THE BINDING

*The photomicrograph
on the binding
depicts giant chromosomes
of the fruit fly (Drosophila virilis).
Each chromosome is striped
with a precise pattern of colored bands.
Dark bands contain the genetic
material DNA; light bands, RNA.
Large dark shape at right
is the nucleolus of the cell, where
RNA is formed. Photomicrograph
was made by Hewson Swift
of the University of Chicago,
and is reproduced here
at a magnification
of about 3000 X.*

THE
SCIENCE
OF
BIOLOGY

McGRAW-HILL BOOK COMPANY

PAUL B. WEISZ
PROFESSOR
OF BIOLOGY
BROWN
UNIVERSITY

THE SCIENCE
OF BIOLOGY

THIRD
EDITION

NEW YORK · ST. LOUIS · SAN FRANCISCO · TORONTO · LONDON · SYDNEY

THE SCIENCE OF BIOLOGY

COLOR PHOTO CREDITS

CHAPTER PHOTO CREDITS

CHAPTER 2

2.4　Courtesy of Dr. Norman E. Williams, University of Iowa.

2.5　Placoderm, American Museum of Natural History; trout, R. H. Noailles.

2.7　Courtesy of Dr. Clifford Grobstein. University of California, Irvine.

2.12　*B*, Ward's Natural Science Establishment, Inc.; *C*, *D*, American Museum of Natural History.

2.13　*A*, Lynwood M. Chace.

CHAPTER 7

7.1　*A*, Dr. Keith R. Porter, Harvard University.

7.2　Dr. Keith R. Porter, Harvard University.

7.3　Courtesy of Dr. W. G. Whaley, University of Texas.

7.4　*A*, Dr. Keith R. Porter, Harvard University; *B*, Dr. H. Fernandez-Moran, University of Chicago, and *J. Cell Biology*, vol. 22, 1964.

7.5　Dr. Keith R. Porter, Harvard University.

7.6　Courtesy of Dr. W. G. Whaley, University of Texas.

7.10　Courtesy of Dr. Melvin S. Fuller, University of California, Berkeley.

7.12　*A*, General Biological Supply House, Inc.; *B*, John L. Schumacher.

7.13　*B*, courtesy of Dr. Norman E. Williams, University of Iowa; *C*, Dr. Keith R. Porter, Harvard University; *D*, courtesy of Dr. Dorothy R. Pitelka, University of California, Berkeley.

7.14　Courtesy of Dr. Melvin S. Fuller, University of California, Berkeley.

7.16　*A*, Ward's Natural Science Establishment, Inc.

7.19　General Biological Supply House, Inc.

7.22　Top, Ripon Microslides, Inc.

7.25　*A*, General Biological Supply House, Inc.; *B*, *C*, Dr. B. J. Serber; *D*, courtesy of Dr. Robert Brenner, Oregon Regional Primate Research Center.

7.28　*A*, Ward's Natural Science Establishment, Inc.; *B*, R. H. Noailles.

7.30　*A*, M. C. Noailles; *B*, courtesy of Dr. William Montagna, Oregon Regional Primate Research Center.

7.31　Ward's Natural Science Establishment, Inc.

7.32　M. C. Noailles.

7.33　Ward's Natural Science Establishment, Inc.

CHAPTER 8

8.1　New York Zoological Society.

8.2　American Museum of Natural History.

8.3　Standard Oil Company, N.J.

8.4　U.S. Fish and Wildlife Service.

8.7　M. Woodbridge Williams.

8.15　U.S. Department of Agriculture.

8.17　Ward's Natural Science Establishment, Inc.

8.18　Courtesy of Buffalo Museum of Science.

8.19　American Museum of Natural History.

8.20　Leonard L. Rue.

CHAPTER 9

9.8　*A*, Paul Popper, Ltd.; *B*, S. Dalton, Natural History Photographic Agency.

9.9　E. W. Teale.

9.10　Paul Popper, Ltd.

9.11　New York Zoological Society.

9.12　U.S. Forest Service.

9.13　*A*, courtesy of Drs. R. M. Herriott and J. L. Barlow, *J. Gen. Physiol.*, vol. 36, p. 17; *B*, courtesy of Dr. R. W. G. Wyckoff, from "Electron Microscopy," Interscience Publishers, Inc., 1949.

9.14　Courtesy of Dr. R. W. G. Wyckoff, from "Electron Microscopy," Interscience Publishers, Inc., 1949.

9.15　General Biological Supply House, Inc.

CHAPTER 10

10.6　U.S. Department of Agriculture.

10.9　Paul Popper, Ltd.

10.10　U.S. Department of Agriculture.

10.11 U.S. Department of Agriculture.

10.12 *A*, U.S. Department of Agriculture; *B*, U.S. Soil Conservation Service.

10.21 General Biological Supply House, Inc.

10.22 American Museum of Natural History.

10.23 American Museum of Natural History.

10.24 R. H. Noailles.

10.25 U.S. Department of Agriculture.

10.26 National Park Service.

10.27 National Park Service.

10.28 National Park Service.

10.29 Top, Paul Popper, Ltd.; Bottom, Australian News and Information Bureau.

CHAPTER 11

11.11 Courtesy of Drs. C. F. Robinow and J. Hillier and Society of American Bacteriologists.

11.12 General Biological Supply House, Inc.

11.13 *A*, courtesy of Dr. C. F. Robinow, from "The Cell," Academic Press, vol. IV; *B*, courtesy of Drs. G. Knaysi, R. F. Baker, and J. Hillier, *J. Bacteriol.*, vol. 53, 1947, and Society of American Bacteriologists.

11.15 General Biological Supply House, Inc.

11.16 Courtesy of Dr. C. F. Robinow, University of Western Ontario, and Academic Press, Inc.

11.17 Courtesy of Dr. I. K. Ross, Yale University.

11.18 Courtesy of Dr. C. F. Robinow, University of Western Ontario.

11.20 Courtesy of Dr. Melvin S. Fuller, University of California, Berkeley.

CHAPTER 12

12.8 *A, C*, courtesy of Dr. Melvin S. Fuller, University of California, Berkeley; *B*, General Biological Supply House, Inc.

12.9 Courtesy of Dr. Melvin S. Fuller, University of California, Berkeley.

12.11 Courtesy of Dr. P. Green, University of Pennsylvania.

12.12 Courtesy of Dr. Melvin S. Fuller, University of California, Berkeley.

12.16 *A*, General Biological Supply House, Inc.; *B*, J. Carel and Larousse Publishing Company.

12.18 Courtesy of Drs. A. J. Shatkin and E. L. Tatum, Rockefeller Institute, and *J. Biophys. Biochem. Cytol.*, vol. 6, p. 423.

12.19 Courtesy of Dr. Melvin S. Fuller, University of California, Berkeley.

12.21 Courtesy of Dr. R. Emerson, University of California, Berkeley, and *Mycologia*, vol. 50, p. 589.

12.25 *A*, courtesy of Dr. C. M. Christensen, University of Minnesota, and University of Minnesota Press; *B*, courtesy of Drs. E. C. Stakman and G. Harrar, from "Principles of Plant Pathology," The Ronald Press Company, 1957.

12.26 *A, B*, courtesy of Dr. Melvin S. Fuller, University of California, Berkeley; *C, D*, General Biological Supply House, Inc.

12.27 Courtesy of Dr. Melvin S. Fuller, University of California, Berkeley.

12.28 Courtesy of Dr. Melvin S. Fuller, University of California, Berkeley.

12.32 Courtesy of Dr. Melvin S. Fuller, University of California, Berkeley.

12.34 Natural History Photographic Agency.

12.35 *B*, R. H. Noailles.

12.38 *B*, Dr. Roman Vishniac, New York.

12.41 Courtesy of Dr. Maria A. Rudzinska and *J. Gerontology*, vol. 16, p. 213, 1961.

CHAPTER 13

13.2 Courtesy of Dr. M. S. Fuller, University of California, Berkeley.

13.9 Courtesy of Dr. M. S. Fuller, University of California, Berkeley.

13.10 *A, B*, U.S. Department of Agriculture; *C*, Brooklyn Botanical Garden.

13.11 Courtesy of Dr. M. S. Fuller, University of California, Berkeley.

13.13 Courtesy of Dr. M. S. Fuller, University of California, Berkeley.

13.16 General Biological Supply House, Inc.

13.21 *B*, J. Carel.

13.23 Courtesy of J. Limbach, Ripon Microslides, Inc.

13.27 Courtesy of J. Limbach, Ripon Microslides, Inc.

13.29 Photo, courtesy of Dr. M. S. Fuller, University of California, Berkeley.

13.30 *A*, courtesy of Dr. M. S. Fuller, University of California, Berkeley; *B*, courtesy of J. Limbach, Ripon Microslides, Inc.

13.31 U.S. Forest Service.

13.32 Courtesy of Dr. M. S. Fuller, University of California, Berkeley.

13.33 Courtesy of Dr. M. S. Fuller, University of California, Berkeley.

13.34 Courtesy of Dr. M. S. Fuller, University of California, Berkeley.

13.36 *A, B*, courtesy of Dr. M. S. Fuller, University of California, Berkeley.

13.37 Courtesy of Dr. R. H. Mohlenbrock, University of Southern Illinois, and *Am. Fern Journ.*, vol. 50, p. 181.

13.38 Courtesy of Dr. M. S. Fuller, University of California, Berkeley.

13.40 *A*, courtesy of Dr. M. S. Fuller, University of California, Berkeley; *B*, Walter H. Hodge.

13.41 Courtesy of J. Limbach, Ripon Microslides, Inc.

13.42 W. H. Hodge.

13.43 J. Carel and Larousse Publishing Company.

13.44 Courtesy of J. Limbach, Ripon Microslides, Inc.

13.45 Chicago Natural History Museum.

13.46 Courtesy of J. Limbach, Ripon Microslides, Inc.

13.47 *A*, General Biological Supply House, Inc.; *B*, courtesy of G. H. Conant, Triarch Products, Inc.; *C*, courtesy of J. Limbach, Ripon Microslides, Inc.

CHAPTER 14

14.2 *A*, American Museum of Natural History; *B*, U.S. Department of Agriculture; *C*, Eastman Kodak Company.

14.17 *A*, M. Woodbridge Williams; *B*, *C*, American Museum of Natural History.

14.25 *A*, Douglas P. Wilson; *B*, Dr. Roman Vishniac, New York; *C*, American Museum of Natural History.

14.26 Photo, Douglas P. Wilson.

14.29 Douglas P. Wilson.

14.32 General Biological Supply House, Inc.

14.34 Photo, Ward's Natural Science Establishment, Inc.

14.39 *A*, courtesy of Dr. W. F. Mai, Cornell U.

CHAPTER 15

15.3 Photo, Douglas P. Wilson.

15.7 Photo, Dr. Richard A. Boolootian.

15.9 Photo, Douglas P. Wilson.

15.11 Photo, American Museum of Natural History.

15.16 Photo, American Museum of Natural History.

15.18 *B*, *C*, R. H. Noailles; *D*, Paul Popper, Ltd.

15.19 Photo, American Museum of Natural History.

15.26 *A*, R. H. Noailles; *B*, *C*, American Museum of Natural History.

15.28 *B*, Lynwood M. Chace; *C*, General Biological Supply House, Inc.

15.33 Paul Popper, Ltd.

15.34 *A*, U.S. Department of Agriculture.

15.38 Photo, R. H. Noailles.

15.39 Photo, Lynwood M. Chace.

15.40 *E*, Eric V. Gravé; *G*, American Museum of Natural History.

15.41 *E*, American Museum of Natural History.

15.44 Photo, R. H. Noailles.

15.47 *A*, Ward's Natural Science Establishment, Inc.; *B*, R. H. Noailles; *C*, Eric V. Gravé; *D*, Leonard L. Rue.

15.48 *A*, M. C. Noailles; *B*, *E*, Natural History Photographic Agency; *C*, R. H. Noailles; *D*, Lynwood M. Chace.

15.49 *A*, *C*, *D*, R. H. Noailles.

15.53 R. H. Noailles

CHAPTER 16

16.3 American Museum of Natural History.

16.7 Photo, Douglas P. Wilson.

16.11 *A*, Paul Popper, Ltd.

16.15 Douglas P. Wilson.

16.16 Douglas P. Wilson.

16.17 *B*, Douglas P. Wilson.

16.18 *A*, M. Woodbridge Williams; *B*, U.S. Fish and Wildlife Service.

16.19 *A*, American Museum of Natural History; *B*, Douglas P. Wilson.

16.20 *B*, U.S. Fish and Wildlife Service; *C*, G. Cripps and Harold V. Green.

16.22 American Museum of Natural History.

16.26 Douglas P. Wilson.

16.27 Courtesy of Dr. William Montagna, Oregon Regional Primate Research Center.

16.34 Courtesy of Dr. William Montagna, Oregon Regional Primate Research Center.

16.35 General Biological Supply House, Inc.

16.39 *A*, L. E. Perkins, Natural History Photographic Agency; *B*, R. H. Noailles.

16.41 *A*, American Museum of Natural History; *B*, Paul Popper, Ltd.; *C*, Ward's Natural Science Establishment, Inc.

16.46 Australian News and Information Bureau.

16.47 *A*, American Museum of Natural History; *B*, Australian News and Information Bureau.

CHAPTER 17

17.7 Courtesy of Dr. K. Esau, from "Plant Anatomy," J. Wiley and Sons, 1953.

17.14 Model designed by Dr. J. F. Mueller, photo by Ward's Natural Science Establishment, Inc.

17.16 Photographic Department, Rhode Island Hospital.

17.19 Courtesy of Dr. Elizabeth Leduc, Brown University.

CHAPTER 20

20.16 *A*, Ward's Natural Science Establishment, Inc.; *B*, Dr. Keith R. Porter, Harvard University.

CHAPTER 21

21.14 Bureau of Human Nutrition and Home Economics.

CHAPTER 22

22.5 Courtesy of Drs. S. H. Wittwer and M. J. Bukovac, Michigan State University, and *Econ. Botany,* vol. 12, p. 213.

22.7 Courtesy of Boyce Thompson Institute for Plant Research.

22.13 Courtesy of Dr. M. S. Fuller, University of California, Berkeley.

22.14 *B, C,* General Biological Supply House, Inc.

22.16 Courtesy of Dr. A. Braun, Rockefeller University.

22.17 Courtesy of Dr. K. Esau, from "Plant Anatomy," J. Wiley and Sons, Inc., 1953.

22.18 Courtesy of Boyce Thompson Institute for Plant Research.

22.28 Ward's Natural Science Establishment, Inc.

22.30 Courtesy of Dr. Robert Brenner, Oregon Regional Primate Research Center.

22.31 New York Zoological Society.

22.32 Dr. B. J. Serber.

CHAPTER 23

23.6 Courtesy of Dr. Robert Brenner, Oregon Regional Primate Research Center.

23.8 *B,* Dr. B. J. Serber; *C,* General Biological Supply House, Inc.

23.9 Photo, Dr. Boris Gueft.

23.10 Photo, Photographic Department, Rhode Island Hospital.

23.11 Dr. Boris Gueft.

CHAPTER 24

24.3 Bell Telephone Laboratories, Inc.

CHAPTER 25

25.1 Photo, Ward's Natural Science Establishment, Inc.

25.3 Inset courtesy of Dr. Mac V. Edds, Brown University.

25.4 *F, G,* Photographic Department, Rhode Island Hospital.

25.6 Ward's Natural Science Establishment, Inc.

25.14 *A,* Ward's Natural Science Establishment, Inc.; *B,* General Biological Supply House, Inc.

25.21 Photo, Ward's Natural Science Establishment, Inc.

25.28 Photo, Ward's Natural Science Establishment, Inc.

CHAPTER 26

26.3 General Biological Supply House, Inc.

26.4 General Biological Supply House, Inc.

26.5 General Biological Supply House, Inc.

26.6 General Biological Supply House, Inc.

26.7 General Biological Supply House, Inc.

26.11 Photo, Douglas P. Wilson.

26.12 Douglas P. Wilson.

26.13 Courtesy of Dr. M. S. Fuller, University of California, Berkeley.

26.19 General Biological Supply House, Inc.

CHAPTER 27

27.1 *A,* courtesy of Dr. C. F. Robinow and Society of American Bacteriologists; *B,* courtesy of Drs. E. A. Duchow and H. C. Douglas, University of Washington, and *J. Bacteriol.,* vol. 58, p. 411.

27.5 General Biological Supply House, Inc.

27.6 *C,* courtesy of Dr. M. S. Fuller, University of California, Berkeley.

27.10 Photo, courtesy of Dr. M. S. Fuller, University of California, Berkeley.

27.11 *A,* courtesy of Dr. W. Koch, University of North Carolina, and J. Elisha Mitchell, *Sci. Soc.,* vol. 67, p. 123; *B, C,* courtesy of Dr. M. S. Fuller, University of California, Berkeley.

27.14 Courtesy of Dr. M. S. Fuller, University of California, Berkeley.

27.19 Photo, Ward's Natural Science Establishment, Inc.

27.20 Photo, General Biological Supply House, Inc.

27.23 Courtesy of Dr. M. S. Fuller, University of California, Berkeley.

27.25 Photo, General Biological Supply House, Inc.

27.26 *B,* courtesy of Dr. M. S. Fuller, University of California, Berkeley.

27.30 *A, B,* courtesy of Dr. M. S. Fuller, University of California, Berkeley.

27.31 Photo, Courtesy of Dr. M. S. Fuller, University of California, Berkeley.

27.34 *A, B,* General Biological Supply House, Inc.

27.37 *A,* courtesy of Dr. M. S. Fuller, University of California, Berkeley; *C,* Ward's Natural Science Establishment, Inc.

27.38 *A,* courtesy of Dr. M. S. Fuller, University of California, Berkeley.

27.39 *C,* courtesy of Dr. M. S. Fuller, University of California, Berkeley.

27.43 R. H. Noailles, from "A Tree is Born," Sterling Publishing Company, Inc.

27.45 Ward's Natural Science Establishment, Inc.

27.46 *A,* Ward's Natural Science Establishment, Inc.

27.47 Photos, courtesy of J. Limbach, Ripon Microslides, Inc.

27.49 Photo, courtesy of Dr. M. S. Fuller, University of California, Berkeley.

27.50 Courtesy of J. Limbach, Ripon Microslides, Inc.

27.51 Photo, courtesy of Dr. M. S. Fuller, University of California, Berkeley.

CHAPTER 28

28.1 Photos, General Biological Supply House, Inc.

28.6 Ward's Natural Science Establishment, Inc.

28.8 Ward's Natural Science Establishment, Inc.

28.13 Photos, Dr. B. J. Serber.

28.16 Photo, courtesy of Carnegie Institution of Washington.

28.20 Courtesy of Dr. G. W. Corner and Carnegie Institution of Washington.

28.21 Dr. A. Gesell, From Fig. 10, "The Embryology of Behavior," Harper and Brothers.

CHAPTER 29

29.2 Courtesy of Dr. W. A. Jensen, University of California, Berkeley.

29.3 Courtesy of Dr. Clifford Grobstein, and 13th Growth Symposium, Princeton University Press, 1954.

29.5 Photo, courtesy of Dr. M. S. Fuller, University of California, Berkeley.

29.6 Courtesy of Dr. Charles Thornton, Michigan State University.

29.17 *A*, courtesy of Drs. T. Steeves and I. Sussex, Harvard University, and *Am. J. Bot.*, vol. 44, p. 665; *B*, courtesy of Dr. Clifford Grobstein, and 13th Growth Symposium, Princeton University Press, 1954.

29.22 American Museum of Natural History.

29.23 Photos, General Biological Supply House, Inc.

29.25 Top, courtesy of Dr. Roberts Rugh, from "Experimental Embryology," Harcourt, Brace, and World, Inc.; bottom left and right, General Biological Supply House, Inc.; bottom middle, M. C. Noailles.

CHAPTER 30

30.23 R. H. Noailles.

CHAPTER 31

31.10 Genetics Laboratory, New York Zoological Society.

31.11 New York Zoological Society.

31.12 *A, B, C*, American Museum of Natural History; *D*, Chicago Natural History Museum.

CHAPTER 32

32.1 American Museum of Natural History.

32.3 *A, D*, Chicago Natural History Museum.

32.5 Chicago Natural History Museum.

32.9 Photo, Chicago Natural History Museum.

32.11 Photo, Chicago Natural History Museum.

32.16 *A*, American Museum of Natural History; *B*, Chicago Natural History Museum.

32.17 American Museum of Natural History.

32.18 Chicago Natural History Museum.

32.21 American Museum of Natural History.

32.22 American Museum of Natural History.

32.24 American Museum of Natural History.

32.25 American Museum of Natural History.

32.26 Chicago Natural History Museum.

32.27 Chicago Natural History Museum.

32.28 American Museum of Natural History.

32.30 American Museum of Natural History.

32.32 American Museum of Natural History.

32.35 *B*, American Museum of Natural History.

32.36 American Museum of Natural History.

32.37 Chicago Natural History Museum.

PREFACE

Because molecular research remains the leading field in biology, it is logical that this approach should be reflected in serious introductory courses. But to avoid the distinct danger of losing organisms from the classroom altogether, it is important to stress and restress the supramolecular phases of biology. Accordingly, the content of this edition differs from the second in two major ways. First, all topics of "molecular" biology are presented in far more breadth and depth than in the preceding edition. Second, this edition includes a much broader, more detailed coverage of ecology and morphology, particularly animal morphology. In addition to these two basic changes, all other subject-matter has been updated and revised thoroughly, with the result that relatively few paragraphs, sections, or chapters are the same as in the previous edition.

The book is now divided into two units of roughly equal length and weight, the first dealing with the *organization* and the second with the *operation* of living systems. In the first unit, Part 1 introduces the scientific and biological basis of living systems. Part 2 begins a level-by-level examination of living organization. The four chapters of the part represent a detailed outline of basic chemistry and biochemistry, and they are designed to serve as a thorough grounding for molecular biology. These chapters actually are written for possible self-study; the instructor need not spend extensive lecture time on them but may assign the bulk of their content as homework. Part 3 continues the examination of organizational levels. Molecules lead to cells, tissues, organs, and organ systems, the higher levels here being discussed separately for plants and animals. The later chapters of the part focus on the supraorganismic, ecological levels, and these accounts now include many topics not dealt with in the second edition, such as biogeography, the nature of ecological niches, and the properties of ecosystems. Part 4 comprises a series of large chapters on the biology and systematics of living types. The conceptual framework is evolutionary; an introductory discussion of the origin of life sets the historical tone at the outset, and the phylogenetic thread is then stressed throughout. Moreover, the basic adaptive traits of very large taxonomic categories are analyzed to much greater depth than in the previous edition, and the morphological traits of each phylum or type are likewise given more thorough attention.

This balance between molecule and organism is repeated in Unit 2, but in a different context. Part 5 comprises a completely revised series of chapters on metabolism. The depth and detail of the presentation correspond with the improved chemical preparation provided through Part 2, and the sequence and scope of the topics have undergone considerable change. The remaining three parts deal with the component processes of self-perpetuation. Part 6, on steady states, provides a transition from the molecular to the higher-level operations within and among organisms; the discussion ranges from rate control via operons to behavior control via hormones and nervous systems. A substantial portion of this part has been rewritten, and the frame of reference has been made broader and somewhat more comparative. Such changes also characterize Part 7, on reproduction, and Part 8, on adaptation, though the scope of these chapters has been altered less than any others.

Apart from these revisions in textual content, this edition also offers several other new features. Most obvious here is the use of color for emphasis in the diagrams, and 32 pages of full-color plates. The diagrams have been newly drawn and, where warranted, redesigned. The lists of collateral readings not only have been updated, but each entry now also includes a brief description of the contents of the cited source. Similarly, the glossary and the index have been expanded and, correlated with the text, revised editions of the Instructor's Manual, the Study Guide, and the Laboratory Manual have been prepared.

These alterations all add up to a measure of improvement and thus to the possibility of more efficient teaching and more meaningful learning. In this connection a statement from the preceding edition is still pertinent.

"A course of study, in biology as in any other field, ideally should be based on three principles of good teaching. The course should probe the *depth* of the subject matter, not merely or even necessarily its total breadth; it should strive to provide a conceptual *synthesis* of diverse data, not simply a disconnected catalogue of so-called facts; and, above all, it should point the way toward a real *comprehension* of significant ideas and should not just require meaningless memorization."

Paul B. Weisz

TABLE
OF
CONTENTS

UNIT ONE
THE
ORGANIZATION
OF LIFE

PART ONE
THE
STUDY
OF LIFE

PART TWO
THE
CHEMICALS
OF LIFE

PART THREE
THE
LEVELS
OF LIFE

PART FOUR
THE
WORLD
OF LIFE

UNIT TWO
THE OPERATIONS OF LIFE

PART FIVE
METABOLISM

PART SIX
SELF-PERPETUATION: STEADY STATES

PART SEVEN
SELF-PERPETUATION: REPRODUCTION

PART EIGHT
SELF-PERPETUATION: ADAPTATION

UNIT ONE
THE ORGANIZATION OF LIFE

PART ONE
THE STUDY OF LIFE

PART TWO
THE CHEMICALS OF LIFE

PART THREE
THE LEVELS OF LIFE

PART FOUR
THE WORLD OF LIFE

Despite their numerous and often obvious differences, living creatures of all kinds have far more in common than might at first be suspected. For example, all are alike in that they occupy specific parts of the environment; in that they have specific past histories; in that they possess body parts which reflect both their present places in the environment and their historical past; and, above all, in that very similar events occur within and among them which collectively make them *living* creatures. In short, all living things share in common their most basic and fundamental traits but differ to greater or lesser degree in their more superficial traits.

Such general similarities and specific differences are expressions of how living material is put together, from atoms to whole individuals and from single individuals to interacting groups of them. The first unit of this book, roughly half the whole volume, is devoted to a study of this living *organization*. The second unit will then deal with the living *operations*, that is, the means by which the organization actually maintains itself in a living state.

PART ONE
THE STUDY OF LIFE
CHAPTER 1
THE SCIENTIFIC BASIS
CHAPTER 2
THE BIOLOGICAL BASIS

The investigation of living things is the concern of the science of biology. The phrase "science of biology" at once suggests two separate, very pertinent questions. First, what is a science? Second, what is a living thing—what, indeed, is the fundamental meaning of the word "life"?

Answers to these two questions are outlined in the two chapters of this introductory part.

CHAPTER 1
THE
SCIENTIFIC
BASIS

Our current civilization is so thoroughly permeated with science that, for many, the label "scientific" has become the highest badge of merit, the hallmark of progress, the dominant theme of the age of atoms and space. No human endeavor, so it is often claimed, can really be worthwhile or of basic significance unless it has a scientific foundation. Moreover, advertisements loudly proclaim the "scientific" nature of consumer goods, and their "scientifically proved" high quality is attested to by "scientific" experts. Human relations too are supposed to be "scientific" nowadays. Conversation and debate have become "scientific" discussions, and in a field such as sports, if one is a good athlete, he is a "scientific" athlete.

There are even those who claim to take their religion "scientifically" and those who stoutly maintain that literature, painting, and other artistic pursuits are reducible to "science," really. And then there are those who believe that science will eventually solve "everything" and that, if only the world were run more "scientifically," it would be a much better place.

Yet in contrast to this widespread confidence in things and activities which claim to be, and in a few cases actually are, scientific, large segments of society doubt and mistrust scientists as persons. To many, the scientist is somehow queer and "different." He is held to be naïve and more or less uninformed outside his specialty. He is pictured as a cold, godless calculating machine living in a strange, illusory world of his own.

Many circumstances in our civilization conspire to foster such false, stereotyped notions about science and scientists. However, no one who wishes to consider himself properly educated can afford to know about the meaning of science only what popular misconceptions, and "common knowledge," may have taught him. Especially is this true for one who is about to pursue studies in a modern science such as biology.

What then *is* the actual meaning of science? How did truly scientific undertakings develop, and how does science "work"? What can it do and, more especially, what can it not do? How does science differ from other forms of activity, and what place does it have in the scheme of modern culture?

THE ORIGIN OF SCIENCE

Science began in the distant past, long before human history was being recorded. Its mother was tribal *magic*.

The same mother also gave birth to religion and, probably even earlier, to art. Thus science, religion, and art have always been blood brothers. Their methods differ, but their aim is the same: to understand and interpret the universe and its workings and, from this, to promote the material and spiritual welfare of man where possible.

This was also the function of tribal magic. For long ages, magic was the rallying point of society, the central institution in which were concentrated the accumulated wisdom and experience of the day. The execution of magical procedures was in the hands of specially trained individuals, the medicine men and their equivalents. These were the forerunners of the scientists and the clergymen of today. How did science and religion grow out of magic? We may illustrate by means of an example.

Several thousand years ago, it was generally believed that magical rites were necessary to make wheat grow from planted seeds. In this particular instance, the rites took one of two forms. Either man intensified his sexual activity, in a solemn spring festival celebrated communally in the fields, or he abstained completely from sexual activity during the planting period.

The first procedure was an instance of *imitative*

3

magic. The reasoning was that, since sowing seeds is like producing pregnancy in a woman, man could demonstrate to the soil what was wanted and so induce it to imitate man and be fertile. The second procedure, an instance of *contagious* magic, grew out of the assumption that only a limited amount of reproductive potency was available to living things. Consequently, if man did not use up his potency, that much more would become available for the soil. Depending on the tribe, the time, and the locality, either imitative or contagious magic might have been used to attain the same end, namely, to make the earth fruitful.

The fundamental weakness of magic was, of course, that it was unreliable. Sometimes it worked, and sometimes it did not work. Bad soil, bad grain, bad weather, and insect pests often must have defeated the best magic. In time, man must have realized that magical rites actually played no role in wheat growth, whereas soil conditions, grain quality, and good weather played very important roles. This was a momentous discovery—and a scientific one.

Magic became science when man accidentally found, or began to look for, situations which could be predictably controlled without magical rituals. In many situations where magic seemed to work successfully most of the time, man discovered an underlying scientific principle.

Yet there remained very many situations where magic did not work and where scientific principles could not be found. For example, in spite of good soil and good weather, wheat might not have grown because of virus or fungus infections. Such contingencies remained completely beyond understanding up to very modern times, and early man could only conclude that unseeable, uncontrollable "somethings" occasionally defeated his efforts. These somethings became spirits and gods. And unless prayers and sacrificial offerings maintained the good will of the gods, their wrath would undo human enterprise. Thus magical rituals evolved into primitively religious ones.

At this stage, medicine men ceased to be magicians and instead assumed the dual role of priest and scientist. Every personal or communal undertaking required both scientific and religious action: science, to put to use what was known; religion, to protect against possible failure by inducing the unknown to work on man's side.

In time, the "two-way" medicine man disappeared and made way for the specialized scientist and priest. In both religion and science, shades of the old magic lingered on for long periods. The religions still retain a high magical content today,

and the sciences only recently dissociated from magic-derived pseudo sciences such as alchemy, astrology, and the occult arts.

Throughout the early development of science and religion, emphasis was largely on practical matters. Science was primitively technological, and religion too was largely "applied," designed to deal with the concrete practical issues of the day. Man was preoccupied mainly with procuring food, shelter, and clothing, and science and religion served these necessities. Later, as a result of technological successes, more time became available for contemplation and cultural development, and this is when researchers and theorists appeared alongside the technologists, and theologians alongside the clergymen.

THE FORMS OF SCIENCE

Today there are three types of scientists carrying on two kinds of science.

One kind of scientist may be symbolized as a man who sits by the river on nice afternoons and who whittles away at a stick and wonders about things. Strange as it may seem to some, the most powerful science stems from such whittlers. Whereas most people who just sit manage merely to be lazy, a few quietly boil with rare powers and make the wheels of the world go round. Thinker-scientists of this sort usually are not too well known by the general public, unless their thoughts prove to be of outstanding importance. Newton, Einstein, Darwin, and Freud are among the best known.

A second kind of scientist is the serious young man in the white coat, reading the dials of monster machines while lights flash and buzzers purr softly. This picture symbolizes the technician, the lab man, the trained expert who tests, experiments, and works out the implications of what the whittler has been thinking.

The third kind of scientist is a relatively new phenomenon. He goes to an office, dictates to secretaries, and spends a good part of his time in conferences or in handling contracts, budgets, and personnel. This symbolizes the businessman-scientist, who gets and allocates the funds which buy time and privacy for the whittler and machines for the lab man.

Note, however, that every scientist worthy of the name actually is a complex mixture of philosopher, technician, and businessman all rolled into one, and none is a "pure" type. But the relative emphasis varies greatly in different scientists.

Whatever type mixture he may be, a scientist works either in basic research, often called *pure science,* or in technology, often called *applied science.*

Basic research is done primarily to further man's understanding of nature. Possible practical applications of the findings are here completely disregarded. Scientists in this field are more frequently of the philosopher–lab-man type than in technology. They may be found principally in university laboratories and research institutes and, in lesser numbers, in industry and government. They have little to show for their efforts beyond the written accounts of their work; hence it is comparatively hard for them to convince nonscientists that they are doing anything essential. However, government and every enlightened industry today either support independent research or conduct such research. And the public is beginning to realize that pure science is the soil from which applied science must develop.

Technology is concerned primarily with applying the results of pure science to practical uses. No lesser inventiveness and genius are required in this field than in basic research, though here the genius is more of a commercial and less of a philosophical nature. Physicians, engineers, crime detectives, drug manufacturers, agricultural scientists, all are technologists. They have services and tangible products to sell; hence the public recognizes their worth rather readily.

Here again, note that no scientist is pure researcher or pure technologist. Mixtures are in evidence once more, with emphasis one way or the other. Moreover, technology is as much the fertilizer of basic research as the other way round. As new theories suggest new ways of applying them, so new ideas for doing things suggest further advances in research. Thus, in most research today, pure and applied science work hand in hand. Many conclusions of pure science cannot be tested before the technologist thinks up the means of testing. Conversely, before the technologist can produce desirable new products, years of basic research may first be required. Insofar as every basic researcher must use equipment, however modest, he is also a technologist; and insofar as every technologist must understand how and why his products work, he is also a basic researcher.

It follows that any science shrivels whenever either of its two branches ceases to be effective. If for every dollar spent on science an immediate, tangible return is expected, and if the budding scientist is prevented from being a whittler by the necessity of producing something salable, then basic research will be in danger of drying up. And when that happens, technology too will become obsolete before long.

THE PROCEDURE OF SCIENCE

Everything that is science ultimately has its basis in the *scientific method.* Both the powers and the limitations of science are defined by this method. And wherever the scientific method cannot be applied, there cannot be science.

Taken singly, most of the steps of the scientific method involve commonplace procedures carried out daily by every person. Taken together, they amount to the most powerful tool man has devised to know and to control nature.

OBSERVATION

All science begins with *observation,* the first step of the scientific method.

At once this delimits the scientific domain; something that cannot be observed cannot be investigated by science. However, observation need not be direct. Atomic nuclei and magnetism, for example, cannot be perceived directly through our sense organs, but their effects can be observed with instruments. Similarly, mind cannot be observed directly, but its effects can be, as expressed, for example, in behavior.

For reasons which will become clear presently, it is necessary, furthermore, that an observation be *repeatable,* actually or potentially. Anyone who doubts that objects fall back to the ground after being thrown into the air can convince himself of it by repeating the observation. One-time events on earth normally are outside science.

Correct observation is a most difficult art acquired only after long experience and many errors. Everybody observes, with eyes, ears, touch, and all other senses, but few observe correctly. Lawyers experienced with witnesses, artists who teach students to draw objects in plain view, and scientists who try to see nature all can testify to this.

This difficulty of observation lies largely in unsuspected bias. People forever see what they *want* to see or what they think they *ought* to see. It is extremely hard to rid oneself of such unconscious prejudice and to see just what is actually there, no more and no less. Past experience, "common knowledge," and often teachers can be subtle obstacles to correct observation, and even experienced scientists may not always avoid them. That is why a scientific observation is not taken at face value until several scientists have repeated the observation independently and have reported the same thing. That is also a major reason why one-time, unrepeatable events normally cannot be science.

A scientific piece of work is only as good as the

original observation. Observational errors persist into everything that follows, and the effort may be defeated before it has properly begun.

PROBLEM

After an observation has been made, the second step of the scientific method is to define a *problem*. In other words, one asks a question about the observation. How does so and so come about? What is it that makes such and such happen in this or that fashion? Question asking additionally distinguishes the scientist from the layman; everybody makes observations, but not everybody shows further curiosity.

More significantly, not everyone sees that there may actually be a problem connected with an observation. During thousands of years, even curious people simply took it for granted that a detached, unsupported object falls to the ground. It took genius to ask, "How come?" and few problems, indeed, have ever turned out to be more profound.

Thus scientists take nothing for granted, and they ask questions, even at the risk of irritating others. Question askers are notorious for getting themselves into trouble, and so it has always been with scientists. But they have to continue to ask questions if they are to remain scientists. And society has to expect annoying questions if it wishes to have science.

Anyone can ask questions. However, good questioning, like good observing, is a high art. To be valuable scientifically, a question must be *relevant*, and it must be *testable*. The difficulty is that it is often very hard or impossible to tell in advance whether a question is relevant or irrelevant, testable or untestable. If a man collapses on the street and passers-by want to help him, it may or may not be irrelevant to ask when he had his last meal. Without experience one cannot decide on the relevance of this question, and a wrong procedure might be followed.

As to the testability of questions, it is clear that proper testing techniques must be available, actually or potentially. This cannot always be guaranteed. For example, Einstein's fame rests, in part, on showing that it is impossible to test whether or not the earth moves through an "ether," an assumption held for many decades. All questions about an ether therefore become nonscientific, and we must reformulate associated problems until they become testable. Einstein did this, and he came up with relativity.

In general, science does best with "How?" or "What?" questions. "Why?" questions are more troublesome. Some of them can be rephrased to ask "How?" or "What?" But others such as "Why does the universe exist?" fall into the untestable category. These are outside the domain of science.

HYPOTHESIS

Having asked a proper question, the scientist proceeds to the third step of the scientific method. This involves the seemingly quite unscientific procedure of guessing. One guesses what the answer to the question might conceivably be. Scientists call this postulating a *hypothesis*.

Hypothesizing distinguishes the scientist still further from the layman. For while many people observe and ask questions, most stop there. Some do wonder about likely answers, and scientists are among these.

Of course, a given question may have thousands of *possible* answers but only one *right* answer. Chances are therefore excellent that a random guess will be wrong. The scientist will not know whether his guess was or was not correct until he has completed the fourth step of the scientific method, *experimentation*. It is the function of every experiment to test the validity of a scientific guess.

If experimentation shows that the first guess was wrong, the scientist then must formulate a new hypothesis and once more test for validity by performing new experiments. Clearly, the guessing and guess testing might go on for years, and a right answer might never be found. This happens.

But here again, artistry, genius, and experience usually provide shortcuts. There are good guesses and bad ones, and the skilled scientist is generally able to decide at the outset that, of a multitude of possible answers, so and so many are unlikely answers. His knowledge of the field, his past experience, and the experience of others working on related problems normally allow him to reduce the many possibilities to a few likelihoods.

This is also the place where hunches, intuitions, and lucky accidents aid science enormously. In one famous case, so the story has it, the German chemist Kekulé went to bed one night after a fairly alcoholic party and dreamed of six monkeys chasing one another in a circle, the tail of one held in the teeth of the other. Practically our whole chemical industry is based on that dream, for it told the sleeping scientist what the long-sought structure of benzene was—as we now know, six carbon atoms "chasing" one another in a circle. And benzene is the fundamental parent substance for thousands of chemical products.

The ideal situation for which the scientist generally strives is to reduce his problem to just two distinct alternative possibilities, one of which, when tested by experiment, may then be answered with a clear "yes," the other with a clear "no." It is exceedingly difficult to streamline problems in this way, and with many it cannot be done. Very often the answer obtained is "maybe." However, if a clear yes or no does emerge, scientists speak of an elegant piece of work, and such performances often are milestones in science.

EXPERIMENT

Experimentation is the fourth step in the scientific method. At this point, science and nonscience finally and completely part company.

Most people observe, ask questions, and also guess at answers. But the layman stops here: "My answer is so logical, so reasonable, and it sounds so 'right' that it must be correct." The listener considers the argument, finds that it is indeed logical and reasonable, and is convinced. He then goes out and in his turn converts others. Before long, the whole world rejoices that it has the answer.

Now the small, kill-joy voice of the scientist is heard in the background: "Where is the evidence?" Under such conditions in history, it has often been easier and more convenient to eradicate the scientist than to eradicate an emotionally fixed public opinion. But doing away with the scientist does not alter the fact that answers without evidence are at best unsupported opinions, at worst wishful thinking and fanatical illusions. Experimentation can provide the necessary evidence, and whosoever then experiments after guessing at answers becomes truly "scientific" in his approach, be he a professional scientist or not.

On the other hand, experiments do not guarantee a scientific conclusion. For there is ample room within experimentation and in succeeding steps to become unscientific again.

Experimentation is by far the hardest part of scientific procedure. There are no rules to follow; each experiment is a case unto itself. Knowledge and experience usually help technically, but to design the experiment, to decide on the means by which a hypothesis might best be tested, that separates the genius from the dilettante. The following example will illustrate the point:

Suppose you observe that a chemical substance X, which has accidentally spilled into a culture dish full of certain disease-causing bacteria, kills all the bacteria in that dish. Problem: Can drug X be used to protect human beings against these disease-causing bacteria? Hypothesis: Yes. Experiment: You go to a hospital and find a patient with the particular bacterial disease and inject some of the drug into the patient.

Possible result 1: Two days later the patient is well. Conclusion: Hypothesis confirmed. You proceed to market the drug at high prices. Shortly afterward, users of the drug die by the dozens, and you are tried and convicted for homicide.

Possible result 2: Two days later the patient is dead. Conclusion: The drug is worthless, and you abandon your project. A year later a colleague of yours is awarded the Nobel prize for having discovered a drug X which cures a certain bacterial disease in man—the same drug and the same disease in which you had been interested.

In this example, the so-called experiment was not an experiment at all.

First, no allowance was made for the possibility that people of different age, sex, eating habits, prior medical history, hereditary background, etc., might react differently to the same drug. Obviously, one would have to test the drug on many categories of carefully preselected patients, and there would have to be many patients in each such category. Besides, one would make the tests first on mice, or guinea pigs, or monkeys.

Second, the quantity of drug to be used was not determined. Clearly, a full range of dosages would have to be tested for each different category of patient. We tacitly assume, moreover, that the drug is a pure substance, that is, that it does not contain traces of other chemicals which might obscure, or interfere with, the results. If impurities are suspected, whole sets of separate experiments would have to be made.

Third, and most importantly, no account was taken of the possibility that your patient might have become well, or have died, in any case, even without your injecting the drug. What is needed here is *experimental control;* for every group of patients injected *with* drug solution, a precisely equal group must be injected with plain solution, *without* the drug. Then, by comparing results in the control and the experimental groups, one can determine whether or not the recovery or death of patients is really attributable to the drug.

Note that every experiment requires at least two parallel tests or sets of tests identical in all respects except one. Of these parallel tests, one is the control series, and it provides a standard of reference for assessing the results of the experimental series. In drug experiments on people, not fewer than about 100,000 to 200,000 test cases, half of them controls, half of them experimentals, would be considered adequate. It should be easy to see why a single test on a single test case may give completely erroneous conclusions. Many repetitions of the same test, under as nearly identical conditions as possible, and at least one control test for each of the experimental tests—these are always prerequisite for any good experiment.

While an actual drug-testing program would be laborious, expensive, and time-consuming, the design of the experiment is nevertheless extremely simple. There are few steps to be gone through, and it is fairly clear what these steps must be. But there are many experiments in which the tests themselves may not take more than an hour or two, whereas thinking up appropriate, foolproof plans for the tests may have taken several years.

And despite a most ingenious design and a most careful execution, the result may still not be a clear yes or no. In a drug-testing experiment, for example, it is virtually certain that not 100 per cent of the experimental, drug-injected group will recover or that 100 per cent of the untreated control group will remain sick.

The actual results might be something like 70 per cent recovery in the experimentals and something like 20 per cent recovery in the controls. The experimentals here show that 30 per cent of the patients with that particular disease do not recover despite treatment, and the controls show that 20 per cent of the patients get well even without treatment. Moreover, if 70 out of every 100 experimental patients recover, then 20 out of these 70 were not actually helped by the drug; since, from the control data, they would have recovered even without treatment. Hence the drug is effective in only 70 per cent minus 20 per cent, or 50 per cent, of the cases.

Medically, this may be a major accomplishment, for having the drug is obviously better than not having it. But scientifically, one is confronted with an equivocal "maybe" result. It will probably lead to new research based on the new observation that some people respond to the drug and some do not and to the new problem of why and what can be done about it.

The result of any experiment represents *evidence*. That is, the original guess in answer to a problem is confirmed as correct or is invalidated. If invalidated, a new hypothesis, with new experiments, must be thought up. This is repeated until a hypothesis may be hit upon which can be supported with confirmatory experimental evidence.

As with legal evidence, scientific evidence can be strong and convincing, or merely suggestive, or poor. In any case, nothing has been proved. Depending on the strength of the evidence, one merely has a basis for regarding the original hypothesis with a certain degree of confidence.

Our new drug, for example, may be just what we claim it to be when we use it in this country. In another part of the world it might not work at all or it might work better. All we can confidently say is that our evidence is based on so and so many experiments with American patients, American bacteria, and American drugs and that under specified hospital conditions, with proper allowance for unspotted errors, the drug has an effectiveness of 50 per cent. Experimental results are never better or broader than the experiments themselves.

This is where many who have been properly scientific up to this point become unscientific. Their claims exceed the evidence; they mistake their partial answer for the whole answer; they contend to have proof for a fact, while all they actually have is some evidence for a hypothesis. There is always room for more and better evidence, or for new contradictory evidence, or indeed for better hypotheses.

THEORY

Experimental evidence is the basis for the fifth and final step in the scientific method, the formulation of a *theory*.

When a hypothesis has been supported by really convincing evidence, best obtained in many different laboratories and by many independent researchers, and when the total accumulated evidence is unquestionably reliable within carefully specified limits, then a theory may be proposed.

In our drug example, after substantial corroborating evidence has also been obtained from many other test localities, an acceptable theory would be the statement that "in such and such a bacterial disease, drug X is effective in 50 per cent of the cases."

This statement is considerably broader than the experiments on which it is based. Theories always are. The statement implies, for example, that drug X, regardless of who manufactures it, will be 50 per cent effective anywhere in the world, under any conditions, and can be used also for animals other than man.

Direct evidence for these extended implications does not exist. But inasmuch as drug X is already known to work within certain limits, the theory expresses the belief, the *probability*, that it may also work within certain wider limits.

To that extent every good theory has *predictive* value. It prophesies certain results. In contrast to nonscientific prophecies, scientific ones always have a substantial body of evidence to back them up. Moreover, the scientific prophecy does not say that something will certainly happen, but says only that something is *likely* to happen with a stated degree of probability.

A few theories have proved to be so universally

valid and to have such a high degree of probability that they are spoken of as *natural laws.* For example, no exception has ever been found to the observation that an apple, if disconnected from a tree and not otherwise supported, will fall to the ground. A law of gravitation is based on such observations.

Yet even laws do not pronounce certainties. For all practical purposes, it may well be irrational to assume that some day an apple will rise from a tree, yet there simply is no evidence that can absolutely guarantee the future. Evidence can be used only to estimate probabilities.

Most theories actually have rather brief life spans. For example, if, in chickens, our drug X should be found to perform not with 50 per cent but with 80 per cent efficiency, then our original theory becomes untenable and obsolete. And the exception to the theory becomes a new observation, beginning a new cycle of scientific procedure.

Thus new research might show that chickens contain a natural booster substance in their blood which materially bolsters the action of the drug. This might lead to isolation, identification, and mass production of the booster substance, hence to world-wide improvement in curing the bacterial disease. And we would also have a new theory of drug action, based on the new evidence.

Thus science is never finished. One theory predicts, holds up well for a time, exceptions are found, and a new, more inclusive theory takes over—for a while. We may note in passing that old theories do not become incorrect but merely become obsolete. Development of a new airplane does not mean that earlier planes can no longer fly. New theories, like new airplanes, merely range farther and serve more efficiently than earlier ones, but the latter still serve for their original purposes. Science is steady progression, not sudden revolution.

Clearly, knowledge of the scientific method does not by itself make a good scientist, any more than knowledge of English grammar alone makes a Shakespeare. At the same time, the demands of the scientific method should make it evident that scientists cannot be the cold, inhuman precision machines they are so often, and so erroneously, pictured to be. Scientists are essentially artists, and they require a sensitivity of eye and of mind as great as that of any master painter, and an imagination and keen inventiveness as powerful as that of any master poet.

THE LIMITATIONS OF SCIENCE

Observing, problem posing, hypothesizing, experimenting, and theorizing—this sequence of procedural steps is both the beginning and the end of science. To determine what science means in wider contexts, we must examine what scientific method implies and, more especially, what it does not imply.

THE SCIENTIFIC DOMAIN

First, scientific method defines the domain of science: *Anything to which the scientific method can be applied, now or in the future, is or will be science; anything to which the method cannot be applied is not science.*

This helps to clarify many a controversial issue. For example, does science have something to say about the concept of God? To determine this, we must find out if we can apply the scientific method.

Inasmuch as the whole universe and everything in it may be argued to be God's work, one may also argue that He is observable. It is possible, furthermore, to pose any number of problems, such as "Does He exist; is the universe indeed His doing?" and "Is He present everywhere and in everything?" One can also hypothesize; some might say "yes," some might say "no."

Can we design an experiment about God? To be reliable, we would need experimental control, that is, two otherwise identical situations, one with God and one without. Now, what we wish to test is the hypothesis that God exists and is universal, that is, that He is everwhere. Being a hypothesis thus far, this could be right or wrong.

If right, He would exist and exist everywhere; hence He would be present in *every* test we could possibly make. Thus we would never be able to devise a situation in which God is not present. But we need such a situation in order to have a controlled experiment.

But if the hypothesis is wrong, He would not exist, hence would be absent from *every* test we could possibly make. Therefore, we would never be able to devise a situation in which God *is* present. Yet we would need such a situation for a controlled experiment.

Right or wrong, our hypothesis is untestable either way, since we cannot run a controlled experiment. Hence we cannot apply the scientific method. The point is that the concept of God is outside the domain of science, and science cannot legitimately say anything about Him. He cannot be tested by science, because its method is inapplicable.

It should be carefully noted that this is a far cry from saying "Science disproves God," or "scientists must be godless; their method demands it." Nothing of the sort. Science specifically leaves anyone perfectly free to believe in any god whatsoever or in none. Many first-rate scientists are priests; many others are agnostics.

Science commits you to nothing more, and to nothing less, than adherence to scientific method.

Such adherence, it may be noted, is a matter of faith, just as belief in God or confidence in the telephone directory is a matter of faith. Whatever other faiths they may or may not hold, all scientists certainly have strong faith in the scientific method. So do those laymen who feel that having electric lights and not having bubonic plague are good things.

THE SCIENTIFIC AIM

A second consequence of the scientific method is that it defines the aim and purpose of science: *The objective of science is to make and to use theories.*

Many would say that the objective of science is to discover truth, to find out facts. We must be very careful here about the meaning of words. "Truth" is popularly used in two senses. It may indicate a temporary correctness, as in saying "It is true that my hair is brown." Or it may indicate an absolute, eternal correctness, as in saying "In plane geometry, the sum of the angles in a triangle is 180°."

From the earlier discussion on the nature of scientific method, it should be clear that science cannot deal with truth of the absolute variety. Something absolute is finished, known completely, once and for all. But science is never finished. Its method is unable to determine the absolute. Besides, once something is already known absolutely, there is no further requirement for science, since nothing further needs to be found out. Science can only adduce evidence for temporary truths, and another term for "temporary truth" is "theory." Because the word "truth," if not laboriously qualified, is ambiguous, scientists try not to use it at all.

The words "fact" and "proof" have a similar drawback. Both may indicate either something absolute or something temporary. If absolute, they are not science; if temporary, we have the less ambiguous word "evidence." Thus, science is content to find evidence for theories, and it leaves truths, proofs, and facts to others.

Speaking of words, "theorizing" is often popularly taken to mean "just talk and speculation." Consider, however, how successfully theorizing builds bridges!

SCIENCE AND VALUES

A third important implication of the scientific method is that *it does not make value judgments or moral decisions.*

It is the user of scientific results who may place valuations on them. But the results by themselves do not carry built-in values. And nowhere in the scientific method is there a value-revealing step.

The consequences of this are vast. For example, the science which produced the atomic bomb and penicillin cannot, of itself, tell whether these products are good things or bad things. Every man must determine that for himself as best he can. The scientist who discusses the moral aspects of nuclear weapons can make weightier statements than a layman only insofar as he may know more about what damage such weapons may or may not do. This will certainly influence his opinions. But whatever opinion he gives, it will be a purely personal evaluation made as a citizen, and any other scientist—or layman—who is equally well informed about the capacities of the weapons may conceivably disagree completely. Human values are involved here; science is not.

In all other types of evaluations as well, science is silent and noncommittal. Beauty, love, evil, happiness, virtue, justice, liberty, property, financial worth, all these are human values which science cannot peg. To be sure, love, for example, might well be a subject of scientific research, and research might show much about what love is and how it works. But such research could never discover that love is wonderful, an evaluation clear to anyone who has done a certain amount of nonscientific research.

It also follows that it would be folly to strive for a strictly "scientific" way of life or to expect strictly "scientific" government. Certainly the role of science might profitably be enlarged in areas of personal and public life where science can make a legitimate contribution. But a completely scientific civilization, adhering strictly to the rules of the scientific method, could never tell, for example, whether it is right or wrong to commit murder, or whether it is good or bad to love one's neighbor. Science cannot and does not give such answers. To be sure, this does not imply that science does away with morals. It merely implies that science cannot determine whether or not one ought to have moral standards, or what particular set of moral standards one ought to live by.

THE SCIENTIFIC PHILOSOPHY

A fourth and most important consequence of the scientific method is that it determines the philosophical foundation on which scientific pursuits must be based.

Inasmuch as the domain of science is the whole material universe, science must inquire into the nature of the forces which govern the universe and all happenings in it. What makes given events in the universe take place? What determines which event out of several possible ones will occur? And what controls or guides the course of any event to a particular conclusion?

Questions of this kind seek to discover the "prime mover" of the universe. As such they are actually philosophic questions of concern not only in science but in all other areas of human thought as well. Depending on how man answers such questions, he will adopt a particular philosophy of nature and this philosophy will then guide him in his various undertakings. Scientific man too must try to find answers, and we already know the framework within which the scientific answers must be given: to be useful in science, any statement about the universe or its parts must be consistent with the procedure of the scientific method. Therefore, if a given philosophy of nature can be verified wholly or even partly through experimental analysis, it will be valuable scientifically. But a philosophy which cannot be so verified will be without value in science, even though it may well be valuable in other areas of human thought.

Vitalism versus Mechanism

In the course of history, two major answers have been proposed regarding the governing forces of the universe. These answers are incorporated in two systems of philosophy called *vitalism* and *mechanism*.

Vitalism is the doctrine of the supernatural. It holds, essentially, that the universe and all happenings in it are controlled by supernatural powers. Such powers have been variously called gods, spirits, or simply "vital forces." Their influence is held to determine the nature and guide the behavior of atoms, planets, stars, living things, and indeed all components of the universe. Clearly, most religious philosophies are vitalistic ones.

Whatever value a vitalistic philosophy might have elsewhere, it cannot have value in science. This is because the supernatural is by definition beyond reach of the natural. Inasmuch as the scientific method is a wholly natural procedure, it cannot be used for an investigation of the supernatural. We have already noted earlier, for example, that science cannot prove or disprove anything about God. Any other vitalistic conception is similarly untestable by experiment and is therefore unusable as a *scientific* philosophy of nature.

A philosophy which *is* usable in science is that of mechanism. In the mechanistic view, the prime mover of the universe is a set of natural laws, that is, the laws of physics and chemistry. Experiments carried out in the course of several centuries have shown what some of these laws are, and any happen-

ing in the universe is held to be governed by the laws. The foundation of mechanism is therefore natural rather than supernatural and is amenable to experimental analysis.

On the basis of the total experimental experience, the mechanistic philosophy holds that if all physical and chemical phenomena in the universe can be accounted for, no other phenomena will remain. Therefore, the controlling agent of the material in the universe must reside within the material itself. Moreover, it must consist of physical and chemical events *only*. As a further consequence, the particular course of any happening must be guided automatically, by the way in which the natural laws permit physical and chemical events to occur within given materials. Note that biological materials are included here; life too must be a result of physical and chemical events *only*. The course of life must be automatically self-determined by the physical and chemical events occurring within living matter.

Clearly, these differences between vitalism and mechanism point up a conceptual conflict between religion and science. But note that the conflict is not necessarily irreconcilable. To bridge the conceptual gap between the two philosophies, one might ask how the natural laws of the universe came into being to begin with. A possible answer is that they were created by God. In this view, the universe ran vitalistically up to the time that natural laws were created and ran mechanistically thereafter. The mechanist must then admit the existence of a supernatural Creator at the beginning of time (even though he has no *scientific* basis for either affirming or denying this; mechanism cannot, by definition, tell anything about a time at which natural laws might not have been in operation). Correspondingly, the vitalist must admit that any direct influence of God over the universe must have ceased once His natural laws were in operation. These laws would run the universe adequately, and further supernatural control would therefore not be necessary (or demonstrable, so long as the natural laws continued to operate without change).

Thus it is not necessarily illogical to hold both scientific and religious philosophies at the same time. However, it is decidedly illogical to try to use vitalistic ideas as explanations of scientific problems. Correct science does demand that supernatural concepts be kept out of natural events, i.e., those which can be investigated by means of the scientific method. However much a vitalist he might be in his nonscientific thinking, man in his scientific thinking must be a mechanist. And if he is not, he ceases to be scientific.

Many people, some scientists included, actually

find it exceedingly difficult to keep vitalism out of science. Biological events, undoubtedly the most complex of all known events in the universe, have in the past been particularly subject to attempts at vitalistic interpretation. How, it has been asked, can the beauty of a flower ever be understood simply as a series of physical and chemical events? How can an egg, transforming itself into a baby, be nothing more than a "mechanism" like a clock? And how can a man, who thinks and experiences visions of God, be conceivably regarded as nothing more than a piece of "machinery"? Mechanism *must* be inadequate as an explanation of life, it has been argued, and only something supernatural superimposed on the machine, some vital force, is likely to account for the fire of life.

In such replacements of mechanistic with mystical thought, the connotations of words often play a supporting role. For example, the words "mechanism" and "machine" usually bring to mind images of crude iron engines or clockworks. Such analogies tend to reinforce the suspicion of vitalists that those who regard living things as mere machinery must be simple-minded indeed. Consider, however, that the machines of today also include electronic computers which can learn, translate languages, compose music, play chess, make decisions, and improve their performance of such activities as they gather experience. In addition, theoretical knowledge now available would permit us to build a machine which could heal itself when injured and which could feed, sense, reproduce, and even evolve. Clearly, the term "mechanism" is not at all limited to crude, stupidly "mechanical" engines. And there is certainly nothing inherently simple-minded or reprehensible in the idea that living things are exquisitely complicated chemical mechanisms, some of which even have the capacity to think and to have visions of God.

On the contrary, if it could be shown that such a mechanistic view is at all justified, it would represent an enormous advance in our understanding of nature. In all the centuries of recorded history, vitalism in its various forms has hardly progressed beyond the mere initial assertion that living things are animated by supernatural forces. Just how such forces are presumed to do the animating has not been explained, nor have programs of inquiry been offered to find explanations. Actually, such inquiries are ruled out by definition, since natural man can never hope to fathom the supernatural. In the face of this closed door, mechanism provides the only way out for the curious. But is it justifiable to regard living things as pure mechanisms, even complicated chemical ones?

Notwithstanding the doubts expressed by some, a mechanistic interpretation of life is entirely justifiable and interjection of touches of vitalism is entirely unjustifiable. Science today *can* account for living properties in purely mechanistic terms. Moreover, biologists are well on their way to being able to create a truly living entity "in the test tube," solely by means of physical and chemical procedures obeying known natural laws. We shall discuss some of the requirements for such laboratory creation in the course of this book. Evidently, vitalistic "aids" to explain the mechanistic universe are not only unjustifiable but also unnecessary.

It may be noted in this connection that, historically, vitalism has tended to fill the gaps left by incomplete scientific knowledge. Early man was a complete vitalist, who for want of better knowledge regarded even inanimate objects as "animated" by supernatural spirits. As scientific insight later increased, progressively more of the universe ceased to be in the domain of the supernatural. Thus it happened repeatedly that phenomena originally thought to be supernatural were later shown to be explainable naturally. So it has been with living phenomena as well. And those today who may still be prompted to fill gaps in scientific knowledge with vitalism must be prepared to have red faces tomorrow. Incidentally, it might also be pointed out in passing that even confirmed vitalists find it prudent on occasion to become ardent believers in mechanism, whether they realize it or not. For example, few vitalists hesitate to accept the mechanistic administrations of a physician at the first signs of disorder in their "machinery."

We conclude that a mechanistic view of nature is one component of the philosophic attitude required in science. A second component may now be considered.

Teleology versus Causalism

Even a casual observer must be impressed by the apparent nonrandomness of natural events. Every part of nature seems to follow a plan, and there is a distinct directedness to any given process. Living processes provide excellent instances of this. For example, developing eggs behave as if they knew exactly what the plan of the adult is to be. A chicken egg soon develops into an embryo with two wings and two legs, *as if* there existed a blueprint which specified that adult chickens should have two wings and two legs each. Moreover, since virtually all chicken eggs undergo the same course of growth, the impression of plan in development becomes reinforced strongly; one is led to conclude that the various parts of a chicken are there not just by random coincidence. Similarly, an earthworm which has been decapitated grows a new head, *as if* there were a plan which specified that every earthworm should have a head—not another tail and not two heads either, but one head.

All known natural processes, biological or otherwise, thus start at given beginnings and proceed to particular endpoints. This observation poses a philosophical problem: How is a starting condition directed toward a given terminal condition; how does a starting point appear to "know" what the endpoint is to be?

It will be noted that such questions have to do with a specific aspect of the more general problem of the controlling agents of the universe. We should expect, therefore, that two sets of answers would be available, one vitalistic and the other mechanistic. This is the case. In view of the discussion in the preceding section, a book on science such as this could properly disregard the vitalistic answers as inadmissible from the outset and proceed at once with an outline of the mechanistic position. It is nevertheless advisable to examine both positions, partly because such a procedure adds to an understanding of the nature and limitations of science, partly because it is important to be able to recognize vitalistic answers if and when they occur (as they occasionally still do) in what is supposed to be scientific thought.

According to vitalistic doctrines, natural events *appear* to be planned because they *are* planned. A supernatural "divine plan" is held to fix the fate of every part of the universe, and all events in nature, past, present, and future, are programmed in this plan. All nature is therefore directed toward a preordained goal, namely, the fulfillment of the divine plan. As a consequence, nothing happens by chance, but everything happens on purpose.

Being a vitalistic, experimentally untestable conception, the notion of purpose in natural events has no place in science. Does the universe exist for a purpose? Does man live for a purpose? You cannot hope for an answer from science, for science is not designed to tackle such questions. Moreover, if you already hold certain beliefs in these areas, you cannot expect science either to prove or to disprove them for you.

Yet many arguments have been attempted to show purpose from science. For example, it has been maintained by some that the whole purpose of the evolution of living things was to produce man. Here the evidence supporting the theory of evolution is invoked to prove that man was the predetermined goal from the very beginning.

This implies several things besides the conceit that man is the finest product of creation. It implies, for example, that nothing could ever come after man, for he is supposed to be the last word in living magnificence. As a matter of record, man is sorely plagued by an army of parasites which cannot live anywhere except inside people. And it is clear that you cannot have a man-requiring parasite before you have a man.

Many human parasites did evolve after man. Thus, the purpose argument would at best show that the whole purpose of evolution was to produce those living organisms which cause influenza, diphtheria, gonorrhea, and syphilis. This even the most ardent purpose arguer would probably not care to maintain.

If one is so inclined, he is of course perfectly free to believe that man is the pinnacle of it all. Then the rest of the universe with its billions of suns, including the living worlds which probably circle some of them, presumably are merely immense and fancy scenery for the microscopic stage on which man struts about. One may believe this, to be sure, but one cannot maintain that such beliefs are justified by evidence from science.

The essential point is that any purpose-implying argument, in this or in any other issue, stands on quicksand the moment science is invoked as a witness; for to say such and such is the goal, the ultimate purpose, is to state a belief and not a body of evidence adduced through the scientific method. Nowhere does this method include any purpose-revealing step.

The form of argumentation which takes recourse to purposes and supernatural planning is generally called *teleology*. In one system of teleology, the preordained plan exists outside natural objects, in an external Deity, for example. In another system, the plan resides within objects themselves. According to this view, a starting condition of an event proceeds toward a specific end condition because the starting object has built into it actual foreknowledge of what the end condition is to be. For example, the egg develops toward the goal of the adult because the egg *knows* what the adult state is to be. Similarly, evolution has occurred as it has because the participating starting chemicals had foreknowledge that the end should be man. Clearly, this and all other forms of teleology "explain" an end state by simply asserting it given at the beginning. And in thereby putting the future into the past, the effect before the cause, teleology negates time.

The scientifically useful alternative to teleology is called *causalism*. It has its foundations in mechanistic philosophy. Causalism denies foreknowledge of terminal states, preordination, purposes, goals, and fixed fates. It holds that natural events take place *sequentially*. Events occur only as other events *permit* them to occur, not as preordained goals or purposes make them occur. End states are consequences, not foregone conclusions, of beginning states. A headless earthworm regenerates a new head because conditions within the headless worm are such that only a head—*one* head—can develop. It becomes the task of the biologist to find out what these conditions are and to see if, by changing the conditions, two heads or another tail could not be produced. Because scientists *can* obtain different end states after changing the conditions of initial states, the idea of predetermined goals loses all validity in scientific thought.

Care must therefore be taken in scientific endeavors not to fall unwittingly into the teleological trap. Consider often-heard statements such as: "the *purpose* of the heart is to pump blood"; "the ancestors of birds evolved wings *so that* they could fly"; "eggs have yolk *in order to* provide food for development." The last statement, for example, implies that eggs can "foresee" the nutritional problem in development and that food will be required; therefore, they proceed to store up some. In effect, eggs are given human mentality. The teleologist is always anthropocentric; that is, he implies that the natural events he discusses have minds like his. Substitute "and" for every "so that" or "in order to" and "function" for every "purpose" in biological statements and they become properly nonteleological.

Clearly then, science in its present state of development must operate within carefully specified, self-imposed limits. The basic philosophic attitude must be mechanistic and causalistic, and we note that the results obtained through science are inherently without truth, without value, and without purpose.

But it is precisely because science is limited in this fashion that it advances. After centuries of earnest deliberation, mankind still does not agree on what truth is, values still change with the times and with places, and purposes remain as unfathomed as ever. On such shifting sands it has proved difficult to build a knowledge of nature. What little of nature we really know and are likely to know in the foreseeable future stands on the bedrock of science and its powerful tool, the scientific method.

THE LANGUAGE OF SCIENCE

SCIENCE AS A WHOLE

Fundamentally, science is a *language*, a system of communication. Religion, art, politics, English, and French are among other such languages. Like them, science enables man to travel into new countries of the mind and to understand and be understood in such countries. Like other languages, science too has its grammar—the scientific method; its authors and its literature—the scientists and their written work; and its various dialects or forms of expression—physics, chemistry, biology, etc.

Indeed, science is one of the few truly universal languages, understood all over the globe. Art, religion, and politics are also universal. But each of these languages has several forms, so that Baptists and Hindus, for example, have little in common either religiously, artistically, or politically. Science, however, has the same single form everywhere, and Baptists and Hindus do speak the same scientific language.

It should be clear that no one language is "truer" or "righter" than any other. There are only *different* languages, each serving its function in its own domain. Many an idea is an idiom of a specific language and is best expressed in that language. For example, the German "Kindergarten" has been imported as is into English and the American "baseball" has gone into the world without change. Likewise, one cannot discuss morality in the language of science, or thermodynamics in the language of religion, or artistic beauty in the language of politics; to the extent that each system of communication has specific idioms, there is no overlap or interchangeability among the systems.

On the other hand, many ideas can be expressed equally well in several languages. The English "water," the Latin "aqua," and the scientific "H_2O" are entirely equivalent, and no one of these is truer or righter than the others. They are merely different. Similarly, in one language man was created by God; in another man is a result of chance reactions among chemicals and of evolution. Again, neither the scientific nor the religious interpretation is the truer. If the theologian argues that everything was made by God, including scientists who think that man is the result of chance chemical reactions, then the scientist will argue back that chance chemical reactions created men with brains, including those theological brains which can conceive of a God who made everything. The impasse is permanent, and within their own systems of communication the scientist and the theologian are equally right. Many, of course, assume without warrant that it is the compelling duty of science to prove or disprove religious matters, and of religion, to prove or to disprove scientific matters.

The point is that there is no single "correct" formulation of any idea which spans various languages. There are only *different* formulations, and in given circumstances one or the other may be more useful, more satisfying, or more effective. Clearly, he who is adept in more than one language will be able to travel that much more widely and will be able to feel at ease in the company of more than one set of ideas.

We are, it appears, forever committed to multiple standards, according to the different systems of communication we use. But we have been in such a state all along, in many different ways. Thus, the color red means one thing politically, something else in a fall landscape, and is judged by a third standard in the fashion world. Or consider the different worth of the same dime to a child, to you, and to the United States Treasury. To be multilingual in his interpretation of the world has been the unique heritage of man from the beginning. Different proportions of the various languages may be mixed into the outlook of different individuals, but science, religion, art, politics, spoken language, all these and many more besides are always needed to make a full life.

BIOLOGY

Within the language of science, biology is an important dialect, permitting travel in the domain of *living things*. Man probably was a biologist before he was anything else. His own body in health and disease; the phenomena of birth, growth, and death; and the plants and other animals which gave him food, shelter, and clothing undoubtedly were matters of serious concern to even the first of his kind. The motives were sheer necessity and the requirements of survival. These same motives still prompt the same biological studies today; agriculture, medicine, and fields allied to them are the most important branches of modern applied biology. In addition, biology today is strongly experimental, and pure research is done extensively all over the world. Some of this research promotes biological technology; all of it increases our understanding of how living things are constructed and how they operate.

Over the decades, the frontiers of biological investigations have been pushed into smaller and smaller realms. Some 100 to 150 years ago, when modern biology began, the chief interest was the whole plant or the whole animal, how it lived, where it could be found, and how it was related to other whole living things. Such studies have been carried on ever since, but, in addition, techniques gradually became available for the investigation of progressively smaller parts of the whole, their structures, their functions, and their relationships to one another. Thus it happened that, during the past few decades, the frontiers of biology were pushed down to the chemical level. And while research with larger biological units continues as before, the newest biology attempts to interpret living operations in terms of the chemicals which compose living creatures.

Biology here merges with chemistry. Today there are already many signs that the next frontier will be the atoms which in their turn compose the chemicals, and biology tomorrow will undoubtedly merge with atomic physics. Such a trend is quite natural; for ultimately, living things are atomic things. Penultimately, they are chemical things, and only on a large scale are they plants and animals. In the last analysis, therefore, biology must attempt to show how atoms, and chemicals made out of atoms, are put together to form, on the one hand, something like a rock or a piece of metal and, on the other, something like a flower or a human baby.

This book is an outline of how successful the attempt has been thus far.

REVIEW QUESTIONS

1. What are the aims and the limitations of science? Review fully. In what sense is science a language, and how does it differ from other, similar languages?

2. What characterizes the different present-day forms of science and the different specializations of scientists?

3. Review the steps of the scientific method and discuss the nature of each of these steps. Define "controlled experiment."

4. How would you show by controlled experiment:

a. Whether or not temperature affects the rate of growth of living things?

b. Whether or not houseflies can perceive differently colored objects?

c. Whether or not plants use up some of the soil they grow in?

5. Suppose that it were found in question *4a* that, at an environmental temperature of 28°C, the growth of fertilized frog eggs into tadpoles occurs roughly twice as fast as at 18°C. What kinds of theories could such evidence suggest?

6. What are the historical and the modern relations of science and religion? Which of the ideas you have previously held about science should you now, after studying this chapter, regard as popular misconceptions?

7. Can you think of observations or problems which so far have not been investigated scientifically? Try to determine in each case whether or not such investigation is inherently possible. Why is mathematics not considered to be a science?

8. Describe the philosophic foundations of science. Define mechanism and causalism and contrast these systems of thought with those of vitalism and teleology. Can conceptual conflicts between science and religion be reconciled?

9. Consider the legal phrases "Do you swear to tell the truth and nothing but the truth?" and "Is it not a fact that on the night of . . . ?" If phrases of this sort were to be used in a strictly scientific context, how should they properly be formulated?

10. Biology is called one of the *natural sciences,* all of which deal with the composition, properties, and behavior of matter in the universe. Which other sciences are customarily regarded as belonging to this category, and what distinguishes them from one another and from biology? What are *social sciences?* Do they too operate by the scientific method?

COLLATERAL READINGS

Bronowski, J.: "Science and Human Values," Harper Torchbooks 505, Harper & Row, New York, 1959. A well-known paperback, containing a stimulating discussion of the role of science in modern society.

Butterfield, H.: The Scientific Revolution, *Sci. American,* September, 1960. A popularly written historical survey of the growth of science from the time of the Renaissance and during the Industrial Revolution.

Conant, J. B.: "Modern Science and Modern Man," Columbia, New York, 1952.

————: "Science and Common Sense," Yale, New Haven, Conn., 1951.

————: "On Understanding Science," Yale, New Haven, Conn., 1947.

In these writings a noted educator discusses the scientific method, its application in research, and the role of science in society.

Dampier, W. C.: "A History of Science," 3d ed., Macmillan, New York, 1942. The growth and development of science and of the various scientific disciplines is traced in this book.

Mausner, B., and J. Mausner: A Study of the Anti-scientific Attitude, *Sci. American,* February, 1955. An analysis of the social problems surrounding the issue of water fluoridation, presented as a case study of anti-intellectualism.

Russell, Bertrand: "The Scientific Outlook," Norton, New York, 1931. A famous philosopher writes most penetratingly on the philosophic and logical foundations of science and on the relation of science to religion.

Singer, C.: "A History of Biology," rev. ed., Abelard-Schuman, New York, 1950. A good survey of the growth of the biological sciences.

Terman, L. M.: Are Scientists Different?, *Sci. American,* January, 1955. A psychologist examines the traits generally characteristic of scientists and compares them with those of nonscientists.

Wilson, E. Bright, Jr.: "An Introduction to Scientific Research," McGraw-Hill, New York, 1952. A good discussion of the nature of the scientific method and its application in scientific investigations.

CHAPTER 2
THE
BIOLOGICAL
BASIS

The property we call life is exhibited by individual living creatures, or *organisms*. What exactly does the concept "living" signify, and what actually is an "organism"—what basic kinds are there and what distinguishes them? Answers to these questions about *the nature of life* and the *forms of life* are sought in this chapter.

THE NATURE OF LIFE

Surely the most obvious difference between something living and something nonliving is that the first *does* certain things the second does not do. Indeed, we may say that the essence of "living" lies in characteristic activities, or processes, or *functions*.

"Nonliving" may mean either "dead" or "inanimate," terms which are not equivalent. If a chicken does not perform its characteristic living functions it is dead, but then it is still distinguishable readily from an inanimate object such as a stone. Chickens, either living or dead, are organisms; stones are not. And we may note that all organisms are put together in such a way that the functions of life are or once were actually possible. Inanimate things, by contrast, are constructed in a way that makes living functions inherently impossible. Accordingly, the essence of "organism" lies in characteristic building materials and building patterns, or *structures*.

A "living organism," therefore, is what it is by virtue of its functions, which endow it with the property of life, and its structures, which make possible the execution of the life-sustaining functions.

What are these functions and structures endowing all organisms with the potential of life?

ORGANISM AND FUNCTION

Most essential to the life of any organism are its *genes*. As later chapters will show in detail, genes are particular kinds of highly complex chemicals that are inherited by every organism from its forebears and that ultimately govern every aspect of living. Genes determine how an organism will form, what structures it will possess, what functions it will be capable of, how it will change during its lifetime in all these respects, and how it will differ from every other organism—in short, they determine both the general and the specific nature of every living organism. Genes play this crucial role by serving somewhat like sets of built-in commands which, directly or indirectly, provide instructions for all other components and parts of an organism to act and react in particular ways. Therefore, keep in mind from the outset that every life-maintaining function or structure referred to below ultimately is a gene-determined and gene-dependent characteristic.

One of the principal life-maintaining functions of organisms is *nutrition*, a process that provides the raw materials of life. All living matter has an unceasing requirement for raw materials, for the very act of living continuously uses up two basic commodities: energy and matter. In this respect a living organism is like a mechanical engine or indeed like any other action-performing system in the universe. Energy is needed to power the system, to make the parts operate, to keep activity going—in short, to maintain function. And matter is needed to replace parts, to repair breakdowns, to continue the system intact and able to function—in short, to maintain structure. Therefore, by its very nature as an action-performing unit, a "living" organism can remain alive only if it continuously expends energy and matter. These commodities must be replenished from the outside at least as fast as they are used up inside; and this replenishment function is nutrition.

The nutritional raw materials are *nutrients*, including foods and required substances such as water and salts. They are available in the general environment of the earth, partly in the physical environment of air, water, and land, partly in the biological environment of other organisms, living or dead. The role of nutrition is to transfer appropriate kinds and amounts of nutrients from the external environment into the living organism. Note generally that, as nutrition permits continuation of life, so life also permits continuation of nutrition; nourished living matter must already preexist if its further nutrition is to be possible.

Organisms carry out this nutritional function in either of two major ways, namely, *autotrophically* or *heterotrophically* (Fig. 2.1). An autotrophic organism obtains *all* required nutritional raw materials from its physical environment alone—the water, air, or soil in which it lives. By contrast, a heterotroph can obtain only some of its needed raw materials from the physical surroundings; the rest must be procured from its biological environment, namely, from other organisms. Thus, autotrophism constitutes an organism-independent form of nutrition, whereas heterotrophism is an organism-dependent form.

Two principal varieties of autotrophism are known, namely, *chemosynthesis* and *photosynthesis*. They differ primarily in the source of the energy the organisms use in transforming their nutrient raw materials into biologically usable substances. Chemosynthesizers, which comprise only certain of the bacteria, obtain such energy from given environmental chemicals. By contrast, photosynthesizers employ the energy of sunlight. These are by far the more abundant and familiar autotrophs for they include the green plants. The green substance (*chlorophyll*) in such plants is one of the agents employed in the utilization of sunlight.

Heterotrophic nutrition occurs in three major forms, namely, *holotrophism, saprotrophism,* and *parasitism.* A holotroph obtains its organism-derived nutrients by swallowing or eating other living organisms in whole or in part. This familiar bulk-feeding mode of nutrition is characteristic of animals. Saprotrophs find nutrients in the juices of dead or decaying organisms or in natural or man-made materials derived from organisms (for example, bread, milk, leather). Saprotrophs include many of the bacteria, fungi, and protozoa, and their nutritional activities initiate or produce further decay. Lastly, a parasite lives right within or on another living *host* organism and draws its nutrients directly from the body of such a host. Viruses, bacteria, fungi, and numerous animal types are parasitic.

Regardless of how given organisms obtain nutrients, one of the primary roles of such substances within a living organism is to supply energy. Nutrients are chemicals, as pointed out, and as such they

2 · 1 Principal forms of nutrition. *Autotrophs (left) acquire all nutrient raw materials from the physical world; energy for internal food manufacture is derived either from chemicals or from light. Heterotrophs (right) must acquire nutrients from both the physical and biological worlds; nutrients from the biological world are either swallowed (holotrophs), absorbed from dead biological materials (saprotrophs), or absorbed from living hosts (parasites). Arrows indicate directions of nutrient flow.*

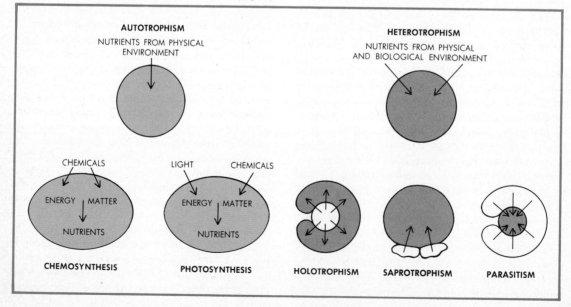

contain chemical energy (see Chap. 3). All living matter runs on the chemical energy obtained from nutrients. The basic pattern here is that nutrient chemicals become decomposed within the organism; their energy thereby becomes available in usable form, and this energy then sustains living activities. In this respect living systems are in principle quite similar to many familiar machines. In a gasoline or a steam engine, for example, fuel is burned, that is, decomposed; the burning process releases energy, and this energy then drives the motor. In the living "motor," nutrients likewise function as fuels, and indeed nutrients and engine fuels belong to the same families of chemical substances. Also, nutrients are decomposed in a way that is actually a form of burning.

In living organisms, the process of energy procurement through decomposition of nutrients is called *respiration*. In most cases respiration requires environmental oxygen as an accessory ingredient, and the collection of oxygen by the organism constitutes *breathing*. Respiration is a second major activity of living matter; it is the basic power-generating process maintaining *all* living functions. Note that such functions include nutrition and even respiration itself. Nutritional activities can be sustained only with the aid of respiratory energy, but respiration in turn depends on the fuel-providing process of nutrition. Moreover, respiration is itself an activity of life and thus must be sustained by respiration. In other words, energy made available by previous respiration is required to make further respiration possible.

The second primary role of nutrients is to serve as construction materials. The whole structure of the living organism must be built from and kept intact with nutrient "bricks." Thus, the chemical stuff that forms living matter is fundamentally the same that forms nutrients. This consideration leads to an interesting inference. If nutrients and living matter are basically equivalent and if nutrients are also respiratory fuels, it should follow that living matter should be able to use *itself* as fuel. This is indeed the case; all living matter is inherently self-decomposing and self-consuming. In this respect a living organism may be likened to an engine that is built out of steel and in which steel is also the fuel. As such an engine runs, it burns up not only fuel supplied from the outside but also its own substance; the motor cannot tell the difference between external fuel and internal structural parts, because both are fundamentally the same. Such an engine would be quite unstable structurally and in fact would burn itself up very quickly. A living organism is similarly unstable structurally, but unlike a machine it counteracts this instability with the aid of nutrients. New structural parts are manufactured continually out of nutrients and the new parts replace those that burn away. Put another way, the structural damage resulting from the unceasing respiratory self-consumption is offset by an equally unceasing self-repair.

Respiration is actually not the only circumstance necessitating the use of nutrients as construction materials. For example, living matter frequently sustains structural damage through injuries from accidents and disease. Parts of the living structure also rub off, evaporate, and dissipate in other ways. Clearly, the structural wear and tear resulting unavoidably from the very activities of living has many forms and causes, and uninterrupted reconstruction must offset this wear and tear if the living structure is to persist. We note that living matter is never the same from moment to moment. As wear and tear and reconstruction occur side by side, the substance of living matter always "turns over"; although the fundamental structural pattern remains the same, every bit of the building material is replaced sooner or later. Moreover, if new building materials accumulate faster than old building materials wear away, the living organism will *grow*. Growth is a characteristic outcome of the use of nutrients in the construction of living matter.

The processes by which nutrients are fashioned into new structural parts of organisms may be referred to collectively as *synthesis* activities. They represent a third basic function of all living things. Like other functions of life, synthesis requires energy, and respiration must provide it: respiration of some of the nutrients provides the energy necessary in the synthesis processes involving other nutrients. Thus, respiration is both the main cause making synthesis necessary and the main means making it possible. In its own turn, synthesis maintains the structural apparatus required for respiration, for nutrition, and indeed for all other life functions as well.

The three functions of nutrition, respiration, and synthesis together constitute a broad living activity known as *metabolism* (Fig. 2.2). Taken as a whole, metabolism may be said to run the machinery of life. By running, the machinery may then carry out continued metabolism. As we have seen, a system which nourishes, respires, and synthesizes is capable of undertaking more nutrition, more respiration, and more synthesis.

However, being capable of continued activity is not the same as actually continuing the activity. Actual continuation becomes possible only if the activity is *controlled*. In this respect living matter is again like an engine. It is not enough that an engine

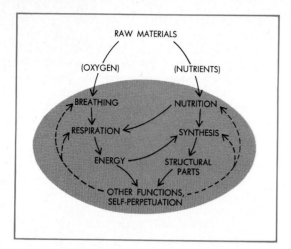

RAW MATERIALS

(OXYGEN)   (NUTRIENTS)

BREATHING   NUTRITION

RESPIRATION   SYNTHESIS

ENERGY   STRUCTURAL
PARTS

OTHER FUNCTIONS,
SELF-PERPETUATION

2 · 2 Metabolism. *The pattern and interrelations of the main processes of metabolism and the main results of metabolism.*

can obtain fuel, can generate energy by burning fuel, and can be repaired. Continuous operation demands that the rates of fuel supply, of burning, and of repair be finely geared to one another, and that if one rate changes for some external or internal reason, all other rates change appropriately. In other words, the various operations of the engine must remain harmonized internally and must be adjusted and readjusted in line with events that may occur externally. Continuous operation, in short, requires control. Just so, continuation of metabolism in living matter depends on control. Metabolism as such is not equivalent to "life," but controlled metabolism in a general sense is.

The necessary control is provided by *self-perpetuation,* a broadly inclusive set of processes (Fig. 2.3). Self-perpetuation ensures that the metabolizing machinery does continue to run indefinitely, without outside help, and despite internal and external happenings that might otherwise stop its operation. We may also note that, in carrying out this controlling role, self-perpetuation uses up respiratory energy and the products of synthesis. Controlled metabolism thus is as much a result of self-perpetuation as a prerequisite.

The most direct and immediate regulation of metabolism is brought about by self-perpetuative processes we may collectively call *steady-state controls.* Fundamentally, such controls permit a living organism to receive information from within itself and from the external environment and to act on this information in a self-preserving manner. The information is received in the form of *stimuli* and the self-preserving actions are *responses.* For example, with the aid of energy and building materials, steady-state controls may cause the organism to procure fresh nutrients when past supplies are used up; may adjust respiration and synthesis in rate and amount according to given requirements; may channel the energy of respiration into protective responses like movement; may direct the repair of damaged parts or the construction of additional parts, as in growth. Taken together, such controls therefore preserve *optimum operating conditions* within living matter; they maintain a steady state. In this state a living

2 · 3 Self-perpetuation. *The pattern and interrelations of the main processes of self-perpetuation and the main results of these processes.*

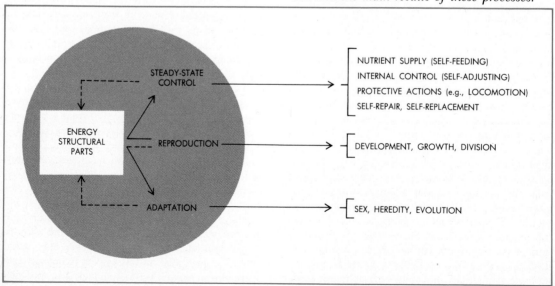

STEADY-STATE
CONTROL

ENERGY
STRUCTURAL
PARTS

REPRODUCTION

ADAPTATION

NUTRIENT SUPPLY (SELF-FEEDING)
INTERNAL CONTROL (SELF-ADJUSTING)
PROTECTIVE ACTIONS (e.g., LOCOMOTION)
SELF-REPAIR, SELF-REPLACEMENT

DEVELOPMENT, GROWTH, DIVISION

SEX, HEREDITY, EVOLUTION

organism may then remain intact and functioning as long as inherently possible.

But span of existence is invariably limited. Indeed, we know that individual life rarely lasts longer than a century and in most cases actually ceases within a single year. Death is a built-in characteristic of living matter because, like all other parts of the organism, those which maintain steady states are themselves subject to breakdown, to respiratory or accidental destruction, to wear and tear generally. When some of its controls become inoperative for any such reason, the organism suffers *disease*. We may define disease as any structural or functional breakdown of steady-state controls, one form of a temporary *unsteady* state. Other, still intact controls may then initiate self-repair. In time, however, so many controls break down simultaneously that too few remain intact to effect repairs. The organism then is in an irreversibly unsteady state and it must die. In this regard the organism again resembles a machine; even the most carefully serviced apparatus eventually becomes scrap, and the destructive impact of the environment ultimately can never be denied.

But unlike a machine, living matter here outwits the environment. For before it dies, the organism may have brought into play a second major self-perpetuative function, namely, *reproduction*. With the help of energy and raw materials, the living organism has enlarged, and such growth in size subsequently permits subdivision and growth in numbers. Reproduction in a sense anticipates and compensates for unavoidable individual death. Through reproduction over successive generations, the tradition of life may then be inherited and carried on indefinitely (Fig. 2.4).

Reproduction implies a still poorly understood capacity of *rejuvenation*. The material out of which the offspring is made is part of the parent, hence is really just as old as the rest of the parent. Yet the one lives and the other dies. Evidently, there is a profound distinction between "old" and "aged." Reproduction also implies the capacity of *development*, for the offspring is almost always not only smaller than the parent but also less nearly complete in form and function.

As generation succeeds generation by reproduction, long-term environmental changes are likely to have their effect on the living succession. In the course of thousands and millions of years, for example, climates may become altered profoundly; ice ages may come and go; mountains, oceans, vast tracts of land may appear and disappear. Moreover, living organisms themselves may in time alter the nature of a locality in major ways. Consequently, two related organisms many reproductive genera-

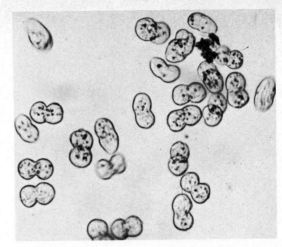

2 · 4 Reproduction: growth in size followed by subdivision and growth in numbers. *The living ciliate protozoa* Tetrahymena *shown here have grown in size for a period of time and are now in various stages of reproduction by subdivision. Repeated at intervals, reproduction may maintain the living succession indefinitely (approx. ×1,000).*

tions apart could find themselves in greatly different environments. And whereas the steady-state controls of the ancestor may have coped effectively with the early environment, these same controls, if inherited unchanged by the descendant, could be overpowered rapidly by the new environment. In the course of reproductive successions, therefore, organisms must change *with* the environment if they are to persist.

They actually do change through *adaptation*. This third major self-perpetuative function includes three subfunctions, namely, *sex, heredity,* and *evolution.* Through sex and heredity, the genes of two parent organisms become joined together within one offspring organism. The offspring thereby inherits the controls, hence also the survival potentials, of both parents. And to the extent that the genes of one parent differ from those of the other, the offspring may inherit a broader range of controls and a wider range of survival potentials. It may therefore be able to adapt to more different environments than either parent alone. Evolution may occur if any of the inherited genes change structurally and also functionally, a process which again alters the controls and the survival potential of an organism (Fig. 2.5). In effect, adaptation of the organism to its environment depends on the genetically determined characteristics of the organism; and insofar as sex, heredity, and evolution may change the genetic characteristics, these processes correspondingly may change—in many cases improve—the adaptation.

Self-perpetuation as a whole thus encompasses three sets of control activities (compare Fig. 2.3).

Steady-state controls maintain optimum operating conditions within individual organisms as long as possible. Reproduction ensures a continuing succession of individual organisms. And adaptation molds and alters the members of this succession in step with the slowly changing nature of the environment. Self-perpetuation thus adds the time dimension to metabolism; regardless of how the environment may change in time, self-perpetuation almost guarantees the continuation of metabolism. Metabolism in turn makes possible uninterrupted self-perpetuation, and the system so able to metabolize and self-perpetuate can persist indefinitely; it becomes a "living" system.

To define, then, the fundamental meaning of "living," we may say that *any structure which metabolizes and self-perpetuates is alive.* And we may add that the metabolic functions of nutrition, respiration, and synthesis make possible and are themselves made possible by the self-perpetuative functions of steady-state control, reproduction, and adaptation.

A first implication of this definition is that, by their very nature, living systems collectively are a highly permanent form of matter, perhaps the most permanent in the universe. They are certainly the most enduring on earth. Every inanimate or dead object on earth sooner or later decomposes and crumbles to dust under the impact of the environment. But every living object metabolizes and self-perpetuates and so may avoid such a fate. We come to realize that living matter, thought soft and weak to the touch, is actually far more durable than the strongest steel, far more permanent than the hardest granite. Oceans, mountains, even whole continents have come and gone several times during the last few billion years, but living matter has persisted indestructibly during that time and, indeed, has become progressively more abundant.

A second implication is that any structure that does not satisfy the above definition in every particular is either inanimate or dead. Life must cease if even one of the fundamental functions of metabolism or self-perpetuation ceases; all these functions must be carried out simultaneously and interrelatedly. This criterion of life offers an instructive contrast to the operation of modern machines, many of which perform some of the functions also occurring in living organisms. As noted, for example, a machine may take on "nourishment" in the form of fuel and raw materials. The fuel may be "respired" to provide operating energy, and, with it, the raw materials may then be "synthesized" into nuts, bolts, and other structural components out of which such a machine might be built. If any one of these processes should stop, the machine would cease to operate even though it is still whole and intact.

Evidently, machines may carry out activities fully equivalent to those of metabolism; and metabolism, therefore, cannot be the special distinguishing feature of living nature. That distinguishing feature must lie, rather, in self-perpetuation. However, note that, like living systems, many "automated" machines have ingenious steady-state controls built into them. For example, such controls may make a machine automatically self-"feeding" and self-adjusting. But no machine is as yet self-protecting, self-repairing, or self-healing to any major extent, and certainly no machine is self-growing. On the other hand, it is known today how, theoretically, such a fully self-controlled, self-preserving machine could be built. If it is ever built, it will have steady-state controls conceivably quite as effective as the ones which have been standard equipment in living organisms for several billion years.

Machines resemble organisms further in that they "die" after a period of time, that is, enter so unsteady a state that they are beyond repair. But whereas

2 · 5 The process of adaptation, or change with *the environment. The upper figure is a drawing of a placoderm, a type of fish long extinct but very common some 300 million years ago. Fishes of this group were the ancestors of modern fish, of which one, a speckled brook trout, is shown in the lower figure. In this evolutionary history, evidently, as in most others, progressive gene change produced evolutionary change. As a result, descendants became different as their physical and biological environment became different, and the descendants so remained adapted to the changing environment.*

living matter may reproduce before death, machines may not. It is in this capacity of reproduction that living systems differ most critically from inanimate systems. No machine self-reproduces, self-rejuvenates, or self-develops. However, it may be noted once again that the theoretical knowledge of how to build such a machine now exists. A device of this kind would metabolize, maintain steady states, and eventually "die" but, before that, would reproduce. It would be almost living. If it had the additional capacity of adaptation, it would be fully living. And here too the theoretical know-how is already available. On paper we may now design machines that could carry out "sexual" processes of a sort, that could pass on hereditary information to their self-reproduced "offspring," and that could "evolve" and change their properties in the course of many "generations."

Today, of course, such fully self-perpetuating machines do not—yet—exist in actuality. Living matter certainly may counteract the disruptive and destructive effect of the environment far more efficiently than any machine. It is primarily this which puts living objects into one category of matter and machines and all other inanimate objects into another. Nonliving objects are what they are because they cannot perform all the functions of metabolism and self-perpetuation. But if the time ever comes when machines are able to carry out all these functions, then the essential distinction between "living" and "machine" will have disappeared.

This consideration brings us to a third implication of the definition above: The property of life basically does not depend on a particular substance. Any substance, of whatever composition, will be "living" provided that it metabolizes and self-perpetuates. It happens that only one such substance is now known. We call it "living matter," or often also *protoplasm*. It has certain clear-cut characteristics of composition and makeup, as will become apparent below; and it is molded into organisms. But if someday we should be able to build a fully metabolizing and self-perpetuating system out of nuts, bolts, and wires, then it too will have to be regarded as being truly alive. Similarly, if someday we should encounter on another planet out in space a metabolizing and self-perpetuating entity made up of hitherto completely unknown materials, it too will have to be considered living. It may not be "life as we know it," that is, life based on the earthly variety of protoplasm, but in any case it will be truly living if it metabolizes and self-perpetuates.

We may conclude, then, that an object is defined as living or nonliving on the basis of its functional properties, not its structural properties. On the other hand, structural properties do determine whether an object is an "organism" or something inanimate. Linguistically as well as biologically, the root of "organism" is *organization*, a characteristic *structural order*.

ORGANISM AND STRUCTURE

Levels of Organization

The smallest structural units of all matter, living matter included, are *subatomic particles*, for example, electrons, protons, and neutrons, to be discussed in the following chapter. The next larger units are *atoms*, each of which consists of subatomic particles. Atoms in turn form still more complex combinations referred to as *chemical compounds*, and the latter are variously joined together into even more elaborate units we may call *complexes of compounds*. We may regard these units as successively higher *levels of organization of matter*. Such levels constitute a hierarchy in which any given level contains all lower levels as components. Moreover, any given level is also a component of all higher levels. For example, atoms contain subatomic particles as components, and atoms are themselves components of chemical compounds (Fig. 2.6).

All structural levels up to and including that of complexes of compounds are encountered both in the nonliving and in the living world. For example, two familiar chemical compounds found both in living and nonliving matter are water and table salt. Examples of complexes of compounds in the nonliving world are sea water and rock, each of which is composed of several compounds in combination (water and table salt among them). Note that differences in mere physical bulk do not necessarily indicate differences in level of organization, Thus, a pebble and a mountain range have the same organizational level, that is, that of complexes of compounds. In living matter, complexes of compounds often occur as microscopic and submicroscopic bodies called *organelles*. We shall identify some of them and their functions in later chapters.

Even in their most elaborate and complicated forms—as organelles, for example—complexes of compounds as such cannot qualify as living units. To reach the level of life, we must go to the next higher structural level, namely, the level of *cells*. A cell is a specific combination of organelles, a usually microscopic bit of matter organized just complexly enough to contain all the necessary apparatus for the performance of metabolism and self-perpetuation. A cell in effect represents the least elaborate known structure that can be fully alive.

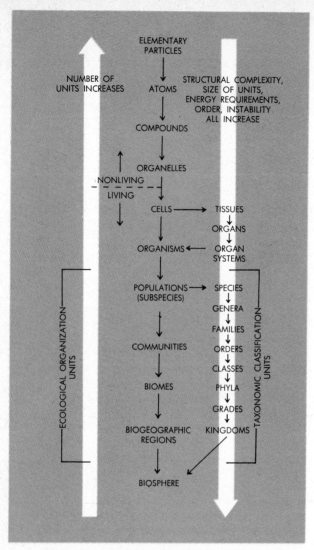

2·6 Hierarchy of levels in the organization of matter. *The definitions of the units in the subhierarchies of taxonomic classification are discussed in this chapter, those of ecological organization, in Chaps. 8 and 9.*

organisms contain not only several tissues, but some of the tissues may also be joined further into one or more units called *organs*. The most complex organisms contain not only many tissues and organs, but groups of organs may also form one or more structural combinations known as *organ systems*. In terms of structural levels, therefore, living organisms exhibit at least five degrees of complexity: the single-celled form, the colonial form, the organism with tissues, the type with organs, and the type with organ systems.

Beyond organisms of all kinds, several still higher levels of life may be distinguished. A few individual organisms of one kind together may make up a *family*. Groups of families of one kind may form a *society*. Groups of families, societies, or simply large numbers of organisms of one kind make up a geographically localized *population*. All populations of the same kind together form a *species*. Different species aggregate into a local *community*. And the sum of all local communities represents the whole living world (compare Fig. 2.6).

This hierarchial organization of matter into levels permits us to formulate a structural definition of life and nonlife. As we have seen, up to and including the level of the complex of compounds, matter is nonliving. At all higher levels matter is living provided that, at each such level, metabolic and self-perpetuative functions are carried out. To be living, a society, for example, must metabolize and self-perpetuate on its own level as well as on every subordinate level down to that of the cell.

Moreover, as life is organized by levels, so is death. Structural death occurs when one level is disrupted or decomposed into the next lower. For example, if a tissue is disaggregated into separate cells, the tissue ceases to exist. Structural death of this sort always entails functional death also, that is, disruption of the metabolic and self-perpetuative processes of the affected level. But note that disruption of one level need not necessarily mean disruption of lower levels. If a tissue is decomposed into cells, the cells may carry on as individuals (Fig. 2.7); if a family is disrupted, the member organisms still may survive on their own. On the other hand, death of one level always entails death of higher levels. If many or all of its tissues are destroyed, the whole organ will be destroyed; if many or all of its families are dismembered, a society may cease to exist. In general, the situation is comparable to a pyramid of cards. Removal of a top card need not effect the rest of the pyramid, but removal of a bottom card usually topples the whole structure. We recognize that neither life nor death is a singular state but is organized and structured into levels.

It follows that a living organism must consist of at least one cell. Indeed, *unicellular* organisms probably constitute the majority of living creatures on earth. All other organisms are *multicellular*, each composed from two up to hundreds of trillions of joined cells.

Several distinct levels of organization may be recognized within multicellular organisms. The simplest multicellular types consist of aggregations of comparatively small numbers of cells. If all such cells are more or less alike, the organism is often referred to as a cellular *colony*. If two or more different groups of cells are present, each such group may be called a *tissue*. Structurally more complex

PLATE I

1. Section through a pine needle (magnified approx. 20×). *Many different types of tissue may be seen; they cooperate to produce and maintain this leaf (an organ). In so doing the tissues surrender much of their freedom and independence of action.*

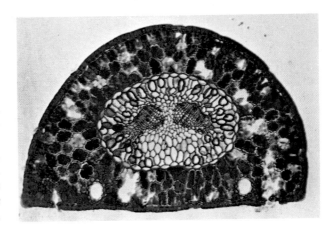

2. General structure of cells. *A, cells from the leaf of a plant. B, red blood cells of a frog. Note the stained nuclei in the cells (red in A, black in B), the external cellular covering membranes, and the cytoplasm between nucleus and cell surface (×3,000).*

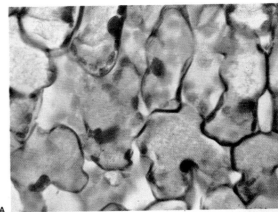

A

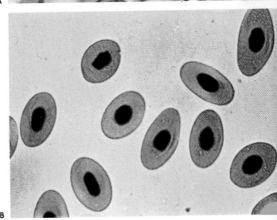

B

3. Fibroelastic connective tissue. *Note the conspicuous fibers forming a meshwork and the cells (small dark dots) embedded in the meshwork.*

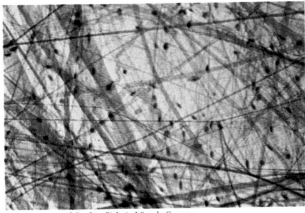

1, 2b, 3, courtesy of Carolina Biological Supply Company

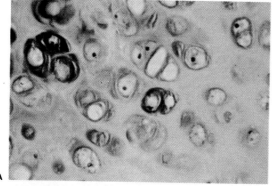

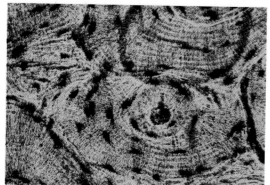

PLATE II

4. Cartilage and bone.
A, histological section through cartilage.
Note many cartilage-producing cells
(chondroblasts), surrounded by
their own secretions.
B, histological section through bone.
Note the concentric layers of a Haversian
system, with the bone-producing cells
(osteoblasts) located in the dark
patches. Hard bone substance, light
in the photo, surrounds the cells.
In the center of each such system
is a wider Haversian canal.

4, 5, courtesy of Carolina Biological Supply Company

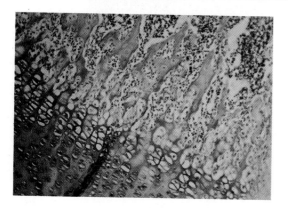

5. The transformation of cartilage into bone.

6. Muscle types.
A, a few fibers of skeletal muscle;
note the cross striations and
the nuclei within each fiber. (See also
Fig. 20.16 for structural details.)
B, smooth muscle; note the spindle-shaped cells.
C, cardiac muscle. Note the branching
fibers, the nuclei, the faint
longitudinal fibrils within each fiber,
and the cross striations.

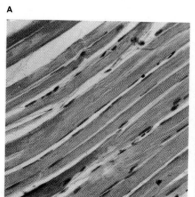

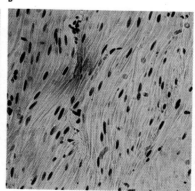

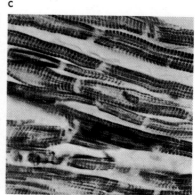

B, C, courtesy of Carolina Biological Supply Company

Note, incidentally, that the hierarchy of levels provides a rough outline of the past history of matter. There is good reason to suspect that the universe as a whole began in the form of subatomic particles. These then became aggregated into atoms and formed galaxies, stars, and planets. As will be shown in Chap. 11, the atoms of planets subsequently gave rise to chemical compounds and complexes of compounds. On earth, some of the complexes of compounds eventually produced living matter in the form of cells, and unicellular types later gave rise to multicellular types. Among the latter, colonial types arose first, forms with organ systems last. Considered historically, therefore, matter appears to have become organized progressively, level by level. The presently existing hierarchy is the direct result, and it still gives mute, built-in testimony of its own historical development.

Several characteristics inherent in the structural hierarchy are of significance. For example, each level of organization includes fewer units than any lower level. There are fewer communities than species, fewer cells than organelles; and there is only one living world, but there are uncountable numbers of subatomic particles. It should be clear also that each level is structurally more complex than lower ones; a given level combines the complexities of all lower levels, and it has an additional complexity of its own. Moreover, we may note that a jump from one organizational level to the next can be achieved only at the expense of energy. It takes energy to build atoms into chemical compounds, and it took energy to create cells out of chemical complexes. Similarly, energy is needed to produce tissues out of cells, societies out of families, or any other living level out of lower ones. Indeed, once a higher living level has been created, energy must continue to be expended thereafter to maintain that level. For example, if the energy supply to the cell, the organ, or the organism is stopped, death and decomposition soon follow and reversion to lower levels occurs. Similarly, maintenance of a family or a society requires work over and above that needed to maintain the organization of subordinate units.

This requirement is an expression of the *second law of thermodynamics*, about which more will be said in Chap. 5: if left to itself, any system tends toward a state of greatest stability. "Randomness," "disorder," and "probability" are equivalent to this meaning of stability. When we say that a system has a higher level of organization, we also say that the system exhibits a high degree of order, that it is nonrandom. The second law tells us that such a system is unstable and improbable and that if we leave it to itself, it will eventually become disordered and therefore more stable. Living systems are the most ordered, unstable, and improbable systems known. If they are to avoid the fate predicted by the second law, a price must be paid. That price is external energy—energy to push the order up, against the constant tug to tear the order down.

But this price of energy is well worth paying, for each higher level exhibits new and useful properties over and above those found at lower levels. For example, a cell exhibits the property of life in addition to the various properties of the organelles which compose it; a multicellular organism with organs such as eyes and brains can see and distinguish objects, whereas cells taken singly at best can only sense the presence or absence of light. In general, the basic new property attained at each higher level may be described as united, integrated function: nonaggregated structure means independent function and, by extension, *competition;* aggregated structure means joint function and, by extension, *cooperation.* Atoms, for example, may remain structurally independent, and they may then be in functional competition for other, suitable atoms with which they might aggregate. Once they do aggregate into a compound, they have lost structural independence and cannot but function unitedly, as a single cooperative unit. Similarly, cells may remain dependent structurally, and they may compete for space and raw materials. But if they aggregate into a tissue, they surrender their independence and become a cooperative, integrated unit.

This generalization applies at every other organizational level as well (see Color Plate I, 1). The

2 · 7 Disaggregated tissue cells of a mouse embryo, cultured in nutrient solution. Originally these cells were part of a compact tissue. Disaggregation destroyed the tissue level of organization but did not destroy the cellular level; the individual cells shown here remain alive.

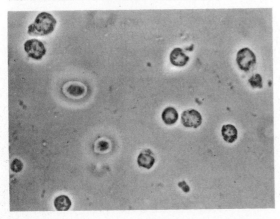

results on the human level are very familiar. Men may be independent and competing, or they may give up a measure of independence, form families and societies, and start cooperating. Note here that sociological laws governing human society are based on and are reflections of the more fundamental laws governing the organization of all matter, from atoms to the whole living universe.

Note also that competition and cooperation are not in any basic sense willful, deliberate, planned, or thought out; atoms or cells neither think nor have political or economic motives. Structural units of any sort simply function as their internal makeup dictates. And the automatic result of such functioning among independent units may be competition; among aggregated units, cooperation. To be sure, human beings may *decide* to compete or to cooperate, but this merely channels, reinforces, makes conscious, and is superimposed on what they would necessarily do in any event.

Specialization

The fundamental advantage of cooperation is *operational efficiency:* the cooperating aggregate is more efficient in performing the functions of life than its subordinated components separately and competitively. For example, a given number of nonaggregated cells must expend more energy and materials to survive than if that same number of cells were integrated into a tissue. Similarly for all other organizational levels.

One underlying reason for this difference is that, in the aggregate, duplication of effort may be avoided. For example, in a set of nonaggregated cells, every cell is exposed to the environment on all sides and must therefore expend energy and materials on all sides to cope with the impact of the environment. However, if the same cells are aggregated into a compact tissue, only the outermost cells are in direct contact with the environment and inner cells then need not channel their resources into protective activities.

In addition to avoiding duplication of effort, aggregation also permits continuity of effort. Such continuity is not always possible in nonaggregated units. We may illustrate the general principle by contrasting unicellular and multicellular organisms, for example. A unicellular organism must necessarily carry out all survival functions within its one cell. In many instances, however, the performance of even one of these functions requires most or all of the capacities of the cell. In many cases, for example, the entire cell surface is designed to serve as gateway for entering nutrients and departing wastes. The entire substance of the cell functions to dis-

2 · 8 An amoeba *(approx. ×5,000). Like all other unicellular organisms, this protozoon carries out all metabolic and self-perpetuative functions within the confines of its single cell. Note nucleus (dark central body), excretory vacuole (light spherical body), and the pseudopodia, fingerlike extensions functioning in locomotion and feeding.*

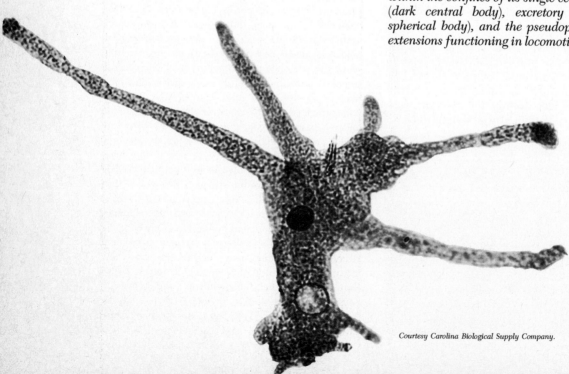

Courtesy Carolina Biological Supply Company.

tribute materials within it. And all parts of the cell may be required directly in locomotion or in feeding, for example (Fig. 2.8).

Very often, therefore, two such functions cannot be performed at the same time. Wherever locomotion and feeding each necessitate action by the whole cell surface, performance of one of these functions more or less precludes the simultaneous performance of the other. We shall find, moreover, that reproduction too involves the operational equipment of the whole cell, and in a unicellular organism this usually necessitates temporary suspension of both feeding and locomotion. Mutual exclusion of some functions by others is a common occurrence in all unicellular forms.

In multicellular forms, by contrast, continuity of effort becomes possible through *division of labor*. In such an organism, the total job of survival may be divided up into several subjobs, and each of these becomes the continuous responsibility of particular cells only. For example, some cells may function in feeding, continuously so, and other cells may function in locomotion, again continuously so. Indeed, division of labor in many cases is so pronounced that given cells are permanently limited in functional capacity; they can perform only certain jobs and no others. Thus, nerve cells can conduct nerve impulses only and are quite unable to reproduce or move. Muscle cells can move by contracting, but they cannot conduct nerve impulses and normally they do not reproduce. Most cells in many multicellular organisms have analogous limitations. Each group of cells is more or less restricted in its functional versatility and exhibits a particular *specialization* (Fig. 2.9).

In a multicellular organism, therefore, an individual specialized cell does not and indeed cannot perform all the functions necessary for survival. This is why, when some cells are separated away from the whole organism, as in injury, for example, such cells must usually die. The specialized cell has lost independence mainly because it is not very versatile, because it can do only some of the jobs necessary for survival. The whole job of survival can be carried out only by the entire integrated multicellular system, which does possess the required versatility by virtue of its many differently specialized cells.

Specialization makes possible not only division of labor but also increased effectiveness of labor. For example, all unicellular organisms are sensitive to environmental stimuli. But such organisms, which must perform all survival functions within their single cells, are not particularly specialized for any one of these functions. Consequently, although they

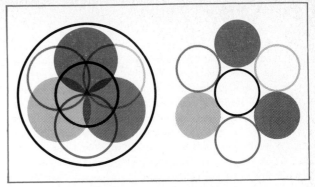

2 · 9 The principle of specialization. *The single-celled organism* (left) *must carry out all required functions* (symbolized by circles of various colors) *of a cell. In the multicellular organism* (right), *by contrast, each cell may specialize to carry out a single function only, with resulting gains in efficiency.*

are sensitive to stimuli, the degree and range of sensitivity are quite modest. By contrast, many multicellular organisms possess highly specialized sensory cells. Such cells can be exceedingly sensitive and may respond to even very weak stimuli. Moreover, several kinds of sensory cells may be present, some specialized specifically for light stimuli, others for sound stimuli, still others for mechanical stimuli, and so on. In short, the degree as well as the range of sensitivity can become enormously greater in cells which can specialize than in cells which cannot. This holds analogously for all other functions.

We may now understand the fundamental advantage of higher organizational levels generally and of multicellularity specifically. First, multicellularity makes possible division of labor, which prevents duplication of effort and permits continuity of effort. Secondly, division of labor leads to specialization, which permits any given effort to become highly effective. The overall result is an enormous saving of energy and materials, hence cheaper operation, and enormous gain in efficiency. Basically, this gain of cheaper yet more efficient operation is what has favored more and more aggregation in matter generally and in living matter particularly; and this is why living history has produced multicellular organisms, equipped successively with tissues, organs, and organ systems, rather than only bigger and better unicellular organisms.

Note, incidentally, that loss of functional versatility in a specialized cell is never total. A cell cannot be so completely specialized that it performs just a single function. Certain irreducible "housekeeping" functions must be carried out by every living cell of a multicellular organism. Every such cell must absorb nutrients, must respire and synthesize, and must maintain steady states relative to its immediate environment. These metabolic and self-perpetuative functions cannot be specialized. Performed continuously and simultaneously in every cell, they are the bedrock of cellular survival. Specialization only affects additional functions, and the fewer of such additional functions a cell performs, the more specialized it is. Analogously, a cell can never be completely unspecialized and be so versatile functionally that it could survive under any or all conditions. All cells, even the most independent, still depend on very *particular* environments, for example. Cells therefore may only be more or less highly specialized; and within limits, the relative degree of functional versatility is an inverse measure of the relative degree of specialization.

Most multicellular organisms actually consist of cells that exhibit widely different degrees of specialization. In view of the earlier discussion about comparative efficiencies, would it not be most efficient if a multicellular organism consisted exclusively of highly specialized cells? Probably not, because certain functions need not be performed continuously. For example, it would be quite wasteful to maintain a permanent set of specialized scar-tissue cells—the organism might never sustain an injury. Analogously, it is a decided advantage that, in many multicellular organisms, reproductive structures become fully developed only during seasons when reproduction actually occurs. Thus, the actual construction of the multicellular system permits the greatest possible economy of energy and materials. The most critical and continuously required functions are the responsibility of sets of permanently specialized cells. But less critical functions, and those required intermittently or only under unusual circumstances, are carried out by initially more versatile, less highly specialized cells.

In summary, the foregoing has shown that living units are organized structural aggregates at or above the cellular level of complexity, carrying out the functions of metabolism and self-perpetuation at every one of these levels. Energy must be expended to maintain the structural hierarchy, and the gain is greater division of labor and more specialization at successively higher levels. As a result of specialization, the versatility and independence of subordinate units is reduced, but the efficiency of maintaining life increases and the comparative cost in materials and energy decreases.

It follows also that a whole organism is more than the sum of its parts, for the organism exhibits properties over and above those of the totality of its components. The difference is a result of specialized organization, or pattern of arrangement. An organism is a collection of parts *plus* organization.

It follows further that the specializations of one level determine the specializations of higher levels. If the cells composing a tissue are specialized as muscle cells, then the whole tissue will be specialized correspondingly for contraction and movement. If the organs of an organ system include teeth, stomach, and intestine, then, since the organs perform nutritional functions, the whole organ system will be specialized for nutrition. Every organism as a whole therefore is itself specialized, in line with the particular specializations of its subordinate parts. For example, every organism is able to live in a *particular* environment only and is able to pursue only a *particular* way of life. A fish must lead an aquatic existence, a tree cannot do without soil, and man too is specialized in his own way. He requires a terrestrial environment of particular properties, a social environment of variously specialized human beings, a community of wheat, cattle, and other food organisms. In effect, the specializations of his body allow him to pursue no other but a characteristically human mode of life. And by being specialized, every organism in effect is a dependent, necessarily cooperating unit of a higher living level: the population, the whole species, the community of several species. These higher-level units are specialized in their own turn, according to the specializations of their members.

We recognize, then, that although all organisms are alike in general characteristics, they differ in specific characteristics because of specialization. Functionally, all organisms pursue life identically through metabolism and self-perpetuation; structurally, all organisms are composed of cells. But in each organism both the functions and the structures are in some respects specialized, and the specializations differ in different cases.

THE FORMS OF LIFE

TAXONOMIC CLASSIFICATION

Organisms can be classified on the basis of their specializations into more or less well-defined types or categories. The discipline dealing specifically with such classification is called *taxonomy* or *systematics*. A taxonomic system of classifying organisms was originated by Carolus Linnaeus, a Swedish naturalist of the early eighteenth century. This Linnaean scheme, now greatly elaborated and in universal use, is based on structural resemblances among organisms; if certain organisms can be shown to have similar construction, they may be regarded as members of the same classification group. Superimposed on such a classification, moreover, evolutionary theory permits formulation of a historical inference: the more closely two organisms resemble each other, the more closely are they likely to be related. Thus, taxonomy correlates the structural organization directly and evolutionary histories indirectly.

Within a given classification group it is often possible to distinguish several subgroups, each containing organisms characterized by even greater similarity of structure and, by inference, evolutionary history. Each such subgroup may then be subclassified still further, and a whole *hierarchy* of classification groups thus may be established. In this hierarchy, the progressively lower levels constitute so-called *taxonomic ranks*, or *categories*, and each is named; in succession from highest (most inclusive) to lowest (least inclusive), the main categories are: *kingdom, phylum, class, order, family, genus,* and *species*. Additional ranks may be interpolated between any two main ranks. In many cases such intermediate categories are identified by the prefixes *sub-* or *super-*; for example, *superclass, subgenus*. The specific organisms encompassed by a given category are often referred to as *taxa*. For example, the moss plants constitute a taxon of phylum rank; mammals are a taxon at the class rank.

Note that, in the hierarchy as a whole, progressively lower ranks consist of progressively more but smaller groups. Also, the progressively smaller groups

2 · 10 Taxonomy. *The pattern of the hierarchy of taxonomic ranks.*

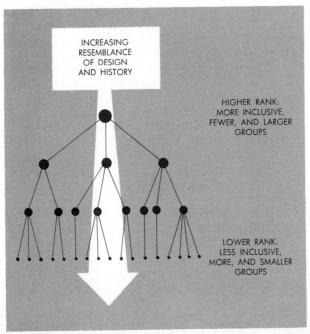

INCREASING RESEMBLANCE OF DESIGN AND HISTORY

HIGHER RANK: MORE INCLUSIVE, FEWER, AND LARGER GROUPS

LOWER RANK: LESS INCLUSIVE, MORE, AND SMALLER GROUPS

TABLE 1 THE TRADITIONAL CLASSIFICATION OF ORGANISMS INTO PLANT AND ANIMAL KINGDOMS

KINGDOM PLANTAE	KINGDOM ANIMALIA
subkingdom Thallophyta *algae, fungi, bacteria,* *slime molds* *subkingdom Embry-* *ophyta* *moss plants, vascular* *plants*	*subkingdom Protozoa* *largely unicellular* *types* *subkingdom Metazoa* *multicellular animals*

at successively lower ranks are characterized by an increasing resemblance of structure and an increasingly similar evolutionary history. For example, the members of a class resemble one another to a great extent, but the families within any of the orders of that class resemble one another to an even greater extent; and an analogous correlation holds for evolutionary histories (Fig. 2.10).

By tradition going back directly to Linnaeus, it has been customary to classify all organisms into two kingdoms, namely, the plant kingdom and the animal kingdom (Table 1). It is highly questionable whether this familiar, simple, and 250-year-old way of subdividing the living world is still justifiable or adequate today. For it is now clear that, in this Linnaean sense, plants and animals are completely undefinable by biological criteria. Every trait usually regarded as characteristic of one kingdom occurs also in the other. For example, plants are defined traditionally as organisms that photosynthesize and do not exhibit locomotion, and animals as organisms that exhibit heterotrophic nutrition as well as locomotion. On such a basis, however, many algae and all fungi and slime molds would have to be animals, for all these organisms are nongreen heterotrophs and a good many of them exhibit locomotion as well, at least in the reproductive stages. Yet sponges, corals, barnacles, tunicates, and other groups could not be strictly labeled as animals since they are sessile as adults, just as many algae are sessile in the mature state. Moreover, certain algal types and carnivorous green plants (such as Venus's flytraps) would be both plant and animal at once, since they are both photosynthetic and heterotrophic. Indeed, algae of this type can also be alternately sessile and motile.

Traits other than nutrition or locomotion fail similarly as distinguishing criteria. If animals are defined as organisms possessing nervous and muscular structures, or at least equivalent conductile and

TABLE 2 THE MAIN CATEGORIES OF LIVING ORGANISMS

CATEGORY	REPRESENTATIVE PHYLA	REPRESENTATIVE MEMBERSHIP
Monera	*Schizophyta*	*bacteria*
	Cyanophyta	*blue-green algae*
Protista	*Chlorophyta*	*green algae*
	Chrysophyta	*golden-brown algae*
	Phaeophyta	*brown algae*
	Rhodophyta	*red algae*
	Mycophyta	*fungi*
	Myxophyta	*slime molds*
	Protozoa	*protozoans*
Metaphyta	*Bryophyta*	*mosses, liverworts*
	Tracheophyta	*vascular plants, e.g., ferns, coniferous seed plants, flowering seed plants*
Metazoa	*Porifera*	*sponges*
	Cnidaria	*coelenterates, e.g., hydras, jellyfishes, corals, sea anemones*
	Platyhelminthes	*flatworms, e.g., planarians, flukes, tapeworms*
	Aschelminthes	*sac worms, e.g., rotifers, roundworms*
	Mollusca	*mollusks, e.g., snails, clams, squids, octopuses*
	Annelida	*segmented worms, e.g., earthworms, leeches*
	Arthropoda	*arthropods, e.g., crustacea (barnacles, shrimps, crabs, lobsters, crayfishes), insects, scorpions, spiders, ticks, millipedes, centipedes*
	Echinodermata	*spiny-skinned animals, e.g., starfishes, sea urchins, sea cucumbers, brittle stars, sea lilies*
	Chordata	*notochord-possessing animals, e.g., tunicates, amphioxus, vertebrates: jawless fishes (lampreys), bony fishes (herring, tuna, etc.), cartilage fishes (sharks), amphibia (salamanders, newts, toads, frogs), reptiles (turtles, lizards, snakes, alligators), birds, mammals*

contractile components, then many photosynthetic algae would have to be animals; and sponges, which are without such structures, would have to be plants. If plants are defined as organisms possessing chemicals such as cellulose, then tunicates would have to be plants and a number of entire phyla of photosynthetic algae without cellulose would have to be animals. In effect, there does not appear to be a single characteristic which would distinguish the traditional plant and animal kingdoms uniquely.

We may note, therefore, that given groups of organisms really fit into neither the plant nor the animal category and should in fact be regarded as something else. At the same time, several other groups fit into both categories. Traditional views notwithstanding, bacteria really have very little in common with either plants or animals, and as pointed out, quite a number of unicellular organisms

and others can be regarded equally well as plants *or* animals. To be sure, no one has much difficulty in deciding whether advanced organisms like cabbages and cats are plants or animals. But such a difficulty does exist with many organisms now known to be primitive, that is, those closely related to the ancestral types that gave rise to both cabbages and cats. As will be shown further in Chap. 12, such ancestral types possessed both plantlike and animallike features *simultaneously,* as is true of their primitive descendants today. And if we go even farther back in time, the very first organisms on earth probably possessed neither plantlike nor animallike features at all, as is again true of their present-day descendants.

The point is that plants and animals, clearly so recognizable, were not in existence right from the beginning. Rather, some of the early organisms *evolved* in plantlike or animallike directions, slowly and gradually; and a definite, finalized "plant" status or "animal" status was attained only relatively late in evolutionary history. Therefore, a division of the living world merely into plant and animal kingdoms is too simple. It does not take into account this gradual evolutionary development, and it allows no place for those primitive organisms which still are neither "plant" nor "animal" or which are both.

In view of this taxonomic difficulty, attempts have been made in recent years to establish alternative classifications that do reflect our present knowledge of evolution. One such alternative scheme recognizes not two but four highest groupings of organisms. Each of the four has a taxonomic rank roughly equivalent to a kingdom, although it may not be desirable to use this rank designation so long as it is technically still reserved for "plants" and "animals." The four highest taxa are the *Monera*, the *Protista*, the *Metaphyta*, and the *Metazoa*. The kinds of organisms included within each of these four groups are listed in Table 2, and the probable evolutionary interrelations of the four are sketched in Fig. 2.11.

The figure indicates that Monera and Protista go back farthest in evolutionary history. Both groups are believed to be descended independently from the earliest organisms on earth. Monera are characterized by a unique cell structure, more specifically, a structure that does not include an internal membrane around the genes of the organism. Modern moneran representatives are the bacteria and the blue-green algae, all basically unicellular organisms and variously plantlike, animallike, both, or neither. Protista do possess internal membranes around the

genes in their cells, and they are also characterized by numerous other common structural features not in evidence among the Monera (see Chap. 12). Ancient protists were undoubtedly unicellular and, as is still the case among many of their present-day descendants, were able to nourish themselves autotrophically as well as heterotrophically, that is, by plantlike and animallike methods simultaneously. From such ancestral types later evolved numerous multicellular descendants which reached the colony level and also the tissue level of structural complexity. Moreover, some of these organisms eventually lost the plantlike modes of nutrition and so became more or less "animal" in character. Conversely, others lost the animallike modes and became more or less distinctly "plant." Among the present representatives of the Protista, the various groups of *algae* include both unicellular and multicellular types, as well as types being either plantlike or animallike or still both simultaneously. The *fungi, slime molds,* and *protozoa* similarly include unicellular as well as multicellular forms, and all three of these groups are exclusively heterotrophic. Apart from their nutrition, however, the other traits of the three groups again have certain joint plantlike and animallike attributes. Fungi are rather more plantlike than animallike, and protozoa are more nearly animallike than plantlike.

Both the Metaphyta and the Metazoa are believed to have evolved from ancient protists, independently and at different times. Both groups are exclusively multicellular, their structural complexity reaching the level of complicated organs and organ systems. Moreover, both Metaphyta and Metazoa typically have life histories that include more or less distinct *embryos*, a characteristic not in evidence (or at best only vaguely suggested) in the Protista.

Metaphyta are almost exclusively photosynthetic

2 · 11 *The four main categories of organisms and their probable evolutionary interrelations.*

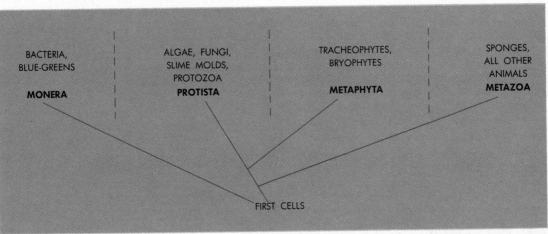

and without locomotion, and they are unmistakably "plants." They include the *bryophytes,* or moss plants, and the enormous and far more important group of *tracheophytes,* or vascular plants. Metazoa are exclusively nonphotosynthetic and largely (but not always) capable of locomotion; they are unmistakably "animals."

Thus, unlike the two Linnaean kingdoms, each of the four more recent major categories can be defined sharply and distinguished clearly from the other categories. Moreover, the present scheme has the important advantage that it is more nearly in line with the known evolutionary and structural characteristics of existing organisms. Throughout this book, therefore, we shall restrict any unqualified reference to plants or animals to mean specifically Metaphyta or Metazoa, respectively. Analogously, we shall not refer to an alga as a plant or to a protozoon as an animal, but shall identify both types of organisms as protists.

As pointed out above, the next highest main taxonomic rank is the *phylum.* In precise traditional usage this term had been reserved for major groups within the animal kingdom, whereas the term *division* had been employed for equivalent major groups within the plant kingdom. In view of the inadequacies of the "kingdoms" scheme just discussed, it is difficult in many cases to decide whether to use the term "division" or the term "phylum." We shall arbitrarily and uniformly use the designation "phylum" throughout.

The phylum rank describes a broad grouping of historically more or less closely related organisms, all characterized by a common structural organization. As indicated in Table 2, for example, all fungi as a group represent a phylum and all sponges as a group represent a phylum. Within a phylum, the next highest main rank is the *class.* For example, sponges may be subdivided into classes on the basis of their skeletons, one group having calcium skeletons, another silicon skeletons, and a third horny skeletons. Similarly, the phylum *Chordata* includes all animals possessing an internal skeleton, the *notochord,* at least as embryos. This phylum contains a subphylum of *vertebrates,* characterized by the presence of a vertebral column (and all other animals are often referred to collectively as *invertebrates*). Within the vertebrate subphylum, one of the classes is represented by the *mammals.* These animals share the possession of a vertebral column with all other vertebrate classes, namely, birds, reptiles, amphibia, and several classes of fishes. But mammals are set off from other vertebrate classes by their possession of hair and by their nursing young with milk. Each other class has its own distinguishing features.

Using such criteria of likenesses and differences among and within groups, one may recognize *orders* within a class, *families* within an order, *genera* within a family, and *species* within a genus. The species normally is the lowest unit; it is defined as an *interbreeding* group: members of two different species usually do not interbreed (see, however, Chap. 8). A species thus encompasses all organisms of the same particular kind. For example, all men now in existence are members of the same single species.

According to Linnaean tradition and internationally accepted rules, a species is always identified by *two* technical names. These names are in Latin or are latinized and are used uniformly all over the world. For example, the species of grass frogs is known technically as *Rana pipiens;* the species to which we belong is *Homo sapiens.* Such species names are always underlined or printed in italics, and the first name is capitalized. This first name always identifies the genus of which the species is a member. Thus, the human species belongs to the genus *Homo* and the grass-frog species to the genus *Rana. Homo sapiens* happens to be the only presently living species within the genus *Homo,* but the genus *Rana* contains *Rana pipiens* as well as many other frog species.

A complete classification of an organism tells a great deal about the nature of that organism. For example if we knew nothing else about corn plants and men except their taxonomic classifications, then we would know that the characteristics of these organisms are as listed in Table 3. By implication, moreover, we would also know that the evolutionary history of corn plants traces back to the common ancestry of flowering plants and that the history of men goes back to a common chordate ancestry. Evidently, even brief taxonomic characterizations such as these place an organism rather well, and we may note that a full, detailed classification would describe an organism completely.

TAXONOMIC COMPARISONS

That classification gives direct and inferential information about *two* kinds of organismic attributes, namely, body structure and evolutionary history, should be clearly kept in mind. Both attributes encompass not only the developmental and the adult stages of organisms but also all levels of structural organization, from the molecular to the organismic. Organisms are characterized by other attributes as well, notably by functions and by ways of life. These, however, play only a limited role in defining organismic types. Because the basic functions of metabolism and self-perpetuation are the same in all organisms,

TABLE 3 A PARTIAL CLASSIFICATION OF CORN PLANTS AND MEN

TAXONOMIC RANK	CORN PLANT	MAN
phylum	Tracheophyta: plants with vascular tissues	Chordata: animals with notochords
subphylum	Pteropsida: types with large leaves	Vertebrata: types with vertebral columns
superclass	Spermatophyta: seed producers	Tetrapoda: terrestrial; four limbs, bony skeletons
class	Angiospermae: flowering plants: seeds inside fruits	Mammalia: types with hair and milk glands
subclass	Monocotyledonae: parallel-veined leaves; single seed leaf; flower parts in threes or multiples	Eutheria: offspring develop within female parent, nourished by placenta
order	Graminales: grasses	Primates: fingers; flat nails
family	Graminaceae: leaves in two rows on round or flattened stem	Hominidae: upright posture; flat face; stereoscopic vision; large brains; hands and feet
genus	Zea: corn plants	Homo: double-curved spine; long life span and long youth
species	Zea mays: cultivated, domesticated corn plants	Homo sapiens: well-developed chins; high forehead; thin skull bones

essentially two kinds of data. And because it encodes a very considerable amount of information about organisms the system is far more than an empty naming scheme. That is why it is in universal use today and why other systems of classification, which *were* mere naming schemes, have not survived beyond the time of Linnaeus.

Another point requires special emphasis. As noted, the taxonomic system tacitly postulates or infers that a common body organization is correlated with a common ancestry. How firmly can such a causal interconnection actually be established? Can it be demonstrated that the body forms within a given taxonomic group resemble one another *because* the organisms have all evolved from a common ancestry?

Structural resemblances of presently living organisms can be studied readily, and indeed they are largely well known. Studies of ancestral fossil organisms and deductions of historical interrelations represent an independent line of investigation, and the amount of information available here varies greatly. In general, evolutionary knowledge is progressively more precise for progressively lower taxonomic ranks. But above the phylum level, and in many cases at the phylum level, such knowledge is lacking almost entirely. It has been found that, for the lower ranks, a classification based on evolutionary history actually does dovetail well with an independently deduced classification based on living body forms. Such agreements justify and lend firm support to the generalization that "common body organization implies common ancestry."

However, where evolutionary information is incomplete or is lacking altogether, classification must be based almost wholly on body organization. Conclusions about common ancestries then rest on very insecure foundations. It is well known, for example, that two structural patterns can have quite different ancestries yet be similar nevertheless, the organisms having made similar adaptive responses to common survival requirements. We shall discuss such phenomena in Chap. 31. In short, unless structural information can actually be supported by independently obtained evolutionary information, inferences as to ancestries may be quite unwarranted. Such evolutionary inferences are being made nevertheless, and different biologists frequently propose different inferences from the same structural data. This explains why the classifications of the higher taxa often vary from text to text. Thus, a particular group of organisms may in one case represent a distinct phylum, in another a superphylum containing several smaller phyla, or in still another a class within a larger phylum. Indeed, general agreement among biologists becomes better with the lower taxonomic

such functions are not very useful as distinguishing traits. Moreover, both the ways of life and the detailed ways of performing functions can become modified greatly and can be adapted readily to fit particular environmental requirements. Such criteria therefore are usually less permanent than the architecture of the body and evolutionary history. Consequently, the taxonomic system incorporates

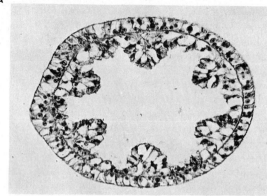

A, *courtesy of Carolina Biological Supply Company.*

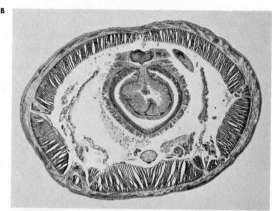

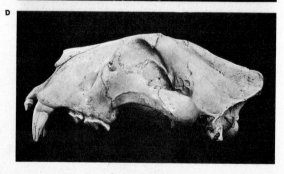

ranks and worse with the higher ranks. The higher-rank categories actually are being reshuffled and reclassified more or less continually. This is probably as it should be, however, for as our knowledge of evolutionary histories improves, the taxonomic rankings must be adjusted accordingly.

We may note that, where structural and evolutionary data are in substantial agreement, classification is said to be *natural;* that is, it reflects an actual interrelation of organisms. The most natural taxonomic group is undoubtedly the *species.* In this instance, a reproductive characteristic, namely, the interbreeding potential, resulting from close similarity of structure and evolutionary history becomes a clearcut taxonomic criterion. On the other hand, where structural and evolutionary agreement is lacking, or where evolutionary histories are known incompletely or are only guessed at, classification remains far less natural. Classification actually tends to become progressively more "unnatural" at ranks above the species level, particularly so above the level of classes. Although most phyla are probably natural groupings, certain ones almost surely are not. For example, it is virtually certain that protozoa represent an unnatural taxonomic group; the different protozoan subgroups appear to have evolved from not one but several separate ancestral stocks (see also Chap. 12). Indeed, most protistan and moneran phyla may be unnatural in this sense. It follows that the very highest ranks probably constitute the most unnatural groupings of all. As noted, the original kingdom designations are no longer adequate in the light of modern knowledge, and it is likely that the present designations of main categories will eventually be made inadequate by improved future evolutionary

2 · 12 Structural and evolutionary comparisons. A, *photomicrographic cross section through a hydra, a coelenterate; B, through an earthworm, an annelid. On the basis of the number of tissue layers present in each, the hydra can be considered to be simpler in structure than the earthworm. Hydra also happens to be more primitive, that is, the evolutionary history of the coelenterate phylum goes back further than that of the annelid phylum. C shows the bones of a fish skull, and D, a lion skull. On the basis of the number of bones present in each, the fish skull is structurally more complex, yet it is more primitive from an evolutionary standpoint than the lion skull. Thus, a given degree of structural complexity does not necessarily or automatically signify a comparable degree of evolutionary advancedness.*

knowledge. The degree of unnaturalness in classification thus is a measure of the degree of our relative ignorance about past events.

In a discussion of different organisms or groups, it is often desirable to make comparative statements about two or more body forms and/or evolutionary histories. The taxonomic system and its evolutionary implications then prescribe what kinds of comparisons are legitimately possible. Several sets of contrasting terms are employed, and it is important to use them correctly.

Simple—Complex

These terms indicate comparative degrees of structural and/or functional elaboration of organisms and their parts. Degrees of elaboration are judged by the *number* of components present and by the number of *interrelations* among the components (Fig. 2.12). The terms therefore describe *organizational* and *operational* attributes of organisms, not evolutionary attributes. If we say that one organism, say a man, is more complex than another, say a bacterium, we mean only that it possesses comparatively more cells, tissues, or other units, and comparatively more interrelations among these units; we do not make *any* evolutionary comparison. A higher level of organization, in the sense defined earlier in this chapter, does signify "more complex." Within a given level of organization, comparative complexity must be judged on the basis of the number of parts and the abundance of interrelations. Note also that it is quite meaningless to speak of "simple" organisms or parts; all units of life are exceedingly complex to begin with, and the terms "simple" and "complex" have biological information content only if they are used in a *comparative* manner.

Primitive—Advanced

These adjectives are often—and wrongly—employed as equivalents for "simple" and "complex." Unlike the latter, "primitive" and "advanced" do have primarily historical, evolutionary connotations. If organisms or their parts are structured according to ancient, ancestral patterns, we may say that such patterns are primitive; newer, more modern patterns superimposed on the ancient ones then are considered advanced, again by comparison only (see Fig. 2.12). Evolutionary "earliness" and "lateness" and similar time-contrasting terms are roughly equivalent to "primitive" and "advanced." Note that an organism or a part of it may be more primitive yet at the same time more complex than another (for example, protistan cells are more primitive and probably more complex than most metazoan or metaphytan cells); more advanced yet simpler than another (for example, a human skull is more advanced but simpler—with far fewer bones—than a fish skull); and also more primitive as well as simpler, or more advanced as well as more complex (for example, jellyfishes are more primitive and simpler than vertebrate fishes).

Generalized—Specialized

These terms have both structural *and* evolutionary connotations. A pattern is generalized (= unspecialized) if it can be and actually has been further modified, for example, through simplification or complication; it is specialized if it is already modified. For example, the segmented body of an annelid,

2 · 13 Generalized and specialized structures. A, *the leg of a grasshopper, a rather generalized leg type within the broad scope of insect design (even though such a leg is already specialized considerably, for example, for jumping). B, the leg of a honeybee, a comparatively more clearly specialized type: a subterminal segment is enlarged into a bristly pollen basket, adapted specifically for pollen transport, and the leg as a whole is equipped abundantly with bristles, a feature which facilitates adherence of pollen.*

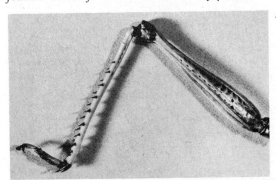

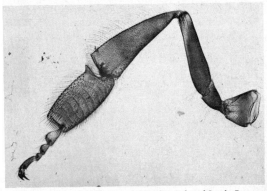

B, courtesy of Carolina Biological Supply Company.

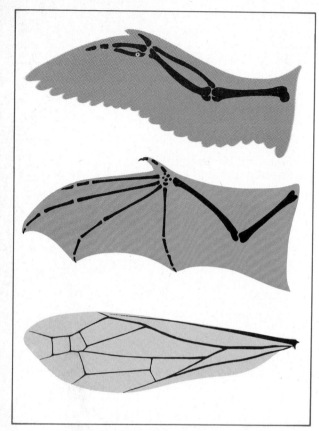

2 · 14 Homology and analogy. *The bird, bat, and insect wings diagrammed here are all analogous, since all serve the same function of flying. Bird and bat wings are also homologous, since they develop in similar fashion and have similar structure. But insect wings are not homologous to either of the other two.*

exemplified by an earthworm, is generalized by comparison with the segmented body of an arthropod, as exemplified by an insect; the arthropod body is a modified annelid body (Fig. 2.13). Generalized structures originate earlier than, and they may later give rise to, specialized structures, both in evolutionary and in embryonic history. Hence generalized patterns are usually more primitive than specialized ones (but they are not always simpler).

Homologous—Analogous

As noted earlier, function and way of life play only relatively small roles as taxonomic criteria. It happens often, therefore, that the various subgroups within a taxonomic rank exhibit widely different methods of executing functions and highly different ways of life. Consider, for example, the different ways of a desert plant like a cactus, an aquatic plant like a water lily, and an underground plant like an onion bulb; or consider the different ways of a fish and a man. Nevertheless, all organisms within a phylum use the same kinds of structures in solving the different problems of their different environments. Thus, the spines of a cactus, the surface float of a water lily, and the white, tear-producing layers inside an onion bulb, all are basically the same kind of structures, namely, leaves; they all have evolved along different paths from one ancestral type of foliation. Analogously, the fins of a fish and the arms of a man are basically the same kind of structures, having evolved from one common ancestral type of body appendage.

Whenever body parts within an organism or in different organisms have evolved from a common ancestral starting point, as in the examples just cited, and whenever they also develop embryologically in like fashion and thus have the same structure at least initially, then such components are said to be *homologous*. Homology therefore connotes similarity of history and structure, without reference to function. Indeed homologous structures may or may not function the same way. For example, the fins of fish and the arms of man do not function in the same manner, yet they are homologous. Whenever two structures do function in like fashion, regardless of history or structure, they are said to be *analogous*. Bird wings and bat wings are analogous. They also happen to be homologous, but note that analogous structures need not always be homologous as well. For example, bird wings and insect wings are analogous inasmuch as both are used for flying, but they are not homologous (Fig. 2.14). We note that "homology" is essentially a single term for the two principal criteria on which taxonomy rests; a study of homologies is the basis of classification.

Higher—Lower

These adjectives have a proper role only in reference to taxonomic and organizational levels and in a literal sense. Thus, a phylum is higher in the taxonomic hierarchy than a class, a tissue is higher in the organizational hierarchy than a cell, and a bird may be higher off the ground than a worm. In other biological respects, the terms are either erroneous, or meaningless if they are used in a structural or evolutionary sense—as they often are. Several decades ago it was believed that evolution occurred in a scalelike or ladderlike pattern, one organismic type giving rise to another in serial fashion. The terms "lower" and "higher" were used to indicate "rung" positions on the evolutionary "ladder." Also, since "highest" generally meant "man," human vanity could be pleasantly satisfied by regarding all other organisms as being "lower."

However, it is now very clearly established that evolution is not ladderlike but has the general pattern of a greatly branching *bush* (Fig. 2.15). All presently living organisms are *contemporaries*, appearing at the uppermost branch tips of the bush. Ancestral types, mostly long extinct, appear lower on the bush, where branches join. Thus, a particular common ancestor may give rise to *several* different types of descendants, each inheriting the characteristics of the common ancestor and evolving innovations of its own. And a particular descendant living today may become a common ancestor of new and different types living tomorrow.

Evidently, it is no longer possible to speak of a ladder or a scale of evolution, implying a straight-line progression from one organism directly to the next, usually from some "low" type like an alga or a protozoon to some "high" type like a tree or a man. For a tree or a man stands only just as "high" (or just as "low") on the evolutionary bush as *every* other organism now living. Yet, although the terms "high" and "low" thus have lost any biological significance, old terminologies become habits that die slowly. Even professional biologists (generally trained in an earlier day) still frequently speak of "higher" or "lower" organisms when the intended reference is to advanced and/or more complex ones or to primitive and/or simpler ones. Indeed, the terms are not only erroneous but also superfluous. For example, in a statement such as "man is a higher animal than a dog inasmuch as man has a more complex brain," the term "higher" is a man-centered value judgment without any biological information content, for the biologically significant information is fully expressed by the statement "man has a more complex brain than a dog." It might be noted that the sense of

2 · 15 Bush pattern of evolution. *The uppermost tips of the branches represent currently living forms, and branches terminating below the top represent extinct forms. Fork points such as B and C are ancestral types. B is more ancient and of higher taxonomic rank than C. A represents the archancestor of all living types.*

smell is developed far better in a dog than in a man, yet this does not make the dog "higher" either. The point is that the terms should be avoided if scientifically meaningful comparisons of organisms are to be made.

Our preliminary characterization of the general nature of life and the entities exhibiting life is now completed. We proceed next to a study of the basic materials out of which all living things are constructed.

REVIEW QUESTIONS

1. What is metabolism? Self-perpetuation? What are the principal component functions of each of these, and what specific roles do these functions play in the maintenance of life?

2. What are the fundamental differences between inanimate, dead, and living systems? Discuss carefully and fully. Define living.

3. Review the hierarchy of levels in the organization of matter, and discuss how living matter is characterized in terms of levels.

4. Review the relation of levels of organization to energy, to aggregation, to complexity, to competition and cooperation, and to operational efficiency.

5. Define cell (*a*) structurally and (*b*) functionally. Define organelle, tissue, organ, organ system, organism.

6. In terms of cellular specializations, how does a cell of a single-celled organism differ from a cell of a multicellular organism? Cite examples of specialization on the tissue, organ, organism, and species levels of organization.

7. What are heterotrophism and autotrophism? Name and characterize the different variant forms of each and cite types of organisms in which these variant forms are encountered.

8. Review the structure of the Linnaean taxonomic system. What are the principal ranks? Name and define them and cite a taxon of each. How is this system related to the size and the numbers of groups at each rank? How is the system related to the hierarchy of organizational ranks?

9. What criteria form the basis of the taxonomic system? What are the advantages of these criteria, and why are other possible criteria not used? Why are organisms not simply classified alphabetically or by some system equivalent to book cataloguing in libraries?

10. What is meant by natural and unnatural taxonomic classifications? Give examples. What rules are in force in the naming of species? Review the taxonomic classification of a corn plant and man, with attention to the definition of each taxon.

11. Explain the proper biological use of the following contrasting sets of terms: simple—complex; primitive—advanced; and generalized—specialized. Criticize and correct the following statements: "Evolution consists of a progression from simple to more complex types of organisms." "In the evolutionary scale, higher organisms such as vertebrates have descended from lower forms such as worms."

12. Define homology, analogy. Give specific examples of each. Why are homologies more important in taxonomy than analogies?

COLLATERAL READINGS

Bonner, J. T.: The Social Amebae, *Sci. American,* June, 1949.

————: Volvox, a Colony of Cells, *Sci. American,* May, 1950. Two case studies of living organization on the level of the cell colony. The impermanent cellular colonies of slime molds are discussed in the first article, the complex spherical colony of a green alga, in the second.

Grobstein, C.: "The Strategy of Life," Freeman, San Francisco, 1965. A thoughtful and stimulating paperback containing a section on levels of organization as well as discussions of other general phenomena of life.

Kemeny, J. G.: Man Viewed as a Machine, *Sci. American,* Apr., 1955. The article shows that computing machines can be built which can learn and even reproduce like living systems.

Mayr, E., E. G. Linsley, and **R. L. Usinger:** "Methods and Principles of Systematic Zoology," McGraw-Hill, New York, 1953. One of the important standard texts on taxonomy, well worth consulting for further information on this subscience of biology.

Penrose, L. S.: Self-reproducing Machines, *Sci. American,* July, 1959. Models of self-duplicating mechanical systems are described, paralleling the action of self-duplicating biological systems.

Schrödinger, E.: "What is Life?," Cambridge University Press, Cambridge, 1944. A stimulating booklet by a noted physicist, discussing some of the basic characteristics of living material.

Wald, G.: Innovation in Biology, *Sci. American,* Sept., 1958. In this article the characteristics of living systems are interpreted in terms of our present knowledge in the physical sciences.

PART TWO
THE CHEMICALS OF LIFE
CHAPTER 3
ELECTRONS AND ATOMS
CHAPTER 4
ATOMS AND BONDS
CHAPTER 5
REACTIONS AND ENERGY
CHAPTER 6
COMPOUNDS AND CELLS

Regardless of where, when, or how we examine the structure of any living creature, we ultimately find it to consist *entirely of chemicals*. And regardless of what particular function of an organism we examine, that function is ultimately always based on the properties of the constituent chemicals. Moreover, it is now clear that before there were living creatures on earth, there were only chemicals; organisms originated out of chemicals (compare Chap. 11). Chemicals in turn are composed of atoms. Thus, the story of life is now known to be largely a story of atoms and of chemicals; and it should not be surprising that physics and chemistry today are among the important background sciences to biology. Indeed, modern biology simply *is* physics or chemistry or both, and very many professional biologists are good physicists or chemists. You too will have to understand certain fundamentals of these background sciences, and the four chapters of this part are designed to provide the beginnings of such understanding. The first three chapters deal with the nature and properties of chemicals generally, and the last chapter examines the specific construction of the particular chemicals found in living material. The part as a whole therefore serves both as an introduction to the basic structural aspects of life and as an essential foundation for much of the functional biology discussed in later parts of the book.

CHAPTER 3
ELECTRONS
AND
ATOMS

The whole material universe, all living matter included, is made up of fundamental substances called chemical *elements*. Iron, silver, gold, copper, and aluminum are some familiar examples of such elements. Altogether, 92 different elements exist naturally, and 11 additional ones have to date been created artificially by man (among them, for example, plutonium).

Each element consists of unimaginably tiny units called *atoms*. An atom may be said to be the smallest complete unit of an element. Thus, a gold atom is the basic unit of the element gold. The first letter or the first two letters of the common or Latin name of an element are used as the chemical symbol of that element. For example, the symbol for hydrogen is H, that for carbon is C, that for silicon is Si (see Table 7, page 52, for complete list). To represent one atom of an element, the appropriate symbol is written alone. For example, the letter H stands for one atom of hydrogen. If more than one atom is to be indicated, the appropriate number is put before the atomic symbol. For example, 5 H stands for five separate hydrogen atoms.

On earth, the atoms of most element actually do not exist as separate units. Instead, given numbers of atoms of given elements are attached to one another more or less firmly and form larger chemical combinations called *compounds*. Virtually all familiar substances consist of one or more of such compounds —liquids like water, gases like air, solids like stones, and also complex liquid-gas-solid mixtures like living things.

The atoms composing any compound are held together by forces referred to as chemical *bonds*. How do atoms form chemical bonds between them— how, in other words, are compounds produced? To answer this question, we must examine the internal structure of atoms.

ATOMS

The atoms of all elements are constructed out of components collectively known as *elementary particles* (or fundamental, or subatomic, particles). Three types of such particles will concern us most: *protons, neutrons,* and *electrons*. Protons and neutrons occur in the center of an atom, where they form an *atomic nucleus*. Electrons are on the outside of a nucleus.

NUCLEAR STRUCTURE

A proton has mass, or "weight." This mass is the same for all protons, and it is given the arbitrary unit value 1. A mass of 1 also characterizes a neutron, which is consequently just as heavy as a proton. By contrast, the mass of an electron is very much less than 1 (specifically, 1,836 times less), which makes its weight practically negligible. Therefore, the total mass of a whole atom is concentrated almost entirely in its nucleus.

The number of protons and neutrons present in an atomic nucleus thus determines the *atomic mass*. For example, the simplest type of atom is that of hydrogen. Its nucleus consists of a single proton, and there is a single electron on the outside; neutrons are absent. Since the nucleus therefore has a mass of 1, the atomic mass of hydrogen is said to be 1. By contrast, the most complex of the naturally occurring types of atoms is the atom of uranium. Its nucleus contains 92 protons as well as 146 neutrons. Therefore, the atomic mass of uranium is 238 (Fig. 3.1). The atomic masses of all other elements range between 1 and 238, according to the specific number of protons and neutrons in the atomic nuclei.

In addition to their mass, the elementary particles also have certain electrical properties. As suggested by their name, neutrons (n) are electrically neutral. Protons are electrically positive; more specifically, each proton carries one unit of positive electric

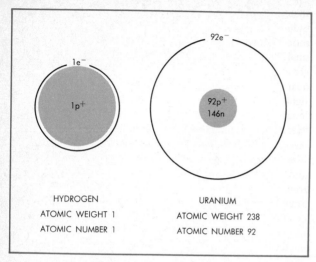

HYDROGEN
ATOMIC WEIGHT 1
ATOMIC NUMBER 1

URANIUM
ATOMIC WEIGHT 238
ATOMIC NUMBER 92

3 · 1   Atomic structure of hydrogen and uranium. The atomic nucleus of hydrogen contains a single proton; that of uranium, 92 protons and 146 neutrons.

charge (p^+). Electrons are electronegative, each carrying one unit of negative charge (e^-).

In each normal atom, the number of protons is exactly equal to the number of electrons. As noted, for example, a hydrogen atom consists of 1 proton (positively charged) and 1 electron (negatively charged). In a uranium atom there are 92 protons in the nucleus (see above), and there are also 92 electrons on the outside. All other atoms similarly display such numerical equality of the positive-charge carriers in the nucleus and the negative-charge carriers on the outside. Hence each atom considered as a whole is electrically neutral.

The number of electrons (or protons) in an atom defines an *atomic number*. Hydrogen has atomic number 1; uranium, atomic number 92. It should be clear that if both the atomic number and the atomic mass of an atom are known, the composition of that atom is also known. For example, if the atomic number is 26 and the atomic mass is 56, then the atom contains 26 electrons on the outside and there must be 26 protons plus 30 neutrons in the nucleus. This happens to be the actual composition of an atom of iron. In certain contexts, rapid reference to either or both the atomic mass and atomic number of an element may be desirable. The appropriate figures are then indicated as a superscript and a subscript to the chemical symbol. For example, iron (Fe) may be symbolized as Fe^{56} or as $_{26}Fe^{56}$.

In virtually any pure sample of an element, most atoms present have a mass normally characteristic of that element. For example, most atoms in a sample of pure hydrogen have a mass of 1, and most atoms in a sample of pure carbon have a mass of 12 $(_6C^{12})$. However, a small number of atoms is usually present in such samples in which the atomic mass differs from the normal by one or two mass units. In a carbon sample, for example, some of the atoms are likely to have a mass of 14; in a hydrogen sample, some atoms usually have a mass of 2. Such differences are due to variations in *neutron* numbers. Thus, some hydrogen atoms do possess one neutron in the nucleus, in addition to a proton. The atomic mass then is 2, and such unusual H atoms are called *heavy* hydrogen, or *deuterium* (symbol D). Analogously, the normal carbon atom possesses 6 protons and 6 neutrons, but an unusual form of carbon contains 6 protons and 8 neutrons in the nucleus. The atomic mass here is therefore 14, and such atoms are referred to as heavy carbon, or carbon 14. The general designation *isotope* is given to any atom in which the nuclear mass differs from the norm due to the presence of fewer or more neutrons.

Note that isotopic atoms differ from normal ones only in *physical* properties, that is, mass, not in chemical properties; the proton and electron counts are identical to those of normal atoms. In naturally occurring elements, it happens that small percentages of the atoms present are isotopic. Hence if a natural sample of a given element is weighed, the weight will not be an integral whole number. For example, the measured *atomic weight* of natural hydrogen is 1.008, that of carbon, 12.011. The fractions in excess of 1 and 12, respectively, result from the presence of heavier isotopes in the samples. We may note, therefore, that atomic *mass* is always a whole number but that atomic weight is not, since the weight reflects the presence of various proportions of slightly different atomic masses. As we shall see, the existence of isotopes is often useful in biological research; for if both isotopic and normal atoms participate in a given chemical process, the different mass of the isotopic atoms provides an identifying *label* through which such atoms may be distinguished physically from the normal atoms.

ELECTRONIC STRUCTURE

We shall soon find that most of the specifically *chemical* properties of atoms are determined by the electrons outside their nuclei. It is therefore necessary to examine the characteristics of these electrons in some detail. Undoubtedly the most basic of these characteristics is that the electrons are not stationary but move around the nucleus. They are kept in orbital paths by electric attraction; the negatively charged electrons are attracted to the positively charged protons in an atomic nucleus. An atom thus resembles a miniature solar system to some extent. Just as gravitational forces maintain planets in orbit around a sun, so also do forces of electric attraction keep the electrons in orbits around an atomic nucleus. Since they all carry identical negative electric charges, electrons repel one another, and their positions will therefore be a compromise between mutual repulsion and collective nuclear attraction.

Their movement endows electrons with *kinetic energy*, or energy of motion. Additionally, electrons possess varying amounts of *potential energy*, according to how close or far away they are from the nucleus. The situation here is comparable to apples on trees and apples on the ground. The potential energy of an apple on a tree is greater than that of one on the ground, for on a tree an apple is farther away from the center of the earth and thus will be attracted less strongly by gravitational force. In atoms, analogously, the energy level of electrons varies in direct proportion to their distance from the nucleus; potential electron energies increase as the distance from the nucleus increases.

Indeed, the electron energies obey the dictates of the *quantum theory*, one of the most significant conceptions in modern science. According to this

3 · 2 *Diagrams of atoms show the seven possible electron orbits, identified by principal quantum numbers. Energy levels increase from the nucleus (at bottom) outward. Left: atom absorbs energy of a photon (wavy line), leading to atomic excitation and escape of an electron (emission of free electrons, or beta particles). Right: capture of a free electron by an atom leads to the escape of energy (emission of photons, or gamma particles); for example, in fluorescence.*

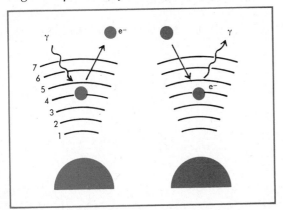

theory, energy is discontinuous; it does not flow or radiate in an uninterrupted stream but exists as a series of distinct packets, each packet representing a smallest possible energy unit. Such minimum units are *quanta*. In the case of light, for example, the quanta are specifically called *photons,* and a beam of light consists of a succession of photons. Each wavelength of light is characterized by photons of particular energy content. In general, the smallest possible difference between any two energy quantities or energy levels is one quantum, and this requirement applies also to the electrons in atoms. Consequently, since electron energies are correlated with distances from the atomic nucleus, it follows that the electrons cannot occupy a continuous space around a nucleus but can be present only at discontinuous intervals from the nucleus. Thus, all electrons having the same energy level will be equally distant from the nucleus. All electrons having energy levels one quantum higher will be farther out, but again all these will be at equal distances. In effect, *all* electrons of an atom must therefore be organized into a series of layers, or *shells*, lying one outside the other around the nucleus. Any given shell represents a given energy level, and the consecutive shells represent energy levels differing by one quantum from one to the next. Electrons can be present only at these set distances from the nucleus.

The shell distances are said to represent *quantum levels*. Each is identified by a number, called the *principal quantum number* (*n*). From the nucleus outward, the values of *n* are 1, 2, 3, 4, 5, 6, 7. In no known atom are there more than 7 electron shells (Fig. 3.2). An electron normally remains in the shell corresponding to its quantum level, and it is then said to be in the *ground state*. Under certain conditions, however, an electron may jump into another shell. For example, if heat or light or other forms of energy are supplied to an atom from the outside, an electron may absorb some of this energy and may thereby acquire a higher energy level. This change is accompanied by an electron jump to one of the shells farther away from the nucleus, and the electron is then said to be in an *excited state*. Absorption of a single energy quantum from the outside will lead to a single *quantum jump;* that is, the electron will move into the next higher shell. If more quanta are absorbed, quantum jumps to correspondingly higher shells will occur. By absorbing a sufficiently large number of quanta (namely, more than 7 in the case of the innermost electrons), an electron may actually become so energetic that it jumps right out of the atom altogether and moves off into space as a *free electron*. The latter are often called beta (*β*) particles, and electron emission from atoms is referred to as *beta radiation*. Radioactive elements give off beta radiation spontaneously. But any other element may become similarly beta-radiating if the electrons of its atoms become sufficiently excited through absorption of external energy.

Conversely, electrons may undergo quantum jumps to shells closer to the atomic nucleus, a process accompanied by loss of energy quanta from the electrons. Such lost energy is emitted from atoms in the form of electromagnetic radiation of a particular wavelength, for example, light. For every single quantum

3 · 3 *The first four main orbital shells and their subshells.*

The number and shape of the subshells are defined by the azimuthal quantum number (l). Thus, the fourth main shell contains four subshells, namely, the circular 4s and the progressively more elliptical 4p, 4d, and 4f subshells. Note that, for clarity, each set of subshells has been drawn distinct from the neighboring sets; in actuality some overlap is in evidence. For example, the 3d subshell actually reaches slightly farther orbits from the nucleus than the 4s subshell (see Fig. 3.4). Even so, the average energy level of any given main shell is greater than that of any lower-numbered main shell.

jump of an electron to the next lower shell, one photon is emitted. These photons are often called gamma (γ) particles, and photon emission is known as *gamma radiation*. Naturally radioactive elements produce such radiation spontaneously but, as in the case of beta radiation, any other element likewise may become gamma-radiating. Fluorescent substances are good examples. If such a substance is illuminated from an external light source, many of its electrons absorb some of the light energy, thereby become excited, and jump to higher orbits. If then the external illumination ceases, the excited electrons soon return to their ground states and in the process they emit photons in amounts equivalent to what they had absorbed originally. The result is that such substances are temporarily self-luminous in the dark (cf. Fig. 3.2).

We may conclude generally that the principal quantum number *n* specifies one of the important attributes of an electron, namely, its ground state position in a particular electron shell, and therefore also its energy level and distance from the nucleus. A second major characteristic is the *shape* of the orbit an electron describes around the nucleus. Orbits can be of four possible shapes, namely, circular,

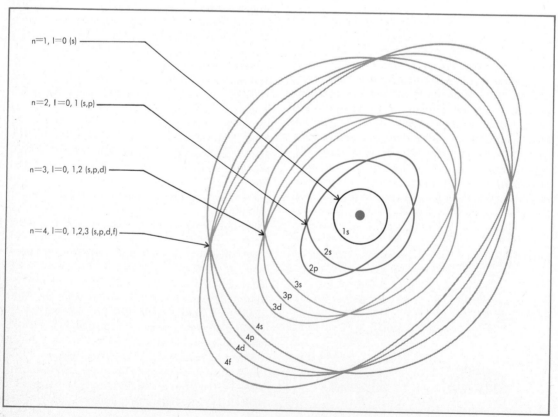

n=1, l=0 (s)

n=2, l=0, 1 (s,p)

n=3, l=0, 1,2 (s,p,d)

n=4, l=0, 1,2,3 (s,p,d,f)

1s
2s
2p
3s
3p
3d
4s
4p
4d
4f

slightly elliptical, moderately elliptical, or extremely elliptical. A so-called *azimuthal quantum number* (l) identifies these shapes. The numerical values of l are 0, 1, 2, and 3, and if $l = 0$ the orbit is circular; the higher values identify the progressively more elliptical orbits. Can the orbits in any shell be of any of the possible shapes? The answer is no, for the position of a shell limits the orbit shapes that can occur in that shell; for any given value of n (principal quantum number), the *maximum* number of orbit shapes is specified by the relation $l = n - 1$. Thus, if $n = 1$ then $l = 0$, which means that in the first shell, closest to the nucleus, all electron orbits are circular. In the second shell ($n = 2$), l can be shown to have the possible values 0 and 1. These numbers signify that some of the electrons will move in circular orbits, all others in orbits having slightly elliptical shape. In the third shell ($n = 3$), the possible l values are 0, 1, and 2. Orbit shapes are therefore in part circular, in part somewhat elliptical, and in part even more elliptical. In the fourth and all higher shells, l values are 0, 1, 2, and 3; that is, only in such shells can all four possible orbit shapes actually occur (Fig. 3.3).

An important consequence now emerges. Whenever the electrons of a given shell follow more than one orbit shape, such electrons cannot all have precisely identical energy levels. In an elliptical orbit, for example, an electron will be farther from the nucleus in some parts of its path than in others, hence its energy will fluctuate considerably as it travels around the nucleus. The pattern of this fluctuation will be different for each value of l. In the case of a circular orbit, to be sure, an energy fluctuation will not occur. But for all elliptical orbits such a fluctuation will be in evidence and it will be the greater the higher the l value, that is, the more elliptical the orbit. Therefore, although all electrons in a given shell do have the same *average* energy level, they must have different *specific* levels in accordance with the geometrical differences of their orbits. This means, in effect, that the number of orbit shapes in a shell defines an equal number of *subshells*, the latter differing from one another in specific energy levels. It can actually be shown that, within the general energy level characteristic of a particular shell, specific energy levels are lowest for circular orbits and highest for the most elliptical ones. Thus, in shells where $l = 3$, as many as four distinct subshells are present, corresponding to the l values 0, 1, 2, and 3. The *average* of the energy levels of all four subshells together defines the quantum level of the shell as a whole, that is, the n value, but each subshell nevertheless has its own specific quantum level. Since this level is lowest for the

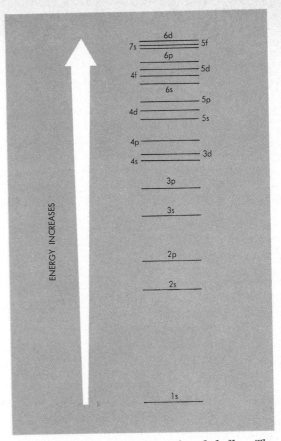

3 · 4 Relative positions of subshells. *The atomic nucleus (not shown) lies toward the bottom of the diagram.*

subshell with circular orbits, the latter must lie nearest to the nucleus.

The four possible subshells are symbolized by the letters s, p, d, and f: s for $l = 0$, p for $l = 1$, d for $l = 2$, and f for $l = 3$. In the first main shell ($n = 1$), we already know that $l = 0$, hence this main shell is equivalent to an s subshell; other subshells are not present. The structure of this first shell may therefore be symbolized as $1s$, the numeral here identifying the shell as a whole (n value), and the letter, the subshell (l value). In the second shell, where $n = 2$, l has the values 0 and 1, hence two subshells may be present, namely, s and p. The whole shell is therefore identified by the symbols $2s$, $2p$, the numerals here again corresponding to the n value and the letters to the two possible l values. Analogously, the third main shell can have three possible subshells, s, p, and d, and the whole shell may be represented as $3s$, $3p$, $3d$. The fourth and all higher shells may possess all four possible subshells, s, p, d, and f. The symbol $6f$, for example, then refers to the outermost subshell in the sixth principal shell (see Fig. 3.3).

Accurate experimental measurements of energy levels have shown that some of the principal shells overlap to a certain extent, such that the outermost subshell of one main shell may have a higher specific energy level (and lie farther away from the nucleus) than the innermost subshell of the next higher main shell. Figure 3.4 indicates the actual relative positions of the successive shells and subshells. The figure shows, for example, that the 4f subshell represents a slightly higher specific energy level than the 6s subshell, even though the fourth principal shell *as a whole* is closer to the nucleus than the sixth principal shell as a whole.

In addition to having specific shell and subshell positions, electrons are characterized further by magnetic properties which determine the *space orientation* of the electron orbits with reference to the nucleus. A *magnetic quantum number* (m_l) describes such orbit orientations. The value of m_l is zero for all s subshells. This correlation signifies that all s orbits are *unoriented* relative to the nucleus; that is, circular orbits may occur in any plane passing through the nucleus. The totality of such possible orbits will mark out a sphere, in which the nucleus lies at the center. The region of space in which an electron may normally move is called an *orbital*. We may say, therefore, that any s subshell is characterized by a single, spherical orbital (Fig. 3.5). For p subshells, m_l has three possible numerical values, namely, -1, 0, and $+1$. These quantum numbers signify that p electrons may have (elliptical) orbits oriented in up to three different directions of space. These may be visualized best as three axes at right angles to one another, with the nucleus at the common point of intersection. The

orbitals may then be envisaged as dumbbell-shaped spaces, one along each axis. In other words, a p electron is most likely to be found in an ellipsoid space to either side of the nucleus, along any of the three axes.

Note that the geometries of electron motions become quite complex in all but the first main shell, 1s, where only a single, spherical orbital exists. In the second shell, the 2s subshell has a spherical orbital and the 2p subshell is split into three dumbbell-shaped orbitals as just described above. In the third shell, the 3s and 3p subshells again have one spherical and three dumbbell-shaped orbitals, respectively, and the 3d subshell is characterized by five additional orbitals. These five are specified by the m_l values -2, -1, 0, $+1$, and $+2$. It is not necessary here to attempt a description of the complex three-dimensional shapes and orientations of these orbitals. We may likewise omit characterization of the seven orbitals into which f subshells are split, as in the fourth and higher shells. The m_l values for the seven possible f orbitals are -3, -2, -1, 0, $+1$, $+2$, and $+3$. Note generally that the maximum possible number of orbitals in all s, p, d, and f subshells is 1, 3, 5, and 7, respectively.

A fourth and final basic characteristic of electrons is that they *spin;* like a planet, each electron rotates around its own axis as it moves along its orbital path. A *spin quantum number* (m_s) describes this axial rotation. Only two values are possible for m_s, namely, $+\frac{1}{2}$ or $-\frac{1}{2}$. The meaning of these figures is roughly comparable to clockwise and counterclockwise. In other words, an electron can spin axially only in one direction or in the opposite direction, but not in any other. In any atom, therefore, any two electrons will have either *parallel* or *antiparallel* spin; they must rotate either in the same or in the opposite sense. Other possibilities are excluded by quantum theory.

The four attributes just outlined and specified by the four quantum numbers n, l, m_l, and m_s together are said to define the *quantum state* of an electron. We may describe the fundamental properties of an atomic electron fully if its quantum state is known. Moreover, the various possible quantum states, summarized in Table 4, provide us with a general blueprint of the "skeletal" structure of any atom. As we have seen, atomic electrons are organized grossly into shells, each shell may be split up more finely into subshells, each subshell in turn may be split up still more finely into orbitals, and in each orbital electrons spin and move around the nucleus. In the atoms of the actual elements, *how many* electrons are present in the various shells, subshells, and orbitals? We already know that different elements can

3 · 5 *Magnetic quantum numbers* (m_l) *determine the shapes of electron orbitals. At left is a spherical s orbital (for* $m_l = 0$). *At right, three dumbbell-shaped p orbitals are set in the three axes of space (for* $m_l = -1, 0, +1$). *For clarity, only the forward half of the p orbital in the z axis is shown.*

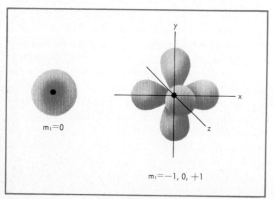

$m_l = 0$

$m_l = -1, 0, +1$

TABLE 4 SUMMARY OF QUANTUM STATES OF ORBITAL ELECTRONS IN FIRST THREE MAIN SHELLS

principal quantum number n; main shells	1	2				3								
azimuthal quantum number l; subshells	0	0	1			0	1			2				
magnetic quantum number m_l; orbitals	0	0	−1	0	+1	0	−1	0	+1	−2	−1	0	+1	+2
spin quantum number m_s	$+\frac{1}{2}$ $-\frac{1}{2}$	$+\frac{1}{2}$ $-\frac{1}{2}$	$+\frac{1}{2}$ $-\frac{1}{2}$	$+\frac{1}{2}$ $-\frac{1}{2}$	$+\frac{1}{2}$ $-\frac{1}{2}$	$+\frac{1}{2}$ $-\frac{1}{2}$	$+\frac{1}{2}$ $-\frac{1}{2}$	$+\frac{1}{2}$ $-\frac{1}{2}$	$+\frac{1}{2}$ $-\frac{1}{2}$	$+\frac{1}{2}$ $-\frac{1}{2}$	$+\frac{1}{2}$ $-\frac{1}{2}$	$+\frac{1}{2}$ $-\frac{1}{2}$	$+\frac{1}{2}$ $-\frac{1}{2}$	$+\frac{1}{2}$ $-\frac{1}{2}$

be arranged in a series of increasing atomic numbers, from 1 to 103, and that an atom of any element normally possesses one electron more than an atom of the preceding element in the series. The problem now is to determine the actual distribution patterns of these increasing numbers of electrons.

THE PERIODIC TABLE

The patterns of electron distribution can be predicted on the basis of an important corollary of the quantum theory, the so-called *Pauli exclusion principle*. This principle states that, in any atom, *no two electrons can have identical quantum states*. Put another way, the values of the four quantum numbers must differ in at least one particular for all of the electrons present in an atom.

A most important consequence is that no orbital can be occupied by more than two electrons; and these two must have antiparallel spins, for any *one* given orbital is characterized by one particular n value, one particular l value, and one particular m_l value. Since all electrons present in this orbital are identical in these respects, they must, if their quantum states are to be different, differ in their spins. And since the only allowable spins are $+\frac{1}{2}$ and $-\frac{1}{2}$, two antiparallel electrons will represent the maximum permitted in any one orbital. If a third electron *were* present, its spin would have to be identical to that of one of the first two electrons, and two of the three electrons would then have identical quantum states—precisely what the exclusion principle excludes.

It follows, therefore, that the maximum numbers of electrons in the successively higher shells of an atom must be 2, 8, 18, 32, 32, . . . , as shown in Table 5. The actual electronic configuration of any atom may now be deduced on the basis of these figures and on the basis of one additional specification: any atom, as indeed any material in the universe, will tend to assume the lowest possible energy level. We shall speak of this important generalization again in Chap. 5, in conjunction with the laws of thermodynamics. Accordingly, as electron numbers

TABLE 5 MAXIMUM ELECTRON NUMBERS POSSIBLE IN SHELLS AND SUBSHELLS; MAXIMUM PER ORBITAL IS 2

MAIN SHELL	s 1 ORBITAL	p 3 ORBITALS	d 5 ORBITALS	f 7 ORBITALS	TOTAL
1	2				2
2	2	6			8
3	2	6	10		18
4	2	6	10	14	32
5 to 7	2	6	10	14	32

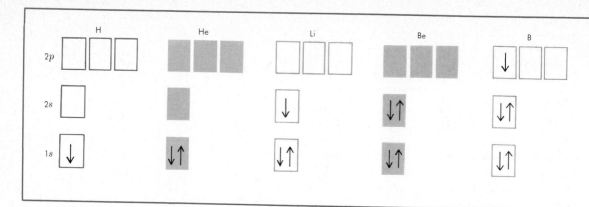

3 · 6 Electron configurations of the first ten elements. Each electron is shown as an arrow. Paired arrows pointing in opposite directions indicate electron pairs with antiparallel spin. The three 2p orbitals are shown as three joined boxes.

increase from 1 to 103 in the series of elements, each additional electron will go to the orbital in which the energy level is lowest and which is not already completely filled by previous electrons. Also, if a choice of two or more orbitals of the same lowest energy level should happen to be available, then an electron will go to a completely empty orbital, not one already containing one electron; for electrons repel one another and will therefore tend to remain as uncrowded as possible.

In hydrogen, with atomic number 1, the single electron present consequently will occupy the 1s space, the lowest available orbital (Fig. 3.6). Helium possesses two electrons. The first will be in 1s as in hydrogen, and the second will likewise occupy 1s, for this orbital can accommodate two electrons and it is still the one with the lowest available energy level. However, the spins of the two electrons must be antiparallel. Helium consequently possesses a completely filled first shell. A third electron, as in lithium, can be accommodated only in the second shell, more specifically, in the 2s orbital, the lowest energy level now available. A fourth electron, as in beryllium, analogously occupies (and fills completely) the 2s orbital, and a fifth electron, as in boron, must go into one of the 2p orbitals. If a sixth electron is present, as in carbon, it too must be situated in a 2p orbital, but because of electron repulsion this sixth electron will occupy a new 2p orbital, not the one already holding the fifth electron. Analogously, a seventh electron, as in nitrogen, likewise will go into a new 2p orbital, so that in nitrogen each of the three 2p orbitals holds one electron. An eighth electron, as

in oxygen, then becomes the second, antiparallel electron in one of the 2p orbitals, and the ninth and tenth electrons, as in fluorine and neon, respectively, fill the remaining 2p orbitals. In neon, therefore, the whole second shell is filled completely (see Fig. 3.6).

In like manner, additional electrons in progressively heavier atoms successively fill the available orbitals in the third and the higher shells (Table 6). Note that, after the 3p orbitals are filled (in argon, atomic number 18), the nineteenth electron (of potassium) does not go into the third subshell but the 4s subshell instead. As Fig. 3.4 indicates, 4s represents a slightly lower energy level than 3d even though 4s belongs to a higher main shell; hence the lowest available energy level for the nineteenth electron is 4s, not 3d. This holds also for the twentieth electron (in calcium), and only the twenty-first (in scandium) begins filling the 3d shell. In effect, argon is the heaviest atom in which the outermost electrons are entirely in the third shell; in all heavier atoms, the fourth or a higher shell forms part or all of the atomic "surface." Note also that uranium, the heaviest natural element, possesses only partly filled fifth, sixth, and seventh shells, 5f, 6d, and 7s here being the highest subshells containing electrons. Even in the man-made elements beyond uranium, 6f and 7p, d, f are empty.

Inspection of Table 6 also shows that, in any atom, the highest-numbered main shell never has more than eight electrons in outermost positions; once a main shell holds more than the eight (which fill the s and p subshells), then the next higher main shell already holds at least one electron as well. We note, therefore, that the electronic configurations in the outermost shells of the different atoms have an inherent repeat pattern. For example, at regular intervals in the series of elements will be found atoms having only one electron in the outer shell. An analogous set can be found with two outer elec-

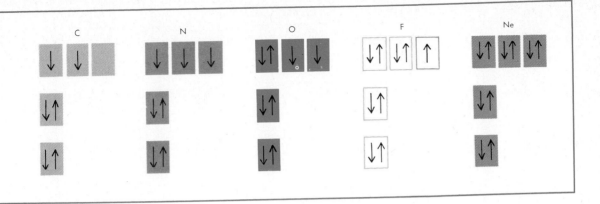

trons, another set with three, and soon up to a final set with eight. Consequently, if one lists the elements by increasing atomic numbers but in such a way that elements with similar configurations of the outer electrons are lined up in vertical columns, then a *periodic table* will result, that is, a chart in which the repeating characteristics are discernible readily. A widely used form of such a chart is depicted in Table 7, page 52.

The table yields the highly significant generalization that elements within a given column (group) possess not only like numbers of outer electrons, but also remarkably similar chemical properties. For example, all elements in group I, namely, H, Li, Na, K, Rb, Cs, and Fr, undergo the same kinds of chemical reactions, and any one of the elements in the group can usually substitute for any of the others in such reactions. Analogous similarities are in evidence within any other group. Such periodically similar behavior had been noted long before electrons were discovered. The first periodic table was constructed in 1869 by the Russian chemist Mendelejev, who did so purely on the basis of known chemical similarities among elements. Since then the electronic foundations of the chemical similarities have become firmly recognized, as has the principle that the *chemical properties of atoms are determined by their outermost electron shells.*

The most fundamental chemical property of an atom is its *reactivity,* that is, its ability to form particular series of combinations with other atoms and thus to participate in the formation of chemical bonds and chemical compounds. This property is examined in the next section.

IONS AND MOLECULES

A filled outermost electron shell is said to be *complete* or *closed.* All elements in group 0 of the periodic table, namely, helium, neon, argon, krypton, xenon, and radon, have closed shells in this sense. In these elements, the first, second, third, fourth, fifth, and sixth shells, respectively, are outermost and filled with electrons (two in the case of helium, eight in all the others). Atoms of all other elements possess *incomplete* or *open* outer shells, elements in group I being the most incomplete, those of group VII the least incomplete.

It can be shown that an atom is electronically and chemically most stable only when its outer electron shell is complete. "Most stable" here is equivalent in meaning to "least reactive." Indeed, elements of group 0, which possess complete outer shells, are quite inert chemically and are normally unable to react with other elements or with one another. These elements are often referred to as the *inert gases.*

All other elements, having variously incomplete outer shells, are chemically unstable and reactive to a greater or lesser extent. That is, if appropriate kinds and numbers of atoms of such elements are brought into contact, then such atoms *will tend to acquire complete shells by appropriating electrons from one another.* The result of such *reactions* is the formation of chemical *bonds* between atoms, that is, the formation of *compounds.* This tendency to acquire complete outer shells is exhibited more or less forcefully by different kinds of atoms, and it constitutes the underlying cause for chemical interactions among atoms. The interactions have been shown to occur in two principal patterns and to result in two principal kinds of chemical bonds and kinds of compounds.

IONS

How can an originally incomplete electron shell become complete? Consider an atom of chlorine ($_{17}Cl^{35}$). Of the 17 orbital electrons, 2 form a com-

TABLE 6 THE ELECTRON CONFIGURATIONS OF THE ELEMENTS

ELEMENT	1	2		3			4				5				6				7
	s	s	p	s	p	d	s	p	d	f	s	p	d	f	s	p	d	f	s
1 H	1																		
2 He	2																		
3 Li	2	1																	
4 Be	2	2																	
5 B	2	2	1																
6 C	2	2	2																
7 N	2	2	3																
8 O	2	2	4																
9 F	2	2	5																
10 Ne	2	2	6																
11 Na	2	2	6	1															
12 Mg	2	2	6	2															
13 Al	2	2	6	2	1														
14 Si	2	2	6	2	2														
15 P	2	2	6	2	3														
16 S	2	2	6	2	4														
17 Cl	2	2	6	2	5														
18 Ar	2	2	6	2	6														
19 K	2	2	6	2	6		1												
20 Ca	2	2	6	2	6		2												
21 Sc	2	2	6	2	6	1	2												
22 Ti	2	2	6	2	6	2	2												
23 V	2	2	6	2	6	3	2												
24 Cr	2	2	6	2	6	5	1												
25 Mn	2	2	6	2	6	5	2												
26 Fe	2	2	6	2	6	6	2												
27 Co	2	2	6	2	6	7	2												
28 Ni	2	2	6	2	6	8	2												
29 Cu	2	2	6	2	6	10	1												
30 Zn	2	2	6	2	6	10	2												
31 Ga	2	2	6	2	6	10	2	1											
32 Ge	2	2	6	2	6	10	2	2											
33 As	2	2	6	2	6	10	2	3											
34 Se	2	2	6	2	6	10	2	4											
35 Br	2	2	6	2	6	10	2	5											
36 Kr	2	2	6	2	6	10	2	6											
37 Rb	2	2	6	2	6	10	2	6			1								
38 Sr	2	2	6	2	6	10	2	6			2								
39 Y	2	2	6	2	6	10	2	6	1		2								
40 Zr	2	2	6	2	6	10	2	6	2		2								
41 Nb	2	2	6	2	6	10	2	6	4		1								
42 Mo	2	2	6	2	6	10	2	6	5		1								
43 Tc	2	2	6	2	6	10	2	6	6		1								
44 Ru	2	2	6	2	6	10	2	6	7		1								
45 Rh	2	2	6	2	6	10	2	6	8		1								

ELEMENT	1	2		3			4				5				6				7
	s	s	p	s	p	d	s	p	d	f	s	p	d	f	s	p	d	f	s
46 Pd	2	2	6	2	6	10	2	6	10										
47 Ag	2	2	6	2	6	10	2	6	10		1								
48 Cd	2	2	6	2	6	10	2	6	10		2								
49 In	2	2	6	2	6	10	2	6	10		2	1							
50 Sn	2	2	6	2	6	10	2	6	10		2	2							
51 Sb	2	2	6	2	6	10	2	6	10		2	3							
52 Te	2	2	6	2	6	10	2	6	10		2	4							
53 I	2	2	6	2	6	10	2	6	10		2	5							
54 Xe	2	2	6	2	6	10	2	6	10		2	6							
55 Cs	2	2	6	2	6	10	2	6	10		2	6			1				
56 Ba	2	2	6	2	6	10	2	6	10		2	6			2				
57 La	2	2	6	2	6	10	2	6	10		2	6	1		2				
58 Ce	2	2	6	2	6	10	2	6	10	2	2	6			2				
59 Pr	2	2	6	2	6	10	2	6	10	3	2	6			2				
60 Nd	2	2	6	2	6	10	2	6	10	4	2	6			2				
61 Pm	2	2	6	2	6	10	2	6	10	5	2	6			2				
62 Sm	2	2	6	2	6	10	2	6	10	6	2	6			2				
63 Eu	2	2	6	2	6	10	2	6	10	7	2	6			2				
64 Gd	2	2	6	2	6	10	2	6	10	7	2	6	1		2				
65 Tb	2	2	6	2	6	10	2	6	10	9	2	6			2				
66 Dy	2	2	6	2	6	10	2	6	10	10	2	6			2				
67 Ho	2	2	6	2	6	10	2	6	10	11	2	6			2				
68 Er	2	2	6	2	6	10	2	6	10	12	2	6			2				
69 Tm	2	2	6	2	6	10	2	6	10	13	2	6			2				
70 Yb	2	2	6	2	6	10	2	6	10	14	2	6			2				
71 Lu	2	2	6	2	6	10	2	6	10	14	2	6	1		2				
72 Hf	2	2	6	2	6	10	2	6	10	14	2	6	2		2				
73 Ta	2	2	6	2	6	10	2	6	10	14	2	6	3		2				
74 W	2	2	6	2	6	10	2	6	10	14	2	6	4		2				
75 Re	2	2	6	2	6	10	2	6	10	14	2	6	5		2				
76 Os	2	2	6	2	6	10	2	6	10	14	2	6	6		2				
77 Ir	2	2	6	2	6	10	2	6	10	14	2	6	7		2				
78 Pt	2	2	6	2	6	10	2	6	10	14	2	6	9		1				
79 Au	2	2	6	2	6	10	2	6	10	14	2	6	10		1				
80 Hg	2	2	6	2	6	10	2	6	10	14	2	6	10		2				
81 Tl	2	2	6	2	6	10	2	6	10	14	2	6	10		2	1			
82 Pb	2	2	6	2	6	10	2	6	10	14	2	6	10		2	2			
83 Bi	2	2	6	2	6	10	2	6	10	14	2	6	10		2	3			
84 Po	2	2	6	2	6	10	2	6	10	14	2	6	10		2	4			
85 At	2	2	6	2	6	10	2	6	10	14	2	6	10		2	5			
86 Rn	2	2	6	2	6	10	2	6	10	14	2	6	10		2	6			
87 Fr	2	2	6	2	6	10	2	6	10	14	2	6	10		2	6			1
88 Ra	2	2	6	2	6	10	2	6	10	14	2	6	10		2	6			2
89 Ac	2	2	6	2	6	10	2	6	10	14	2	6	10		2	6	1		2
90 Th	2	2	6	2	6	10	2	6	10	14	2	6	10		2	6	2		2
91 Pa	2	2	6	2	6	10	2	6	10	14	2	6	10	2	2	6	1		2
92 U	2	2	6	2	6	10	2	6	10	14	2	6	10	3	2	6	1		2

plete first shell, 8 a complete second shell, and the remaining 7 an incomplete third shell (see Table 6). We already know that the third shell can hold eight electrons in outermost position. Evidently, the chlorine atom is just one electron short (in one of its $3p$ orbitals) of having a complete set of outer electrons. If the atom could in some way *gain* one more electron, it would satisfy its very strong tendency for electronic completeness and stability.

Consider now an atom of sodium ($_{11}Na^{23}$). Of the 11 electrons here present, 2 form a complete first shell, 8 a complete second shell, and the remaining 1 a highly incomplete third shell (see Table 6). If this atom were to *lose* its single $3s$ electron, its second shell would then in effect become the outermost shell. Inasmuch as this second shell is complete, the atom would have satisfied its tendency for completeness and would be stable.

It appears therefore that chlorine is unstable because it has one electron too few and that sodium is unstable because it has one electron too many. In view of this circumstance, could not *both* atoms become stable simultaneously if they transferred one electron from one atom to the other—if chlorine were to gain the one electron that sodium were to lose? This can indeed happen under appropriate

TABLE 7 THE PERIODIC TABLE OF ELEMENTS

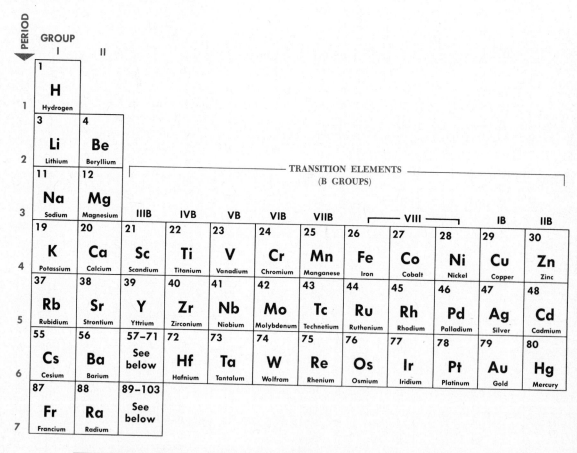

conditions. When it does, it represents an example of one major class of chemical reactions: an *electron-transfer reaction* (Fig. 3.7).

More than two atoms may participate in such a reaction and more than one electron may be transferred. For example, consider the interaction of magnesium and fluorine. Magnesium possesses two electrons in its incomplete third shell; if it were to lose these two, it would become stable. Fluorine possesses seven electrons in its nearly complete second shell; if it were to gain one more electron, its second shell would contain a full set of eight. Magnesium and fluorine may now interact by electron

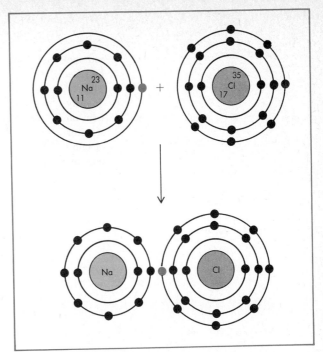

3 · 7   Electron-transfer reactions. *In a reaction between one atom of sodium and one of chlorine, the single electron in the third shell of sodium becomes transferred to the third shell of chlorine. As a result, sodium now has a complete outer (second) shell of eight electrons and chlorine has a complete outer (third) shell of eight electrons. In this joined form, the sodium and chlorine atoms constitute the compound sodium chloride.*

transfer. However, magnesium must lose *two* electrons, yet fluorine need gain only *one*. To make the transaction balance, therefore, each magnesium atom would have to interact with *two* fluorine atoms. This is how the reaction actually occurs (Fig. 3.8). In other words, if a magnesium-fluorine reaction is to achieve electronic stability for all participating atoms, then three atoms must interact and two electrons must be transferred. This reaction illustrates the general principle that a reaction can occur only if all participants achieve electronic stability. Different reactions therefore require the interaction of different numbers of given atoms and the transfer of different numbers of electrons.

Because of the negative charges of electrons, electron transfers have important electrical consequences. Consider again the transfer reaction between sodium and chlorine. Before the reaction, the sodium atom is electrically neutral, i.e., its total of 11 electrons is counterbalanced exactly by the 11 positively charged protons in the nucleus. During the reaction, one unit of negative charge, in the form of an electron, is lost from sodium. After the reaction, therefore, the sodium atom must be posi-

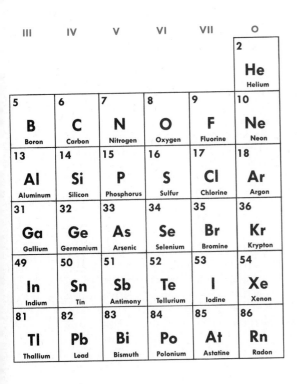

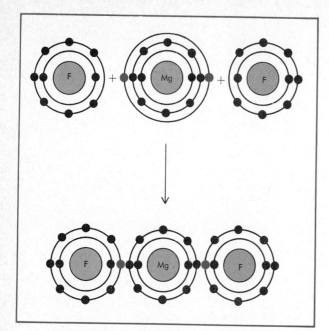

3 · 8 Electron-transfer reactions. *A magnesium atom, with two electrons in its third shell, may lose these two electrons by reacting with two fluorine atoms, each of which requires one more electron for a complete second shell. The result of such an electron transfer is the compound magnesium fluoride, in which each of the three participating atoms now possesses a complete outer shell.*

tively charged, for now there are only 10 electrons but the 11 protons are still present. Hence through the loss of one electron, sodium exhibits one unit of positive charge:

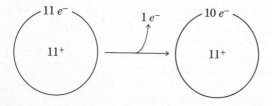

If we indicate a unit of positive charge by a superscript plus sign, we may also write

$$Na \longrightarrow e^- + Na^+$$

Analogously, chlorine is electrically neutral at the outset. During the reaction, it acquires one additional unit of negative charge in the form of an

electron. After the reaction it must therefore be negatively charged:

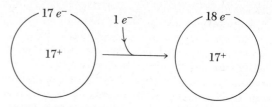

If we indicate a unit of negative charge by a superscript minus sign, we may write

$$Cl + e^- \longrightarrow Cl^-$$

We may now symbolize the sodium-chlorine reaction as a whole by writing

$$Na + Cl \longrightarrow Na^+ + Cl^-$$

or

$$Na + Cl \longrightarrow Na^+Cl^-$$

The equation implies that one electron has been transferred from sodium to chlorine, and it shows that the two atoms have acquired opposite unit charges as a result.

Similarly, in the reaction of magnesium and fluorine, the magnesium atom loses two electrons and then exhibits *two* units of positive charge. The two fluorine atoms accept the two electrons and so acquire negative charges. Symbolically,

$$Mg + 2 F \longrightarrow Mg^{++} + 2 F^-$$

or

$$Mg + 2 F \longrightarrow Mg^{++}F_2^-$$

Atoms or groups of atoms carrying electric charges are known as *ions*. The symbols Na^+ and Mg^{++} stand for sodium ion and magnesium ion, respectively; the symbols F^- and Cl^- similarly stand for fluoride ion and chloride ion, respectively. Electron-transfer reactions may also be referred to as *ionic reactions*.

In such reactions, note that the total number of positive charges carried by one group of ions equals the total number of negative charges carried by the other group. Substances with opposite electric charges are attracted to each other, and we should therefore expect that positive and negative ions exert mutual electric attraction. This is the case; the force of attraction actually binds oppositely charged ions together. Any two ions so coupled are in effect united by a chemical bond, and the bonded group of ions represents a compound, an *ionic compound*. For example, in the reaction

$$Na + Cl \longrightarrow Na^+Cl^-$$

the endproduct is the ionic compound sodium chloride. It contains one bond between the sodium ion and the chloride ion, produced by the electric attraction these two ions have for each other.

The chemical bonds formed in electron-transfer reactions are called *ionic bonds*. Every electron transferred establishes one ionic bond. Thus the magnesium ion Mg^{++}, resulting from the transfer of two electrons, forms two ionic bonds with other ions.

In writing ionic compounds symbolically, it is not always necessary to indicate the electric charges of the ions. For example, instead of writing Na^+Cl^-, one may also write Na—Cl, the dash here representing the ionic bond. Or one may write, even more simply, NaCl. Similarly, the ionic compound magnesium fluoride, $Mg^{++}F_2^-$, may also be depicted simply as MgF_2. Even though such shorthand notations do not indicate the ionic nature of the components, ions are nevertheless present and ionic bonds unite them. The number of bonds an atom can form with others by electron transfer indicates the *valence* or, more specifically, the *electrovalence* of the atom. Thus, sodium and chlorine each has an electrovalence of 1, since each can form one ionic bond. Analogously, magnesium has an electrovalence of 2. Because this bond-forming potential of an atom is governed by its outer electrons, the latter are often referred to as *valence electrons.*

What determines whether an atom loses electrons and thus behaves as an *electron donor* or gains electrons and so functions as an *electron acceptor?* For example, could not fluorine become stable by losing its seven valence electrons instead of gaining an additional one? The answer is no, since it is exceedingly difficult to dislodge as many as seven electrons from the atom. Recall that electrons are negatively charged and are attracted to the positively charged protons in the atomic nucleus. Seven electrons are actually attracted very strongly, and they cannot be removed readily in one batch. Indeed, the nucleus exerts a sufficiently strong attracting force to capture and hold on to an additional electron from another atom. The situation is quite similar for chlorine and in general for all atoms in which the outermost shell is almost complete to begin with. Such atoms normally act as electron acceptors in transfer reactions.

Conversely, could not magnesium become stable by gaining six more electrons instead of losing the two in its outer shell? Here again the answer is no. In a shell capable of holding eight electrons, as few as two electrons are not attracted very strongly to the electropositive nucleus. Moreover, the attracting force of such a nucleus is not great enough to capture six additional electrons. Thus, magnesium normally acts as an electron donor. This holds also for sodium, for example, and usually for all atoms in which the outer shell is nearly empty to begin with.

In general, therefore, we may say that electron donors and acceptors differ in that the former contain fewer valence electrons than the latter. Even a small difference in the number of such electrons suffices, in theory at least, to make possible electron transfers. In practice, however, transfers take place most readily if the numerical differential is great, that is, if one participant has very few valence electrons and is an *active* donor, and if the other has very many valence electrons and is an *active* acceptor. Sodium or magnesium, for example, are active donors. As a group such donors are commonly known as *metals*. By contrast, fluorine and chlorine are among the active acceptors, which are collectively known as *nonmetals*. Electron-transfer reactions occur most readily between metals and nonmetals.

Donors and acceptors of electrons have a patterned distribution in the periodic table. Group I elements, which may lose their single outer electrons most readily, are the most metallic in character; and group VII elements, which accept electrons most readily, are the most nonmetallic in character. The intermediate groups are the less metallic, and the more nonmetallic the higher the group number. Elements in groups III, IV, and V actually display transitional properties. They may behave as electron donors in the presence of very active acceptors or as electron acceptors in the presence of very active donors. A regular distribution pattern is in evidence also *within* given groups. The lighter a metal, the closer to the nucleus is the shell in which its few outer electrons are located, hence the more strongly are these electrons attracted to the nucleus. Thus, heavier metals may act as electron donors more readily than lighter ones. Potassium is actually more metallic than sodium, which in turn is more metallic than lithium. Conversely, the lighter a nonmetal, the more strongly will it attract electrons to the atomic nucleus. Indeed, fluorine is more nonmetallic in character than chlorine, which in turn is more nonmetallic than bromine.

Note that the position of an element in the periodic table is an important clue to its valence. For electron donors, the group number is usually directly equivalent to the electrovalence. Thus, group I elements such as Na or K have a valence of 1, group II elements such as Mg or Ca have a valence of 2. For electron acceptors, the electrovalence can often be obtained by subtracting the group number from 8. For example, group VII elements have a valence of 1, group VI elements, a valence of 2.

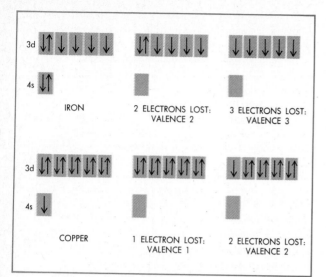

3 · 9 *Electron configurations in the 4s and 3d subshells of iron and copper, respectively, when these elements display various valences. The 4s subshell lies slightly closer to the atomic nucleus than the 3d subshell.*

Most elements display a fixed electrovalence in all chemical reactions, but some, particularly the "transition elements" between groups II and III, exhibit multiple electrovalences, that is, different ones in given different reactions. In iron, for example, the usual electrovalence is 2, as should be expected from the presence of two outer electrons (in the 4s subshell, see Table 6). However, in many reactions iron has an electrovalence of 3. As shown in Fig. 3.9, the 3d subshell of iron contains four half-filled orbitals and one completely filled orbital. Moreover, Fig. 3.4 indicates that the 3d and 4s subshells have rather similar energy levels, that of 3d actually being a little greater. Consequently, iron may readily lose not only the two 4s electrons but also one electron from the filled 3d orbital. Thus, according to whether the element loses two or three electrons, it will display an electrovalence of 2 or 3. (On rare occasions iron may even lose six electrons, two from the 4s subshell and four from the 3d subshell; the electrovalence then is 6.)

Copper, analogously, has a fundamental electrovalence of 1, reflecting the ease of removal of the single electron in its 4s subshell (see Fig. 3.9). The 3d subshell here is filled completely, but again one electron may become dislodged quite readily from one of the 3d orbitals. Under such conditions copper displays an electrovalence of 2. We may note in general that, where the outermost and the next inner

subshells of an atom have quite similar energy levels, multiple electrovalences are likely to be in evidence in given different circumstances.

Consideration of energy levels underscores another important aspect of electron transfers. Every electron present in an atom endows this atom with a certain energy content, and loss of an electron from a donor atom must therefore be equivalent to energy loss. In other words, the positively charged ion remaining after an electron is removed will contain less energy than the original atom, the difference amounting to the energy carried away with the electron. Conversely, electron gain by an acceptor atom will be equivalent to energy gain, and a negatively charged ion will contain more energy than the original atom. Note now that any process involving electron loss is also called *oxidation*, any process involving electron gain, *reduction*. Thus, any electron transfer between donor and acceptor atoms, that is, any ionic reaction, is a joint *oxidation-reduction* process, also called *redox* process for short. In losing an electron an atom is said to become *oxidized*, and in gaining an electron an atom is said to become *reduced*. For example, in the reaction

$$Na \longrightarrow e^- + Na^+$$
$$Cl + e^- \longrightarrow Cl^-$$
$$\overline{Na + Cl \longrightarrow Na^+Cl^-}$$

sodium is oxidized and chlorine is reduced. Chlorine may be said to be the *reductant* or *reducing agent* of sodium, and sodium, the *oxidant* or *oxidizing agent* (Fig. 3.10).

The degree of oxidation or reduction can be described through a series of arbitrary numbers, called *oxidation numbers* or *oxidation states*. In electron-transfer processes, this state is equivalent to the sign and number of the electric charges present on an atom or ion. For example, the oxidation state of Na^+ is $+1$, that of Mg^{++} is $+2$, that of Cl^- is -1. Neutral atoms, being uncharged, are assigned oxidation states of 0. In terms of such numbers, oxidation may then be defined as *increase* in oxidation state, and reduction, as *decrease* in oxidation state. For example, in the following reactions the oxidation state increases; hence they represent oxidations:

$$\underset{0}{Na} \longrightarrow \underset{+1}{Na^+} + e^-$$

$$\underset{+2}{Fe^{++}} \longrightarrow \underset{+3}{Fe^{+++}} + e^-$$

An example of an oxidation-state-decreasing reaction, that is, a reduction, is the following:

$$\underset{0}{Cl} + e^- \longrightarrow \underset{-1}{Cl^-}$$

The earlier discussion of quantum levels in atoms has shown that if a donor atom is to lose an electron, that is, if it is to become oxidized, then the energy level of that electron must be raised sufficiently to allow it to escape the atom. Such a raising of the energy level cannot take place by itself but requires a supply of external, environmental energy. In other words, energy must be introduced from the environment into an atom, some of this external energy must be absorbed by an electron, and the latter must thereby become excited sufficiently to escape from the atom. We note that oxidation is an energy-*requiring* process, the amount required from the environment being equivalent to the energy necessary to produce electron escape. Such a free electron then possesses more energy than is needed to make it part of an atom. Consequently, if such an electron is acquired by an acceptor atom, not all the electron energy need become part of this atom. Only the amount required to maintain the electron in a ground-state orbit around the nucleus will be gained by the atom, and any energy excess will dissipate into the environment (typically as heat). Thus, reduction is an energy-*releasing* process (see Fig. 3.10).

In general, therefore, every oxidation *requires* environmental energy (to dislodge electrons) and results in a net energy *loss* in the atom being oxidized (due to electron loss); and every reduction *yields* energy to the environment (amounting to the excess electron energy) and results in a net *gain* in the atom being reduced (due to electron gain). We may make one further generalization in this context. Since oxidation represents energy loss and since lower energy contents signify greater stability, we may conclude that oxidation of a substance leads to an increased stability of that substance. Conversely, because reduction involves energy gain and thus lesser stability, reduction tends to decrease the stability of a substance. As we shall find later, these various correlations have an exceedingly important bearing on the energy management in living systems.

MOLECULES

Electron Sharing

Atoms may become electronically stable not only by transferring electrons but also by *sharing* electrons. For example, consider again a chlorine atom. As noted, it possesses seven outer electrons but it re-

3 · 10 An oxidation-reduction process in electron transfers. *A is the electron donor, B the electron acceptor, and both have an initial oxidation state (and number) of zero. After the electron transfer, A has become oxidized to A^+ and to an oxidation state of $+1$; B has been reduced to B^- and to an oxidation state of -1. Moreover, A^+ is now more stable than the original A (and this oxidation requires energy); and B is less stable than the original B (and this reduction yields energy).*

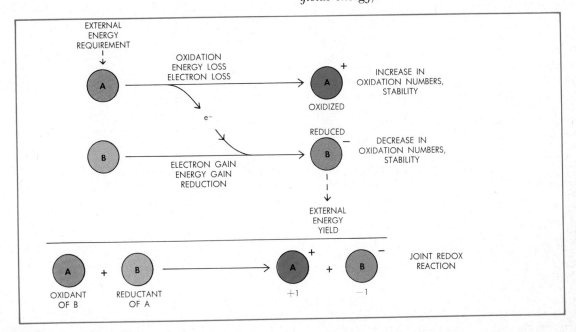

quires eight for a complete shell. If appropriate electron donors such as sodium atoms happen to be in the vicinity, the eighth electron may be gained by ionic reaction, as discussed above. However, suppose that appropriate electron donors are not available and that only chlorine atoms are present. Under such circumstances, a chlorine atom may complete its outer shell by reacting with another chlorine atom. We know that a chlorine atom can attract one additional electron rather strongly. Therefore, if two chlorine atoms come into contact, each will attempt to capture an electron from the other atom. But since each atom holds on strongly to its own electrons, an actual transfer cannot take place. Instead, a mutual "tug of war" will continue, each atom holding its own electrons and at the same time trying to pull one electron away from the other. The net result is a mutual attraction which will keep the two atoms in contact. Moreover, the atoms will *share* one pair of electrons: the sphere of influence

3·11 Electron sharing. *The 3s and 3p subshells of two chlorine atoms are shown. After the reaction, the two atoms share one pair of electrons in the 3p subshells and each atom thereby acquires a complete third shell of eight electrons. The result is a molecule of chlorine, Cl_2.*

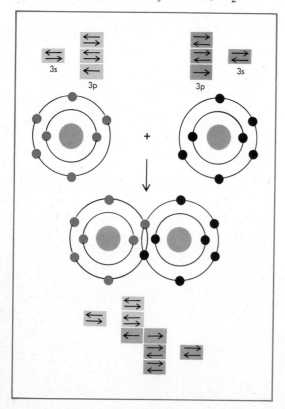

of each atom will include seven outer electrons of its own plus one which is attracted from the other atom. Both atoms then behave as if they actually possessed eight outer electrons each, and this suffices to establish their electronic stability (Fig. 3.11). Electrons so shared fill an orbital (that is, a 3p orbital in the case of chlorine) and they must therefore have antiparallel spins.

Electron sharing may also occur among hydrogen atoms, for example. Hydrogen possesses a single 1s electron and, in the absence of electron acceptors, pairs of hydrogen atoms may share their electrons:

$$H\cdot \ + \ H\cdot \ \longrightarrow \ H{:}H$$

Through such pooling of the two electrons, the electrons no longer "belong" to either atom but belong equally to both. In effect, therefore, each of the two atoms attracts the two electrons necessary to complete its shell. As in all other such cases, the shared electrons fill an orbital (1s in this instance) and spin in opposite directions. We may note generally that only a half-filled orbital, that is, one containing a single, unpaired electron, may normally participate in electron sharing. Also, two originally unpaired electrons in two atoms may form a single shared pair only if the spins of these electrons happen to be antiparallel.

More than one pair of electrons may be involved in a sharing process. For example, oxygen possesses six outer electrons and requires *two* more for a complete shell. Completion may be achieved if two oxygen atoms share *two* pairs of electrons. An oxygen atom possesses two half-filled 2p orbitals, and if two such atoms combine these orbitals pairwise, both atoms will jointly acquire completely filled 2p orbitals, hence completely filled outer shells (Fig. 3.12).

If we indicate electrons by dots and symbolize only those present in the outer shells, we may write, for oxygen,

$$\ddot{O}{:} \ + \ {:}\ddot{O} \ \longrightarrow \ \ddot{O}{::}\ddot{O}$$

The two pairs of electrons shown between the two O's in the endproduct are the shared pairs. Each O atom now attracts eight electrons, the required number for a complete shell. In nitrogen, each atom possesses three half-filled 2p orbitals, and these three may be shared with, for example, the three half-filled orbitals of another nitrogen atom (see Fig. 3.12):

$$:\!\overset{\cdot}{N}\!\cdot \ + \ \cdot\!\overset{\cdot}{N}\!: \ \longrightarrow \ :\!N\!\vdots\!N\!:$$

In this instance, evidently, three pairs of electrons are shared and each atom thereby completes its outer shell.

Electron sharing may also occur among more than two atoms, and the atoms may be of different kinds. For example, one oxygen atom may share the two electrons in its partially filled $2p$ orbitals with two hydrogen atoms. All three atoms may so acquire complete outer shells, that is, oxygen a shell of eight electrons and each hydrogen a shell of two electrons (see Fig. 3.12):

$$\cdot \ddot{O} \cdot \ + H \cdot + H \cdot \longrightarrow H : \ddot{O} : H$$

We may conclude generally that electron sharing characterizes a second major class of chemical reactions. Atomic combinations formed through electron sharing are called *molecules,* and the reactions which produce them are called *molecular reactions.* In a molecule, the shared electrons represent the chemical bonds which hold the atoms together. Each shared electron pair represents one chemical bond, and we may note that bonds of this type are known as *covalent bonds.*

If two atoms are joined by one pair of shared electrons, the covalent union is said to represent a *single bond,* as in $H:H$. Two pairs of shared electrons between two atoms form a *double bond,* as in $\ddot{O} : : \ddot{O}$, and three pairs, a *triple bond,* as in $: N \vdots N :$ Molecules with single bonds may be regarded as being *saturated;* that is, they contain as many separate bonds as can be formed. By contrast, molecules with one or more double or triple bonds are *unsaturated,* inasmuch as any one such bond may give rise to two or three single bonds. For example:

$$\ddot{O} : : \ddot{O} + 4 H \cdot \longrightarrow 2 H : \ddot{O} : H$$

1 double bond,   2 single bonds,
unsaturated   *saturated*

$$: N \vdots N : + 6 H \cdot \longrightarrow 2 \ \overset{\displaystyle H}{\underset{\displaystyle H}{N:H}}$$

1 triple bond,   3 single bonds,
unsaturated   *saturated*

It can be shown that, in a double bond, the distance between the two united atoms is less great than in a comparable single bond. Analogously, two triple-bonded atoms lie closer together than two double-bonded ones. Moreover, the energy holding two atoms together is greatest if the union is a triple bond, less great if it is a double bond, and least if it is a single bond. As we shall see later, bond energies are roughly inversely proportional to bond stabilities, single bonds being the most stable, triple bonds, the least stable.

In shorthand symbolizations of molecules, bonds

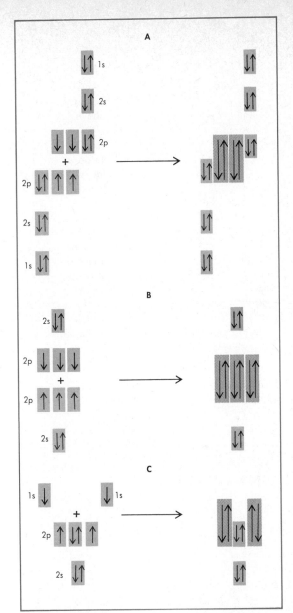

3 · 12 Electron configurations in sharing reactions. *A, two oxygen atoms share two pairs of electrons and form a molecule of oxygen, O_2. B, two nitrogen atoms share three pairs of electrons and form a nitrogen molecule, N_2. C, two hydrogen atoms and one oxygen atom share two pairs of electrons and form a water molecule, H_2O. In B and C, only the outer electrons are indicated. Colors indicate the sphere of influence of each atom. See also Fig. 3.13.*

may be indicated either by pairs of dots representing electron pairs or by dashes. Alternatively, bonds need not be indicated at all. For example, see Fig. 3.13. A condensed shorthand formula obviously does not

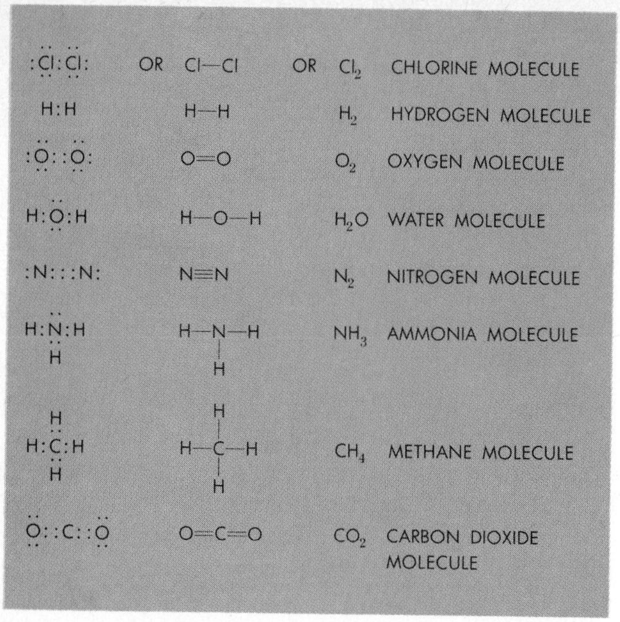

:Cl:Cl:	OR Cl—Cl	OR Cl$_2$	CHLORINE MOLECULE
H:H	H—H	H$_2$	HYDROGEN MOLECULE
:O::O:	O=O	O$_2$	OXYGEN MOLECULE
H:O:H	H—O—H	H$_2$O	WATER MOLECULE
:N:::N:	N≡N	N$_2$	NITROGEN MOLECULE
H:N:H H	H—N—H H	NH$_3$	AMMONIA MOLECULE
H:C:H H	H—C—H H	CH$_4$	METHANE MOLECULE
O::C::O	O=C=O	CO$_2$	CARBON DIOXIDE MOLECULE

3 · 13 Molecular symbolization. *Different ways of representing various molecules.*

show whether a given compound is ionic or molecular. Only prior knowledge makes clear that a compound such as MgF$_2$ is ionic and a compound such as CO$_2$ is molecular. Where the distinction is important, ionic charges must be shown in one case and dot pairs or dashes in the other.

Since the formation of covalent bonds does not involve actual transfers of electrons, the participating atoms remain whole, electrically neutral atoms. The number of electrons an atom shares indicates its valence, more specifically, its *covalence*. Hydrogen exhibits a covalence of 1 when it shares its electron, oxygen, a covalence of 2, nitrogen, a covalence of 3, and carbon, a covalence of 4.

Redox Changes

Although shared electrons are not transferred outright, they are nevertheless pulled more closely toward one or the other atom by nuclear attraction. We already know that atomic nuclei differ in their electron-attracting capacity; attraction is the greater the more nonmetallic the atom. Fluorine, the most nonmetallic element, attracts electrons most strongly, and when fluorine shares electrons with another atom, it will tend to pull the shared pair toward it. If the other atom happens to lose electrons readily, an outright electron transfer will occur, as in

$$Na + F \longrightarrow Na^+F^-$$

But if the other atom holds its own electrons more strongly, a sharing process will take place in which

the shared electron pair will merely come to lie closer to the fluorine nucleus than to the other nucleus. For example

$$H\cdot + :\ddot{F}\cdot \longrightarrow H \quad :\ddot{F}:$$

In general, the different relative strengths by which electrons are attracted to their own nuclei will determine whether two atoms will transfer or share electrons between them. If two atoms differ very greatly in their electron-attracting capacity, as is the case between active metals and active nonmetals, then ionic transfer reactions will take place. But if the differential is less great, or if such a differential is absent altogether (as between two identical atoms), then a sharing reaction will occur.

If we refer to the electron-attracting capacity of an atom as its *electronegativity*, we may say that elements of group I in the periodic table are least electronegative (or most electropositive), those in group VII, most electronegative (or least electropositive). Within a given group, moreover, the lighter nonmetallic elements are more electronegative than the heavier ones, and the heavier metallic elements are less electronegative than lighter ones. In a sharing process between atoms, therefore, the shared electron pairs will come to lie closest to the most electronegative atom. In a water molecule, for example, oxygen (group VI) is more electronegative than hydrogen (group I), hence the shared electrons will be pulled nearer to the oxygen nucleus than to the hydrogen nuclei (Fig. 3.14),

$$H\cdot + \cdot\ddot{O}\cdot + \cdot H \longrightarrow H \quad :\ddot{O}: \quad H$$

Even though such shifts of shared electrons do not amount to outright gains or losses, they are nevertheless equivalent to corresponding shifts or redistributions of energy. They therefore qualify as oxidation-reduction processes. A relative shift of an electron pair *away from* an atom is an oxidation, a relative shift *toward* an atom is a reduction. Thus, in the covalent union of two hydrogen atoms and one oxygen atom, the hydrogens in the resulting water molecule are oxidized, the oxygen is reduced. To assess such redox changes quantitatively we may again use the arbitrary convention of oxidation states. However, since actual charge transfers do not take place in molecular reactions, we must treat relative shifts of electrons *as if* they were equivalent to actual transfers. For example, in the formation of a water molecule from 2 H and 1 O, the oxygen behaves *as if* it acquired two electrons, hence its oxidation state changes from the original zero of the free atom to −2 in the molecule. Each hydrogen atom analogously changes its oxidation state from an original zero to $+1$, for it behaves *as if* it actually lost an electron. Note that in covalent unions between identical atoms the oxidation states do not change at all, for all such atoms are identically electronegative. In H:H, for example, neither atom can be said to behave as if it acquired electrons (or both must be considered to acquire electrons equally). Oxidation states consequently remain zero, and neither oxidation nor reduction takes place in this case.

Inasmuch as they represent the least electronegative elements, the active metals of groups I and II generally tend to become oxidized if they participate in sharing reactions. As already noted, most metal reactions actually involve outright electron transfers. The only notable sharing processes of metals are covalent combinations with hydrogen, yielding hydrides; for example,

$$Na\cdot + H\cdot \longrightarrow Na:H \quad NaH, \text{sodium hydride}$$

Metals such as sodium are more electropositive than hydrogen, hence the oxidation state of sodium changes from 0 to $+1$, that of hydrogen from 0 to -1. In other words, sodium becomes oxidized, hydro-

3·14 Oxidation-reduction in electron sharing. *The formation of a molecule of water is illustrated. Two H atoms and one O atom originally have oxidation states (and numbers) of zero. The H atoms are more electropositive than oxygen and serve as reductants; that is, they become oxidized. Conversely, the O atom is more electronegative and, as an oxidant, becomes reduced. The shared electrons are pulled more toward the O nucleus than toward the H nuclei.*

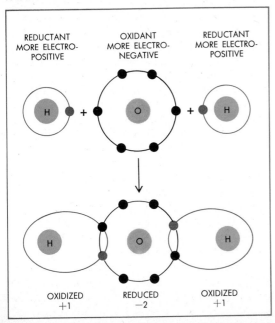

REDUCTANT
MORE ELECTRO-
POSITIVE

OXIDANT
MORE ELECTRO-
NEGATIVE

REDUCTANT
MORE ELECTRO-
POSITIVE

OXIDIZED
$+1$

REDUCED
-2

OXIDIZED
$+1$

gen becomes reduced. By contrast, group VII elements, being the most electronegative, generally become reduced if they participate in sharing processes. The most electronegative element of all, namely, fluorine, is always reduced (that is, always acts as an oxidizing agent) no matter what reaction it participates in. Oxygen, as the next most electronegative element, can be oxidized only by fluorine, and oxygen thus is an oxidizing agent for all elements but fluorine. In general, the result of an electron-sharing process between any two atoms is that the more electronegative will become reduced, the less electronegative, oxidized.

Most elements actually may become either oxidized or reduced depending on whether they react with more electronegative or less electronegative elements. Hydrogen, for example, can become reduced by metals, as just noted, but in virtually all other instances hydrogen is the less electronegative element and becomes oxidized, to an oxidation state of $+1$. As shown in Fig. 3.14, for example, a reaction of hydrogen and oxygen produces a $+1$ state in hydrogen and a -2 state in oxygen. (We may note that, apart from oxygen-fluorine combinations, the only compounds in which oxygen does not have an oxidation of -2 are the so-called *peroxides*, for example, H_2O_2, or $H:\overset{..}{\underset{..}{O}}:\overset{..}{\underset{..}{O}}:H$; the oxidation state of each hydrogen here is $+1$, as is usual, but that of each oxygen is -1.)

Elements transitional between metals and nonmetals, that is, many of those in groups III, IV, and V, should be oxidizable more or less just as readily as they should be reducible, and this is the general case. In group IV, for example, carbon is oxidizable by more electronegative nonmetals such as chlorine or reducible by less electronegative elements such as hydrogen (Fig. 3.15). Note here that, as in ionic compounds, stability increases with an increase in the oxidation state of electron-sharing atoms. Thus, CH_4, methane, possesses a far less stable carbon atom than CCl_4, carbon tetrachloride.

Note further that the sum of all oxidation numbers in a chemical complex must add up arithmetically to the electric charge of that complex. In a molecule, the overall net charge is zero, hence the sum of all oxidation numbers must be zero. For example, in the molecule H_3PO_4, phosphoric acid, the phosphorus atom is neither metallic nor strongly nonmetallic. The oxidation state of hydrogen must therefore be $+1$ (since metals are not present), that of oxygen, -2 (since fluorine or peroxides are not present). Consequently, the oxidation state x of phosphorus must be:

$$+3 + x - 8 = 0$$
$$x = +5$$

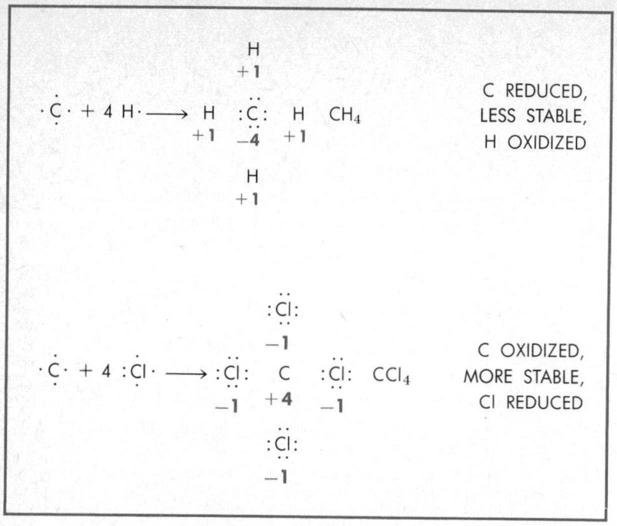

$$\cdot \overset{\cdot\cdot}{C}\cdot + 4\,H\cdot \longrightarrow \underset{+1}{H}\ \underset{-4}{\overset{\cdot\cdot}{\underset{H}{C}}}\ \underset{+1}{H}\quad CH_4$$

C REDUCED, LESS STABLE, H OXIDIZED

$$\cdot \overset{\cdot\cdot}{C}\cdot + 4\,:\overset{\cdot\cdot}{Cl}\cdot \longrightarrow \underset{-1}{:\overset{\cdot\cdot}{Cl}:}\ \underset{+4}{C}\ \underset{-1}{:\overset{\cdot\cdot}{Cl}:}\quad CCl_4$$

C OXIDIZED, MORE STABLE, Cl REDUCED

3 · 15 Oxidation and reduction of carbon. *In the upper reaction, carbon is reduced by H atoms and the electrons move closer to the carbon nucleus. In the lower reaction, carbon is oxidized by chlorine, electrons now moving closer to the chlorine nuclei. The two reactions illustrate the extreme oxidation states of carbon, −4 and +4.*

In electronic terms, the +5 value means that the phosphorus atom is in an oxidized state, more specifically, that all five of its shared electrons have undergone shifts away from the nucleus, as if the electrons had become transferred. To find the oxidation state of carbon in the bicarbonate ion, HCO_3^-, we note that all oxidation numbers must add up to −1, the net charge of the ion. The oxidation state of H is again +1, that of oxygen is −2, hence that of C will be:

$$+1 + x - 6 = -1$$
$$x = +4$$

The carbon is in an oxidized +4 state.

Probably the greatest variety of possible oxidation states is displayed by nitrogen, an atom which contains five valence electrons and can have any oxidation number from −3 to +5, including certain fractional numbers (Table 8). In other words, nitrogen can obtain a stable valence shell by acquiring three electrons through sharing with other atoms, but any number of the eight electrons so available may lie

TABLE 8   COMPOUNDS OF NITROGEN

OXIDATION STATE		VALENCE OF NITROGEN
−3	NH_3, *nitrogen hydride (ammonia)*, $H:\overset{\cdot\cdot}{N}:H$, H—N—H (with H above)	3
−3	HCN, *hydrogen cyanide*, $H:C:::N:$, H—C≡N	3
−2	N_2H_4, *hydrazine*, $H:\overset{\cdot\cdot}{N}:\overset{\cdot\cdot}{N}:H$, H—N—N—H	3
−1	NH_2OH, *hydroxylamine*, $H:\overset{\cdot\cdot}{N}:\overset{\cdot\cdot}{O}:H$, H—N—O—H	3
−⅓	NH_3, *hydrogen azide*, $H:N::N::N:$, H—N=N=N	3, 4, 2
0	N_2, *molecular nitrogen*, $:N;:::N:$, N≡N	3
+1	N_2O, *nitrous oxide*, $:N:::N:\overset{\cdot\cdot}{O}:$, N≡N→O	3, 4
+2	NO, *nitric oxide*, $:N::\overset{\cdot\cdot}{O}$, N=O	2
+3	HNO_2 (NO_2^-), *nitrous acid (nitrite)*, $H:\overset{\cdot\cdot}{O}:\overset{\cdot\cdot}{N}::\overset{\cdot\cdot}{O}$, H—O—N=O	3
+4	NO_2, *nitrogen dioxide*, $:\overset{\cdot\cdot}{O}:N::\overset{\cdot\cdot}{O}$, O←N=O	3
+5	HNO_3 (NO_3^-), *nitric acid (nitrate)*, $H:\overset{\cdot\cdot}{O}:N::\overset{\cdot\cdot}{O}$, :O: H—O—N=O (with O below)	4

closer to either the nitrogen nucleus or the other nuclei present. Phosphorus, the next heavier group V element, has nearly as many possible oxidation states.

Coordinate Covalence

Table 8 demonstrates several general phenomena correlated with covalent bonding. First, note that the oxidation number is not necessarily equivalent to the valence number. Valence merely indicates the total number of bonds formed by an atom, regardless of whether or to what extent the atom is thereby oxidized or reduced. (It may be pointed out here that in H_2O_2, referred to above, oxygen has a valence of 2 but an oxidation state of -1—another of many instances where the two numbers differ). Second, in certain exceptional cases covalent bonding does not give an atom a full set of eight valence electrons. In nitric oxide or nitrogen dioxide, for example, the sphere of influence of the nitrogen atom includes only seven outer electrons. Such violations of the octet rule are very rare, however; they are without importance in biological systems and may be disregarded for present purposes.

By contrast, a third phenomenon implicit in Table 8 occurs fairly frequently. We know that, of the five valence electrons of nitrogen, two fill the $2s$ orbital completely and the other three half-fill each of the three $2p$ orbitals (see Fig. 3.6). These half-filled orbitals normally participate in sharing reactions, which explains the characteristic nitrogen valence of 3. When these three of the five valence electrons are being shared, the two electrons in the $2s$ orbital remain unshared. This circumstance is reflected in the electron formula for ammonia, for example, in which the two unshared valence electrons appear as unbonded dots (see Table 8). Since these two unshared electrons fill the $2s$ orbital completely, they cannot participate in the usual covalent bonding process. However, they can *together* contribute to filling the valence shell of another atom, if the latter happens to be two electrons short of a complete shell. In effect, therefore, a bond between two atoms can be formed even where one atom contributes *both* electrons and the other contributes none. For example, the nitrogen atom of ammonia can supply a complete pair of antiparallel electrons to any atom in which such a pair would fill a valence shell. A hydrogen ion, H^+, qualifies in this sense; the ion is without electrons and its vacant $1s$ shell can just be filled completely by a pair of antiparallel electrons. Thus, H^+ may become bonded to ammonia, the nitrogen atom here supplying both bonding electrons:

$$H:\overset{\cdot\cdot}{\underset{H}{N}}:\ +\ H^+ \longrightarrow$$

ammonia   *hydrogen ion*

$$H:\overset{\cdot\cdot}{\underset{H}{N}}:H^+ \quad \text{or} \quad \left[H-\overset{H}{\underset{H}{N}}\rightarrow H \right]^+ \quad \text{or} \quad NH_4^+$$

ammonium ion

Any covalent bond in which a single atom serves as donor of both electrons is referred to as a *coordinate covalent* bond. In dash symbolizations of such a bond, an arrowhead is added to the dash in the direction pointing away from the donor atom.

Table 8 shows that nitrogen may form coordinate bonds in a variety of compounds. In each such case the valence number is increased by 1, since the coordinate bond is present in addition to the usual number of regularly formed covalent bonds. Coordinate bonds are established not only by nitrogen, however. In the oxygen of water, for example, two pairs of unshared valence electrons are present, and one of these pairs is known to produce a coordinate bond with hydrogen ions:

$$H:\overset{\cdot\cdot}{\underset{H}{O}}:\ +\ H^+ \longrightarrow$$

water

$$H:\overset{\cdot\cdot}{\underset{H}{O}}:H^+ \quad \text{or} \quad H-\overset{}{\underset{H}{O}}\rightarrow H^+ \quad \text{or} \quad H_3O^+$$

hydronium ion

Like oxygen, sulfur too possesses six valence electrons, of which two are normally shared in regular covalent fashion. In hydrogen sulfide, for example, the valence of sulfur is 2 and the oxidation state is -2:

$$\overset{}{\underset{+1}{H}}\ \ :\overset{\cdot\cdot}{\underset{-2}{S}}:\ \ \overset{}{\underset{+1}{H}}$$

Two unshared electron pairs are therefore available for coordinate bonding (as in oxygen), and here both pairs actually come into play in, for example, sulfuric acid, H_2SO_4 (Fig. 3.16). The valence of sulfur in this case is 4 (2 more than normal because of two coordinate bonds), and the oxidation state is $+6$. To cite another example of biological importance, phosphorus possesses five valence electrons and, as in nitrogen, three of these are in half-filled orbitals and are shared in regular manner. The remaining pair then may participate in coordinate bonding, as in phosphoric acid, H_3PO_4 (see Fig. 3.16).

$$
\begin{array}{ccc}
\ddot{\,:}\!O\!:\!\!\cdot & & \overset{-2}{O} \\
H:\!\ddot{O}\!:\!\overset{\cdot\cdot}{S}\!:\!\ddot{O}\!:\!H \quad \text{OR} & & \overset{+6}{\underset{+1\ -2}{H-O-}}\overset{\uparrow}{\underset{\downarrow}{S}}\overset{}{\underset{-2\ +1}{-O-H}} \\
:\!\ddot{O}\!:\!\cdot & & \overset{O}{\underset{-2}{\ }}
\end{array}
$$

SULFURIC ACID
H_2SO_4

$$
\begin{array}{ccc}
\ddot{\,:}\!O\!:\!\!\cdot & & \overset{-2}{O} \\
H:\!\ddot{O}\!:\!\overset{\cdot\cdot}{P}\!:\!\ddot{O}\!:\!H \quad \text{OR} & & \overset{+5}{\underset{+1\ -2}{H-O-}}\overset{\uparrow}{\underset{|}{P}}\overset{}{\underset{-2\ +1}{-O-H}} \\
:\!\ddot{O}\!:\!\cdot & & \underset{-2}{O} \\
H & & H \\
& & \underset{+1}{H}
\end{array}
$$

PHOSPHORIC ACID
H_3PO_4

3 · 16 *Coordinate covalent bonds of sulfur and phosphorus. The electrons of sulfur and phosphorus are shown in color. Sulfur forms two coordinate bonds in sulfuric acid, phosphorus forms one in phosphoric acid. The oxidation states of all atoms are shown in the right formula of each pair.*

Hybrid Orbitals

Coordinate bonding is not the only cause of multiple covalences of given atoms. Another is the occurrence of electron shifts among orbitals of equivalent energy, as in the multiple electrovalences discussed earlier.

For example, we know that carbon possesses four valence electrons, of which two fill the $2s$ orbital and the other two half fill two of the $2p$ orbitals. The third $2p$ orbital is vacant (see Figs. 3.6 and 3.17). The expected valence of carbon thus should be 2, and the two half-filled orbitals should participate in regular covalent bonding. This is actually the case in some reactions. For example, electrons of carbon may be shared with four of oxygen, resulting in carbon monoxide:

$$
:\!C\!: \; + \; :\!:\!O\!: \; \longrightarrow \; :\!C\!:\!:\!:\!O\!:, \quad \underset{+3\quad-3}{C\!\!\equiv\!\!O}, \quad CO
$$

The formulas here indicate that two electron pairs are shared in regular covalent manner between the two atoms, and that oxygen by itself additionally contributes a third electron pair in coordinate fashion. This pair fills the vacant $2p$ orbital of carbon. The noteworthy point is not primarily this coordinate bond, but the circumstance that, considered by itself, carbon shares only two of its four valence electrons, that is, its $2s$ electrons remain unshared. Its own valence contribution is therefore 2 (though if the coordinate bond is counted as well, the overall valence between C and O is 3). However, the usual and biologically most significant valence of carbon is

3 · 17 *Multiple valences may be exhibited by given atoms as a result of electron shifts. As here shown for each of three atoms, valences differ according to whether the atom is in a ground state or an excited state.*

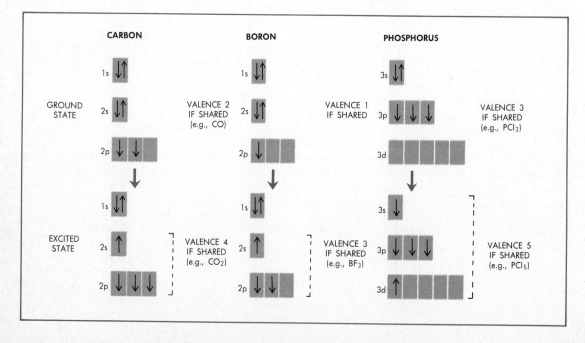

4, as exhibited, for example, in CCl_4 and CH_4. Such a valence results from a shift of one of the $2s$ electrons present in an uncombined carbon atom into the third available $2p$ orbital, which had been vacant (Fig. 3.17). A shift of this type may occur readily, inasmuch as the energy levels of orbitals in the second shell do not differ too greatly. The excited carbon atom then possesses one half-filled $2s$ orbital and three half-filled $2p$ orbitals. All four of these now may add one antiparallel electron through sharing. In reacting with two oxygen atoms, for example,

$$:C: + 2 :\ddot{O} \longrightarrow \ddot{O}::C::\ddot{O}, \quad O{=}C{=}O, \quad CO_2$$
$$-2 \quad +4 \quad -2$$

Carbon here exhibits its common valence of 4. Its oxidation state is $+4$, that is, it is more highly oxidized in CO_2 than in CO. The CO_2 molecule as a whole is also more stable than CO. It is precisely because a valence of 4 produces more stable complexes that this valence is far more common for carbon than any other.

Atoms other than carbon may likewise display their characteristic covalences as a result of displacements of given electrons from filled orbitals to free orbitals of the same principal quantum level. For example, boron has three valence electrons, two in $2s$, one in $2p$ (see Fig. 3.17). The atom should therefore exhibit a valence of 1, but its actual valence is 3, as in BF_3, due to a shift of one of the $2s$ electrons into a free $2p$ orbital. In phosphorus,

the five valence electrons are in the third shell; two fill the $3s$ orbital, three half fill the $3p$ orbitals (see Fig. 3.17). A valence of 3 is actually displayed in many phosphorus compounds, as in PH_3 or PCl_3. However, the third shell of phosphorus also contains vacant $3d$ orbitals, hence one of the two $3s$ electrons should be able to shift into one of the $3d$ orbitals. All five valence electrons should then be able to participate in bond formation. This is the case in many instances, and phosphorus may form compounds such as PCl_5, in which its valence is 5.

One important aspect of covalent bonding remains to be considered. When two atoms share a pair of electrons, two orbital spaces must be shared as well. Inasmuch as each orbital has an original shape, what will happen to such shapes during sharing? We may envisage the formation of a covalent bond as an overlapping or interpenetration or fusion of two half-filled orbitals of two atoms, resulting in the establishment of a single common new orbital, called an atomic *hybrid*. The shape of this new hybrid depends on the original shapes of the orbitals that participate in its formation. Three principal possibilities may be considered. In one, a spherical s orbital joins with another spherical s orbital, as in the formation of a hydrogen molecule from two H atoms. Interpenetration of two spheres here results in a single new orbital shaped like a distorted sphere, or an ellipsoid (Fig. 3.18). A mixed hybrid orbital of

3 · 18 *Hybrid orbitals.* *The formation of ss and pp hybrid orbitals.*

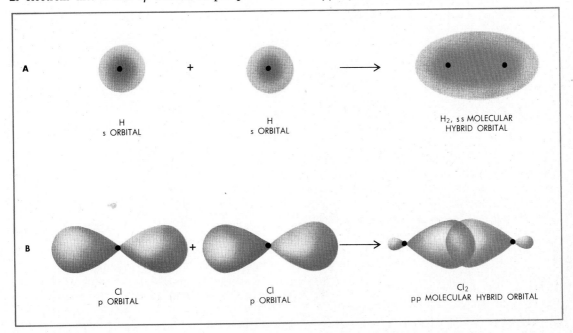

A
H
s ORBITAL
+
H
s ORBITAL
H₂, s s MOLECULAR HYBRID ORBITAL

B
Cl
p ORBITAL
+
Cl
p ORBITAL
Cl₂
pp MOLECULAR HYBRID ORBITAL

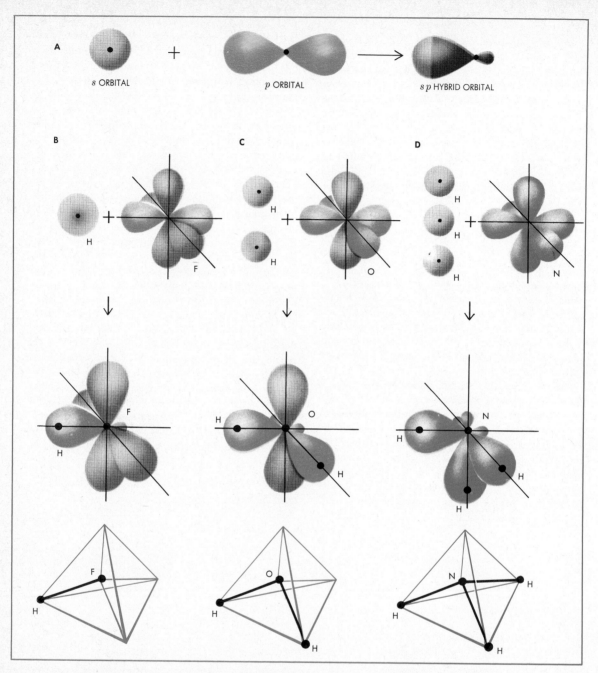

3 · 19 Hybrids and symmetries. A, fusion of an s and a p orbital yields the dumbbell-shaped sp hybrid orbital shown. B, C, D illustrate one type of sp hybrid, formed in different molecules. In all these cases, orbitals actually containing electrons are shown in color, and empty orbitals are gray. B, one s orbital of H combines with one p orbital of F, yielding HF. C, two s orbitals of H combine with two p orbitals of O, yielding H_2O. D, three s orbitals of H combine with three p orbitals of N, yielding NH_3. The sym- metries of the resulting molecules are indicated in the bottom row.

3 · 20 Formation of molecular hybrids. In the ▶ diagram on opposite page, the left column illustrates the ground state of the indicated atoms; the middle column shows the excited state in which molecules are formed; the right column depicts molecular hybrids. In beryllium, the two

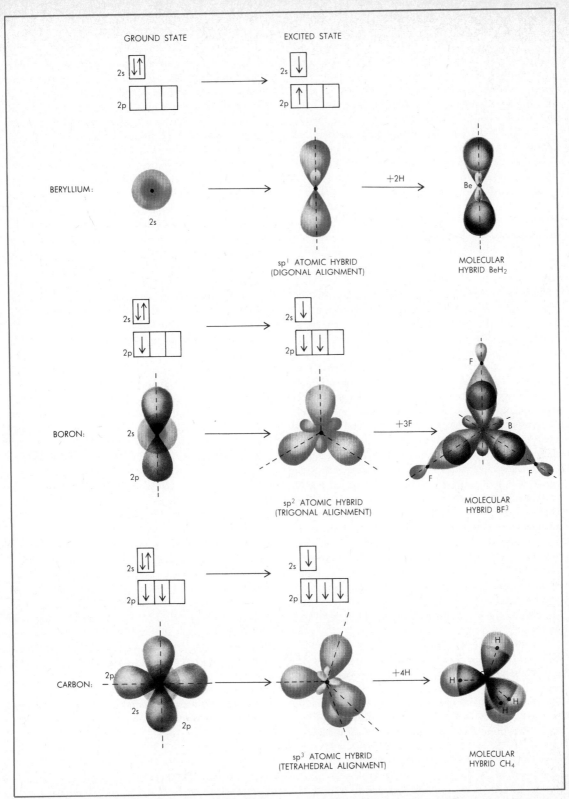

GROUND STATE

EXCITED STATE

2s

2p

2s

2p

BERYLLIUM:

2s

sp¹ ATOMIC HYBRID
(DIGONAL ALIGNMENT)

+2H

Be

MOLECULAR
HYBRID BeH_2

2s

2p

2s

2p

BORON:

2s

2p

sp² ATOMIC HYBRID
(TRIGONAL ALIGNMENT)

+3F

F

B

F

F

MOLECULAR
HYBRID BF^3

2s

2p

2s

2p

CARBON:

2p

2s

2p

sp³ ATOMIC HYBRID
(TETRAHEDRAL ALIGNMENT)

+4H

H

H

H

H

MOLECULAR
HYBRID CH_4

sp¹ atomic hybrid orbitals of an excited atom react with two H atoms, and the digonal fusion product is the molecular hybrid BeH_2. In boron, three sp² atomic hybrid orbitals of an excited atom may form a trigonal BF_3 molecule. In carbon, the four sp³ atomic hybrid orbitals of the excited atom yield a tetrahedral molecule after fusion with four H atoms.

this type may be said to form an *ss* bond. A second type of hybrid orbital arises when two *p* orbitals interpenetrate, resulting in the formation of a *pp* bond, as in a chlorine molecule. In such cases, the originally dumbbell-shaped orbital of each of the two atoms (that is, the half-filled 3*p* orbital of each chlorine atom) becomes distorted into a double teardrop with a smaller and a larger side, the latter facing the other atom (see Fig. 3.18).

The third type of hybrid orbital results from a mixing of *s* and *p* orbitals and the consequent formation of *sp* bonds. Several variants of these may be distinguished (see Fig. 3.19). A simple set of variants is illustrated by the molecules HF, H_2O, and NH_3. In all three, one 1*s* orbital of hydrogen overlaps separately with one of the 2*p* orbitals of the other atom. One such *sp* hybrid is present in HF, two in H_2O, and three in NH_3, corresponding to the covalences of F, O, and N. The shape of each *sp* is again somewhat like a distorted double teardrop, the larger side representing the fusion of the *s* orbital with one part of the *p* orbital. Note that the presence of such *sp* hybrids tends to alter the original symmetry of the atoms. For inasmuch as some of the electrons now no longer move symmetrically around the atomic nuclei, the latter will become effective centers of fields of positive electricity and will repel one another in new patterns. In NH_3, for example, the three hydrogen nuclei are repelled by the nitrogen nucleus as well as by each other. The overall result is that the molecule assumes somewhat tripodlike shape, with the N nucleus at the center of an imaginary tetrahedron and the H nuclei at three of the corners (see Fig. 3.19). The *sp* bonds here correspond to lines drawn from the center to these corners of the tetrahedron. The shape of the H_2O molecule analogously can be fitted into the geometry of a tetrahedron, the oxygen nucleus now being at the center and the hydrogen-oxygen bonds pointing to two of the corners.

Another set of *sp* hybrids is illustrated by molecules in which beryllium, boron, or carbon is present. These atoms normally possess a filled 2*s* orbital, and when they form molecules, one of the two 2*s* electrons moves into an empty 2*p* orbital (as already pointed out above for boron and carbon, see Fig. 3.17). Beryllium then can form two covalent bonds,

boron three, and carbon four. In such shifts of electrons from 2*s* to 2*p*, the orbital shapes of the atoms themselves change and atomic hybrid orbitals result. Such atomic hybrids subsequently become changed even more, to *molecular hybrids*, when other atoms are joined through electron-sharing.

In beryllium, for example, an atomic hybrid forms when a 2*s* electron moves into one of the available 2*p* orbitals (Fig. 3.20). The half-filled 2*s* and the single half-filled 2*p* orbitals so formed now fuse, yielding two so-called sp^1 atomic hybrid orbitals. The designation sp^1 here indicates that the atomic hybrid is produced from an *s* and *one p* orbital *of the same atom*. The two sp^1 are equivalent in shape; they resemble a pair of distorted double teardrops aligned along a single common axis (*digonal* alignment). Beryllium may now share its two valence electrons with, for example, two H atoms, and this process will be accompanied by interpenetration of the two 1*s* orbitals of hydrogen with the two sp^1 orbitals of beryllium. The resultant *molecular* hybrids are as in Fig. 3.20.

In the case of boron, the atomic hybrids are produced from *one 2s* and *two 2p* orbitals, a combination yielding three equivalent sp^2 hybrids (see Fig. 3.20). These three atomic hybrids lie in a single common plane and subtend angles of 120° (*trigonal* alignment). Boron may then share its three valence electrons with, for example, three fluorine atoms, resulting in three molecular hybrid orbitals. Each of the latter is a mixture of a *p* orbital of fluorine and one of the sp^2 orbitals of boron.

A particularly important case is that of carbon, in which the atomic hybrids arise from a mixing of *one 2s* and *three 2p* orbitals (see Fig. 3.20). The resultants are four equivalent sp^3 hybrids, in *tetrahedral* alignment: the carbon nucleus is at the center of the tetrahedron and the sp^3 orbitals point toward the four corners. The angle subtended by any two of these orbitals is 109°28′, the tetrahedral angle. If now a carbon atom shares its four valence electrons with, for example, four H atoms, the resulting methane, CH_4, has *molecular* hybrid orbitals as shown in Fig. 3.20.

As will become apparent in the next chapter, molecular geometries such as these contribute directly to the physical state in which large numbers of molecules may exist.

REVIEW QUESTIONS

1. Define element, atom, compound, ion, molecule, chemical energy, chemical bond, valence.

2. What is an electrovalent bond? How is such

a bond formed? Explain in terms of atomic structure. What is a covalent bond? How is such a bond formed? Again explain in terms of atomic structure.

3. Consider the following equation:

$$Ca(OH)_2 + 2\ HCl \longrightarrow CaCl_2 + 2\ H_2O$$

a. Identify the different atoms by name and determine the valence of each.

b. Rewrite the equation to show the bonds, ionic, molecular, or both, within each compound.

4. Distinguish between: atomic mass and weight; kinetic and potential energy; ground state and excited state; beta and gamma radiation; covalence and co-ordinate covalence; metals and nonmetals; groups and periods in the periodic table.

5. Which four characteristics define the quantum state of an electron, and in how many ways can each of these characteristics be expressed? What is a quantum jump? An orbital?

6. State the Pauli exclusion principle. How does it contribute to the determination of electron configurations of atoms? Write out the actual electron configuration of the 10 lightest elements, and from this deduce the position of these elements in the periodic table.

7. What factors determine whether a given atom will transfer or share electrons in given reactions? What is meant by the relative electronegativity of atoms?

8. What is a redox process? Show how such processes differ in electron transfer and sharing. Why is the oxidation state of hydrogen usually $+1$, that of oxygen usually -2?

9. Why must shared electrons have antiparallel spins? Show how two nitrogen atoms share their electrons. Distinguish between saturated and unsaturated bonds.

10. How is a coordinate covalent bond formed? Cite specific examples. Explain why and how certain atoms display different valences in different circumstances. Why do valences and oxidation states often differ numerically?

11. What are atomic hybrid orbitals? Molecular hybrid orbitals? Distinguish between *ss*, *pp*, and *sp* bonds. How are sp^1, sp^2, and sp^3 hybrids formed? Give an example of each of the hybrid types here mentioned.

12. Which substance in each of the following sets is the most stable: Na, Na^+; CO, CH_4, CO_2; NH_3, NO_2; PCl_3, PCl_5. Explain.

COLLATERAL READINGS

Asimov, I.: "Inside the Atom," Abelard-Schuman, New York, 1958. For those without prior background; popularly written.

Baker, J. J. W., and G. E. Allen: "Matter, Energy, and Life," Addison-Wesley, Reading, Mass., 1965. A recommended paperback covering not only topics dealt with in this chapter but also many of those of the succeeding three.

Bush, G. L., and A. A. Silvidi: "The Atom: A Simplified Description," Barnes, Noble, New York, 1961. An introductory account, dealing briefly also with quantum states.

Darrow, K. K.: The Quantum Theory, *Sci. American*, Mar., 1952. A popular article on the development and significance of the theory.

Gamov, G.: The Exclusion Principle, *Sci. American*, July, 1959. An explanation of atomic structure on the basis of the Pauli principle.

Grunwald, E., and R. H. Johnsen: "Atoms, Mole-cules, and Chemical Change," Prentice-Hall, Englewood Cliffs, N. J., 1960. Introductory, well suited for those without adequate background.

Hiller, L. A., and R. H. Herber: "Principles of Chemistry," McGraw-Hill, New York, 1960. A recommended basic text, college level, covering atomic structure, bonds and bond types, and topics also dealt with in subsequent chapters.

Sienko, M. J., and R. A. Plane: "Chemistry," 2d ed., McGraw-Hill, New York, 1961. A widely used introductory college-level text, recommended for general and specific background data on most chemical topics dealt with here.

White, E. H.: "Chemical Background for the Biological Sciences," Prentice-Hall, Englewood Cliffs, N.J., 1964. This paperback contains a brief chapter on atomic and molecular structure and then covers numerous topics also dealt with in the next three chapters of this book.

CHAPTER 4
ATOMS
AND
BONDS

By virtue of the internal properties—particularly the bonding potentials—of atoms, compounds exhibit a variety of larger-scale attributes of both a physical and a chemical nature. Such attributes are manifested whenever ions or molecules occur in bulky accumulations, either as pure samples of single compounds or as mixtures of several. Most of these larger-scale characteristics are of considerable biological importance, since the ions and molecules of living matter normally do form aggregates of at least microscopically and often macroscopically visible bulk. Indeed, many of the gross, overt properties of organisms are direct reflections of the group properties of the accumulated compounds.

Among these effects resulting from the bonding of atoms, some influence the *physical state* in which compounds can exist. Others determine the manner of *physical dispersion* if a sample of a compound is in contact with another one serving as an environmental medium. Chemical consequences of bonding include primarily the existence of many different *kinds of compounds* of widely differing internal complexities, a subject examined in this chapter, and the occurrence of *reactions* among compounds, a topic discussed in the next.

PHYSICAL STATES

The ionic or molecular units of a compound exist in either a gaseous, a liquid, or a solid physical state. In a gas, ions or molecules (referred to below simply as particles) are comparatively far apart and are able to move independently of one another; the particles influence one another very little. In a liquid, by contrast, particles are packed very close together and perhaps may even touch, yet they may still move and shift freely around one another. In a solid too the particles are packed closely together, but here their positions are more or less fixed and they are not free to move around one another. It can be shown that the particular physical state a substance can actually exist in depends principally on three variables: the *pressure* the substance is subjected to, the *temperature* of the substance, and the *electric polarity* of the substance.

PRESSURE AND TEMPERATURE

The influence of pressure may be assessed readily. If the pressure applied on a group of particles from the outside is low, the particles will be constrained very little. They may then disperse readily and occupy as large a volume of space as is available. Low pressures thus favor a gaseous state. On the other hand, higher pressures will crowd the particles into progressively smaller volumes and will gradually restrict their mobility. Rising pressures therefore favor first a liquid and then a solid state. Significant variations in external pressure actually play an important role in changes of physical state, that is, in interconversions of gases to liquids to solids or vice versa.

Temperature is an expression of particle motion. At a given temperature all particles possess a given amount of kinetic energy, and they move at certain rates and with particular intensities. In a gas, each particle tends to move in a straight line until it collides with and bounces off another particle or the walls of a container. The totality of particles in a gas sample thus undergoes random motions in all directions, and these directions change frequently and randomly as a result of collisions. If the temperature is raised, the rate of such *thermal motion* increases; the particles possess greater kinetic energies and move more violently. If the container of the gas sample has a fixed volume, the internal pressure of the gas will then increase, the collision rate among the particles will increase as well, and, as we shall see, the result may be faster chemical reactions. Or, if the container does not restrict gas volume, the increased thermal motion of the particles will lead to an expansion of the gas into progressively larger volumes (and to a consequent rarefaction, or decrease in density).

Conversely, a lowering of the temperature reduces the thermal motion of the particles and also their collision rate. The particles may then crowd together more, and as they move progressively less they may assume first a liquid and ultimately a solid state. Like pressure, therefore, temperature too plays an important role in interconversions of state. Note that if the temperature were reduced sufficiently, a point should eventually be reached at which thermal motion would be zero and the particles would be entirely stationary. This point can be shown to occur at −273°C, the theoretical absolute zero of temperature. In practice such a temperature has been approached closely in laboratory experiments but not actually attained; every known natural or experimental material contains at least some heat, and the amount of heat is proportional to the amount of thermal motion. Evidently, heat motion occurs even in a solid. Particles here are not free to move around one another, to be sure, but each nevertheless vibrates back and forth within a small space. If then the temperature is raised sufficiently, the amplitude of the vibrations will increase until the particles escape their positional constraints. At such a stage the solid will melt, and if the resulting liquid is heated further it will eventually vaporize into a gas.

We may note therefore that, by changing pressures, temperatures, or both, every material may be made to undergo interconversions of state. However, different materials differ greatly with respect to the actual pressures and temperatures at which changes of state will occur. The result is that, at room temperature and at ordinary atmospheric pressure, for example, compounds such as methane or ammonia are gases, water is a liquid, and sodium chloride is a solid. Such differences are due to the third principal variable determining physical states, namely, the internal atomic structure of molecules or ions. Of particular significance in this respect is the electric *symmetry* of particles.

ELECTRIC POLARITY

We already know that particles such as atoms, ions, and molecules all contain electrically positive and negative subunits, namely, protons and electrons. We may now add that the totality of such subunits within a particle creates *electric fields* around the particle, just as a body with mass creates a gravitational field around it. Specifically, all protons in, for example, a molecule, produce a field of positive electricity around them. This field has different "strengths" in different regions, that is, different attractive effects, depending on the spatial distribution of the protons. Such a field also has a center, just as a massive body has a gravitational center. Analogously, all the electrons present in a chemical produce a field of negative electricity, again with different strengths at different points and with a center.

We may now distinguish two classes of substances on the basis of the electric field symmetries of their particles (Fig. 4.1). A *nonpolar* particle is one in which the centers of the positive and the negative field are coincident at the same point in space, so that the attractive effects of the two fields cancel out. Such a particle will be electrically *symmetrical*, and it will not exert any electrostatic attraction beyond its own limits, for example, on other nonpolar particles in the vicinity. By contrast, a *polar* particle is one in which the positive and negative fields do not overlap exactly, the two fields being centered at different points in space. Such a particle is *asymmetrical* electrically, and a greater or lesser portion of both the positive and the negative field will extend beyond the particle. These projecting, uncanceled portions of the fields then do exert external attraction effects. We may say, therefore, that a polar particle has a *dipole,* that is, a negative electric pole some distance away from a positive electric pole. And in a close group of numerous polar particles, all the negative poles will attract all the positive poles present and vice versa.

Hence it should readily be appreciated that, if pressure and temperature are given, electric polarities will play an important role in determining the degree to which particles are packed together and thus the physical state of a substance. Consider, for example, substances such as helium atoms, hydrogen molecules, and methane molecules (Fig. 4.2). In helium, the outer electron shell (1s) is complete and forms a spherical orbital around the atomic nucleus. The atom is structurally symmetrical, and it is therefore also electrically symmetrical, or nonpolar; the centers of the positive and negative field are coincident at the center of the atom. Groups of helium atoms will therefore be without any mutual attraction, a condition reflected in the gaseous state of helium. Hydrogen molecules, H_2, have quite similar field characteristics. In such a molecule, the two shared electrons form a slightly ellipsoid ss orbital around the two nuclei. These nuclei lie a certain distance apart as a result of their mutual repulsion. However, the positive and the negative field are again coincident, both being centered at the midway point between the nuclei. Hydrogen molecules therefore are gaseous. Methane too is nonpolarized. We already know that the C and the four H atoms are arranged in the form of a regular tetrahedron (see Chap. 3), and this structural regularity is matched by an electric symmetry; the field centers are coincident and symmetrical around the carbon nucleus at the center of the tetrahedron.

But if such nonpolar particles do not attract one another, how can they ever "hang together" as closely packed groups and exist as liquids or solids? The answer is that electric symmetries may become disturbed. For example, if helium atoms collide, such impacts may displace a nucleus relative to its electrons, and a temporarily polarized atom will result (see Fig. 4.2). Or if a helium atom happens to come under the influence of an external electric field (produced, for example, by a polar particle in the vicinity), then the normal electric symmetry of helium may again be disturbed and a temporary dipole will be created. In any gas, actually, enough temporarily polarized particles are present at any given time to produce weak attractive forces which tend to hold the gas together to some extent. Such weak electrostatic forces in nonpolar substances are known as *van der Waals forces*. Along with pressure and temperature, they aid in producing liquid or solid states. To be sure, the more difficult it is to make nonpolar particles temporarily polar, the less readily will such a substance become a liquid or a solid. In general, the heavier the individual atoms

4 · 1 Electric fields of chemical units. *A, in a nonpolar material, the centers of positive and negative electric fields are coincident. B, in a polar material, the fields are not coincident, and the line between the two field centers marks out a dipole. C, electrically asymmetrical materials attract each other and form aggregates.*

or the more atoms present in a nonpolar ion or molecule, the more readily liquefaction or solidification can occur. This conclusion is valid because electric symmetries are far more likely to be upset if a particle contains numerous electrons and protons than if it contains only a few; large numbers of parts can become disarranged more easily than small numbers. Consequently, helium gas, which consists of single atoms, should liquefy less readily than hydrogen gas, in which there are two atoms per molecule; and hydrogen in turn should liquefy less readily than methane gas, in which the molecules contain five atoms. Indeed, the boiling points of these three substances are, respectively, -268.9, -252.7, and $-161.4°C$. Helium actually has the lowest boiling point of any substance known and is least readily convertible into liquid form.

Consider next compounds such as sodium chloride. Each unit is composed of two ions, Na^+ and Cl^-, and the very presence of such oppositely charged subunits indicates that the substance must be inherently strongly polar. All ionic compounds have powerful inherent dipoles, and groups of such units tend to cling together tenaciously through electrostatic attraction. At room temperature sodium chloride is actually a solid, more specifically, a *crystal* in which the ions are arranged in a regular pattern; each sodium ion attracts chlorine ions all around it and each chlorine ion attracts sodium ions all around it (see Fig. 4.2). The ions here oscillate back and forth in thermal motions but the general positions relative to one another are rigidly maintained.

Almost all pure metals likewise exist as solids at room temperature (mercury being the notable exception). Metal atoms are characterized by highly incomplete outer electron shells, and the few outer electrons that are present can be dislodged readily, leaving the atoms as positively charged ions. A group of metal atoms may therefore be considered to consist es-

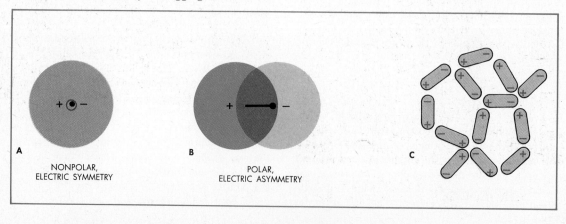

NONPOLAR,
ELECTRIC SYMMETRY

POLAR,
ELECTRIC ASYMMETRY

PLATE III

7. _Physalia_, the Portuguese man-of-war.
Each tentacle suspended from the
gas-filled float represents a portion of
a single coelenterate individual. The several
different types of tentacles here
indicate the high degree of polymorphism
encountered in such colonies.

8. _Egg-laying queen bee on brood cells._

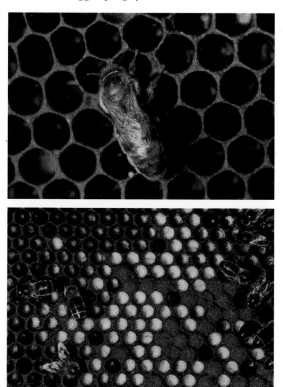

9. _Workers_ tend sealed
brood cells and brood cells with larvae.

PLATE IV

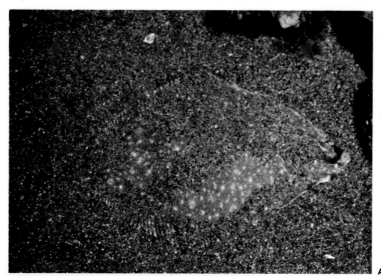

A

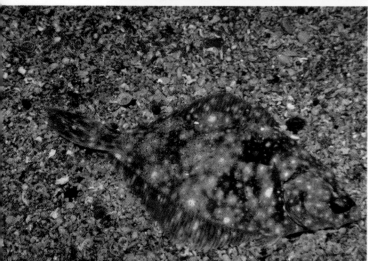

B

10. A flatfish (plaice) *against three different backgrounds.*
The animal can adapt its skin pigmentation pattern to the environment. In such cases of adjustable camouflage, information about the environment is communicated to the skin via eyes, nerves, and hormones. . Pigment cells in the skin respond to the information by contracting or expanding, thus altering body coloration.

C

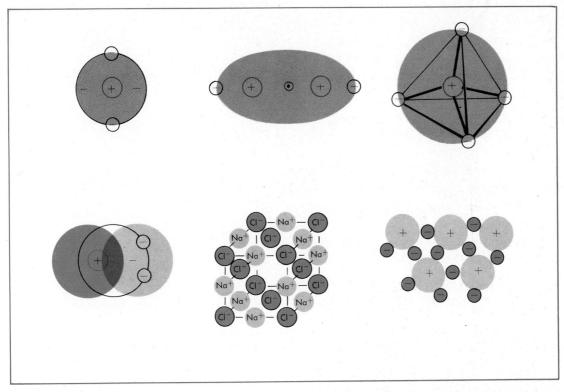

sentially of a group of positive ions and of comparatively loose groups or clouds of electrons which do not "belong" to any specific nuclei but to all of them together. The positive ions then will attract the electrons collectively, and the result of such electrostatic group attractions will be a strong mutual bonding of the atoms, producing a solid. Through such *metallic bonds*, metals actually form crystallike solids, in which the nuclei are equidistant and attract any electrons that happen to lie between them. The geometric arrangement here resembles a stack of balls (see Fig. 4.2). The metal atoms are therefore free to roll around one another, a property contributing to the well-known malleability and deformability of metallic solids.

Consider now covalent compounds such as HF, NH_3, and H_2O. These are not so strongly polar as ionic compounds, but they are variously asymmetric in structure and are also inherently polar to different extents (Fig. 4.3). Of the three compounds, the most nearly symmetrical is ammonia; an NH_3 molecule is shaped somewhat like a three-rayed star. A not very powerful dipole is present, hence groups of NH_3 molecules will attract one another, though comparatively weakly. This condition is reflected in the relatively high boiling point of ammonia, which is

$-33.4°C$. At room temperature ammonia is therefore a gas, but it liquefies at a far higher temperature than methane, for example. Considerably stronger mutual attraction is exhibited by hydrogen fluoride molecules, HF, in which the dipole is quite pronounced. The fluorine atom shares one of its seven valence electrons with hydrogen, and the six unshared electrons shift the center of the negative electric field of HF close to the fluorine atom. The hydrogen atom shares its single electron with fluorine, hence the hydrogen nucleus, not surrounded by any other electrons, produces a powerful positive electric field centered close to that nucleus. HF is consequently strongly polar. It exists just barely as a liquid at room temperature; the boiling point is $+19.5°C$, which means that on a warm day hydrogen fluoride will transform into a gas.

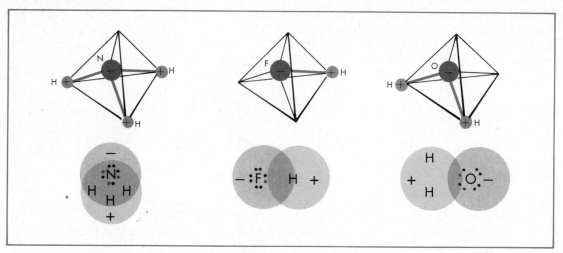

4·3 Symmetries of weakly polarized substances. In ammonia (left), *centers of positive and negative fields are not far apart; the dipole is therefore fairly weak. The dipole of hydrofluoride* (middle) *is more pronounced. The dipole of water* (right) *is fairly strong.*

Water is the most polar of the three compounds above. In a H_2O molecule, the center of the negative electric field lies close to the oxygen atom, which possesses four unshared valence electrons. The two hydrogen atoms produce a strong positive field centered roughly midway between these two atoms. By virtue of their strong dipoles, water molecules tend to hang together tenaciously. As is well known, water boils only at 100°C and it may even become a solid at the relatively high temperature of 0°C. Indeed, in the process of forming ice a new type of electrostatic force comes to play a highly significant role. This force operates between the four unshared electrons of an oxygen atom and the hydrogen nuclei of *other* water molecules in the vicinity. At or near the freezing point, water molecules are already so close together that the attraction between oxygen of one molecule and hydrogen of another results in the establishment of actual intermolecular bonds, called *hydrogen bonds*. The overall effect of hydrogen bonding is that water molecules come to be arranged in a repeating pattern in which the oxygen of one molecule forms the center of a tetrahedron and the oxygens of four other molecules are at the corners of such a figure (Fig. 4.4). A H atom lies between any two such O atoms, the bond with one O atom being covalent, the somewhat longer bond with the other O atom being a hydrogen bond. A bond of this type, depicted symbolically as a broken line, is less strong than a covalent bond but is considerably stronger

than, for example, a van der Waals bond. So oriented tetrahedrally, the molecules of water form an indefinitely enlargeable crystal structure, namely, ice.

Hydrogen bonds arise not only between H and O atoms but also between H and any other atoms in which unshared valence electrons are available. For example, hydrogen bonds will form when compounds such as HF or NH_3 freeze, both fluorine and nitrogen being atoms with unshared valence electrons. In HF, the six unshared electrons of fluorine actually form exceedingly strong hydrogen bonds. Unlike ice, however, neither solid HF nor solid NH_3 have their molecules arranged in tetrahedral patterns, and neither substance forms continuous, indefinitely ·enlargeable crystals. Note also that, in an ice crystal, the water molecules are not packed together so densely as they could be. When ice melts, the H bonds and the orderly tetrahedral spacing of the molecules are disrupted, and as a result of dipolar attraction the molecules then do pack together even more intimately. Such closer packing reveals itself by an increase in the density of water. The greatest density is attained at 4°C, hence ice swims on liquid water colder than 4°C (and this is why, for example, lakes and ponds freeze from the top down). Above 4°C, thermal motion of the water molecules becomes progressively greater than the dipolar attraction, and water then does become less and less dense and therefore lighter. Water is anomalous in that its liquid form may be denser than its solid form. Most other substances, NH_3 for example, are most dense in the solid state, and solid NH_3 will sink in the liquid form of this compound.

Polar substances tend to be good solvents of other polar substances. As is well known, for example, water is an excellent solvent of most highly polar materials, particularly ionic compounds, for example sodium chloride. Solvation in such cases is a result of a stronger electrostatic attraction between the particles of water and those of the ionic material than between the particles of the ionic material itself (Fig. 4.5). In water, additionally, either the H or the O atoms or both sets of atoms together may participate in hydrogen bonding, with the result that water is able to dissolve other hydrogen-bondable materials, for example, substances containing N, O, or H atoms. Numerous compounds of living matter are in this category, as we shall see. Water is actually the best of all solvents, dissolving more different substances and larger amounts of each than any other known material. Evidently, water exhibits numerous properties unique either quantitatively or qualitatively. We shall find this circumstance to be of crucial biological significance.

We may now note quite generally that, whereas electrostatic repulsion of like charges tends to keep the units of matter separated, so electrostatic attraction between opposite charges tends to keep matter together. As an important result, matter neither flies apart in all directions nor does it congeal into a single huge lump. Instead it attains varying degrees of physical dispersion, reflecting a balance between the forces of repulsion and those of attraction. We may conclude,

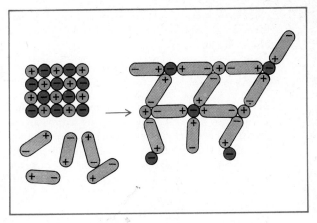

4 · 5 The mutual solvent action of two polar substances. Circles (left) represent ions of sodium chloride and the bars below represent water molecules. Mixing of the two leads to mutual separations of the particles (right). In general, one polar material will disrupt the continuity of, and thereby dissolve, another polar material if the attraction between particles of the two is greater than the attraction among the particles of each.

moreover, that the small-scale forces which do keep matter together are all fundamentally electric. As outlined above, electric attraction produces electron-proton bonding within atoms and metallic bonding between atoms; ionic and covalent bonding within compounds; and van der Waals bonds, crystal-forming ionic bonds, and hydrogen bonds between compounds. The visible consequences are the different physical states of given materials at different pressures and temperatures.

DISSOCIATION AND pH

Strongly polar substances tend not only to dissolve other materials but also to break other polar molecules into ions. Formation of ions from originally molecular units is called *dissociation*. The process is illustrated most clearly by the ion-producing effect of water, a strongly polar solvent as noted.

When a covalent polar compound such as HF is placed into water, electrostatic attraction will occur between the electronegative oxygen of water and the electropositive hydrogen of HF. This attraction is strong enough to pull hydrogen away altogether from HF. However, fluorine is sufficiently electronegative itself to maintain its hold on the electron pair shared between H and F. In effect, therefore, the oxygen of water exerts an attraction just sufficient to acquire

4 · 4 Hydrogen bonds in water (left) and hydrogen fluoride (right) are shown as broken colored lines. Water molecules are depicted as they are arrayed in ice. Hydrogen bonds are weaker and longer than covalent bonds.

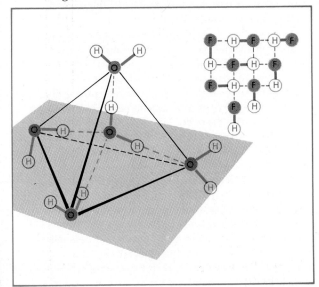

the hydrogen *nucleus* of HF, whereas fluorine retains the hydrogen *electron*. The net result is the formation of an ion pair:

$$\text{H:}\overset{..}{\underset{..}{\text{O}}}\text{:} + \text{H:}\overset{..}{\underset{..}{\text{F}}}\text{:} \longrightarrow \text{H:}\overset{..}{\underset{..}{\text{O}}}\text{:H}^+ + \text{:}\overset{..}{\underset{..}{\text{F}}}\text{:}^-$$
$$\text{H} \qquad\qquad\qquad\quad \text{H}$$

In other words, HF loses a hydrogen ion, H^+, and so becomes a fluoride ion, F^-. This hydrogen ion may then bond coordinately to an unshared electron pair of oxygen, yielding a hydronium ion, H_3O^+. In symbolizations of such dissociations, the role of water is not always shown explicitly, and the equation

$$\text{HF} \xrightarrow{\ H_2O\ } H^+ + F^-$$

has the same meaning as the one above. Note, however, that *active* participation of water is nevertheless always implied.

We may ask why, if HF and water are mixed, dissociation could not occur in such a way that *water* would lose a hydrogen ion and HF would gain it, rather than the other way round. Thus, could not the following take place:

$$\text{H:}\overset{..}{\underset{..}{\text{O}}}\text{:H} + \text{H:}\overset{..}{\underset{..}{\text{F}}}\text{:} \longrightarrow \text{H:}\overset{..}{\underset{..}{\text{F}}}\text{:H}^+ + \text{H:}\overset{..}{\underset{..}{\text{O}}}\text{:}^-$$

In actuality such a process does not occur to any appreciable extent, for the covalent bond between H and O in water is stronger than the covalent bond between H and F. Fluorine is so highly electronegative that the shared electron pair "belongs" far more strongly to F than to H; the "sharing" is exceedingly unequal and HF virtually is an ionic compound to begin with. By contrast, oxygen is less electronegative than fluorine, and the electrons shared between H and O of water are attracted correspondingly less strongly to oxygen. In a mixture of HF and H_2O, therefore, far more HF molecules tend to become dissociated than H_2O molecules.

Note generally that, of two H-containing compounds participating in a dissociation process, the one containing a more electronegative atom will be the one that loses H^+ to the other. It follows that, in a mixture of water and a compound containing a less electronegative atom than oxygen (in effect, any compound other than one containing fluorine), it will be water which dissociates and loses a H^+ ion. For example, nitrogen is less electronegative than oxygen, and if ammonia is mixed in water, water will relinquish hydrogen ions more readily to ammonia than vice versa:

$$\text{H:}\overset{\text{H}}{\underset{\text{H}}{\text{N}}}\text{:} + \text{H:}\overset{..}{\underset{..}{\text{O}}}\text{:} \longrightarrow \text{H:}\overset{\text{H}}{\underset{\text{H}}{\text{N}}}\text{:H}^+ + \text{H:}\overset{..}{\underset{..}{\text{O}}}\text{:}^-$$

ammonia   water   ammonium ion   hydroxyl ion

The H^+ ion pulled away from water forms a coordinate bond with ammonia, yielding an *ammonium* ion, NH_4^+, and a *hydroxyl* ion, OH^-.

What will happen if the electronegativities of the atoms of two molecules are identical? For example, a given quantity of water can be regarded as a mixture of water in water. In this case, *mutual* dissociations should take place. Any given molecule should be able to lose a H^+ ion but, with equal facility, should also be able to gain one; dissociation of water into ions should equal the reassociation of these ions into whole molecules. The end state should therefore be the same as the beginning state and there should be no *net* dissociation. In actuality, however, a given quantity of water does contain a very small net quantity of ions, indicating that dissociation occurs at a very slightly faster rate than reassociation. In other words, the reaction

$$\text{H:}\overset{..}{\underset{..}{\text{O}}}\text{:} + \text{H:}\overset{..}{\underset{..}{\text{O}}}\text{:} \longrightarrow \text{H:}\overset{..}{\underset{..}{\text{O}}}\text{:H}^+ + \text{H:}\overset{..}{\underset{..}{\text{O}}}\text{:}^-$$
$$\text{H} \qquad\quad \text{H} \qquad\qquad \text{H}$$

is slightly in excess of the reverse reaction. Measurements have shown that 1 liter of pure water normally contains 10^{-7} mole of H^+ (or H_3O^+) as well as 10^{-7} mole of OH^-. A *mole* is defined as that amount of a substance which numerically equals in gram weights the atomic or molecular weight of that substance. For example, inasmuch as the molecular weights of H^+ and OH^- are 1 and 17, respectively, 1 mole of H^+ weighs 1 gram, 1 mole of OH^-, 17 grams.

Note again that dissociation is particularly characteristic of polar molecules. Nonpolar molecules (for example, CH_4) generally do not ionize in water. Note also that ionic compounds consist of ions to begin with (for example, NaCl contains Na^+ and Cl^-), hence if these are dissolved in water, they are already dissociated from the start.

Inasmuch as dissociation of any compound produces equal numbers of positively and negatively charged ions, solutions containing dissociated compounds remain electrically neutral as a whole. However, the presence of free ions permits passage of electric currents through such solutions. Dissociating compounds are therefore also called *electrolytes*, and nondissociating compounds are called *nonelectrolytes*. Flow of an electric current in electrolyte solutions is equivalent to an oriented migration of the ions. If electrodes are put into such a solution and a current is passed through, the positive ions will be attracted and will migrate to the negative electrode, called the *cathode*. Positive ions are therefore referred to as *cations*. Analogously, negative ions will be attracted to the positive electrode, known as the *anode*. Negative ions are correspondingly called *anions*.

1	$HF \longrightarrow H^+ + F^-$
2	$HCl \longrightarrow H^+ + Cl^-$
3	$H_2CO_3 \longrightarrow H^+ + HCO_3^-$
4	$CH_3COOH \longrightarrow H^+ + CH_3COO^-$
5	$NH_3 + H_2O \longrightarrow H\!:\!\overset{\displaystyle H}{\underset{\displaystyle H}{N}}\!:\!H\;:\!\overset{..}{\underset{..}{O}}\!:\!H \longrightarrow NH_4^+ + OH^-$
6	$Na^+OH^- \longrightarrow Na^+ + OH^-$
7	$H_2O \longrightarrow H^+ + OH^-$

4 · 6 *Acids and bases. The first four equations symbolize the dissociation (in water) of hydrofluoric, hydrochloric, carbonic, and acetic acids, respectively. These substances are acids inasmuch as each raises the H^+ ion concentration; the negative ions formed are fluoride, chloride, bicarbonate, and acetate, respectively. Equations 5 and 6 symbolize the dissociation of bases, that is, they raise the OH^- concentration. Ammonia in water forms covalent ammonium hydroxide, which dissociates so that the electrons* (colored dots) *go with the hydroxyl ion. The resulting ammonium ion (NH_4^+) is therefore positive (having lost one electron), and the OH^- ion is negative (having gained one electron). Equation 7 symbolizes the dissociation of water, which is chemically neutral because it raises both the H^+ and OH^- concentrations equally.*

Any compound which in aqueous solution increases the concentration of hydrogen ions, H^+ (or hydronium ions, H_3O^+) is known as an *acid*. Examples are HF, HCl, H_2CO_3, or CH_3COOH, all of which give rise to H^+ concentrations higher than in water itself (Fig. 4.6).

Any compound which in aqueous solution increases the concentration of hydroxyl ions, OH^-, is known as a *base* or an *alkali*. Ammonia, NH_3, and also initially ionic compounds such as sodium hydroxide (NaOH, or Na^+OH^-) are bases because in water they all raise the OH^- concentration above that of water itself (see Fig. 4.6).

Certain ions may themselves be acids or bases. For example, the bicarbonate ion is an acid since it may dissociate further and increase the H^+ concentration even more:

$$HCO_3^- \longrightarrow H^+ + CO_3^=$$
bicarbonate ion   *carbonate ion*

Inasmuch as H^+ ions are protons, that is, hydrogen nuclei, acids may also be defined as proton donors and many bases as proton acceptors. Thus, HCl is a proton donor and therefore an acid, NH_3, a proton acceptor and therefore a base. (However, such a definition does not reveal NaOH to be a base.) Water evidently is both an acid and a base simultaneously, since it produces H^+ as well as an equal number of OH^-. Water consequently may be said to be chemically *neutral*, that is, the acid and alkaline properties cancel out exactly.

When an acid such as HCl is mixed with a base such as NaOH, the solution will contain both H^+ and OH^- ions. Indeed, many more of these ions will be present than can actually remain in the solution; for H^+ and OH^- are components of water, and we already know that the maximum possible dissociation of water is very slight. In effect, therefore, any H^+ and OH^- in excess of the maximum dissociation capacity of water will reassociate into whole intact molecules of H_2O. In other words, a chemical *neutralization* will take place in which water molecules are formed:

$$NaOH + HCl \longrightarrow H_2O + Na^+ + Cl^-$$

If then the water is boiled away, the remaining sodium and chloride ions will form solid, crystalline NaCl, or table salt. We may note generally that interactions between acids and bases yield water as well as *salts*. Such salts normally remain as dissolved ions, and solid ionic compounds may form if the water is removed.

Salts in aqueous solution are always dissociated completely, that is, *all* chemical units of a salt exist in the form of ions. By contrast, acids and bases are not always dissociated fully, different ones dissociating to different degrees. In a solution of HF, for example, only about 1 per cent of the original molecules dissociate into ions; the rest remain in solution as intact molecules. HF is said to be a *weak* acid. Acetic acid similarly is a weak acid, most of the molecules remaining as intact wholes. On the contrary, almost all molecules of HCl put into water dissociate, and HCl is therefore spoken of as a *strong* acid. Analogously, NaOH is a very strong base, for the compound is ionic to begin with and all units present will be ionized in water. Ammonium hydroxide correspondingly is a much weaker base, many units remaining as intact NH_4OH molecules. Salts are ionic and can therefore be regarded as very strong electrolytes. Water qualifies as a very weak electrolyte. The weakest of all electrolytes in effect are the nonelectrolytes, which do not dissociate at all.

The actual acidic or basic strength of given electrolytes is a property of considerable significance, particularly so in living matter, which contains numerous dissolved acids and bases (as well as salts and nonelectrolytes). In determinations of the acidity or alkalinity of given solutions, the concentrations of free H^+ and OH^- ions present are measured with the aid of appropriate electrical equipment. The results obtained are compared with the H^+ (and OH^-) concentrations of pure water, which is taken as a reference standard. Comparative acidity or alkalinity is then expressed as a number, called the *pH* of a solution. This number has been defined arbitrarily by the expression

$$pH = \log \frac{1}{[H^+]}$$

where $[H^+]$ indicates the concentration of free hydrogen ions in 1 liter of solution. As already indicated above, 1 liter of pure water contain 10^{-7} gram of H^+. The pH of pure water therefore is

$$pH_{H_2O} = \log \frac{1}{10^{-7}} = 7$$

Inasmuch as water is chemically neutral, a pH of 7 signifies chemical neutrality. Hence any solution having a measured pH of 7 will be neutral, for its net H^+ (and OH^-) concentration will be as in pure water.

Suppose, however, that a solution contains so much acid that a liter of it contains 10^{-1} gram of H^+, that is, 1 million times as much as pure water. The pH then will be

$$pH = \log \frac{1}{10^{-1}} = 1$$

This solution will be very strongly acid. Analogously, if a solution contains 1 million times less H^+ than pure water, its pH will be

$$pH = \log \frac{1}{10^{-13}} = 13$$

and the solution will be very strongly alkaline.

In general, the *lower* than 7 the pH of a solution, the *more acid* it is, that is, the more H^+ ions are present relative to OH^- ions. Analogously, the higher than 7 the pH, the *more alkaline* is a solution, that is, the fewer H^+ ions are present relative to OH^- ions. Most electrolyte strengths of biological interest fall within a pH range from 0 to 14, that is, acidities do not normally go below pH 0 and alkalinities do not exceed pH 14 (Fig. 4.7). Indeed, living matter generally has a pH very near neutrality. For example, the pH of human blood normally is

7.3. Distinctly higher or lower pH levels do occur, however (for example, in lemons and stomach cavities, both of which contain characteristically quite acid regions, and in ponds, which are often distinctly alkaline).

Living matter does not tolerate significant variations of its normal acid-base balance, and its pH must remain within fairly narrow limits. If these limits should be exceeded, major chemical and physical disturbances would result which would be lethal. Yet we shall find later that many normal processes within living matter yield small amounts of excess acids or bases. Such small additions produce only negligible alterations of the pH. This is largely because living matter is *buffered*, or protected to some extent against pH change.

For example, suppose we consider a solution of sodium bicarbonate ($NaHCO_3$), a salt normally present in living matter. This salt exists as sodium ions (Na^+) and bicarbonate ions (HCO_3^-). If now a little hydrochloric acid (HCl) is added, we should expect the solution to become more acid. Actually, however, the pH change will be rather slight. This is because the hydrogen ions formed by hydrochloric acid (H^+) have a chance to react with the bicarbonate ions (HCO_3^-), resulting in the production of carbonic acid (H_2CO_3):

$$NaHCO_3 \longrightarrow Na^+ + HCO_3^-$$
$$\underline{HCl \longrightarrow H^+ + Cl^-}$$
$$H^+ + HCO_3^- \longrightarrow H_2CO_3$$

Carbonic acid is a *weak* acid and does not dissociate to any great extent. But the solution above at first contains very many H^+ and HCO_3^- ions, far more than are consistent with the maximum dissociation of carbonic acid. Therefore, H^+ and HCO_3^- will bond together (covalently) into intact mole-

4 · 7 The pH scale.

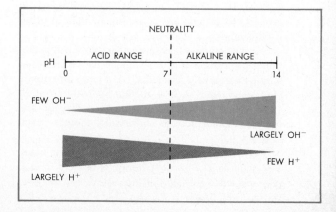

cules of H_2CO_3, as above, until the amounts of the free ions are reduced appropriately. In effect, the free H^+ ions formed by the added HCl are being "taken out of circulation," and the HCl consequently will not be able to change the pH appreciably.

We say that the presence of HCO_3^- ions *buffers* the solution, that is, protects it from major pH change if a little acid is added. Analogous buffering effects against added bases are produced by a number of positively charged ions. Inasmuch as living matter contains complex mixtures of various ionic compounds, it is buffered by virtue of its composition. Ions of the weak phosphoric acid are particularly important biological buffers. This acid dissociates in three ways:

$$H_3PO_4 \longrightarrow H^+ + H_2PO_4^-$$
$$\longrightarrow 2\,H^+ + HPO_4^=$$
$$\longrightarrow 3\,H^+ + PO_4^\equiv$$

Dissociation is slight in all cases but occurs to the greatest degree according to the first equation and least according to the third. Thus, if a strong acid is added to $PO_4^\equiv$, for example, far more H^+ ions are likely to be formed than is consistent with the maximum dissociation of H_3PO_4. Some of the free H^+ ions will then combine with $PO_4^\equiv$ and yield $HPO_4^=$, $H_2PO_4^-$, and even H_3PO_4:

$$H^+ + PO_4^\equiv \longrightarrow HPO_4^=$$
$$H^+ + HPO_4^= \longrightarrow H_2PO_4^-$$
$$H^+ + H_2PO_4^- \longrightarrow H_3PO_4$$

The solution will thereby become less acid. To be sure, if a living system (or any buffered solution) is flooded with large quantities of additional acids or bases, then buffer protection will become insufficient and pH will change noticeably.

COLLOIDAL SYSTEMS

As noted, a compound in contact with water may or may not dissolve, depending on its polarity properties. If it does dissolve, the compound will form a *true solution* of electrolytes or nonelectrolytes. In any such solution, the particles of the solute (that is, the dissolved substance) are small molecules or ions and these are dispersed thoroughly throughout the solvent. They can be neither seen nor filtered out and they stay dispersed indefinitely; they do not settle out. If the solvent is removed (for example, by boiling), then the solute particles may conglomerate into solid crystals. Hence true solutions may also be called *crystalloids*. Alternatively, the compound may not dissolve in water but form a more or less coarse *suspension*. In this case the molecules or ions of the compound remain as incompletely dispersed and

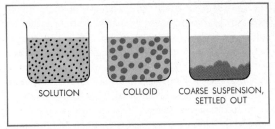

SOLUTION   COLLOID   COARSE SUSPENSION, SETTLED OUT

4 · 8 *The size of particles in water determines whether they will form a solution, a colloid, or a coarse suspension that settles out.*

more or less bulkily aggregated particles. These are large enough to be seen, and they may settle out by gravity or they can be separated out by filtration.

A third alternative arises if a compound in water forms particles intermediate in size between those in a solution and those in a suspension. A system of this type is known as a *colloid*. It is composed of a *dispersed* phase, formed by the colloidal particles, and of a *continuous* phase, formed by the water medium (Fig. 4.8).

COLLOID PROPERTIES

Colloidal systems are like solutions in that the particles are not filterable and do not settle out by gravity, but remain dispersed indefinitely. However, colloids do not form crystals and in this respect they are unlike true solutions. Also, again unlike true solutions, the particles of colloids are large enough to scatter a beam of light passing through the system. Known as the *Tyndall effect*, such light scattering is visible to the unaided eye as a more or less brilliant luminescence. The color of this luminescence tends to white if the colloid particles are comparatively large and to bluish if they are small. Only the size of dispersed particles, not their chemical nature, determines whether or not they will exist in a colloidal state. Appropriate particle sizes can be shown to range from $1/1,000,000$ to $1/10,000$ millimeter (mm). The larger figure corresponds very nearly to the limit of vision under a good microscope. In biological practice, the unit $1/1,000$ mm $=$ 1 micron (μ) is frequently used. Hence the colloidal range is from $1/1,000$ to $\frac{1}{10}\,\mu$. Particles smaller than $1/1,000\,\mu$ therefore form solutions, and particles larger than $\frac{1}{10}\,\mu$ form suspensions. A single colloidal particle can be a complex of many small molecules or ions aggregated together, or it can be a solitary large molecule or ion.

The continuous phase of a colloid need not necessarily be water. Any diphasic system is a colloid if one of the two components consists of particles of appropriate size. Eight general types of colloid systems are actually possible: a gas within either a solid or a liquid; a liquid within either a liquid, a solid, or a gas; and a solid within either a liquid, a solid, or a gas. The most common types are *sols*, in which colloidal solid particles are dispersed within liquids (for example, colloidal $Mg(OH)_2$ in water, as in milk of magnesia); *gels*, in which colloidal liquid particles are dispersed within solids (for example, colloidal water in protein, as in stiff gelatin or Jell-o); *emulsions*, in which colloidal liquids are dispersed within liquids (for example, colloidal fat in water, as in milk); and *aerosols*, in which either solids or liquids are dispersed within a gas (for example, colloidal ash in air, as in cigarette smoke, or colloidal water in air, as in fog; note that the bluish color of cigarette smoke is an example of the Tyndall effect).

Living matter is both a true solution and a colloidal system, the colloid types being sols, gels, and emulsions. Water serves as the solvent for numerous compounds and also as one of the components of the colloidal systems. For example, blood plasma is partly a sol and partly an emulsion in which water

is the continuous phase; and skin is largely a gel, colloidal water droplets here being the dispersed phase.

What prevents the particles of a colloid from settling out by gravity? As noted earlier, the molecules of a liquid are under continuous thermal agitation; the more intense the agitation, the higher the temperature. When the liquid freezes, molecular motion is reduced sharply. Above the boiling point, molecules move so rapidly that many escape; the liquid vaporizes at high rates. If dispersed particles are present in a liquid, they are buffeted and bombarded constantly by the molecules of the liquid. Very large particles are unaffected by these tiny forces, and they fall straight to the bottom of a container. But smaller bodies of colloidal size may be pushed back and forth, up and down. Gravitational pull may thereby be counteracted partly or wholly and the particles thus may be kept suspended. This random movement of small particles, called *Brownian motion*, is easily demonstrable under the microscope.

Brownian movement aids in keeping colloidal particles from settling out, but they cannot remain suspended by this force alone. Colloids stay dispersed mainly because of their *electrical charges*. Being divided up very finely, colloidal particles have an enormous surface in relation to their volume, a circumstance facilitating *adsorption* of dissolved ions present in the medium. For example, the physicochemical properties of a given colloid might be such that, if Na^+ and Cl^- ions happen to be dissolved in the water medium, the Cl^- ions become adsorbed to the surfaces of the colloid particles. The result would be that all such particles carry negative charges. And since like charges repel, the colloid

4 · 9 Adsorption and dispersion in colloids. *Colloid particles* (left, gray circles) *may adsorb ions such as* Cl^-, *and the repulsion produced by these charges may keep the colloid dispersed. If a material dissociates in water and if one of the ion types formed is of colloidal size* (X^-, *middle*), *the repulsion of like charges can maintain dispersion of the colloid. If particles of opposite charge* (H^+) *are added to dispersed and charge-carrying colloidal particles* (X^-, *right*), *the colloid may be electrically neutralized and settle out.*

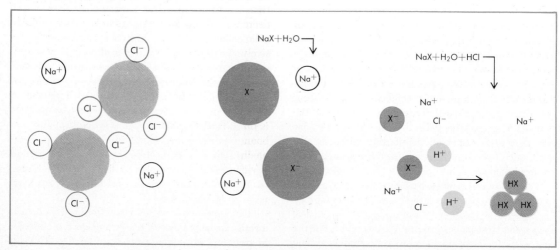

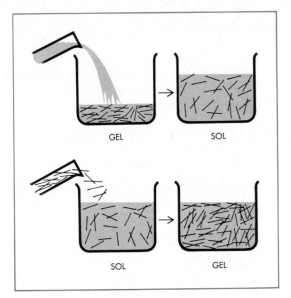

4 · 10 *Phase reversals. A gel may be transformed into a sol either by addition of more liquid* (top) *or by withdrawal of solid particles. A sol may be transformed into a gel either by addition of more solid particles* (bottom) *or withdrawal of liquid.*

particles would be kept apart and prevented from aggregating and settling (Fig. 4.9). Moreover, many types of colloid particles are themselves ionic and charged. For example, suppose that the compound NaX dissociates in water into Na^+ and X^-, and that X^- is of colloidal size. Na^+ then will dissolve, whereas X^- will form a colloidal system with water. Again the X^- ions will repel one another and will thereby remain suspended. Most colloids of biological interest actually contain particles all of which are either electropositive or electronegative, and such like charges prevent them from settling out. To be sure, if a strong acid such as HCl were added to the $Na^+ + X^- + H_2O$ system, then Cl^- ions would go into solution and the H^+ ions could combine with X^-, forming undissociated or less strongly dissociated HX. Although HX would then still be of colloidal size, the compound would no longer be charged and would therefore tend to settle out (see Fig. 4.9). It is in part because of this colloid-destroying effect that strong acids or bases kill living material.

The relative quantities of the two components of a colloid often determine whether the system will form a sol or a gel. For example, if a little gelatin is added to a comparatively large amount of water, a sol will be formed. But if then more gelatin

is added or, alternatively, if water is withdrawn, the gelatin particles will be brought closer together until they ultimately come into contact. They will then interlock into a spongelike meshwork of solid material and in the spaces of the mesh water will be dispersed in discontinuous droplets. The original sol has become transformed into a quasi-solid, pliable jelly, that is, a gel. Conversely, addition of water or removal of solid particles may convert a gel into a sol (Fig. 4.10). In living material, *sol-gel transformations* of this sort occur normally and repeatedly as local concentrations of particles or of water vary. In other cases, a region may remain more or less permanently in a gel state (for example, as in skin) or a sol state (for example, as in blood plasma—which, however, becomes a gel upon clotting). We may note, incidentally, that gels may have reasonably solid consistency and may exhibit definite forms and shapes yet still contain very large quantities of water. For example, a jellyfish is predominantly a gel, with a water content of 95 or more per cent. Analogously, brain tissue is largely a gel with a water content of about 80 per cent.

Sol-gel reversals may be brought about also by temperature changes. If the temperature of a gel is raised, the colloidal particles become more agitated and the gelled meshwork is disrupted (for example, liquefaction of Jell-o by heating). Conversely, lower temperatures promote conversions of sols into gels. Many other physical and chemical influences, for example, low or high pH or pressure, likewise affect sol-gel conditions.

All colloids *age*. The particles in a young, freshly formed colloidal system are enveloped by layers of *bound water;* water molecules are adsorbed to the particle surfaces by electrostatic attraction. It is largely because of these forces that water within a gel does not "run out" through the gel meshes. With time, however, the binding capacity of the particles decreases and some of the water does run out. The colloid "sets," that is, contracts and gelates progressively; examples are exudation of water from long-standing milk curd, custard, or mustard. Such aging of colloids in living systems may be a factor contributing to the aging of organisms.

Another important property of colloidal systems is that they tend to form boundary *membranes.* The boundary between a colloidal system and a different medium (air, water, solid surfaces, or another colloid of different type) is called an *interface.* The colloid particles there are usually subjected to complex physical forces which act on and from both sides of the interface. The result is that the particles at the interface pack together tightly and become *oriented* in parallel, in layers, or both; an interfacial membrane forms (for example, the "skins" on puddings, custards, boiled milk). Moreover, if colloid particles are electrically charged, formation of an interfacial membrane by such particles will be equivalent to the establishment of a charged interface. Such a layer then will either repel or attract other charged materials in the environment.

Interfacial membranes arise also in living colloids. This property may well be the fundamental reason why living material does not occur in large undivided masses but is organized into discrete units such as cells and, within cells, into numerous discrete smaller organelles. As will be shown in greater detail in Chap. 7, the internal cellular organelles are separated from one another by interfacial membranes, and cells themselves are likewise bounded by such membranes. The structure of these various living membranes is more complex than that of a simple colloidal one, yet the greater complexity is superimposed secondarily and a simple colloidal structure appears to be basic. That this is so is suggested by many properties shared in common by living and nonliving colloidal membranes. For example, the interfacial boundaries of living units are usually charged. Also, if a cell membrane is punctured, a new *surface precipitation membrane* develops over the opening within seconds, before appreciable amounts of the interior can flow out—a property displayed also by the boundary membranes of nonliving colloids.

Interfacial membranes have different *permeability* to different substances. Most membranes are completely permeable to water; water molecules can pass through freely in either direction. As for other materials, there is no rule by which their passage potential can be determined beforehand. In general, three classes of materials can be distinguished: those that can pass through a membrane in either direction; those that can pass in one direction but not in the other; and those that cannot penetrate at all. These categories vary considerably for different membranes.

DIFFUSION, OSMOSIS

What forces actually produce directed movement of water or other particles, either through a permeable membrane as just noted or simply through a continuous medium? Basically, such movements are brought about both in true solutions and in colloids as a direct result of the thermal motion of the dissolved or colloidal particles. For if ions, molecules, or colloidal particles happen to be distributed unevenly, more collisions will take place in more concentrated regions. Thus, if a particle in the circle in

Fig. 4.11 is displaced by thermal motion (or by Brownian bombardment) *toward* a region of higher concentration, it will soon be stopped in its track by collision with other particles. But if it is displaced *away* from a high concentration, its movement will not be interrupted so soon, since neighboring particles are farther apart. On the average, therefore, a greater number of particles is displaced into more dilute regions than into more concentrated ones. In time, particles throughout the system will become distributed evenly. This equalization resulting from net displacements of particles is called *diffusion*. The process plays an important role in living matter. For example, it happens often inside a cell that particles are unevenly distributed. Diffusion will then tend to equalize the distribution. Evidently, this is one way through which materials in cells can migrate about.

How will diffusion be affected if a membrane separates one colloid or solution from another one or from a different kind of medium? In that case the membrane is likely to be permeable to some of the particles present on either side of the membrane and impermeable to others. If, initially, the *transmissible* particles are unequally concentrated on the two sides, diffusion will equalize the concentration, as above, and the membrane is not likely to interfere with such movements. What happens when *nontransmissible* particles are unequally concentrated? For simplicity, let us assume that transmissible substances are not present at all and that we deal only with water containing nontransmissible particles. What events occur in such a system? Consult Fig. 4.12:

1. In the initial state, relatively more water molecules are in contact with the membrane X on

4 · 11 Diffusion. In the initial state, particles are distributed unevenly (left). A given particle (for example, the circled one) will therefore have more freedom to move in the direction of lower concentrations. This eventually leads to an even distribution of particles, as in the end state shown at right.

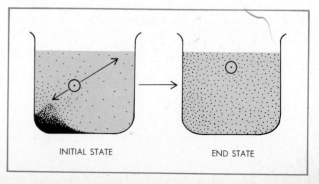

INITIAL STATE   END STATE

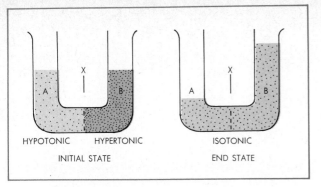

HYPOTONIC   HYPERTONIC   ISOTONIC

INITIAL STATE   END STATE

4 · 12   Osmosis. In the initial state, because A is less concentrated than B, water will be pulled from A into B. This eventually leads to the isotonic end state, where concentrations in A and B are equal. From this point on, no further net migration of water occurs (that is, just as much water moves from A into B as from B into A). A semipermeable membrane is represented by X.

the A side than on the B side, since fewer of the solid particles occupy membrane space on the A surface than on the B surface.

2. Therefore, more water molecules, on an average, are transmitted through the membrane from A to B than from B to A.

3. As a result, the water content decreases in A and increases in B. Particles in A become crowded into a smaller and smaller volume, and more and more of them therefore take up membrane space on the A surface. On the B side, the increasing water content permits the spreading of the particles into progressively larger volumes, thus reducing particle concentration along the B surface of the membrane.

4. A stage will be reached at which the number of particles along the A surface equals that along the B surface. From then on, the number of water molecules transmitted from A to B equals the number transmitted from B to A. Thereafter, no further *net* shift of water occurs.

This movement of water is called *osmosis*.

Note that the extent of osmosis depends on the *concentration differential*, the relative *numbers* of particles in A and B. Actually, it makes no difference whether the particles involved are transmissible or not. If, as normally happens in living matter, both kinds are present, transmissible particles on the more concentrated side will eventually diffuse over to the other side until concentrations are equal; but before this equality is reached, transmissible particles still exert a temporary osmotic effect. Nontransmissible particles, not being able to penetrate the membrane, exert a permanent osmotic effect.

If the difference in particle number is great enough (for example, if A contains pure water only and B contains water and a large number of particles),

then the A side may dehydrate completely and collapse, while the B side might burst and so collapse also. Since this does not normally happen in living systems, their parts, clearly, must be in general osmotic equilibrium. The concentration of particles must be the same on both sides of membranes, or as often stated, the two sides must be *isotonic* to each other. If the initial concentration on an arbitrary A side is lower than on a B side (as in Fig. 4.12), then the A side loses water. The B medium here is said to be *hypertonic* to A, that is, initially more highly concentrated than the A medium. The B side, having the higher initial concentration of particles, gains water. The A medium is said to be *hypotonic* to the B medium.

Note that the net effect of osmosis is to pull water *into* the region of higher colloidal concentration, that is, from the hypotonic to the hypertonic side. The process will continue until the two sides are isotonic. Osmosis will occur whenever certain particles cannot or do not pass through a membrane. Then nothing migrates through the membrane except *water* (plus any particles present which *can* diffuse through).

Like diffusion, osmosis plays an important role in living matter. It is one agency by which water is distributed and redistributed across membranes.

In the past, traffic through living membranes has been compared with traffic through nonliving ones like cellophane. Such nonliving membranes let water or small ions through, but not very large molecules, for example. Particle penetration here can be explained rather readily in terms of diffusion. Ions, for example, would strike the barrier; most of them would bounce off, but some would pass through *pores* in the membrane. If the ion concentration were greater on one side of the membrane than on the other, more ions on an average would migrate into the dilute side, thus equalizing concentrations.

However, a hypothesis postulating diffusion through pores is generally inadequate for living membranes. If cellular membranes were indeed passive, inert films with holes, like cellophane, then it should not matter if such a membrane were poisoned; being nonliving, it could not be affected by a poison. But experiments actually show that the activity of cellular membranes *is* stopped or severely impaired by poisons, indicating that such membranes are not simply passive films. Moreover, if living membranes actually contained small holes, then the size of a particle should determine whether or not it could pass through such holes. However, particle size is often of little importance. For example, under certain conditions very large molecules may pass through a given membrane whereas very small molecules sometimes may not. Again, many kinds of molecules in living material have the same physical size, yet the different kinds are passed through living membranes at substantially different speeds.

Clearly, living membranes are highly *selective*; they act as if they "knew" which substances to transmit and which to reject. Moreover, it is now known that active, energy-consuming work is often done by a living membrane in transmitting materials, and that complex chemical reactions take place in the process. Therefore, rather than visualize a passive membrane with small holes, we are led to consider cellular membranes as dynamic structures in which entering or leaving particles are actively "handed" across from one side to the other.

Accordingly, if we encounter a situation where materials other than water pass through a living membrane, we shall be quite wrong if we simply say offhandedly that this can be explained "by diffusion." Diffusion does play some role in most cases, but *active transport* by the membrane usually plays an equally important role.

ORGANIC BONDING

CARBON COMPOUNDS AND RADICALS

Apart from hydrogen and oxygen compounds, among them notably water, the single most important types of chemicals in living matter are the carbon compounds. By virtue of the structural properties of its atoms, carbon happens to be a fairly unusual and exceedingly versatile element; and it is precisely because of this circumstance that carbon has actually become so crucial a component in material we now call "living."

With a usual covalence of 4 (see Chap. 3), carbon atoms can link up with as many as four other atoms of the same or of different kinds. Carbon is bonded to four hydrogens in methane, as noted earlier, but any or all of these hydrogen atoms may be replaced rather readily by other atoms. For example, in reactions of methane with chlorine or chlorine-containing compounds, one may obtain new compounds such as CH_3Cl, CH_2Cl_2, $CHCl_3$, and CCl_4.

Apart from bonding possibilities such as these, carbon atoms may link directly to other carbon atoms. In this respect carbon is a rather unusual element. The atoms of most other elements may similarly bond to atoms of like kind, but the number of atoms so bondable is generally quite limited. For example, a hydrogen atom may link to one other hydrogen atom at most ($H—H$, H_2); an oxygen atom may link to two others at most ($.\overset{..}{O}. \quad .\overset{..}{O}.$, O_3, ozone); and

as many as eight sulfur atoms may link together into

molecules (S_8). But a carbon atom may combine with a practically unlimited number of other carbons. More or less long *chains* of carbon atoms may form in this way:

Such chains represent parts of molecules in which various other atoms or groups of atoms are attached to the carbons. For example, hydrogen may be joined to all free bonds:

Alternatively, one or more types of atoms other than hydrogen may be bonded to such chains.

Chains, or *aliphatic* structures, are by no means the only possible kinds of carbon-to-carbon combinations. If we imagine that one end of a carbon chain becomes connected to the other end, then a carbon *ring* will be the result. Benzene is one of such ring-containing, or *aromatic*, compounds:

Many additional types of configurations exist. For example, carbon chains can be branched, rings and chains can become joined to one another, and any of these "patterns in carbon" can extend into three as well as two dimensions. Such carbon structures form molecular "skeletons," as it were, and the other atoms bonded to the carbons may be thought of as the "flesh" on the skeletons.

No other element even approaches the self-bonding versatility displayed by carbon. To be sure, all elements of group IV in the periodic table display the same valence characteristics as carbon, but the outer electrons of these other elements lie farther from the nucleus, in higher shells, and thus are bound less strongly. The result is that not even silicon, the next-larger group IV atom after carbon, can form nearly so many different, stable compounds as carbon. In effect, the properties of carbon introduce the possibility of tremendous *complexity* as well as *variety* into molecular structure. Actually, carbon-containing substances, including particularly those with two or more *linked* carbon atoms, display more complexity and more variety than all other chemicals put together.

The vast majority of naturally occurring carbon compounds is found in *living* matter or in materials derived from living and once-living matter. Compounds associated most specifically with the living attributes of any organism are carbon compounds; and earth fuels such as coal, oil, and natural gas are carbon compounds derived from living organisms of past ages. Because of this, all such carbon chemicals are collectively called *organic compounds.* Excepted from this organic category are a few types of carbon compounds of mineral origin, for example, carbon dioxide (CO_2) and materials containing carbonate ions ($CO_3^=$) or their derivatives—in short, carbon-oxygen compounds, or compounds in which the oxidation state of carbon is $+4$. By contrast, organic compounds almost always contain carbon in which the oxidation state is not $+4$, carbon being bonded to hydrogen, to carbon itself, and often also to nitrogen, oxygen, sulfur, phosphorus, or other atoms as well. Among the simplest organic compounds, for example, is methane, CH_4 (as well as derivatives of methane such as CCl_4). All compounds not in the organic category are collectively called *inorganic compounds.* Among these are water, mineral substances, metals, nonmetals, and also the mineral carbon derivatives just referred to above, such as CO_2 (including CO, even though here the oxidation state of carbon is not $+4$ but $+2$). In general, inorganic substances include all materials composing the physical, nonliving world. But note that whereas the nonliving world contains inorganic materials only, the living world contains *both* inorganic and organic materials. For example, water, an inorganic substance, is a conspicuous component of every living organism.

If one examines the structure of different molecular compounds, organic ones in particular, he finds that certain groupings of atoms tend to recur in very many of them. The atoms of such groupings are often bonded to one another more firmly than to other atoms, and they then tend to behave as relatively more stable subunits of the compound. Subunits of this type are called *groups,* or *radicals.* In organic molecules, for example, one or both ends of a carbon chain frequently carry the combination

$$-\overset{\displaystyle H}{\underset{\displaystyle H}{\overset{\displaystyle |}{\underset{\displaystyle |}{C}}}}-H,$$

or $-CH_3$, called the *methyl* group. In the interior of such chains may be present one or more

$$H-\overset{\displaystyle |}{\underset{\displaystyle |}{C}}-H$$

or $-CH_2-$ combinations, referred to as *methylene* groups. An $-OH$, or hydroxyl group, is found in water ($H-OH$) as well as in numerous organic compounds. On occasion two or more groups may together form a single larger group. For example, a methyl and a methylene group together, CH_3CH_2-, constitute an *ethyl* group. Analogously, a *carboxyl* group, $-\overset{\displaystyle |}{\underset{\displaystyle OH}{C}}=O$, or $-COOH$, consists of one *carbonyl* group, $-C=O$, and one hydroxyl group, $-OH$. Numerous whole compounds are simply combinations of two or more radicals. For example, a methyl group joined to a carboxyl group forms acetic acid, CH_3-COOH; an ethyl group joined to a hydroxyl group forms ethyl alcohol, CH_3CH_2OH. Some of the most commonly encountered groups of organic compounds are shown in Fig. 4.13; they will be referred to frequently throughout this book.

All such radicals are normally linked by covalent bonds to the other portions of a molecule. However, in some cases a group may split off as an ion or, conversely, an ion may become bonded covalently to a molecule as a group. Many of these transformations of radicals into ions or vice versa involve hydrogen atoms; we already know that such atoms may either share or transfer their electrons. Thus, water is normally a molecule, $H-OH$, with a hydroxyl group bonded covalently to hydrogen. Under certain conditions, however, water may split apart into two ions. One of the hydrogens leaves its electron on the oxygen and departs as a positively charged hydrogen ion. The remaining hydroxyl group then possesses an extra electron and becomes a negatively charged hydroxyl *ion:*

$$H:\overset{..}{\underset{..}{O}}:H \longrightarrow H:\overset{..}{\underset{..}{O}}:^- + H^+$$

This is an important reaction in living material, and we shall deal with it again in later contexts. (Note that it differs from the dissociations discussed earlier in that here a *single* water molecule forms two ions, whereas in the earlier dissociations *two* water molecules interact and form two ions.)

Also of considerable biological significance are ion-radical interconversions among phosphates (Fig. 4.14). All phosphates are derivatives of phosphoric acid, H_3PO_4. This acid may be considered to consist of a covalent union between a hydrogen atom and a phosphate radical, namely, $H-H_2PO_4$. If the hydrogen atom splits away and in the process leaves its electron behind, the phosphate radical will become a phosphate ion, namely, $H_2PO_4^-$. This ion may now be considered to represent a covalent union between a hydrogen atom and another type of phosphate radical, namely, $H-HPO_4^-$. If the hydrogen atom again splits away and leaves its electron behind, a

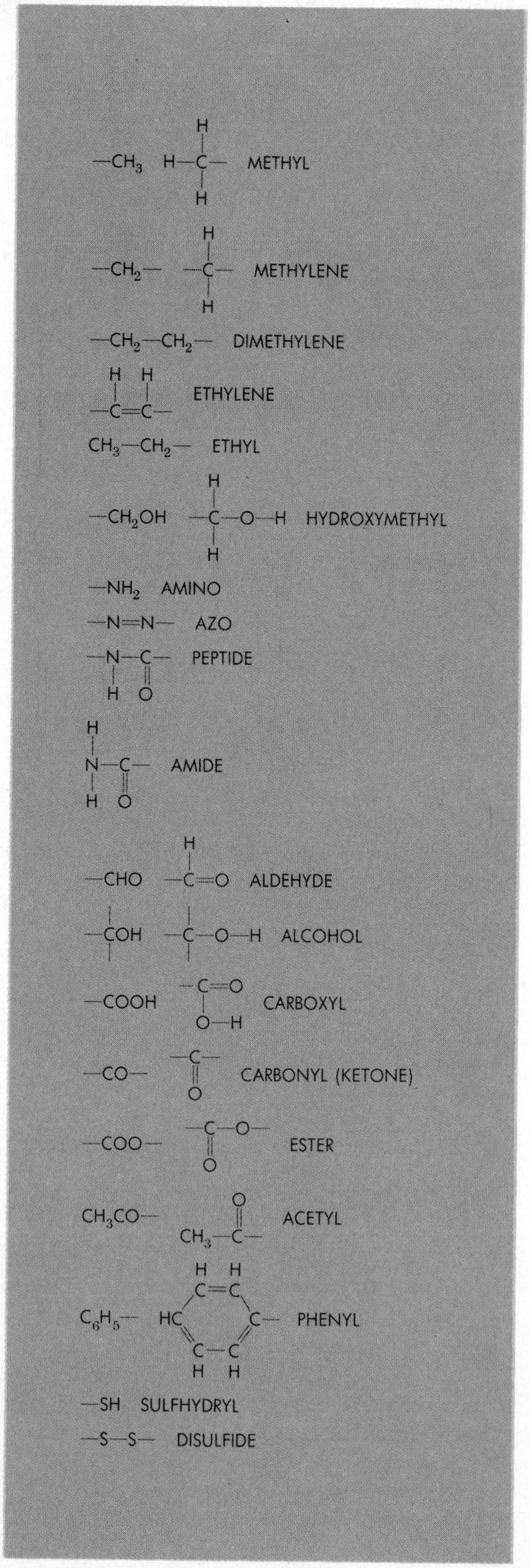

-CH₃ H—C— METHYL

-CH₂— —C— METHYLENE

-CH₂—CH₂— DIMETHYLENE

ETHYLENE —C=C—

CH₃—CH₂— ETHYL

-CH₂OH —C—O—H HYDROXYMETHYL

-NH₂ AMINO

-N=N— AZO

-N—C— PEPTIDE H O

N—C— AMIDE H O

-CHO —C=O ALDEHYDE

-COH —C—O—H ALCOHOL

-COOH —C=O O—H CARBOXYL

-CO— —C— O CARBONYL (KETONE)

-COO— —C—O— O ESTER

CH₃CO— CH₃—C— O ACETYL

C₆H₅— PHENYL

-SH SULFHYDRYL

-S—S— DISULFIDE

4 · 13 *Common radicals,* or atomic groupings, encountered in organic compounds.

new type of ion will result, namely, $HPO_4^=$. In its turn, this ion consists of a hydrogen atom and a radical, $H—PO_4^=$, and if this last hydrogen splits away without its electron, the ion $PO_4^{\equiv}$ will be left. We note therefore that phosphoric acid can be transformed into two series of phosphates, one consisting of three types of phosphate *radicals* ($—H_2PO_4$, $—HPO_4^-$, $—PO_4^=$), the other of three types of phosphate *ions* ($H_2PO_4^-$, $HPO_4^=$, $PO_4^{\equiv}$). By addition of H^+ ions, moreover, the phosphate ions can become radicals, and by removal of H^+ ions the radicals can become ions. Phosphate radicals are often joined to organic compounds, and in biological practice such phosphates are often referred to as *organic phosphates*. Free phosphate ions, by contrast, are spoken of as inorganic phosphates.

POLYMERS AND ISOMERS

The numbers and types of atoms in a compound determine its size and mass. A molecule composed of but a few atoms of low atomic weight will obviously be smaller and lighter than a molecule composed of many atoms of high atomic weight. Of the organic compounds present in living matter, most consist of atoms of relatively low atomic weights. Carbon itself is of low weight, and the most abundant other atoms are H, O, and N, all likewise of low weight. But although the atomic weights are low, the *molecular* weights can be exceedingly high; given molecules in living matter are of very large size, contain hundreds and thousands of atoms each, and may have molecular weights in the order of millions. Here it is the huge number of atoms, not their individual weights, that endows such compounds with high molecular weights. The term *macromolecule* is applied to such exceedingly large molecules. We shall find later that the most fundamental "living" characteristics of organisms are due particularly to specific types of macromolecules.

Very high molecular weights usually result when a given grouping of atoms is repeated many times within a molecule. For example, the repeat unit might be the methylene radical, $—CH_2—$, and an exceedingly long molecule can form when dozens of such radicals are joined together via their carbon atoms. In other instances, the repeat unit may be a fairly large, whole molecule itself. For example, one of the sugars we shall deal with frequently is *glucose*, a complete, whole molecule containing a chain skeleton of six carbon atoms. Through reactions involving

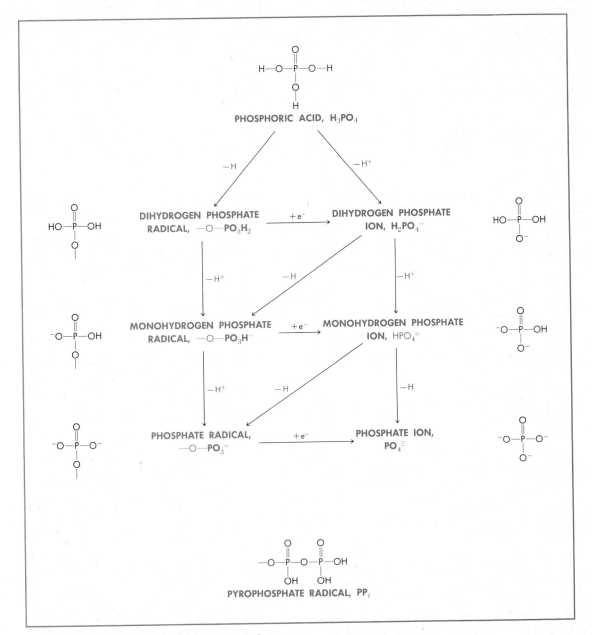

4 · 14 Phosphate ions and radicals *are derivatives of phosphoric acid. The radicals, or organic phosphates, are groupings attached to other (organic) compounds. The ions are independent charged particles. Ions and radicals can become interconverted as shown.*

some of the H and O atoms bonded to the ends of this carbon chain, two or more glucose molecules may become joined to one another end to end. Chains composed of several thousand glucose units

(and six times as many carbon atoms) are obtained in this fashion, the whole glucose molecule here representing the basic repeat unit. Among the familiar compounds produced in this way are, for example, starch and cellulose, two kinds of true macromolecules (see Chap. 6).

The general process of uniting numerous molecular units of the same type into far larger supermolecules (not necessarily straight chains only) is called *polymerization*. Each molecular unit (such as glucose) is said to be a *monomer*. If only two, three, four, or a few more monomers are linked together, the resulting compounds are referred to as dimers, trimers, tetramers, etc. A macromolecular result (such as starch) is a *polymer*. As we shall see, virtually all the fundamentally significant macromolecules of living matter are polymeric structures, each composed of often thousands or tens of thousands of specific monomeric units. Some of these polymers are actually large enough to be visible under the electron microscope as distinct filamentous or granular particles, and we may note here that such polymeric macromolecules include the largest chemical complexes known.

One of the consequences of the great structural variation among organic compounds is that two or more of them may possess identical atoms yet nevertheless represent different compounds, with different properties. Such substances differ in the *patterns* in which the atoms are bonded. For example, the molecules

contain identical atoms and both may be symbolized as C_4H_{10}. But since their atoms are bonded in different patterns, they are in fact different kinds of molecules with different properties. A family of compounds in which the bonding patterns differ as above is called a set of *structural isomers*. For example, the molecule on the left above is *butane,* and that on the right is the structural isomer *isobutane.* It may

4 · 15 Structural isomerism. *The diagram depicts the four structural isomers of a six-carbon chain. Any other chainlike arrangement of six carbon atoms corresponds to one of the patterns depicted here.*

be verified readily that the number of possible isomers increases rapidly as the number of carbon atoms in a molecule increases. Thus in a 4-carbon chain, as in butane, only the single T-shaped aliphatic isomer as in isobutane is possible, for any other arrangement of the carbon skeleton is again a linear butane chain. But in a 6-carbon chain the possible isomeric configurations are more numerous, as indicated in Fig. 4.15. As we shall see, isomeric families of organic compounds play conspicuous roles in the chemistry of living matter; and it is an important generalization that two isomers of even slightly different bonding patterns may have vastly different biological functions and effects.

The tetrahedral alignment of the four bonds of a carbon atom give rise to another kind of isomerism, namely, *optical isomerism*. If two, three, or all four bonds of carbon are linked to the *same* atoms or atomic complexes, then the resulting molecule will have at least one mirror plane; it will be so constructed that at least one of its possible mirror images forms an identically arranged structure. For example, assume that a carbon atom is bonded to atoms *a, a, b,* and *c* (Fig. 4.16). If we now visualize a plane passing through *b, c,* and carbon itself, we find that the whole molecule is bilaterally symmetrical with reference to this plane. The latter constitutes the mirror plane. Also, a mirror placed next to the molecule parallel to the mirror plane will produce an image which will be structurally identical with the molecule itself. The molecule and its mirror image are therefore *superimposable*. A carbon-containing molecule characterized by a superimposable mirror image is said to possess a *symmetric* carbon atom.

On the contrary, if all four carbon bonds link to *different* atoms or atomic groups, then the carbon atom will be *asymmetric*. Thus, if the groups bonded to carbon are *a, b, c,* and *d,* then a mirror plane cannot be found no matter how the molecule is positioned. Moreover, none of the possible mirror images will be superimposable on the molecule, just as a left hand cannot be superimposed on a right hand; some part of the structure always points in a different direction in the mirror image (see Fig. 4.16).

It follows that two molecules can be identical in atomic composition and structure, yet if they contain asymmetric carbons they need not be identical in their "handedness"; they can represent nonsuperimposable mirror images of each other. Pairs of this kind generally share in common properties such as chemical reactivities, melting points, boiling points, and others, but they behave differently toward asymmetric physical agents. For example, a well-known asymmetric physical agent is polarized light, that is,

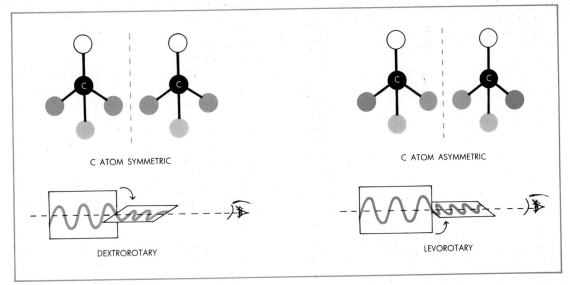

C ATOM SYMMETRIC

C ATOM ASYMMETRIC

DEXTROROTARY

LEVOROTARY

a beam in which the energy waves oscillate in a single plane only (somewhat like a snake undulating from side to side in the plane of the ground). Compounds with asymmetric carbons have the property of changing the plane of oscillation if a beam of polarized light is passed through them. Symmetric carbon atoms do not produce such an effect. Asymmetric molecules are therefore said to be *optically active*, and mirror-image pairs of molecules are referred to as *enantiomorphs, enantiomers,* or *optical isomers* of each other. Both members of such a pair rotate the plane of polarized light to the same extent, but one produces rotation in a clockwise sense, the other in a counterclockwise sense. If the observer faces the beam of light emerging from samples of the optical isomers, the sample giving the clockwise rotation is arbitrarily designated as a *dextrorotary* isomer and is identified by the prefixes *d-* or (+)-; and the sample giving the counterclockwise rotation is referred to as *levorotary* and is identified by the prefixes *l-* or (−)-. Mixtures of paired (+) and (−) isomers of a compound are called *dl mixtures, racemic* mixtures, or *racemates*.

Like structural isomerism, optical isomerism is of considerable biological significance. For example, many a compound in living matter has different effects in its *d* and its *l* configuration. Note, incidentally, that an organic molecule may contain more than one asymmetric carbon atom. Many very large molecules contain hundreds, as will become apparent later. Note also that atoms other than carbon may be asymmetric. For example, nitrogen is asymmetric if all three of its bonds hold different atoms or atomic groups. Such asymmetries are negligible in consider-

4 · 16   Optical isomerism. *If at least two groups attached to a carbon atom are identical (top left), then an identical mirror image of the molecule can be formed and the carbon atom is symmetric. But if all groups on carbon are different (top right), then an identical mirror image cannot be formed and the atom is asymmetric. The lower figures illustrate the convention of calling a compound dextrorotary if it rotates the plane of polarized light clockwise from the viewpoint of the observer; and levorotary if the rotation is counterclockwise.*

ing living systems, however, asymmetric carbons being the most important not only quantitatively but also in terms of effects.

RESONANCE AND HIGH-ENERGY BONDS

The preceding discussion of spatial symmetries in chemical units leads to a consideration of a related phenomenon, encountered particularly when a group of linked atoms contains both double and single bonds. We have already found, for example, that the structure of benzene can be represented as a ring of six —CH— groups, linked alternately by single and double bonds; and if we consider the —CH— groups to have fixed positions, we may write two formally equivalent diagrams for this structure:

However, neither formula could correspond to the actual configuration of benzene, for double bonds are known to be somewhat shorter and slightly stronger (as well as slightly less stable) than single bonds. Hence the geometric configuration of benzene should be

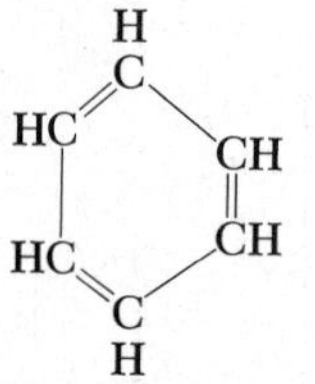

Yet experimental analysis has shown unequivocally that the six —CH— groups are in actuality equidis-

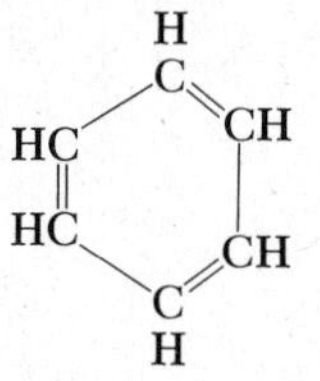

4 · 17 Resonance hybrids. *For each of the four ions considered here, the column at far left indicates the atomic composition. The column at left center outlines the general electron distribution. The center column shows (as colored dots) the electrons contributed by the central atoms and (as colored minus signs) the places where the ion has acquired extra electrons. The column at right center indicates the conventional structural formula; bonds with arrowheads symbolize coordinate covalent bonds. The groups of formulas at far right depict some of the resonance hybrids required to represent the ions adequately.*

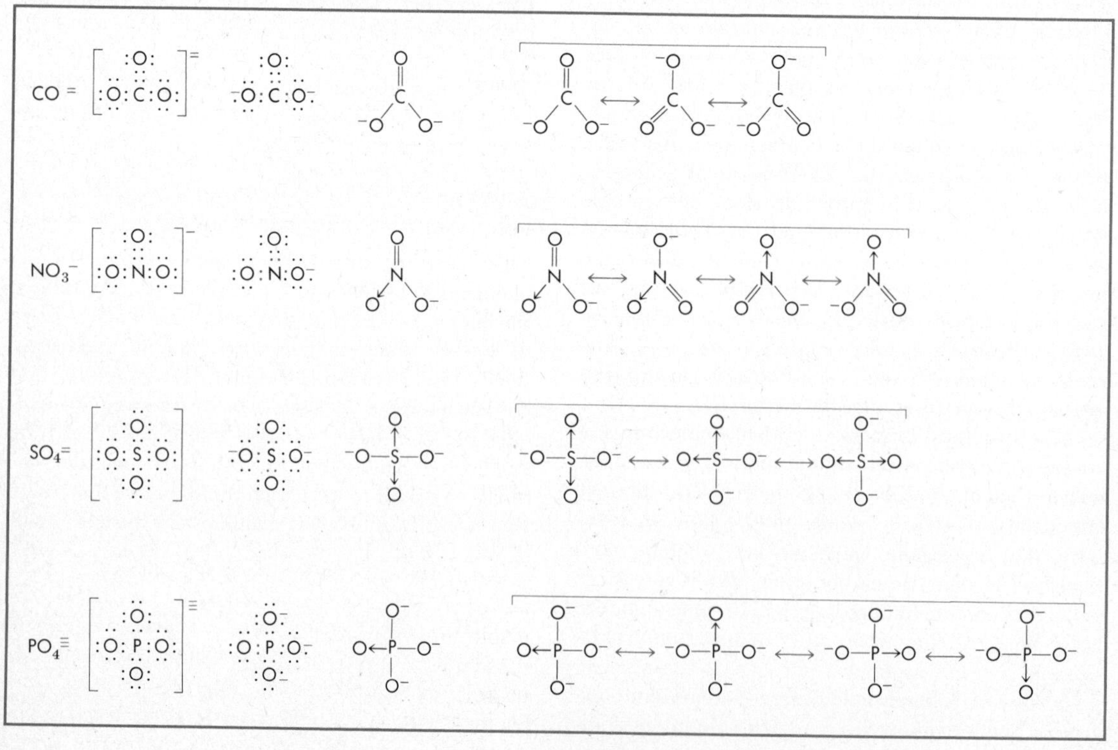

tant, located at the corners of a regular hexagon, and that all bonds are of *equal* length, stability, and energy content. This discrepancy between theory and experiment has been resolved formally by representing benzene by two structural formulas simultaneously, interconnected with a double-headed arrow:

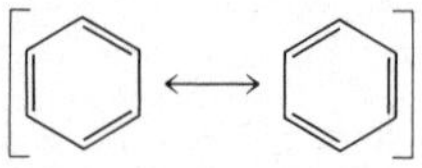

This dual representation signifies that either formula alone does not correctly describe the molecular structure and that a better description is obtained if both formulas are taken together and superimposed in one's mind. The double-headed arrow thus does *not* indicate a reversible conversion of one form to the other; if that were to be indicated, the symbol $\rightleftharpoons$ would be used. Instead, the arrow $\longleftrightarrow$ signifies that both formulas need to be combined if the one compound is to be depicted.

Any compound or atomic complex which cannot be properly described by a single structural formula is said to exhibit *resonance*, or to be a *resonance hybrid*. The term resonance does not imply, however, that electron pairs flip back and forth to either side of a —CH— group, alternately converting a given single bond into a double bond or vice versa. Instead,

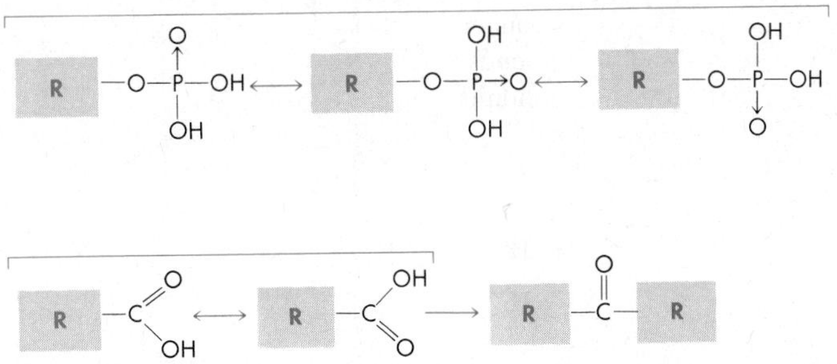

R —O—P—OH ⟷ R —O—P→O ⟷ R —O—P—OH

R —C⟍OH ⟷ R —C⟍OH ⟶ R —C— R

the term merely implies that our presently available symbolic tools, both pictorial and verbal, are inadequate to give a single unambiguous description of electronic configurations. This difficulty is underscored further by the word "hybrid," which suggests that a resonating compound is analogous to a biological hybrid, that is, an offspring produced by crossbreeding two genetically different parents. In the biological situation we *can* describe the result unambiguously (for example, we can photograph it), but in the chemical situation we cannot.

Resonance is displayed by many polyatomic ions, some of them of major significance in living matter precisely because of their resonance properties. Consider, for example, the inorganic ions NO_3^-, $CO_3^=$, $SO_4^=$, and $PO_4^{\equiv}$. Each represents a covalent group that has acquired one or more electrons by transfer from suitable donors (for example, H atoms), and all atoms of these ions thus can have complete octets of outer electrons. Figure 4.17 indicates the conventional structural configurations. Note that each ion contains both single and double bonds, suggesting that bond lengths and bond energies should differ accordingly. Yet experiment again shows that the ions are symmetrical, all bonds in each being of equal length and energy content. In other words, each ion must be a resonance hybrid, and more than one formula will be needed to provide a reasonably adequate representation (see Fig. 4.17).

An important property of resonating complexes is that they contain less energy and thus are more stable than nonresonating derivatives of such complexes. For example, one of many derivatives of benzene is quinone:

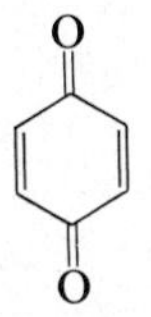

4 · 18 Resonance restriction. *If a phosphate becomes attached as a radical to an organic carrier compound R (top), such bonding restricts the resonance of the phosphate to three hybrid forms as shown, rather than the four indicated in Fig. 4.17 for the free phosphate. The free carboxyl group (—COOH) normally resonates in two forms, as shown at bottom, but if the —OH group is replaced by another organic carrier (R′) then the resonance is restricted to a single form, that is, the resonance is abolished.*

Like benzene, quinone contains a 6-carbon ring, but a single formula is fully adequate to depict the electron configuration of this compound. Evidently, conversion of benzene to quinone abolishes resonance, and the substitution of O for H at two of the carbons apparently "fixes" the structure of the benzene ring into a conventionally describable form. Furthermore, quinone is less stable than benzene and its total energy content is greater. The situation is roughly analogous to a motor-driven wheel with the brake off and then on. The freely turning wheel compares with the resonating compound, the braked wheel with the nonresonating derivative. If the brake is on, the wheel is prevented from turning and the energy normally expended in turning is now not being dissipated. Thus the braked wheel, straining to slip the brake, will have a greater energy potential, the difference corresponding to the energy which must be expended to keep the brake applied tightly. Just so do resonating hybrids acquire extra energy if their resonance is restricted, the excess being equivalent to the energy expended in producing the restriction.

Several specific instances of resonance restriction are of considerable biological importance. For example, a phosphate ion is a resonance hybrid, as noted; four formulas are required to depict it adequately (see Fig. 4.17). However, the resonance will be restricted if the free ion becomes a phosphate

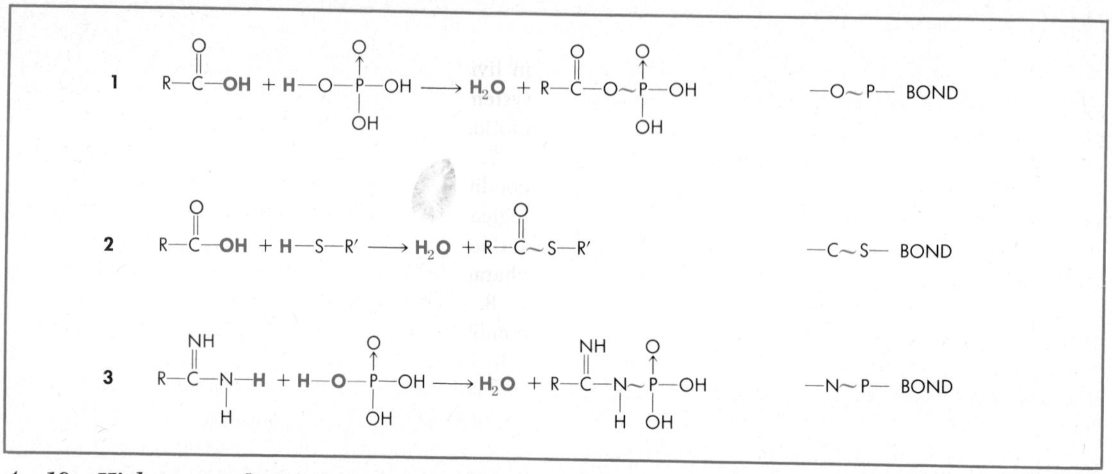

4 · 19 *High-energy bonds and resonance in three biologically important kinds of reaction types. In the reaction 1 a carboxyl and a phosphate group combine with mutual restriction of resonance, yielding a high-energy O~P bond in the product. In the reaction 2 the resonance of the carboxyl group is abolished by combination with a sulfhydryl group (—SH), yielding a high-energy C~S bond. In the reaction 3, the resonance of phosphate is restricted by union with an amino group (—NH$_2$), and a high-energy N~P bond then appears in the product.*

radical bonded to an organic compound. Resonance then still occurs, but the number of resonance forms has decreased from four to three (Fig. 4.18). In a sense the organic carrier compound of phosphate is analogous to a brake lightly applied to a turning wheel, so that the turning becomes reduced. The restricted resonance hybrid of phosphate now contains more energy (in the —O—P bond) than the original ion.

Another common resonance hybrid is the carboxyl radical of organic molecules, R—COOH (see Fig. 4.18). Here again the energy may increase and the resonance is restricted—indeed abolished—if the —OH group is replaced by another atomic complex, for example, R′ in Fig. 4.18.

Suppose now that two *different* resonating groups are joined, such that in the product one radical restricts the resonance of the other, in reciprocal fashion. For example, an organic phosphate radical might serve as R′ and might substitute for the —OH group in carboxyl (Fig. 4.19, reaction 1). In the product, the organic phosphate abolishes the resonance

of the carboxyl-derived —C— group, and R—C— in turn restricts the resonance of the phosphate.

The net effect of this mutual restriction is that the —O—P— bond becomes enormously energetic, so energetic, indeed, that it is spoken of as a high-energy bond. It is symbolized by ~, as in Fig. 4.19. As we shall see, high-energy —O ~ P bonds represent the principal energy source in all internal operations of living matter.

Several other types of high-energy bonds will be found to be of significance in various later contexts. One is the C ~ S bond, produced when a carboxyl group becomes joined to a sulfhydryl radical, —SH (see Fig. 4.19, reaction 2). The increase in bond energy here results as above from an abolition of resonance in the carboxyl group. (Note, incidentally, that H—S—R′ in reaction 2 of Fig. 4.19 is formally equivalent to phosphoric acid, H—O—PO$_3$H$_2$, participating in reaction 1; both S and O belong to group VI of the periodic table.) A high-energy bond arises also when nitrogen becomes linked to organic phosphate. For example, the radical

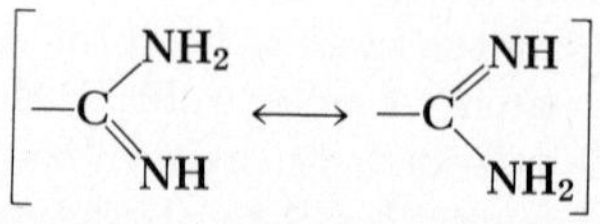

$$\left[-C\begin{array}{c} NH_2 \\ \\ NH \end{array} \longleftrightarrow -C\begin{array}{c} NH \\ \\ NH_2 \end{array} \right]$$

is a resonance hybrid, and a union with phosphate may yield the product shown in reaction 3 of Fig. 4.19. In this case the phosphate abolishes the resonance of the carbon-nitrogen radical and the latter in turn reciprocally restricts phosphate resonance. The result is the appearance of a high-energy N ~ P bond.

Throughout this chapter, chemical *reactions* either have been implicit in the discussion or have been considered explicitly in particular instances. We next shift our attention to the general nature of such reactions among chemical units.

REVIEW QUESTIONS

1. How do temperature and pressure affect the physical states of materials? Distinguish between polar and nonpolar substances. What is a dipole, and how can a temporary dipole form in symmetrical substances? How are electronic symmetries related to boiling points? To solubilities?

2. What are van der Waals forces? Hydrogen bonds? Between what types of atoms can H bonds become established? Why does water but not ammonia, for example, exist in solid crystalline form? In what ways is water physically anomalous? What kinds of bonding forces make almost all metals solids at room temperature?

3. Define dissociation, electrolyte, acid, base, salt. Is H_2SO_4 an acid, a base, or a salt? How does sodium sulfate (Na_2SO_4) dissociate? Distinguish between dissociation and ionization. What are cations and anions? Give examples. Distinguish between strong and weak electrolytes.

4. Define pH. What does the pH of a solution indicate? What would you expect the pH of a solution of NaCl to be? Of HCl? Of NaOH? Compared with pure water, how many more or fewer grams of H^+ ions will there be in a liter solution of (a) pH 5 and (b) pH 10? The pH of human blood is 7.3; what is the actual H^+ ion concentration per liter?

5. What is the biological significance of dissociation and pH? What are buffers and how do they work? Give examples. How do phosphates work as buffers?

6. What is a colloidal system? How does such a system differ from a solution? What kinds of colloidal systems are possible, and what kinds are found in living matter? Review the properties of colloidal systems. What are the Tyndall effect, Brownian motion, and sol-gel transformations?

7. Define diffusion and show how and under what conditions this process will occur. What is the biological significance of diffusion? How and where do surface precipitation membranes form? What are the characteristics of such membranes?

8. Define osmosis. Show how and under what conditions this process will occur. Distinguish carefully between osmosis and diffusion. Cite examples of biological situations characterized by isotonicity, hypertonicity, and hypotonicity.

9. What are inorganic compounds? Organic compounds? Characterize both types in terms of oxidation states of carbon. Name and state the composition of several common types of radicals. Distinguish between organic and inorganic phosphates.

10. Define polymer, macromolecule, isomer. What are structural isomerism and optical isomerism? Under what conditions is a carbon atom (a) asymmetric, (b) optically active? How are d- and l- isomers of a substance defined?

11. Define chemical resonance. In what sense is the concept of resonance a reflection of our ignorance of nature? Give examples and write symbolizations of resonating chemicals.

12. How do the energy contents of resonating and related nonresonating substances compare? Explain. What are high-energy bonds and how do they form? Show how specific high-energy bonds of importance in living matter may arise.

COLLATERAL READINGS

Alder, B. J., and T. E. Wainwright: Molecular Motions, *Sci. American*, October, 1959. A description of the properties of molecules in bulk in terms of the behavior of individual particles.

Baker, J. J. W., and G. E. Allen: "Matter, Energy, and Life," Addison-Wesley, Reading, Mass., 1965. This paperback, already referred to in the previous chapter, contains an account of dissociation and also covers other topics of basic chemistry in an introductory manner.

Bent, R. L.: Stereoisomerism, *J. Chem. Ed.*, vol. 30, 1953. An article on structural isomers for those who wish to have more extensive information.

Buswell, A. M., and W. H. Rodebush: Water, *Sci. American*, Apr., 1956. A popular article describing the physical and chemical attributes of water, including the anomalous properties of this vital substance.

Christensen, H. N.: "pH and Dissociation," Saunders, Philadelphia, 1964. A booklet designed for programmed self-study, covering the indicated topic very thoroughly. Recommended.

Fieser, L., and M. Fieser: "Organic Chemistry," 3d ed., Reinhold, New York, 1956. A good basic text recommended for further background on organic compounds.

Herz, W.: "The Shape of Carbon Compounds," Benjamin, New York, 1963. A paperback dealing with atomic and molecular symmetries, isomerism, resonance, orbitals and hybrids, and other topics dealt with in this chapter. Highly recommended.

Moore, W. J.: "Physical Chemistry," Prentice-Hall, Englewood Cliffs, N.J. This text includes a good treatment of the states of matter.

Noller, C. R.: A Physical Picture of Covalent Bonding and Resonance in Organic Chemistry, *J. Chem. Ed.*, vol. 27, 1950. The title of this general article is self-explanatory.

Pauling, L.: "The Nature of the Chemical Bond," Cornell, Ithaca, N.Y., 1960. An authoritative discussion covering all aspects of bonding, including those referred to in the present chapter.

Sienko, M. J., and R. A. Plane: "Chemistry," 2d ed., McGraw-Hill, New York, 1961. Already referred to in the last chapter, this general text includes good accounts of physical states and colloids.

CHAPTER 5
REACTIONS
AND
ENERGY

A chemical reaction may be considered to be any process in which at least one bond between two atoms is either formed or broken. Several questions emerge from this generalization. What kinds of chemical changes can be produced by such bond-forming or bond-breaking events? What conditions or agents can initiate, promote, or halt these events? And what physical changes accompany the chemical ones? For example, what alterations take place in the energies of the participating chemicals? Issues such as these are examined below; we shall find most of them to be crucial in later contexts.

CHEMICAL CHANGE

Reactions generally occur as a result of *collisions* among molecules or ions; direct contact is necessary between molecular or ionic units if they are to be close enough together for bond breaking or bond formation. The more collisions there are the more reaction will be possible and, as will be shown shortly, any factor or condition that promotes collision among chemical units also promotes reactions.

Inasmuch as reactions always imply formation or abolition of bonds, the most fundamental chemical outcome of any reaction must be a *rearrangement* of atoms and bonding patterns. For example:

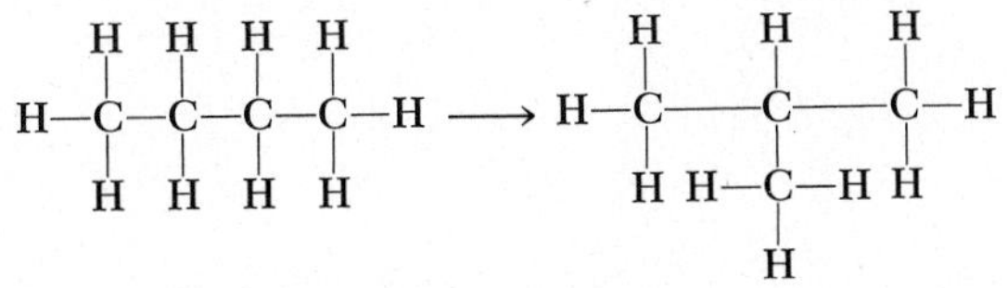

Or, generally, $A \longrightarrow B$.

If reactions take place between two or more types of compounds, then, superimposed on the atomic rearrangements, three classes of broader results may usually be distinguished as well. First, two or more molecules or ions may become added together into a single larger unit; a *synthesis* may occur. For example:

$$H_2O + CO_2 \longrightarrow H_2CO_3$$

Or, generally,

$$A + B \longrightarrow AB$$

Second, a single molecule or ion may become divided up into two or more smaller units; a chemical *decomposition* may take place, the reverse of synthesis. For example,

$$H_2CO_3 \longrightarrow H_2O + CO_2$$

Or, generally,

$$AB \longrightarrow A + B$$

Third, synthesis and decomposition may occur simultaneously, that is, the decomposition products of one set of compounds become the building blocks for the syntheses of another set. Processes of this type are *exchange* reactions. For example, in the reaction

$$HCl + NaOH \longrightarrow HOH + NaCl$$

the ionic units H^+, Cl^-, Na^+, and OH^- are decomposition products of the compounds to the left of the arrow and building blocks of the compounds to the right. We may also say that Na^+ exchanges OH^- for Cl^- while H^+ exchanges Cl^- for OH^-. In general,

$$AB + CD \longrightarrow AD + BC$$

Note that each of these types of reactions actually does include a rearrangement of atoms and bonding patterns; in every case one or more preexisting bonds are broken and one or more new ones are formed. However, the total numbers and types of atoms are exactly the same before and after a reaction, and atoms are neither gained nor lost. In symbolic representations of reactions, therefore, it is important to make sure that equations *balance;* the total numbers and types of atoms to the left of the reaction arrow must equal exactly those on the right.

Regardless of the nature of the gross results, any reaction has two fundamental attributes. One of these is *direction*. In the examples above, the directions of the reactions have been indicated by arrows, but this has been possible only because of knowledge gained from prior experience. If such experience were lacking, it would not necessarily be clear in which direction a given reaction would proceed. For example, if H^+, Na^+, Cl^-, and OH^- ions were in close enough proximity to react and if we did not know the result beforehand, it could be possible *either* that HOH + NaCl would accumulate *or* that HCl + NaOH would accumulate; theoretically the exchange might occur in either direction. What determines the actual direction? The second fundamental attribute is reaction *rate,* a measure of how fast and for how long a reaction proceeds. We already know that reactions result from collisions of chemical units, and we may generalize that reaction rate is directly proportional to collision rate. As noted, any factor or condition promoting collisions will also promote rates. What are these rate determinants?

The direction of a reaction is a function of the *energetics* of the reacting system, and the rate is determined by *temperatures and pressures,* by *concentrations,* and by *catalysts.*

ENERGETICS

Like all other kinds of changes in the universe, chemical changes obey and are governed by the laws of *thermodynamics.* These most fundamantal rules of nature deal with the *energy* relations of a system and its surroundings. A "system" in this context may be regarded as any set of materials on which we concentrate our attention at the moment; for example, a set of chemicals undergoing reactions. The surroundings then are all other parts of the universe, that is, the total environment in which the system exists.

The *first law* of thermodynamics, often also called the law of *conservation of energy,* states that, in any process, the sum of all energy changes must be zero. Expressed differently, energy can be neither created nor destroyed. Thus, if a given chemical system gains energy, that amount of energy must be lost by the environment of the system. Or if a chemical system loses energy, that amount must be gained by the environment. The first law therefore implies that energy can only be redistributed, changed in form, or both. Indeed, chemical, thermal, radiant, mechanical, or other energy forms are mutually interconvertible. Moreover, energy may also be transformed into mass or vice versa.

The *second law* of thermodynamics states that, if left to itself, any system tends toward a state of greatest stability. The phrase "if left to itself" here implies that the system is *closed,* or completely insulated from the environment, and that exchanges of energy or mass between system and environment do not take place. Actually, the only system that can be considered to be truly closed is the whole universe taken as a unit. Any subcomponent of the universe is to a greater or lesser extent *open,* that is, it does exchange energy or mass with the environment. However, for practical purposes such openness is very often entirely negligible or is at most exceedingly limited. For example, a stone on a hillside is very largely unaffected by events in any but the most immediate surroundings, and for many purposes the stone together with its nearby environment may in effect be regarded as a closed system. Similarly, a chemical reaction together with its container and the room in which it takes place can usually be taken as a closed system.

As already pointed out in Chap. 2, the phrase "greatest stability" in the second law also means "most random," "most probable," or "least ordered." A stone near the top of a hillside represents a more ordered, less probable, hence less stable system than a stone at the bottom of the slope. The second law now indicates that such a stone may well tend to roll downhill to a more stable state but that, by itself, it can never roll uphill. To be sure, a stone can be *brought* uphill if an environmental agent expends energy and pushes the stone up, but in that case the system is no longer "left to itself." Evidently, natural processes tend to be *unidirectional,* even though they are inherently reversible. Analogously, *all chemical processes are theoretically reversible,* but in actuality they proceed either in one direction or in the opposite direction, according to which one of these leads to a more stable state (Fig. 5.1).

5 · 1 *Stone on a hillside may be regarded as a closed thermodynamic system. If the stone is left to itself a unidirectional process can occur: the stone may fall into the valley and thereby assume a more stable state.*

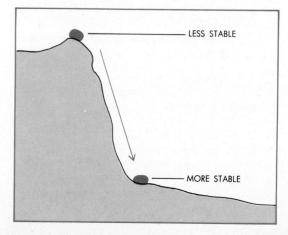

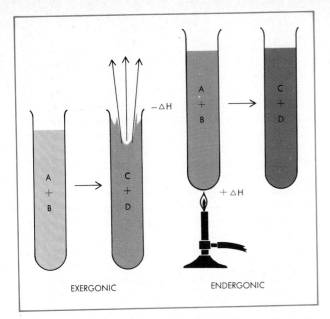

EXERGONIC   ENDERGONIC

5 · 2 Exergonic and endergonic reactions. *In the exergonic reaction* (left), *the mixture A + B contains more total energy than C + D; the energy difference, or total energy change* $(-\Delta H)$, *escapes the reacting system. In the endergonic reaction* (right), *the mixture A + B contains less energy than C + D. Hence, if a reaction is to take place, the energy difference,* $+\Delta H$, *must be supplied to the reacting system from an external source.*

The actual stability of chemical systems depends primarily on two factors, both involving the energy of compounds. One factor is *enthalpy*, symbolized by the letter *H*; it denotes the *total energy content* of a chemical system. Compounds are most stable if *H* is at a minimum. It can be shown that, of all possible states of a system, a state of minimum energy content is the most likely; and it is because of this greatest likelihood, or greatest statistical probability, that minimum energy states are the most stable. Chemical reactions will therefore tend to proceed in such a way that, at the end, the total energy content of all participants will be least. For example, assume that in the generalized reaction

$$A + B \longrightarrow C + D$$

the total energy of all the bonds in *A* and *B* together is greater than the total energy of all the bonds in *C* and *D* together. In other words, more potential energy is available in the bonds of the starting materials than is needed to form the bonds of the endproducts. If all other conditions are suitable, such a reaction can occur readily because *C* + *D*, containing less total energy, is more stable than *A* + *B*. The energy difference will be lost from the reaction

system into the environment, usually in the form of heat. We may symbolize the energy differential as ΔH, or *total energy change*. And since ΔH passes *from* the reaction system *to* the environment, it is given a negative sign. We may then write:

$$A + B \longrightarrow C + D - \Delta H$$

Energy-yielding reactions of this sort are said to be *exergonic* or *exothermic* (Fig. 5.2).

Conversely, assume that the total energy of *A* + *B* is less than that of *C* + *D*. In this case *A* + *B* is more stable, and the second law stipulates that, by itself, no process proceeds from a more stable to a less stable state. However, the reaction could be made to occur if energy were supplied *from* the environment *to* the reaction system, in an amount at least equal to ΔH. Then the total energy of *A* + *B*, together with ΔH from the environment, would actually suffice to form *C* + *D*. We would then write

$$A + B \longrightarrow C + D + \Delta H$$

Energy-requiring reactions of this sort are said to be *endergonic* or *endothermic*. Note that, by standard convention, a $-\Delta H$ on the right of an equation indicates energy *loss* from the system, a $+\Delta H$, energy *gain* by the system; the reacting system, not the environment, is the point of reference (see Fig. 5.2).

The second factor determining the relative stability of a chemical system is *entropy*, symbolized as *S*; it denotes the *energy distribution* in a chemical system. A system is most stable if *S* is at a maximum, that is, if energy is distributed as uniformly or randomly as possible. It can be shown that, of all possible energy distributions in a system, the most random or unordered is the most likely; and it is because of this greatest statistical probability that states with the highest entropy are the most stable (Fig. 5.3). For example, consider again the reaction *A* + *B* $\longrightarrow$ *C* + *D*, and assume that ΔH is zero, that is, the total energy content is the same before and after the reaction. Assume, however, that *A* is very rich in energy, that *B* is very poor in energy, and that *C* and *D* each contain intermediate amounts of energy. Under such conditions, the energy distribution in the *A* + *B* state is more uneven, or less random, than in the *C* + *D* state; the latter will therefore be the more stable. If other conditions are suitable, the reaction may consequently occur and it will increase the entropy of the system. If we symbolize the net entropy change as ΔS, we may write

$$A + B \longrightarrow C + D + \Delta S$$

Consider now the reaction

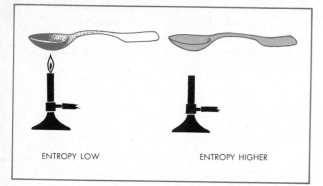

ENTROPY LOW   ENTROPY HIGHER

5 · 3 *Low entropy* (left) *results when a spoon is heated at one end, producing a nonuniform and comparatively unstable energy distribution. If the system is left to itself (and assuming heat is not lost to the environment), the energy will become distributed more evenly throughout the spoon. Such a state is more stable and has a higher entropy* (right).

$$A + B + C \longrightarrow D$$

and again assume that ΔH is zero. On the left side the total energy is distributed among three particles, but on the right all the energy is concentrated in one particle. Since, everything else being equal, the $A + B + C$ state has a more scattered, hence more random, energy distribution, this state will be more stable and will have a greater entropy than the D state. The reaction will therefore not be possible if the system is left to itself. However, by supplying energy from the environment, we could conceivably lower the entropy of $A + B + C$ sufficiently to make the reaction to D possible. We may write

$$A + B + C \longrightarrow D - \Delta S$$

Note that entropy is a directly temperature-dependent factor. For example, if equal amounts of water under otherwise equivalent conditions exist in the form of ice, liquid water, and steam, then ice will have the lowest and steam the highest entropy; water molecules are most scattered and disordered in the form of steam. In general, entropy tends to increase with rising temperature. For this reason, entropy changes are usually symbolized as a mathematical product of ΔS and T, where T is the absolute temperature at which a reaction occurs.

The overall stability change during a reaction thus is a function of two variables, ΔH and $T \Delta S$. By conceptual definition, these two are of opposite algebraic sign, since stability changes as enthalpy increases and entropy decreases or as enthalpy de-creases and entropy increases. This circumstance finds expression in the formulation

$$\Delta F = \Delta H - T \Delta S$$

an important equation representing a symbolic statement of the second law. The term ΔF denotes over-all change in system stability and is generally referred to as the *free-energy change*. If ΔF in a given reaction is numerically negative, the system has become more stable; and if it is positive, the system has become less stable. We may readily see why this should be so. If we disregard the entropy term for the moment, then ΔF will be negative if ΔH is negative, since in that case $-\Delta F = -\Delta H$; and we already know that a negative ΔH signifies an exergonic reaction system, one which has lost energy to the environment and thus has become more stable. If we now disregard the enthalpy term, then ΔF will be negative if ΔS is positive, since in that case $-\Delta F = -(+T \Delta S)$; but a positive ΔS means that the system has acquired a more randomized energy distribution and is therefore more stable. Conversely, if ΔF in the above equation is numerically positive, then the reaction system has become less stable; it must have gained total energy from the environment and/or the energy distribution of the system must have become less random.

Thus, the algebraic sign of ΔF indicates whether or not a given reaction possible on paper is likely to occur by itself in actuality; reactions with a positive ΔF lead to less stability and therefore require a supply of external energy if they are to take place. Note also that the ΔF is a measure of the theoretical amount of *usable* work one may obtain from a reacting system. For example, if a piece of wood is burned in a fireplace, the total energy content of the original wood minus the energy content of all the ashes and other combustion products represents ΔH, the total energy change. This total is not usable as such to perform work, for example, to heat a room; for in the process of burning, the compact piece of wood has become dispersed into scattered ashes and into gases escaping into the air. Such scattering represents an increase in entropy, that is, a loss of some of the potential energy of the original wood, dissipated in the scattering process. The amount of this lost energy is equivalent to the amount of energy we would have to spend to reassemble the dispersed combustion products back in one place. This quantity, equal to $T \Delta S$, is therefore not available to heat the room, and the net amount which does remain available is $\Delta H - T \Delta S$, or ΔF.

Changes in free energy, enthalpy, and entropy are expressed as *heat equivalents*, the units of heat being *calories*. A calory (cal) is defined as the amount of heat (or equivalent quantities of other energy forms) required to raise the temperature of 1 gram (g) of water by 1°C. For example, if 1 g of sugar at room temperature is decomposed in the presence of oxygen into water and carbon dioxide, the ΔF of this reaction can be shown to be -3810 cal. The reaction evidently is feasible in practice, for it leads to an increase in stability. The ΔH here can be calculated to be -3738 cal; the reaction is exergonic, or energy-yielding. And $T\,\Delta S$ is $+72$ cal; the reaction also increases the entropy. Thus, $-3810 = (-3738) - (+72)$. Note that the calory units referred to here and in later chapters are "small" calories, as distinct from "large," or dietary, calories (Cal), each of which is equal to 1000 cal.

We may note generally that a negative ΔF is largely characteristic of *decomposition* reactions, a positive ΔF, of *synthesis* reactions. Under suitable conditions, some of the energy produced by a decomposition reaction may be made to perform useful work. For example, it may drive an engine, as in the decomposition of fuels by burning, or it may simply provide useful heat as such, or, indeed, it may make possible energy-requiring synthesis reactions. In living systems, actually, decomposition reactions are *coupled* intimately to synthesis reactions. As we shall see, reactions with negative ΔF's yield the energy needed to sustain those with positive ΔF's. It is this circumstance that makes the sign and value of ΔF's of considerable biological significance.

The laws of thermodynamics generally and the energetics of a system specifically thus determine one fundamental attribute of a reaction, namely, its direction. As noted earlier, the second attribute, rate, is specified by several factors influencing the collision frequency among chemical units.

REACTION RATES

PRESSURE AND TEMPERATURE

The effect of pressure on reacting systems varies greatly, depending on the physical state of the participating reactants. It should be appreciated readily that reaction rates among gases will be the higher the greater the environmental pressure. For the effect of increasing pressure is to force gaseous reactants closer together into a progressively smaller volume, thereby enhancing the possibility of direct contact among them. Practical examples come to mind readily. To cite one, oxygen combines with hemoglobin of blood at a certain rate at sea level, but at the lower pressures at higher altitudes this reaction can occur only at correspondingly lower rates. This is one reason why breathing is more difficult on a high

mountain. The effect of pressure is far less pronounced on liquid reactants, which are virtually incompressible, and on solids, which may or may not be compressible.

More significant than pressure for reactants in any of the physical states is the environmental temperature. We already know that at any given temperature chemical units undergo a certain amount of thermal motion, and that such motion is the basic cause of collisions among chemical units. Thus collision rates, hence reaction rates, vary in direct proportion to temperature. At the absolute zero of temperature, at $-273°C$, heat motion is by definition absent entirely, and collisions as well as reactions are correspondingly absent entirely. Any increase in environmental temperature above absolute zero increases the thermal motion of particles, hence their collision rates, hence also their reaction rates. Pressure then reinforces the effect of temperature; at any given fixed temperature reaction rates vary with pressure, and at any given fixed pressure reaction rates vary with temperature. But note that pressure alone does not produce particle motion. Particles could be subjected to very high pressure yet they would not react if they were stationary. Conversely, moving particles could react even under low pressure.

To be sure, not all collisions between chemical units necessarily lead to reaction. Mere contact as such is probably ineffective in most cases to produce formation or abolition of bonds. The impact of a collision among particles must be energetic or forceful enough if it is to produce changes in bonding patterns. It is therefore more nearly correct to say that reaction rates are proportional to *effective* collision rates, not simply to collision rates as such. The external energy required to produce effective collisions is called the *activation energy*, E_{act}. The amount of this energy differs for different reactants, but at least this critical amount must be supplied by the environment in each case if a reaction is to take place. Heat is the most common form of activation energy. In certain instances, the heat of the ordinary environment suffices to activate a reaction. For example, water and metallic sodium react spontaneously at room temperature. Evidently, the general environment produces enough heat motion in water and sodium to cause effective collisions. By contrast, water and fat do not react appreciably at room temperature. Although molecular collisions unquestionably do occur at that temperature, a sufficient number of *effective* collisions does not. However, by heating a fat-water mixture to a high enough temperature critical activation may be achieved and a reaction then does occur.

Most materials in the physical world, as also in the living world, actually require activation energies far greater than provided by ordinary temperatures. This is why, for example, the oxygen molecules in air and the molecules of wood or coal do not interact spontaneously all over the earth, despite the numerous collisions between these substances. As is well known, combustible fuels must be heated substantially, that is, must be activated effectively, before they will react with aerial oxygen and thus burn. We therefore recognize generally that, to start any reaction, a sufficient amount of activation energy must first be supplied from the outside. Interaction of the chemical units may then begin at some critical collision rate specific for each type of reaction.

Activation energies are interrelated with free-energy changes, as may be illustrated by considering a stone lying near the edge of a cliff. If the stone fell over the edge, its descent into the valley would yield kinetic energy which could be used to perform work. But some external agency is first required to move the stone over the cliff edge to begin with; and this external agency is equivalent to activation energy. Assume that, in Fig. 5.4, point A represents the degree of stability (or free energy, F_A) of a chem-

5 · 4 Free energy change and activation. *The assumption in the diagram is that A is more stable than B (the free energy F_A of A is greater than the free energy F_B of B). If a reaction now proceeds from A to B, activation energy E_{act} must be supplied from the outside and the energy yield (free energy change) is then E_{act} plus ΔF, or $-\Delta F$ net. But if a reaction proceeds from B to A, the external energy supply must amount to ΔF plus E_{act}, and only E_{act} is then gained back. Hence the free energy change here is $+\Delta F$.*

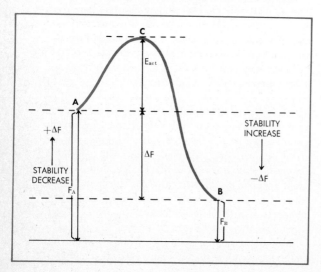

ical system before a reaction has started, and position B, the degree of stability (F_B) at the end of the reaction. The net stability change, or free-energy change ΔF, therefore may be represented as the difference in the levels of A and B. The lower position of B signifies that, as with a falling stone, stability is greater at the end of the reaction, and that the ΔF therefore is negative. But note that the stability curve from A to B passes through point C, located at a higher level than either A or B. This means that the stability of the system first *decreases* from A to C before it increases from C to B. The amount of this decrease from A to C represents the activation energy, E_{act}, which must be supplied from the outside to bring the reaction system "over the cliff." Subsequently, just as a stone falls on its own, the reaction proceeds by itself; and in the process it not only "pays back" the energy expended for activation but also yields net free energy usable for work, in the amount of ΔF.

If we now consider the reverse reaction, from B to A, we note that, to provide adequate activation, we must supply external energy to the extent of ΔF plus E_{act}. Here only E_{act} is paid back when the reaction subsequently "falls" from C to A, and our net energy expenditure therefore is ΔF, which in this case is positive. In terms of our analogy, a great deal more work must be done to move a stone up from a valley over a cliff edge than in the opposite direction.

After adequate activation, a reaction will proceed the faster the more heat is supplied to it. It has been found that every temperature increase of 10°C approximately doubles to triples the speed of reactions. A *temperature coefficient*, conventionally designated by the letter Q, expresses how many times a reaction is speeded up by any stated increase of temperature. Thus, $Q_{10} = 2$ to 3 for chemical reactions generally. This statement reads: a 10° rise of temperature accelerates reactions two to three times. The implications for reactions in living systems are important. For example, the life-maintaining chemical processes in a housefly will occur two or three times as fast on a day that is 10°C warmer than another.

CONCENTRATION AND EQUILIBRIUM

It should be readily apparent that, if all other conditions are fixed, reaction rates will depend on the concentration (amount per volume) of the reacting compounds present; for the greater the concentration of the starting materials, the more frequently collisions among the materials become possible and the faster the reaction will therefore be. We may say that, other factors being equal, the rate of a reaction is proportional to the concentrations of the participating compounds. This generalization is sometimes referred to as the *law of mass action* (Fig. 5.5).

Assume that, in the generalized reversible reaction system

$$A + B \rightleftharpoons C + D$$

thermodynamic conditions are such that they do permit a reaction to occur in either direction. Assume also that the system initially contains compounds A and B only:

$$A + B \longrightarrow$$

The rate of the ensuing reaction will be proportional to the concentrations of A and B, according to the mass-action law. If we symbolize these concentrations as $[A]$ and $[B]$, we may write

$$\text{forward rate} = k_{A,B}[A] \cdot [B]$$

where $k_{A,B}$ is a proportionality constant characteristic of the compounds A and B and of the particular conditions under which this reaction occurs. As A and B are transformed progressively into C and D, the concentrations of A and B will fall and the forward reaction rate will therefore decrease as well. On the other hand, as C and D accumulate, their concentrations—originally zero—will rise, and a reverse reaction will now take place at a gradually increasing rate. For this reverse reaction we may write

$$\text{reverse rate} = k_{C,D}[C] \cdot [D]$$

where $k_{C,D}$ again is a characteristic proportionality constant.

Eventually, a point will be reached at which the decreasing forward rate becomes just equal to the increasing reverse rate. This is the *equilibrium* point of the reaction system. At this point, A, B, C, and D will all be present in certain particular concentrations, and since the reaction rates in both directions now are equal, these concentrations will not change subsequently. For the equilibrium condition we may therefore write

$$k_{A,B}[A] \cdot [B] = k_{C,D}[C] \cdot [D]$$

or

$$\frac{k_{A,B}}{k_{C,D}} = \frac{[C] \cdot [D]}{[A] \cdot [B]}$$

Since both $k_{A,B}$ and $k_{C,D}$ are constants, the expression $k_{A,B}/k_{C,D}$ is also a constant. It is called the *equilibrium constant* and is symbolized as K. Each reaction, taking place under specified conditions (particularly temperature and pressure), has its own characteristic

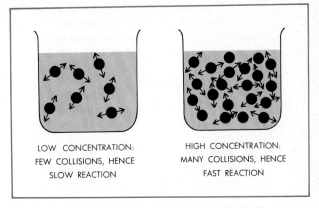

LOW CONCENTRATION: FEW COLLISIONS, HENCE SLOW REACTION

HIGH CONCENTRATION: MANY COLLISIONS, HENCE FAST REACTION

5 · 5 *The principle of mass action. At left, few molecules are present and collisions are infrequent, hence reaction is slow. At right, at the same temperature as at left, many molecules are present and collisions are frequent, hence reaction is fast.*

K value; it is an index of the concentrations of the participating compounds at equilibrium.

Note, however, that, depending on the nature of a given reaction system, an equilibrium state may or may not be reached in practice. For example, if a reaction has the form

$$A + B \rightleftharpoons C + D \qquad \Delta F = 0$$

then an equilibrium may in fact be attained; for a zero ΔF indicates that both sides of the system are equally stable and that free energy is neither lost nor gained during a reaction in either direction. Since the forward and reverse reactions are therefore equally possible, the concentration product $[A] \cdot [B]$ will at equilibrium actually equal the product $[C] \cdot [D]$. In such a case, $K = 1$, and after an equilibrium has been attained, further *net* changes will not take place; the net reaction will in effect have stopped.

If, however,

$$A + B \longrightarrow C + D - \Delta F$$

then $C + D$ represents the more stable side. If the negative numerical magnitude of the ΔF is very great, then the forward reaction may proceed beyond the equilibrium state, and all of A and B might be converted into C and D. In that case a reverse reaction might not occur at all, and the forward reaction may stop only when A and B are no longer present. Such a system is in practice without equilibrium. But if the ΔF is only slightly negative, that is, close to zero, then a comparatively larger forward reaction may be accompanied by a comparatively smaller reverse reaction, and an equilibrium point might be attained. At that point the concentration product $[C] \cdot [D]$ will be greater than the product $[A] \cdot [B]$, and K will be greater than 1. If

$$A + B \longrightarrow C + D + \Delta F$$

then, again depending on the (positive) magnitude of the ΔF, an equilibrium may or may not be attained in practice. If it is, $[A] \cdot [B]$ will be greater than $[C] \cdot [D]$, and $K < 1$.

We may note in passing that the mathematical interrelation of K and ΔF can be shown to be

$$\Delta F = -RT \ln K = -2.303RT \log K$$

where T is the absolute temperature, $\ln K$ the natural logarithm of K, and R the so-called gas constant, a proportionality factor interrelating pressure, volume, absolute temperature, and concentration. The expression indicates, for example, that if $\Delta F = 0$, K is indeed 1. Also, the relation makes it possible to determine by how much K is greater or smaller than 1 when ΔF is negative or positive, respectively.

Large free-energy changes are not the only factors preventing attainment of equilibrium states. Even when $\Delta F = 0$, for example, if one of the reaction products is an escaping gas or an insoluble precipitate, then the loss of such compounds from a reaction mixture clearly will make a reverse reaction impossible. Here again the forward reaction will proceed beyond the equilibrium point and go to completion, or to maximum yield. In general, therefore, we may note that equilibria imply *closed systems:* only if both energy (ΔF) and matter (reactants) are neither gained nor lost by a system can an equilibrium be attained and maintained. In practice, such closed conditions are seldom if ever realized completely. Yet even an analysis of the theoretical equilibrium state for any given reaction system is nevertheless of considerable significance. As we have seen, such an analysis gives information about the direction, rate, and duration of a reaction, and it interrelates concentrations and energy changes.

When actual reaction rates are measured experimentally, it is found that rates and concentrations vary linearly in some cases, exponentially in others. For example, in the reaction $A + B \longrightarrow AB$ the rate is given by

$$\text{rate} = k\,[A] \cdot [B]$$

which indicates a linear proportionality. Thus, if the concentration of A is doubled, twice as many collisions per unit time can occur between A and B, and the product AB can therefore form at twice the original rate. If then the concentration of B is doubled as well, the rate of product formation will double again. A reaction obeying such a linear relation is said to be of the *first order* with respect to A separately and also with respect to B separately. But it is said to be of the *second order* overall, or with respect to A and B jointly.

If B, above, is taken to be the same as A, then the reaction becomes $A + A \longrightarrow A_2$, or $2A \longrightarrow A_2$. The rate is then given by

$$\text{rate} = k[A]^2$$

A reaction of this type is of the second order, for if the amount of A is doubled, the rate of formation of the product A_2 will quadruple. An exponential relation also governs reactions of the type $2A + B \longrightarrow C$, for example. The rate expression here is

$$\text{rate} = k[A]^2[B]$$

that is, the reaction is second-order with respect to A, first-order with respect to B, and third-order overall. In general, experimental measurements show reaction rates to be governed by the expression

$$\text{rate} = k[A]^p[B]^q[C]^r \cdots$$

On the basis of this *rate law,* a reaction is of the pth order with respect to A, qth order with respect to B, rth order with respect to C, and of the $(p + q + r + \cdots)$th order overall.

An important generalization applies to reactions in which more than two components participate. In the reaction $2A + B \longrightarrow C$, for example, three particles (two of A, one of B) participate in the formation of the one endproduct C. Yet the probability that three (or more) randomly moving particles would collide simultaneously is exceedingly low. Indeed, it is so low that anything other than *two-body collisions* can in practice be discounted as a contributing factor to chemical reactions (but see the next section). Consequently, any reaction involving more than two starting participants must be interpreted as a *succession* of intermediate subreactions, each consisting of a two-body collision. In the reaction above, for example, either of the two following two-step sequences might occur:

	alternative I	*alternative II*
step 1	$A + A \longrightarrow [A_2]$	$A + B \longrightarrow [AB]$
step 2	$[A_2] + B \longrightarrow C$	$[AB] + A \longrightarrow C$
net	$2A + B \longrightarrow C$	$2A + B \longrightarrow C$

Sequences of this sort are said to constitute *reaction mechanisms,* and temporary compounds such as A_2 or AB, above, are called reaction *intermediates.* Whenever several alternative mechanisms are possible theoretically, experimental analysis must show which one (or more) of these mechanisms actually takes place and to what extent.

It should also be clear that, whatever the mechanism of a specific reaction might be, the overall rate of the total reaction will depend on the rates of the successive subreactions. More specifically, an overall reaction cannot take place any faster than the *slowest* subreaction will permit. The situation is analogous to a bucket brigade, where objects are handed one after the other along a chain of people; the output rate of the objects at the end of the chain will be determined by the slowest passer. The slowest subreaction in a sequence is often referred to as the *rate-limiting* or *rate-determining* step of the overall reaction. Note incidentally that, in any reaction consisting of two or more steps, *each* step has its own activation-energy requirement. Moreover, the rate-determining step will have the highest requirement, for only if that step is properly activated may the whole reaction proceed.

In many cases the overall rate of a reaction can be increased by adding ingredients to the mixture that make an alternative reaction mechanism more feasible. This circumstance relates to the phenomenon of catalysis, the third major rate determinant of reactions and of special significance in living systems.

CATALYSIS

Consider the comparatively slow reaction

$$SO_2 + O \longrightarrow SO_3$$

It has been found that, without raising temperatures or concentrations, the rate of this reaction can be increased substantially by adding NO, nitrogen oxide, to the reaction mixture. Product formation then occurs via an intermediate in a two-step sequence, as follows:

$$
\begin{array}{ll}
\text{step 1} & NO + O \longrightarrow [NO_2] \\
\text{step 2} & \underline{[NO_2] + SO_2 \longrightarrow SO_3 + NO} \\
& SO_2 + O + NO \longrightarrow SO_3 + NO
\end{array}
$$

Evidently, added NO serves as a temporary carrier of O, and free NO then reappears again unchanged among the endproducts. The important point is that steps 1 and 2 together take place faster than the single original reaction. Both steps happen to have a lower activation-energy requirement than the original reaction, hence at the same temperature the number of effective collisions between NO and O and between NO_2 and SO_2 is greater than between SO_2 and O directly. NO in this case is said to function as a *catalyst*. The compound is one of a large group of substances that increases rates of reactions. Catalysts

of a special sort are present in all living matter and are called *enzymes*. Like all catalysts, enzymes have the property of reappearing essentially unchanged at the end of a reaction and, more importantly, of lowering the activation-energy requirements and thereby increasing reaction rates without necessitating a rise in temperature.

Catalysis is thus of crucial biological importance. Most reactions of biological interest actually require fairly high activation energies—so high, indeed, that most living processes should ordinarily necessitate environments far hotter than room temperature. This is evidently not the case. Moreover, if living matter were heated substantially above room temperature it would quickly be killed. It remains true, nevertheless, that at the comparatively low temperatures at which living matter normally exists, the thermal motion produced by the environment is insufficient to activate many reactions. As already pointed out, for example, a fat-water mixture at room temperature, or even at body temperature, remains virtually unchanged for days. Within the body, however, fat and water react appreciably within an hour or so and become converted to fatty acids and glycerin. The high rate of this and all other biological processes is due to the presence of enzymes. These agents evidently represent a supplement to environmentally produced thermal motion, a device through which reactions requiring high temperatures otherwise can occur at low temperatures within living matter.

Enzymes are *proteins*, a class of organic compounds about which much more will be said in the next chapter. Like catalysts generally, enzyme proteins produce their reaction-accelerating effect by combining temporarily with the reactants, thus forming intermediates. Reactants in this context are generally called *substrates*, and the intermediates are referred to as *enzyme-substrate complexes*. If we symbolize substrates as S and endproducts as P, then the role of an enzyme E in the generalized reaction $S \longrightarrow P$ can be described as follows:

$$
\begin{array}{lll}
\text{step 1} & S + E \longrightarrow [ES] & \text{enzyme-substrate} \\
& & \text{intermediate} \\
\text{step 2} & [ES] \longrightarrow P + E & \text{product formation} \\
\hline
& S + E \longrightarrow [ES] \longrightarrow E + P
\end{array}
$$

Note that, because the complex ES is interposed between S and P, the rate of product formation is not linearly proportional to the concentration of S, contrary to what might be expected if an enzyme were not present. If enzyme activity is plotted on a graph showing substrate concentrations along the abscissa and product increase along the ordinate, then a

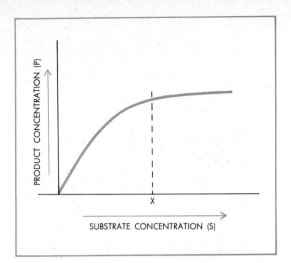

5 · 6 *An enzyme-activity curve. Note that if* S *is lower than point X, then* S *and* P *are almost directly proportional. But if* S *is higher than* X, *then* P *remains nearly constant.* P *depends on the concentration of the enzyme-substrate complex, not on* S *directly; the enzyme is the limiting factor.*

curve as in Fig. 5.6 is obtained. It indicates that, when substrate concentrations are high and increasing (that is, higher than point X on the curve), then the rate of product formation nevertheless remains substantially unchanged. This is because the rate of product formation depends primarily on *ES*, not on S directly. In its own turn, formation of *ES* is limited by the concentration of *E*, which is usually very much lower in living matter than that of S. As a result, the concentration of *E* is normally rate-limiting for formation of *ES*, and the latter is rate-limiting for formation of *P*. Put another way, once S is present in concentrations above a certain level, the rate of product formation is virtually independent of the concentrations of S. Note here that, because enzymes reappear unchanged at the end of reactions, very small amounts of enzymes, used over and over, can catalyze very large quantities of substrates.

The protein nature of enzymes is essential to their reaction-accelerating effect. Protein molecules are huge, and an almost unlimited number of different kinds of proteins exists. Accordingly, proteins have distinct molecular surfaces and the geometries of these surfaces differ as the internal structure of the proteins differs. The nature of the surface appears to be the key to enzyme action. Consider the reaction

fat + water ⟶ fatty acids + glycerin

A fat molecule has a given unique structural configuration, and so does a water molecule. Enzymatic acceleration of this reaction may now occur if the structures of both fat and water happen to fit closely into the surface of a particular protein molecule. In other words, if the substrates can become attached to a suitably shaped surface of an enzyme, then these substrates will be so close to each other that they may react chemically (Fig. 5.7). The enzyme itself remains almost passive here. It may provide a uniquely structured "platform," or *template*, on which particular molecules may become trapped. Such trapping evidently brings substrates into contact far faster than chance collisions at that temperature; hence reactions are accelerated. When they are held by the enzyme, fat and water interact via formation of a fat-enzyme intermediate and become fatty acid and glycerin subsequently. These endproducts then disengage from the enzyme surface.

Formation of enzyme-substrate complexes thus may be thought of as a "lock-and-key" process. Only particularly shaped keys fit into particularly shaped locks. Just so, only certain types of molecules will establish a close fit with a given type of enzyme protein. For example, the enzyme in Fig. 5.8 may be effective in reactions involving substrates *a* and *b*, but not in those involving *c*.

Because enzyme proteins are huge molecules compared to most substrates, the whole surface of an enzyme is probably not required to promote a given reaction; only limited surface regions, called *active sites*, need be involved (see Chap. 6). Therefore, even if other parts of enzyme molecules become altered chemically or physically, the enzymes may still be effective so long as their active sites remain intact. Until recently, it has been generally believed that enzymes were rigid molecular structures, templates of fixed shapes, and that enzyme activity depended on this permanence of configuration. Newer research indicates, however, that enzyme

5 · 7 *Active sites on the surface of the enzyme fit into the surfaces of molecules A and B. Reaction between A and B is thus speeded up, for contact between them does not now depend on chance collision.*

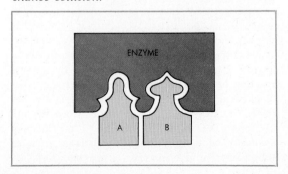

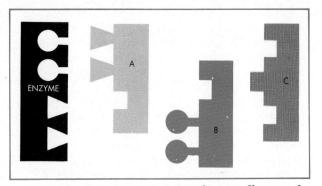

5 · 8 *Reactants A and B fit partially into the surface of the enzyme but reactant C does not. Hence the enzyme may speed up reactions involving A and B but not those involving C.*

molecules may actually be flexible in a physical sense and that the structure of a particular substrate may *induce* the enzyme to bend or mold itself over the substrate. Such an "induced fit" hypothesis is consistent with the observation that only the active sites, not the whole enzyme molecules, need to retain permanent configurations. Moreover, the hypothesis may account in part for the long-established observation that many enzymes operate adequately only in the presence of certain *cofactors*. These are of various kinds and include, for example, metal ions such as Mg^{++}. Also included are *coenzymes*, organic materials of diverse types but usually less complex structurally than the enzymes (or *apoenzymes*) themselves. It is possible that cofactors of all kinds are agents which, by virtue of their own chemical or physical properties or both, aid in molding an enzyme (or its substrates) into the shape required for a proper fit between enzyme and substrate (Fig. 5.9). In later contexts we shall deal more fully with particular types of cofactors.

Differences in the surface configuration of different enzymes or their active sites undoubtedly account for the phenomenon of *enzyme specificity*; a given type of enzyme normally accelerates only one particular type of reaction. For example, the enzyme in the fat-forming reaction above, called *lipase*, is specific and catalyzes only that particular type of reaction. In living matter there are actually almost as many different kinds of enzymes as there are different kinds of reactions. This specificity of enzymes is an important corollary of the more general phenomenon of *protein specificity*, about which more will be said in Chap. 6. Because of protein specificity, some proteins are enzymes to begin with and some are not. If a protein happens to have surface regions into which some other molecules could fit, then that protein could function as an enzyme in reactions involving those molecules.

Note that a given enzyme can speed up a reaction in *either* direction; the reaction fat + water $\longrightarrow$ fatty acids + glycerin is accelerated by the *same* enzyme, namely lipase, that speeds up the reverse reaction. This is understandable if we keep in mind that enzymes are primarily passive reaction platforms. Thus, like heat, enzymes only influence rates; we already know that directions are determined by thermodynamic conditions.

In living matter it happens often that a process in one direction requires one type of enzyme whereas the same process in the reverse direction requires another. In such cases, however, "process" generally means more than a single reaction, and reverse processes are not exact *chemical* mirror images. For example, a transformation of A to B might occur via an intermediate step X, whereas the reverse conversion from B to A might pass through an intermediate step Y. Different sets of enzymes would then be required even though the net starting and end conditions appeared to be mirror images:

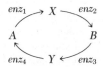

It remains true, however, that enz_1, for example, would be effective in the individual reaction A $\longrightarrow$ X *as well as* in the reverse of it, X $\longrightarrow$ A.

The effectiveness of enzymes varies greatly with changes of temperature, pH, and environmental conditions generally, just as all proteins are affected by such changes. For example, if enzyme activity

5 · 9 *Effect of cofactors. The enzyme shown here has an active site at each end. A cofactor may aid in fitting together the active sites of enzyme and substrate. Cofactors include Mg^{++} and other mineral ions, as well as a variety of organic materials collectively called* coenzymes (*principal enzymes are* apoenzymes).

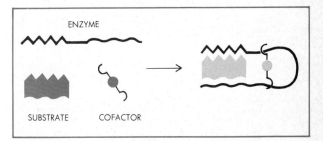

is plotted in relation to temperature or to pH, curves as in Fig. 5.10 are obtained. These indicate that as either temperature or pH rises, the effectiveness of enzymes increases up to a certain *optimum* but decreases thereafter. Though each particular type of enzyme has its own specific optimum, most enzymes operate optimally in a temperature range of about 25 to 40°C (human body temperature is 37°C) and in a pH range of about 6.0 to 7.5 (human blood pH is 7.3). At lower than optimal temperatures enzymes are less effective, primarily because reactions of all kinds decrease in rate in a colder environment; and at higher than optimal temperatures the physical structure of enzyme proteins begins to be destroyed, leading ultimately to coagulation. Analogously, pH changes to either side of the optimum range produce structural changes and also precipitation of enzyme proteins (see Chap. 6). Enzyme inactivation is the result, a basic reason why drastic temperature or pH changes are lethal to living matter.

We may note in passing that, just as certain substances may function as rate-increasing catalysts and enzymes, so also other substances may happen to operate as rate-decreasing *anticatalysts* and *antienzymes*, also called *inhibitors*. Their net effect is to *raise* the activation-energy requirements of given reactions, thereby reducing or stopping them entirely at that temperature. Inhibitors generally act by combining either with the substrates of given reactions, making such substrates less reactive at that temperature, or with the enzymes normally required by given substrates, making such enzymes ineffective. In either event an inhibitor blocks a

particular reaction pathway. In living material inhibitors are of importance in two ways. An inhibitor blocking a normal reaction represents a disease-producing *poison;* and an inhibitor blocking a disease-producing reaction represents a *medicinal drug* (Fig. 5.11).

In this context we may also make note of another form of reaction block, produced by so-called *analogs*. A chemical analog is a substrate resembling another one so much that the same enzyme may catalyze either one. For example, if A is a normal substrate in a reaction requiring enzyme X, then a substance A′ could be so similar to A that A′ is an analog to A. Enzyme X could therefore be effective with either A or A′:

In effect, A and A′ *compete* for the same limited amount of enzyme. The practical importance of analogs should be appreciated readily, for if A ⟶ B is a normal biological reaction, then introduction of A′ could crowd out or reduce this reaction. The analog thus could be a poison. Alternatively, it could serve as a beneficial drug which could crowd out an abnormal, disease-causing reaction. By way of example, carbon monoxide (CO) is an analog to both carbon dioxide and oxygen, and CO is poisonous because it crowds out the normal interactions of hemoglobin in blood with oxygen and with CO_2. Conversely, drugs used to combat many infectious bacterial diseases are analogs of disease-causing compounds in bacteria.

Enzymes are named in various ways. For example, they may be classified according to the kind of substrate they affect. Any enzyme accelerating reactions of compounds called carbohydrates is referred to as a *carbohydrase*. Analogously, *proteinase* and *lipase* are

5 · 10   *Effect of temperature and* pH *on enzyme activity. Graph at left shows that enzymes tend to be most active in a temperature range of 25 to 40°C, and that rapid inactivation takes place beyond 40°C. Graph at right shows that optimum enzyme activity occurs in a* pH *range of about 6 to 7.5.*

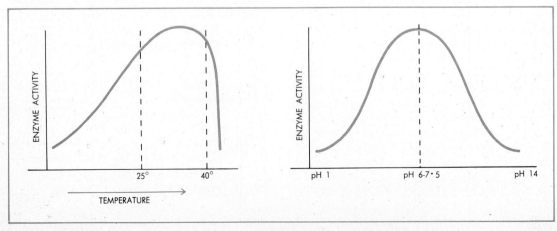

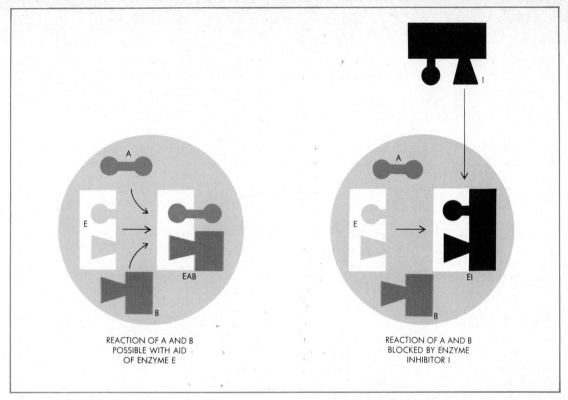

REACTION OF A AND B
POSSIBLE WITH AID
OF ENZYME E

REACTION OF A AND B
BLOCKED BY ENZYME
INHIBITOR I

5 · 11   Enzyme inhibition. *The enzyme E normally speeds up reactions involving reactants A and B. But if an inhibitor molecule I, which fits into the surface of E, is supplied from the outside, then I may combine preferentially with E, thus preventing the normal reaction of E, A, and B. Poisons may act by causing such inhibiting effects. On the other hand, if the reaction of E with A and B gives an abnormal, disease-producing result, then a beneficial chemical may be introduced which acts like I and so prevents the disease.*

enzymes catalyzing reactions of proteins and of fatty substances (= lipids), respectively. Enzymes may also be classified according to the nature of the reaction they catalyze. For example, one may distinguish "splitting" and "synthesizing" enzymes, "transferring" enzymes (*transferases*), "rearranging" enzymes (*mutases*), and numerous others. We shall encounter many specific types during later discussions. Note that a suffix -ase always signifies that the substance in question is an enzyme. However, not all enzyme names necessarily end in -ase. In writing an enzymatic reaction symbolically, the name of the enzyme is conventionally put over the reaction arrow. Thus,

$$\text{fat} + \text{water} \xrightarrow{\textit{lipase}} \text{fatty acids} + \text{glycerin}$$

We have found that, like temperature, pressure, and concentration, enzymes increase reaction rates. At this point we have a substantially complete outline of the main attributes of any reacting chemical system. If we wanted to symbolize all these attributes, we would write

$$[A] + [B] \underset{k_{C,D}}{\overset{k_{A,B}}{\underset{\textit{enzyme}}{\rightleftarrows}}} [C] + [D] \qquad \Delta F \lesseqgtr 0; K \lesseqgtr 1$$

and we would specify particular values for each term in this expression. Indeed, even where such values are not actually given, they are nevertheless implied in every real reaction; no reaction could occur without obeying the various specifications of direction and rate implicit in the terms above.

We may now conclude with the following general summary. If chemical reactions occur in water, the participating substances will be more or less completely dissociated acids, bases, and salts as well as whole, nondissociated molecular compounds. Reactions will be possible if sufficient activation energy is made available. If it is, the chemical changes will always involve atomic rearrangements and can also result in synthesis, decomposition, or exchange. In the course of the reactions, the energy contents and energy distributions of the compounds will become altered and the resulting free-energy changes will affect the directions and rates of the reactions. These system properties will also be influenced by other variously related and unrelated factors, including environmental temperature and pressure, reactant concentrations, and catalysts. Equilibria may or may not be attained in the process, but in any event the endproducts will differ from the starting materials in the numbers, types, and bonding arrangements of the atoms present.

Most of the discussion in this and the two preceding chapters applies to chemicals generally. We are now ready to consider *biological* chemicals specifically.

REVIEW QUESTIONS

1. What is a chemical reaction and what kind of event produces it? What general types of reactions may occur? What factors determine the directions and rates of reactions?

2. State the first and second laws of thermodynamics and describe their general implications. Describe also their specific implications for chemical processes. What are closed and open systems? Why are most natural processes unidirectional in practice?

3. Define enthalpy, entropy, free-energy change. How does each of these concepts apply to a reacting system? What does the algebraic sign of a ΔF tell about a reaction? How do energy changes differ for exergonic and endergonic reactions? Define calory.

4. How does pressure affect a reaction? Review the role of environmental heat in chemical reactions. What is activation energy? How is this energy related to free energy changes in exergonic and endergonic processes?

5. State the law of mass action. What is the equilibrium point of a reaction system? What is an equilibrium constant? Under what conditions is a reaction reversible? Irreversible? How are ΔF's and equilibrium constants correlated?

6. Distinguish between first-order and second-order reactions. Give examples. State the rate law of reactions. Define reaction mechanism, and give an example. What is rate-limiting factor?

7. What is a catalyst? What is an enzyme and how does it work? What is an active site of an enzyme? A cofactor? How does enzyme activity affect the activation energy of a reaction?

8. Show how enzyme activity varies with different substrate concentrations, with temperature, and with pH. What are the usual optimal conditions for enzyme activity?

9. Why is a carbohydrase ineffective in accelerating the reaction glycerin + fatty acids $\longrightarrow$ fat + water? What kind of enzyme does such a reaction require? What are enzyme inhibitors and analogs, and how do they work? Give examples.

10. In the complete symbolic representation of a general reaction on p. 107, name and explain each term shown, and indicate how each term contributes to specifying the direction and rate of a reaction.

COLLATERAL READINGS

Baker, J. J. W., and G. E. Allen: "Matter, Energy, and Life," Addison-Wesley, Reading, Mass., 1965. This paperback contains accounts on reaction energetics and kinetics, including sections on catalysis, reaction rates and equilibria, and thermodynamics. Recommended.

Frieden, E.: The Enzyme-Substrate Complex, *Sci. American,* Aug., 1959. A popularly written article on the central intermediate in enzymatic reactions.

Green, D. E.: Enzymes in Teams, *Sci. American,* Sept., 1949. The integrated action of groups of enzymes in living systems is described in this article.

Grunwald, E., and R. H. Johnsen: "Atoms, Molecules, and Chemical Change," Prentice-Hall, Englewood Cliffs, N.J., 1964. Introductory, directly pertinent to the topics of this chapter.

Hiller, L. A., and R. H. Herber: "Principles of Chemistry," McGraw-Hill, New York, 1960. This basic text is recommended particularly for further background reading on the rate law, on reaction orders, and on reaction mechanisms. Other topics of this chapter are covered as well.

King, E. L.: "How Chemical Reactions Occur," Benjamin, New York, 1963. A paperback, most specifically pertinent to the contents of this chapter. Highly recommended.

Roberts, J. D.: Organic Chemical Reactions, *Sci. American,* Nov., 1957. Reactions among simple organic compounds are analyzed in detail, to illustrate the nature of reactions generally and the fate of individual atoms specifically.

Sienko, M. J., and R. A. Plane: "Chemistry," 3d ed., McGraw-Hill, New York, 1966. This basic text has already been recommended in the readings for earlier chapters. Contains good accounts of the energetics and nature of reactions.

White, E. H.: "Chemical Background for the Biological Sciences," Prentice-Hall, Englewood Cliffs, N.J., 1964. A chapter on chemical reactions is included in this paperback.

CHAPTER 6
COMPOUNDS
AND
CELLS

Different kinds of cells differ vastly in almost all their characteristics; it is a commonplace though nonetheless important biological generalization that no one kind of cell is ever exactly like any other. Moreover, no one cell is ever exactly the same from moment to moment, for the substance of a living cell is not a static, passive material. New materials enter a cell continuously; wastes and manufactured products leave continuously; and substances in the cell interior are continuously transformed chemically and redistributed physically. As a result, a living cell is in persistent internal turmoil. To the human observer a tree, for example, may appear to be a rather placid, inactive structure. But if the internal cellular components of the tree could be seen, they would all be noted to be in constant, violent motion, colliding with one another and interacting and changing. Consequently, the tree as a whole changes continuously, and so indeed does every kind of living material.

However, despite such differences between cells and changes within cells, all cells nevertheless share certain very basic features; and it is this circumstance, actually, which makes the cell the universal minimum unit of all life. Representing the basic heritage passed on by the very first living things on earth, the common features of cells have partly chemical and physical aspects, partly biological ones. In chemical and physical respects, many types of compounds in cells are of a kind and exhibit properties largely not encountered in the inanimate world.

The characteristics of such primarily life-associated and life-maintaining substances are our concern in the present chapter.

CELL COMPOSITION

Four of the most widely distributed chemical elements on earth make up approximately 95 per cent of the weight of cellular matter: oxygen, about 62 per cent; carbon, about 20 per cent; hydrogen, about 10 per cent; and nitrogen, about 3 per cent. Some 30 other elements contribute the remaining 5 per cent of the weight. The elements listed in Table 9 occur in almost all types of cells. Trace amounts of others are found only in particular types, and still other elements may become incorporated into living matter accidentally, along with nutrient materials. All these elements are present in the ocean; cells originated in water, as we shall see, and even today they still largely reflect the composition and content of the sea.

Virtually all the elements occur in the form of compounds. Both great classes of compounds are present in cells, namely, mineral, or *inorganic*, compounds and variously complex, carbon-containing, *organic* compounds. Directly or indirectly, all inorganic compounds in cells are of mineral origin; they are derived in finished form from the external physical environment. *Water*, the most abundant cellular mineral, is present in amounts ranging from 5 to 90 or more per cent. For example, the cellular water content of certain plant seeds and of tooth enamel is about 5 to 10 per cent; of bone and of timber, about 25 to 50 per cent; of muscle, 75 per cent; of brain, milk, or mushrooms, 80 to 90 per cent; and of algae and jellyfish, 90 to 95 or more per cent. As a general average, cellular matter is about 65 to 75 per cent water, overall.

Mineral solids constitute the other inorganic components of cells. Such solids are present in amounts ranging from about 1 to 5 per cent, on an average. A considerable fraction of the minerals may exist in the form of hard bulk deposits, either as crystals within cells or as secreted precipitates on the outside of cells. Such deposits are often silicon- or calcium-containing substances. For example, diatoms, certain protozoa, and the surface cells of certain grasses are protected externally with layers of glasslike silica;

TABLE 9 THE RELATIVE ABUNDANCE OF CHEMICAL ELEMENTS IN LIVING MATTER

ELEMENT	SYMBOL	WEIGHT, PER CENT
oxygen	O	62
carbon	C	20
hydrogen	H	10
nitrogen	N	3
calcium	Ca	2.50
phosphorus	P	1.14
chlorine	Cl	0.16
sulfur	S	0.14
potassium	K	0.11
sodium	Na	0.10
magnesium	Mg	0.07
iodine	I	0.014
iron	Fe	0.010
		99.244
trace elements		0.756
		100.00

the hard part of bone is largely a deposit of calcium phosphate, secreted in layers around individual bone-forming cells; clamshells consist of calcium carbonate, secreted to the exterior by sheets of cells.

All other cellular minerals are in solution, either free or combined with organic compounds. These inorganic constituents exist largely in the form of ions. The most abundant positively charged inorganic ions are H^+, hydrogen ions; Ca^{++}, calcium ions; Na^+, sodium ions; K^+, potassium ions; and Mg^{++}, magnesium ions. Abundant negatively charged mineral constituents include OH^-, hydroxyl ions; $CO_3^=$, carbonate ions; HCO_3^-, bicarbonate ions; $PO_4^{\equiv}$, phosphate ions; Cl^-, chloride ions; and $SO_4^=$, sulfate ions. Note that the mineral constituents of cells are also major constituents of the ocean and of rocks and ores. This is not a coincidence, for rocks are dissolved by water, water finds its way into the ocean and into soil, and living matter ultimately draws its mineral supplies from these sources.

Cells contain hundreds of different categories of organic constituents. Of these, four broad categories in particular are found in all types of cells, and they form the organic basis of living matter. These four are:

1. carbohydrates and derivatives
2. fats and derivatives
3. proteins and derivatives
4. nucleotides and derivatives

Like mineral compounds, some of these organic substances may contribute to the formation of hard parts. For example, wood and various kinds of horny materials present in many animal skeletons and also in structures such as claws and hoofs are predominantly organic. More generally, however, organic materials are dissolved or suspended in cellular water, some in ionized, some in nonionized form. Their relative abundance varies considerably for different types of cells and for different types of organisms. For example, in a plant such as corn, carbohydrates make up about 18 per cent of the total weight, proteins about 2 per cent, and all other organic constituents together not more than about 1 per cent. By contrast, an animal such as man contains about 15 per cent protein, about 15 per cent fat, and other organic components to the extent of about 1 per cent (Fig. 6.1). In both cases, evidently, the inorganic matter (mainly water) far outweighs the organic. It is also generally true that, per unit weight, plant cells contain less organic matter and more water than animal cells.

CARBOHYDRATES AND DERIVATIVES

Organic compounds in this category are called carbohydrates because they consist of carbon, hydrogen, and oxygen, the last two in a 2 : 1 ratio, as in water. The general atomic composition usually corresponds to the formula $C_x(H_2O)_y$, where x and y are whole numbers.

If x and y are low numbers (from 3 to about 7 or 8 in naturally occurring molecules), then the formula describes the composition of the most common carbohydrates, the *simple sugars*, or *monosaccharides*. In these, the carbon atoms form a chain to which H and O atoms are variously attached. On the basis of the numbers of carbons present, different classes of monosaccharides may be distinguished: C_3 sugars are *trioses;* C_4 sugars, *tetroses;* C_5 sugars, *pentoses;* C_6 sugars, *hexoses;* and C_7 sugars, *heptoses.* The ending -ose always identifies a sugar. On the basis of how the H and O atoms are attached to the carbon chains, two basic series of sugars can be distinguished (Fig. 6.2). In one, called the *aldose* series, one end of the sugar molecule always consists of an aldehyde group, H—C=O; the carbon of this aldehyde is referred to as the 1 position of the whole molecule. The other end has the form H_2C—OH (also written as CH_2OH); and the intermediate carbons all carry H and O in the pattern H—C—OH. In the other series, called the *ketose* series, both ends of the sugar

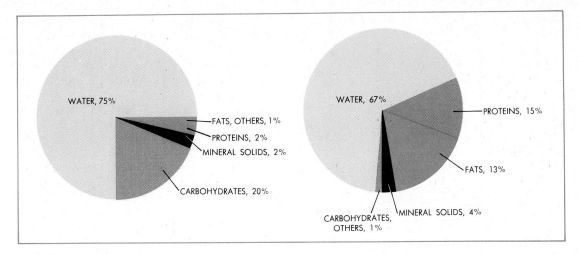

6 · 1 Average overall composition of *plant cells* (left) *and animal cells* (right).

have the form H₂C—OH; the second carbon near one end (position 2) is a carbonyl group here called a *ketone,* C=O; and all other carbons again carry H and O in the pattern H—C—OH. Thus, aldoses and ketoses differ principally in that a —C=O group is terminal at position 1 in one case, subterminal at position 2 in the other.

On the basis of both class and series, given sugars may be named *aldotrioses* or *ketotrioses, aldotetroses* or *ketotetroses,* and so forth. The aldotriose category is represented by *glyceraldehyde,* the ketotriose category, by *dihydroxyacetone:*

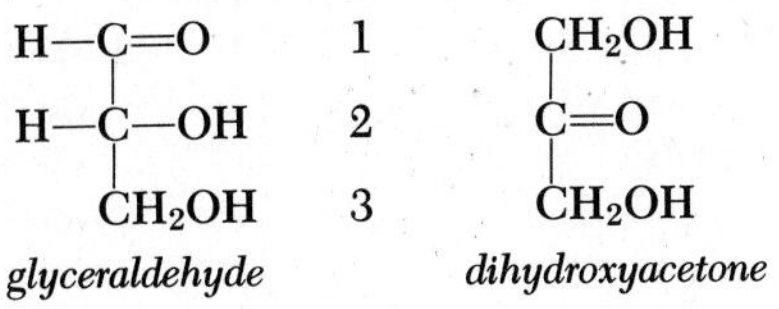

H—C=O	1	CH₂OH
H—C—OH	2	C=O
CH₂OH	3	CH₂OH
glyceraldehyde		*dihydroxyacetone*

It will be noted that glyceraldehyde possesses an asymmetric carbon atom at position 2. The molecule therefore exists in two structurally isomeric configurations, shown in Fig. 6.3. Of these two, one is known as the D- form, the other as the L- form, according to the alignment of the groups at positions 2 and 3 (see Fig. 6.2).

Both glyceraldehydes above also happen to be dextrorotary, that is, they twist the plane of polarized light to the right (see Chap. 4). This experimentally determined optical activity can be indicated in the names of the compounds by + and − signs: D(+)-glyceraldehyde, L(+)-glyceraldehyde.

In aldoses containing more than three carbons, more than one of these is asymmetric. Correspondingly larger numbers of structural isomers therefore exist. In an aldotetrose, for example, carbons 2 and 3 are asymmetric and four isomeric configurations are possible (see Fig. 6.3). (Note again that D- and L-forms refer to terminal carbon configurations, that is, the alignment of the groups on carbon 3 relative to those on carbon 4.) Three asymmetric carbons and eight different isomers are found among the aldopentoses, four asymmetric carbons and sixteen isomers among the aldohexoses, and so forth, as summarized in Fig. 6.3.

In the corresponding ketose series there are fewer isomers, for in the parent ketotriose, dihydroxyacetone, all three carbons are symmetric (see formula above).

6 · 2 General structure of *aldose and ketose sugars* (left) *and configuration of* D- *and* L-*forms of the terminal carbons of a carbohydrate chain* (right).

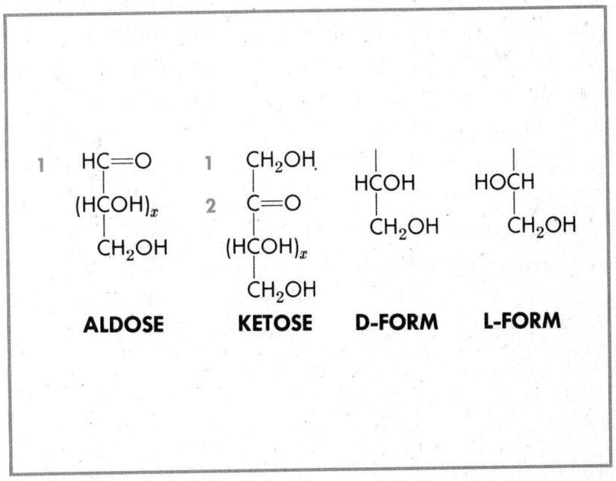

1 HC=O	1 CH₂OH	HCOH	HOCH
(HCOH)ₓ	2 C=O	CH₂OH	CH₂OH
CH₂OH	(HCOH)ₓ		
	CH₂OH		
ALDOSE	**KETOSE**	**D-FORM**	**L-FORM**

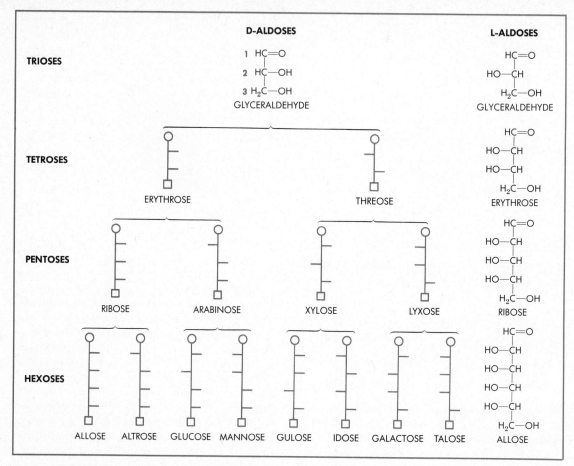

6 · 3   The aldose sugars. *For each of the D-al-doses shown symbolically, there exists a corresponding L-aldose which is roughly a mirror image. For example, L-erythrose in the far right column has configurations of carbons 2 and 3 mirroring that of D-erythrose at far left.*

In ketotetroses, therefore, only a single asymmetric carbon and two structurally isomeric forms exist (Fig. 6.4). Ketopentoses have two asymmetric carbons and four isomeric variants, and ketohexoses, three asymmetric carbons and eight isomeric variants. Note that the name of a ketose is usually formed by the insertion of the syllable -ul- in the name of the corresponding aldose. For example, the aldopentose *ribose* corresponds to the ketopentose *ribulose*. Similarly, the aldohexose *glucose*, possibly the most common of all sugars, corresponds to a ketohexose which should be named "gluculose" but is actually known more familiarly as *fructose*.

Experimental evidence indicates that certain sugar molecules do not always exist as straight-chain structures but that they often form closed rings, oxygen being one of the members of such rings. Sugar structures of this type are known as *pyranoses*. For example, the ring configuration for glucose (or *glucopyranose*) is as shown in Fig. 6.5. Note from this figure that not only carbons 2 to 5 but also carbon 1 is now asymmetric. Hence there should be, and there actually are, two isomeric types with reference to carbon 1. They are named α- and β- isomers, or *anomers*. Anomeric configurations are superimposed on and exist in addition to all other isomeric types discussed above, and they are known not only for glucose but also for other hexoses, for pentoses, and for derivatives of these.

Two or more monosaccharides of different or identical type may become joined together end to end, forming chainlike larger molecules. As a class, the latter are referred to as *glycosides*. If two monosaccharide units become so joined, a "double sugar," or *disaccharide*, results. For example, a combination of two glucose units forms the disaccharide *maltose*, malt sugar; a combination of glucose and fructose forms *sucrose*, the cane or beet sugar used familiarly

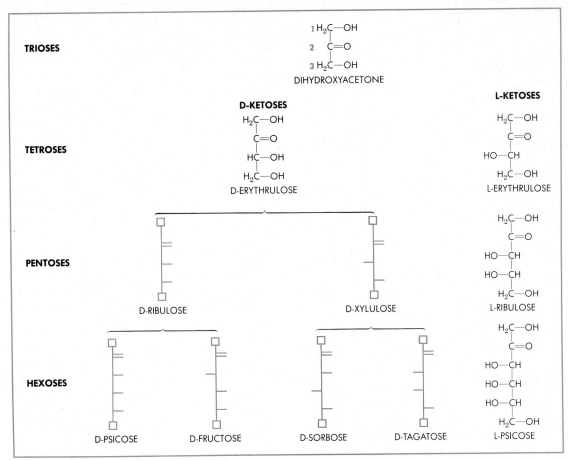

TRIOSES

1 H$_2$C—OH
2 C=O
3 H$_2$C—OH
DIHYDROXYACETONE

TETROSES

D-KETOSES
H$_2$C—OH
C=O
HC—OH
H$_2$C—OH
D-ERYTHRULOSE

L-KETOSES
H$_2$C—OH
C=O
HO—CH
H$_2$C—OH
L-ERYTHRULOSE

PENTOSES

D-RIBULOSE

D-XYLULOSE

H$_2$C—OH
C=O
HO—CH
HO—CH
H$_2$C—OH
L-RIBULOSE

HEXOSES

D-PSICOSE   D-FRUCTOSE

D-SORBOSE   D-TAGATOSE

H$_2$C—OH
C=O
HO—CH
HO—CH
HO—CH
H$_2$C—OH
L-PSICOSE

as a sweetening agent; and a union of glucose and galactose forms *lactose,* milk sugar. All three of these disaccharides have the atomic formula $C_{12}H_{22}O_{11}$ and their formation is described by the same equation:

$$2\ C_6H_{12}O_6 \longrightarrow H_2O + C_{12}H_{22}O_{11}$$

The structures of these three disaccharides are shown in Fig. 6.6. Note that, in both maltose and lactose, carbon 1 of one hexose unit is joined to carbon 4 of the other. In both cases one of the hexoses is a β-anomer of glucose (hence the designation of these disaccharides as β-maltose and β-lactose). The 4th carbon of that glucose unit is bonded to carbon 1 of the other hexose, which is α-glucose in the case of maltose, β-galactose in the case of lactose. Both disaccharides thus may be said to contain 1,4-*glycoside linkages;* in maltose the link is of the 1,4-α type and in lactose it is of the 1,4-β type. In sucrose, carbon 5 of fructose is bonded to carbon 1 of α-glucose; the glycosidic link here is therefore of the 1,5-α type.

Glycosides of more than two monosaccharide units yield "multiple sugars" called *oligosaccharides* if only

6 · 4 *The ketose sugars. As in the aldose series, D- and L-ketoses correspond like mirror images. Note that since carbon positions 1 as well as 2 are identical for all ketoses, there are only half as many structural isomers compared with aldose isomers. Also note that the ketotriose dihydroxyacetone exists in a single form only; D- and L-variants begin with the ketotetroses.*

a few units are joined and *polysaccharides* if very many units are joined. Among polysaccharides of major significance are high polymers of glucose, that is, chains of several hundreds or thousands of linked glucose units. One of these is *cellulose,* a principal constituent of plant cell walls. Another is *amylose,* a main component of plant starches. And a third is *glycogen,* a common animal carbohydrate (Fig. 6.7). In cellulose, the glycosidic links are of the 1,4-β type; a repeating unit of two glucose molecules joined by such a link is a disaccharide called *cellobiose.* In amylose, the links are of the 1,4-α type, hence the disaccharide repeating units here are malt-

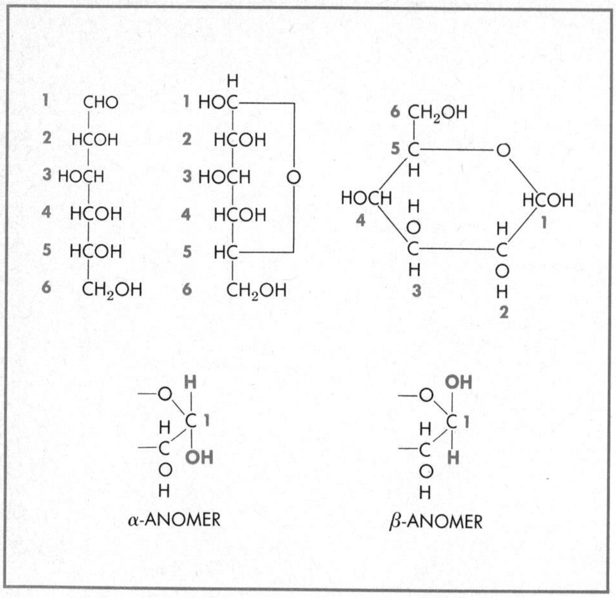

6 · 5 *The structural formula of glucose can be written in different ways shown above. Note that the structure may be depicted either as a chain or a ring. Note also that α and β anomers are distinguished according to how the H and OH groups of carbon 1 are aligned.*

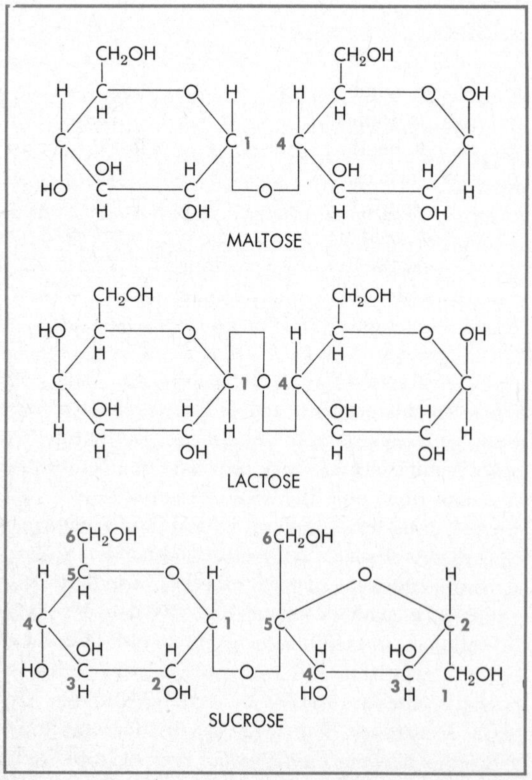

oses. This is true also for glycogen, but present additionally in this molecule are 1,6-α glycosidic links: a given glucose unit may connect to *two* other glucose units, namely, to one via its fourth carbon and a 1,4-α link, and to a second via its sixth carbon and a 1,6-α link. As a result, glycogen consists of variously branched and forked chains.

Unmodified carbohydrates like the above function in cells in two general capacities. They are structural building blocks of the cellular substance, and they are energy-rich molecules suitable as energy-yielding fuels in respiration. Simple carbohydrates are manufactured in green cells of plants by photosynthesis, and nongreen plant cells as well as animals and other heterotrophs then obtain these carbohydrates as basic foods. Monosaccharides such as ribose, glucose, fructose, and others are used as construction materials in the manufacture of other, more complex constituents of cells (see also below). Moreover, free glucose is the chief form in which carbohydrates are transported within organisms, both from cell to adjacent cell and over greater distances via sap or blood. Carbohydrates are stored principally as amylose in plants, as glycogen in animals. In all organisms, both monosaccharides and polysaccharides are also used directly as respiratory energy sources.

Apart from the unmodified carbohydrates, numerous derivatives play equally significant roles in cells. Important derivatives of monosaccharides include, for example, *phosphorylated* molecules, that is, sugars to which organic phosphates are attached.

$$\begin{array}{ll} 1 & H-C=O \\ & (HCOH)_4 \\ 6 & CH_2-O-PO_3H_2 \end{array}$$

glucose-6-phosphate

Note that the organic phosphate group $-O-PO_3H_2$ here substitutes for the $-OH$ group on the terminal carbon of the parent sugar. As we shall see, very many carbohydrates actually participate in cellular reactions not directly as unmodified molecules but rather as phosphorylated derivatives. The unmodified carbohydrates are far less reactive, and indeed this is why free glucose, for example, can serve as a transport form of carbohydrates. The molecule is sufficiently unreactive to make immediate chemical change during transit unlikely.

6 · 6 *The structure of three disaccharides. In maltose, the hexose units are joined via a 1,4-α link: carbon 1 of the glucose unit (left) was an α-anomer. In lactose the bond is a 1,4-β link; in sucrose, an α-anomer of glucose is bonded to fructose via a 1,5-α link.*

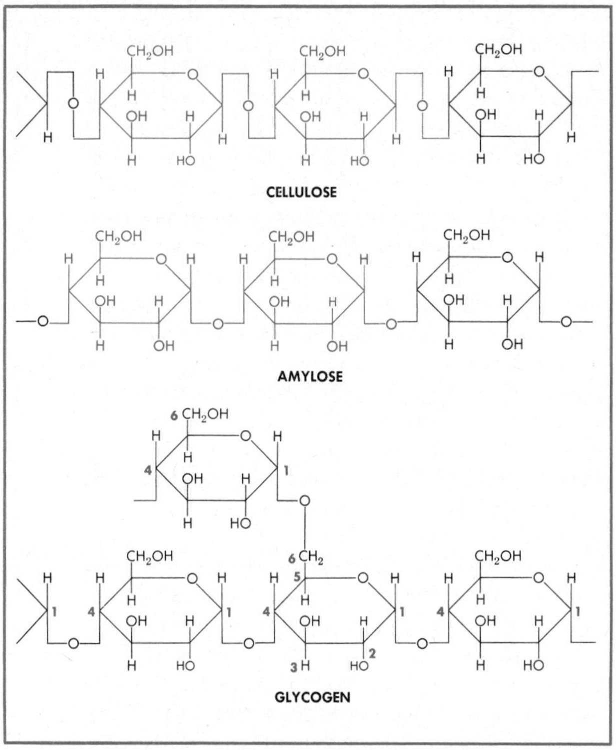

6 · 7 *The structure of three polysaccharides,* all composed of glucose units. In cellulose, the repeating disaccharide unit (color-shaded area) is called cellobiose, a combination of two glucose units joined via a 1,4-β link. In amylose the repeat unit is maltose (see Fig. 6.6) and bonds here are thus of the 1,4-α type. In glycogen, straight-chain portions have 1,4-α links and branch chains are joined via 1,6-α links (i.e., carbon 6 of one glucose unit joins to carbon 1 of an α-anomer of another glucose unit).

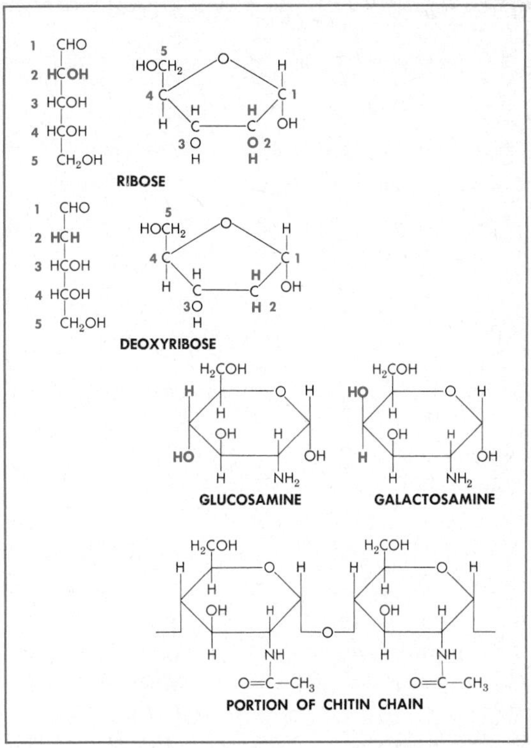

6 · 8 *The chemical structure* of various carbohydrates and derivatives.

Other monosaccharide derivatives are the *deoxysugars*, which, as their name indicates, possess one oxygen atom less than the parent sugars. The most important of the sugars so modified is the aldopentose *deoxyribose*, about which a great deal more will be said below (Fig. 6.8). Closely related derivatives are the *amino sugars*, for example, *glucosamine*, in which an amino group, —NH_2, replaces the —OH group of carbon 2 in aldohexose (see Fig. 6.8). High polymers of slightly modified glucosamine form polysaccharides which are major constituents of *chitin*, the hard, horny material found on the body surfaces of certain fungi, arthropods, and other organisms. Galactosamine is a component of a polysaccharide found particularly in cartilage.

A large number of important carbohydrate derivatives is formed from *sugar acids*. Three basic types may be distinguished (Fig. 6.9). In *aldonic* acids, the first carbon of a sugar molecule is part of an acid group. In *uronic* acids, the last carbon is part of an acid group. And in *aldaric* acids, both the first and the last carbons are parts of acid groups. One example of an aldonic acid is *glyceric acid*, formed as an intermediate in carbohydrate respiration (see Chap. 18). A more familiar example is *ascorbic acid*, or vitamin C, a slightly modified aldonic acid. Aldaric acids are represented by, for example, *tartaric acid*, derived from the aldotetrose threose. Derivatives of it are formed as intermediates in respiratory reactions. Another aldaric acid is *mucic acid*, which, along with derivatives of it, is a component of mucus. Among the uronic acids, the glucose derivative *glucuronic acid* and the galactose derivative *galacturonic acid* are important and widely occurring components in both plants and animals. Thus, high polymers of glucuronic acid are present in the *mucopolysaccharides*, substances found in, for example, mucus, cartilage, and particularly the cementing substance between animal cells. Present in plants as

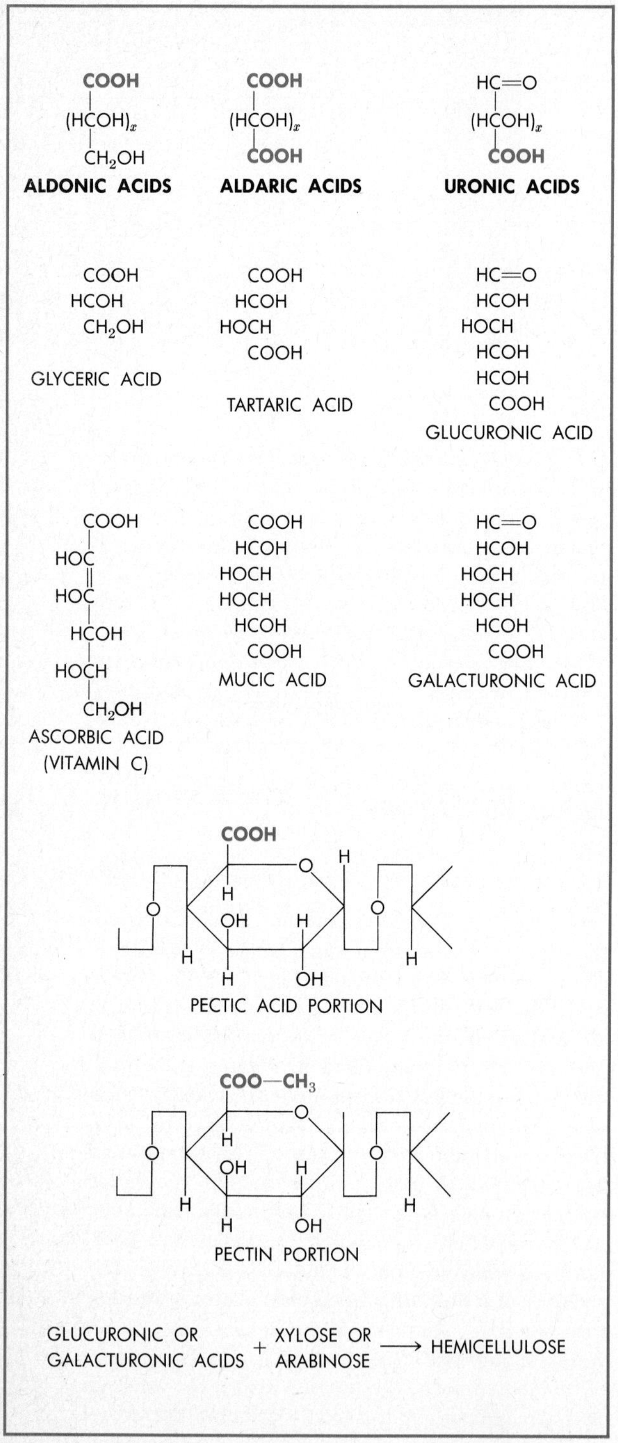

COOH
|
(HCOH)$_x$
|
CH$_2$OH
ALDONIC ACIDS

COOH
|
(HCOH)$_x$
|
COOH
ALDARIC ACIDS

HC=O
|
(HCOH)$_x$
|
COOH
URONIC ACIDS

COOH
HCOH
CH$_2$OH

GLYCERIC ACID

COOH
HCOH
HOCH
COOH

TARTARIC ACID

HC=O
HCOH
HOCH
HCOH
HCOH
COOH

GLUCURONIC ACID

COOH
|
HOC
||
HOC
|
HCOH
|
HOCH
|
CH$_2$OH

ASCORBIC ACID
(VITAMIN C)

COOH
HCOH
HOCH
HOCH
HCOH
COOH

MUCIC ACID

HC=O
HCOH
HOCH
HOCH
HCOH
COOH

GALACTURONIC ACID

PECTIC ACID PORTION

PECTIN PORTION

GLUCURONIC OR
GALACTURONIC ACIDS + XYLOSE OR
ARABINOSE → HEMICELLULOSE

6 · 9 *Sugar acids. The general categories of such acids are shown along top. Below are specific examples and portions of polymeric derivatives. Note that vitamin C is given in its* L-*configuration.*

a common constituent of cell walls (along with cellulose) is *hemicellulose,* a polymer of uronic acids and pentose sugars. A 1,4-β high polymer of galacturonic acid forms *pectic acid,* another major constituent of plant cell walls (see Fig. 6.9). If the hydrogen in the acid groups of pectic acid is substituted by methyl (—CH$_3$), then the result is *pectin,* abundant in fruits and in vegetable matter generally. Closely related is *amylopectin,* a branching glycogenlike polysaccharide with 1,4-α as well as 1,6-α linkages. Starches consist principally of mixtures of amylose and amylopectin. Plants also contain carbohydrate-derived compounds so complex that their detailed structure is as yet known only incompletely. Two examples are *suberin* and *lignin.* Suberin is a widely occurring waterproofing substance found in bark and the interior of roots, for example, and lignin is a strengthening material. The hard part of wood is approximately 50 per cent lignin, the rest largely cellulose.

Finally, mention may be made of the *sugar alcohols,* in which all carbons of a parent sugar molecule carry —OH groups and in which aldehyde or ketone groups are therefore not present (Fig. 6.10). The sugar alcohol corresponding to glucose is *sorbitol,* found widely in plants, and that corresponding to mannose is *mannitol,* a storage food present particularly in brown algae. But the most important of the sugar alcohols is undoubtedly the one derived from the aldotriose glyceraldehyde, namely, *glycerol,* or *glycerin.* This substance is a component of all fats, as will become clear in the next section.

LIPIDS AND DERIVATIVES

Fats and their derivatives are known collectively as *lipids.* The principal lipids are the *fatty acids.* Like the sugars, these are composed of C, H, and O, the carbon atoms being arranged as chains of various lengths (Fig. 6.11). All such chains carry a terminal

carboxyl group $-\overset{\displaystyle O}{\overset{\displaystyle \|}{C}}-OH$, and all other carbons hold hydrogen only.

The simplest fatty acid is *formic acid,* HCOOH. This compound occurs occasionally in cellular excretions such as sweat and urine and also plays a protective role in some ants, where it may be squirted out as an irritant spray against potential enemies. A series of increasingly complex fatty acids is formed by successive addition of —CH$_2$— groups to HCOOH. For example, addition of one such group produces *acetic acid,* CH$_3$COOH, the active ingredient of vinegar. Acetic acid serves a vital function in all cells, a derivative of it being an important intermediate in the respiratory decomposition of foods. Beyond acetic acid, fatty acids may be represented by the general formula $CH_3(CH_2)_nCOOH$, where n is any number other than zero. If $n = 1$, the acid is *propionic acid*, CH_3CH_2COOH; if $n = 2$, the result is *butyric acid*, $CH_3CH_2CH_2COOH$. The carbon atoms of fatty acids are numbered in sequence from the carboxyl end; the carbon *next* to the carboxyl group is referred to as the α carbon; the carbon adjacent to that is the β carbon, and so on.

In most naturally occurring fatty acids, n is an even number. As we shall see, this is because cells synthesize fatty acids from acetic acid building units which themselves are 2-carbon, that is, even-numbered, chains. Very common fatty acids in this category, present as components of most plant and animal fats, are *palmitic acid,*

$$CH_3(CH_2)_{14}COOH \text{ (or } C_{16}H_{32}O_2)$$

and *stearic acid,*

$$CH_3(CH_2)_{16}COOH \text{ (or } C_{18}H_{36}O_2)$$

Fatty acids like these are said to be *saturated;* all available bonds of the carbon chains are filled with hydrogen atoms. This contrasts with *unsaturated* fatty acids, characterized by the presence of one or more double bonds in a carbon chain. Such double bonds can become single bonds by the addition of more hydrogen:

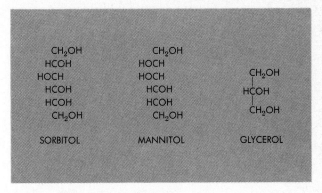

A widely occurring example of an unsaturated fatty acid is *oleic acid*, $CH_3(CH_2)_7CH=CH(CH_2)_7COOH$ (or $C_{18}H_{34}O_2$). If the double bond of this acid is converted to a single bond by addition of 2 H, then the result is the saturated compound

$$CH_3(CH_2)_{16}COOH$$

that is, stearic acid, as above. If more than one double bond is present, the acid is said to be *poly-unsaturated*. In many such cases, the double bonds alternate regularly with single bonds:

$$-CH=CH-CH=CH-$$

Such acids are said to have *conjugated* double bonds.

The carboxyl group of a fatty acid is polar; it may dissociate and thereby dissolve in water (itself a polar substance): $-COOH \longrightarrow -COO^- + H^+$. It is this reaction that makes a fatty acid an acid. However, the rest of the fatty acid chain is nonpolar and thus may not dissolve in water. The result of

6 · 10 *Three sugar alcohols.*

such joint *hydrophilic* and *hydrophobic* properties is that short-chain fatty acids, particularly formic, acetic, and proprionic acid, are completely water-soluble, whereas slightly longer chains are only sparingly soluble and long-chain acids are completely insoluble. Nevertheless, even long-chain acids still possess the polar hydrophilic carboxyl groups, and this circumstance accounts for the cleaning action of soaps and detergents. A soap is a salt formed by a fatty acid and an inorganic base, for example, NaOH or KOH:

$$\underset{\text{fatty acid}}{NaOH + R-COOH} \longrightarrow \underset{\text{soap}}{R-COO^-} + Na^+ + H_2O$$

Suppose we consider an oil-water mixture. The surface tension of water is very great compared to that

6 · 11 *Fatty acids* arranged according to increasing molecular complexity. Carbon positions are identified by Greek letters, starting at the carbon next to the carboxyl group.

STRUCTURE	COMPOSITION	NAME
H—COOH	CH_2O_2	FORMIC
$\overset{\alpha}{CH_3}$—COOH	$C_2H_4O_2$	ACETIC
$\overset{\beta}{CH_3}$—$\overset{\alpha}{CH_2}$—COOH	$C_3H_6O_2$	PROPIONIC
$\overset{\gamma}{CH_3}$—$\overset{\beta}{CH_2}$—$\overset{\alpha}{CH_2}$—COOH	$C_4H_8O_2$	BUTYRIC
$CH_3(CH_2)_4COOH$	$C_6H_{12}O_2$	CAPROIC
$CH_3(CH_2)_6COOH$	$C_8H_{14}O_2$	CAPRYLIC
$CH_3(CH_2)_{14}COOH$	$C_{16}H_{32}O_2$	PALMITIC
$CH_3(CH_2)_{16}COOH$	$C_{18}H_{36}O_2$	STEARIC

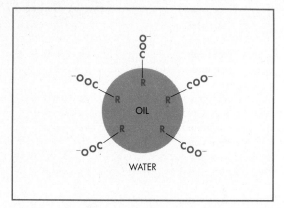

6 · 12 Emulsifying action of soap (R—COO^-). *The water-insoluble (hydrophobic) portion of the soap molecule (R—) dissolves in an oil droplet and the water-soluble (hydrophilic) portion (—COO^-) sticks out into the water. The oil drops thereby acquire an exterior layer of like negative charges, and the resulting repulsion prevents the oil droplets from coalescing.*

of oil, and the water-oil interface will therefore tend to attain and retain a minimum area. If therefore the mixture is shaken vigorously, colloidal oil droplets will form. But such droplets will soon coalesce and the oil will separate out completely from the water. If a soap is now introduced and the mixture is again shaken, then the R—COO^- ions of the soap will aggregate in neatly oriented monomolecular layers at the interfaces between the oil droplets and water: the hydrophobic R— portions will dissolve in the oil, the hydrophilic —COO^- portions will dissolve in the water (Fig. 6.12). The result is that the surface tension of water is lowered greatly and that each oil droplet has become surrounded by a layer of negative charges. Such droplets will therefore repel one another and will not coalesce. In everyday use, soaps and detergents have just this emulsifying effect; they permit layers or bulky accumulations of grease to be broken up into separate colloidal droplets, which may then be flushed away readily from areas to be cleaned. In biological contexts, an analogous emulsifying action is brought about by the bile salts secreted from the vertebrate liver into the gut. These salts are detergents acting on masses of fat present in food. The resulting colloidal droplets then offer an enormous surface area to the enzymes (lipases) dissolved in the surrounding water, and enzymatic digestive decomposition of the droplets is thereby facilitated.

Fatty acids not only contribute to the composi-

tion of fat cleaners but are themselves structural components of fats. A *fat* is a fatty acid *triglyceride*, that is, a complex in which three fatty acid units are joined to one glycerol unit (Fig. 6.13). The fatty acids here may be of the same or of different types, and the bonding to glycerol is an *ester* link, a saltlike bond formed whenever one organic molecule is an —OH donor and another is an —H donor. Water is then a byproduct, as in salt formation between inorganic acids and bases. Note, however, that in fat formation it is the fatty acids which serve as —OH donors and glycerol which serves as —H donor.

The physical nature of a fat is determined by the chain lengths and the degrees of saturation of the fatty acids present. Fats containing fatty acids that are short-chained, unsaturated, or both tend to be volatile liquids or oils. For example, oleic acid is oily, and fats containing oleic acid tend to be similarly liquid. By contrast, fats containing long-chained and saturated fatty acids tend to be hard tallow. This is the case, for example, in *tristearin*, a common animal fat containing three stearic acids per fat molecule. We may note, incidentally, that fats are highly insoluble in water because the originally hydrophilic carboxyl groups are now no longer free but have become incorporated into ester links. If fats are water-insoluble, however, how can they be utilized as foods in cells, a process which must occur in aqueous solution? Fat utilization in organisms is achieved, first, by emulsification as outlined above, and second, by digestive decomposition, a process which is the reverse of fat formation. In the presence of lipase and H^+ ions (supplied in vertebrates by HCl secreted from the stomach wall), fats decompose into fatty acids and glycerol. The latter is completely water-soluble and, as noted, fatty acids may make intimate contact with water via their free hydrophilic carboxyl groups.

6 · 13 Formation of a fat. *Three molecules of fatty acid combine with one molecule of glycerin via ester links (—COO—), resulting in three water molecules and one fat molecule.*

$$CH_3(CH_2)_n-\overset{\overset{\displaystyle O}{\|}}{C}-OH \quad HO-CH_2$$

$$CH_3(CH_2)_n-\overset{\overset{\displaystyle O}{\|}}{C}-OH \; + \; HO-CH \xrightarrow{-3\,H_2O}$$

$$CH_3(CH_2)_n-\overset{\overset{\displaystyle O}{\|}}{C}-OH \quad HO-CH_2$$

$$CH_3(CH_2)_n-\overset{\overset{\displaystyle O}{\|}}{C}-O-CH_2$$

$$CH_3(CH_2)_n-\overset{\overset{\displaystyle O}{\|}}{C}-O-CH$$

$$CH_3(CH_2)_n-\overset{\overset{\displaystyle O}{\|}}{C}-O-CH_2$$

3 FATTY ACIDS   GLYCERIN   FAT

Fats and fatty acids represent the chief food storage compounds of animals and are among the important storage foods in all other organisms. Like carbohydrates, moreover, fats and fatty acids also play significant roles as structural components of cells, and they are even richer sources of respiratory energy than carbohydrates. As among carbohydrates, furthermore, chemical derivatives of fats and fatty acids occur abundantly, and these play a wide variety of roles.

For example, one important group of fatlike compounds comprises the *phospholipids*, or *phosphatides*. In a molecule of this type, glycerol is joined to *two* fatty acid units, and the place normally taken by a third in a fat is here occupied by a phosphate group or by a grouping containing phosphate and, usually nitrogen as well (Fig. 6.14). Among widely occurring members of this class of compounds is *lecithin*, present in small amounts in most accumulations of fats but particularly abundant in the lipid fraction of seeds and egg yolk. Moreover, lecithin is a major constituent in the surface and interior membranes of cells. As the formula of the compound indicates, the phosphate-choline end of the molecule is charged

and polar and therefore hydrophilic. It is this property which makes lecithin an important surface-active material. Other phospholipids include *plasmalogen*, *cephalin*, and *sphyngomyelin*, high concentrations of which are found in brain, nerves, and neural tissues generally.

A widely encountered class of lipid derivatives comprises the *waxes*. These are fatty acid esters of any sugar alcohol other than glycerol. In most cases, the carrier alcohols of waxes are chains containing numerous carbon atoms, though not all of these generally carry fatty acids. Waxes occur abundantly as waterproofing layers on the exposed surfaces of plant cells, on the body surfaces of many types of animals, and in a large variety of animal secretion

6 · 14 Lipid derivatives. *In lecithin, the grouping to the right of the phosphate is the choline fraction. R and R' represent different fatty acids. The structure for waxes is very general; more than one fatty acid, and other alcohols, may be present. The structure of the xanthophyll lutein corresponds to that of carotene except for differences in the terminal rings, as indicated.*

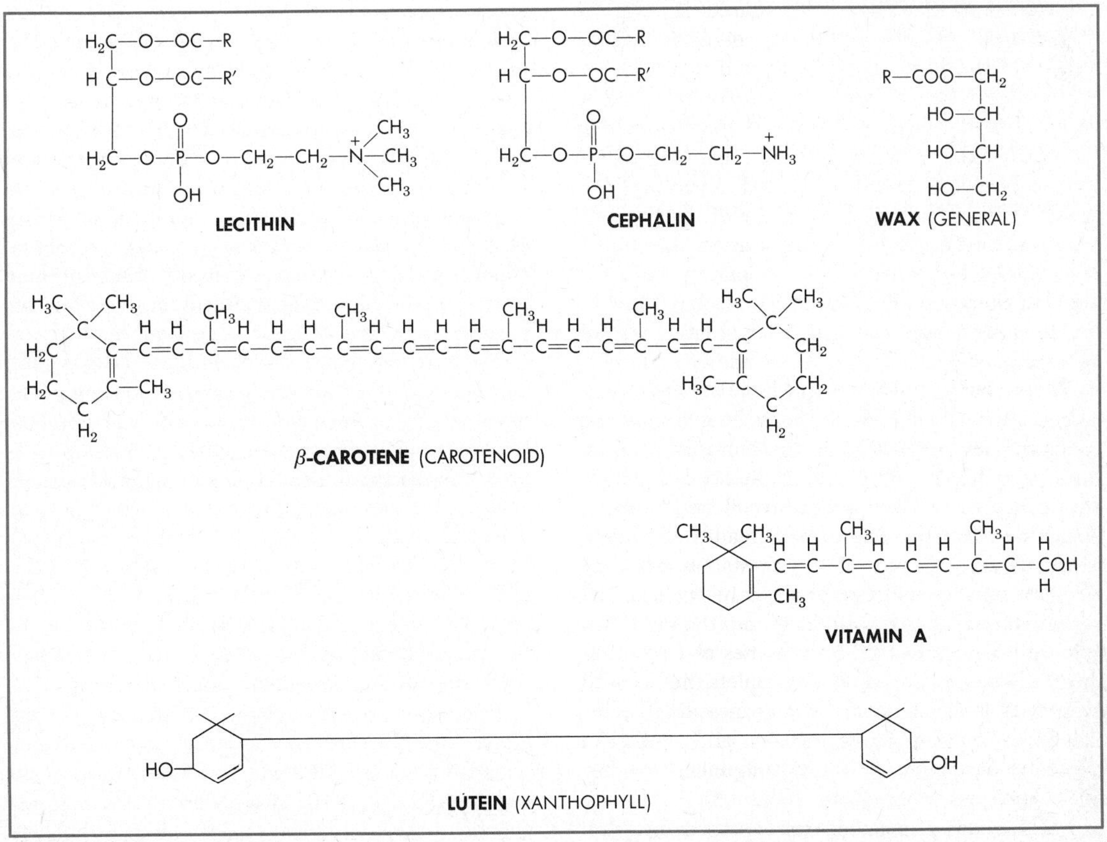

LECITHIN

CEPHALIN

WAX (GENERAL)

β-CAROTENE (CAROTENOID)

VITAMIN A

LUTEIN (XANTHOPHYLL)

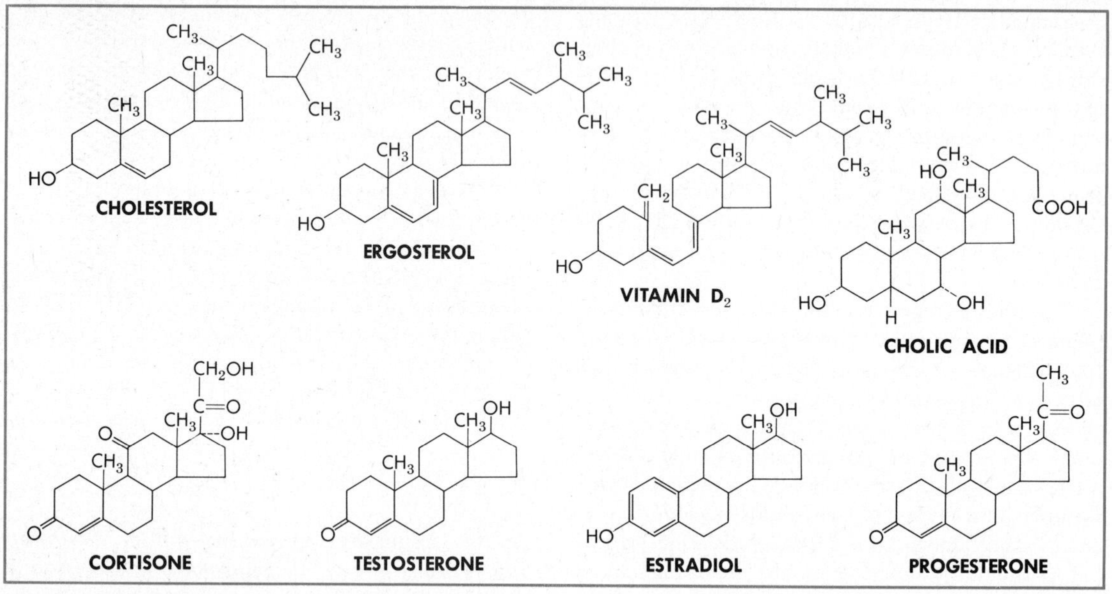

CHOLESTEROL

ERGOSTEROL

VITAMIN D$_2$

CHOLIC ACID

CORTISONE

TESTOSTERONE

ESTRADIOL

PROGESTERONE

6 · 15 Lipid derivatives: steroids. The four basic fused rings of a steroid are well seen in cholesterol and in ergosterol. Note that vitamin D is quite similar to ergosterol, differing only in the openness of the second ring. Cholic acid is one of the bile acids; a bile salt may form by dissociation at the terminal carboxyl group. Cortisone is one of the adrenocortical hormones. Testosterone and estradiol are the most potent male and female sex hormones, respectively (note the very slight structural differences). Progesterone, structurally very similar to cortisone, is the pregnancy hormone in man and other mammals.

products (for example, spermaceti in the head of sperm whales, beeswax, and in the outer ears of mammals).

More distantly related to lipids are the *carotenoids*, fatty-acid-like carbon chains containing conjugated double bonds and carrying six-membered carbon rings at each end (see Fig. 6.14). These compounds are pigments, and they produce red, orange, yellow, cream, and brown colors in both plant and animal matter. Two subgroups of the carotenoids are the *carotenes* and the *xanthophylls*. Carotenes have the general formula $C_{40}H_{56}$, and it may be noted that vitamin A is a derivative. Named after the carrot, in which carotenes are abundant, the pigments also occur widely in all leaves and are responsible for the red, yellow, or cream-white colors of, for example, tomatoes, pumpkins, egg yolk, butter, milk, and other plant and animal products. Xanthophylls contain oxygen in addition to carbon and hydrogen. They are

as widely distributed as the carotenes. For example, a common xanthophyll of leaves is *lutein* ($C_{40}H_{56}O_2$), which is responsible for the yellow colors in autumn foliage. An important xanthophyll in brown and other algae is *fucoxanthin* ($C_{40}H_{56}O_6$).

Manufactured from lipid precursors in cells and rather lipidlike in their solubility properties are the *steroids*, molecules having a fused four-ring skeleton (Fig. 6.15). Among important and well-known steroids are *cholesterol*, found in most animal fats and also in blood; *ergosterol*, and other plant steroids; *vitamin D;* the *adrenocorticosteroids*, a group of hormones produced in the cortex of the vertebrate adrenal gland (including *cortisone*, the most familiar of these hormones); the *androgens* (including *testosterone*, the most powerful of these compounds), which are the male sex hormones of vertebrates; the *estrogens*, which are the female sex hormones of vertebrates; *progesterone*, a hormone playing a variety of reproductive roles among vertebrates generally and serving as pregnancy-maintaining hormone in mammals specifically; and the *bile salts* of vertebrates, which have an emulsifying effect on food fats, as pointed out above. Note that, in many cases, two steroids may differ only very slightly in chemical structure yet their biological effects may differ greatly. For example, the chemical differences between male and female sex hormones are exceedingly slight.

Still more distantly related to lipids are the *tetrapyrrols*, or *porphyrins*, a group of pigmented compounds serving a wide variety of functions in plants and animals (Fig. 6.16). A so-called pyrrol molecule contains a skeleton of five atoms, four of carbon and

PLATE V

11. Insect Camouflage.
A, a stick insect and B, a caterpillar,
both resembling
the branches of plants.

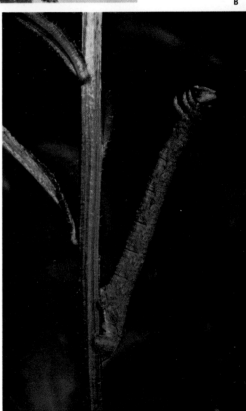

12. Mutualism.
A, lichens, shown here
encrusting a tree branch, are mutualistic
associations of algae and fungi.
B, root nodules, representing
mutualistic associations of nitrogen-fixing
bacteria and roots of clover plants,
as below, or other legumes.

PLATE VI

13. Caterpillar of a moth,
carrying the pupal cocoons of
a parasitic wasp.

Courtesy of Carolina Biological Supply Company

14. Freshwater plankton.
The algal components
here are largely Volvox,
and the animals are
crustacean water fleas
and copepods.

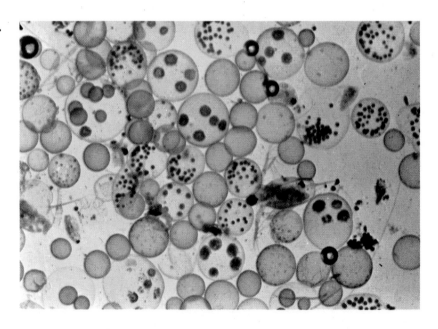

one of nitrogen, and the five are arranged as a ring. Four such pyrrol rings joined together form a tetrapyrrol. In certain cases, the four joined pyrrol rings form a straight chain. Tetrapyrrols of this type include red, blue, yellow, and other varieties of pigments found, for example, in several algal groups, in the shells of robin and other bird eggs, and in mammalian feces and urine. In other tetrapyrrols, the four pyrrol rings are joined to form a larger ring in turn, and in the center of this larger ring is present a single atom of a metal. Major pigments of this type are the red *cytochromes*, in which the metal atom is iron. Cytochromes serve as hydrogen-carrying coenzymes in the respiration of all cells. Quite closely related structurally to the cytochromes are the *hemes*, which function as oxygen-transporting compounds in the blood of many animals. In cells the cytochromes and hemes normally do not occur as free compounds but are bonded to carrier proteins (see below).

Chlorophyll, the green pigment of photosynthetic organisms, likewise is a ringlike tetrapyrrol, the central metal atom here being magnesium.

Note again, as illustrated clearly in steroids and tetrapyrrols, that chemical differences or similarities are by no means or necessarily proportional to biological differences or similarities. This principle is underscored particularly well also by the proteins, the next major group of cellular compounds to be examined.

6 · 16   Tetrapyrrols (porphyrins). *The straight-chain skeleton shown is chemically very similar to bilirubin, one of the breakdown products of hemoglobin in blood. Note the similarities and differences among heme, cytochrome, and chlorophyll. In the latter, the tetrapyrrol ring with the magnesium center forms the "head" of the molecule, and a "tail" is represented by the 20-carbons-long chain at the lower left corner of the molecule.*

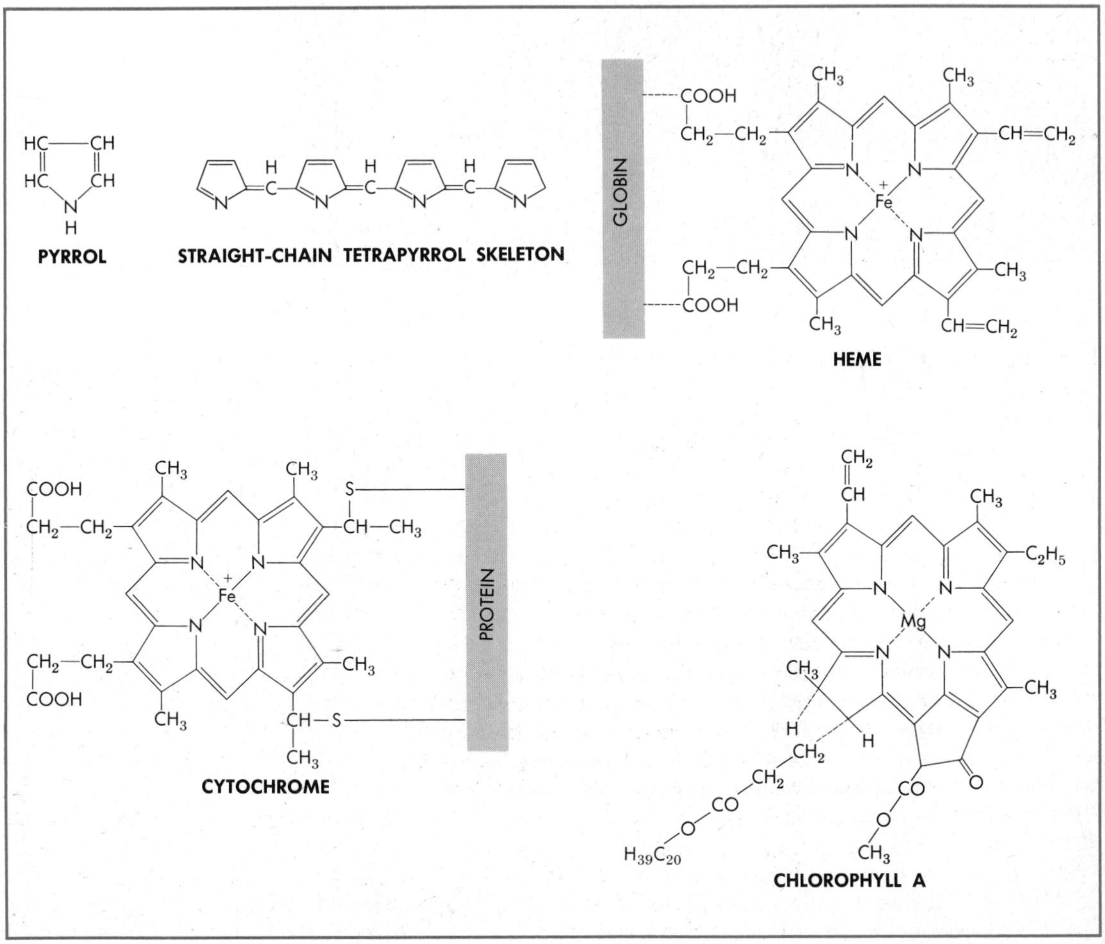

PYRROL

STRAIGHT-CHAIN TETRAPYRROL SKELETON

GLOBIN

HEME

CYTOCHROME

PROTEIN

CHLOROPHYLL A

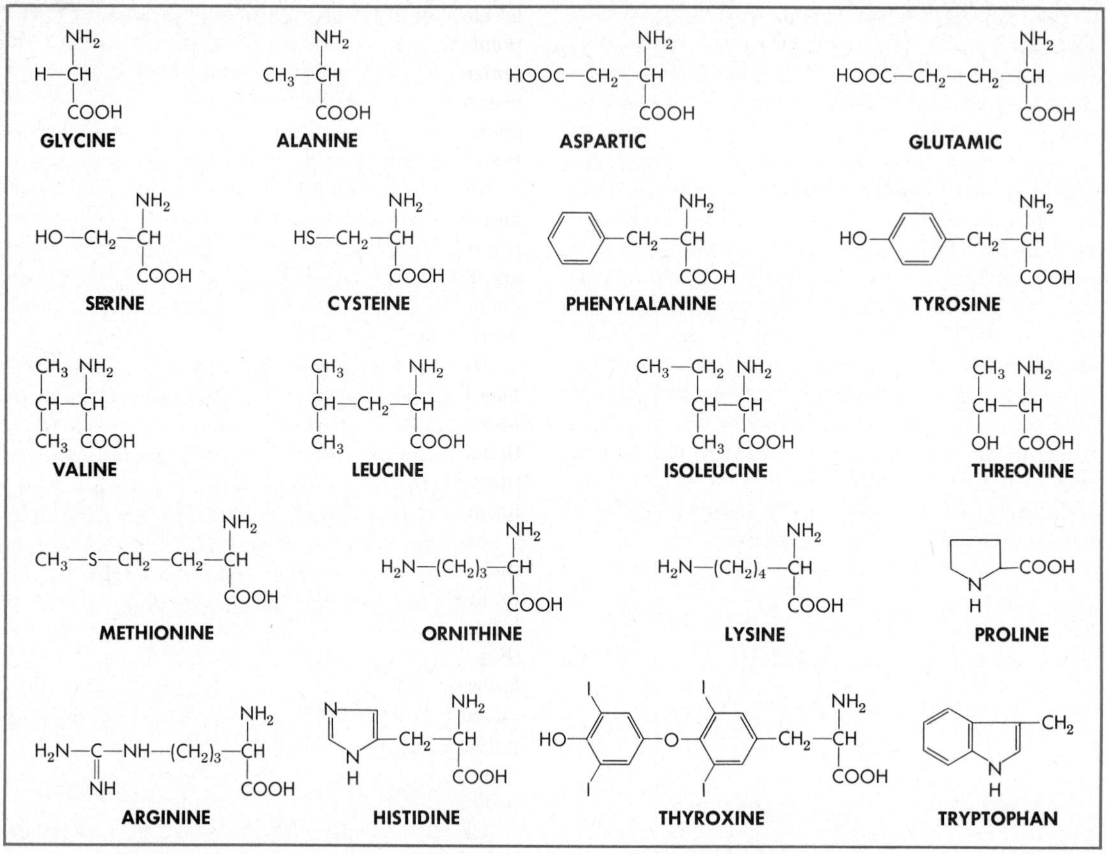

6 · 17 The structure of 20 amino acids.

PROTEINS AND DERIVATIVES

Proteins are polymers of molecular units known as *amino acids*. The general structure of an amino acid may be represented as

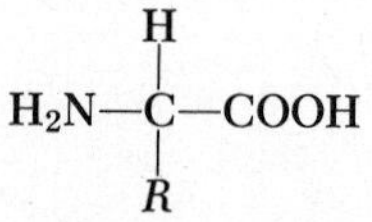

$$H_2N-\underset{R}{\overset{H}{\underset{|}{\overset{|}{C}}}}-COOH$$

where —NH_2 is an *amino* group, —COOH a carboxyl group, and —R an atomic grouping which may vary in structure considerably. For example, the simplest amino acid is *glycine*, where R = H. If R = OH, the amino acid is *serine*, and if R = CH_3, the acid is called *alanine*. Many other amino acids are characterized by comparatively more complex R— groups, some being carbon chains both straight and branched, others being rings. Altogether some 70 different amino acids are known, but only about 20 to 24 occur naturally in living organisms (Fig. 6.17).

With the exception of glycine, all other amino acids possess an asymmetric carbon atom and can therefore exist in two structurally isomeric series. The acids are designated D- or L- according to the following configurational patterns:

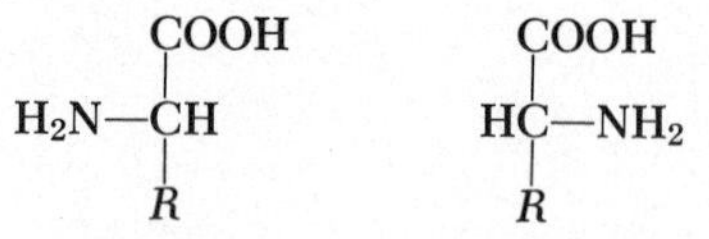

$$\underset{\text{L-amino acid}}{\overset{COOH}{\underset{R}{\underset{|}{H_2N-CH}}}} \qquad \underset{\text{D-amino acid}}{\overset{COOH}{\underset{R}{\underset{|}{HC-NH_2}}}}$$

These patterns follow the formal relation between the amino acid alanine, in which R = CH_3, and the D- and L- forms of the triose sugar glyceraldehyde, the standard for configurational nomenclature:

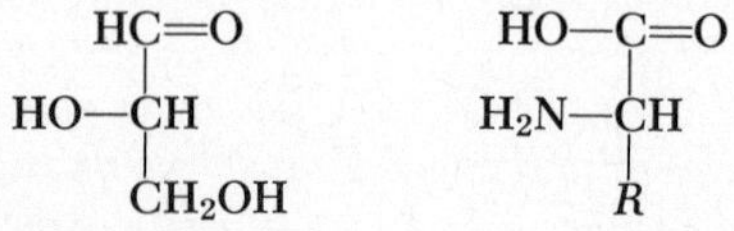

$$\underset{\text{L-glyceraldehyde}}{\overset{HC=O}{\underset{CH_2OH}{\underset{|}{HO-CH}}}} \qquad \underset{\text{L-alanine}}{\overset{HO-C=O}{\underset{R}{\underset{|}{H_2N-CH}}}}$$

With very few exceptions, all naturally occurring amino acids, both as free molecules and as components of proteins, are of the L- type. (The exceptions are D- alanine, D-glutamic acid, and a few other D- isomers isolated from the cell wall material of certain bacteria.) Note that here, as in sugars, the configurational pattern is essentially unrelated to measured optical activity. For example, alanine is dextrorotary and may therefore be designated as L.(+)-alanine.

Amino acids are weak electrolytes. Indeed, each is both a weak acid and a weak base simultaneously, for the —COOH group may dissociate and yield H^+ and the —NH_2 group of the same compound may accept the H^+:

$$NH_2—RCH—COOH \rightleftharpoons NH_3{}^+—RCH—COO^-$$

The compound as a whole thus remains electrically neutral, but it is ionized at both ends and is therefore strongly dipolar. Consequently, amino acids dissolve well in water when they are in this ionized state. Electrolytes like amino acids, which are both acidic and basic at once, are called *ampholytes*, *amphoteric* substances, or *zwitterions*.

It should be appreciated readily that such ions may migrate in an electric field. Thus, if ionized amino acids in water are placed between the positive and negative poles of an electric field, then the acids will tend to migrate to a position where the attraction of the positive pole for the —COO^- groups equals the attraction of the negative pole for the —$NH_3{}^+$ groups. The pH of the medium will influence this positioning. In an acid solution excess H^+ ions are present in the medium, and such ions will react with some of the amino acid ions and reduce their electronegative properties:

$$NH_3{}^+—RCH—COO^- + H^+ \rightleftharpoons$$
$$NH_3{}^+—RCH—COOH$$

In such a case, therefore, a preponderant number of amino acid ions will be electropositive and these will migrate more toward the side of negative pole. Conversely, in an alkaline medium the electropositive property of the amino acid ions will be reduced by the excess of OH^- ions in the medium:

$$OH^- + NH_3{}^+—RCH—COO^- \rightleftharpoons$$
$$H_2O + NH_2—RCH—COO^-$$

In this case a preponderant number of the acid ions is electronegative and will migrate to the side of the positive pole. Hence in a medium of a given pH, in which both H^+ and OH^- are present in given concentrations, dissolved ionized amino acids will migrate until they come to rest in a region where the attraction by the two poles balances. This region may lie more toward one pole or more toward the other, depending on the specific pH of the medium; and in this region the total electropositivity of the amino acids will just equal their total electronegativity. The pH at which amino acids no longer migrate in

an electric field is called the *isoelectric point*. At that point the total positive and negative charges of the ionized amino acids are equal and their overall net charge is zero. At that point, moreover, the amino acids are in their most strongly dipolar form and are therefore also most soluble in water.

Most types of amino acids undergo reactions and give rise to derivatives that play widely significant roles within cells; we shall discuss this structural and functional individual importance of the acids in Chap. 19. Collectively, by far their most important derivatives are the proteins.

Hundreds and even thousands of amino acid units may be polymerized into a single protein molecule. Most proteins are clearly macromolecules; among them, indeed, are some of the largest chemical structures known. As such, proteins are associated most intimately with the phenomenon we call "life."

Adjacent amino acids in a protein are united in such a way that the amino group of one acid links to the carboxyl group of its neighbor; the bond is formed by the removal of one molecule of water (Fig. 6.18). The resulting grouping —NH—CO— is known as the *peptide bond*, and two amino acids so joined constitute a *dipeptide*. If many amino acids are polymerized by means of peptide bonds, the whole complex is a *polypeptide*. Such chains are the basis of protein structure.

Chemically, polypeptides may vary in practically unlimited fashion:

1. they may contain any or all of the two dozen or so naturally occurring *types* of amino acids.
2. they may contain almost any *number* of each of these types of amino acids.
3. the specific *sequence* in which given numbers and types of amino acids are joined into a chain can vary almost without restriction.

In other words, amino acid units may be envisaged to represent an "alphabet" of some 20+ "letters," and an astronomically large number of different

6 · 18 Formation of a peptide bond. Two amino acids combine with loss of water, resulting in a dipeptide. The peptide link in the dipeptide is indicated within the tinted area at right.

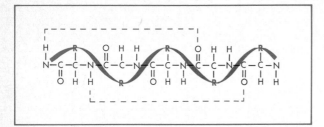

6 · 19   The α helix. *Shown here is a portion of a polypeptide chain, illustrating the primary structure of a protein molecule. If a line is drawn to connect all R— fractions of the consecutive amino acid units, such a line marks a spiral called an α helix. Note that the helix is held together by hydrogen bonds between the H of the —NH of one amino acid unit and the O of a —CO— in another amino acid three units distant (colored broken lines).*

polypeptide "sentences" may be constructed from this alphabet. Correspondingly, the possible number of chemically different proteins is likewise astronomical. Indeed, no two organisms possess the same types of proteins.

A polypeptide chain with its particular sequence of amino acid units and peptide bonds forms what is known as the *primary structure* of a protein. A *secondary structure*, superimposed on the primary structure, is also recognized. More specifically, a polypeptide chain has the physical form of a spiraling ribbon. That is, if a line were drawn through all the *R—* portions of the consecutive amino acids present, that line would mark out a spiral (Fig. 6.19). Such spirals are in some cases "right-handed" (α-helix), in others "left-handed" (β-helix). In either configuration, the backbone of the spiral is a bonded sequence of —N—C—C—N—C—C—N— atoms, each —N—C—C— portion representing the skeleton of one amino acid unit. Projecting to the side from this ribbon are the H—, O=, and R— groups of the amino acid units. A polypeptide spiral of this sort has quite uniform geometrical properties for most proteins. For example, there are on the average 3.7 amino acid units per turn of the spiral. Accordingly, a chain of some 18 units forms a helix with five complete turns.

This conformation of the spiral is maintained by hydrogen bonds, formed here by the sharing of an H atom between the nitrogen of one amino acid unit and an oxygen of another, nearby unit. More precisely, it can be shown that the H of the —NH of one unit is bonded to the O of —C=O three amino acid units away (see Fig. 6.19). Indeed, all

—NH and —C=O groups present in the chain are hydrogen-bonded in this fashion, each such bond linking amino acids three units apart. By virtue of such bonds, the helical configuration becomes quite stable; it represents the secondary structure of a protein.

Long coils of this sort may remain extended and threadlike, and the protein molecule then is said to be *fibrous*. In many cases, however, such coils may be looped and twisted and folded back on themselves, in an infinite variety of ways. Protein molecules then are *globular*, that is, balled together somewhat like entangled twine. Such loops and bends give a protein a *tertiary structure*. Where present, a tertiary configuration is held together chiefly by three types of bonds (Fig. 6.20). One is again the hydrogen bond, which in this case links together more or less distant portions of a polypeptide chain. Another is an *ionic bond*, or salt bond, formed when the —NH$_3^+$ and —COO$^-$ groups of two distant terminal amino acid units come to lie near and attract each other electrostatically. A third type of link is the *disulfide bond*, which arises between sulfur-containing amino acids. Sulfur is present most often in the form of —SH groups, and the principal —SH-carrying amino acid is *cysteine*. If, for example, two distant cysteine units in a folded polypeptide come to lie close to each other, then their —SH groups may link together and form a "disulfide bridge," —S—S—. Such bridges, and probably also a variety of bonds formed between the R— groups of near-lying amino acid units, contribute importantly toward maintenance of the tertiary structure (see Fig. 6.20).

Some proteins consist of not only one but several

6 · 20   Separate polypeptide chains *or segments of a single chain (vertical lines) may be held together by bonds such as shown below. In a hydrogen bond, an H atom is held in common by two side groups of the polypeptide chains. Disulfide bridges are formed by S-containing amino acid units, like cysteine. Ionic links between charged side groups of polypeptide chains hold together by electric attraction.*

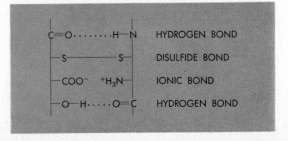

C=O·······H—N	HYDROGEN BOND
S————S	DISULFIDE BOND
COO$^-$ $^+$H$_3$N	IONIC BOND
O—H·····O=C	HYDROGEN BOND

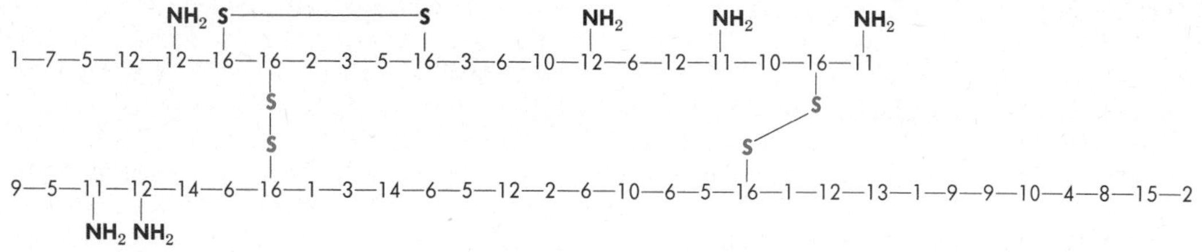

```
         NH₂ S————————————————S              NH₂        NH₂           NH₂
          |  |                |                |          |             |
1—7—5—12—12—16—16—2—3—5—16—3—6—10—12—6—12—11—10—16—11
                   |                                          |
                   S                                          S
                   |                                          |
                   S                                  S
                   |                                  |
9—5—11—12—14—6—16—1—3—14—6—5—12—2—6—10—6—5—16—1—12—13—1—9—9—10—4—8—15—2
          |   |
         NH₂ NH₂
```

1 GLYCINE	5 VALINE	9 PHENYLALANINE	13 ARGININE
2 ALANINE	6 LEUCINE	10 TYROSINE	14 HISTIDINE
3 SERINE	7 ISOLEUCINE	11 ASPARTIC ACID	15 LYSINE
4 THREONINE	8 PROLINE	12 GLUTAMIC ACID	16 CYSTEINE

6 · 21 Structure of the insulin molecule. The molecule consists of two polypeptide chains held together by two disulfide bridges. The numbers represent amino acid units, which are listed below the diagram. Note that disulfide bridges are formed by the amino acid cysteine.

separate polypeptide chains bonded to one another, often in the form of a bundle. Proteins of this type are said to possess a *quaternary structure*. Bundles of polypeptides are held together largely by the bond types already referred to: ionic bonds, hydrogen bonds, and disulfide bonds. For example, one of the hormones of the pancreas, *insulin*, is a protein consisting of two parallel polypeptide chains, held together by two disulfide bonds (Fig. 6.21). The composition of this protein was determined in 1954, the first time that the exact structure of any protein could be established. One of the polypeptides of insulin was shown to consist of 30 amino acid units, the other of 21. With only 51 units altogether, insulin is probably one of the smallest proteins. Most others are far more complex, and their exact structure is correspondingly less well known as yet. In the very large protein of the vertebrate red blood cell, *hemoglobin*, it is now known that four polypeptide chains are linked, held together mainly by ionic bonds. Two of these chains appear to be identical to each other and to be arranged as α-spirals, the two others analogously identical to each other but arranged as β-spirals. Several other functionally important proteins have been found to be made up of four polypeptides.

It should be clear that proteins will differ not only according to their primary structure but also according to their secondary, tertiary, and quaternary structures. Thus, two proteins might have identical amino acid sequences, but if, for example, the folding pattern of the chains differs, the two molecules will have different properties and will in effect be different proteins. Many of the physical and biological properties of proteins actually depend on a specific secondary or tertiary structure.

Many of the *R*— side chains in proteins are ionized, particularly common ionic components here being —NH_3^+ and —COO^-. As a result, a protein as a whole is a multiple ampholyte and displays electric properties quite similar to those of individual amino acids. In an acid medium, for example, the —COO^- groups on a protein will become —COOH and leave the protein with a net positive charge. Conversely, in an alkaline medium the —NH_3^+ groups will become —$NH_2 + H_2O$ and leave the protein with a net negative charge. At a certain pH, the isoelectric point of the protein, the total positive and negative charges will be equal. At that point a protein will be most polar and therefore most soluble. Indeed, many proteins precipitate out of solution if the pH changes substantially to either side of the isoelectric point. Most proteins in the nongenetic (cytoplasmic) region of cells have an isoelectric point at a pH of about 6. Since the pH of this cytoplasmic region is about 7, the proteins are in a medium more alkaline than their isoelectric point and thus carry net negative charges. Also, they will be not quite fully dissolved, a circumstance which permits them to form the discrete structural framework of a cell; complete protein dissolution would yield a formless soup. In the gene-containing (nuclear) region of a cell, some proteins, notably the so-called *histones* and *protamines*, have alkaline isoelectric points. Inasmuch as the average pH of the nuclear region again is about 7, histones and protamines there carry net positive charges. These proteins too are therefore not fully dissolved and will be able to form discrete structure

—specifically, gene-containing filaments, or chromosomes (see Chap. 7). We may recognize here a major reason why drastic pH changes would be lethal; proteins would be brought either closer to or farther away from their isoelectric points, resulting either in more dissolution or more precipitation. Either happening would destroy cell structure and consequently also cell function.

By virtue of their charges, proteins, like amino acids, will migrate in an electric field at any pH except that of the isoelectric point. The rate and direction of migration depend entirely on the size and sign of the net charge, and different types of proteins differ in these respects. This circumstance makes possible the separation of a mixture of several proteins into individual ones. If a protein mixture is put between the poles of an electric field in a medium of a given fixed pH, then the different protein types present will move for various distances toward one or the other pole, or may remain stationary, depending on their different charge characteristics at that pH. So spread out between the two poles according to type, each type of protein may then be isolated from the others. Such an isolated sample may itself subsequently be subjected to an electric field, at a new and different pH level, and this procedure may be repeated until a final sample no longer separates into differently moving fractions. This last sample will be a pure protein of a single type. The property of proteins to migrate in electric fields is known as *electrophoresis,* and electrophoretic separation of mixed proteins is a common method of laboratory analysis.

Not only pH changes but also salts and heavy metals disrupt the normal states of proteins. Salt and metal ions bond preferentially and very strongly to the positive or negative charges on proteins, thus reducing the electric polarity of the ampholytes. Solubility in water is thereby reduced correspondingly, regardless of pH. Proteins can actually be "salted out," that is, precipitated, by strong salt solutions, and heavy metals are biological poisons because of their analogous precipitating effects. Moreover, temperature and pressure changes likewise disrupt the structure of proteins. In this connection, we may note that hydrogen bonds, and also the disulfide and ionic bonds which maintain a globular configuration of the molecules, are comparatively much weaker than peptide bonds. As a result, hydrogen bonds may be disrupted more readily by changes in the physical and chemical environment of a protein. When bonds are so disrupted, the globular configuration of a protein will no longer hold together as before, and the molecule will lose its specific secondary or tertiary or quaternary structure. The originally highly folded protein may now stretch out and become a straight, fibrous protein; and a large collection of fibrous molecules may pile together like a log jam. Such piled-up molecules often cannot disperse freely in water, and in many cases fibrous proteins actually are water-insoluble.

Changes in the physical configuration of proteins as above are called *denaturation*. If the environmental effect is mild and of brief duration, denaturation may be temporary and the protein may subsequently revert to its original *native* state. But if the environmental effect is drastic and persisting, then denaturation becomes permanent and irreversible, and the protein will be *coagulated*. For example, the protein of egg white, albumen, is globular (and water-soluble) in the raw native state, but becomes fibrous (and water-insoluble) in the cooked, coagulated state (like boiled egg white). A biological property a protein may have in the native state usually is lost after denaturation. This is a major reason why undue heat, or virtually any undue environmental change, kills cells.

Because proteins thus may vary in as many as four aspects of structure, they differ considerably in this respect from carbohydrates or fats. Even a highly complex carbohydrate, for example, is the same whether we obtain it from mushrooms or mangoes, from mice or from men. A given lipid, similarly, is the same lipid regardless of where we find it. Not so for proteins, however; these compounds can, and do, vary so much that, as noted, no two organisms contain precisely the same types. Even twin organisms have slightly different proteins. The differences between proteins can be shown to be the greater the more unrelated two organisms are evolutionarily. We say that proteins have a high degree of *specificity:* the proteins of a given living unit have a unit-"specific" character; they are unique for that unit.

Protein specificity has major well-known consequences. For example, transfer of protein from one organism into the cells of another amounts to the introduction of foreign bodies, and disease may result. Thus, the proteins of plant pollen may produce allergy in animals such as mammals. Blood of one animal mixed with blood of another, if not of compatible type, may produce protein shock and death. Bacteria, partly because their proteins differ from those of other organisms, may produce many diseases if they infect given hosts. And portions of one animal, when grafted onto another animal, normally do not heal into place, because the two sets of proteins differ.

Proteins may be classified into *simple* and *conjugated* varieties. A simple protein consists entirely of amino acids, whereas a conjugated type consists of a simple protein fraction plus at least one other non-protein fraction. Each class may be subclassified further according to chemical and physical characteristics. For example, simple proteins include *albumins* and *globulins,* which are predominantly globular, and *scleroproteins,* which are predominantly fibrous. Among conjugated proteins, one may distinguish, for example, *lipoproteins* and *mucoproteins,* in which a protein fraction is joined to lipid or polysaccharide derivatives, respectively; *chromoproteins,* in which the nonprotein components are pigmented molecular units; *metalloproteins,* in which metal atoms are an integral part of protein structure; *nucleoproteins,* in which the simple protein components are histone and protamine mentioned above and the nonprotein components are nucleic acids (see below); and various other categories.

Both simple and conjugated proteins play a variety of roles in living cells. To some extent, normally far less so than carbohydrates or fats, proteins are used in cells as foodstuffs. But by virtue of their special characteristics, proteins serve primarily in two far more important cellular functions. First, they represent the vital construction materials out of which the basic framework of cells is built. Proteins form the essential molecular "scaffolding," as it were, around which the carbohydrates, fats, minerals, and other cellular components are organized. Far more so than these other constituents, the proteins include building "bricks" of the required size and diversity to make possible the construction of something so elaborate that it can have the properties of life. Indeed, structural differences among organisms, and differences among the parts within an organism, are due primarily to the differences in the protein building materials present. As might be expected, insoluble fibrous proteins are particularly well suited to serve as cellular scaffolding. Good examples of such *structural proteins* in cells are *myosin,* one of the characteristic proteins of muscle; *keratin,* the characteristic protein of hair and skin in mammals; and *collagen,* the fiber-forming protein produced by cells in bone, cartilage, tendons, and many other parts of many animals.

Second, proteins play crucial functional roles in cells. For example, among the conjugated proteins are many in which the protein fractions are physical *carriers* of the other, functionally important fractions. A good illustration is provided by *hemoglobin* of blood. In this chromoprotein, the protein portion is a globulin called *globin,* and it appears to be mainly a carrier vehicle for the nonprotein portion, the porphyrin pigment heme. The latter performs the principal function of hemoglobin, namely, ferrying oxygen throughout the animal. The analogously

iron-containing *cytochrome* porphyrins (see above) likewise belong to this category of chromoproteins. In conjugated proteins of all types, analogously, the nonprotein portion of the molecule performs some specific task in the cell whereas the protein usually serves as a carrier. In some cases the protein carrier may actually contribute more directly to a particular cell function.

Some of the conjugated types and, above all, very many of the simple proteins perform by far their most significant function in cells by serving as reaction-catalyzing *enzymes.* Life depends on enzymatic acceleration of reactions, and "living" therefore implies protein-dependency. Enzyme proteins share the chemical and physical characteristics of proteins generally. Thus, as proteins are specific, so enzymes are specific: by virtue of its particular structural attributes, including the presence of one (or more) segments in the polypeptide chain which may serve as active sites, a given enzyme can catalyze only one particular type of reaction (Fig. 6.22). Also, enzymes are just as sensitive to environmental influences as proteins generally. Hence, if denaturation of enzyme proteins alters or destroys the native configuration of the active sites, specific enzyme activities will be lost. Note that enzymes, and most *functional proteins* of cells generally, tend to have a globular tertiary structure.

Clearly then, both for structural and functional reasons, cellular life would be unimaginable without molecular agents such as proteins. On the other hand, even if we grant the presence of proteins and all the other cellular constituents already described, a cell cannot yet be alive; the molecular components discussed thus far only endow a cell with the potential of having a structure (proteins and other constituents),

6 · 22 *Four hydrolytic enzyme proteins (named at left) contain the indicated sequences of amino acid units near their active sites. In each case the active site is apparently associated specifically with serine (SER) and the two amino acid units at each side of it. GLY, glycine; MET, methionine; ASP, aspartic acid; PRO, proline; LEU, leucine; VAL, valine; PHE, phenyl alanine; GLU, glutamic acid; ALA, alanine; THR, threonine.*

CHYMOTRYPSIN:	MET–GLY–ASP–SER–GLY–GLY–PRO–LEU
TRYPSIN:	GLY–GLY–ASP–SER–GLY–PRO–VAL–ASP
CHOLINE ESTERASE:	PHE–GLY–GLU–SER–ALA–GLY–GLY
ALK. PHOSPHATASE:	VAL–THR–ASP–SER–ALA–ALA–SER

the potential of performing functions (enzymes), and the potential of possessing usable foods (carbohydrates and fats). The cell has not yet been equipped molecularly to make these potentials actual: *how* to use the foods, *what* actual structure to develop, and *which* functions to carry out. These all-important capacities emerge from the organic compounds to be dealt with next.

NUCLEOTIDES AND DERIVATIVES

A nucleotide is a molecular complex of three united subunits: an organic *phosphate* group, a *pentose* sugar, and a so-called *nitrogen base*.

Recall from Chap. 4 that organic phosphates may be represented as $-O-PO_3H_2$. For present purposes we shall symbolize the $-PO_3H_2$ portion here simply as P and write $-O-P$ for organic phosphate. The pentose sugar in a nucleotide is one of two kinds,

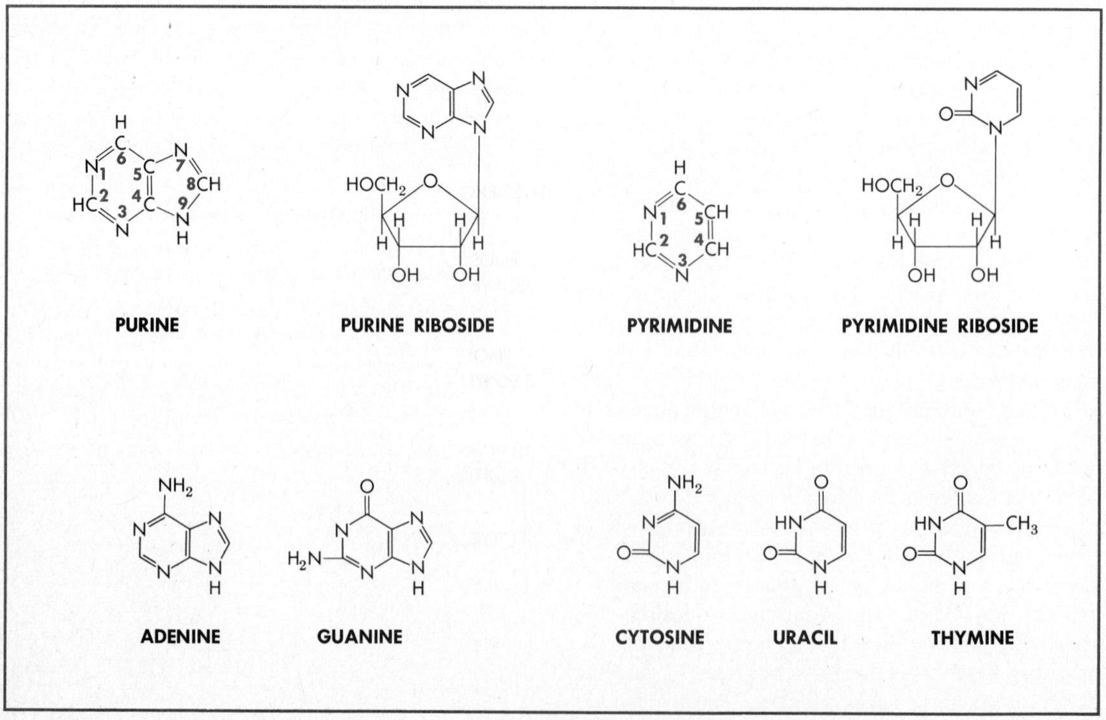

6 · 23   Purines, pyrimidines, and nucleosides. The principal specific purines and pyrimidines are shown in lower row. Any of these N bases can be joined to ribose to form a nucleoside. Thus, a purine riboside is a nucleoside composed of ribose (bottom part) and adenine or guanine (top part). Similarly, a pyrimidine riboside consists of a ribose fraction and one of the pyrimidines cytosine, uracil, or thymine.

namely, *ribose* or *deoxyribose* (Fig. 6.23). A nitrogen base is one of a series of ring compounds, the rings containing nitrogen as well as carbon. In *pyrimidines*, a single ring is present; a double ring characterizes *purines*. Pyrimidines include three variants of significance, namely, *thymine, cytosine,* and *uracil*. Among purines are two important types, namely, *adenine* and *guanine*.

If one nitrogen-base unit is joined with one pentose unit, the complex is referred to as a *nucleoside*. For example, an adenine-ribose combination forms a nucleoside called *adenosine* (see Fig. 6.23). If now a nucleoside is joined at the sugar end to a phosphate group, then such a complex forms a *nucleotide*. For example, the combination adenine—ribose—O—P is a nucleotide. It has at least three different but equivalent names: *adenosine monophosphate,* or AMP for short; or *adenylic acid;* or *adenine ribotide*. So far as is known, nucleotides in organisms occur in two distinct series, depending on whether the pentose component is ribose or deoxyribose. Each series includes mainly four specific kinds of nucleotides differing in their N-base components (Fig. 6.24). Note that uracil occurs only in the ribose series, thymine only in the deoxyribose series; adenine, guanine, and cytosine occur in both series.

Nucleotides are building blocks in larger molecular complexes serving three crucial functions in

PURINE   PURINE RIBOSIDE   PYRIMIDINE   PYRIMIDINE RIBOSIDE

ADENINE   GUANINE   CYTOSINE   URACIL   THYMINE cells: some are *energy carriers;* others are *coenzymes;* and still others are components of *genetic systems.*

ENERGY CARRIERS

Nucleotides have the property of being able to link up, at their phosphate ends, with one or two additional phosphate groups, in serial fashion. For example, if to adenosine monophosphate (AMP) is added one more organic phosphate, *adenosine diphosphate,* or ADP, is formed; and if a third phosphate is added to ADP, *adenosine triphosphate,* or ATP, results:

adenine—ribose—O—P	AMP
adenine—ribose—O—P—O~P	ADP
adenine—ribose—O—P—O~P—O~P	ATP

The wavy symbol in the —O~P links signifies the presence of a *high-energy bond,* already discussed in Chap. 4. Recall that formation of such bonds results from resonance restriction and requires inputs of particularly large amounts of energy. The bonds also release correspondingly large amounts of energy when they are broken. Thus, to convert AMP to ADP and ADP to ATP requires not only additional phosphate groups but also large energy inputs. Energy is derived in cells from respiratory fuels, and respiration actually functions primarily to create high-energy bonds in ATP. This latter compound may be said to be the significant energy-rich endproduct of respiration. ATP subsequently supplies all parts of a cell with energy usable in other activities: ATP is split again to ADP and —O—P, and in this breaking of high-energy phosphate bonds large packets of energy become available to a cell (Fig. 6.25).

We shall examine these processes in detail in Chap. 18, but we may note here that ATP is evidently an *energy carrier.* Indeed, it happens to be the most abundant and most universal of such carriers. Others, playing a more limited energy-carrying role, are derivatives of some of the other nucleotides, for example, as outlined in Fig. 6.25, guanosine di- and triphosphates (GDP, GTP), uridine di- and triphosphates (UDP, UTP), cytidine di- and triphosphates (CDP, CTP), and thymidine di- and triphosphates (TDP, TTP).

COENZYMES

A coenzyme is a particular kind of cofactor, that is, a carrier molecule functioning in conjunction with a

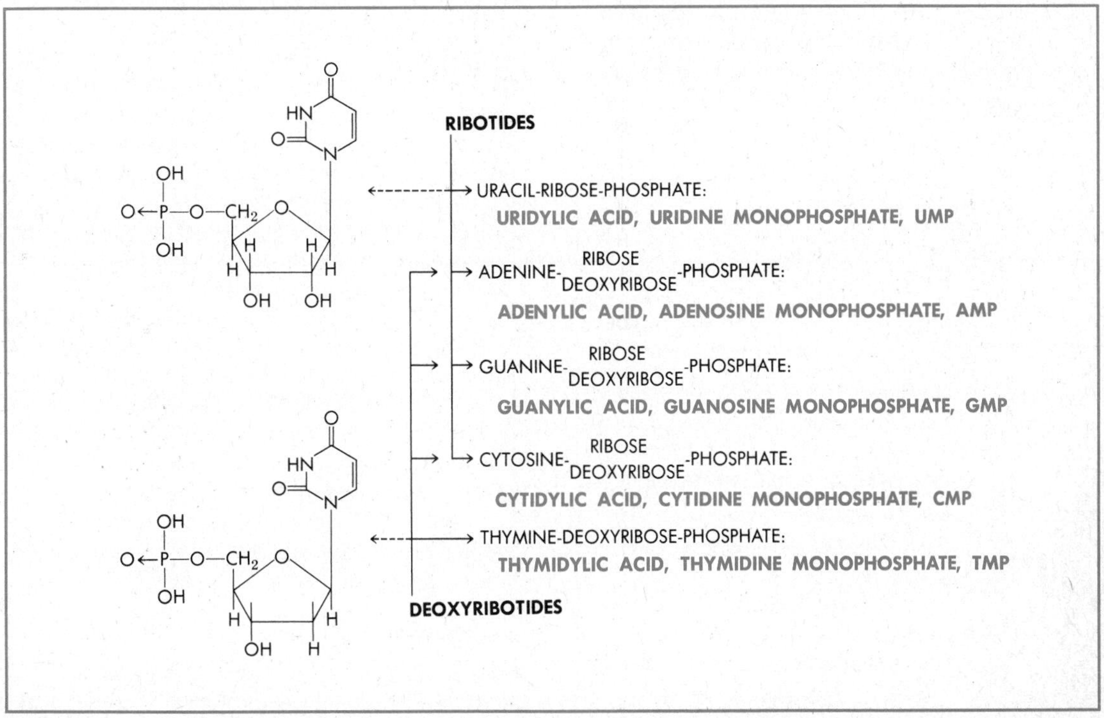

***6 · 24 Nucleotides** are formed when nucleosides are combined with phosphate groups* (—O—PO_3H_2, *in exchange for the* —O—H *in position 5 of the pentose sugar). Two nucleotide series are of importance, ribotides and deoxyribotides, each with four members. The structures of the ribotide* UMP *and the deoxyribotide* TMP *are depicted at left.*

particular enzyme. It happens often in cellular processes that a group of atoms is removed from one compound and is transferred to another. In such cases a specific enzyme catalyzes the removal, but a specific coenzyme must also be present to carry out the transfer. The coenzyme temporarily joins to, or accepts, the removed group of atoms and may subsequently "hand" it off to another acceptor compound. The majority of coenzymes happen to be chemical derivatives of nucleotides (Fig. 6.26).

More specifically, in most coenzymes the nitrogen-base portion of nucleotides is substituted by another chemical unit. This unit itself is usually a derivative of a particular vitamin. For example, one of the B vitamins is riboflavin (B_2). This is a compound consisting of a ribose portion and, attached to it, a *flavin* portion, the latter being a complex triple-ring structure. In cells, a phosphate group becomes linked to riboflavin, resulting in a nucleotidelike complex

$$\text{flavin—ribose—O—P}$$

This compound is known as *flavin mononucleotide*, or FMN for short. If now FMN joins to AMP, a dinucleotide is formed:

$$\text{flavin—ribose—O—P—O—P—O—ribose—adenine}$$

This combination is known as *flavin-adenine-dinucleo-*

6 · 25 ATP *produced during respiration is used subsequently to supply the energy necessary for all cellular activities* (top). *The nucleotide derivatives shown at bottom occasionally play energy-carrying roles in cells. The high-energy bonds in such cases are* O~P *bonds as in ATP.*

tide, or FAD. Both FMN and FAD function as coenzymes in cells. Their specific role is to serve as hydrogen carriers in many processes in which hydrogen is transferred from one compound to another. Being a light gas, hydrogen probably would not transfer properly by itself. The presence of carriers such as FMN and FAD thus becomes highly advantageous. In these coenzymes it is the flavin portion of the molecule that provides the specific place for temporary hydrogen attachment (see Fig. 6.26).

Two other hydrogen-carrying coenzymes are constructed from derivatives of *nicotinic acid* (or *niacin*), another B vitamin. A molecule of niacin possesses a so-called *pyridine* ring, and a derivative of such a ring (*nicotinic amide*) participates in the formation of the following complexes:

$$\begin{array}{cc} \text{nicotinamide} & \text{adenine} \\ | & | \\ \text{ribose—O—P—O—P—O—ribose} \end{array}$$

$$\begin{array}{cc} \text{nicotinamide} & \text{adenine} \\ | & | \\ \text{ribose—O—P—O—P—O—ribose—O—P} \end{array}$$

The first has been referred to as *diphosphopyridine nucleotide* (DPN), but is today more commonly known as *nicotinamide-adenine-dinucleotide,* or NAD for short. The second can be referred to as *triphosphopyridine nucleotide* (TPN), but its more common name today is *nicotinamide-adenine-dinucleotide-phosphate,* NADP for short. In both, it is the pyridine (nicotinamide) part of the molecule that serves specifically as the H carrier (see Fig. 6.26).

One of the coenzymes carrying not hydrogen but another specific group of atoms is *coenzyme A,* or CoA. A molecule of this compound consists of three parts, namely, a phosphate derivative of ADP, a B vitamin known as *pantothenic acid,* and a chain of nitrogen, carbon, and sulfur atoms to which hydrogen is attached (see Fig. 6.26). CoA serves as a carrier of a molecular group called *acetyl,* a two-carbon combination of importance in respiration and synthesis. An acetyl group becomes attached to the sulfur end of CoA, and the product, *acetyl CoA,* is held together by an —S~C— bond. Recall that, like the —O~P bond, the —S~C— bond too is a high-energy bond. Thus, CoA may be considered to be both an acetyl carrier and an energy carrier.

Several coenzymes that are not nucleotide derivatives will be encountered in later contexts.

GENETIC SYSTEMS

If any single entity could qualify as "the secret of life," that entity would unquestionably have to be the

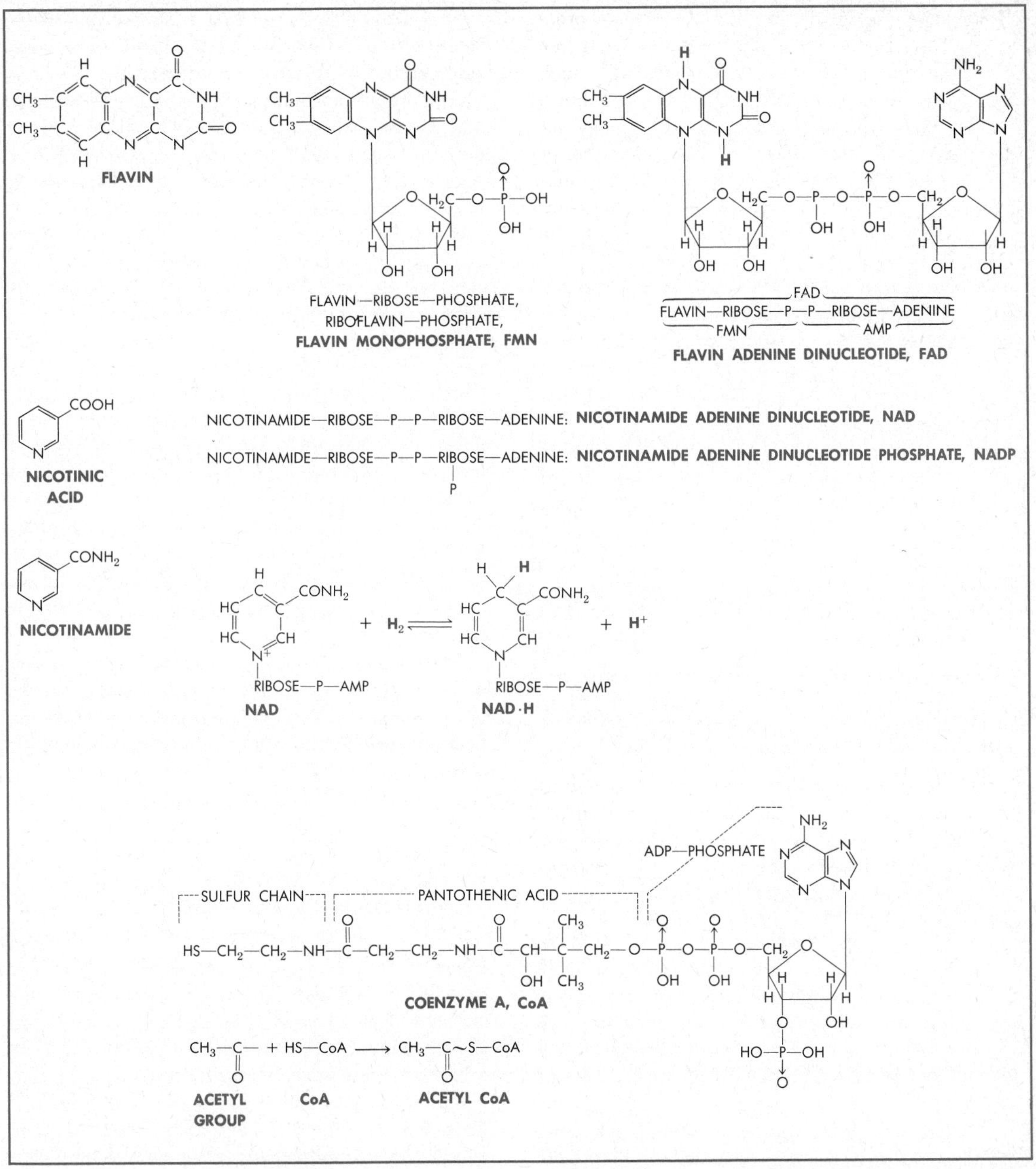

FLAVIN

FLAVIN—RIBOSE—PHOSPHATE,
RIBOFLAVIN—PHOSPHATE,
FLAVIN MONOPHOSPHATE, FMN

FAD
FLAVIN—RIBOSE—P—P—RIBOSE—ADENINE
FMN   AMP
FLAVIN ADENINE DINUCLEOTIDE, FAD

NICOTINIC ACID

NICOTINAMIDE—RIBOSE—P—P—RIBOSE—ADENINE: **NICOTINAMIDE ADENINE DINUCLEOTIDE, NAD**

NICOTINAMIDE—RIBOSE—P—P—RIBOSE—ADENINE: **NICOTINAMIDE ADENINE DINUCLEOTIDE PHOSPHATE, NADP**
                              P

NICOTINAMIDE

NAD   **NAD·H**

COENZYME A, CoA

$CH_3-\underset{O}{\overset{}{C}}- \;+\; HS-CoA \longrightarrow CH_3-\underset{O}{\overset{}{C}}\sim S-CoA$

ACETYL GROUP   **CoA**   **ACETYL CoA**

6 · 26 Coenzymes. *Among the flavin derivatives, flavin joined to ribose is riboflavin, and the latter joined to phosphate becomes FMN. This coenzyme joined to AMP as shown yields FAD. The places where FAD carries hydrogen are indicated by colored H atoms. FMN carries H at corresponding locations. Among the pyridine derivatives, similarly, the H-carrying locations in NAD are shown by colored H atoms; NADP functions analogously as H carrier. The structural components of coenzyme A are indicated above, as is the way in which this substance functions in carrying an acetyl group. Note the high-energy —C~S— bond in acetyl CoA.*

6 · 27 *The Watson-Crick model of* **DNA** *structure* (top). *P, phosphate; D, deoxyribose; A, T, G, C, purines and pyrimidines. A P—D—A unit represents one of the nucleotides. In this —P —D—P—D— double chain, four kinds of purine-pyrimidine pairs are possible, namely, A · T, T · A, G · C, and C · G. Each of the four may occur very many times, and the sequence of the pairs may vary in unlimited fashion. Bottom, the hydrogen bonding between T · A and C · G pairs* (colored broken lines).

nucleic acids. To be sure, inasmuch as we can actually make such an identification today, it is really no longer possible to speak of any "secret." Nucleic acids are *polynucleotides,* extended chainlike polymers of up to thousands of nucleotide units. Nucleic acids thus are macromolecules (and it is because of this, as we shall see, that proteins themselves are macromolecules).

Nucleic acids are of two types, according to whether the nucleotides composing them are of the ribose series or the deoxyribose series. A polymer consisting of ribose nucleotides is called a *ribose nucleic acid,* or RNA for short; and a polymer of deoxyribotides is a *deoxyribose nucleic acid,* DNA for short. In either type, nucleotide units are linked so that the sugar component of one unit bonds to the phosphate component of the next. If we symbolize nitrogen bases as *N,* sugars as S, and phosphates as *P,* we may write, for a combination of four nucleotides,

$$-P-S-P-S-P-S-P-S-$$
$$\quad\;\; N \quad\;\; N \quad\;\; N \quad\;\; N$$

In other words, the sugar and phosphate components form an extended molecular thread from which nitrogen bases project as side chains.

In the case of RNA, the particular types, numbers, and sequences of the four possible kinds of nucleotide units can vary in an infinite variety of ways. A given segment of a long RNA molecule might, for example, read as follows

$$-P-R-P-R-P-R-P-R-P-R-$$
$$\quad\;\; A \quad\;\; U \quad\;\; G \quad\;\; G \quad\;\; C$$

where *R* stands for ribose and *A, U, G, C,* for adenine, uracil, guanine, and cytosine, respectively. Evidently, RNA molecules differ according to their different N-base sequences—and that, as we shall see, is the key to their importance. The four possible N bases may be regarded as a four-letter "alphabet" out of which, just as with amino acids in proteins, any number of "sentences" may be constructed. Indeed, we shall find that the protein sentences precisely match and are in fact determined by the RNA sentences.

Carrying this analogy one step further, we may say that the original "author" of the sentences is not RNA itself, but DNA. This type of nucleic acid appears to be a long *double* chain of polynucleotides:

$$-P-D-P-D-P-D-P-D-$$
$$\quad\;\; N \quad\;\; N \quad\;\; N \quad\;\; N$$
$$\quad\;\; N \quad\;\; N \quad\;\; N \quad\;\; N$$
$$-P-D-P-D-P-D-P-D-$$

D here stands for deoxyribose, and *N* and *P* for nitrogen base and phosphate, respectively, as before. N bases are held together pairwise by hydrogen bonds, which thus maintain the double-stranded structure of DNA. Moreover, there are only four different ways in which N bases may be paired, as outlined in Fig. 6.27. Note that *adenine is always paired with thymine, guanine always with cytosine.* The chemical properties of these purines and pyrimidines, and the space available between the parallel —P—D— chains, are such that only combinations shown in Fig. 6.27 can be formed.

But there is apparently no limit to the number of times each of these combinations can occur in a long double chain. Nor, apparently, are there restrictions as to their sequence. Thus *A·T, T·A, G·C,* and *C·G* may again be regarded as an alphabet of four symbols, and sentences of any length may be constructed by using these symbols as often as desired and in any order. Evidently, the possible number of compositionally different DNA's is practically un-limited.

A final structural characteristic of DNA is that its double chain is not straight but spiraled into a helix (Fig. 6.28). The DNA structure as outlined here is designated as the *Watson-Crick model,* after the investigators who proposed it.

Functionally, DNA exhibits three properties which make it the universal key to life. First, as will be shown in greater detail in Chap. 20, the specific sequence of nitrogen-base pairs in DNA represents *coded information,* which provides the cell with instructions on how to manufacture specific proteins. These coded instructions first are "transcribed" into matching nitrogen-base sequences within RNA, and the instructions in such RNA subsequently are translated into particular sequences of amino acid units within polypeptide chains and proteins. By so controlling protein manufacture, DNA ultimately controls the entire structural and functional makeup of every cell.

Second, under appropriate conditions (such as actually exist within cells), DNA has the property of being *self-replicating* or self-duplicating; DNA is a *reproducing* molecule. That a mere chemical should be able to multiply itself may perhaps be astounding, but this is nevertheless a known, unique property of DNA. Without doubt, this property is a direct result of the atomic complexity and the specific organization of the molecule. The reproduction of DNA is at the root of all reproduction—cellular, organismic, species, as well as communal; in a fundamental sense even the reproduction of a whole organism is, after all, a reproduction of "chemicals." Through its reproduction, moreover, DNA is also the key to *heredity.*

Third, DNA has the property of being *mutable,* that is, under certain conditions a given sequence of nitrogen-base pairs may become altered slightly. Such alterations then are stable and persist into succeeding molecular generations of DNA. As the coded information of DNA becomes changed, however, the structural and functional traits of a cell become changed correspondingly. Through changes in its cells a whole organism and its progeny may thus become changed in the course of successive generations; and this is equivalent to *evolution.*

In short, DNA is the material which forms *genes,* the ultimate controllers of all living operations, short-range or long-range. Together with RNA, DNA represents the substance of the *genetic systems* which direct metabolism and self-perpetuation and so are the basis of life. In Chap. 20 we shall examine *how*

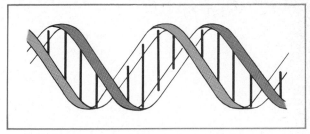

6 · 28 **DNA** *double chain is spiraled as shown. The two spirals symbolize the* —P—D—P—D— *chains, and the connections between the spirals represent the purine-pyrimidine pairs.*

the structure of the nucleic acids actually permits genes to function in such crucial ways.

Carbohydrates, lipids, proteins, and nitrogen-base derivatives such as nucleic acids and nucleotide phosphates form the organic bulk of living matter. However, hundreds of other kinds of organic substances exist in cells. Although such substances are often present in only very small quantities, they may nevertheless be of extreme importance in the maintenance of life. Some of these constituents are not related chemically to the four main categories above. Others are derivatives of one of the four groups, and still others are combinations of two or more of the basic four.

Thus, although the listing of special cellular compounds could be extended enormously, a general principle may be glimpsed nevertheless: virtually the whole vast array of organic constituents in cells is related to or derived from only a half dozen or so fundamental types of compounds; and among these, the principal types are sugars, fatty acids, amino acids, and nucleotides. Nature apparently builds with but a limited number of fundamental construction units, yet the possible combinations and variations among these units are practically unlimited.

It should also be kept in mind that these diverse constituents of a cell are not "just there," randomly dissolved or suspended in water like the ingredients of a soup. Instead, as already emphasized earlier, the constituents must be organized if they are to form something living. This consideration leads us from the primarily chemical and physical attributes of living material, discussed throughout the chapters of this part, to the primarily biological ones, examined in the following part.

REVIEW QUESTIONS

1. What kinds of inorganic materials are present in cells and in what general proportions? What are the main classes of organic materials? What defines an organic compound as a carbohydrate? A lipid? A protein? A nucleic acid?

2. What are aldoses, ketoses, pentoses, hexoses? How are structural isomers distinguished? Write out the D- and L- configurations of several specific aldoses and ketoses. What is a pyranose? Write out several ways in which the structure of glucose may be depicted. What are anomers? Give examples.

3. Give examples of glycosides in monosaccharide, disaccharide, and polysaccharide forms. Distinguish between 1,4- and 1,6-glycosidic linkages, and give specific examples of 1,4-α, 1,4-β, and 1,6-α links. Show the structural difference between ribose and deoxyribose.

4. What are amino sugars? Give examples. What kinds of sugar acids are known? Again give specific examples. What is the composition of starch? What are sugar alcohols?

5. Review the composition and structure of fatty acids. Distinguish between saturated and unsaturated kinds, and give examples. Show how the hydrophilic and hydrophobic properties of fatty acids account for the cleaning action of soap.

6. What are triglycerides? Phospholipids? Give examples of each. How is a fat formed? What is an ester? Review the structure of waxes and of carotenoids. What are steroids? Give specific examples. Describe the structure of tetrapyrrols and again give examples.

7. Describe the structure of an amino acid, distinguish between L- and D- forms, and explain the amphoteric nature of these acids. What is the isoelectric point? What are the properties of amino acids at that point and at different pH levels?

8. Write out the formation of a peptide bond. Show how different amino acids differ structurally. What is a polypeptide chain? An α-helix? What are the properties of such a helix and how is it held together? How is the behavior of proteins correlated with the isoelectric point and the pH of the medium? What is electrophoresis?

9. What is the primary, secondary, tertiary, and quaternary structure of a protein, and what kinds of bonds produce such structures? How is a coagulated protein different from a native or a denatured protein? What are fibrous and globular proteins?

10. How are proteins classified? Give specific examples. What is protein specificity and what is it due to? Review the biological roles of proteins. Describe the structure of an active site in an enzyme.

11. Distinguish between nitrogen bases, nucleosides, nucleotides, ribotides, and deoxyribotides. Give examples of each. What are adenosine phosphates? Which nucleotides form coenzymes? Review the structure and function of such coenzymes.

12. What is the chemical composition and molecular structure of nucleic acids? In chemical terms, what are DNA and RNA? How are nucleotides related to DNA and RNA? What different kinds of nucleotides occur in nucleic acids? What are the general functions of such acids?

COLLATERAL READINGS

Baker, J. J. W., and G. E. Allen: "Matter, Energy, and Life," Addison-Wesley, Reading, Mass., 1965. This paperback contains good general discussions of all classes of cellular constituents. Recommended for further reading.

Fieser, L., and M. Fieser: "Organic Chemistry," 3d ed., Reinhold, New York, 1956. A good basic text on the topics of this chapter.

White, A., P. Handler, and E. L. Smith: "Principles of Biochemistry," 3d ed., McGraw-Hill, New York, 1964. The first part of this large volume contains comprehensive but not too difficult chapters on carbohydrates, lipids, proteins, and nucleic acids.

The following articles in *Scientific American* all are popularly written, and they deal with particular cell constituents or processes identified in the titles:

Buswell, A. M., and W. H. Rodebush: Water, Apr., 1956.

Crick, F. H. C.: Nucleic Acids, Sept., 1957.

Doty, P.: Proteins, Sept., 1957.

Fieser, L. F.: Steroids, Jan., 1955.

Frank, S.: Carotenoids, Jan., 1956.

Fruton, J. S.: Proteins, June, 1950.

Gray, G. W.: Electrophoresis, Dec., 1951.

Gross, J.: Collagen, May, 1961.

Kramen, M. D.: A Universal Molecule of Living Matter: The Tetrapyrrol Ring, Aug., 1958.

Kendrew, J. C.: The 3-dimensional Structure of a Protein Molecule, Dec., 1961.

Nord, F. F., and W. J. Schubert: Lignin, Oct., 1958.

Pauling, L., R. B. Corey, and R. Hayward: The Structure of Protein Molecules, July, 1954.

Perutz, M. F.: The Hemoglobin Molecule, Nov., 1964.

Preston, R. D.: Cellulose, Sept., 1957.

Schmitt, F. O.: Giant Molecules in Cells and Tissues, Sept., 1957.

Stein, W. H., and S. Moore: The Chemical Structure of Proteins, Feb., 1961.

Thompson, E. O. P.: The Insulin Molecule, May, 1955.

PART THREE
THE LEVELS OF LIFE
CHAPTER 7
CELL AND ORGANISM
CHAPTER 8
SPECIES AND POPULATION
CHAPTER 9
ECOSYSTEM AND COMMUNITY
CHAPTER 10
BIOSPHERE AND HABITAT

In this part we examine the structure of the living hierarchy in some detail. Our first concern is the basic unit of the hierarchy, namely, the *cell*, the smallest complex of substances capable of carrying out all the metabolic and self-perpetuative functions by which we define "living." How are cells organized—what kinds of organelles are common to all of them, and what kinds occur specifically in particular cell types only? Moreover, which kinds of the chemicals encountered in the preceding part are found in which organelles of a cell, and which parts of the cell actually perform the various life-maintaining metabolic and self-perpetuative processes?

Cells can form organisms singly, but they are also constituents of multicellular organisms. In these, we already know, the main structural levels are the tissue, the organ, and the organ system. We must inquire here just how each of these levels is constructed out of components of the preceding level, and again how metabolic and self-perpetuative functions are performed on these levels. Further, organisms of all kinds are themselves structural and functional units of still higher living levels, namely, the population and species, the community and supercommunity. Groups of this kind live in, and indeed are greatly influenced by, the geographic localities that serve as their *habitats*, or homes. These most inclusive levels thus encompass all living matter on earth as well as the total physical environment of the globe. Their organization constitutes the final topic in this series of chapters.

CHAPTER 7
CELL AND ORGANISM

The generalization that all organisms consist of cells and cell products is known as the *cell theory*. Principal credit for its formulation is usually given to the German biologists Schleiden and Schwann, whose work was published in 1838. But the French biologist Dutrochet had made substantially the same generalization as early as 1824. The cell theory rapidly became one of the fundamental cornerstones of modern biology and, with minor qualifications, it still has that status today.

Cells came to be recognized early as the "atomic" units of living matter, structurally as well as functionally. In 1831, the English biologist Robert Brown discovered the presence of nuclei within cells, and in 1839 the Bohemian biologist Purkinje coined the general term *protoplasm* for the living substance out of which cells are made. Virchow in 1855 concluded that *"omnis cellula e cellula"*—new living cells can arise only by reproduction of preexisting living cells. This important recognition of the continuity of life, and thus of the direct derivation of all cells from ancient cellular ancestors, introduced the notion of history into the study of cells. Ever since, such studies have revolved around three interrelated problems, namely, cell *structure*, cell *function*, and short- and long-range cell *development*. The first of these concerns us here particularly.

CELLS

GENERAL STRUCTURE

Examination of living or killed cells under various kinds of microscopes shows that cell sizes vary considerably, ranging in diameter from about 2μ to as much as several millimeters and more. However, the order of size of the vast majority of cells is remarkably uniform; a diameter of 5 to 15 μ is fairly characteristic of cells generally. We surmise that, notwithstanding the exceptions, cells can be neither much smaller nor much larger than a certain norm. Too small a size presumably would not provide enough room to accommodate the necessary parts, and too large a size would increase the maintenance problem and at the same time reduce the efficiency of compact operation. Note here that as a cell increases in size, its surface enlarges as the *square* of its radius, and that the available surface area determines the amount of nutrient uptake and waste elimination possible. However, cell volume increases with the *cube* of its radius, and the volume determines how much cellular mass must be kept alive. Hence if a cell enlarges unduly, its mass would soon outrun the food-procuring capacity of its surface, and cell growth then would have to cease. The size limits of cells actually are such that available surfaces can adequately service the living volumes they delimit.

The two fundamental subdivisions of most cells are the *nucleus* and the living substance surrounding the nucleus, called the *cytoplasm*. The nucleus is bounded by a *nuclear membrane*, the cytoplasm by a *cell membrane*, also called *plasma membrane*. Surrounding the cell membrane in many cases is a *cell wall* (see Color Plate I, 2).

Most cells usually contain a single nucleus each, but there are many exceptions. For example, bacteria and blue-green algae, that is, organisms constituting the taxonomic category Monera (see Chap. 2), do not contain structurally defined nuclei at all. Analogously, we shall encounter several cell types among plants which, in the mature state, are without nuclei. Mature mammalian red blood cells are likewise without nuclei (and are therefore referred to as "corpuscles" rather than as complete "cells"). Conversely, given cells of various organisms often contain more than one nucleus. A *binucleate* or *multinucleate* condition of this sort is particularly common among the cells of many Protista but is encountered also with some frequency in the Metaphyta and Metazoa.

There are exceptions too concerning the individ-

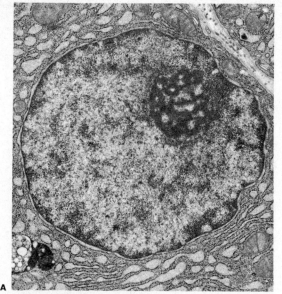

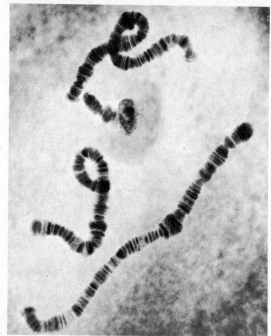

B, courtesy of Drs. D. F. Poulson and C. W. Metz, from Fig. 1, J. Morph, vol. 63, p. 366, 1938.

7 · 1 *A, electron micrograph of a cell nucleus. The whole round structure covering most of the photo is the nucleus; cytoplasm is outside it. Note the nuclear bounding membrane. Within the nucleus, the large dark patch is a nucleolus and the dark speckle elsewhere is the gene-containing chromatin (×16,000). B, a stained preparation of insect chromosomes. Note the characteristic crossbands, found in all chromosomes studied (×2,600). See also Fig. 30.29.*

uality of cells, normally maintained by the cell membrane. In certain cases, for example, in latex-forming cells of rubber trees and in the embryos of many animals, cell membranes at first form boundaries between individual cells. But at a later stage of development these boundaries dissolve, the result being a fused, continuous living mass with nuclei dispersed through it. Such a structure, in which cellular individuality has been lost, is called a *co-enocyte* in plants and a *syncytium* in animals.

Despite variations in the number of nuclei or the occasional loss of the structural discreteness of cells, the fundamentally cellular character of living matter is undeniable even in such exceptional cases. And in all other cases the cellular character is unequivocal, for there we deal with distinct bits of living matter, each bounded by a plasma membrane (and often a cell wall) and containing one nucleus.

NUCLEUS AND CYTOPLASM

A nucleus typically consists of three kinds of components: the more or less gellike nuclear sap, or *nucleoplasm*, in which are suspended the *chromosomes*, and one or more *nucleoli* (Fig. 7.1).

Chromosomes are the principal nuclear structures. Indeed, a nucleus as a whole may be regarded primarily as a protective housing for these slender, threadlike organelles. Chemically, chromosomes consist largely of protein (histones and protamines) and of nucleic acids, both kinds of components joined together as conjugated *nucleoproteins*. DNA is the principal nucleic acid of the nucleoproteins, but RNA is also present. Functionally, chromosomes are the carriers of the genes which, as noted in previous contexts, are the ultimate controllers of cellular processes. Particular cell types may not contain formed nuclei, as we have seen, and thus they may not contain formed chromosomes; but all cell types contain genes.

Chromosomes are conspicuous only during cell reproduction, when they become thickly coated with additional nucleoprotein. At other times such coats are absent, and chromosomes then are very fine filaments not easily identifiable within the nuclear sap. The exact number of chromosomes within each cell nucleus is an important species-specific trait. For example, cells of human beings contain 46 chromosomes each. Analogously, the cells of every other type of organism have their own characteristic chromosome number. A cell rarely contains more than in the order of 100 chromosomes. Therefore, since there are at least 2 million different species of organisms, many species share the same chromosome number. To be sure, possession of the same number

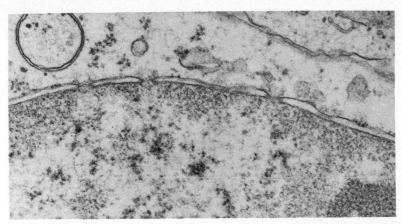

of chromosomes does not mean possession of the same kinds.

A nucleolus ("little nucleus") is a spherical body also consisting largely of nucleoprotein. But the only type of nucleic acid present here is RNA. As we shall see in a later chapter, nucleoli are derivatives of chromosomes, and they appear to play an important role in the control of protein synthesis within cells. Given cell types contain a fixed number of nucleoli per nucleus.

The whole nucleus is separated from the surrounding cytoplasm by the nuclear membrane. This structure, like most other living membranes, is constructed mainly of proteins and lipids. It governs the vital traffic of materials between cytoplasm and nucleus. Examination with the electron microscope shows that the nuclear membrane is actually a double layer pierced by tiny pores (Fig. 7.2).

If the nucleus, by virtue of its genes, is the control center of cellular activities, then the cytoplasm is the executive center in which the directives of the nucleus are carried out. But it should be emphasized at once that such a functional distinction between nucleus and cytoplasm must not be taken too rigorously. Although the nucleus primarily controls, it also executes many directives of the cytoplasm; and although the cytoplasm primarily executes, it also influences many nuclear processes. A vital reciprocal interdependence binds nucleus and cytoplasm, and experiment has repeatedly shown that one cannot long survive without the other. For example, amoebae can readily be cut into halves, so that one half is with nucleus, the other without. A nucleated half then carries on in every respect like a normal amoeba, but a nonnucleated half invariably dies. An amoeba without nucleus may persist for as long as a month and at first it may even move and feed. However, it never grows, it never reproduces,

and soon it cannot digest or metabolize food. Yet just as survival of the cytoplasm depends on the nucleus, so does survival of the nucleus depend on the cytoplasm; a naked isolated nucleus dies sooner or later. Inasmuch as the cytoplasm is the site of food management, respiration, and synthesis, a nucleus freed of cytoplasm undoubtedly succumbs from lack of energy and raw materials. Cellular life must therefore be viewed against a background of cyclical interactions between nucleus and cytoplasm.

Cytoplasm consists of a semifluid *ground substance,* which is in a sol or a gel state at different times and in different cellular regions, and in which are suspended large numbers of several kinds of organelles. Such organelles may be shaped into films, granules, rodlets, filaments, or droplets. Each of these may have various sizes and chemical compositions and may have a variety of functions. Particular cell types often possess unique organelles not found elsewhere. The following organelles are widespread among many or all cell types.

Endoplasmic reticulum. Also known as *ergastoplasm,* this structure is demonstrable under the electron microscope and is present in probably all but the moneran cells (Fig. 7.3). Composed largely of lipoproteins, the endoplasmic reticulum is a network of exceedingly fine double membranes that traverses all regions of the cytoplasm and that in many cases also passes from a given cell into adjacent ones. The double membranes extend from plasma membrane to nuclear membrane, with which they are continuous,

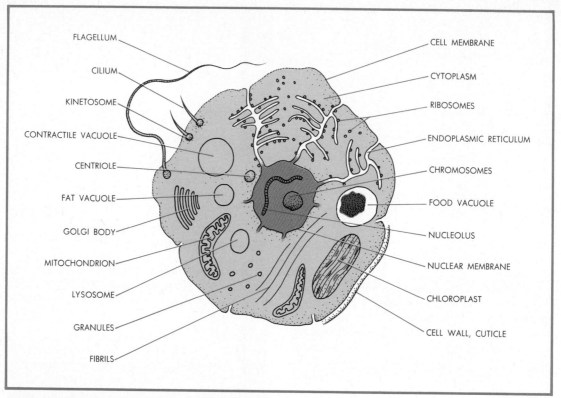

FLAGELLUM — CELL MEMBRANE
CILIUM — CYTOPLASM
KINETOSOME — RIBOSOMES
CONTRACTILE VACUOLE — ENDOPLASMIC RETICULUM
CENTRIOLE — CHROMOSOMES
FAT VACUOLE — FOOD VACUOLE
GOLGI BODY — NUCLEOLUS
MITOCHONDRION — NUCLEAR MEMBRANE
LYSOSOME — CHLOROPLAST
GRANULES — CELL WALL, CUTICLE
FIBRILS

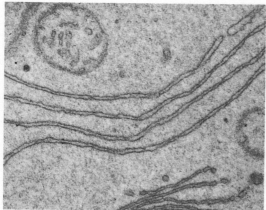

7 · 3 *Diagram: some of the principal cellular organelles. Any single actual cell does not contain all the structures shown in this composite drawing. For clarity and simplicity, most components are shown in only part of the cell. Thus the endoplasmic reticulum, for example, occurs not only where indicated but throughout the cytoplasm. Photo: electron micrograph of portions of the endoplasmic reticulum. The latter consists of an array of double membranes. A cross section through a mitochondrion is seen above the reticulum and a portion of a Golgi body below it. (×60,000)*

and attached to them are many of the other types of organelles present in cytoplasm. The membrane network appears to function broadly in two ways. First, it may serve as a system of traffic pathways and conducting channels. Materials in transit from one cellular region to another, or from cell to exterior and the reverse, may migrate along the narrow spaces within the double membranes. Second, by interconnecting other organelles, the endoplasmic reticulum forms an extensive cytoplasmic scaffolding, an ultrastructural framework that keeps the nonfluid components of cytoplasm in particular relative positions. The membranes may form, dissolve, and re-form rapidly, and in different regions such changes apparently take place often in conjunction with the frequent shifts of position and streaming movements of the cell contents. Thus, even though the cell as a whole is readily deformable and the interior contents flow and intermix unceasingly, the endoplasmic reticulum nevertheless keeps other organelles properly stationed and distributed in relation to one another. Evidently, little is really "loose" in a cell, and an orderly interior organization persists. Such a structural order actually is quite essential if cellular functions are to remain integrated.

Mitochondria. Found in all but the moneran cells,

these organelles too are constructed predominantly out of lipids and proteins. Small amounts of DNA and RNA are known to be present as well. The principal functional constituents of mitochondria are respiratory enzymes and coenzymes, that is, the compounds required in energy-liberating reactions. Mitochondria are the chief chemical "factories" in which cellular respiration is carried out. Under the light microscope, mitochondria appear as short rods or thin filaments averaging 0.5 to 2 μ in length. The electron microscope shows that the surface of a mitochondrion consists of two fine membranes (Fig. 7.4). The inner one is greatly folded, the folds projecting into the interior of the mitochondrion. These folds, known as *mitochondrial cristae*, bear numerous tiny stalked microgranules. The latter are probably the specific locations where respiratory reactions take place (see also Chap. 18).

Ribosomes. Present universally in all cells, these organelles are exceedingly tiny granules visible under the electron microscope (Fig. 7.5). Many of them are usually attached to the endoplasmic reticulum, others lie free in the cytoplasm. Ribosomes contain RNA (hence the "ribo-" portion of their name) and the enzymes required in the manufacture of proteins; ribosomes (probably functioning in groups as *polyribosomes*) appear to be the principal "factories" where protein synthesis is carried out (see also Chap. 20).

Golgi bodies. Depending partly on the way in which cells are prepared for microscopic study, Golgi bodies, often also called *lipochondria*, appear variously as complexes of droplets or as stacks of thin platelike layers or as mixtures of these and other configurations (Fig. 7.6). These organelles apparently function in the manufacture of cellular secretion products, for Golgi bodies are particularly conspicuous in actively secreting cells. For example, whenever gland cells are producing their characteristic secretions, the Golgi bodies of such cells become very prominent.

Lysosomes. Known to occur in various animal cell types and possibly present in the cells of all organisms, such organelles appear under the electron microscope as tiny membrane-bounded sacs or vesicles (see Fig. 7.3). These vesicles contain high concentrations of digestive (hydrolytic) enzymes which, when the vesicles burst open, are released into the free cytoplasm. Lysosomes thus probably play a role in various normal decomposition processes taking place in a cell; for example, chemical breakdown of previously stored or presently incoming nutrients prior to their utilization, breakdown of formed structural cell parts prior to their reconstruction or remodeling during growth or repair, breakdown of

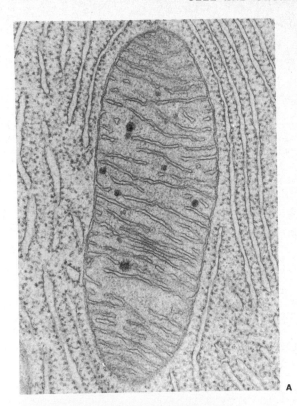

A

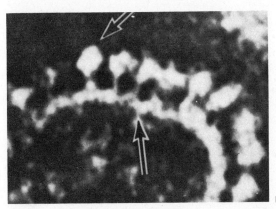

B

7·4 A, electron-micrographic section through a mitochondrion (of a mammalian pancreatic cell). Note the double-layered exterior boundary and, in places along it, the infolding of the inner boundary membrane, forming the internal partitions called cristae. The dark spots in the interior of the mitochondrion are calcium-rich granules ($\times 45,000$). B, highly enlarged portion of a mitochondral crista (in beef heart muscle), showing array of stalked particles attached to the cristal membrane. Arrows point to head piece and base piece of such a particle. Particles of this kind may contain the actual enzymatic apparatus for respiratory reactions ($\times 700,000$).

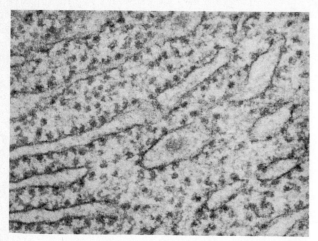

7 · 5 *Electron micrograph of ribosomes (of a mammalian pancreatic cell). The ribosomes are the small dark granules. The double-layered membranes also visible here are portions of the endoplasmic reticulum, illustrated also in Fig. 7.4 (×90,000).*

extraneous foreign particles which happen to enter a cell accidentally, and the like. It is known also that simultaneous disruption of many or all lysosomes of a cell brings about rapid dissolution and death of that cell. Conceivably, therefore, lysosomes may be associated with normal turnover processes on the tissue level, that is, replacement of old cells with new ones generated by cell reproduction.

Plastids. These round, oval, or disk-shaped bodies are found in the cells of plants and other photosynthetic organisms. Three kinds of plastids may be distinguished on the basis of their pigment content. Plastids of one kind, known as *leucoplasts,* are without pigment. Colorless plastids of this sort may function in the storage of starch, in which case they are given the name *amyloplasts.* In the second kind of plastid pigments are present, but these do not include chlorophyll. Instead, carotenes and xanthophylls are abundant. Plastids of this type are known as *chromoplasts.* For example, carrots and tomatoes owe their color to pigments localized in chromoplasts. The third variety of plastid contains pigments like the chromoplasts, but chlorophyll is present also. Such green plastids are called *chloroplasts* (Fig. 7.7).

Averaging 4 to 6 μ in diameter, chloroplasts contain a structural framework composed largely of protein. This framework is arranged as a stack of parallel layers, each layer being separated from the next by a definite space. Set into this framework are smaller organelles, so-called *grana.* Each of these in turn contains a framework of parallel protein layers, but

here the layers are stacked more densely than in the chloroplast as a whole. Present within the framework of the grana are DNA, enzymes, chlorophyll and the other pigments, and indeed the whole chemical machinery necessary for food manufacture; grana are the "factory" locations where photosynthesis takes place.

Centrioles and kinetosomes. In the cells of some algae, some fungi, and all animals, a single small granular body, the *centriole,* is located near or in some cases within the nucleus (see Fig. 7.3). Such centrioles function specifically in cell reproduction, as we shall see. Also, all cells of any organism possessing flagella or cilia contain granular organelles near the cell surfaces which anchor and control the motion of the flagella or cilia. These granules are *kinetosomes* (or *basal granules,* or *blepharoplasts*). It can be shown that centrioles and kinetosomes are homologous and have probably arisen from a common evolutionary source, namely, a single type of granule serving simultaneously as a centriole and a kinetosome. Many primitive protistan cells today still possess such granules with joint dual functions. In later cellular evolution, evidently, the single original granule must have become two separate ones, one retaining the centriolar function only, the other, the kinetosomal function only.

The electron microscope reveals centrioles and kinetosomes to have a common, highly complex structure (Fig. 7.8). Each such granule contains nine sets of minute parallel tubules, the nine sets being arranged in the form of a ring. Surrounding this ring is a fine layer of boundary material. The tubules extend beyond the body of the granule. On one side

7 · 6 *Electron micrograph of portion of cytoplasm showing two Golgi bodies. Each such body consists of stacks of parallel lamellae (×50,000).*

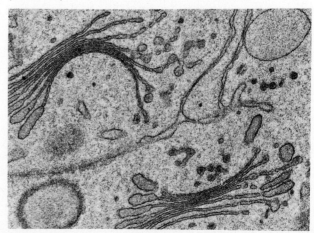

they continue into the free cytoplasm as a spreading array of *microtubules*, and, in the case of a kinetosome, on the other side they lead into the basal parts of a flagellum or cilium (see also below). It is far from clear as yet what the specific functional significance of these structural components might be, but it is clear that the very considerable operational complexity of centrioles and kinetosomes is matched fully by their organizational complexity.

Apart from organelles just listed, cytoplasm generally contains additional *granules* and larger fluid-filled droplets bounded by membranes called *vacuoles* (see Fig. 7.3). Such granules and vacuoles serve in a large variety of functions. They may be vehicles transporting raw materials from the cell surface to interior processing centers (for example, *food vacuoles*) or finished products in the opposite direction (for example, *secretion granules*); they may be places of storage (for example, *starch granules, glycogen granules, fat vacuoles, water vacuoles, pigment granules*); they may be vehicles transporting waste materials to points of elimination (for example, *excretory vacuoles*); or they may be special processing centers themselves.

In addition to all these, cytoplasm may or may not contain a variety of long, thin *fibrils* made predominantly out of protein (for example, contractile *myofibrils*, conducting *neurofibrils*). Various other inclusions, unique to given cell types and serving unique functions, may also be present. In general, every function a cell performs, common or not, is based on a particular structure in which the machinery for that function is housed.

As already noted, cytoplasm as a whole is normally in motion. Irregular eddying and streaming occur at some times, and at others the substance of a cell is subjected to cyclical currents, a movement known as *cyclosis*. The organelles, nucleus included, are swept along passively in these streams. The specific cause of such motions is unknown, but there is little doubt that they are a reflection of the uninterrupted chemical and physical changes taking place on the molecular level. Whatever the specific causes may be, the apparently random movements might give the impression that nothing is fixed within a cell and that cytoplasm is simply a collection of loose particulate bodies suspended in "soup." As pointed out earlier, however,

7 · 7 *A, diagram of cell showing disposition of chloroplasts. B, electron micrograph showing section through a whole chloroplast (×28,000). Note laminate structure and denser grana. C, a higher magnification of one of the grana in a chloroplast (×160,000).*

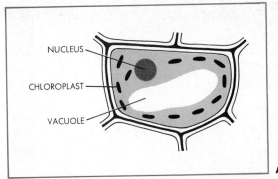

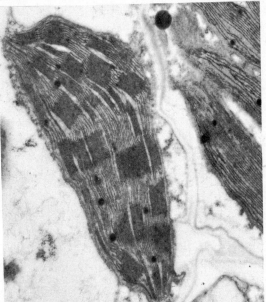

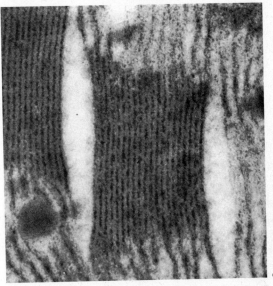

B, C, courtesy of Dr. A. J. Hodge, California Institute of Technology, and J. Biophys. Biochem. Cytol., vol. 1, p. 605.

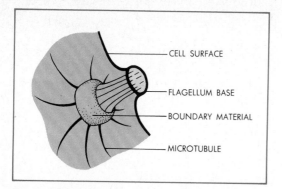

7 · 8 *The fine structure of a kinetosome. Nine microtubules ramify into the cytoplasm and continue into the flagellum as the outer wreath of nine of the 11 fibrils present there.*

such an impression is erroneous, for by virtue of its ultrastructural membrane systems a cell does have an orderly and persisting interior organization.

THE CELL SURFACE

Every cell as a whole is bounded by a *cell* (or *plasma*) *membrane*. Composed predominantly of protein and lipid substances, this important structure is far more than a passive outer skin. As already indicated in Chap. 4, it is an active, highly selective, semipermeable membrane which regulates the entry and exit of materials into and out of a cell. The membrane therefore plays a critical role in *all* cell functions, since directly or indirectly every cell function neces-

7 · 9 *Diagram of plant cells showing plasmodesmata and primary and secondary cell walls.*

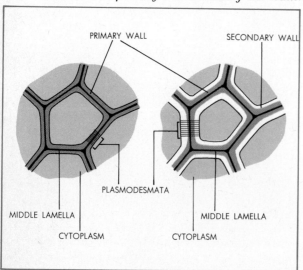

sitates *absorption* of materials from the exterior, *excretion* of materials from the interior, or both.

Nearly all plant cells possess a *cell wall* around the cell membrane. Usually composed of cellulose, hemicellulose, and pectin or pectin-derived substances (but of chitin in many fungi), cell walls vary in thickness depending on the functions of cells and their position within the plant body. A *primary cell wall* is that part of the wall which is formed while a cell grows and develops. Mature, nongrowing cells often deposit additional materials on the inner surfaces of their primary walls, and such additions form a *secondary cell wall* (Fig. 7.9).

Adjacent plant cells in a tissue are held together by a thin layer called a *middle lamella*, composed of pectin-derived cementing substances. In many cases, adjacent cells are interconnected further by fine strands of cytoplasm known as *plasmodesmata*. These pass through the cell walls and the middle lamella, thus forming minute but continuous cytoplasmic bridges between one cell and the next. Parts of the endoplasmic reticulum are included in such plasmodesmata.

Thin cell walls are more or less elastic; thicker ones, more or less rigid. These envelopes maintain *cell shape* and aid in mechanical *support* against gravity. Plant cells exposed directly to the external air also secrete *cuticles* on their exposed surfaces, in addition to cell walls. Such cuticles are made of waxy and fatty materials. They make the exposed cells relatively impermeable to water (Fig. 7.10).

Unlike plant cells, most animal cells and also many algae and protozoan cells are without exterior cell walls. In many cases, the surfaces of such naked cells are fairly smooth, and in compact animal tissues the cells press against one another and assume more or less irregular, somewhat angular shapes. In certain packed tissues, however, the cell contours are far from smooth. Instead, numerous fingerlike extensions may project from one cell and interlock with similar extensions from neighboring cells. Such protrusions, or *microvilli*, usually are not fixed structures; they may slowly retract, re-form again, and the whole cell so may change its contours in the course of time. Moreover, some of the microvilli of one cell occasionally may nip off a microvillus of an adjacent cell. The first cell thus acquires an internal vacuole, filled with a droplet of cytoplasm derived from an adjacent cell. This process is one of the means by which material may be transferred from cell to cell. Also, a cell may occasionally form a deepening surface depression which eventually nips off on the inside as a fluid vacuole. Through such fluid engulfment, or *pinocytosis*, a cell may transfer liquid droplets into its interior (Fig. 7.11).

All such transfers may be regarded as specialized forms of the more general phenomenon of *amoeboid* motion, in which transient, shifting fingerlike extensions, or *pseudopodia*, are again formed at any point on the cell surface (see Fig. 2.8). The protrusion-retraction process cannot be fully explained as yet, but it appears to involve sol-gel transformations in the layer of cytoplasm located just under the cell membrane. Some algae and protozoa are very obviously amoeboid, and they move and feed by means of pseudopods. In feeding, pseudopods flow all around a bit of food, which thus comes to be engulfed and forms a food vacuole in the cell cytoplasm. Many kinds of nonprotistan cells are similarly capable of amoeboid movement, for example, many types of eggs, which engulf sperm cells in fertilization, and several categories of blood cells, which engulf foreign bodies, bacteria, and other potentially harmful bodies in blood. When one cell "swallows" such bodies or solid particles generally in amoeboid fashion, the term *phagocytosis* is often applied. Note that the intake by one cell of a microvillus of another is also a form of phagocytosis.

Some protistan and animal cells, particularly animal cells exposed directly to the external environment, are not naked but are enveloped partially or wholly with wall-like cuticles, or *pellicles*. For example, a protective coat of secreted chitin is found on the skin cells of insects and arthropods generally. Numerous other invertebrate animals secrete horny protein coats on their outer cells. Analogously, the surface cells of most vertebrates secrete external protective coats made of the protein *keratin*, a substance which also covers surface structures such as feathers and hair. In many other cases, surface cells secrete slimy films of mucus, composed of polysaccharide derivatives. In tunicates, surface deposits of cellulose are present. Many mollusks manufacture *shells* over the surface cells, usually composed of lime. Shells of lime, glass (silica), or horny organic materials also characterize the cells of numerous algae and protozoa (Fig. 7.12).

Many cell types have the capacity of locomotion, and those that do not move in amoeboid fashion usually are equipped with specialized locomotor organelles on the cell surface. Principal among these are *flagella*, long, slender, threadlike projections from cells (Fig. 7.13). The base of a flagellum is anchored in the cell cytoplasm on a kinetosome. In some cases, a threadlike fibril, or *rhizoplast,* connects the kinetosome with the centriole in the cell interior. As already pointed out, kinetosomes and centrioles are homologous and some protists possess single granules with joint kinetosomal and centriolar functions. A kinetosome appears to control the motion of the

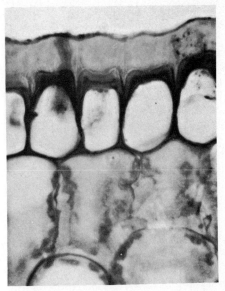

7 · 10 *Portion of a leaf showing epidermal cells with thick, dark walls and a waxy cuticle on their exposed surfaces.*

flagellum it bears. If a flagellum has a smooth external surface, it is said to be of the *whiplash* type; if it possesses exceedingly fine side branches set on the main stem like the bristles of a brush (*mastigonemes*), it is said to be of the *tinsel* type. A cell usually bears one flagellum, but in some cases many more are present, all anchored in the same kineto-

7 · 11 *Amoeboid engulfment. Diagram depicts portions of cell surfaces during pinocytosis, the cellular engulfment of fluid droplets* (top), *and phagocytosis, the cellular engulfment of solid particles* (bottom).

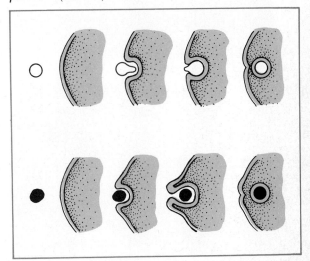

some or complex of kinetosomes. Numerous cell types possess shorter variants of flagella, called *cilia*. These are usually present in very large numbers and may cover all or major portions of a cell like tiny bristles. Each cilium has its own, separate kinetosome complex at its base, and cilia and flagella may be distinguished on this basis.

Internally, all flagella and cilia have the same structure. The electron microscope reveals a flagellum or cilium to be a bundle of 11 exceedingly fine fibrils (continuations of the microtubules of the kinetosome). Two of the fibrils are central, and nine are arranged in a ring around the central two. All the fibrils connect with the kinetosome at the base. How motion is

7 · 12 Pellicles and cuticles. *A, the organic chitinlike pellicle of the ciliate protozoon Para-mecium. The dark dots are tiny pores through which the cilia project (×3,000). B, the chitin cuticle of the head of a carpenter ant, illustrating the high degree of structural elaboration possible in arthropod exoskeletons generally.*

A

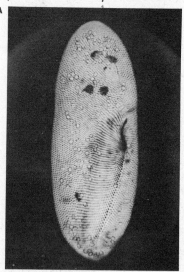

B

TABLE 10 SOME STRUCTURAL COMPONENTS OF CELLS AND THEIR PRINCIPAL FUNCTIONS

STRUCTURE		FUNCTION
nucleus	*chromosomes*	*gene carriers, ultimate control of cell activities*
	nucleolus	*auxiliary to protein synthesis*
	nuclear membrane	*traffic control to and from cytoplasm*
cytoplasm	*endoplasmic reticulum*	*secretion channels, connection between cell parts, attachment surfaces*
	mitochondria	*site of respiration*
	ribosomes	*site of protein synthesis*
	Golgi bodies	*site of specific secretion synthesis*
	lysosomes	*stores of hydrolytic enzymes*
	chloroplasts	*site of photosynthesis*
	centrioles	*auxiliary to cell division*
	kinetosomes	*anchor and control of flagella, cilia*
	myofibrils	*contraction*
	neurofibrils	*conduction*
	granules *vacuoles*	*transport, storage, processing centers*
surface	*plasma membrane*	*traffic control to and from cell*
	cell wall	*support, protection, cell shape*
	cuticles, pellicles	*support, protection, waterproofing*
	cilia *flagella*	*locomotion, current creation, feeding*
	pseudopodia	*locomotion, feeding, phagocytosis*

actually produced is as yet understood only poorly (see Fig. 7.13).

Flagella are the locomotor structures in numerous Protista and in most sperm cells of plants and animals generally. In the large majority of flagellum-possessing protists, the flagellum is at the anterior end of a cell and its sinuous beat pulls the cell behind it. In many sperms and in some fungal cells, by contrast, the flagellum is at the posterior end and its beat pushes the cell forward. Flagella are also encountered

in stationary animal cells. For example, many of the interior cells of sponges are flagellate, the flagella being used here to create food-bearing water currents. Analogously, the principal excretory cells of many invertebrate animals, so-called *flame cells*, bear flagella used to produce currents in waste-laden body fluids. Greatly modified flagellate cells exist in the retinas of mammalian eyes, in the form of rod and cone cells (see Fig. 25.23).

Cilia are even more widely distributed. They occur in a major group of protozoa, and most animal embryos, many types of larvae, and numerous groups of adults are ciliated externally. In such cases the surface cilia serve in locomotion, in creation of feeding currents, or both. Most animals also possess ciliated cells in the interior of the body, for example, in the pressure-sensitive cells of certain sense organs, in the lining tissues of breathing, alimentary, and reproductive channels, and generally in any other location where movement of air, water, or solid materials must take place. Numerous modifications of cilia are encountered as well. For example, cilia are permanently stationary in some cases and enormously increase the surface area of a cell. Or, adjacent cilia may be fused together and form stiff, strong *cirri*, which may be used as tiny walking legs, as in certain protozoa.

We clearly note that, in any cell, certain of the components of the nucleus, the cytoplasm, or the surface may be associated directly with well-circumscribed cell functions. For example, photosynthesis, respiration, and protein synthesis are distinct functions performed in distinct cytoplasmic structures; see Table 10 for a summary of such correlations. But many cell functions cannot be localized so neatly. Thus, cellular reproduction or amoeboid movement requires the cooperative activity of many or all of the cell components present. Functions of this kind cannot be referred to any particular part of a cell; they must be referred to the cell as a whole.

Note also that, whereas many organelles are bulky enough to be visible under the microscope, even more are not visible; individual molecules in a cell "function" no less than larger molecular aggregates. Be it a single dissolved molecule or a whole group of large suspended organelles, each cellular structure performs a function, and as the structures differ among cells, so do the functions.

TISSUES AND ORGANS

As an organism matures, most of its cells specialize in given ways; they become more or less diversified in external appearance and internal structure, and they develop the capacity to perform some function

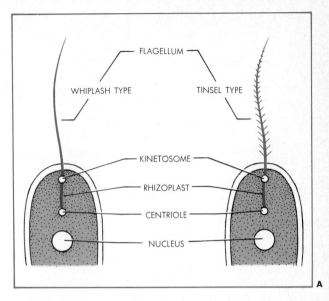
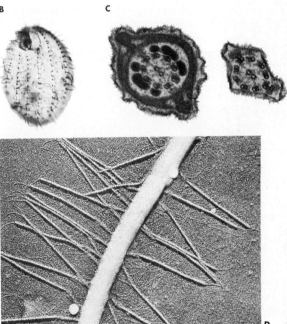

7 · 13 Cilia and flagella. A, types of flagella (color) and their insertion in cells. B, the ciliate protozoon Tetrahymena stained to show the cilia and their arrangement on the body surface. C, electron-micrographic section through two regions of the flagellum of a mouse sperm, showing the two central and nine peripheral filaments characteristic of flagellar structure (×60,000). D, electron micrograph of a portion of the tinsel-type flagellum of a unicellular flagellate organism, showing the mastigonemes projecting laterally from the main shaft of the organelle (×35,000).

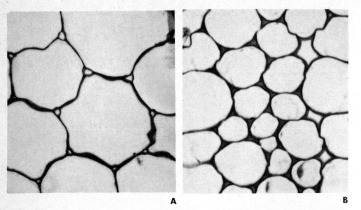

A   **B**

7 · 14   *A, parenchyma. B, collenchyma* (×4,700).

or functions especially well. Such characteristics tend to become fixed and irreversible. Once a cell has become specialized—particularly highly specialized—in one way, it normally cannot change and respecialize in another way.

A *tissue* may be defined as an aggregation of cells in which each *cooperates* with all others in the performance of a particular group function. In a *simple tissue,* all cells are of the same type. Two or more different cell types are present in a *composite tissue.* The cells of a tissue need not necessarily be in direct physical contact, but this is actually the case in most instances. Tissues may be highly or less highly specialized, according to the degree of specialization of the component cells.

An *organ* is an aggregation of tissues all of which cooperate in the performance of a group function. Analogously, an *organ system* is a cooperating aggregation of organs. Several organ systems may be present in an organism. But note again that not all multicellular organisms necessarily possess organs and organ systems. In some of the most primitive multicellular organisms, the whole body consists of but a single tissue. More advanced organisms usually possess several tissues, and certain ones in given cases form organs. Numerous organs and sets of organ systems occur only in the most advanced organisms.

THE PLANT PATTERN

Cell Types

Among the least specialized and most abundant cell types present in plant tissues are so-called *parenchyma* cells (Fig. 7.14). Such cells may variously photosynthesize, manufacture numerous chemical constituents of living matter, store some of these constituents, and transport others in solution from one parenchyma cell to another. Above all, parenchyma cells remain so indistinctly specialized that, under appropriate stimulation, they may specialize further and develop into a large variety of other cell types. Groups of parenchyma cells collectively may even develop into whole roots or stems or into complete new plants. Evidently, parenchyma cells retain more or less *embryonic,* undeveloped characteristics even in an adult plant.

Parenchyma cells are usually packed closely together, and the pressure the cells exert on one another gives them a typically 14-sided shape. The cell walls of parenchyma cells remain relatively thin and consist most often of primary wall only. When such cells become more specialized and develop into other cell types, secondary walls may be formed inside the primary ones. Given points along these walls may remain thin, however, and such points are known as *simple pits.* Opposing pits in two adjacent cells form a *simple pit pair.* The two pits here are separated by the middle lamella and a thin layer of primary wall on either side. These dividing layers constitute a *pit membrane.* Transport of materials from cell to cell takes place particularly through such pit pairs (Fig. 7.15).

A somewhat more specialized variant of parenchyma cells is a cell type called *collenchyma* (see Fig. 7.14). These cells possess quite thick, yet nevertheless fairly elastic, primary walls. Wall thickenings are especially noticeable at the corners of the prismatic cells. Collenchyma cells are abundant in devel-

7 · 15   *Pits in cell walls. Left, cell with primary wall only; right, cell with primary and secondary walls.*

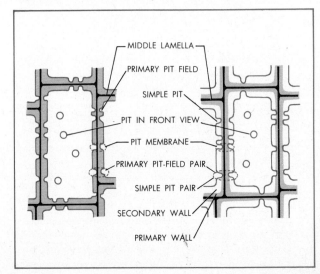

MIDDLE LAMELLA
PRIMARY PIT FIELD
SIMPLE PIT
PIT IN FRONT VIEW
PIT MEMBRANE
PRIMARY PIT-FIELD PAIR
SIMPLE PIT PAIR
SECONDARY WALL
PRIMARY WALL

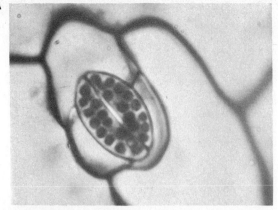

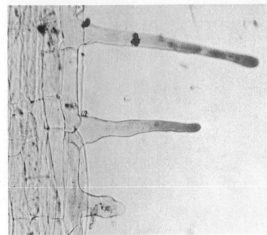

7 · 16 Epidermal specializations. *A, surface view of epidermis showing a pair of chloroplast-containing guard cells enclosing a stoma (×4,800). B, root epidermis with root hairs (×400).*

kind, known as *guard cells*, occurs on the surfaces of leaves and green stems. Guard cells are sausage- or crescent-shaped, and they are placed pairwise in such a way that the concave side of one faces the concave side of another. Along these concave sides the cell walls are thicker than elsewhere. The open space left between two such paired cells is a *stoma*. Through changes of osmotic conditions within guard cells stomata may be opened or closed, an important process controlling the entry and exit of atmospheric gases through the body surface of a plant (see Chap. 22).

Another special kind of epidermal cell is found on the surfaces of roots, at certain stages of root development. Present there are so-called *root-hair cells*. Like epidermal cells of roots generally, these cells are without cuticles. As their name indicates, root-hair cells possess thin, elongated fingerlike extensions of the cytoplasm on the side exposed to soil. Such "hairs" greatly increase the surface area of the cells, a significant feature in nutrient absorption (see Chap. 17).

Among the most highly specialized cells of plants is a group which functions primarily in providing mechanical support. The cell type is known as *sclerenchyma* (Fig. 7.17). Such cells possess thick primary walls and also very thick, lignin-impregnated

oping leaves and stems, where the thick cell walls aid materially in support against gravity.

The body parts of a plant are covered externally by various types of *epidermal cells*. They have greatly diversified shapes, and they serve not only as protective coverings but also in procurement, manufacture, and storage of nutrients. Indeed, any activity relating a plant to its external environment necessarily involves epidermal cells in one way or another. In epidermal cells of stems and leaves, the parts of the cell walls which face the atmosphere are usually thicker than elsewhere and are thickened even further by the deposition of waxy cuticles (see Fig. 7.10). As a group, epidermal cells are not very highly specialized, and in this and other respects they rather resemble parenchyma cells.

Two particular kinds of epidermal cells are somewhat more specialized than others (Fig. 7.16). One

7 · 17 Sclerenchyma. *The diagram depicts fibers in longitudinal view (A), in cross section (B), and a section through a part of a sclereid (C) as well as a whole sclereid (D).*

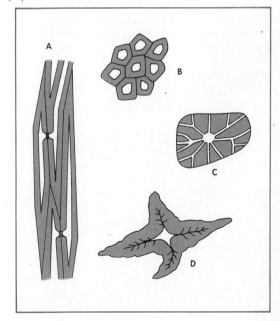

secondary walls. Cells of this type are strong, quite
inelastic, and well suited to lend rigidity and hardness to mature, nongrowing body parts of a plant.
Two variant forms of sclerenchyma may be distinguished, namely, *fibers* and *sclereids*. Fibers are
greatly elongated and they usually have tapered
ends. The cells function mainly in lending support
to elongated plant parts such as stems. For example,
the stems of flax plants are rich in fibers used commercially in the manufacture of linen. Sclereids
have more varied and irregular shapes. Their main
function is to provide rigidity or hardness. For example, sclereids known as *stone cells* are present in
the flesh of pears, and they give this fruit a characteristic gritty texture. Once a cell begins to develop
as a distinct sclerenchyma type, it can thereafter no
longer respecialize as any other type. In this respect,
sclerenchyma cells are like all other highly specialized cell types. Often, indeed, sclerenchyma cells
manufacture their walls and then the nucleus and
the cytoplasm disintegrate altogether. Only the walls
are left, and mature sclerenchyma may therefore be
wholly nonliving and no longer "cellular" in character at all.

Several highly specialized cell types serve particularly in transport of water. One group of such
cells, found largely in stems, is known as *tracheids*
(Fig. 7.18). Mature tracheids are spindle-shaped and
comparatively huge. They may be up to 5 mm long

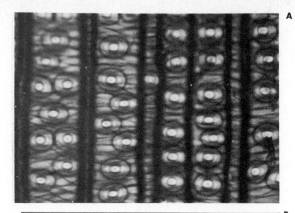

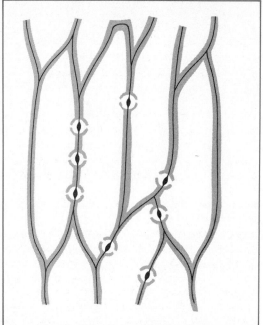

*7 · 19 Xylem pits. A, section through the wood
of a fir, showing xylem pits in surface view.
B, the appearance of pits in longitudinal section.
A few xylem cells are illustrated. The thin
pit membranes provide lateral pathways from
one cell to an adjacent one. The thickening in
the middle of the pit membrane serves as a stop-
per, which prevents the membrane from ballooning out too far to either side.*

*7 · 18 Types of tracheids showing various
kinds of secondary thickenings.*

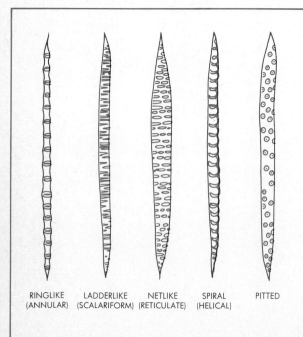

RINGLIKE (ANNULAR) LADDERLIKE (SCALARIFORM) NETLIKE (RETICULATE) SPIRAL (HELICAL) PITTED

and 0.03 mm wide. Their cell walls contain primary
as well as secondary layers, both rigid and impregnated with lignin. In many cases the secondary wall
lines the primary layer completely, as an uninterrupted inner coat. In other cases the secondary wall
is incomplete and is deposited in the form of rings or
spiral bands or transverse bars or networks. Such
incomplete patterns add strength yet still permit a

long tracheid to bend without breaking. Like a sclerenchyma cell, a mature tracheid has lost its nucleus and cytoplasm and is represented only by its nonliving walls.

Transport of water from one tracheid into the next occurs through elaborate *bordered pits* in the cell walls, specialized regions similar in some respects to the simple pits of parenchyma cells (Fig. 7.19). In a bordered pit, the primary cell wall of a tracheid is very thin except at a small central area. Here primary-wall material forms a *torus,* a small round or oval plug attached to the pit membrane. The secondary wall overhangs the pit around its rim and is absent in the region of the torus. Thus, if water pressure in an adjacent cell pushes the pit membrane and the torus into the tracheid, the torus is prevented from moving too far inward by the rim of the secondary wall. The torus in effect functions like a valve. Like the simple pits of parenchyma cells, bordered pits most frequently occur in pairs, the pit of one tracheid joined directly to the pit of an adjacent cell. If the adjacent cell is another tracheid, the double pit is known as a *bordered pit pair;* if the adjacent cell is parenchymatous, the double pit is referred to as a *half-bordered pit pair.* In either case the pits permit easy passage of liquid between cells, and in the case of the rigid tracheids the pluglike action of the torus guards against entry or exit of too much water.

Serving like tracheids in water conduction are highly specialized, cell-derived structures called *vessels* (Fig. 7.20). A vessel develops from embryonic cells which lie end to end and form a continuous column often many feet long. Each cell here gives rise to a *vessel element.* As the cell matures it produces primary and secondary cell walls as well as bordered pits, just like tracheids. The secondary walls may be incomplete and may be deposited in spiral bands or in rings or in other patterns. Eventually the nucleus and the cytoplasm disintegrate and disappear. Moreover, the transverse end walls, where one cell of the column abuts against the next, may develop one or more openings or may dissolve altogether. In effect, therefore, the mature vessel elements in a column become a continuous nonliving hollow tube, with remnants of transverse cross walls still present in places. Such a final structure is a vessel.

Specialized for the conduction of organic compounds are cellular complexes called *sieve tubes* (Fig. 7.21). A sieve tube usually develops from a column of embryonic cells lying end to end, just as in the development of vessels. Each of these embryonic cells divides, and one of the two resulting cells is a *sieve-tube cell.* Remaining joined to it, the other cell forms one or more smaller *companion cells.* Subsequently, primary cell walls (only) are deposited; they

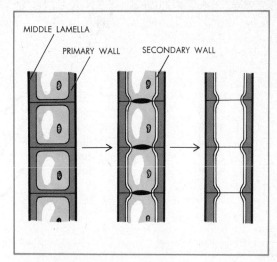

7 · 20   *Development of a vessel.*

are quite thin where the sieve-tube cell is attached to the companion cells. Also, many simple pits form in these regions. As the sieve-tube cell continues to mature, *sieve areas* appear at various points of its wall. These areas represent modified pits, and they are actually openings or perforations in the cell wall. Passing through these openings are strands of cytoplasm which interconnect the sieve-tube cell with adjacent cells. In some plants, comparatively large sieve areas develop only on the end walls, where one sieve-tube cell in the column abuts against others above and below. Conduction of organic materials through a long sieve tube depends particularly on the cytoplasmic bridges between adjacent sieve-tube cells.

A characteristic feature of mature sieve-tube cells is the absence of a nucleus. This organelle persists through the period of cell maturation, but then it disintegrates and disappears. Thereafter, such nuclear

7 · 21   *Sieve tubes and their development.*

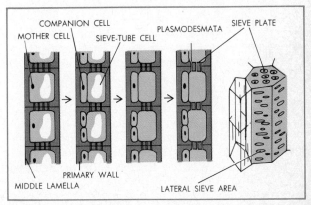

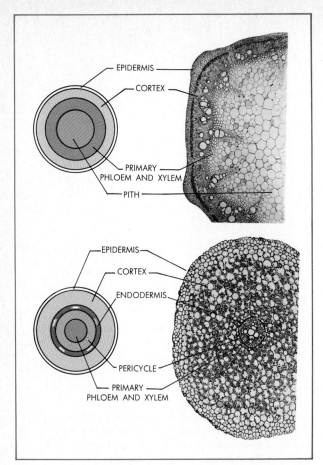

7 · 22 Tissues. *Top, the typical arrangement of tissues in a stem; a portion of a section through a bean stem is shown at right. Bottom, the typical arrangement of tissues in a root; a section through a buttercup root is shown at right. (Right bottom, courtesy of Carolina Biological Supply Company.)*

activities as are required appear to be carried out by the persistently nucleated companion cells. These maintain a close cooperation with their associated sieve-tube cell. Thus, if a mature sieve-tube cell stops functioning for any reason, its associated companion cells also stop functioning and die.

The categories of cells here described represent some of the most widespread and abundant types among plants. In various groupings and combinations, such cells are the structural building blocks of numerous plant tissues. Other, less common types are known, however, and we shall encounter some of these in specific later contexts.

Tissues and Organs

The structural patterns by which cells of various types may be joined into tissues are illustrated clearly by young stem-root systems in flowering plants (Figs. 7.22 and 7.23).

In such a system, the tissues are arranged in a concentric, radially symmetrical pattern. The outermost tissue is the *epidermis,* a protective cover one cell layer thick and composed of various kinds of epidermal cells. In the stem portion, such cells include guard cells; in the root portion, nutrient-absorbing root-hair cells are present. Underneath the epidermis are several layers of parenchyma cells which form a tissue called the *cortex.* This tissue is green and food-producing in stems, nongreen and food-storing in roots. In both root and stem, the cortex also transports water. Adjacent to the innermost layer of the cortex is the *endodermis.* In most stems the endodermis is developed very incompletely, and in some it may not be present at all. But in roots the endodermis is usually quite prominent. It is composed of a single layer of fairly large cells, most of them impregnated with suberin on their outer surfaces. In certain regions of the root, small groups of endodermis cells do not manufacture suberin. These are called *passage cells;* as we shall see later, they play an important role in water transport through the root.

Toward the inside of the endodermis is a group of tissues known collectively as the *stele.* The arrangement of these stelar tissues differs greatly for different plant groups, and we shall discuss various specific arrangements in Chap. 13. Here we shall consider only the basic, primitive arrangement from which all others are probably derived.

The outermost tissue of the stele, directly adjacent to the endodermis, is the *pericycle.* In most stems the pericycle, like the endodermis, is developed very incompletely, and in some stems it may not be present at all. But in roots the pericycle is fairly conspicuous, being composed here of one or more layers of parenchyma cells.

Toward the inside of the pericycle a second tissue of the stele is the *primary phloem.* This is a highly composite tissue consisting of parenchyma cells, sclerenchymatous fiber and sclereid cells, companion cells, and sieve-tube cells formed into sieve tubes. Primary phloem is a conducting tissue; it transports organic materials and foodstuffs over long distances. By virtue of this transporting function, primary phloem is also referred to as a *vascular tissue.*

A third tissue of the stele is located typically toward the inside of the primary phloem. This tissue is the *primary xylem.* It too is highly composite; it consists of parenchyma cells, sclerenchymatous fiber cells, tracheids, and, above all, vessel elements formed into vessels. These components make primary xylem both a vascular and a supporting tissue; it functions in long-distance conduction of water and dissolved inorganic nutrients, and it supports a plant against

TISSUES	EPIDERMIS	CORTEX	ENDODERMIS	PERICYCLE	PHLOEM	XYLEM	PITH
CELL TYPES	EPIDERMAL CELLS	PARENCHYMA	ENDODERMAL CELLS	PARENCHYMA	PARENCHYMA	PARENCHYMA	PARENCHYMA
	GUARD CELLS	COLLENCHYMA	PASSAGE CELLS	SCLERENCHYMA	SCLERENCHYMA	SCLERENCHYMA	SCLERENCHYMA
	ROOT-HAIR CELLS	SCLERENCHYMA			COMPANION CELLS	TRACHEIDS	
					SIEVE-TUBE CELLS	VESSEL ELEMENTS	

7 · 23 *The principal cell types* composing each of the tissues in a mature stem and root.

gravity. Note that possession of the two vascular tissues, primary phloem and xylem, defines a group of plants appropriately called "vascular plants" (or phylum Tracheophyta, plants with vascular tissues). Note also that another name for xylem is *wood*. However, if only a little is present, as is usually the case in primary xylem, this tissue usually represents too little wood to make a plant distinctly "woody" in external appearance. For example, although a green bean stem technically contains wood, that is, primary xylem, the stem of such a plant is not "woody."

The innermost of the basic tissues of the stele is the *pith*. It is not present in roots, and in stems it is located right at the center, surrounded by primary xylem. Pith is composed of parenchyma cells; as in the cortex, pith cells store foods and conduct water from cell to cell.

Clearly, these various tissues are not "just there," but are organized in a definite structural pattern.

7 · 24 *Fibrocytes* growing in tissue culture.

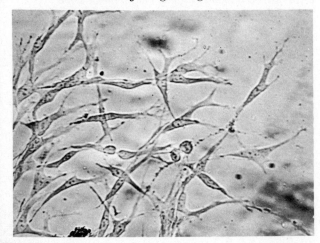

Because of it, functional cooperation among the tissues becomes possible. The main cooperative functions of the tissues are, in the stem, support against gravity, conduction, and manufacture of organic nutrients; and, in the root, support in soil, conduction, and absorption of inorganic nutrients. Group functions performed by several tissues are characteristic of *organs*, and we may note that stems and roots actually are two of the kinds of organs found in a plant.

Two other sets of organs occur in vascular plants, namely, *leaves* and *reproductive organs*. As we shall find later, these organs are again formed largely from the same kinds of cell types and tissue types present in stems and roots. In at least one instance among plants, several whole organs cooperate functionally and form a still more complex organization, namely, an *organ system*. This is the case in cones and flowers. As we shall see, these consist of several reproductive and other associated organs, all contributing to the one overall function of propagation.

A far more elaborate organization, including many more than one type of organ system, is characteristic of advanced animals.

THE ANIMAL PATTERN

Most tissues of most animals may be classified generally either as *connective tissues* or as *epithelia*. Not normally included in this classification are three specific tissues, namely, *nerve, muscle,* and *blood*. Also not included are less common tissue types unique to given animal groups.

Connective Tissues

These are identified by comparatively widely separated cells, the spaces between the cells being filled with various fluid or solid materials. Another identifying characteristic is the relatively unspecial-

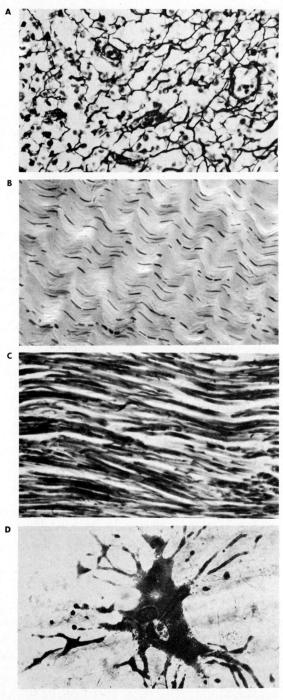

7 · 25   Some variants of fibroelastic connective tissue. A, reticular tissue, composed of fibrous and cellular components. This tissue type is found in lymph nodes and lungs, and in pre-adult stages it is also a forerunner of mature fibroelastic tissue. B, tendon. C, ligament. D, pigment cell.

ized nature of the cells. With appropriate stimulation, they may transform from one connective tissue cell type to another. In this respect the cells are roughly equivalent to the parenchyma and parenchymalike cells of plants. Variants of connective tissues are distinguished on the basis of the types of intercellular deposits present and the relative abundance and the arrangements of the cells.

The most fundamental variant of the connective tissues may be considered to be *fibroelastic tissue* (see Color Plate I, 3). In this tissue, the most conspicuous components are large numbers of threadlike fibers, some of them tough and strong (and made of the protein *collagen*), some of them elastic. These fibers are suspended in fluid and form an irregular, loosely arranged meshwork. The cells of the tissue are dispersed throughout the mesh. Materials secreted by the cells give rise to the fibers outside them.

The cells are of various types. Many are so-called *fibrocytes* (Fig. 7.24), generally spindle-shaped and believed to be the chief fiber-forming cells. Other cells, the *histiocytes*, are capable of amoeboid locomotion and of engulfing foreign bodies (for example, bacteria in infected regions). Also present are *pigment cells* (*chromatophores*), *fat cells*, and, above all, *mesenchymal cells*. The latter are embryonic, undeveloped, and relatively quite unspecialized. The connective tissues of an embryo at first are entirely mesenchymal, and these cells later give rise to the various types of cells which compose adult connective tissues. Such adult tissues usually still contain mesenchymal cells "left over" from embryonic stages, and the cells then serve as developmental reserves; they may develop into any kind of connective tissue cell. Indeed, it is possible to define connective tissues as all those that have a mesenchymal origin in the embryo. In many embryonic or adult animals, mesenchymal cells play an important role in healing and regeneration. The cells may migrate to injured body regions and contribute to the redevelopment of lost body parts and to scar-tissue formation. Actually, most of the adult cell types of fibroelastic tissue may likewise transform into one another. For example, a fibrocyte might become a fat cell, then perhaps a histiocyte, then a fibrocyte again, and then a pigment cell. The specializations of any of these cells evidently are not fixed.

By virtue of its cellular components, fibroelastic tissue thus functions in food storage and in body defense against infection and injury; and by virtue of its fibers, the tissue is a major binding agent which holds one body part to another. For example, fibroelastic tissue connects skin to underlying muscle. The tough fibers provide connecting strength, yet the elastic fibers still permit the skin to slide over the muscle to some extent. In man, fat stored in fibroelastic tissue under the skin is responsible for the generally rounded contours of females and is partly responsible for the obese appearance of overweight persons. The binding action of the tissue is also in evidence deep within an animal, where fibroelastic layers often form a tough but flexible link between different tissues within an organ or between different organs.

The relative quantities of both the cellular and the fibrous components may vary greatly, and on the basis of such variations one may distinguish other types of connective tissues (Fig. 7.25). For example, *tendons* are dense tissues containing only fibrocytes and tough collagen fibers, the fibers being arranged as closely packed parallel bundles. Tendons typically connect muscles to parts of the skeleton. A *ligament* is similar to a tendon, except that both collagen and elastic fibers are present and that these are arranged in more or less irregular manner. Another variant of fibroelastic tissue is *adipose tissue*, of which fat cells are the most abundant components. Each fat cell contains a large fat droplet which fills almost the entire cellular space. A large collection of such cells has the external appearance of a continuous mass of fat. Still another variant of fibroelastic tissue occurs in several (but not all) types of tissue *membranes*. In these, the cellular components are abundant and packed together fairly densely, and the intercellular components are minimal. Various other types of loose connective tissues are known in addition. These arise in special locations at special times during animal development.

Many animals possess *jelly-secreting* connective tissues. The cells in such cases are mesenchymal, and they secrete gelatinous mucoid substances. As the latter accumulate, the cells become separated from one another more and more. Mesenchymal jelly tissue may become quite bulky, as in jellyfishes, for example. Such tissues also occur abundantly in numerous other groups, either as parts of whole body layers (for example, flatworms) or as parts of specific organs (for example, around and in the eyes of man and other vertebrates).

In some connective tissues, the cellular components secrete organic and, especially, inorganic materials, which form a solid precipitate around the cells. Thus the cells appear as islands embedded in hard intercellular deposits. The chief variants of this tissue type are *cartilage*, encountered in several invertebrate groups, as well as in all vertebrates, and *bone*, characteristic of vertebrates (see Color Plate II, 4). The hard constituents of both tissue types include organic as well as inorganic substances, the main inorganic material in bone being calcium phosphate. Both cartilage and bone arise from mesenchymal cells, and both function as skeletal components in two ways; they support (for example, the long bony rods of the appendages, which hold other tissues around them) and they protect (for example, the flat bony plates of the skull which cover the underlying brain).

Among vertebrates, cartilage is the sole supporting tissue in forms such as lampreys and sharks. In these, the skeleton remains permanently cartilaginous. In other vertebrates, man included, the skeleton is very largely bony, bone developing in two ways. Most of the skull and part of the pectoral girdle, that is, skeletal parts consisting of flat plates and lying close to the body surface, arise as *dermal bones*, directly from the connective tissue in the inner layers of the skin. All other skeletal parts, that is, those which

7 · 26 The development of dermal bone is outlined in these diagrams.

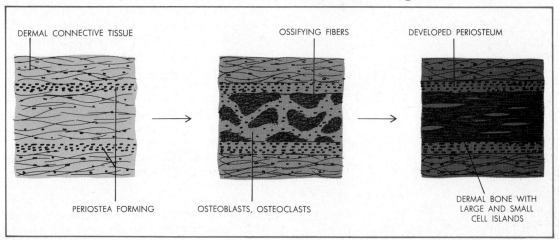

DERMAL CONNECTIVE TISSUE   OSSIFYING FIBERS   DEVELOPED PERIOSTEUM

PERIOSTEA FORMING   OSTEOBLASTS, OSTEOCLASTS   DERMAL BONE WITH LARGE AND SMALL CELL ISLANDS

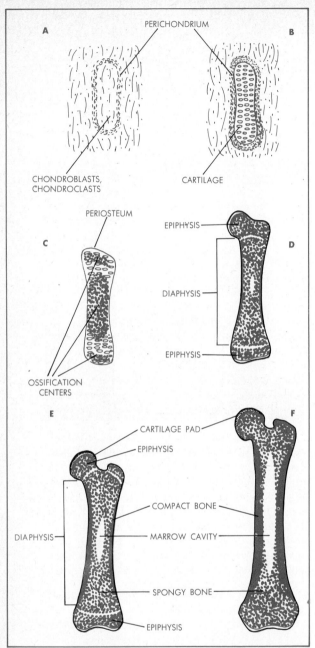

7·27 Development of replacement bone.
A, cartilage-forming cells aggregate in position of future bone. B, formed cartilage rod. C, perichondrium has become periosteum and bone-forming cells (osteoblasts) have begun secretion of bone substance at three centers. D, spongy bone has replaced all cartilage except in regions near joints (white bands); compact bone begins to form at surface of shaft, and marrow cavity, in center of shaft. E, compact bone (solid black) extensive, marrow cavity enlarging. F, mature bone; cartilage layers near joints have been replaced by bone; in shaft, marrow cavity large and spongy bone largely replaced by compact bone.

Labels in figure: PERICHONDRIUM, CHONDROBLASTS, CHONDROCLASTS, CARTILAGE, PERIOSTEUM, EPIPHYSIS, DIAPHYSIS, EPIPHYSIS, OSSIFICATION CENTERS, CARTILAGE PAD, EPIPHYSIS, COMPACT BONE, DIAPHYSIS, MARROW CAVITY, SPONGY BONE, EPIPHYSIS

form deep-lying and predominantly elongated supports, develop as *replacement bones;* they are first laid down in cartilage, which is replaced subsequently by bone substance.

In the case of dermal bones, some of the mesenchymal cells in the inner skin layers aggregate and form two parallel tissue sheets, the *periostea* (Fig. 7.26). These bud off new cells into the space between them; and the cells, known as *osteoblasts,* become specialized for the formation of bone substance. They produce a meshwork of fibers around themselves which later *ossifies,* that is, becomes impregnated with hard mineral deposits. The bone substance does not form as a solid mass but is honeycombed by channels, and in these are present not only the osteoblasts but also blood cells, fat cells, more mesenchymal cells—in short, the usual constituents of connective tissue. Also present are mesenchyme-derived *osteoclasts,* bone-destroying cells capable of resorbing the bone substance near them. Operating together, osteoblasts and osteoclasts may reshape and remold bone and alter its thickness and general configuration, in response to changes of stress and the growth of the animal as a whole.

Replacement bone similarly arises from mesenchymal cells in connective tissue (Color Plate II, 5). Such cells first form a *perichondrium,* a layer which buds off cartilage-forming *chondroblasts* and cartilage-destroying *chondroclasts.* Through their activity, cartilage in the shape of a future long bone is produced. Later the perichondrium specializes as a periosteum, and from then on bone formation occurs essentially as in dermal bones; as chondroclasts resorb cartilage, newly specialized osteoblasts secrete bone substance in substitution. Near the surface of a bone shaft, in the vicinity of the periosteum, the osteoblasts deposit bone substance in dense parallel layers. Some distance away from the surface, bone is laid down in dense concentric patterns, forming so-called *Haversian systems* (Color Plate II, 4). Present in such a system is a central canal and concentrically placed islands, filled with blood cells and the other cellular components of bone. Such densely organized *compact bone* contrasts with loosely organized *spongy bone,* formed in the core of the shaft and at the ends of a long bone (see Fig. 7.27). The bone substance here is traversed by comparatively wide, irregularly patterned channels, all again filled with soft tissue. Such tissue constitutes *marrow;* it is reddish in color if blood cells predominate in it, as at the ends of a bone, and it is yellowish if fat cells predominate, as in the shaft. As a long bone matures, osteoclasts gradually resorb the spongy bone in the core of the shaft and a distinct *marrow cavity* appears. Like dermal bones, replacement bones too may be remolded and reshaped by the combined action of osteoblasts and osteoclasts. In man, replacement of cartilage by bone is usually not completed until approximately the twentieth year of life. A few regions do not become bony at all, for example, the cartilages of the nose and the outer ears.

We may note that, as a group, the connective tissues serve largely as structural scaffolding of the animal body. By contrast, the primarily functional parts are formed chiefly by the epithelial tissues.

Epithelia

An epithelium is a tissue in which the cells are cemented directly to one another and so form single-layered sheets, multilayered sheets, or irregular, compact, three-dimensional aggregates (Fig. 7.28). The "cement" in such cases usually is complexly organic, one of the constituents often being *hyaluronic acid,* a carbohydrate derivative. Epithelia forming layered sheets generally rest on so-called *basement membranes,* flat networks of collagen-containing fibers secreted as supporting fabrics for the epithelial sheets. The periostea of bone, referred to above, qualify as epithelia.

Sheets consisting of a single layer of cells are called *simple* epithelia (Fig. 7.29). Distinctions among them are made principally on the basis of cell shape. If the cells are flattened and are joined along their edges, the tissue is known as a "pavement" or *squamous* epithelium. Many tissue membranes and the surface layer of the skin of many animals are of this type. If the cells have the shape of cubes, the tissue is a *cuboidal* epithelium. The walls of ducts and glands frequently consist of such tissues. Analogously, if the cells are prismatic and are joined along their long sides, the tissue is a *columnar* epithelium. In many animals, this type forms, for example, the innermost, digestive-juice-secreting layer of the intestine.

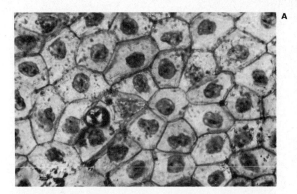

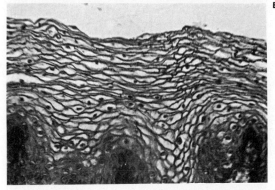

7 · 28 **Epithelia.** A, *surface view of frog epidermis. Note the close packing of the cells and the angular outlines, produced by the pressure of cells against one another. B, section through the lining of the human uterus. Note the progressive flattening of the closely packed cells toward the inner surface (top) of the organ.*

7 · 29 **Simple epithelia.** *Diagrams: A, squamous epithelium. B, cuboidal epithelium. C, columnar epithelium. Photos: A, simple to cuboidal columnar epithelium in lining of kidney tubule. B, simple ciliated columnar epithelium in inner lining of frog gut wall. (Photos courtesy of Carolina Biological Supply Company.)*

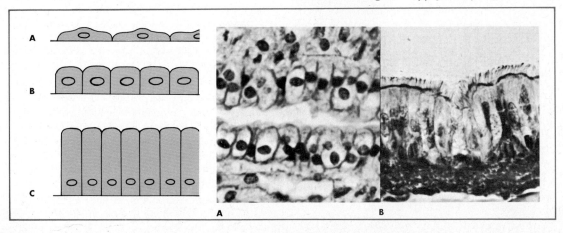

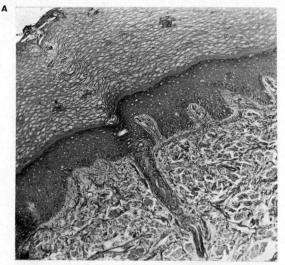

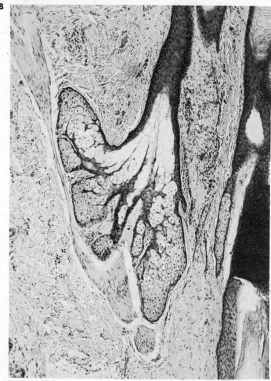

7 · 30 Mammalian skin. A, histological section through the whole skin. Note the stratified epithelial layers of the epidermis near the top of the photo. The underlying dermis consist largely of connective tissue. Parts of the duct of a sweat gland may be seen meandering from the dermis through the epidermis to the skin surface. B, section through sebaceous gland of man. Such glands open along shafts of hairs and their oily secretions keep hair soft and pliable.

Intergradations between such cell shapes are very common, and many simple epithelia therefore cannot be classified into definite categories. If several epithelial layers of a given type are stacked into a multilayered sheet, the term *stratified* epithelium is often applied. Such complex epithelia thus may be of stratified squamous, stratified cuboidal, or of stratified columnar type. The mammalian epidermis, that is, the outermost tissue of the skin, is a good example of a mixed stratified epithelium; the cells are squamous along the outer surface and become increasingly cuboidal with increasing distance from the surface (Fig. 7.30).

In contrast to the connective tissues, the epithelia are all fairly highly and permanently specialized. Once their cells are mature, they do not thereafter change in their basic structural characteristics. Also, by the time maturity is reached, the cells have acquired given fixed functions which are then performed throughout the life of the animal.

Some common animal tissues cannot be classified strictly as either connective tissues or epithelia, as noted earlier, and they may share certain of the characteristics of both. Included here are particularly the *blood, nerve,* and *muscle* tissues. Blood is generally like a connective tissue in that it contains cellular components and extensive intercellular deposits, fluid in this case (see Chap. 23); but although some of the blood cells have a mesenchymal origin, some do not. Nerve tissue on the contrary has an epithelial origin, and it resembles an epithelium in some respects; but in others, for example, its frequent netlike arrangement, it does not (see Chap. 25). Muscle tissue has a mesenchymal origin, yet adult muscle resembles an epithelium more than a connective tissue. Muscle is usually the most abundant tissue in most animals. In a man, as much as two-thirds of the total body weight is muscle weight. Muscle is also one of the most characteristically "animal" tissues, and there is no general body function that does not involve muscular contraction in some way.

Three types of muscle tissue may be distinguished: they are *smooth* muscle, *striated* muscle, and *cardiac* muscle (see Color Plate II, 6). In the smooth variety, the cells are elongated and spindle-shaped. Contraction of lengthwise intracellular myofibrils shortens and thickens the cell. Many of such cells may be oriented in parallel, forming a muscular layer. For example, the intestinal wall of vertebrates contains two such layers. In one, the cells are aligned longitudinally and in the other they are placed circularly. Contraction of the one shortens and widens the gut; contraction of the other lengthens and narrows it. Contraction of both maintains firmness and a tubular shape. In vertebrates, smooth muscle is generally not connected with the skeleton and is not under voluntary nervous control. Contractions take place relatively slowly.

Striated, "skeletal," or "voluntary" muscle is made up of syncytial units. Each such unit, a *muscle fiber*, develops through repeated division of a single cell, and in this process the boundaries between daughter cells disappear. The resulting fiber therefore contains many nuclei embedded in a continuous mass of muscular cytoplasm. The whole fiber is elongated, and its internal contractile myofibrils are aligned longitudinally. Under the microscope these fibrils exhibit cross striations (alternate dark and light bands), hence the name of this type of muscle tissue. More will be said about the internal fine structure of this muscle type in Chap. 20.

A group of parallel muscle fibers makes up a *muscle bundle*. Such a bundle is enveloped by layers of loose fibroelastic connective tissue. Several bundles form a muscle, which is enclosed within a connective tissue sheath of its own. At either end, a muscle may merge gradually into tendon. Like smooth muscles, striated muscles may be arranged into consecutive layers, each contracting in a different direction (for example, the layers of the body wall in man).

Cardiac muscle composes the bulk of the heart. Like smooth muscle, it is not under voluntary control; like striated muscle, its fibers are syncytial. Indeed, cardiac fibers are themselves fused together in intricate patterns. Consequently, the whole heart is a continuous, multinucleate mass of contractile living matter.

All muscle fibers innervated by a single nerve fiber form a *motor unit* (Fig. 7.31). Hundreds of such units may be present in a whole muscle. Each motor unit operates in an *all-or-none* manner; either it contracts fully or it does not contract at all. The motor units within a whole muscle work in relays, different ones contracting or being at rest at any given moment. Moreover, whereas a single motor unit operates in all-or-none fashion and thus cannot produce a graded response, a whole muscle may; its contraction will be the stronger the more motor units are active. We shall inquire in Chap. 20 just how muscle contraction is brought about.

Muscles actually are never relaxed completely. Even during periods of rest, muscles are held in a partially contracted state in which very little energy is expended. Such mild contractions constitute *tonus*, or muscle "tone," and it is through this that muscles preserve the shape of body parts, maintain posture, and provide mechanical support in general. (Note here that numerous animals, for example,

worms, do not possess a skeleton; muscles then are the principal supporting structures.) Only stronger contractions, above and beyond tonic ones, result in outright movement of parts (and in pronounced energy expenditure).

Striated muscles operate far more rapidly than smooth muscles, and usually there are also many more motor units in a striated muscle than in a smooth muscle of equivalent size. Consequently, the striated musculature can produce faster, more abruptly alterable, and more finely adjustable motions. On the other hand, the smooth musculature requires comparatively less energy, and its slower, more sustained motions are well suited in steady, continuing activities; for example, maintenance of digestion through gut-wall contractions.

Organs and Organ Systems

An organ typically consists of one or more epithelia and one or more connective tissues. The internal division of labor is such that the epithelia carry out the characteristic specialized functions of the organ, whereas the connective tissues serve in the necessary auxiliary roles. Thus, the connective tissues maintain the shape and the position of the organ as a whole, and they lead nerves, blood vessels, and other ducts to and from the epithelia.

For example, a complete bone is actually an organ,

7 · 31 Motor end plates, the knobbed terminals of the branches of a motor nerve on individual muscle fibers. The group of muscle fibers so innervated by a single nerve fiber and its terminal branches constitutes a motor unit, that is, a set of muscle fibers functioning together.

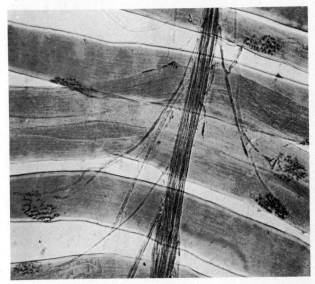

inasmuch as it is composed of an epithelial periosteum, a connective tissue containing cells and hard bone substance, as well as blood and nerves leading to and from the bone. Analogously, a complete muscle is an organ. It contains epitheliumlike muscle fibers and bundles, connective tissues surrounding such units, in many cases also tendons attaching the muscle to bone, and again nerves and blood vessels to and from the muscle. In compact three-dimensional organs such as the liver, the connective tissues envelop the whole organ exteriorly and partition it extensively

7 · 32 *Histological section through a mammalian (pig) liver, showing a few of the epithelial lobules separated from one another by the stroma, that is, layers of connective tissue. Branches of the hepatic portal vein in the stroma carry blood to a lobule. Blood then passes freely through the canallike spaces between the strands of lobule cells, and it eventually collects in and is carried off by a branch of the hepatic vein, seen as a large clear space in the center of a lobule. See also Figs. 17.12 and 17.19 for additional details on liver structure.*

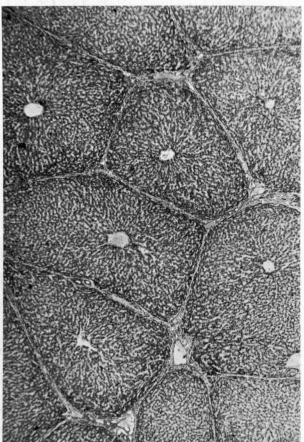

interiorly. The connective tissues here are said to form a *stroma*, a supporting framework that divides up the interior of the organ into islands of epithelial cells (Fig. 7.32). Such islands usually represent complete functional units of the organ, and the traffic of materials to and from the units is carried by the surrounding stroma. Small groups of such islands or each individual island may form a distinct *lobule*, and numerous lobules may be recognizable collectively as an anatomically distinct *lobe* of the organ.

In sheetlike organs such as skin, epithelia and connective tissues form adjacent layers. For example, vertebrate skin consists of two principal layers, an outer *epidermis*, which is a stratified epithelium, and an inner *dermis*, a fibroelastic connective tissue (see Fig. 7.30). Both are many cell layers thick and each produces other characteristic tissues and organs. Thus, the epidermis gives rise to, for example, various glandular ingrowths into the dermis (for example, excretory *sweat glands*, oil-secreting *sebaceous glands*, see Fig. 7.30), as well as numerous outgrowths such as beaks, claws, hoofs, nails, scales, feathers, and hair. The dermis produces dermal bones, as already noted (the scales of fishes are included here), as well as teeth, combs and wattles in birds, and pigment cells which give various vertebrates their characteristic skin colorations. Evidently, the skin as a whole, or *integument*, is not merely a single organ but an integrated group of numerous organs; it is an organ system.

In tubular organs such as the gut, epithelia and connective tissues likewise form alternating layers. For example, the wall of the mammalian small intestine consists of four main layers formed by at least six or seven different tissues (Fig. 7.33). The innermost layer is the *mucosa*, composed principally of a sublayer of simple columnar epithelium and a sublayer of underlying fibroelastic connective tissue. Its chief function is to complete the digestion of foods and to absorb the digested nutrients from the cavity of the gut. Adjoining the mucosa toward the outside is the *submucosa*, a substantial layer of fibroelastic connective tissue in which are present numerous blood vessels, lymph vessels, and nerve fibers. The principal function of the submucosa is to transfer nutrients from the mucosa into the blood and lymph streams for further distribution into other parts of the body. Surrounding the submucosa is the *muscularis*, the chief muscle tissue of the gut wall. As already noted above, this tissue is composed of smooth muscle, and it contains an inner circular and an outer longitudinal sublayer. More nerve tissue is present between these two muscle layers. The muscularis maintains the tubular shape of the

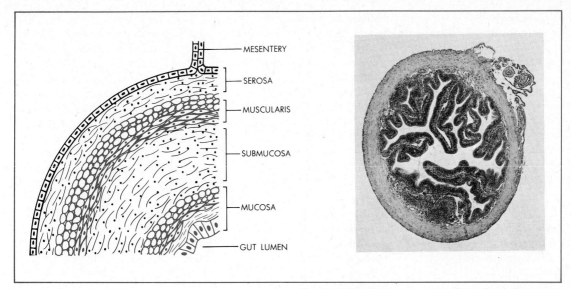

7 · 33 Diagram: cross section through a portion of the intestinal wall of mammals (left). The mucosa, adjacent to the lumen (gut cavity), consists of columnar epithelium, connective tissue, and thin layers of muscle; the submucosa, of connective tissue, nerves, and blood vessels; the muscularis, of thick layers of inner circular and outer longitudinal muscles; and the serosa, of connective tissue and squamous epithelium, the latter continuous with the mesentery and representing part of the peritoneum. Note that the mucosa is usually extensively folded and that the gut lumen is far wider in proportion to the thickness of the gut wall than suggested in the diagram. Photo: histological section through the intestine (at the level of the duodenum), showing the highly folded condition of the mucosa.

gut, and it also produces a series of gut movements playing important roles in digestion (see Chap. 17). The outermost layer of the intestinal wall is the *serosa*, composed of an inner sublayer of fibroelastic tissue and an outer sublayer of squamous epithelium. The serosa as a whole is the limiting membrane of the gut, and it is continuous with the membranes that keep the entire intestine in place within the body.

All these component tissues of the small intestine cooperate in performing the one group function of food processing. The small intestine is therefore an organ. Several dozens of organs, each similarly constructed out of two or more tissues, may be identified in animals as complex as vertebrates. Of these organs, given ones cooperate in carrying out a single complex group function and they therefore form *organ systems*. For example, numerous organs in addition to the small intestine function in food processing: mouth, stomach, liver, pancreas, salivary glands, large intestine, and others. Together these organs constitute the *alimentary system*. In this instance, as in most others, the component organs interconnect physically. But this is not always the case. For example, the endocrine system consists of a series of hormone-producing glandular organs not interconnected directly.

The animal body may contain up to ten organ systems. Directly or indirectly, all of them are necessary and just sufficient to maintain the life-sustaining functions of metabolism and self-perpetuation. Conversely, all functions also contribute importantly to the maintenance of all systems. For example, although the alimentary system serves primarily in nutrition, it also serves indirectly in all

other functions of metabolism and contributes additionally to all processes of self-perpetuation, including even evolution: without a properly nourished reproductive system there can be no reproduction, hence also no heredity and no evolution. Analogously, it is easy to verify that every body part must provide functional support for every other part, and that only through such interdependent activities can all of metabolism and self-perpetuation take place.

It is true nevertheless that some systems are more intimately concerned with given metabolic or self-perpetuative processes than others. Thus, five systems serve primarily in various supporting, protecting, and coordinating activities; as a group they function particularly in correlating the interior operations of the animal with the requirements imposed by the external environment. These five are:

1. The *integumentary* system, which includes skin and all skin-derived structures and which serves as boundary and protective cover for the whole animal.

2. The *skeletal* and *muscular* systems, which provide support, protection, and the means of motion, and which also maintain body shape and the position of body parts.

3. The *nervous* and *endocrine* systems, which coordinate the activities of all body parts into a harmonious pattern and which make the behavior of the whole animal relate meaningfully to particular environmental situations.

Four other systems may be regarded as internal "service" systems; their primary functions are supply, removal, and transport of all the materials associated with the proper operation of individual cells. These four are:

1. The *alimentary* system, which processes nutrients available in the environment into actually usable ones.

2. The *breathing* system, which brings respiratory oxygen into the animal and respiratory CO_2 out of it.

3. The *excretory* system, which ensures the retention of usable substances and the elimination of unusable wastes.

4. The *circulatory* system, which is the general internal transport apparatus; as the circulation passes by all cells of the body, it supplies the cells with nutrients and oxygen and carries off their wastes; and as the system passes through the alimentary, breathing, and excretory systems, it delivers the wastes to all three of these and picks up fresh nutrient supplies from the first and oxygen supplies from the second.

The remaining tenth system is the *reproductive* system, which accomplishes the propagation of the animal. We shall later examine the makeup of most of these systems in the context of their functions.

In various animal groups, some or others of these systems may not be present. As already noted, for example, worms of all kinds do not possess skeletal systems. Many primitive animals do not possess circulatory or breathing or excretory systems. And endocrine systems are conspicuous in only a few groups, most notably arthropods and vertebrates. In all such animals, as indeed also in plants, the functions performed elsewhere by systems are performed by individual cells or individual tissues or individual organs. Keep in mind here that an organism consisting of but a single cell is alive just as fully and completely as one composed of ten elaborate organ systems. The differing degrees of structural complexity or simplicity are reflections of the comparative *specializations* of organisms and their parts, and, as pointed out in Chap. 2, such specializations in turn endow organisms with various degrees of functional efficiency and operational versatility.

Keep in mind further that organisms as variously specialized individuals are themselves but units of higher organizational levels, a consideration leading to our next topic.

REVIEW QUESTIONS

1. What are the structural subdivisions of cells? What are the main components of each of these subdivisions, where are they found, and what functions do they carry out?

2. List cytoplasmic inclusions encountered in all cell types and inclusions found only in certain cell types. What is cyclosis? How do plant and animal cells differ structurally? How do moneran cells differ structurally from others?

3. What structures are found on the surfaces of various cell types? Which of these structures are primarily protective? What do they protect against? What are the functions of other surface structures? How do the surfaces of plant and animal cells differ?

4. Define "cell" (*a*) structurally and (*b*) functionally. Define tissue, organ, organ system, organism.

5. Review the structural and functional characteristics of moderately and highly specialized cell types among plants. Which cell types function primarily in conduction? In mechanical support? What cell types are unique to roots? To aerial portions of a plant?

6. Describe the development and structure of xylem vessels and of sieve tubes. What is a stele? What justifies the designation of a stem or a root as an organ?

7. What is a connective tissue? Describe the makeup of several types of connective tissues and state their general functions in animal organization.

8. What is an epithelium? Describe the structure and function characteristic of an epithelium and list several variants of this type of tissue. Give specific examples of each. How are tissues joined into organs? What is a stroma and what is its role?

9. Describe the development and structure of bone. What types of muscle tissue are there and how

are they distinguished? What makes a muscle or a bone an organ?

10. Name and state the function of the various organ systems of man. Which familiar organs belong to each of these systems? How many organ systems are present in a flowering plant?

COLLIATERAL READINGS

Bloom, W., and D. W. Fawcett: "Textbook of Histology," Saunders, Philadelphia, 1962. This is a detailed and comprehensive volume on the cells, tissues, and organs of animals.

Brachet, J.: The Living Cell, *Sci. American,* Sept., 1961. A very good general account of our modern knowledge of cell structure.

deDuve, C.: The Lysosome, *Sci. American,* May, 1963. The structure and function of this cytoplasmic organelle are discussed in a nontechnical manner.

Dippell, R. V.: Ultrastructure of Cells in Relation to Function, in "This Is Life," Holt, New York, 1962. An exceedingly good and well-illustrated article on the electron-microscopic fine structure of various cellular organelles. Highly recommended.

Esau, K.: "Anatomy of Seed Plants," Wiley, New York, 1960. A leading text containing authoritative accounts on the cells, tissues, and organs of plants; it may serve like the Bloom and Fawcett volume cited above for animals.

Gabriel, M. L., and S. Fogel (eds.): "Great Experiments in Biology," Prentice-Hall, Englewood Cliffs, N.J., 1955. Included in this very useful compilation are abstracts from original papers on the cell theory, written well over a century ago. Recommended for historical background.

Galston, A. W.: "The Life of the Green Plant," 2d ed., Prentice-Hall, Englewood Cliffs, N.J., 1964. This paperback contains a section on the structure of plant cells.

Green, D. E.: The Mitochondrion, *Sci. American,* Jan., 1964. An up-to-date description of the structure and function of this organelle.

Jensen, W. A.: "The Plant Cell," Wadsworth, Belmont, Calif., 1964. In this paperback the structure of plant cells is discussed in relation to their functions. Recommended.

Montagna, W.: The Skin, *Sci. American,* Feb., 1965. A good review of the structure and function of this organ system in man.

Robertson, J. D.: The Membrane of the Living Cell, *Sci. American,* Apr., 1962. A good account of the exterior cell membrane and its continuations in the cellular interior.

Satir, P.: Cilia, *Sci. American,* Feb., 1961. A thorough description of the electron-microscopic fine structure of these surface organelles.

Solomon, A. K.: Pores in the Cell Membrane, *Sci. American,* Dec., 1960. The structure of cellular membranes is discussed in relation to the traffic of materials through them.

Swanson, C. P.: "The Cell," Prentice-Hall, Englewood Cliffs, N.J., 1960. This paperback is recommended particularly for further background reading on the structure and function of cells, both plant and animal.

CHAPTER 8
SPECIES
AND
POPULATION

Inasmuch as every organism is specialized to greater or lesser degree, it invariably depends on other organisms and on the environment generally for some essential product or process; survival requires group association. Indeed, interacting and interdependent natural groupings of organisms are as ancient as the organisms themselves, and as the organisms evolved, so did their groupings. The interrelations of organisms with one another and with the physical environment are the special concern of the biological subscience of *ecology*. In this chapter we shall examine the characteristic ecological properties of the *species* level.

A geographically localized group of individuals of the same species represents a *population;* a whole species normally consists of many such populations. The populations of certain species are composed of individuals which interact far more intimately than those in populations of other species. We refer to highly specialized populations of this sort as *societies.* Thus, populations and societies constitute major organizational sublevels of a species, and we shall examine their particular attributes as well.

THE SPECIES

STRUCTURAL AND FUNCTIONAL ATTRIBUTES

We recall (Chap. 2) that a species is a taxonomic unit encompassing organisms capable of interbreeding with one another. A species is therefore the sum of all organisms of the same kind; all the corn plants on earth, all the bullfrogs on earth, or all the human beings on earth, each group represents a species. But a species is not only a taxonomic unit, and several types of bonds additionally unify the members of a species into an associated *natural* grouping of organisms.

First and foremost, each species is an *evolutionary* unit; because they are able to interbreed, all member organisms share as their common group possession all the genes present in the species, and thus the members are more closely related to one another than to members of any other species. As a result, the members of a species have in common a basic set of structural and functional traits.

However, no two organisms are exactly alike, and despite their close relation the members of a species actually differ from one another quite considerably; superimposed on the common traits, *individual variations* are characteristic within each species (Fig. 8.1). Indeed, the range of such variations within one species may be directly continuous with the range within a closely related species. It may happen, therefore, that two organisms belonging to two different species do not differ very much more structurally and functionally than two organisms belonging to the same species.

Individual variations can be *inheritable* or *noninheritable.* The first are produced by gene mutations and are controlled by genes. They may therefore be transmitted to offspring. Noninheritable variations are the result of developmental processes within organisms and are not (directly) controlled genetically. They therefore disappear from a species with the death of the individuals which exhibit them. Evidently, only inheritable variations can be significant in determining the permanent characteristics of a species. If a man is an athlete, his muscular system is likely to be developed much more than in the average person. This is an individual variation and a noninheritable one. The degree of muscular development does not depend on heredity, primarily, but only on whether or not a person goes in for athletics. On the other hand, the blood type, the skin color, and the hair color are examples of hereditary variations. They are part of the genetic inheritance from parents and earlier forebears and will, in turn, influence the traits of future offspring generations (Fig. 8.2).

Most of the noninheritable variations encountered within a species actually represent genetically controlled traits that have been modified in noninheritable fashion. For example, body weight is a general, inherited species characteristic. But what the actual weight of an individual will be depends partly on his eating habits. Similarly, a generalized level of intelligence is characteristic of the human species and is inherited, but actual mental capacities depend greatly on the education of each individual and on other noninherited factors.

Inherited variations are often correlated with the environmental characteristics of the different geographic regions a species inhabits. In warm climates, for example, individuals of many animal species tend to have smaller body sizes, darker colors, and longer ears, tails, and other protrusions than fellow members of the same species living in cold climates (Fig. 8.3). Such structural variations are adaptive; that is, they are advantageous to the individuals in the different environments. Smaller bodies and longer ears, for example, make for a large body surface relative to the body volume. Under such conditions evaporation from the skin surface is rapid and the cooling effect of this enhanced evaporation is of considerable benefit in a warm climate. The converse holds in a cool climate. In many instances it may be very difficult to recognize the adaptive value of a variation. And some variations conceivably may be nonadaptive, without inherent advantage to the possessors. Human eye colors may conceivably be in this category.

Still other kinds of variations are adaptive not primarily in an environmental but in a developmental or functional sense. For example, any species always includes temporarily variant individuals in the form of embryos, larvae, and young and mature

A   B

8 · 1 Individual variation. These two umbrella birds belong to the same species, namely, Cephalopterus ornatus. But they are members of different populations, and the structural differences between the birds are quite pronounced. Technically these birds are said to belong to different subspecies (also referred to as varieties) of the same species. For other variations cf. Fig. 8.2.

8 · 2 Inheritable, gene-controlled trait variations. These are litter-mate rats, produced by the same two parents. Considerable variation in coat color is evident. Such differences among offspring are due to the gene-shuffling effects of sex, and as a consequence even brothers and sisters of the same family may be different genetically. Variant traits of this type are superimposed on common, more basic traits; for example, despite the color differences all the litter mates above are distinctly rats and, indeed, members of a single breeding line with specific fine characteristics.

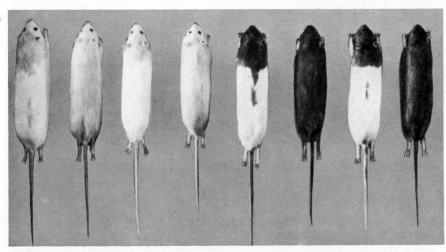

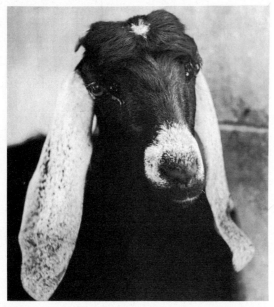

8 · 3 *Evaporation surfaces tend to be larger in warm-climate than in corresponding cool-climate animals. For example, the Arabian desert goat illustrated here possesses external ears very much longer than those of related types in temperate regions.*

organisms generally. Also present in most species are permanently variant individuals in the form of males and females. Moreover, a species usually encompasses subordinate classification groups such as subspecies (*varieties*), subsubspecies (*races*), and *strains,* and these too are distinguished by particular, unique variations (see Fig. 8.1).

By virtue of the structural variations of their members, all species may be said to exhibit a greater or lesser degree of *polymorphism,* that is, to be composed of individuals of "many shapes." The structural differences between males and females are instances of *dimorphism,* a form of polymorphism (Fig. 8.4). But polymorphism may be far more pronounced. Two individuals of the same species may be so different structurally that their common traits become evident only through the most careful study. For example, many coelenterate species are highly polymorphic. These animals occur in two structurally quite different forms, namely, as free-swimming *medusae* like jellyfish and as sessile *polyps* like sea anemones. Indeed, polyps and medusae may themselves be highly polymorphic. For example, *Physalia,* the Portuguese man-of-war, is a colonial coelenterate that is commonly found on the surface of warm seas (see Color Plate III, 7). A colony is made up of several dozens or hundreds of individuals and several classes of polymorphs are present: *feeding* individuals, with tentacles and mouths adapted for the ingestion and digestion of small fish; *protective* individuals, whose long trailing tentacles are equipped with batteries of sting cells which paralyze prey and ward off predators; individuals modified into the air-filled *float,* which buoys the whole colony; and *reproductive* individuals, which propagate the species. Many species of several other phyla exhibit analogously pronounced forms of polymorphism. The most familiar probably are the social insects, a given species of which includes queens, drones, soldiers, workers, and others, all structurally quite dissimilar (see below).

All such instances of polymorphism are expressions of structural *specialization.* And where organisms exhibit great polymorphic diversity, a high degree of functional interdependence usually follows as well. In *Physalia,* for example, only the feeding individuals can feed and the whole colony depends on that. Only the protective individuals can protect and all other polymorphs depend on that

8 · 4 *Sexual dimorphism, a form of polymorphism: fur seals, male at right, female at left. Note sexual differences in size and structure.*

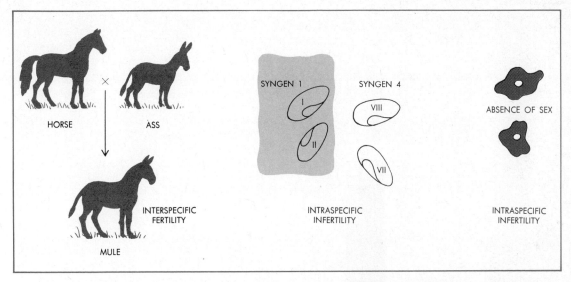

also. And only the whole, tightly integrated colony is a self-sufficient unit. Indeed, such units display all the attributes of a society. We note that structural variation generally and polymorphism specifically produce functional bonds which tend to link the members of a species into a cooperating association of organisms.

However, regardless of the scope of their structural variations, the members of a species usually must cooperate functionally in any case; for by virtue of being an evolutionary unit, a species is also a *reproductive unit*. Males and females must be interdependent reproductively, and interbreeding therefore links the members of a species into a functionally cohesive association. As noted, the interbreeding potential is the customary criterion used to define a species as a taxonomic unit.

Not all species can actually be defined uniquely by this criterion of interbreeding, for *interspecific fertility* is a well-known phenomenon; closely related species, and occasionally even more distantly related ones, are known to be interfertile in some cases, although in nature they may often be isolated from one another by various geographic or biological barriers to interbreeding. Among plants, for example (where interspecific fertility occurs far more commonly than among animals), cross-breeding of cabbages and radishes is known to produce new organisms which may themselves be fertile. And among animals, matings between male lions and female tigers may produce *"ligers"*; the reverse crosses may yield *"tiglons"*; and horses and asses have long been used for the production of *mules*. These and many other known interspecific results among animals are usually sterile, but they do illustrate the occasional

8 · 5 Interspecific fertility is illustrated by matings between horses and asses (left) *and also by tigers and lions, two species of the same genus* (Felis leo, Felis tigris). *Middle diagram: mating types I and II of* Paramecium aurelia *belong to syngen (or "variety") I, within which mating may occur. Individuals of types VII and VIII belong to syngen 4, and mating within this group may also occur. But interbreeding between syngens may not occur, even though such individuals may live in close proximity and belong to the same species. Right: exclusively vegetative reproducers such as* Amoeba proteus *are by definition infertile, hence also intraspecifically infertile.*

possibility of interbreeding between members of two different animal species.

In some cases, on the contrary, interbreeding is not possible between two members of the same species. Such *intraspecific infertility* is encountered among protozoa, for example. Certain protozoan species are split up functionally into several *mating types*, such that one type can mate only with a particular one among all the other types. The best illustration is the ciliate protozoan species *Paramecium aurelia*, which consists of 34 hereditary mating types forming 16 distinct mating groups, or *syngens*. Of these, 15 syngens contain two mating types each and one syngen contains four mating types. Mating within a syngen is possible, but mating between syngens is not. Intraspecific infertility is even more pronounced in all asexually developing species among organisms, in which fertilization does not occur at all and in which interbreeding is therefore completely absent (Fig. 8.5).

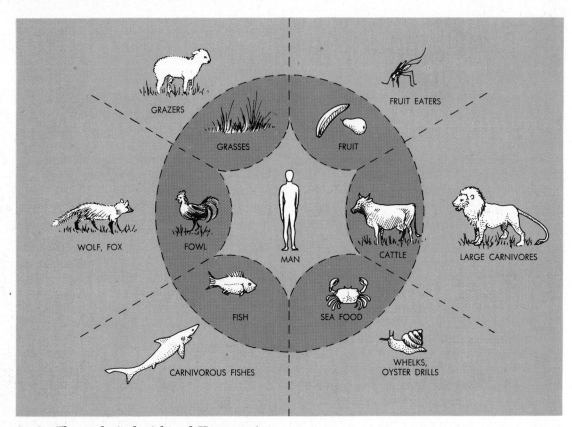

8 · 6 *The ecological niche of* Homo sapiens *is characterized in part by man's requirement of foods such as are shown within the circle around man. These food organisms also happen to form parts of the ecological niches of other animals, as indicated outside the circle. However, the latter animals also use foods not used by man. Thus, although these various ecological niches partly overlap that of man, each niche is nevertheless distinct in its entirety and characteristic of a particular species. Ecological niches are defined not only by the food organisms but also by the geographic territory, the waste products, the structures, and other attributes of given species.*

Evidently, common reproductive bonds characterize more than a single species in some cases (or what appears to be more than a single species) and less than a whole species in others. The definition of a species as a reproductive unit consequently does not always hold, and the derived taxonomic definition similarly is not applicable in all instances. It remains true, nevertheless, that reproduction does represent an important unifying link among the members of most species.

Another type of link is probably even more im-portant and universal. By virtue of being evolutionary units, all species are also *ecological units*. Each species is defined by its *ecological niche*, its place in nature; it inhabits a certain territorial range, it uses up particular raw materials in that range, and it produces particular byproducts and endproducts. For example, the environment offers numerous opportunities for carnivorous modes of animal existence, all differing from one another in hundreds of fine details. Such opportunities represent ecological niches, and given species occupy them. Thus, animal species can subsist carnivorously by being terrestrial, aquatic, or aerial; sessile or motile; cold-, temperate-, or warm-climate types; daytime or nighttime hunters; small-prey or large-prey specialists. And each such coarse category additionally encompasses innumerable finer categories of possible carnivorous ways of life. Analogously, all other opportunities of pursuing specific ways of life in the available environment constitute ecological niches occupied by particular species. Consequently, just as each species is identified by a particular set of structural, functional, and evolutionary characteristics, so is it also identified by its ecological niche (Fig. 8.6).

Such niches are correlated strongly with geography; in similar kinds of environments, even if

PLATE VII

15. Marine plankton,
including diatoms, copepods,
crustacean larvae, protozoa,
animal eggs, and other organisms.

PLATE VIII

16. A bed of cattails,
plants adapted secondarily to water.

17. The desert habitat.
In this particular view,
giant cacti (Cereus giganteus)
are conspicuous.
Note the absence of grasses.

18. The tundra.
Note the complete
absence of trees, characteristic
of the tundra.

17, 18, courtesy of Carolina Biological Supply Company

widely separated, species with similar ways of life will be found. For example, widely different localities offering similar conditions of soil and climate will support prairies composed of grass species having similar requirements. In their turn, prairies offer opportunities for grazing animals, and each prairie region of the world actually has its own animal species filling available grazing niches; for example, antelopes in Africa, bisons in North America, kangaroos in Australia. Analogously, plant and animal species on different high mountains occupy similar ecological niches. At the same time, several similar niches may be available in a single territory. For example, the Central African plains support not only one but several species of grasses, and not only numerous types of antelopes but also zebras, giraffes, and other grazing species. The ways of life of such species overlap in many respects, but they are not precisely identical in all details; each species normally fills a unique ecological niche.

By being adapted to the same niche, the members of a species are linked together through powerful ecological bonds. These have cooperative as well as competitive aspects. Thus, *intraspecific cooperation* is often necessary to execute the way of life of a species. Among animals, for example, hunting may have to be done in cooperative packs, migrations may have to be undertaken in the comparative safety of herds or flocks, and groups may be required for the construction of complex nests, hives, or dams. At the same time, inasmuch as the members of a species must share the living space and the food sources within their common ecological niche, *intraspecific competition* occurs as well. However, such competition is generally quite indirect, as when adjacent individuals of a plant species draw from the same pool of soil nutrients or compete for sunlight by growing as tall and wide as space permits. Intraspecific competition among animals is likewise largely indirect. Although direct competition by combat does occur,

8 · 7 *Intraspecific cooperation is usually pronounced in herding animals, as in this walrus herd. But note that, since the members of a herd use the same restricted space and limited food sources, a measure of intraspecific competition is usually likely to be manifested as well.*

in most cases one member of the species affects another via the environment only, and physical or even visual contact need not be involved (Fig. 8.7).

DEVELOPMENTAL AND GEOGRAPHIC ATTRIBUTES

Each species occupies a particular ecological niche for the duration of its evolutionary life, that is, in the order of a million years on the average. In the course of this time, the history of a species typically follows a characteristic pattern. A species originates in a small home territory, spreads from there over as wide a geographic range as it can, then dies out in various localities of that range and eventually becomes extinct altogether (Fig. 8.8). Species extinction is not a theoretically inherent necessity, but no past species is known to have survived longer than a few million years at most. What factors govern this pattern of species development?

8 · 8 *The general life history of a species.*

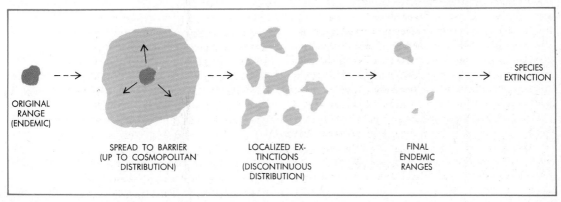

ORIGINAL RANGE (ENDEMIC)

SPREAD TO BARRIER (UP TO COSMOPOLITAN DISTRIBUTION)

LOCALIZED EXTINCTIONS (DISCONTINUOUS DISTRIBUTION)

FINAL ENDEMIC RANGES

SPECIES EXTINCTION

As will be shown in Chap. 31 in greater detail, species formation, or *speciation*, occurs when, in a parent species, a population becomes isolated reproductively from neighboring sister populations. Such isolation may be brought about in various ways, but the common consequence of all these ways is that the isolated population can no longer interbreed with the rest of the parent species and so forms a new descendant species. In the process of being "born," a new species also acquires its own ecological niche. It may do so, for example, by occupying a niche that had been free in the territory. Or if a change in the physical environment has created a new niche, the new species may come to occupy it. Or the new species may itself create its own niche, by evolving a way of life which overlaps partially with the ways of life of several similar species living in the same area. Or the new species may simply encroach on a niche that another species in the area already occupies. The result then is *interspecific competition*, with consequences to be described below.

During its early development, a new species is said to be *endemic:* its members may form just one or at most a few populations, all localized in a single small territory. Further development depends on the geographic extent of the ecological niche of the species. In general, a species tends to expand in widening circles around the home territory until the boundaries of its niche are reached, that is, until ecological barriers impose conditions to which the species is not adapted. Such barriers are biological as well as physical. For example, spreading in a given direction may be blocked by the presence of competing species or by the absence of appropriate food sources in the path of expansion. Physical barriers can be crudely geographic; for example, water, deserts, or mountains may stop the spread of a terrestrial species, and land may halt an aquatic species. More subtle physical barriers exist as well. On land, for example, the area of an ecological niche is usually delimited by temperature ranges, by the extent of seasonal and daily climatic changes, by precipitation and soil characteristics, by proximity of water, and by numerous other environmental factors. In the ocean, species may be confined to given temperature zones, salinity zones, pressure zones, oxygen zones, illumination zones, current zones, and many more. Analogously, dispersal opportunities in fresh water may depend on the strength of currents, amount of silting and pollution, oxygen content, bottom conformation, and a wide variety of other conditions.

Thus, if the boundaries of its ecological niche are close to the original home territory, a species cannot spread significantly and it must then remain endemic. Such species usually become extinct fairly rapidly,

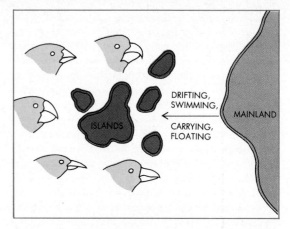

8 · 9 Sweepstake bridges operate unidirectionally from mainland to islands via accidental and fortuitous means of transport, as indicated. The ancestral finches of the Galapagos islands probably came there from South America via sweepstake routes, as Darwin had surmised, and then evolved on each island into unique types by genetic drift. The heads of five such finches are shown above; counterclockwise from the top: Geospiza difficilis, *a ground finch;* Camarhynchus cassirostris, *a vegetarian tree finch;* C. psittacula, *an insect eater;* Pinarolaxias inornata, *a warbling finch; and* C. heliobates, *another insect eater. (Birds after Lack.)*

namely, as soon as changes in the physical or biological environment make survival impossible. However, most species can find the living conditions they require in more extensive areas and they usually succeed in spreading quite widely. Many cover all or major parts of a continent or an ocean, and many others expand even farther and become *cosmopolitan*, or distributed around the world. In numerous instances, a species may expand to a physical barrier and may subsequently cross that barrier and reexpand on the other side of it. Barrier crossing may occur in one of three general ways, namely, by *sweepstake bridges*, by *filter bridges*, and by *corridor bridges*.

A sweepstake bridge provides variously fortuitous or accidental means of species expansion. For example, terrestrial species of plants or animals may cross even extensive water barriers by floating across. Also, plant spores, animal eggs, and microscopic organisms of all kinds may be carried across water in mud clinging to the feet of birds. Moreover, if a water barrier is not too wide, even large plants and animals may be forced across by currents or storms and many animals additionally may swim across. Most small oceanic islands were probably populated via sweepstake bridges of this sort. Islands contain comparatively few species of organisms, and those that are present often are quite unique and are found nowhere else. However, they do resemble related species present on the nearest mainland. Such a pattern of island life is fully consistent with the hypothesis (first proposed by Darwin) that islands have been colonized from the closest continent (Fig. 8.9).

Whereas a sweepstake bridge normally operates in one direction only, a filter bridge accommodates traffic in both directions. Such a bridge is a narrow land connection between two continents, and it usually exists for only brief geologic periods. It is a filter inasmuch as it prevents many species from crossing over it. A good example of a filter bridge is the land link which once interconnected Asia and Australia (Fig. 8.10). This link remained open till about 100 million years ago and permitted the spread of, for example, the first mammals (such as egg-laying and pouched marsupial types) from South Asia into Australia. When the bridge later became submerged except for island chains still present today, the more modern placental mammals evolving at that time in Asia could no longer reach Australia. Thus, in the absence of placental competitors, that continent then became an exclusive preserve for early mammals. The occurrence of marsupials such as kangaroos in

Australia but not in Asia is the present result. Only the recent introduction of placental mammals in the form of man and animals associated with him has seriously jeopardized the survival of the Australian marsupials.

Probably the most studied filter bridge is the link between Alaska and Siberia (see Fig. 8.10). At present this bridge is submerged under the shallow waters of the Bering Strait, but an intermittent land connection existed during the ice ages of the last million years. As water became locked into continental ice, the global ocean level sank enough to expose the Bering land bridge, and as ice melted (as it does now) the bridge became submerged again. During its inter-

8 · 10 The three best-known filter bridges. An intermittently open land bridge between Siberia and Alaska during the last million years (Pleistocene) permitted exchange of animals such as those named below. A land connection open till about 100 million years ago (late Mesozoic) permitted marsupials, but not the later placental mammals, to spread from Asia into Australia. And a Caribbean land bridge during the late Mesozoic allowed marsupials to migrate northward, placentals such as sloths, armadillos, and anteaters to migrate southward.

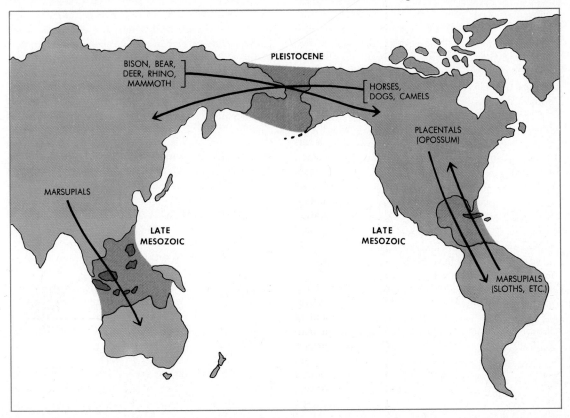

PLEISTOCENE

BISON, BEAR, DEER, RHINO, MAMMOTH

HORSES, DOGS, CAMELS

PLACENTALS (OPOSSUM)

MARSUPIALS

LATE MESOZOIC

LATE MESOZOIC

MARSUPIALS (SLOTHS, ETC.)

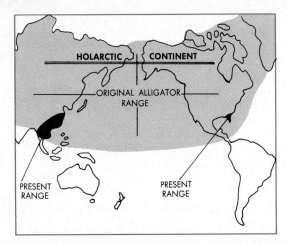

8 · 11 *A postulated Holarctic land mass (color) formed a corridor bridge between Asia and North America. This bridge later disappeared by sinking of land and northward extension of the Pacific Ocean. Originally alligators presumably ranged throughout Holarctica. The present restricted distribution of alligators is indicated in black.*

mittent existence, the link permitted the crossing of successive waves of species. For example, among the mammals spreading from Asia to North America are believed to have been bisons, bears, deer, rhinos, mammoths, and cats; and a reverse crossing was probably achieved by horses, dogs, and camels (the latter then spreading throughout Asia into Africa). The bridge acted as a filter inasmuch as its far northern location permitted only cold-adapted species to make the crossing.

Corridor bridges are far rarer than either filter or sweepstake routes. A corridor is a broad land connection between continents which persists for long geologic periods and allows free and substantial exchange of species. The best known corridor of the past was the land link between North America and Asia, the same which much later became reduced to the Bering filter bridge. Until about 200 million years ago the land connection between Asia and North America was very extensive (and these two land masses may actually have been part of a single continent; see below). Plants and animals of the time could cross quite freely, and this probably accounts for the present distribution of, for example, sequoia trees and alligators. Today these organisms are found only in China and North America, but their original forebears probably ranged throughout Asia and North America. The organisms probably became extinct in all but their present localities when climates became cooler during later ages and when the Pacific Ocean

came to extend northward and submerged the corridor between the two continents (Fig. 8.11). Corridors undoubtedly exist today, but their location will become apparent only in future ages. If some continuous continental land mass of today should later become subdivided into two subcontinents, then future biologists may discover that the subcontinents were joined by a connecting corridor in the present age.

The example of sequoias and alligators above illustrates a very general phenomenon in the life history of species. After a species becomes cosmopolitan, or at least manages to become distributed widely, its populations in numerous localities cease to exist sooner or later. Such local disappearances are brought about in three ways, namely, a population either dies out, or it emigrates, or it evolves into a new species. The underlying causes can be physical, biological, or both.

Thus, if a locality undergoes a change in physical characteristics, a population living there must respond to the change in one of the three ways above. Evidently, sequoias and alligators (as well as numerous other plant and animal types) responded by dying out in all regions except those which remained suitable. Tapirs provide a similar example. These animals are found today only in South America and in the Malay Archipelago. Presumably they originated somewhere in Central Asia and spread to Southern Asia and across the Bering bridge into the Americas. Then they became extinct in all intermediate regions as a result of the cooler climates of more recent ages (Fig. 8.12).

Biological change in a locality is brought about by other species living in the same locality. For example, if two populations of different species have a predator-

8 · 12 *The present distribution of tapirs through Malaya, Sumatra, Borneo, and most of central and northern South America.*

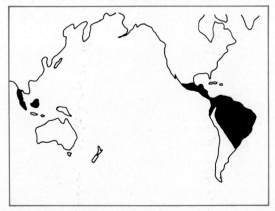

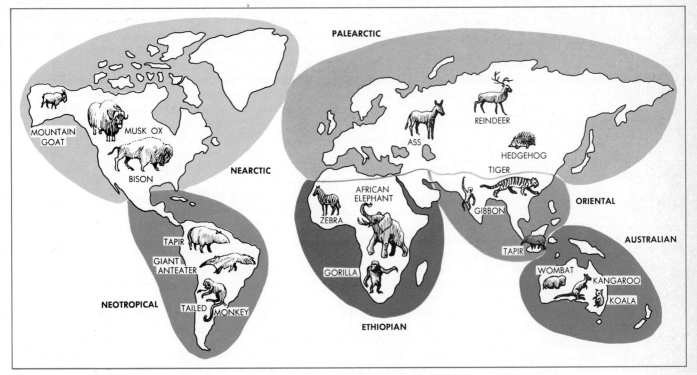

8 · 13 The six biogeographic regions. *For each supercommunity, three representative and characteristic mammals are indicated. Note that, within each supercommunity, the positioning of the animals is dictated largely by the drawing space available, not by geographic considerations.*

prey relationship, then disappearance of the prey for any reason will constitute a biological change to which the predator must respond in one of the three ways above. Another frequent cause of biological change is the invasion of a region by members of other species which occupy an ecological niche very similar to that occupied by the earlier inhabitants. Such a condition leads to *interspecific competition* for the same living space or the same food sources or both. Coexistence may be possible at first, though each competing species is usually hampered in some way by the others. In time, however, one population usually becomes dominant and those of other species then must emigrate, evolve into new species, or die out.

In widely distributed and cosmopolitan species, therefore, population gaps are likely to appear in various parts of the territorial range. Over an extended period of time, such gaps tend to become progressively more numerous, and what may have been a fairly continuously distributed species earlier may eventually become a discontinuous array of more or less isolated populations. Literally hundreds of species are known, those of sequoias, alligators, and tapirs among them, that consist of widely separated, isolated populations in various parts of the globe. They represent remnant populations in what origi-

nally had been continuous species ranges. Ultimately, a species may again become endemic and may consist of but a few localized populations or even just a single one. Total extinction then is often not far away (see Fig. 8.8).

Note that a species may be endemic either because it is young or because it is old. Old endemic species are more numerous today (and probably at any time) than young endemic ones, presumably because young endemic species become cosmopolitan more rapidly than old endemic ones become extinct. A progressive increase in the total number of existing species is the result.

About 2 million species of organisms are known and identified today, and possibly 10 or more times that many may actually exist. Some 10,000 new ones are described each year. Apart from cosmopolitan species, characteristic groups of terrestrial species are found on each of the continental land areas of the world. Based especially on the types of birds and mammals present, six major *biogeographic regions* can be identified. The locations and a few of the most typical mammals of these regions are shown in Fig. 8.13. This figure indicates, for example, that the widely separated faunas of Alaska and northern Mexico by and large resemble each other more than the directly adjacent faunas of northern Mexico and southern Mexico.

If species are considered singly, the pattern of their life histories in most cases accounts adequately for their present global distribution. However, the distribution of groups of species is not always explainable so readily. For example, we know that marsupial mammals exist today not only in Australia but also in North America, the only presently surviving representative on the latter continent being the opossum. We also know that, about 100 million years ago, groups of marsupials lived in South America as well as in South Asia, and that from these regions they later spread to North America and Australia, respectively. We could now assume that the first ancestral marsupials evolved either in some Asian or in some American territory, and that they then expanded from this single original location to South Asia as well as to South America. If so, the migration route would have had to pass over the Bering bridge, as a glance at a map clearly indicates. Yet fossil evidence does not support a hypothesis of a Bering cross-

ing. Indeed, the nonoccurrence of such a crossing might actually be expected since marsupials are predominantly temperate- and warm-climate types. How then can the present distribution of marsupials be explained? Did these pouched mammals migrate from southern Asia directly to South America or vice versa, via sweepstake routes over South Pacific islands and Antarctica? Possibly. Or did they evolve twice independently in two different regions of the world? Again, possibly. Another explanation has also been advanced, namely, the hypothesis of *continental drift.*

According to the most common form of this hypothesis (first proposed in the early part of this century), all the land mass of the globe formed a single continent, *Pangaea,* until roughly 250 million years ago (Fig. 8.14). Pangaea then is assumed to have split into a northern *Laurasia* (or *Holarctica*) and a southern *Gondwana,* with a *Tethys* sea between them. Later each of these land masses is postulated to have split further, Laurasia into what eventually was to become North America and Eurasia, Gondwana into land now represented by Antarctica, Africa, India, Australia, most Pacific islands, and South America. All these fragments subsequently are thought to have drifted to their present locations and to have become joined here and there into the familiar land masses of today.

The hypothesis was suggested originally by the contours of the present continents, some of which seem to fit together like pieces of a jigsaw puzzle (for example, South America and Africa). Moreover, continental drift could account for numerous other geographic and geologic features of the earth. Above all, the drift hypothesis was clearly and neatly consistent with the known biogeographic attributes of the world (as outlined, for example, by Fig. 8.13 above). Indeed, it was possible to explain distributions such as those of the marsupials. In line with the drift concept, marsupials would have originated on

8 · 14   The continental drift hypothesis. *Continental areas at right are identified by abbreviations; they are assumed to have drifted to their present positions since the late Mesozoic (100 million years ago). Dark-shaded areas in Holarctica and at right indicate how the origin and later distribution of eels might be accounted for; dark-shaded areas in Gondwana and at right, analogously for origin and later distribution of marsupials. The Carboniferous referred to in the figure ended about 250 million years ago.*

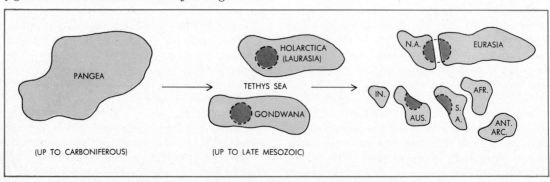

Gondwana, and when this continent later foundered, the animals would have become split into South Asian and South American groups. A drift hypothesis could also explain curious migration patterns such as those of eels, animals which travel to common North Atlantic spawning grounds from both American and European rivers (see also below). North America and Europe may have been part of the postulated Holarctic land mass, and the ancestral eels once may have spawned in a common central Holarctic river system. Correspondingly, their present descendants still are assumed to travel from both west and east to the same ancestral spawning area, which now however happens to lie in the middle of an ocean (see Fig. 8.14).

Geologic evidence for continental drift has been generally absent, and during the last 50 years the idea has been alternately abandoned and resurrected. Various other hypotheses have been proposed instead, most of them based on the assumption of permanently stationary continents. Very recently, the notion of continental drift has again come into prominence, mainly because for the first time good—though still indirect—evidence for it has become available through modern geologic studies. Indeed, it appears that the evidence is becoming more and more convincing. If the hypothesis now does attain the status of a well-supported theory, the task of the biogeographer will be clarified considerably.

THE POPULATION

STRUCTURAL AND FUNCTIONAL ATTRIBUTES

A population, often also called a *species-population*, is a relatively stable, geographically localized association of members of the same species. All species are substructured into population units. Such units are exemplified by the dandelions in a field, the minnows in a pond, the earthworms in a plot of ground, or the people in a village. Individual organisms multiply and die, emigrate or immigrate, but collectively a population persists. It may split into subpopulations or fuse with adjacent sister populations, yet the basic characteristics of the group as a whole do not thereby change. The fundamental unifying links within a population are that all members share the same ecological niche and the same local territory, and particularly also that they interbreed more or less preferentially with one another. However, fairly frequent interbreeding with members of sister populations does occur in addition. A population thus is a reproductively cohesive unit, integrated more loosely with other such units.

The significant structural characteristics of populations are their *dispersion* and their *growth* patterns. Dispersion is a measure of the density of the organisms present and also of their distribution pattern within the population territory. A random distribution is typical in populations of solitary organisms, for example, earthworms, spiders. Distribution tends to be more or less uniform in nonmotile populations, for example, rooted plants, permanently sessile animal groups such as colonial corals, or temporarily sessile animal groups such as flocks of birds nesting on an island. In highly mobile populations, for example, in birds or insects in flight or in moving herds, the distribution is usually clumped in shifting patterns of densities (Fig. 8.15).

The growth characteristics of a population are determined by the rates of reproduction, mortality, and mobility (that is, emigration and immigration), by age distribution, and by the effects of population density on growth. Such effects can be of three kinds. In some species, the growth rate of a population is inversely proportional to the density of the member organisms. Thus, population growth may occur more rapidly if the density is low. In such cases, lessened intraspecific competition promotes faster propagation of the fewer individuals present. In other species, population growth rates tend to increase geometrically until the limits of the available living space and food supply are reached. And in still other species, population growth is most intense at intermediate densities, that is, both undercrowding and overcrowding depress growth.

In all patterns, we may note, population growth is restricted by *limiting factors*. These include not only population density but also the territory available and the abundance of the food supply, or any conditions contributing to intraspecific competition. Moreover, growth is limited also by interspecific competition and by mortality resulting from predation, parasites, and epidemic diseases. Such factors are usually linked to population density, for both predation and epidemics have more pronounced effects if a population is denser.

The important net result of all such variables is that, over appreciable periods of time, *natural populations tend to remain constant in size*. The conditions which promote and those which limit growth normally attain a balanced steady state such that the numbers of individuals in a population do not change significantly on a long-term basis. We shall see in the next chapter how such steady states are automatically self-adjusting.

The most significant functional attribute of populations is that they *interact* with all components of their surroundings. The members of a population interact with their physical environment, with members of other species-populations (interspecific interaction), and with one another (intraspecific interaction).

Reference to interactions with the physical world has already been made. For example, the external environment provides inorganic nutrients, a living space with certain physical characteristics, and it orients the life history of a population by remaining stable or by changing in various ways. In turn, a population also affects its physical surroundings through the sheer chemical and mechanical impact of the living mass on the nonliving environment. We shall discuss such effects more fully in Chap. 10. Furthermore, the physical environment is often responsible for certain forms of population behavior, especially *rhythmic behavior*. For example, the populations of virtually all plant and animal species, that of man included, respond behaviorally to the seasonal and daily motions of the sun. They do so differently in different parts of the world, as if populations possessed internal clocks set to local time. For example, breeding seasons and flowering seasons are set to local time. In a species of habitual spring breeders, a population in the Northern Hemisphere will attain its reproductive period between March and June, whereas a sister population in the Southern

Hemisphere will reproduce between September and December. Similarly governed by local time are daily feeding rhythms, seasonal migration rhythms, and activity rhythms in general. The moon exerts its own effects, particularly on aquatic populations living in the tide zone. If members of two widely separated tidal populations of the same species are brought together in the laboratory, each group continues to behave in accordance with the tidal rhythm of its own locality, as if it responded to built-in tide tables computed for local latitude, longitude, and season. Numerous other environmentally regulated types of population behavior are known, and we shall encounter some of them in later contexts.

Interspecific interaction of a population with those of other species living in the same area produces *community* life, a subject treated in detail in the next chapter. Of more immediate concern are the intraspecific interactions of the members within single populations, particularly single animal populations. In the majority of animal species, as indeed in *all* plant species, the members of a population live as solitary individuals and, as pointed out earlier, interactions other than reproductive ones are largely indirect, mediated by the environment. By contrast, a few animal species are characterized by extensive direct interactions within populations. The animals in such cases live not as solitary individuals but as more or less closely knit *social* populations. In all of these, cooperative interdependence is correlated with various functional specializations of the member animals; and in many instances structural specializations in the form of polymorphism are encountered as well. Societies based primarily on structural specializations are exemplified best by insects, those

8 · 15   Patterns of population dispersion. *This photo of nesting cormorants illustrates uniform distribution, the birds occupying nesting mounds more or less exactly equidistant from one another. Moving herds usually exhibit clumped distributions, that is, distances between animals vary considerably and in shifting patterns.*

based primarily on functional specializations, by vertebrates.

SOCIAL POPULATIONS: INSECTS

Highly developed societies occur among termites, ants, bees, and wasps. Each member of such populations is adapted structurally from the outset to carry out specific functions in the society. Insect societies, organized somewhat differently in each of the four groups just named, operate in fixed, stereotyped, largely unlearned behavior patterns. In its rigid, inflexible ways, the insect society resembles a human dictatorship, except that among insects there is no dictator, no rule by force. Each member is guided by inherited, instinctive reactions and is unable to carry out any functions other than those for which built-in instincts exist. Insects *can* learn, though only to a limited extent. For example, a bee may be taught to respond differently to different colors and scents, and it may learn a new route to its hive if the hive has been moved.

All social insects build variously intricate *nests*, and their societies are stratified into structurally distinct *castes*. In each of the four groups, different species form populations of different degrees of social complexity. We may profitably examine the organization of a few of the more complex associations.

Honeybees

A population of honeybees is made up of three social ranks: a *queen*, tens or hundreds of male *drones*, and from 20,000 to 80,000 *workers* (Fig. 8.16). The queen and the stingless drones are fertile, and their main functions are reproductive. The smaller-bodied workers are all sterile females. They build the hive, ward off enemies, collect food, feed the queen and the drones, and nurse the young.

When a hive becomes overcrowded, the queen together with some drones and several thousand workers secedes from the colony. The emigrants swarm out and settle temporarily in a tree or other suitable place until a new hive is found. In the old hive, meanwhile, the workers remaining behind raise a small batch of the old queen's eggs in large, specially built honeycomb cells. These eggs develop into new queens. The first one to emerge from its cell immediately searches out the other queen cells and stings their occupants to death. If two new queens happen to emerge at the same time, they at once engage in mortal combat until one remains victorious. The young queen, her succession now undisputed, soon mates with one of the drones. In a nuptial flight high into the air, she receives millions of sperms which are stored in a receptacle in her

8 · 16 Honeybees. Worker on left, queen in middle, drone on right. Workers and queens are illustrated also in Color Plate IV, 8 and 9.

abdomen. The sperms from this single mating last through the entire egg-laying career of the queen.

Among the eggs laid individually into honeycomb cells (see Color Plate IV, 8), some escape fertilization, even in a young queen. None is fertilized in an older queen once her sperm store is exhausted. Unfertilized eggs develop into drones. Fatherless development of this sort, or *natural parthenogenesis*, is widespread among social insects generally. Fertilized eggs develop into larvae and these either into queens or into workers, depending on the type of food the larvae receive from their worker nurses. Larvae to be raised into workers are fed a "regular" diet of plant pollen and honey. Queens form when the larvae receive an especially rich *royal jelly*, containing pollen, honey, and comparatively huge amounts of certain vitamins (particularly pantothenic acid). But new queens are not raised while the original queen remains in the hive, healthy and fertile. If the queen produces eggs faster than honeycomb cells can be built, she receives less food from her attendants. Egg production then slows down. Conversely, if she is behind in her egg laying, she is fed more intensively.

In the six weeks or so of its life, a worker bee does not perform the same duties continuously. The age of a bee determines what work it can do; housekeeping tasks are performed by young bees, food-collecting trips are made by older ones. On a food-collecting trip, the bee gathers pollen, rich in protein, and nectar, a dilute sugar solution. Pollen is carried home in *pollen baskets* on the hind legs. Nectar is swallowed into the *honey crop*, a specialized part of the alimentary tract, where saliva partially digests the sugar of nectar. On arriving at the hive, the bee first passes a security check on the way in, then

8 · 17   A queen ant.

unloads its pollen into one cell and regurgitates its nectar into another. Other bees which happen by pack the pollen tight and start converting nectar into honey. They rapidly beat their wings close to a nectar-filled cell, a process which is continued until most of the water has evaporated. Every now and then a bee samples the product (probably more a matter of hunger than of professional pride in the work). And when the honey is just right (or when all the bees standing by have had their fill?) the cell is sealed up with wax. This is the principal food store for the winter. Pollen is unobtainable at that

*8 · 18   **Portion of termite nest.** In central chamber note queen, her abdomen swollen with eggs, being cared for by workers. Winged king in lower right corner, larval queen in upper left corner.*

time and, being perishable, cannot be stored so readily.

Bees and other social insects possess remarkable powers of orientation and communication. On food-collecting trips, bees have been shown to navigate by the sun. They are able to relate the position of their hive with the direction of polarized light coming from the sky; hence they may steer a beeline course home from any compass point. On arrival in its hive, a scouting bee which has found a food-yielding field of flowers communicates with its fellow workers by means of an *abdominal dance,* a side-to-side wiggle of the hind portion of the bee's body. The violence of the dance gives information about the richness of the food source. Flight distance is indicated by the duration of the dance, and flight direction, by the specific body orientation the dancing bee assumes on the honeycomb surface.

In winter, bees cling together in compact masses. Animals in the center always work their way out; those near the surface work their way in. A clump of bees thereby withstands freezing, even when exposed to very low temperatures. Smoke calms bees, as is well known. The animals react to smoke by rushing to their food stores and gorging themselves with honey. They are too busy at that time to sting an intruder. This is probably an inherited adaptive response to fire. Smoke might indicate a burning tree, and it is of obvious advantage if the bees are well fed when they are forced to abandon their nest. Similarly adaptive is the expulsion of all drones from

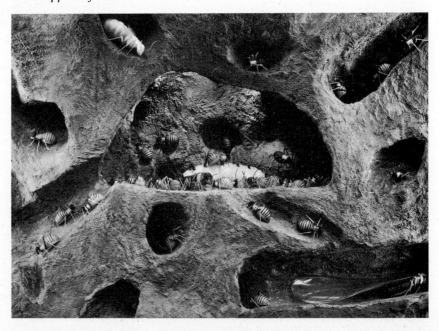

the colony at the approach of winter. Not contributing to the well-being of the population, males merely use up food, which is at a premium in the cold season. Reactions such as these might appear to be thought out. Yet bees probably do not "reason" at all.

Other Insect Societies

Polymorphic castes and functional division of labor are in evidence among other social insects also. Many species of ants and termites include, in addition to sterile wingless workers, sterile wingless *soldiers*. These are strong-jawed, heavily armored individuals which accompany work crews outside and keep order within the nest. Soldiers in many cases cannot feed themselves and are cared for by workers. Besides a winged fertile queen (Fig. 8.17) and one or several winged fertile males (kings), ant and termite societies may maintain structurally distinct lesser "royalty," probably developed by overfeeding larvae; not enough to produce queens, but more than enough to produce workers (Fig. 8.18).

Agricultural societies occur among both termites and ants. Populations of certain termite species make little garden plots of wood, excrement, and dead termites. There they plant and rear fungi for food. *Leaf-cutting ants*, similarly, prepare pieces of leaves on which fungi are grown. The fungi are systematically pruned and cared for by gardening crews. *Magnetic termites* of Australia are of interest because they appear to be sensitive to the magnetic field of the earth. They build their hive in such a way that its long axis points precisely north and south, its short axis, exactly east and west. The adaptive significance of such hive orientation is not known.

Dairy ants exist which keep aphids, tiny green insects (plant lice), as food suppliers. The aphids secrete honeydew, a sugar- and protein-containing mixture, on which the ants depend. A common species of garden ant, for example, places "domesticated" plant lice on the roots of corn. The aphids feed there, and the ants thereafter milk these "ant cows" by gently stroking them. At the approach of winter, the aphids are carried into the ant nest and are put back on corn roots the following spring (see Fig. 9.9).

Slave-making ants exist which can neither build nests, feed themselves, nor care for their larvae. They form workerless soldier societies capable only of making raids on populations of other ant species. These victims are robbed of their pupae. The captive pupae mature, and the emerging slaves then care for their masters, performing all the functions they would have carried out in their own nest.

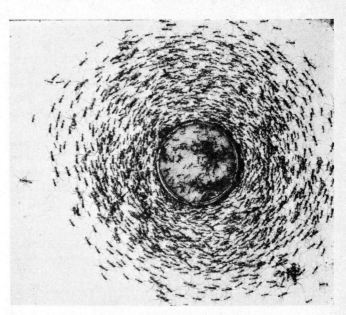

8 · 19 *A marching column of army ants. If such a column is made to travel in a circle, as in the photo, then these ants will continue to circle endlessly. Unless they are diverted by an outside force, they may march themselves to death. Each ant evidently is governed by inherited instinct so completely that it is capable only of following the ant before it and is incapable of thinking itself out of an even slightly altered situation.*

Tropical *army ants* (also called *driver* or *legionary* ants) march cross-country in raiding expeditions. They travel in columns, and larger-bodied "officer" ants march alongside. Everything living in the path of such columns is devoured, even large animals, including man, if they should be unable to move away. The instinctive, unreasoned nature of insect behavior is shown particularly well in these ants. If a column of army ants is made to travel in a circle, so that the first animals of the column come to march right behind the last, then these ants will continue to circle endlessly. And unless they are diverted by an outside agency they may march themselves to death. Each ant evidently is so completely "disciplined" that it is incapable of thinking itself out of even a slightly changed situation (Fig. 8.19).

Certain desert ants, called *honeypot ants*, collect nectar from flowers and feed it to some of their fellow workers which are kept within the nest. These "living bottles" become greatly distended and serve as bacteria-free storage bins; during the dry season they dispense drops of honey to their thirsty mates.

Among insect societies generally, the fixed specialization of each individual constitutes a potential long-range disadvantage. Death of a queen bee and the destruction of honeycomb cells which contain larvae still young enough to be reared into queens usually spell the end of a bee population; new workers are not produced, and old ones die out. Local eradication of the fungus on which agricultural termites depend and the destruction of their gardens spell the end of the termite population, its members not being equipped to grow any other food. The victims of slave-making ants could better preserve their population if all the workers could be mobilized into defending soldiers at the moment of attack.

Among insects, destructive social crises of this sort are offset by the establishment of numerous populations and by enormously high reproduction rates. The safety of the population lies in the number of its individuals. We recognize, however, that it would be immediately advantageous if, in addition

8 · 20 Family organization and territoriality. *The photo shows a family of elks, consisting of a bull, a cow (right foreground), and their calves. Family groups such as this occupy and control a particular territory and the animals tend to ward off any fellow members of the species, or other potential competitors, which might invade this territory accidentally or deliberately.*

to safety through numbers, the society were organized more flexibly: if each member could perform the functions of every other member and if the population as a whole could learn to adopt new ways of life in the face of changed environmental conditions. Flexible social organization is actually in evidence to greater or less degree among vertebrate populations.

SOCIAL POPULATIONS: VERTEBRATES

In contrast to insects and apart from the sexual dimorphism of males and females, the members of vertebrate populations are structurally more or less alike, at least during the early stages of adult life. If specialization does become pronounced later, it is predominantly functional and behavioral and is based on variations in physical strength, developed skills, mental acuity, and in man also on social tradition. Group behavior may be minimal or well developed. In either case the main determinant of behavior is inherited instinct, tempered here and there with a more or less thin veneer of *learning*. Learning goes hand in hand with *training*, and both are made possible largely by *family* groupings. Populations substructured into families are particularly characteristic of vertebrates.

Group behavior is quite distinct in populations such as schools of fish, packs of wolves, flocks of birds, or herds of deer. In most of these, functional specialization is not particularly pronounced. In travel, the individual which happens to be in the

lead position, usually a male, guides the population temporarily. Other males, often stationed along the outskirts of the group, may take the lead in frequent rotation. The advantages of such associations are largely protective. Many eyes see more than two; a huddled herd stays warm; a group is more effective in attack and in defense. Family life within such populations may or may not be evident. There is hardly any in schools of fish. But a duck or a doe trains its young.

Closely associated with family life specifically and reproductive behavior generally is the phenomenon of *territoriality*, that is, the tendency of each family or mating unit to maintain its own physical space within the population territory. For example, in a herd of seals resting on an island, males take up stations at more or less regular intervals, and each male gathers his family around him. The individual patriarch jealously guards his territory, driving off bachelor males and keeping a sharp eye on his females (Fig. 8.20). A strongly developed territorial sense is in evidence also among birds, where the males of a population stake out the borders of their domains by flying around them. Song birds then protect their claim vocally and they later also use song to attract females into their domain. A domain is usually just large enough to provide sufficient nesting materials and adequate food for the prospective family. Not only terrestrial but also numerous aquatic animals display territory-claiming behavior. Indeed, such behavior is more or less characteristic of all animals, vertebrate as well as invertebrate, for all have distinct territorial requirements for reproduction and for survival generally. The result of territoriality may be reduced intraspecific competition within a population (and often also interspecific competition with members of other species claiming the same territory).

Group behavior becomes particularly pronounced during seasonal *migrations* of populations. Not all species are migratory. Those that are undertake migrations in search of richer or safer pastures, in response to seasonal changes in climate, or to reach geographically fixed breeding grounds. Eels, seals, salmon, and many types of birds are among familiar migrants. When not migrating, solitary individuals or families of these animals may be dispersed widely over a considerable territory. At specific times, as if on cue, individuals draw together from far and near to a common jumping-off point, and then they travel to their destination together.

How do these animals know where to gather before the journey? How do they time their arrival there, often exactly to the day? And what leads them unerringly to their destination, thousands of miles away in many cases? The navigation problem is sufficiently puzzling among types which make the same trip every year, like seals and birds. If nothing else, a remarkable memory for landmarks, prevailing winds, or ocean currents may be indicated. The problem becomes even more puzzling, however, when none of the migrating animals has ever been at its destination before. This is the case among eels.

The spawning grounds of both European and American eels are situated in the deep waters of the Sargasso Sea, southeast of Bermuda and northeast of Puerto Rico. The eggs hatch there, and the near-microscopic larvae, or *elvers*, then travel toward the coasts; larvae of American eels turn west, those of the European eel turn east. The spawning beds of the American type lie farther west. Differences in the direction of ocean currents probably contribute to the initial separation of the two species.

Elvers of the American species travel for about a year before they reach continental waters—and maturation of the larvae requires just 1 year. The voyage of European elvers lasts 3 years—and their maturation requires precisely 3 years.

In coastal estuaries the elvers change into adults. The glassy transparency of the larval body changes to an opaque brown-gray, and the fishlike larval shape changes to the characteristic elongated form of the adult. Adult males remain in estuaries. Females ascend rivers and settle in headwaters and in lakes. Some 7 to 15 years now pass. Then the females migrate back to the estuaries, rejoin the males, and all head out into the Atlantic. Reproductive organs mature during this migration, and upon arrival in the Sargasso the females spawn and the males fertilize the eggs. The adults then die.

How do the adults find their breeding grounds? It is hardly conceivable that they memorized the route in reverse when they made the trip as immature larvae, a decade earlier. And how do the larvae find coastal waters from which to ascend rivers? In line with the hypothesis of continental drift (see above), it might be postulated that the Atlantic spawning grounds corresponded to the location of ancient Holarctic river systems. If so, however, then it is still not clear how a "geographic memory" could survive countless generations of fishes as well as geographic changes themselves stretching over some 70 million years. Nor is it clear how, in eels and migrating populations generally, migration behavior is regulated in terms of neural, sensory, or other internal control mechanisms. On the other hand, it is rather obvious that banding together during travel has great adaptive value.

In migrating as well as nonmigrating social species,

the behavioral structure of a population is influenced greatly by the mating structure. In many populations mating occurs promiscuously, as in numerous rodent groups, and a distinct familial organization is then usually absent. In other types of social populations family units are distinguishable, such units being polygamous in some instances, monogamous in others. For example, herds of seals and flocks of many types of birds consist of polygamous families, whereas flocks of other types of birds are made up of monogamous units. Families are not always associated as herds or herdlike groups but may also live as solitary units. For example, chickens form solitary polygamous family units and sticklebacks, parrots, bears, and wolverines form solitary monogamous units. In some cases, monogamy persists for a single breeding season only, in others it lasts for life. Bears and wolverines are among animals which usually mate for life.

A solitary polygamous family, like that of chickens, for example, is generally made up of a single dominant male, a series of females, their young, and sometimes a few unrelated young bachelor males. The rule of the dominant male is frequently challenged by the bachelors. If one of these succeeds in defeating his opponent in battle, the loyalty of the females is transferred to the winner. In this way the group is assured of continuously fit, healthy leadership.

An interesting social organization exists among the females of a polygamous family. In a flock of chickens, for example, hens are ranked according to a definite *peck order*. A given hen may peck without danger all hens below her in social rank but may be pecked in turn by all hens above her in the scale. If a new hen is introduced into the flock, she undertakes or is made to undertake a pecking contest with each fellow hen. Winning here and losing there, she soon finds her level in the society. A high rank carries with it certain advantages, such as getting

first to the food trough and obtaining a position of prestige on the perch. Very-high-ranking birds often are so aggressive that they persistently reject the attentions of the rooster. More submissive hens then produce most of the offspring. Social rankings of a similar nature are found also among female elephants as well as in most other polygamous families.

The success of vertebrate societies as a whole lies primarily in the functional versatility of the individual. In the insect society, as we have noted, reproduction of the majority is suppressed, and reproduction of the minority serves not only toward the new formation of individuals, but also toward the new formation of the whole society. Thus, among insects, the fate of the society hinges on the fate of a single female, and her genes alone provide continuity from one social generation to the next. By contrast, almost all members of a vertebrate society are reproducers. Social continuity consequently is the responsibility of many, and reproduction of any one individual is less vital for the propagation of the society.

The phenomenon of "society" as a whole appears to be bound up with advanced evolutionary status; both insects and vertebrates are elaborately evolved groups. And although societies have evolved independently in these two groups and have different detailed organization, remarkably similar patterns of social behavior are in evidence nevertheless. Ants and man are unique among animals in making war, in practicing slavery, in pursuing agriculture, and in domesticating other organisms.

Social populations of all kinds, like populations generally, are components of species. At the same time, populations of social and nonsocial animals are also units within communities, associations which will occupy our attention next.

REVIEW QUESTIONS

1. What are individual variations? Distinguish between inheritable and noninheritable variations and give examples of each. Why are noninheritable variations without direct importance in species evolution? What are adaptive variations?

2. Define ecology, ecosystem, biosphere, species, polymorphism, dimorphism, and give an example of each. What characteristics does a species possess as an evolutionary unit? As a reproductive unit?

3. Distinguish between interspecific fertility and intraspecific infertility. What is a syngen? Is the usual

definition of "species" universally applicable? What is an ecological niche? Give examples. Distinguish between intraspecific cooperation and intraspecific competition and again give examples.

4. Through what evolutionary processes does a new species originate? Describe the typical life cycle of a species. What are endemic and cosmopolitan species? What effect does interspecific competition have on species survival?

5. Define and give specific examples of sweepstake bridges, filter bridges, and corridor bridges. What

are the biological characteristics of small oceanic islands and how can such characteristics be accounted for? Describe the geographic and biological characteristics of the six biogeographic zones.

6. How can widely discontinuous distributions of given types of organisms be explained? Describe the hypothesis of continental drift and show how it may contribute to explaining distribution patterns of organisms.

7. What is a population and what is its relation to a species? What are the structural characteristics of a population with reference to dispersion and growth pattern? What are some of the physical and biological limiting factors of population growth? How does a population interact with its physical environment? Its biological environment?

8. Distinguish between interspecific and intraspecific interactions of populations. What is a social population? Review the structural and functional organization of honeybee societies.

9. What forms of polymorphism are encountered in honeybee and other insect societies? Describe the characteristic structure of vetebrate societies and contrast it with that of insects. What are the adaptive advantages and disadvantages of each? What is meant by territoriality of animals? What is the adaptive advantage of this behavior trait?

10. What is the significance of animal migrations? Which animal groups are migratory? How does the mating structure of different vertebrate populations vary? What is a peck order and what is its significance?

COLLATERAL READINGS

Billings, W. D.: "Plants and the Ecosystem," Wadsworth, Belmont, Calif., 1964. Strongly recommended for background reading on ecology generally and plant ecology specifically. The paperback contains a section on plant distribution.

Brown, F. A.: Biological Clocks and the Fiddler Crab, *Sci. American*, Apr., 1954. An interesting study of rhythmic, environment-influenced behavior.

Cole, L. C.: The Ecosphere, *Sci. American*, Apr., 1958. The amount of life sustainable on earth is assessed from the ecological interrelations of organisms and their environment.

Dodson, E. O.: "Evolution: Process and Product," Reinhold, New York, 1960. This book contains good and comprehensive sections on biogeography and species distribution, both plant and animal; discussions of sweepstake routes and other distribution mechanisms are included, as are statements on the continental drift hypothesis.

Griffin, D. R.: Navigation of Bats, *Sci. American*, Aug., 1950. A discussion of the interesting sound "radar" in bats.

Guhl, A. M.: The Social Order of Chickens, *Sci. American*, Feb., 1956. A close look at peck orders.

Hess, E. H.: Imprinting in Animals, *Sci. American*, Mar., 1958. A case study in social behavior, showing how ducklings come to learn who (or what) their mother is.

Hesse, R., W. C. Allee, and K. P. Schmidt: "Ecological Animal Geography," 2d ed., Wiley, New York, 1951. A standard, advanced-level reference work, recommended for further background on specific points.

Kay, M.: The Origin of Continents, *Sci. American*, Sept., 1955. Pertinent supplementary reading in the context of the continental drift hypothesis.

Lack, D.: Darwin's Finches, *Sci. American*, Apr., 1953. An account of the most famous case study of species distribution and evolution on islands.

Odum, E. P.: "Ecology," Holt, New York, 1963. This is a useful paperback for general background on topics covered in this and the following chapters.

Sauer, E. G. F.: Celestial Navigation by Birds, *Sci. American*, Aug., 1958. An interesting article on a specific instance of animal migration.

Schneirla, T. C., and G. Piel: The Army Ant, *Sci. American*, June, 1948. The senior author of this article is the foremost authority on these social insects.

Thorpe, W. H.: "Learning and Instinct in Animals," 2d ed., Methuen, London, 1963. This book contains discussions of many topics introduced in the present chapter. Recommended.

Tinbergen, N.: "Social Behavior in Animals," Wiley, New York, 1953.

———: The Evolution of Behavior in Gulls, *Sci. American*, Dec., 1960.

In these two readings, a well-known student of animal behavior discusses various expressions of the phenomenon of society.

Von Frisch, K.: "Bees, Their Vision, Chemical Senses, and Language," Cornell, Ithaca, N.Y., 1950.

Von Frisch, K.: Dialects in the Language of Bees, *Sci. American*, Aug., 1962.

The discoverer and foremost "translator" of bee language discusses the forces and phenomena on which bee society is based.

Wilson, E. O.: Pheromones, *Sci. American*, May, 1963. The title of this article refers to chemicals by which members of given animal species are now known to communicate.

Wilson, J. T.: Continental Drift, *Sci. American*, Apr., 1963. The history of the concept is discussed and its present status is assessed in the light of modern evidence.

Wynne-Edwards, V. C.: Population Control in Animals, *Sci. American*, Aug., 1964. Various forms of social behavior may introduce reproductive limitations through which population control may be achieved.

CHAPTER 9
ECOSYSTEM
AND
COMMUNITY

A community, technically often referred to as a *biota* or a *biotic* community, is a localized association of several populations of *different* species. Almost always, a community contains representatives of Monera, Protista, Metaphyta, and Metazoa, all being required for group survival. Moreover, the populations of a community consist only partly of free-living organisms; also present are parasites and other types living together in so-called *symbiotic* associations.

Whole communities together with the physical environments in which they live represent *ecosystems* (Fig. 9.1). All ecosystems on earth collectively form the biosphere, which thus encompasses the entire inhabited part of the globe including all nonliving and living components. Ecosystems represent the largest subunits of the biosphere; examples are a pond, a forest, a meadow, a section of ocean shore, a portion of the open water of the sea, a coral reef, or a village with its soil, grasses, trees, people, bacteria, cats, dogs, and other living and nonliving contents. We shall examine the properties of ecosystems generally in the first part of this chapter and those of the symbiotic components specifically in the second.

THE ECOSYSTEM

STRUCTURE AND GROWTH

The living portion of an ecosystem, that is, a community, exhibits a characteristic species structure: a few species are represented by large populations and many species are represented by small populations. For example, large populations of just two or three kinds of monkeys may form the bulk of a jungle community. The remainder may consist of small populations of numerous kinds of birds, bats, snakes, and other animals. Analogously, several dozen species of trees may be present, but populations of just two or three may constitute some 70 to 80 per cent of the total number of trees. In general, species diversity in an ecosystem is inversely proportional to the sizes of organisms. Thus, a forest is likely to contain more species of small trees than of large ones, more species of insects than of birds, and more species of birds than of large mammals. The reasons for such correlations will become apparent presently.

Species diversity probably contributes to the stability of a community; the presence of many different kinds of organisms may provide a reservoir of adaptive types able to withstand many changes in the physical environment. Ecosystems are actually highly stable. In some cases, their stability has been estimated to be up to five times greater than that of the physical parts of the systems alone. Yet even such a high degree of stability is relative only, for like other living entities, communities grow, develop, pass through mature phases, reproduce, and ultimately die. To be sure, the time scale is in hundreds and thousands of years.

Such life cycles result from an interplay between the living and the nonliving components of an ecosystem. Being specialized to occupy particular ecological niches, different species must live in different types of environments. Consequently, the physical characteristics of a given region determine what types of organisms can settle there originally. Temperature, winds, amount of rainfall, the chemical composition of the surroundings, latitude and altitude, soil conditions, and other similar factors decisively influence what kinds of plants will be able to survive in a given locale. Vegetation in turn, as well as the physical character of the locale, has a selective effect on the types of animals that may successfully settle in the region.

By its very presence, however, a particular set of organisms gradually alters local conditions. Raw materials are withdrawn from the environment in large quantities and metabolic wastes are returned. To the

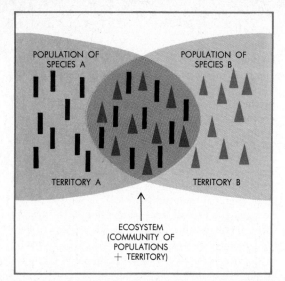

9 · 1 Communities. *When the territorial ranges of several species overlap, populations of these different species may coexist within a given limited area as a community. The organisms in such a community, plus the territory they occupy, represent an ecosystem.*

extent that these wastes differ from the original raw materials, the environment becomes altered. Moreover, the components of dead organisms also return to the environment, but not necessarily in the same place or necessarily in the same form in which they were obtained. In time, therefore, communities bring about profound redistributions and alterations of vast quantities of the earth's substance.

This means that later generations of the original community may find the changed local environment

9 · 2 Ecological succession. *Left to right, a sequence of seres from virgin land (sand) to climax (trees). The total living mass increases during this sequence.*

no longer suitable. The populations of the community must then resettle elsewhere or readapt or die out, and the result is the gradual development of population gaps within species, as already noted in the last chapter. A new community of different plants and animals thus may come to occupy the original territory, and as this community now alters the area according to its own specializations, type replacement, or *ecological succession,* may eventually follow once more. We note how closely the nonliving and the living components of an ecosystem are interlinked; change in one produces change in the other, and the passage of time alone is bound to initiate change.

Continued ecological succession ultimately leads to the establishment of a *climax community:* a set of populations which alters the local environment in such a way that the original conditions are repeatedly re-created more or less exactly. The North American prairie and forest belts are good examples of climax communities; so are the communities in large lakes and in the ocean. Climax communities represent ecological steady states, and they are perpetuated within a territory as long as local physical conditions are not altered drastically by climatic or geologic upheavals. If that happens, communal death usually follows. Development of new communities by immigration or major evolutionary adjustment of the remnants of the old community may then occur.

In an ecological succession culminating in a climax community, each developmental stage is called a *sere* (Fig. 9.2). A sequence of seres is characterized not only by changes in the sets of populations present, but also by a progressive increase in the diversity of species and the total quantity of the living mass. The sequence of seres for a given region is often fully predictable, both with respect to the general types of populations expected at each sere and to seral durations. On land, for example, a climax stage is often represented by a forest community. If the

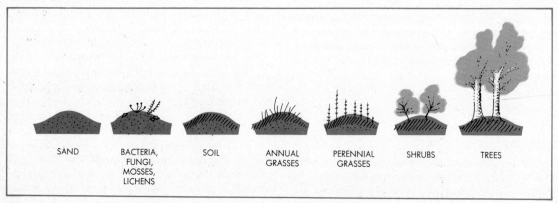

original physical environment is sand or equivalent virgin territory, then the succession of seres generally follows the pattern: soil-forming organisms (bacteria, lichens, mosses) —→ annual grasses —→ perennial grasses —→ shrubs —→ trees. Characteristic animal populations are associated with each of such seral plant populations. It can be shown that, from sand to forest climax, on the order of 1,000 years may have to elapse. If denuded but previously cultivated land is the starting condition, that is, if soil is already present, then a grass climax may be attained in about 50 years, a forest climax in about 200 years. We may note here also that successive generations of the same plant population gradually exhaust the soil in specific ways. Moreover, the dead bodies of the plants add materials to the soil which often prove to be toxic to subsequent generations of the same plants. Thus, both specific exhaustion of soil and specific additions to it promote seral succession, not only among the plants but also among the animal populations dependent on them.

Clearly, *turnover* occurs on the level of the ecosystem just as it does on all other levels of living organization. Population flux continues even after a climax has been attained, for example, given populations emigrate or die out, and the ecological niches so emptied come to be reoccupied by other, similar populations. The important point is that, after a climax has been reached, such population flux is automatically self-adjusting, and the community remains balanced internally with respect to types of populations present. Furthermore, the community also exhibits a *numerical* steady state: in all populations present, the numbers of individuals remain relatively constant on a long-term basis. In a large, permanent pond, for example, the numbers of algae, frogs, minnows, and other organisms stay more or less the same from decade to decade. Annual fluctuations are common, but over longer periods of time constancies of numbers are characteristic in most natural communities.

Three main factors create and control these striking numerical balances: *food, reproduction,* and *protection.* They are the principal links which make the populations of a community interdependent.

LINKS AND BALANCES

From the standpoint of its nutritional structure, a stable ecosystem generally consists of four parts (Fig. 9.3). The *abiotics* are the *nonliving* physical components of the environment on which the living community, or *biomass,* ultimately depends. The *autotrophs* are the photosynthetic organisms, the *producers* which subsist entirely on the abiotic por-

tion of the ecosystem. The *heterotrophs* are the *consumers,* largely animals. Herbivorous consumers subsist on the producers, and carnivorous consumers consume one another as well as the herbivores. Lastly, the *saprotrophs* are the *decomposers,* that is, bacteria and fungi. These subsist on the excretion products and the dead bodies of all producers and consumers, and thus they bring about decay and the return of raw materials to the abiotic part of the ecosystem. Evidently, the physical substance of an ecosystem *circulates,* from the abiotic part through the biomass back to the abiotic part. The circulation is maintained by the continuous influx of energy from the sun.

However, energy dissipates in the course of such cycles, and only a small fraction of a given amount of solar energy is recoverable in the form of new living plant matter. Similarly, a pound of plant food cannot make a pound of new living animal matter; for much of what a plant consists of, cellulose, for example, cannot be digested or used otherwise by animals. Moreover, even the usable portions of plants yield energy which dissipates as heat and thus cannot become useful in animal metabolism. Therefore, as raw materials are transferred from soil to plants and from plants to animals, these transfers are not 100 per cent efficient. *More* than a pound of soil is needed to make a pound of plant matter, and *more* than a pound of plant matter is needed to make a pound of animal matter. Similarly, more than 300 lb

9 · 3 *The nutritional structure of an ecosystem.* Abiotics represent the physical, nonbiological components of the system. Arrows indicate flow of energy and materials.

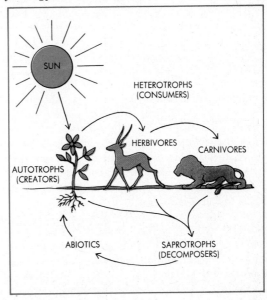

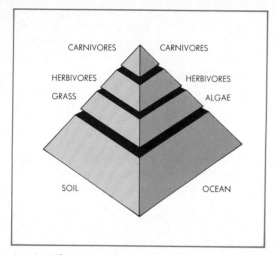

9 · 4   The general pattern of food pyramids.
Soil and ocean support plant life; herbivorous animals subsist on the plants; and carnivorous animals subsist on the herbivores.

of antelope meat or even lion meat is required to produce a 300-lb lion.

This inescapable condition leads to the establishment of *food pyramids* in the community (Fig. 9.4). So many tons of soil can support only so many fewer tons of grass. Grass in turn supports herbivores which together weigh less than the grass. And only a relatively small weight of carnivores can find sustenance in such a community. Several acres of ground thus might just suffice to support a 150-lb man. Such a pyramid of total weights and relative productivity also delineates a pyramid of individual numbers and individual sizes, for prey is generally smaller than predator; hence the balanced community may contain millions of individual grasses, but only one man.

Pyramids of this sort are one of the most potent factors in balancing communal populations; significant variations of numbers at any level of a pyramid entail automatic adjustments at every other level. For example, overgrowth of land by plants soon results in nutritional depletion of soil, since more raw materials are withdrawn from the soil. This depletion eventually leads to a starvation of the plants and decimation of their numbers. But the bodies of the dead plants now enrich the soil again, and the fewer plants which still live make less total demand on the raw materials once more present in soil. These living plants therefore can become well nourished. Hence they may reproduce relatively rapidly, and this circumstance increases their numbers again. The cycle then is repeated (Fig. 9.5).

Analogous cycles probably occur among animals.

For example, overpopulation of carnivores might result in the depletion of herbivores, since a greater number of herbivores is eaten. This depletion might lead to starvation of carnivores, hence to a reduction of their numbers. Underpopulation of carnivores then could result in overpopulation of herbivores, since fewer herbivores are eaten. But the fewer carnivores could be well fed. They might therefore reproduce relatively rapidly, and this would increase their numbers again (see Fig. 9.5). As a general result, although the numbers of all kinds of organisms would undergo short-term fluctuations, the total quantities could remain relatively constant over the long term.

The territory of an ecosystem usually supports more than one food pyramid. Each of these is characterized by a different *food chain,* culminating in a different carnivore. For example, a lion would find it extremely expensive in terms of locomotor energy to live on insects, worms, or even lizards and mice. Bigger prey, like antelope or zebra, is obviously more appropriate. On the other hand, insects and worms are suitable food for small birds; and small birds, lizards, and mice provide adequate diet for larger predatory birds. In this example, two food pyramids are based on the same plot of land. The pattern is generally much more complex. Different types of plants in one territory may sustain many different herbivores. These may form the basis of different, intricately interlocking animal food chains. As in the case of elephants, a herbivore may itself represent the peak of a food pyramid (Fig. 9.6).

It may be noted also that, in a balanced ecosystem, the total biomass yields just enough dead matter and other raw materials to replenish the soil or the ocean. This permits the continued existence of the various food pyramids above ground or in water. In such delicate nutritional interdependencies, minor fluctuations are rebalanced fairly rapidly. But serious interference, by disease, by man, or by physical factors, is likely to topple the whole pyramid. If that happens, the entire community may cease to exist.

A second link between the members of a community is reproductive interdependence. A familiar and most important example of this is the pollinating activity of insects. In some well-known cases of remarkable specialization, a given insect visits only one or a few specific flower types for pollen and nectar. The flowers (for example, snapdragons) in turn are structurally adapted to facilitate entry of the insect. Such intimate reciprocity testifies to a closely correlated evolutionary development of animal and plant. It is fairly obvious how such interdependence contributes to population balance: reduction of the insect population entails reproductive restriction of the plant, and vice versa. Similarly significant in

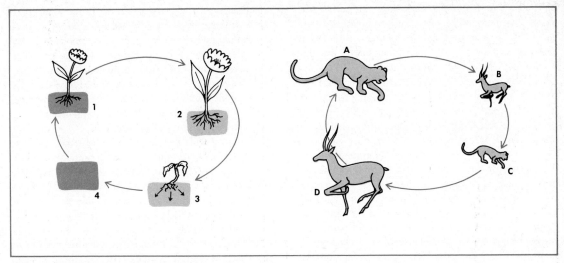

9 · 5 *Population balance in plants* (left) *and animals* (right). *A large plant population on land reduces the soil nutrients available (1, 2). This eventually leads to starvation of plants and reduction of their numbers (3). But the dead plants now enrich the soil (4), and this again permits an increase in the number of living plants. Through continued repetition of such a cycle, the size of the plant population is maintained fairly constant over the long term. In animals, a large carnivore population reduces the herbivore population by predation (A, B). This eventually decreases the food supply of carnivores and leads to starvation and decrease of the carnivore population (C). This in turn then permits the herbivore population to flourish again (D), which also permits an increase in the numbers of carnivores.*

food and absence of competition promote high reproduction rates and a rapid increase of numbers at all levels of the pyramid. The base of the pyramid therefore widens, and a larger area of the territory will be occupied. Sizable herbivores and even a few larger carnivores may gradually be assimilated into the community. As a result, the rate of predation will increase, which in turn will slowly decrease the net reproductive population gain. A turning point will

9 · 6 *Several different food chains, each culminating in a different animal, may be supported by a single plot of ground.*

balancing the reproductive growth of plant populations is the seed-dispersing activity of birds and mammals, man in particular.

Other examples of reproductive dependence are many. Birds such as cuckoos lay eggs in nests of other birds. Insects such as gall wasps embed their eggs deep in the tissues of particular plants, where the hatching larvae find food and protection. Other insects deposit eggs on or under the skin of various animals. Certain wasps, for example, kill tarantulas and lay their eggs in them.

Reproductive growth and geographic expansion of a community are intimately correlated with nutritional balances. In new territory, a pioneer association of populations will first form a small food pyramid, occupying perhaps only part of the available territory. The pyramid may still be too "low" to support any big herbivores or carnivores. Abundance of

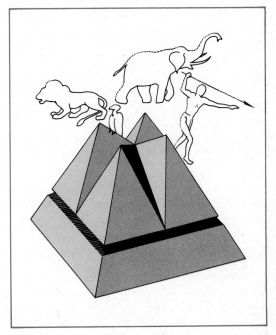

be reached eventually. Prior to it the community grows at an increasing rate; after it the community still grows, but at a decreasing rate. Net expansion finally comes to a standstill, and from then on the pyramid retains relatively stable proportions (Fig. 9.7).

In such a growth pattern, it is assumed that territorial and numerical expansion can follow its inherent trend without external restriction. Yet geographic and biological barriers often delimit an area. A small forest may be surrounded by water or by land on which trees cannot grow; a meadow may be ringed in by forest, or a valley by high mountains. In such cases, growth of a community is stopped before its inherent potential is fully expressed. The food pyramid on such a limited territory may never become high enough to support large herbivorous or carnivorous members. One searches in vain for stag in a tiny forest, for large fish in a small pond. But the one is likely to abound in worms, mice, and small birds, the other in algae, protozoa, and frogs.

In a community incapable of further expansion, steady reproduction may produce a centrifugal *population pressure*. This condition may be relieved by emigration of the overflow population. If emigration is not possible or if it is not sufficiently effective, numbers will be decimated by starvation or even sooner by epidemic diseases. The latter spread rapidly through an overpopulated, undernourished, spatially delimited community. Even if disease affects only one of the component populations, the whole communal web is likely to be disrupted.

The third main link among the populations of a community is protective interdependence. Plants in forest and grassland usually protect animals by providing shelter against enemies and adverse weather. If the opportunities for protection are reduced, both the animal and the plant population may suffer. For example, if an overpopulation of insects makes available plant shelter inadequate, the insects will become easier prey for birds and bats. But this circumstance may also decimate the plant populations, for their major pollinating agents may no longer be sufficiently effective.

Given animals in many cases are protected from other animals by *camouflage*. Such a protective device may involve body color or body shape or both (Fig. 9.8). Probably the most remarkable instance of protective coloration is the phenomenon of *mimicry*, widespread particularly among butterflies and moths. In certain of these animals, pigmentation patterns exist which are virtually indistinguishable from those of other, unrelated species. Usually those species are mimicked which are poisonous or distasteful and have few natural enemies. The advantage is that an animal resembling even superficially another more protected one will be protected too, by scaring off potential predators. Insects also display a variety of structural camouflages. For example, the individuals of certain species possess the detailed shape of leaves, of branches, or of thorns. This serves not only defensively but also as a disguise against potential victims (Fig. 9.8).

Other protective devices vary widely in type. Various birds and some mammals mimic the song and voice of other species, either defensively or as an aggressive lure. The hermit crab protects its soft abdomen in an empty snail shell of appropriate size. Schools of small pilot fish scout ahead of large sharks, leading their protectors to likely prey. Significant protection is also afforded by man, through domestication, game laws, parks, and sanctuaries.

These various examples illustrate how the member populations of a community are specialized nutritionally, reproductively, and protectively. Carnivorous populations cannot sustain themselves on plant food and not even on every kind of animal food. Herbivorous populations require plants and are incapable of hunting for animals. The populations of green plants depend on soil or ocean, and the populations of saprotrophs cannot do without dead organisms. These are profound specializations in structure and function, and they imply loss of individual self-sufficiency correlated with cooperative interdependence. Communal associations of populations evidently are a necessity. They are but extensions, on a higher biological level, of the aggregation of cells into tissues, organs, and organ systems.

Indeed, the development of "community" appears to be as integral a part of organic evolution as the

9 · 7 Population growth and geographic expansion. *As the number of individuals increases, more territory will be occupied and the food pyramid will become wider and higher* (left part of diagram). *Rates of population increase are indicated in the curve at right; rates increase to a turning point* (arrow), *then decrease.*

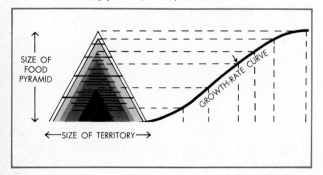

development of individual organisms. Events were probably not such that a particular organism first evolved structurally and functionally in a certain way and then happened to find the right community into which it could fit. Rather, the community probably existed from the very beginning, and all its member populations evolved together; the community itself evolved. The histories of the bumblebee and the snapdragon are linked as intimately as the histories of every man's hand and foot.

A community within a given territory includes not only free-living organisms in loose cooperative association but also organisms which live together in more or less permanent *physical* contact. Two individuals of different species may be joined so intimately that one lives right within the other. All such instances of physically intimate living together of members of different species are instances of *symbiosis*, a special form of communal life.

SYMBIOSIS

A free association in which an animal habitually shelters under a plant might, in a relatively simple evolutionary step, become an association in which the animal and the plant have entered a more permanent protective union. A plant which depends on some animal for seed dispersal might advantageously live in, or on, the animal altogether, not only at the time of seed production but throughout life. A soil bacterium or a scavenging protozoon living on the undigested elimination products of larger forms might find a surer food supply if it could adapt to an existence right in the gut cavity of its supplier.

Among ancestral populations of free-living forms, ample opportunity existed for the development of such symbiotic relationships. These opportunities were exploited to the full, and many associations arose in which two organisms of different species came to live together in intimate, lasting physical contact. Today there is no major group of organisms which does not include symbiotic species, and there is probably no individual organism which does not play *host* to at least one *symbiont*.

The phenomenon of symbiosis is expressed in two basic patterns. In *facultative* associations, two different organisms "have the faculty" of entering a more or less intimate symbiotic relationship. But they need not necessarily do so, being able to survive as free-living forms. In *obligatory* associations, on the other hand, one organism *must* unite symbiotically with another, usually a specific one, if it is to survive. The ancestors of obligatory symbionts have invariably been free-living organisms which in the course of history have lost the power of living on their own.

A

B

9 · 8 Animal disguise. A, *great resemblance to the stems and branches of a bush is exhibited by the body shapes of South African mantises. B, the forms and colors of foliage are in evidence in the bodies of dead-leaf butterflies* (top of photo).

Before becoming obligatory symbionts, they formed facultative associations with organisms on which they came to depend more and more.

Symbionts affect each other in different ways. Thus, *mutualism* describes a relationship in which both associated partners derive some benefit, often a vital one, from living together. *Commensalism* benefits one of the partners, and the other is neither helped nor harmed by the association. *Parasitism* is of advantage to the parasite but is detrimental to the host to greater or lesser extent. These categories intergrade imperceptibly, and in many boundary cases clearcut distinctions cannot be made.

MUTUALISM

An example of a loose mutualistic association is the tickbird-rhinoceros relationship. The tickbird feeds on skin parasites of the rhinoceros, and in return the latter is relieved of irritation and obtains warning of danger when the sharp-eyed bird flies off temporarily to the security of the nearest tree. Another example is the relationship between dairy ants and aphids, already cited in Chap. 8 in the section on insect societies. The ant obtains food from the aphid, and the aphid in turn secures protection, food, and care from the ant. These two examples also illustrate the difference between facultative and obligatory mutualism. Both tickbird and rhinoceros can get along without each other if necessary; but the ant cannot do without its aphids and the aphid cannot do without its ants (Fig. 9.9).

9 · 9 Mutualistic symbiosis: carpenter ant protecting a larva of a tree hopper insect. The larva benefits from the protection and in return secretes sugary honeydew, which is licked off by the ant and serves as its food.

A somewhat greater degree of physical intimacy is exhibited in the mutualistic symbiosis of sea anemones and hermit crabs. Sea anemones attach themselves to empty snail shells, and hermit crabs use these shells as protective housings. The sea anemone, an exceedingly slow mover by itself, is thus carried about on the shell of the hermit crab—an obvious advantage to the anemone in its search for food and in geographic dispersal. The hermit crab in turn benefits from the disguise. Moreover, since the anemone is not a dainty eater, scraps of food become available to the crab when the anemone catches prey. This is a facultative association; sea anemones and hermit crabs may, and largely do, live on their own.

An example of rather more intimate mutualism is provided by *lichens,* grayish and yellowish incrustations commonly found on rock surfaces as well as on tree bark (see Color Plate V, 12). These crusts are associations of photosynthesizing single-celled algae and saprotrophic threadlike fungi. The meshes of the fungal threads support the algae, and they also hold rain water like a sponge. The algae produce food for themselves and for the fungus. The fungus in turn contributes water, nitrogenous wastes, and respiratory carbon dioxide, substances which allow for continued photosynthesis and food production. Lichens may consequently survive in relatively dry terrestrial environments. The fungus may live alone in a water-sugar medium, and the alga may persist by itself in mineral-containing water. Separately, they are merely two types of organisms not particularly different from many others like them. But together they become a combination of considerable evolutionary importance. Lichens were among the first organisms capable of eking out a terrestrial existence. Contributing to the crumbling of rock and the formation of soil, they paved the way for a larger-scale colonization of the land.

The most intimate forms of mutualism involve organisms which live directly *within* other organisms. For example, the roots of certain vascular plants, particularly legumes like soybeans, clover, and peas, form important mutualistic associations with so-called *nitrogen-fixing bacteria.* The bacteria invade the roots of the hosts and the infected root cells respond by increasing in size and number. The result is the development of *root nodules* (Plate V, 12). In them, the host provides nutrients for the bacteria and the bacteria in turn fix atmospheric nitrogen; that is, they make this essential element chemically usable for both themselves and the host plant. As we shall see in the next chapter, this is a major source through which usable nitrogen becomes available to animals.

Analogously invasive forms of mutualism occur in associations between algae and various other organisms. For example, many free-living protozoa (for example, a species of *Paramecium*) and coelenterates (for example, several species of *Hydra* and various types of corals) harbor green single-celled algae within their translucent bodies. Known as *zoochlorellae* and *zooxanthellae,* the algae supply food and oxygen, as in lichens, and in turn receive protection, water, and other materials essential for continued photosynthesis.

In the gut of termites live flagellate protozoa which secrete an enzyme capable of digesting the cellulose of wood. Termites chew and swallow wood, the intestinal flagellates then digest it, and both organisms share the resulting carbohydrates. Thus, to the detriment of man, termites may exploit unlimited food opportunities open to very few other animals. And the protozoa receive protection and are assured of a steady food supply.

Virtually every animal possessing an alimentary canal houses billions of intestinal bacteria, particularly in the lower gut. These bacteria draw freely on materials not digested or not digestible by the host, and as a result of their activities, they initiate fecal decay (see Chap. 17). The host generally benefits from the auxiliary digestion carried out by the bacteria and in many instances is also dependent on certain of the bacterial byproducts. For example, man and other mammals obtain many vitamins in the form of "waste" materials released by the bacterial symbionts of the gut.

Parasitic associations may sometimes develop into mutualistic ones. In the course of successive generations, a relationship in which one partner originally lives at the expense of the other may change gradually into an association beneficial to both. Thus, mutualistic intestinal bacteria might have evolved from originally parasitic ancestors. As we shall see shortly, it is adaptively advantageous to a parasite not to jeopardize its own survival opportunity, and in the course of evolution this factor often tends to change a parasitic relation into either a commensalistic or a mutualistic one.

COMMENSALISM

Just as the chance association of two free-living organisms may develop into mutualism, so an analogous chance association may develop into commensalism. As far as can be demonstrated, the commensal neither harms nor helps its host, and the host appears neither to resist nor to foster the relationship in any way.

Among plants, commensalism is illustrated by numerous *epiphytes.* An epiphyte is a plant which grows on another host plant, but the latter is neither

9 · 10 Epiphytes. *The photograph shows ferns growing epiphytically on a tree trunk.*

harmed nor helped. Tropical ferns and plants closely related to the pineapple, for example, the *bromeliads,* frequently occur as epiphytes on jungle trees. The symbionts obtain water and minerals from pockets in the host tree. In many cases, such epiphytes also possess modified cup-shaped leaves which catch rain water. Aerial roots of the epiphyte then may grow into these cups and absorb the water collected there (Fig. 9.10).

Animal commensalism is illustrated, for example, by a species of small tropical fish. Individuals of this species find shelter in the cloacae of sea cucumbers. The fish darts out for food and returns, to the utter indifference of the host. The so-called shark sucker, or *remora,* provides another example. This fish (Fig. 9.11) possesses a dorsal fin modified into a holdfast device. By means of it, the fish attaches to the underside of sharks and thereby secures scraps of food, wide geographic dispersal, and protection. The shark neither benefits nor suffers in any respect. In still another example, barnacles may attach to the skin of whales, an association which secures geographic distribution and wider feeding opportunities for the sessile crustaceans. In this instance, a trend toward parasitism is in evidence; in some cases the barnacles send rootlike processes into the whale, outgrowths which eat away bits of host tissue.

9 · 11   Commensalism. *Shark with three remoras, or suckerfish, attached to underside.*

These and most other existing commensalistic unions tend to be facultative; for a symbiont is not likely to be allowed to impose on a host in intimate, obligatory fashion unless the host derives at least some benefits from such an imposition and therefore fosters the association, or unless the symbiont has overcome the host's defenses and is frankly parasitic. Consequently, although obligatory commensalistic associations may have evolved quite often, most of them have probably been unstable; they would soon have changed either into mutualism or into parasitism.

PARASITISM

Parasitic Ways of Life

It has probably become apparent in the above that symbiosis revolves largely, though not exclusively, around the problem of food. We might suspect, therefore, that symbiosis in general and parasitism in particular would be most prevalent among organisms in which competition for food is most intense. This is actually the case. Although some parasitic green plants do exist (for example, mistletoes, Fig. 9.12), photosynthesizing organisms by and large are not under competitive pressure for basic nutrients; air, water, and sunlight are present everywhere in virtually inexhaustible quantities. Parasitism flourishes primarily among organisms that must obtain food from others, that is, in heterotrophs—viruses, bacteria, fungi, and animals.

All viruses are parasitic. They consist mainly of nucleic acids, the only other structural part being an external mantle of protein (Fig. 9.13). Note therefore that viruses are not cells and not organisms; they are considerably less than cells or organisms. We know also that at least some viruses arise as fragments broken off from the nucleic acid material of a donor cell. Such fragments then direct that cell to manufacture protein mantles around them. The so-formed viruses subsequently escape from their host, often disintegrating the host cell in the process, and exist free in air or water. They are quite inert in the free state and become reactivated if, and only if, they enter some new cell. In such infections, a virus becomes attached to the surface of the new host and then the nucleic acid mass of the virus is squeezed out from the protein mantle, through the cell surface, into the cell interior. The empty mantle itself does not enter the host. Within the host cell, the viral nucleic acids now may parasitize the living apparatus of the cell for renewed virus formation; the nucleic acids reproduce and new protein mantles are constructed around them.

Among bacteria, those not photosynthetic or saprotrophic are parasitic. Among fungi, some are saprotrophic, the rest are parasitic. And in animals, many phyla and classes are wholly parasitic; virtually all others include important parasitic subgroups.

As will become apparent in Chap. 11, parasitism is almost as old as life itself. So advantageous and economical is the parasitic mode of living that many parasites may be infested with smaller parasites of their own and these in turn may support still smaller ones. For example, a mammal may harbor parasitic worms; these may be invaded by parasitic bacteria; and the bacteria may be infected by *bacteriophages*, or viruses that parasitize bacteria (Fig. 9.14). *Hyperparasitism* of this sort, that is, one parasite inside another, is very common. It represents a natural exploitation of the very condition of parasitism. Inasmuch as the parasite is generally smaller than the host and inasmuch as one host may support many parasites, parasitic and hyperparasitic relationships form inverted

9 · 12   Mistletoe, *parasitic on branch of pine tree.*

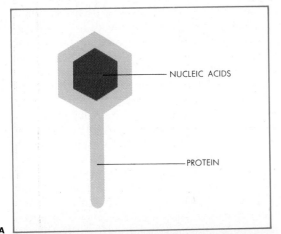

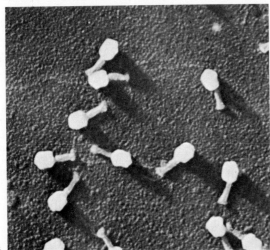

9 · 13 *Viruses.* A, *diagram of virus structure.* B, *electron micrograph of actual viruses.* C, *a virus crystal. In this state viruses are nonliving; they exhibit living properties only when present within host cells.*

food pyramids contained within the pyramids of the larger community.

The first problem a potential parasite faces is the defense mobilized by a potential host. Attachment to the outer body surface can be prevented only with difficulty, particularly if the host does not possess limbs. Numerous *ectoparasites* exploit this possibility. Equipped with suckers, clamps, or adhesive surfaces, they hold onto skin or hair, and with the aid of cutting, biting, or sucking mouth parts, or with rootlike outgrowths, they feed on the body fluids of the host. Examples are leeches, lice, ticks, mites, lampreys, and many fungi.

Endoparasites, within the body of the host, must breach more formidable defenses. Cellular enzymes of a host, digestive juices and strong acids in the alimentary tract, antibodies in the blood, white blood cells and other cells which engulf foreign bodies in amoeboid fashion (for example, histiocytes), these are among the defensive agents guarding against the invader. Overcoming such defenses means *specialization:* development of resistant outer coverings, bacteria, fungi, and as in most parasitic worms; development of cyst walls and calcareous capsules; development of hooks or clamps with which to hold onto the gut wall; development of enzymes which, when secreted, erode a path through host tissues.

Specialization of the parasite also involves the selection of *specific* hosts. Highly advanced parasites cannot pick a host at random, even if many similar ones offer the same type of nutrients. During the evolution of a parasite, structural and functional

9 · 14 *Electron micrograph of the remnants of a bacterium after attack by bacteriophages. The virus parasites are the small rodlets with knobbed ends.*

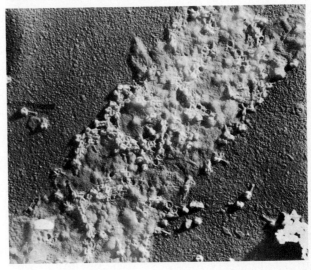

specializations have developed in adaptation to particular hosts only. Thus, most parasites enter a host's body by fixed routes, then settle in fixed regions, as if in the course of time they had learned to channel their attack through points of weakness characteristic of particular hosts.

Breaching the host's defenses is a perennial problem to the parasite. No sooner has it developed an avenue to a comfortable existence than the infected individual is discriminated against in his environment; healthy hosts which have evolved a resistance to the parasite have a better chance of surviving. For example, large-scale infection of a population with parasites will lead to the preferential survival of those hosts which, through random mutations, develop specific means of combating the infectious agents. Hence if a parasite is to prevail against host defenses continually improved by evolution, it too must readjust and evolve. Through its own random mutations, it must develop new means of attack.

We recognize that parasite and host evolve *together*, first the parasite, then the host being one jump ahead. The very fact that free-living organisms exist at all today signifies that they are resistant to a good many potential parasites by which they are constantly besieged. The very fact that parasites continue to exist signifies that free-living organisms are not completely resistant—and they probably can never be,

in view of the evolutionary inventiveness of the parasites.

It may be noted in this connection that it is to the obvious advantage of the parasite to keep the host alive. We find, indeed, that the virulence of a parasite often decreases with time. When a parasite-host relationship is first established, the invader is likely to be *pathogenic,* or disease-producing. Two parallel evolutionary trends then tend to reduce this pathogenicity. One is natural discrimination against infected hosts, as indicated above; the least resistant will be eliminated through plagues and epidemics. At the same time, less virulent populations of a given parasite will be favored; for when a parasite kills a host, the killer is generally killed as well. Therefore, the more harmful the parasite, the more difficult is its perpetuation. Many parasites are only mildly pathogenic, or not at all, often indicating long association with a particular host. In time the parasitic relation may actually become commensalistic or mutualistic.

Parasitic Simplification

Once established in the body of a host, the parasite may pursue a life of comparative ease. Embedded in food, it needs no locomotor equipment, few sense organs, no fast nervous reflexes. Indeed, structural and functional *simplification* is a nearly universal characteristic of parasites. Here we encounter the ultimate expression of the principle that loss of self-sufficiency tends to be proportional to the degree of interdependence of organisms.

Structural simplification is exhibited, for example, by mistletoes. The dwarf mistletoe, common on western cone-bearing trees, has only the slightest vestiges of leaves. Moreover, absorption of water and inorganic materials from the host occurs not through true roots, but through rows of parenchyma cells which grow like fungus filaments through the host tissue. Among animal parasites, structural simplification is pronounced in tapeworms, for example (Fig. 9.15). These parasitic flatworms possess only a highly reduced nervous system, a greatly reduced muscular system, and not even a vestige of a digestive system. Almost like blotting paper, the worms soak up through their body walls the food juices in the host gut. Even more simplified is the adult of *Sacculina*, a crustacean parasitizing its not too remote relatives, crabs. The parasitic adult is little more than a formless, semifluid mass of cells which spreads through a crab like a malignant tumor. The invader later produces sperms and eggs, and fertilized eggs then develop into recognizably typical, free-swimming crustacean larvae. These attach to crabs, enter them, and change into the simplified adults (Fig. 9.16).

9 · 15 Tapeworms. *A, head, or scolex, with hooks and suckers. B, segmental sections, or proglottids, near middle of body. C, proglottids near hind end of body. Tree-shaped structures in B and C are reproductive organs. Note testes filling proglottids in B and genital pores opening on the sides of the proglottids. In C, the uterus filled with eggs is conspicuous. A digestive system is absent in these worms.*

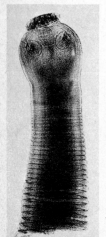 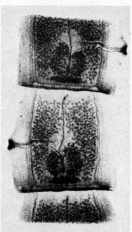 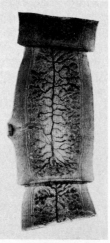

A   B   C

Simplification also extends to metabolic activities. In particular, the synthetic capacities of a parasite are almost invariably restricted. For example, in the presence of nitrogen sources and simple carbohydrates like glucose, a *free-living* soil bacterium or fungus may synthesize amino acids, proteins, vitamins, numerous antibiotics useful to man, in short, all the complex compounds that make up the living matter of the organism. By contrast, an obligatorily parasitic bacterium or fungus promptly dies when given nitrogenous and simple organic substances alone. It has reduced synthesizing capacities and has become dependent on its host to supply it with most of the components of its living substance in prefabricated form.

In this respect, the modern viruses are the most simplified. They cannot metabolize or self-perpetuate at all except within living host cells. Removed from cells, they become lifeless crystals of complex chemicals; and they may resume metabolic and self-perpetuative activities only when they are reintroduced into living host cells (see Fig. 9.13). Other parasites may be free-living at least at some stage of their life cycle, but viruses are never free-living. Their parasitism is total, complete, obligatory. It should be noted here, however, that viruses actually cannot be considered to be in the same category as other parasites; viruses are chemical complexes and not cellular organisms like other parasites. Moreover, the ancestors of all other parasites were free-living organisms, whereas the ancestors of viruses probably were the genetic substances of bacteria (see Chap. 11). These substances were never free-living to begin with.

In parasitic organisms, simplification is probably an adaptive advantage, for the reduced condition may be more economical than the fully developed condition of the free-living ancestor. A tapeworm, for example, being structurally reduced, may concentrate all its resources into parasitizing the host; it need not divert energy and materials into maintaining elaborate nervous, muscular, or digestive systems, which are unnecessary anyway in this parasitic way of life.

Parasitic Reproduction

In one respect parasites are far from simplified: reproduction. In this function they are as prolific as the most prolific free-living forms. The practical necessity of an enormous reproductive potential is correlated with a major problem confronting the parasite, particularly the endoparasite, namely, how to get from one host to another. The problem is severely compounded by the requirement that not

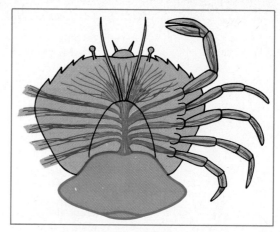

9 · 16 *The crustacean parasite* Sacculina (colored), *attached to the abdomen of a crab. The exteriorly formless adult parasite, related to barnacles, spreads tissue outgrowth into the host.* (Adapted from Calman.)

any new host will do. Another individual of the same host species must be found.

Parasites succeed in two ways, both of which involve reproduction: *active transfer* and *passive transfer*. In the former, one stage of the life cycle of the parasite is free-living and motile, and this stage transfers from one host to another through its own powers of locomotion. For example, the adult phase may be parasitic and the free-living embryo or larva may be capable of locomotion, as in *Sacculina*. Or the larval phase may be the parasite, the adult then being free-living and capable of locomotion. This is the case in a number of parasitic insects which deposit their eggs within or on individuals of other species (see Color Plate VI, 13).

Passive transfer is encountered among parasites in which no phase of the life cycle is capable of locomotion. Propagation here is accomplished by wind, by water, or by *intermediate hosts*. The latter offer a means of transfer not quite so chancy as random distribution by wind or water. What is involved here is well illustrated in the propagation of tapeworms (Fig. 9.17).

These parasites of man and other mammals, like numerous others, exploit one of the easiest routes into and out of the host, namely, the alimentary tract. Entering through the host's mouth by way of eaten food and leaving through the anus by way of feces, tapeworms spend their adult life directly in the gut cavity of the host. Other endoparasites utilize the gut as a springboard from which to invade interior tissues. The problem is to transfer offspring from one host, for example, a man, to another by passive means.

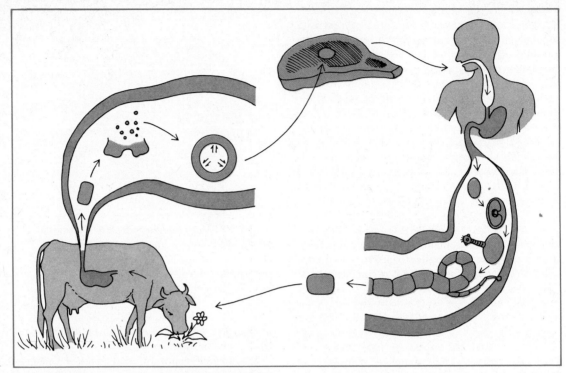

9 · 17 *The life cycle of a beef tapeworm* (color). *Ripe sections of the worm pass with the feces from the human gut. Eggs are released from these sections in the gut of cattle. Walled, hook-bearing tapeworm embryos then encapsulate in beef muscle, and the embryos become adults in the intestine of man. The head (scolex) of the worm is invaginated at first, but it soon everts and with the hooks and newly developed suckers it attaches to intestinal tissues.*

Tapeworms accomplish a first phase of this readily; namely, mature eggs are released to the outside with the host's feces.

Since man does not eat feces, the eggs evidently cannot reach new human hosts directly. However, tapeworms ingeniously take advantage of the food pyramids of which man is a member; man eats beef, and cattle eat grass. A ready-made pathway from grass to man thus exists, and the transfer chain becomes complete if, as happens on occasion, human feces are deposited on grass. Tapeworm eggs clinging to such vegetation may then be eaten by cattle.

In the intestine of a cow, a tapeworm egg develops into an embryo and such an embryo bores a path through the gut wall into the cow's bloodstream. From there the embryo is carried into beef muscle, where it encapsulates and matures. If man then eats raw or partially cooked beef, the capsule surrounding

the young tapeworm is digested away in the human gut and the free worm now hooks on to the intestinal wall of its new host (see Fig. 9.17).

This history illustrates a very widely occurring phenomenon. Many kinds of parasites utilize well-established food pyramids in transferring to new hosts. Often there is more than one intermediate host, as in the life cycle of the Chinese liver fluke (Fig. 9.18). The adults of this parasitic flatworm infest the liver of man. Fertilized eggs are released via the bile duct into the gut of the host and pass to the outside with the feces. If the feces get into ponds or rivers, as happens frequently, the eggs develop into so-called *miracidium* larvae.

Such a larva must then enter a snail, and in the tissues of this animal the miracidium develops into another larval type, called a *sporocyst*. The latter subsequently gives rise to many *redia* larvae, which feed on snail tissue and grow. Then each of the rediae produces yet another set of many larvae, called *cercariae*. These fourth-generation larvae escape from the snail and swim about freely. If within a short time they happen to find a fish, they bore into it and encapsulate in muscular tissue. And if man subsequently eats raw or incompletely cooked fish, the young adult flukes find their way from the human gut into the liver.

Note that this cycle involves two intermediate

9 · 18   The life-cycle of a Chinese liver fluke.
The detailed structure of the adult is shown in
Fig. 14.33. A, adult in liver of man; B, egg,
passing out with feces and eaten by snail; C,
miracidium larva in snail; D, sporocyst; E, one
of many rediae, formed from sporocyst; F, cer-
caria; G, cercariae escape from snail and en-
capsulate in fish muscle.

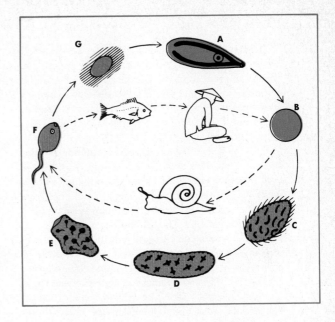

hosts, the snail and the fish. Transfer is partly passive (man to snail, fish to man), partly active (snail
to fish). Note particularly the multistage, larva-within-
a-larva type of development. Characteristic of flukes
generally, larval polymorphism of this sort constitutes
a highly efficient method of enormously increasing
the number of reproductive units. A single fluke egg
is estimated to yield a final total of some 10,000
cercariae—and a single adult fluke may produce many
tens of thousands of eggs. Hence the chances become
fairly good that at least some of the millions or billions of larvae will reach final hosts.

Through active locomotion, through physical
agents such as air and water, and through routes involving food pyramids and intermediate hosts, parasites have solved their transfer problems most successfully. So successfully, indeed, that there are
many more individual parasites in existence than
free-living organisms.

A community consists of various kinds of free-
living and various kinds of symbiotic populations.
Which particular ones of each type actually compose
a given community, hence the nature of a whole
ecosystem, is determined largely by the nature of
the physical environment. We shall examine this
abiotic part of the biosphere in the following chapter.

REVIEW QUESTIONS

1. Define ecosystem, biomass, biota, community.
What is the species structure of a community? What
factors produce and maintain such a structure?

2. Describe the life cycle of a community. What
are ecological succession, climax communities, seres?
Describe the nutritional structure of a community.
What maintains such a structure?

3. What are food pyramids and food chains, and
what factors produce and maintain them? Show how
nutritional factors contribute to the long-range
numerical constancies within communities.

4. Describe reproductive links that make the components of communities interdependent. What are
the growth characteristics of communities? What is
population pressure?

5. What kinds of protective links unite the members of communities? Show how such links contribute
to numerical population balances. Give examples of
mimicry and various forms of camouflage in animals.

6. What are the various forms of symbiosis and

how are they defined? Give specific examples of each.
What are lichens, root nodules, zoochlorellae? To
what other organisms is man a host in mutualistic
or commensalistic relationships?

7. What general structural and functional characteristics distinguish parasites from free-living
organisms? Distinguish between ectoparasites and
endoparasites and give examples.

8. What is hyperparasitism? In what ways are
parasites adapted to ectoparasitic or endoparasitic
modes of life? What is the adaptive advantage of
parasitic simplification? In what ways are parasites
simplified?

9. Distinguish between active and passive transfers in parasite life cycles. What is the role of food
pyramids in parasite transfers? What are intermediate
hosts?

10. Review the life cycles of tapeworms and liver
flukes and show what general principles of parasite
transfer are illustrated by these cycles.

COLLATERAL READINGS

Billings, W. D.: "Plants and the Ecosystem," Wadsworth, Belmont, Calif., 1964. This paperback, already referred to in the last chapter, may again be consulted at this juncture. The sections on dynamics and types of ecosystems are particularly pertinent.

Burnet, F. M.: Viruses, *Sci. American,* May, 1951. A good general discussion.

Carson, R. L.: "Silent Spring," Houghton Mifflin, Boston, 1962. This book (which caused considerable controversy when it first appeared) intends to document the disruptive effect of man's use of chemicals and other agents on the ecological balance of nature.

Dunbar, M. J.: The Evolution of Stability in Marine Environments: Natural Selection at the Level of the Ecosystem, *Am. Naturalist,* vol. 94, 1960. A case study of the development of stable communities.

Harzen, W. E.: "Readings in Population and Community Ecology," Saunders, Philadelphia, 1964. A compilation containing discussions of many topics covered in this chapter.

Jacob, F., and E. L. Wollman: Viruses and Genes, *Sci. American,* June, 1961. An account of how bacteriophage infections have thrown light on the mechanism of heredity.

Kendeigh, S. C.: "Animal Ecology," Prentice-Hall, Englewood Cliffs, N.J., 1961. This book may likewise be consulted for further data on topics of this chapter.

Lamb, I. M.: Lichens, *Sci. American,* Oct., 1959. A case study of symbiosis.

Limbaugh, C.: Cleaning Symbiosis, *Sci. American,* Aug., 1961. This article describes mutualistic and commensalistic relationships among marine fishes.

Lwoff, A.: The Life Cycle of a Virus, *Sci. American,* Mar., 1954. A noted virologist and biologist writes on a subject clearly described by its title.

Odum, E. P.: "Fundamentals of Ecology," 2d ed., Saunders, Philadelphia, 1959. One of the standard texts, recommended for background data on specific points.

————: "Ecology," Holt, New York, 1963. A recommended paperback; includes sections on the cyclical processes within ecosystems.

Oosting, H. J.: "The Study of Plant Communities," 2d ed., Freeman, San Francisco, 1956. Like the preceding text by Odum, recommended as a comprehensive source book.

Rogers, W. P.: "The Nature of Parasitism," Academic, New York, 1962. Well worth consulting for a more thorough study of this aspect of symbiosis.

Slobodkin, L. B.: "Growth and Regulation of Animal Populations," Holt, New York, 1961. This small book represents a good introduction to quantitative animal ecology; some (but not extensive) facility with mathematical concepts is desirable.

CHAPTER 10
BIOSPHERE
AND
HABITAT

All individuals, populations, and communities depend directly on their physical *environment;* their evolution is oriented by it and their continued existence is made possible by it. In the first section below we shall examine this interrelation between the non-living and the living components of the biosphere. In the second section, our attention will be focused on the different types of homes, or *habitats,* that the environment actually provides for living communities.

THE ENVIRONMENT

All living functions begin with raw materials, and all basic raw materials ultimately come from the physical environment of the earth. The environment also influences organisms in other major ways. For example, every cellular reaction, hence every organism as a whole, is affected greatly by environmental temperature, pressure, the nature of the surrounding medium, in short, by geography and weather generally. In this respect, forces of global dimensions have a direct bearing on forces of molecular dimensions. We may note, therefore, that the environment sets the stage for life principally in two ways: the environment is the ultimate supplier of all raw materials, and it provides the physical and chemical background against which living processes must be carried out. How does the environment function in these roles?

The most important general observation we can make about the environment is that it is forever changing, on every scale from the submicroscopic to the global. The physical world is subjected unceas-

ingly to various astrophysical, meteorologic, geologic, and geochemical forces which alter every component of the earth sooner or later, very rapidly in some cases, rather slowly in others. Being part of the earth's substance, living matter too is subjected to these forces and it therefore undergoes unceasing change. The very origin of living matter on earth was itself a result of environmental change, and organisms then became a powerful cause of continued change.

The fundamental reason for uninterrupted environmental change is that the earth as a whole, hence also living matter and every other component, is an *open system.* Such systems exchange materials, energy, or both with their surroundings. By contrast, a *closed system* exchanges nothing with its surroundings (see Chap. 5). On earth, to be sure, the amounts of material entering from space or leaving into space are negligible. However, *energy* both enters and leaves, and this makes the earth an open system. Most importantly, various forms of solar energy—heat, light, X rays, ultraviolet rays, and many others—beam to earth uninterruptedly; and enormous amounts of energy radiate out, principally in the form of heat. As a result, the earth's material substance can never attain static equilibrium; so long as the sun shines and the earth spins, energy flux creates balance-upsetting disturbances. Every imbalance creates new imbalances of its own, and, as a general consequence, the earth's environment is forever changing.

Such changes, being produced primarily by sun and planetary motion, occur predominantly in rhythmic, patterned *cycles.* Daily and seasonal climatic cycles are familiar examples. Other environmental cycles may be less readily discernible, particularly if their scale is too vast or too minute or if they occur too fast or too slowly for direct observation. Organisms are interposed into these cycles; and as the earth's components circulate, some of these components become raw materials in living processes.

The physical environment is the ultimate source which supplies organisms with all required *inorganic* nutrients. From some of these, the required *organic* nutrients, or *foods,* must then be manufactured and distributed within the living world itself. Thus, all organisms build up their bodies at the ultimate expense of inorganic materials withdrawn directly from the physical environment. Excretion products formed within organisms return to the environment largely while the organisms live. And when they die, all other materials of their bodies return to the environment as well. As we shall see, *decay* caused by saprotrophic bacteria and fungi gradually retransforms all the returned substances into the same kinds of inorganic materials which were withdrawn from the environment originally (Fig. 10.1).

Living organisms may therefore be envisaged as transient constructions built out of materials "borrowed" temporarily from the environment. One important corollary of this is that, despite its material contribution to the formation of organisms, the physical earth *conserves* all its raw materials on a long-term basis; and this makes possible an indefinitely continued, repeated re-creation of living matter. Therefore, the continuity of life depends on the parallel continuity of death.

A second corollary is that, because of their life and their death, organisms contribute in major ways to the movement of earth substances in cycles. Billions of tons of materials are withdrawn from the environment into billions of organisms all over the world, are made components of living matter, are

10 · 1 *Cyclical interaction between the physical environment and living matter. Raw materials taken by living matter from the physical environment return to the latter through excretion and decay.*

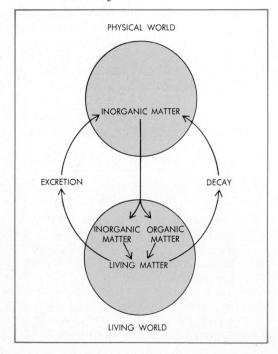

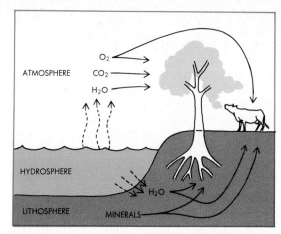

10 · 2 *The material contributions of each of the three subdivisions of the environment to the maintenance of living matter are depicted in this diagram.*

redistributed among and between organisms, and are finally put back into the environment as they were obtained. Such life-involving cycles become part of and often reinforce and contribute to the physical cycles on earth. As in the purely physical cycles, those in which living matter participates run on energy supplied by the sun. Solar energy is trapped by living organisms via photosynthesis, and some of this energy is later spent by organisms in moving parts of the earth through their bodies.

The global environment consists of three main subdivisions. The *hydrosphere* includes all liquid components, that is, the water in oceans, lakes, rivers, and on land. The *lithosphere* comprises the solid components, that is, the rocky substance of the continents. And the *atmosphere* is the gaseous mantle which envelops the hydrosphere and the lithosphere. Living organisms require inorganic raw materials from each of these subdivisions. The hydrosphere supplies liquid *water;* the lithosphere supplies all other *minerals;* and the atmosphere supplies *oxygen, nitrogen,* and *carbon dioxide.* Together, these inorganic materials provide all the chemical elements needed in the construction and maintenance of living matter (Fig. 10.2). In addition to being sources of supply, the three subdivisions of the environment also affect organisms in various other specific ways. We shall examine the contributions of each of the subdivisions in turn.

THE HYDROSPHERE

Water is the most abundant surface mineral of the planet. It covers some 73 per cent of the earth's surface entirely and it is a major constituent of the lithosphere and the atmosphere. As noted in Chap. 6, water is also the most abundant component of living matter. It is not surprising, therefore, that it is the major inorganic nutrient required by all living organisms. In metabolism, water is the exclusive source of the element hydrogen and one of several sources of oxygen.

The basic water cycle which moves and conserves water in the environment is quite familiar. Solar energy evaporates water from the hydrosphere into the atmosphere. Subsequent cooling and condensation of the vapor at higher altitudes produces clouds, and precipitation as rain or snow then returns the water to the hydrosphere. This is the most massive process of any kind on earth, consuming more energy and moving more material than any other (Fig. 10.3).

In using water as metabolic raw material, organisms withdraw it principally from the hydrospheric segment of the global cycle. Aquatic organisms absorb water directly from their liquid environment; they excrete some of it back while they live; and after death the remainder, still in the form of liquid water, is returned through decay. Terrestrial organisms are interposed more extensively in the global cycle, and indeed they contribute substantially to its continuance. These organisms absorb liquid water from the reservoir present in soil and in bodies of fresh water. Plants and animals move such water through their bodies and in the process they retain required quantities. The remainder is excreted, partly as liquid water but more particularly as water vapor which raises the moisture content of the atmosphere. We may note that a given quantity of environmental water is moved from hydrosphere to

atmosphere far faster through the metabolic agency of living organisms than if that water were simply allowed to evaporate directly from the hydrosphere. In other words, the metabolism of terrestrial organisms actively accelerates the global water cycle. Sometimes this may have an effect on the climate. For example, the trees of tropical jungles release so much water vapor that the air over vast areas remains permanently saturated with moisture, cloudbursts occurring almost every evening. After terrestrial organisms die, any liquid water in their bodies again returns to the hydrosphere through decay.

Water influences organisms not only through its function as a prime nutrient but also through its effect on almost all aspects of climate and weather, both in the sea and on land. Very largely, these effects are immediate or distant consequences of the interplay between solar energy, the rotation and revolution of the earth, and the hydrosphere—the same interplay which also produces the global water cycle.

In the ocean, water warmed in the tropics becomes light and rises to the surface, whereas cool polar water sinks. These up-down displacements bring about massive horizontal shifts of water between equator and pole. The rotation of the earth introduces east-west displacements. These effects, reinforced substantially by similarly patterned wind-producing air movements, result in *oceanic currents*. The latter influence climatic conditions not only within the seas, but also in the air and on land (Fig. 10.4).

Another climatic effect is a result of the thermal properties of water. Of all liquids, water is one of the slowest to heat or cool, and it stores a very large amount of thermal energy. The oceans thus become huge reservoirs of solar heat. The result is that sea air chilled by night becomes less cold because of *heat radiation* from water warmed by day. Conversely, sea air warmed by day becomes less hot because of *heat absorption* by water cooled by night. Warm or cool onshore winds then moderate the inland climate in daily patterns. Analogous but more profound effects are produced by heat radiation and absorption in seasonal summer and winter patterns.

Third, global climate over long periods of time is determined by the relative amount of water locked into *polar ice*. Temperature variations averaging only a few degrees over the years, produced by still poorly understood geophysical changes, suffice for major advance or retreat of polar ice. Ice ages have developed and waned during the last million years, and warm *interglacial* periods, characterized by ice-free poles, have intervened between successive

10 · 3   The global water cycle. Evaporated water eventually returns to earth through precipitation.

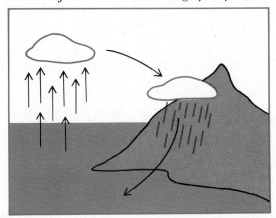

advances of ice. At the present time, the earth is
slowly emerging from the last ice age, which reached
its peak some 50,000 to 20,000 years ago. As polar
ice is melting, water levels are now rising and coast
lines are gradually being submerged. If trends during
the past 50 years are reliable indications, the earth
appears to be warming up generally. Deserts are
presently expanding; snow lines on mountains are
receding to higher altitudes; in given localities, more
days of the year are snow-free; and the flora and
fauna native to given latitudes are slowly spreading
poleward. It is difficult to be sure whether these
changes are merely part of a short warm cycle or
are really indicative of a long-range trend.

All these various cyclic changes in the hydrosphere have a profound impact on all organisms. By
influencing temperature, humidity, amount of precipitation, winds, waves, currents, and indeed the
very presence or absence of water in given localities,
they play a major role in determing what kinds and
amounts of metabolism are possible in such localities,
hence what kinds and amounts of organisms may
live there.

THE LITHOSPHERE

This subdivision of the environment plays two vital
roles. First, as already pointed out above, it is the
exclusive source of most *mineral* raw materials for all
organisms, terrestrial as well as aquatic; and, second,
it forms the bulk component of *soil*, required specifically by terrestrial plants and by numerous subterranean animals.

Minerals

Like the world's water, the rocky substance of the
earth's surface moves in a gigantic cycle, but here
the rate of circulation is measured in thousands
and millions of years. One segment of this global
mineral cycle is *diastrophism*, the vertical uprising

10 · 4   The circulation of ocean water. *A cross-
sectional profile of the ocean between equator and
pole is shown at top. Water warmed in equatorial
regions rises and water cooled in polar regions
sinks. This produces north-south and up-down
circulation as indicated. However, this basic
equator-to-pole movement is modified by the
rotation of the earth, by winds, and by the position of the continents. The map at bottom indicates the actual surface circulation produced
and the names and flow directions of the chief
currents.*

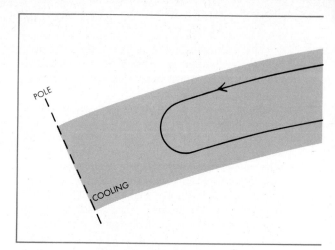

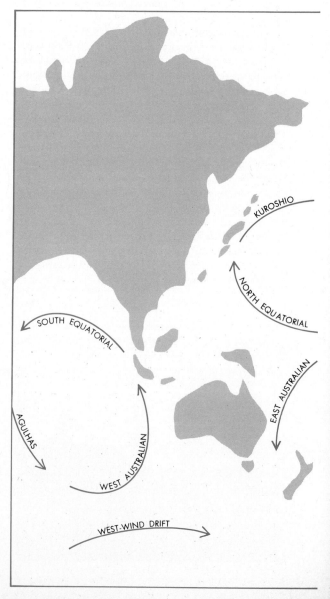

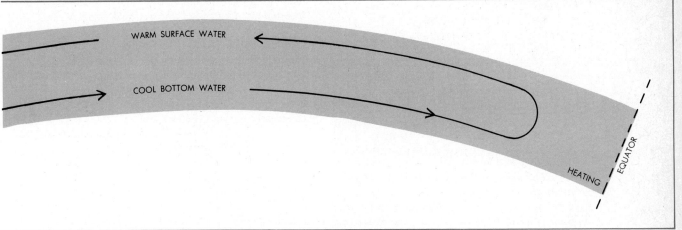

WARM SURFACE WATER

COOL BOTTOM WATER

HEATING

EQUATOR

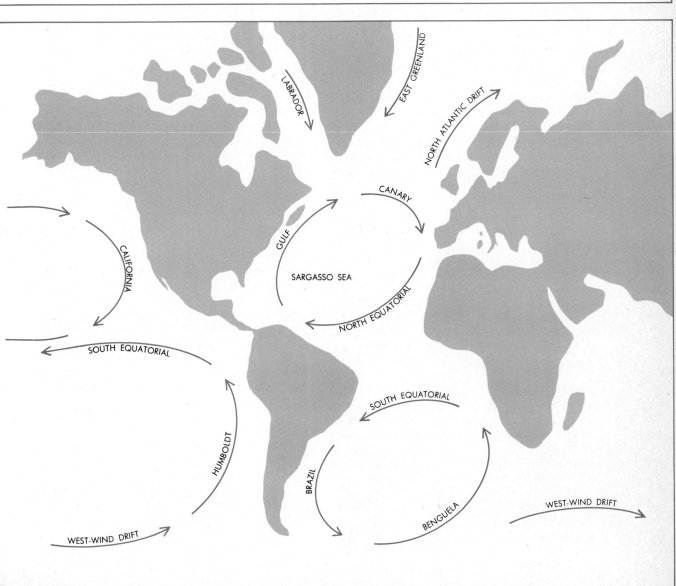

LABRADOR

EAST GREENLAND

NORTH ATLANTIC DRIFT

CANARY

GULF

CALIFORNIA

SARGASSO SEA

NORTH EQUATORIAL

SOUTH EQUATORIAL

SOUTH EQUATORIAL

HUMBOLDT

BRAZIL

BENGUELA

WEST-WIND DRIFT

WEST-WIND DRIFT

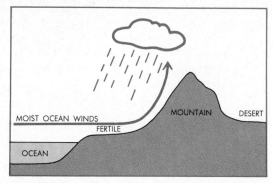

10 · 5 The effect of a mountain on climate. *A mountain deflects moisture-rich ocean winds upward and causes rain to remain confined to the slope facing the ocean. That slope will therefore be fertile, but the far slope will become a desert.*

of large tracts of the earth's crust. Major parts of continents or indeed whole continents may undergo such diastrophic movements. They occur when a land mass is pushed up from below or is subjected to great lateral pressure, generated in adjacent por-

10 · 6 The cutting, erosive effect of a river. *The canyon was channeled out by the stream flowing through it.*

tions of the earth's crust. Uplifting or upbuckling then follows. Changes of this sort take place exceedingly slowly. The most striking instance of diastrophism is *mountain building*. Presently the youngest and highest mountain ranges are the Himalayas, the Rockies, the Andes, and the Alps. All of them were thrown up some 70 million years ago, and we may note that the earth crust in these regions is not completely settled even now.

Quite apart from the tremendous upheaval caused by mountain formation itself, such an event has long-lasting effects on climate, hence on organisms. A high, massive mountain barrier is likely to interfere drastically with continental air circulation. For example, moisture-laden ocean winds may no longer be able to pass across the barrier. Continual rain will therefore fall on the near side and the region may become lush and fertile. By contrast, the far side will be arid and desert conditions are likely to develop (Fig. 10.5). The following are two good examples: fertile California on the ocean side of the Sierras and the deserts of Arizona and New Mexico east of the Rockies; fertile India on the ocean side of the Himalayas and the belt of deserts north of them. Organisms living on either side of a newly formed mountain range must adapt to the new environmental conditions by evolution. Periods of extensive mountain building have always been followed by major evolutionary turnover among organisms (see Chap. 32).

The second segment of the global lithospheric cycle involves *gradation*, the lowering of high land and the leveling of mountains. These changes are brought about in part by actual geologic sinking of land and in part by actions of the hydrosphere and the atmosphere. These actions usually take the form of *erosion* and *dissolution* of rock. Many erosive processes are quite familiar. For example, water and gravity produce shearing, canyon-cutting rivers (Fig. 10.6). Water and high temperatures produce corrosive humidity. Water and low temperatures produce grinding, rock-pulverizing glaciers. And as freezing water expands in rocky crevices, it carves boulders and stones off the face of a mountain. Water, wind, and sun in time thus reduce mountain to hill and hill eventually to plain. Together with geologic sinking, these processes often may make land lie so low that substantial parts of it become overrun by the ocean.

Accompanying the physical forces of gradation are chemical forces, and these are of particular direct and indirect importance to organisms. First, the chemical action of water, and also chemical processes which accompany the decay of dead terrestrial organisms, are major erosive factors. They contribute to breaking large stones into smaller ones and small pebbles into tiny sand grains and microscopic rock fragments. Gradation thus plays a principal role in the formation of the rocky components of soil.

Second, whenever water is in contact with rock, it dissolves small quantities of it and so acquires a mineral content. The dissolved minerals are carried largely in the form of ions. Accordingly, as rain water runs off high land, it becomes progressively laden with minerals. Streams and rivers form, and these irrigate adjacent areas and contribute to the water content of soil. Rain adds to soil water directly. In soil, the water leaches more minerals out of the many rock fragments present and the total supply then serves as the mineral source for terrestrial organisms. After the organisms die and decay, the mineral ions of their bodies return to the soil.

Dissolved soil minerals eventually drain back into rivers, and rivers drain into the ocean. Therefore, as the lithosphere is slowly being denuded of mineral compounds, the hydrosphere fills with them. It was partly by this means that the early seas on earth acquired their original saltiness, and as the global water cycle now continues, it makes the oceans even saltier. Organisms in the sea freely use the mineral ions as nutrient raw materials.

The death of marine organisms subsequently helps to complete the global mineral cycle. Many protists and animals use mineral nutrients in the construction of protective shells and supporting bones. After these organisms die, their bodies sink down toward the sea floor, in a slow, steady rain (see also below). All organic and some of the inorganic matter dissolves during the descent, but much of the mineral substance persists in solid form and reaches the sea bottom. So abundant and uninterrupted is this rain that it forms gradually thickening layers of ooze over huge tracts of the sea floor. Various types of Protista contribute particularly to these mineral accumulations. In the course of millennia, the older, deeper layers of the ooze may compress into rock. The global lithospheric cycle then becomes complete when a section of sea bottom or low-lying land generally is subjected to new diastrophic forces. High ground or mountains are thereby regenerated, and such parts as were sea floor originally may be thrust up as new land in the process (Fig. 10.7).

The lithospheric cycle supplies many more *types* of minerals than organisms normally require. Those withdrawn and used by most organisms include, for example, ions of nitrates (NO_3^-), phosphates ($PO_4^=$),

chlorides (Cl^-), carbonates ($CO_3^=$), and sulfates ($SO_4^=$); and ions of sodium (Na^+), potassium (K^+), calcium (Ca^{++}), manganese (Mn^{++}), magnesium (Mg^{++}), copper (Cu^{++}), and iron (Fe^{+++}). From the standpoint of quantities, the relatively *least* plentiful mineral circulating in the environment will determine the maximum quantity of living matter that can be supported on earth. Despite the dense cover of life now carpeting the earth, available quantities of most minerals are still well in excess of currently required amounts. However, because of the uninterrupted global growth of organisms for millions of years, a few key minerals now tend to be in relatively short supply. In particular, phosphates and nitrates have become significant limiting factors. For example, agriculturally used soils may often be burdened with so much vegetation that they may become exhausted unless artificially enriched with fertilizers—largely phosphates and nitrates. Similarly, the amount of microscopic life sustainable in the ocean is now determined principally by the amounts of available phosphates and nitrates. As we shall see presently, however, nitrates are supplied not only by the lithospheric cycle but by an atmospheric cycle as well.

Soil

As noted, the lithosphere plays a special role in the life of land plants in that it contributes importantly to the formation of soil. This complex material

10 · 7   The global mineral cycle. *Minerals absorbed by terrestrial plants and animals return to soil by excretion and death. Rivers carry soil minerals into the ocean, where some of them are deposited at the bottom. Portions of sea bottom then may be uplifted geologically, reintroducing minerals to a global cycle.*

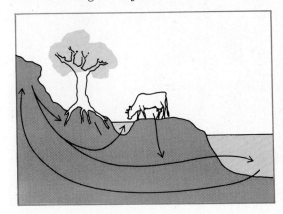

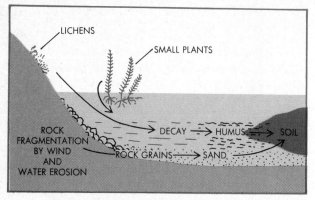

LICHENS
SMALL PLANTS
ROCK FRAGMENTATION BY WIND AND WATER EROSION
DECAY → HUMUS → SOIL
ROCK GRAINS → SAND

10 · 8 *The formation of soil. Chemical and physical decomposition of rock yields humus and sand, respectively, and these two components together form soil.*

serves in plant maintenance in two major ways: it provides mechanical *anchorage* for plants, without hindering growth and aeration of roots, and it holds water and mineral ions, the source from which

10 · 9 *Hydroponics, the soilless culture of plants. A nutrient solution (bottom) maintains these tobacco plants, which are held mechanically in a box filled with wood shavings. This box normally rests directly on top of the nutrient container.*

land plants must obtain supplies of these *inorganic nutrients.*

Before ancestral plants invaded the terrestrial environment, the land was bare of soil. But processes making possible its later formation were already under way. A profusion of stones and rock chips, produced by the forces of gradation, was steadily fragmented and ground into powder by the milling of rivers, the shear of ice sheets, and the battering impact of coastal surf. Silt was deposited in floodplains and along river and ocean shores. Winds spread the dust farther inland. Small rock grains of rough, jagged texture formed *sand*, and even smaller microscopic and submicroscopic particles formed *clay*. Sand and clay became the hard mineral fraction of soil.

The other major component of soil was contributed by living organisms. Early terrestrial Monera and Protista, organisms which do not require soil themselves, shed their excretion products into the sand layers, and upon death their bodies came to be added as well. Saprotrophic bacteria and fungi carried in by air or water found sustenance in this organic material. Decay ensued which transformed the formerly living substance into a variety of complex chemicals, the organic fractions of soil, collectively called *humus*. Acids produced by decay also roughened the surfaces of rock fragments, and so monerans and protists contributed to the formation of sand.

Humus mixed in with sand and clay constituted soil (Fig. 10.8). Formed first in isolated patches, it provided a foothold for small metaphytes. As these died and decayed, more soil was produced, larger plants could root there, and over the centuries continuous soil layers developed in large areas. At the present time, perhaps a foot of soil, on an average, covers the arable land. In barren regions, moreover, new soil may still be developing today by the same processes which were effective earlier. Thus, various monerans and protists may come to inhabit lifeless sandy areas. Subsequent decay and partial dissolution of the sand grains may slowly lead to the enrichment of the area with humus and dissolved minerals. In effect, new soil may be being formed.

Actually, soil is not an essential medium for plant maintenance. For example, floating aquatic plants do very well without it. Moreover, land plants too can be maintained adequately without soil—for example, by immersing their roots in mineral-rich water. Such procedures are called *hydroponic* cultures. They are used today in many experimental and commercial situations (Fig. 10.9). Evidently, so long as the environment provides water and minerals at all, it does not matter too much through what medium the plant obtains these materials. On land, soil happens to be the usual and the cheapest large-scale supplier. And it has the additional, very essential property of anchoring plants mechanically, without halting the continuous expansion of root systems.

General references to "soil" are usually references to the *topsoil*, the upper, most valuable layer. Topsoils differ widely in color, according to the types of minerals and humus components contained in them. The roots of small plants are embedded entirely in topsoil. Larger plants send their roots into the extensive subjacent layer, the *subsoil*. Here the proportion of clay may be higher than in topsoil and subsoil may therefore be relatively dense. Also, the proportion of humus may be reduced. Subsoil is usually underlain by *loose rock*, and this layer extends down to the continuous *bedrock* of the continent (Fig. 10.10).

The quality of topsoil depends on a wide variety of factors. Where a soil layer is too thin or where soil particles are blown away by wind or washed away by water, plants cannot obtain firm anchorage. Moreoever, if the sand particles are too small or if there is too much clay, the soil is likely to be packed tight and root growth will be difficult. But if the sand grains are too large, roots slip through the free spaces and plant anchorage is insecure. One important determinant of soil quality thus is the *size* of the soil particles. Another is the *shape* of the particles, for smooth round grains leave spaces between them through which water would drain off rapidly. On the other hand, coarse grains with rough, jagged edges still leave sufficient room for aeration and root growth. Despite such particle shape, however, water would still be lost by drainage. It is the organic matter which aids in endowing soil with its crumbly, spongelike, water-retaining properties. In a good soil, this water-retaining action of humus is augmented by the subsoil, which prevents water from seeping away too rapidly.

From the standpoint of their physical characteristics, therefore, the best soils form layers of considerable thickness, contain rock fragments of appropriate size and shape, and are rich in humus. Moreover, they are protected against water erosion by appreciable amounts of subsoil and against wind erosion by hedges, trees, and plant cover in general. For as the soil holds the plant, so the plant also holds the soil (Fig. 10.11). In agriculturally important regions, practices designed to conserve the physical values of soil are now widespread. For example, wind and water erosion can be reduced through flood control,

10 · 10 Profile of soil. Note dark topsoil, underlain by light-colored layer of subsoil. Streaked layers of clay lie under the subsoil, and the clay merges into rock near the bottom of the photo.

through appropriate rain drainage, through contour plowing, and through provision of adequate windbreaks (Fig. 10.12).

The chemical value of a soil depends on its usable water and mineral content. Soil particles are enveloped by thin films of water. This water is

10 · 11   Erosion. *As soil holds the plant, so the plant also holds the soil. A, eroded land. Sandy gullies are present, which would enlarge gradually. B, same landscape as above, after planting and about three years of growth. Erosion has been halted.*

bound; that is, electrostatic forces hold the water molecules tightly against the rock fragments. Even relatively dry soil still retains its films of bound water. If there is much water in soil, some of the fluid is bound, but most of it is beyond the range of soil-particle attraction. Held loosely in the spaces between the hard particles, *unbound* water is the immediate water source for plants.

Dissolved in the water are the mineral ions. We have already discussed three major ways by which these nutrients are replenished: inflow of new mineral-laden water, direct chemical dissolution of soil particles by soil water, and decay of dead plants and animals. Decay not only returns minerals but also adds new organic substances, and it so raises the humus content of soil. These relatively slow natural processes of replenishment may be augmented by man, through conservation procedures

designed to prevent nutritional exhaustion of soil. For example, he may add mineral-rich *fertilizers* to soil. He may let soils *rest* for one or more seasons. He may grow crops and, instead of harvesting them, plow them right back into the ground. Or he may adopt a program of *crop rotation*, whereby different crops are planted in successive seasons, each crop requiring a different set of minerals from the soil.

Some natural replenishment of soil minerals is accomplished also by certain bacteria, and we shall see in the next section how this occurs (Fig. 10.13).

10 · 12 *A, soil leaching and gully erosion by water. Drainage ditches are not available for water runoff from mountainous areas in background. B, aerial view of contour-plowed region. In contour plowing, plow lines are run at right angles to the slope of the land to reduce wind and water erosion.*

THE ATMOSPHERE

Like the hydrosphere, the atmosphere as a whole is subjected to physical cycles by the sun and the spin of the earth. Warmed equatorial air rises and cooled polar air sinks, and the axial rotation of the earth shifts air masses laterally. The resulting global air currents basically have the same general pattern as the ocean currents, and the winds of the former strongly reinforce the latter. Also, the motions of air substantially influence climatic conditions.

Equally significant to organisms are the chemical cycles of the atmosphere. Air consists mainly of oxygen, O_2 (about 20 per cent); carbon dioxide, CO_2 (about 0.03 per cent); nitrogen, N_2 (about 79 per cent); water (in varying amounts, depending on conditions); and minute traces of inert gases (helium, neon, krypton, argon, xenon). Except for the inert gases, all these components of air serve as raw materials and each circulates in a global cycle in which organisms play a conspicuous role. Also, all the gases are dissolved in natural water, and in this respect the hydrosphere is in equilibrium with the atmosphere. Regardless of whether they are aquatic or terrestrial, therefore, all organisms have access to the aerial gases.

The role of the water vapor in air has already been discussed, for this vapor represents the atmospheric segment of the global water cycle. The cycles of the other gases are as follows.

The Oxygen Cycle

Atmospheric oxygen enters the living world as a gas required in respiration (Fig. 10.14). As will be shown in Chap. 18, the function of oxygen in respiration is to collect hydrogen, resulting in the formation of water. This water joins all other water present in organisms and as such it may undergo three possible fates. Some of it may be excreted immediately and so add to the water content of the environment. Another fraction may be used as a building material in the construction of more living matter, water here being the source of the elements hydrogen and oxygen. Such structural oxygen remains within an organism until death, and subsequent decay returns it to the environment. However, the return is not usually in the form of free atmospheric oxygen, but is either in the form of water or in the form of carbon dioxide. Evidently, the global oxygen cycle is closely interlinked with the global water and CO_2 cycles. A third possible fate of water within organisms is its utilization as a fundamental raw material in photosynthesis. In this process, water is split

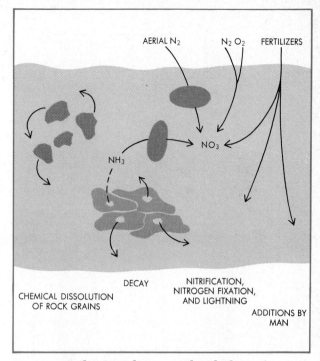

10 · 13 *Soil minerals are replenished in the four principal ways indicated in this diagram.*

apart into hydrogen and oxygen (see Chap. 19), the hydrogen then being used in food manufacture. The oxygen is a byproduct. Such free oxygen may now again be used in respiration, or it may be returned to the environment as molecular atmospheric oxygen, completing the cycle.

In sum, atmospheric molecular oxygen enters

10 · 14 *The oxygen cycle. Components of the cycle within organisms are inside the colored rectangle.*

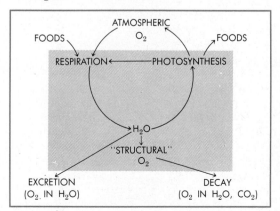

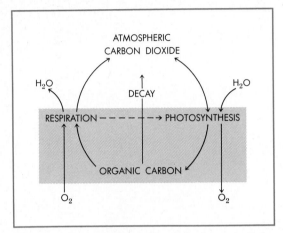

10 · 15 The carbon cycle. *Components of the cycle within organisms are inside the colored rectangle.*

organisms only through respiration and leaves organisms only through photosynthesis. In intervening steps, the oxygen is incorporated into water and in this form it may interlink with the water cycle or, indirectly, with the carbon cycle.

We may note here that atmospheric oxygen is the source of the ozone (O_3) layer which envelops the earth at an altitude of some 10 miles. This layer prevents a great deal of the high-energy radiation of the sun (ultraviolet rays, X rays) from reaching the earth's surface, and so it affects organisms indirectly, by shielding out potentially lethal rays.

10 · 16 Interrelations of the oxygen, water, and carbon cycles.

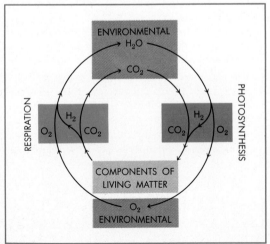
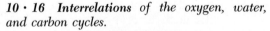

The Carbon Cycle

Atmospheric carbon dioxide is virtually the exclusive carbon source and, with water, one of the two major oxygen sources for the construction of living matter. The gas enters the living world through photosynthesis, in which it is a fundamental raw material (Fig. 10.15). Photosynthesis incorporates CO_2 into organic substances, which serve two principal functions. One fraction is used in the construction of more living matter. The carbon and oxygen thus supplied by CO_2 remain in living matter until death. Decay subsequently returns CO_2 to the atmosphere, and this completes one possible carbon cycle. Another fraction of the organic substances is used as fuel in respiration. This process releases CO_2 as a byproduct. Such carbon dioxide may now be used in photosynthesis again, or it may return to the environment and complete a second possible carbon cycle. The interrelations of the CO_2, O_2, and H_2O cycles are outlined in Fig. 10.16.

The carbon dioxide content of the atmosphere is replenished not only through biological combustion, that is, respiration, but also through nonliving combustion, that is, real fires. For example, forest fires and burning of industrial fuels release CO_2 into the air. Such events represent a long-delayed completion of the carbon cycle, for wood, coal, oil, and natural gas all contain combustible organic substances which were manufactured through photosynthesis, in many cases millions of years ago. Aerial CO_2 was then used up, and the gas is returned to the atmosphere only now. The rapid, very voluminous release of CO_2 by man-made combustions today may increasingly affect global climates, for atmospheric CO_2 acts as a heat screen. That is, it permits various solar energies other than heat to reach the earth's surface readily, where some of them are transformed into heat, but it retards the radiation of earth heat into space. Carbon dioxide therefore has a "greenhouse" effect, which in some measure probably contributes to the present warming up of the earth. Note, finally, that occasional net additions of CO_2 to the atmosphere are brought about by volcanic eruptions.

The Nitrogen Cycle

Nitrogen is required by all organisms in the construction of proteins, nucleic acids, and other nitrogenous compounds. Atmospheric nitrogen serves as the ultimate source (Fig. 10.17). But aerial N_2, the most abundant component of air, is rather inert chemically and it actually cannot be used as such by the majority of organisms. The most common usable nitrogen source frequently is the *nitrate* ion,

NO_3^-. This ion may be absorbed by plants as a mineral raw material from the environment and may be converted by them (but not by animals) into amino groups ($—NH_2$) and other nitrogen-containing components of living matter. Some of the environmental sources of nitrate have already been referred to above; that is, the mineral accumulates through dissolution of rock by water or through addition of soil-fertilizers by man. Small quantities also form in the air when the energy of lightning bolts combines aerial nitrogen and oxygen. Rain then carries such nitrates to the ground. As we shall see presently, another major nitrate source is the global nitrogen cycle.

Nitrogen incorporated into the organic structure of plants stays there until death. Animals must obtain their usable nitrogen from one another and, ultimately, by eating plants. Eventually animals die as well. Through subsequent decay, all organic nitrogen of dead plants and animals becomes converted into *ammonia*, NH_3. This substance becomes available in the environment, where it forms a nutrient for so-called *nitrifying bacteria*. These are of two types. One type absorbs ammonia and converts it into *nitrite* ions, NO_2^-, which are excreted into the environment. The second type absorbs the nitrite and converts it into nitrate ions, NO_3^-, which are similarly excreted. Thus, the combined metabolic activities of the nitrifying bacteria provide environmental nitrates. This is a major source from which plants obtain their nitrogen supplies.

Environmental nitrates are also acted upon by *denitrifying bacteria*. These are of various kinds, and the net result of their combined metabolic activities is that nitrate is converted into molecular, atmospheric nitrogen, N_2. They therefore reduce the available supply of environmental nitrates and increase the nitrogen content of the air. However, still another set of bacteria indirectly compensates for this loss of nitrates. Atmospheric N_2 can be used directly by so-called *nitrogen-fixing* organisms, namely, certain bacteria and blue-green algae which live in water and soil. These absorb aerial nitrogen as a raw material and are able to incorporate it into their amino acids and proteins. Some nitrogen-fixing bacteria are free-living soil saprotrophs. When they die, the nitrogenous materials of their bodies decay and yield ammonia to the soil, which is then transformed into nitrates by the nitrifiers. Other nitrogen-fixing bacteria are mutualistic symbionts on the roots of leguminous plants. The bacteria here bring about the formation of characteristic root nodules (see Chap. 9), and the nitrogen fixed by the bacteria becomes available to the legumes as usable nitrogen. Legumes actually may in some situations acquire

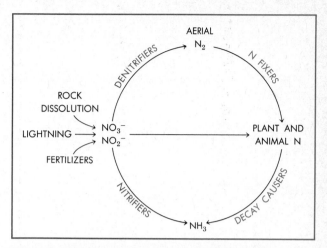

10 · 17 The nitrogen cycle, simplified. Participating bacterial types are indicated in color over the curved arrows.

most or all of their nitrogen from the nitrogen-fixing bacteria in the nodules.

Thus, by converting aerial nitrogen into usable nitrogen, the nitrogen-fixing organisms complete the global nitrogen cycle. We note that this cycle depends on at least four different sets of bacteria: the decay causers, the nitrifiers, the denitrifiers, and the nitrogen fixers. We may emphasize also that these bacteria act as they do, not because they are aware of the grand plan of the global nitrogen cycle, but because they derive immediate metabolic benefits from their action. For example, the decay causers are saprotrophs which require dead organisms as their source of food. Ammonia happens to be the excretory byproduct of their gathering and processing activities involving nitrogen-containing foods. Analogously, the other bacterial types above utilize one kind of nitrogenous compound as nutrient and eliminate an altered kind as excretion product.

So long as the global environment makes available water, mineral ions, and atmospheric gases, and so long as it provides suitable operating conditions generally, the living components of the biosphere may obtain not only their required basic nutrients but also their necessary *living space:* the places in which communities must pursue life are portions of the hydrosphere, the lithosphere, or the atmosphere.

HABITATS

With the possible exception of the most arid deserts, the high, frozen mountain peaks, and the perpetually icebound polar regions, probably no place on earth is devoid of life. The subdivisions of the planetary environment represent *habitats* in which communities live. The two principal habitats are the *aquatic* and the *terrestrial*. Both range from equator to pole and from a few thousand feet below to a few thousand feet above sea level. *Ocean* and *fresh water* are the principal components of the aquatic habitat and *air* and *soil* of the terrestrial.

THE OCEAN

The Ocean Basin

Even the land dweller will appreciate readily that the sea is not a single, unified environment. Indeed, an examination of its structure and of its content of living matter shows clearly that this birthplace of life comprises nearly as many distinct habitats as the land.

The most conspicuous attribute of sea water is its high mineral content. The proportions of the different types of salt present in sea water are almost the same all over the globe, as a result of thorough mixing of all waters by currents. More than four-fifths of the total mineral content consists of the ions of table salt; 55 per cent of all ions present are chlorine, 30 per cent are sodium. However, although the proportions are invariant, the total salt concentration, or *salinity*, varies greatly from region to region. The highest salinities are encountered in tropic waters, where high temperatures and exten-

sive evaporation concentrate the quantities of oceanic salts. In the Red Sea, for example, ocean water is a 4 per cent solution; every 100 parts of sea water include 4 parts of minerals (and 55 per cent of these 4 parts are chlorine, as just noted above). By contrast, sea water in higher latitudes, north or south, evaporates less and is therefore less salty. In such latitudes, moreover, the fresh water melt from the polar ice caps dilutes the oceanic salt considerably. As might be expected, furthermore, salinities are lower for often several hundred miles around the mouths of great rivers. The lowest known salinity occurs in the Baltic Sea, where ocean water is a 0.7 per cent solution (comparable to the total salinity of the blood of frogs and somewhat less than that of human blood). Salinity determines the buoyancy (density) of ocean water, buoyancy being the greater the higher the salinity. Both salinity and buoyancy are of considerable significance to all marine life (see below).

An ocean basin has the general form of an inverted hat (Fig. 10.18). A gently sloping *continental shelf* stretches away from the coast line for an average distance of about 100 miles (discounting often extreme deviations from this average). The angle of descent then changes more or less abruptly and the shelf grades over into a steep *continental slope*. Characteristically, this slope is scored deeply by gorges and canyons, carved out by slow rivers of mud and sand discharging from estuaries. Several thousand feet down, the continental slope levels off into the ocean floor, a more or less horizontal expanse known as the *abyssal plain*. Mountains rise from it in places, with peaks sometimes so high that they rear up above sea level as islands. Elsewhere

10 · 18   The structure of an ocean basin. The littoral zone is not labeled; it is the part of the benthonic zone which forms the floor of the continental shelf (and is covered by the waters of the neritic zone).

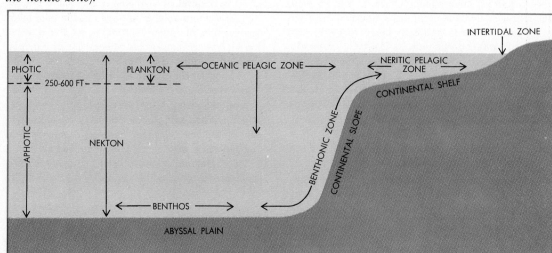

the plain may be scarred by deep rifts, for example, the Japan and Philippine Deeps along the western edge of the Pacific. These plunge 35,000 ft down and are the lowest parts of the earth's crust.

Three major habitats may be distinguished in such a basin. The sea floor from the shore out to the edge of the continental shelf forms the *littoral* zone. Its most important subenvironment is the narrow *intertidal* belt, between the high- and low-tide lines. Beyond the littoral, the sea floor along the continental slope and the abyssal plain constitutes the *benthonic* habitat. The third principal habitat is the *pelagic*—the water itself which fills the ocean basin. This habitat includes a *neritic* subdivision over the littoral zone and an *oceanic* subdivision over the benthonic zone.

A most important vertical subdivision of the pelagic habitat is brought about by the sun. Acting directly or via the overlying medium of air, the sun produces "weather" in the surface layers of the sea: waves, currents, storms, evaporation, seasons, daily, climatic rhythms, and other changes. Deep water is not affected in this way. Moreover, sunlight penetrates into water only to an average depth of about 250 ft and to at most 600 ft in certain seas. Within this sunlit layer, called the *photic zone,* light dims progressively to zero with increasing distance from the surface. The most significant consequence of this circumstance is that photosynthesizing vegetation can exist only in the uppermost layers of the sea. Heterotrophs directly dependent on photosynthesizers therefore must similarly remain near the surface. As a result, the top 250 ft or so of the oceans contains a concentration of living matter as dense as any on earth. In sharp contrast, the *aphotic zone,* that is, the dark region underneath the photic zone, is completely free of photosynthetic organisms and contains only animals, bacteria, and possibly fungi.

On the basis of its relationship to these various habitats, marine life has been classified into three general categories: *plankton, nekton,* and *benthos.* Plankton includes all passively drifting or floating forms. Most of them are microscopic and are found largely in the surface waters of the sea, that is, in the photic zone. Even though some of these forms possess locomotor systems, they are nevertheless too weak or too small to counteract currents and movements of water. Nekton comprises the active swimmers, capable of changing stations at will. All nektonic types are therefore animals, and they are found in all waters, along the surface as well as in the sea depths. The benthos consists of crawling, creeping, and sessile organisms along the sides and the bottom of the ocean basin.

The Photic Zone

Since photosynthetic organisms do not possess powerful locomotor systems such as muscles, such organisms in open water can stay within the range of sunlight only if they float. And since living material is usually slightly heavier than water, passive floating is possible only if an organism possesses a special floating device or if it is small enough to be buoyed up by the salt water.

Thus, the predominant marine photosynthesizers are planktonic. They include teeming trillions of algae which, as a group, probably photosynthesize more food than all land plants combined. Collectively called *phytoplankton,* this oceanic vegetation represents the richest pasture on earth; directly or indirectly, it forms the nutritional basis of all marine life (see Color Plate VII, 15).

Most of the algal types included in this "grass of the sea" are microscopic. Unquestionably the most abundant are the *diatoms.* Each of these single-celled protists is enclosed within a delicate, intricately sculptured, silicon-containing shell. Reddish *dinoflagellates* also abound in surface waters, sometimes in populations so dense that they tint acre upon acre of ocean with a coppery hue (for example, "red" tides). Other marine algae include many types of variously pigmented forms, and some of these, as well as countless numbers of marine bacteria, are bioluminescent. They emit flashes of cold light, which dot the night seascape with a billion pin points of greenish fire.

Surrounded on all sides by raw materials and bathed in sunlight, the passively drifting phytoplankton community inhabits a highly favorable, chemically rather stable habitat. The death rate resulting from animal feeding is high, but rapid reproduction sufficiently offsets it. Physical and climatic changes do not affect an algal cell too greatly. In winter, the temperature of surface waters may fall below the freezing point, but the salts of the ocean prevent actual freezing. Cold merely reduces the rate of metabolic processes and algal life continues at a slower pace.

Indeed, low temperatures indirectly promote algal growth. When surface temperatures are high, as in tropical waters throughout the year and in northern and southern waters in summer, pronounced *temperature layering* of water prevents much vertical mixing. A warm-water layer is less dense and thus lighter than a colder layer below it; it "swims" on top of the colder layer without mixing. The boundary between the two layers is known as a *thermocline.* Organisms above such a thermocline deplete the surface waters of mineral raw materials, and at

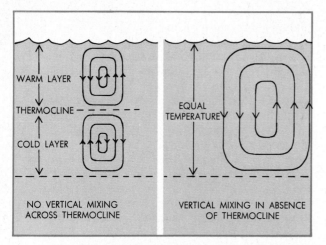

WARM LAYER

THERMOCLINE

COLD LAYER

EQUAL TEMPERATURE

NO VERTICAL MIXING ACROSS THERMOCLINE

VERTICAL MIXING IN ABSENCE OF THERMOCLINE

10 · 19   Temperature layering of surface water, as in summer, leads to the formation of a thermocline, a temperature barrier responsible for poor vertical circulation of water (left). In early spring, late fall, and winter, surface waters do acquire the same temperature as deeper layers; the thermocline then disappears, and vertical mixing does become possible (right).

death these materials sink down without being brought back to the surface by vertical mixing. As a result, the amount of surface life is limited, and warm seas are actually relatively barren (Fig. 10.19).

By contrast, when surface and deeper waters have roughly the same low temperature, a thermocline is absent and vertical mixing becomes possible. Minerals are then recirculated more rapidly and surface life may therefore be more abundant. The perennially cold artic, antarctic, and subpolar waters actually support huge permanent populations of algae. And, as is well known, the best commercial fishing grounds are in the high north and south, not in the tropics, and the best fishing seasons are spring and fall, not summer.

Warm and cold waters differ not only in the total amount of life but also in its diversity. Although the biomass in tropic seas is comparatively smaller than in temperate and polar seas, its species diversity is far greater. Thus, whereas warm oceans sustain small populations of many species, cold oceans harbor large populations of few species. The reason is that higher temperatures promote all reactions, including those leading to evolution. Warm-climate life will therefore tend to become more diverse than cold-climate life. However, the limited mineral content of warm seas will keep individual numbers low. Note also that, in all oceans, the sun produces *diurnal migrations* of most planktonic

organisms. During the night the organisms are distributed vertically throughout the surface layers of the sea, but during the day most of the plankton shuns the bright light and moves down into the lower strata of the photic zone. Larger animals feeding on plankton migrate up and down correspondingly. As a result, even richly populated seas are quite barren on the surface during the daytime, and it is well known that surface fishing is most fruitful at night (Fig. 10.20).

In certain circumscribed regions, phytoplankton also includes larger, multicellular algae: flat, sheet-like seaweeds, often equipped with specialized air bladders which aid in keeping the organisms afloat. Such seaweeds may sometimes aggregate in considerable numbers over wide areas, particularly if a region is ringed in by ocean currents and therefore remains relatively isolated and stagnant. The Sargasso Sea in the mid-Atlantic is a good example. This sea has figured prominently in marine lore. For example, stories are told of ships trapped in "floating jungles," rapidly overgrown by plants, and sunk without a trace. Such accounts are wholly legendary, since the organisms are nowhere dense enough to prevent a ship's passage. Yet the Sargasso *is* unique from a biological standpoint. The comparative isolation of the region had led to the evolution of a distinct flora not found elsewhere on earth, and an equally distinct fauna finds shelter and food in this vegetation (Fig. 10.21).

Living side by side with the photosynthetic phytoplankton in the open waters of the photic zone are the small nonphotosynthetic forms. These include bacteria and members of the *zooplankton:* protozoa, eggs, larvae, tiny shrimp (krill) and other crustacea (particularly *copepods*), and countless other small animals carried along by surface drift (Color Plate VII, 15). They feed directly on the microscopic vegetation; hence as the phytoplankton waxes and wanes, so does the zooplankton. A good part of the nekton, largely fishes and marine mammals, comes into these waters to feed either on zooplankton or on phytoplankton directly.

Nearer to shore, in the neritic waters above the littoral zone, the problem of remaining afloat is not so critical for a photosynthesizer as in open water, for here even a bottom dweller is likely to be within the range of sunlight. The problem, rather, is to remain attached to solid ground, for close to shore the force of waves and of ground swells is considerable. In the intertidal belt, moreover, an even more profound problem is the ebbing of water twice daily and the consequent rhythmic alternation between aquatic and essentially terrestrial conditions. Also, in waters in and for miles beyond estuaries, fresh water discharging from rivers mixes with ocean

PLATE IX

19. *Hormogonales.*
Portion of a colony of Nostoc.
Note the enlarged heterocysts. The cellular
filaments are embedded in
gelatinous sheaths.

19, courtesy of Carolina Biological Supply Company

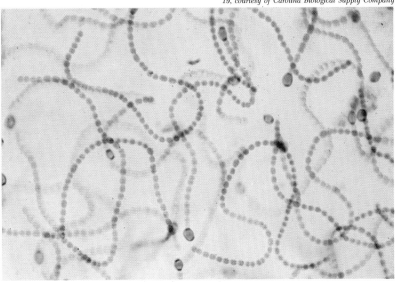

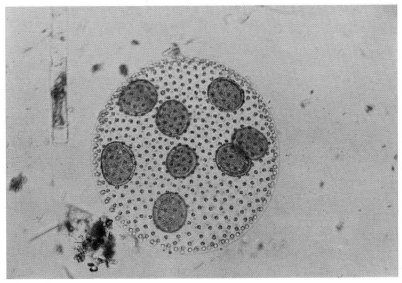

20. *Volvox,*
a colonial green alga consisting of
many flagellate cells. The cells are arranged
as a single-layered sphere, with each
cell in direct contact with the
water environment.
In the interior of the sphere are
several offspring colonies, which
develop there and eventually
burst through the parent.

PLATE X

21. Diatoms.

water, a circumstance introducing additional environmental inconstancies. Being the meeting ground of water, land, and air, the intertidal belt is actually among the most violently changing habitats on earth.

Vegetation here and in the littoral and the overlying neritic region as a whole is again largely algal. In addition to the single-celled and small planktonic types, attached multicellular forms abound. Most of these are equipped with specialized holdfasts which anchor the organisms to underlying ground. Green, brown, and red algae are particularly common. For example, the soft, slippery mats of vegetation encrusting rocks along the shore are familiar to many, as is *Fucus*, a common leathery brown alga found in dense populations on coastal rock.

Animals in coastal waters include representatives of almost all major groups. In addition to the abundant planktonic types, sessile and creeping animals occur which are variously adapted to rocky, muddy, or sandy bottoms. The animals make use of all conceivable dwelling sites—for example, tide pools left on rock by ebbing water, crevices and hollows in and under rock, burrows in sand or mud, the sheltered water among vegetation and among sessile animal growths, empty shells and other skeletons of dead animals, and flotsam and jetsam along the shore and in deeper water. Among the very abundant nektonic animals in these regions, largely fish, many normally do not stray very far from a particular home, even though an efficient locomotor system would permit them to do so. They foray into surrounding waters for food and mates, but they always tend to return to the same base of operations. However, another group of nektonic animals consists of perpetual wanderers without permanent homes.

The Aphotic Zone

The contrast between the surface habitats within reach of the sun and those underneath is dramatic. As the ones are forever fluctuating, so the others are perennially steady and relatively unchanging. The deep ocean is still little explored, and, for many, this "last frontier" has acquired a romance and mystery all its own. Several unique physical conditions characterize this world of the sea depths.

First, the region is one of eternal night. In the total absence of sunlight, the waters are pervaded with a perpetual blackness of a kind found nowhere else on earth. Second, seasons and changing weather are practically absent. Localized climatic changes do occur as a result of occasional submarine volcanic activity or, more regularly, through deep-sea currents. These produce large-scale shifts of water masses and, incidentally, bring oxygen to even the deepest parts

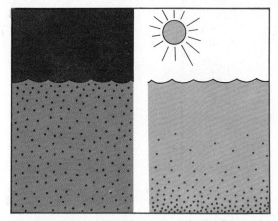

10 · 20 Diurnal migrations of plankton. At night (left) plankton is distributed throughout the dark surface water. In daytime (right) plankton migrates away from the surface and accumulates in darker, deeper waters.

of the ocean. Being beyond the influence of the sun, the deep waters are cold, unchangingly so. Temperatures range from about 10°C at the top of the dark zone to about 1°C along the abyssal plain.

Third, water pressure increases steadily from the surface down, 1 atmosphere (atm) for every 33 ft of

10 · 21 Sargassum weed, a brown alga. The bulbous structures are air bladders. A species related to the one shown in the photograph forms the principal seaweed of the Sargasso Sea.

10 · 22 *The deep-sea angler fish shown here is a female. The structure above the eye is a parasitic male, which is carried about perman- ently attached. This neatly solves the problem of finding a mating partner in the dark. Many of these large-mouthed, dagger-toothed fishes are surprisingly small; for example, the fish above fits comfortably into a person's palm.*

descent. Thus, in the deepest trenches of the ocean, the pressure is about a thousand times as great as at sea level. And fourth, a continuous slow rain of the dead remnants of surface organisms drifts down to- ward the sea bottom. Much of this material, partic- ularly the organic fraction, dissolves completely during the descent. But much microscopic mineral matter reaches the abyssal plain, where it forms ever-thickening layers of ooze. Accumulating over

10 · 23 *A deep-sea angler fish with a stalked, luminescent "lantern" over the mouth. Note the vertical position of the mouth, a feature which facilitates catching prey lured to the light of the lantern.*

the millennia, the older layers eventually compress into rock. Vertical bore samples of such rock have revealed a great deal of the past history of the oceans and their once-living surface inhabitants.

Contrary to early beliefs that life should be im- possible in such an environment, a surprisingly rich diversity of organisms has been found to exist virtually everywhere in the free water and along the floor of the deep sea. Apart from containing bacteria and perhaps fungi, the community is characteristically animal—photosynthesizing organisms are confined to the sunlit surface. Virtually all animal groups are represented, many by—to us—strange and bizarre types uniquely adapted to the locale (Fig. 10.22).

If a deep-sea animal is to avoid death from explosion or implosion, its internal pressure must equal the external pressure of the water. A few of the nektonic animals, toothed whales, for example, are adapted to resist the harmful effects of rapid changes of external pressure. These animals are capable of traversing the whole ocean from bottom to surface. They may therefore feed directly on the rich food supplies in surface waters. But the bulk of the deep-sea nekton is adapted to particular water pressures only, and given animals are rigidly confined to limited pressure zones at given depths. Such animals must therefore obtain food either from the dead matter drifting down from the surface—a meager source, particularly in deeper water—or from within the nekton itself.

This last condition makes the deep sea the most fiercely competitive habitat on earth. The very struc- ture of the animals underscores their violently carniv- orous, "eat-or-be-eaten" mode of existence. For example, most of the fishes have enormous mouths equipped with long, razor-sharp teeth, and many can swallow fish larger than themselves.

Since the environment is pitch-black, one of the critical problems for these animals is to *find* food to begin with. A highly developed pressure sense pro- vides one solution. Turbulence in the water created by nearby animals can be recognized and, depending on the nature of the turbulence, may be acted upon either by flight or by approach.

Another important adaptation to the dark is bio- luminescence. Many of the deep-sea animals possess light-producing organs on the body surface, of different shapes, sizes, and distributions in different species. The light patterns emitted may include a variety of colors and probably serve partly in species recogni- tion. Identification of a suitable mate, for example, must be a serious problem in an environment where everything appears equally black. Another function of the light undoubtedly is to warn or to lure. Some of the bioluminescent lures have evolved to a high degree of perfection. Certain fish, for example, carry a "lantern" on a stalk protruding from the snout (Fig. 10.23). An inquisitive animal attracted to the light of the lantern will discover too late that it has headed straight into powerful jaws.

THE FRESH WATER

Physically and biologically, the link between ocean and land is the fresh water. Rivers and lakes were the original invasion routes over which some of the descendants of ancestral marine organisms reached land and, in the process, evolved into terrestrial forms. Certain of the migrant types never completed the transition but settled along the way, in fresh water.

Among such organisms, some adapted to the brackish water in estuaries and river mouths or to a life spent partly in the ocean, partly in fresh water (for example, salmon, eels). Very many types could leave the ocean entirely and adapt to an exclusively freshwater existence. The descendants of these organisms include representatives of virtually all groups present in the ocean. Certain of the freshwater types later managed to gain a foothold on land. Of these, some continued to spend part of their lives in or near fresh water (for example, mosses, frogs), but more became wholly terrestrial. And among the terrestrial forms, some subsequently returned to water and adapted secondarily to an aquatic existence (for example, reed grasses, many insects). Thus, organisms inhabiting the fresh water today constitute a rich and major subdivision of the living world.

In addition to rivers, freshwater habitats also include lakes, ponds, and marshes. Contrary to what might be expected, each category of these environments harbors communities which are remarkably similar throughout the world. Thus, lakes of a given size in any part of the world are likely to contain roughly identical types of communities. Such similarities are probably due to several factors. First, if a given marine ancestor could give rise to a particular freshwater descendant in one part of the world, any such descendant in another part would probably have been quite similar, since the freshwater environments are themselves similar. Second, freshwater systems within a continent are often interconnected, and direct migration from one part of such a system to a far distant part is possible in many cases. Third, many freshwater animals are able through their own locomotion to travel overland for longer or shorter distances; and small organisms of all kinds also are carried overland accidentally, by sweepstake routes which often involve birds as carrying agents (for example, organism-containing mud clinging to the feet of birds). Whether or not such explanations are fully adequate, it is true nevertheless that freshwater communities are far more similar on a global basis than either marine or terrestrial communities.

Three main conditions distinguish the freshwater habitat from the ocean. First, the salinity is substantially lower. If an organism has evolved in and still lives in the sea, the internal salt concentration of its body matches that of the marine environment. If such an organism moves to fresh water, the external salt concentrations will be much lower than the internal. As a result, water will move osmotically from the environment through the body surface into the organism. The amount of water in the organism will therefore tend to increase and the substance of cells will tend to become diluted.

Freshwater organisms evidently require, and they actually possess, means of counteracting this tendency of shipping too much water. Where rigid cell walls are present, as in plants, such walls protect against internal dilution. The walls withstand the outward pressure generated by the accumulation of water within cells; once such cells contain given amounts of water, no more can be drawn in osmotically because the walls will not permit any further cell enlargement. Where cell walls are not present, as in animals, water balance is maintained by the excretion of any excess internal water. Excretory systems and also digestive systems and gills serve in this function. In animals inhabiting estuaries, where external salt concentrations fluctuate almost continuously, and in organisms whose life cycle includes both marine and freshwater phases, water- and salt-balancing mechanisms are particularly well developed.

A second condition characterizing much of the freshwater environment is the presence of strong, swift currents. Where these occur, passively floating life so typical of the ocean surface is not likely to be encountered. On the contrary, the premium will be either on maintaining firm anchorage along the shores and bottoms of rivers or on ability to resist and to overcome the force of currents by muscle power.

Indeed, the vegetation found in swift rivers consists almost entirely of plants possessing rootlike holdfasts or actual roots. Since true roots are characteristic only of terrestrial plants, the presence of such plants in rivers means that some ancestral land plants have adapted secondarily to a life in water. Pertinent examples are reed grasses, water foxtails, wild rice, and watercress (see Color Plate VIII, 16). In contrast to this, where fresh water is not flowing strongly, as in lakes, ponds, bogs, and marshes, not only rooted but also floating planktonic vegetation may be exceedingly abundant. In stagnant or near-stagnant water, algal communities forming continuous layers of green surface scum are particularly conspicuous.

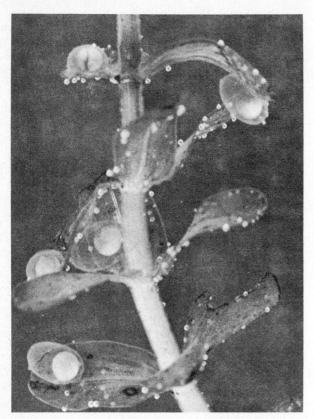

10 · 24 *Amphibian eggs, each surrounded by a sticky jelly coat which attaches such eggs to vegetation or other objects in the water.*

Among animals, analogously, those in quiet fresh waters include both planktonic and nektonic types, but those in swiftly flowing water are either attached and sessile or nektonic and swimming. The eggs of nektonic animals cannot swim, to be sure, but they are enveloped by sticky jelly coats which adhere firmly to plants or other objects in the water (Fig. 10.24). And the young are strongly muscled from the moment they hatch (for example, freshwater vertebrates).

We may note in this connection that most modern fishes and vertebrates in general probably are an evolutionary product of the fresh water, not of the ocean. The ancestors of vertebrates were marine. They laid small, relatively yolk-free eggs which developed rapidly, and the adults were small and not very muscular. Some of the descendants of these forms then evolved adaptations which permitted them to become successful in fresh water. Principally, eggs enlarged and became very yolky. Well supplied with food in this manner, the eggs could develop

slowly and for a relatively long period, which allowed ample time for the elaboration of internal structures, muscular systems included. At hatching, therefore, the young were already well muscled and could maintain station against river currents.

The first fish probably arose in this way, as forms well adapted to the freshwater environment. Some of these early fishes stayed in fresh water and their descendants may still be encountered there today. Others, however, invaded the ocean, returning along the reverse route their ancestors had taken. Marine fishes so came into being, and today they are among the dominant life forms of the ocean. A third group of the early freshwater fishes took the path to land, and from these eventually evolved the modern land vertebrates—amphibia, reptiles, birds, and mammals, including man. Large, yolky eggs are still characteristic of vertebrates today, a silent reminder of their probable freshwater origin (see also Chap. 32).

A third major distinction between fresh water and ocean is that the former, with the exception of only the very large lakes, is affected much more by climate and weather than any part of the latter. Bodies of fresh water often freeze over in winter and may dry up completely in summer. Water temperatures change not only seasonally but also daily, frequently to a considerable extent. Gales or flood conditions may bring bottom mud and silt to the surface and upset the freshwater habitat in major ways. A large number of factors may alter flow conditions and produce, for example, stagnant water or significantly altered chemical content or situations facilitating infectious epidemics. We note that the fresh water shares the environmental inconstancies of the land in very large measure. Notwithstanding the aquatic nature of the freshwater habitat, its living component reflects the ebb and flow of land life as much as that of ocean life.

THE LAND

That land habitats differ vastly in their characteristics is eminently clear to a land dweller as efficient and far-ranging as man. It should also be clear that, regardless of which particular subdivision of the terrestrial environment one considers, the sustaining foundations of all land life are air and, directly or indirectly, also soil. Air and soil are to the terrestrial habitat what the surface waters of the ocean are to the marine.

Like air, soil is itself a terrestrial home, providing a habitat for a vast array of subsurface organisms. And by creating the conditions necessary for the

10 · 25   The habitat of the grassland. *A landscape in Arizona is shown.*

survival of all other terrestrial organisms, soil becomes a major agency which transforms terrestrial environments into life-sustaining "habitats." Two other agencies play a vital role here: annual temperature and rainfall. As these vary with geographic latitude and altitude, they divide the soil-covered land surface into a number of distinct habitat zones, or *biomes: desert, grassland, rain forest, deciduous forest, taiga,* and *tundra.*

In the tropics are found representatives of the first three of the six biomes just named. They are characterized here by comparatively high annual temperatures and by daily temperature variations greater than the seasonal variations. Differences in the amount of precipitation largely account for the different nature of these habitats.

A *desert* (Color Plate VIII, 17) usually has less than 10 in. of rain per year, concentrated largely in a few heavy cloudbursts. Desert life is well adapted to this. Plants grow, bloom, are fertilized, and produce seeds, all within a matter of days after a rain. Since the growing season is thus greatly restricted, such plants stay relatively small. Leaf surfaces are often reduced to spines and thorns (as in cacti), minimizing water loss by evaporation. Desert animals too are generally small, and they include many burrowing forms which may escape the direct rays of the sun under the ground surface. In most deserts mammals and birds, which maintain constant internal body

temperatures, are comparatively rare or are absent altogether; maintenance of constant body temperature is difficult or impossible under conditions of great heat and practically no water. By contrast, animals which match their internal temperature to the external can get by much more easily.

Grassland is not an exclusively tropical habitat but extends into much of the temperate zone as well (Fig. 10.25). The more or less synonymous terms "prairie," "pampas, "steppe," "puszta," and many other regional designations underscore the wide distribution of this biome. The common feature of all grasslands is intermittent, erratic rainfall, amounting to about 10 to 40 in. annually. Grasses of various kinds, from short buffalo grass to tall elephant grass and thickets of bamboo, are particularly adapted to irregularly alternating periods of precipitation and dryness. Grassland probably supports more species of animals than any other terrestrial habitat. Different kinds of mammals are particularly conspicuous.

In those tropical and subtropical regions where torrential rains fall practically every day and where a well-defined rainy season characterizes the winter, plant growth continues the year round. *Rain forests* have developed here (Fig. 10.26), typified particularly by the communal coexistence of up to several hundred different species of trees. Rain forests are the "jungles" of the adventure tale. They cover much of central Africa, south and southeast Asia, Central America, and the Amazon basin of South America. Trees in such forests are normally so crowded together that

10 · 26 *The habitat of the rain forest. Many dozens of different plant types, coexisting in dense formations, are generally characteristic of it. Note moss plants hanging from many tree branches.*

they form a continuous overhead canopy of branches and foliage which cuts off practically all the sunlight, much of the rain water, and a good deal of the wind. As a result, the forest floor is exceedingly humid and quite dark, and it is populated by plants requiring only a minimum of light. Animal communities too are stratified vertically, according to the several very different habitats offered between canopy and ground. The tropical rain forest is singularly quiet during the day, but it erupts into a cacophony of sound at night, when the largely nocturnal fauna becomes active.

In the temperate zone, apart from extensive grasslands and occasional deserts, the most characteristic biome is the *deciduous forest* (Fig. 10.27). The fundamental climatic conditions here are cold winters, warm summers, and well-spaced rains bringing some 30 to 40 in. of precipitation per year. The habitat is characterized also by seasonal temperature variations which are greater than the daily variations. Winter makes the growing season discontinuous, and the flora is adapted to this. Trees are largely deciduous, that is, they shed their leaves and hibernate; and small annual plants produce seeds which withstand the cold weather. A deciduous forest differs from a rain forest in that trees are spaced farther apart and in that far fewer species are present. Compared with the hundreds of tree types in the one, there may be only some ten or twenty in the other. Maple, beech, oak, elm, ash, and sycamore are among the common trees of a deciduous forest. The many familiar animal types in this biome include deer, boars, raccoons, foxes, squirrels, and, characteristically, woodpeckers.

North of the deciduous forests and the grasslands, across Canada, northern Europe, and Siberia, stretches the *taiga* (Fig. 10.28). This is a biome of long, severe winters and of growing seasons limited largely to the few months of summer. Hardy conifers, spruce in particular, are most representative of the flora, and moose, wolves, and bears of the fauna. The taiga is preeminently a zone of forests. These differ from other types of forests in that they usually consist of a single species of tree. Thus, over a large area, spruce, for example, may be the only kind of tree present. Another conifer species might be found in an adjacent, equally large area. Occasional stands of hardy deciduous trees are often intermingled with conifers. An accident of geography makes the taiga a habitat characteristic of the Northern Hemisphere only: little land exists in corresponding latitudes of the Southern Hemisphere.

The same circumstance makes the *tundra*, most polar of terrestrial biomes, a predominantly northern phenomenon (Color Plate VIII, 18). Much of the tundra lies within the Arctic Circle. Hence its climate is cold and there may be continuous night during the winter season and continuous daylight, of comparatively low intensity, during the summer. Some distance below the surface, the ground is permanently frozen (*permafrost*). Above ground, frost can form even during the summer—plants often freeze solid and remain dormant until they thaw out again. As in the desert, the growing season is very brief and the limiting factor is again water supply: frozen water is functionally equivalent to absence of water. Plants are low, ground-hugging forms, and trees are absent. Lichens, mosses, coniferous and other shrubby growths, and

10 · 27 The habitat of the deciduous forest.
In this type of forest, generally characteristic of the temperate zone, trees lose their foliage during the winter.

herbs with brilliantly colored flowers, all blooming simultaneously during the growing season, are characteristic of the habitat. Conspicuous among the animals are hordes of insects, particularly flies, and a considerable variety of mammals: caribou, arctic hares, lemmings, foxes, musk oxen, and polar bears. Birds are largely migratory, leaving for more southern latitudes with the coming of winter.

Life does not end at the northern margin of the tundra but extends farther into the ice and bleak rock of the soilless polar region. Polar life is almost exclusively animal. And it is not really terrestrial

10 · 28 The habitat of the taiga. *Note the predominance of a single tree species over large areas, a phenomenon typical of the taiga.*

10 · 29 The polar and subpolar habitats, *based on the sea. Two animals characteristic of these regions are shown: top, seal; bottom, king penguin (molting).*

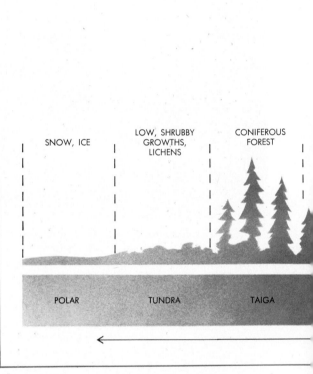

10 · 30 The sequence of habitat zones *between equator and pole is repeated between the base and the top of a mountain.*

anyway but is based on the sea (for example, walrus, seals, penguins; Fig. 10.29).

The horizontal sequence of biomes between equator and pole is repeated more or less exactly in a vertical direction, along the slopes of mountains (Fig. 10.30). Here too temperature and precipitation are the decisive variables. On a high mountain in the tropics, for example, the succession of biomes from mountain base to snow line is tropical rain forest, deciduous forest, coniferous forest, and lastly, low shrubby growths and lichens. The farther north a mountain is situated, the more northern a biome covers its base and the fewer biomes cover its slopes. In the taiga, for example, the foot of a mountain is coniferous forest and the only other biome higher

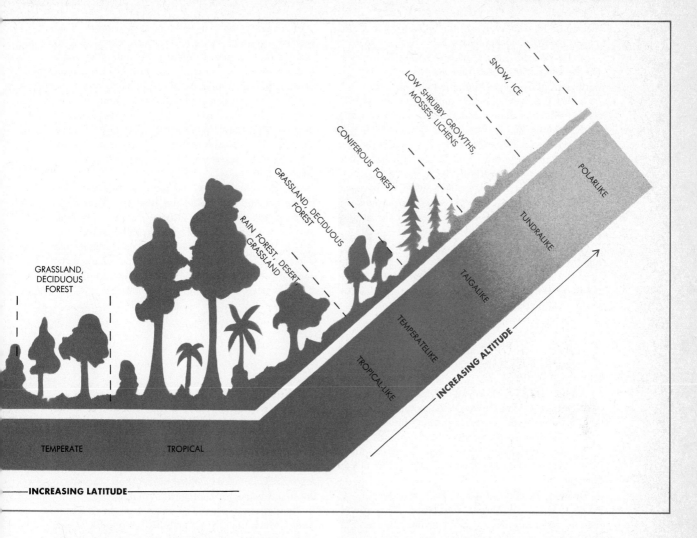

along the slopes is the zone of low shrubby plants. Thus, habitat zones spread over thousands of miles latitudinally are telescoped altitudinally into a few thousand feet.

The foregoing should make it clear that the nature of any kind of habitat, terrestrial, freshwater, or marine, is determined by a few persistently recurring physical variables. Among them are solar light, solar heat, geographic latitude, vertical depth and altitude, rainfall, wind and water currents, and the chemical composition of the locale. As such environmental variables differ in different geographic regions of the world, the habitats present there, hence the ecosystems as a whole, differ accordingly.

This account concludes our characterization of the biosphere and the living hierarchy of organizational levels within it. We next shift our attention from the associations of organisms to the various specific kinds of organisms actually found in these associations.

REVIEW QUESTIONS

1. Why is the global environment always changing and never stable? What are open and closed physical systems? How do organisms contribute to cyclic environmental change?

2. Review the global water cycle. What forces maintain it? How do organisms participate in this cycle? In what different ways does the world's water influence climates?

3. What are diastrophism and gradation? How does the formation of mountains influence climates? Cite

examples. In what ways is the global lithospheric cycle of nutritional importance?

4. Review the general pattern of mineral cycles. On the basis of this, construct diagrams showing the pattern of global phosphate and calcium cycles.

5. What is the chemical composition of the atmosphere? Which of these components do not play a role in the maintenance of organisms?

6. Review (a) the oxygen cycle, (b) the carbon cycle. Show how these cycles are interlinked with each other and with the global water cycle.

7. Review the global nitrogen cycle. How many different groups of bacteria aid in the maintenance of this cycle? What is the role of decay in the atmospheric, lithospheric, and hydrospheric cycles?

8. What is the structure of an ocean basin? What are the major habitats in such a basin? What role does the sun play in creating subdivisions in these habitats? What physical conditions characterize the various subdivisions?

9. Define plankton, nekton, and benthos. Give specific examples of each. Where in the ocean are each of these types of organisms found? Why is life in tropical waters generally less abundant but more diverse than in temperate and subpolar waters?

10. What physical and biological conditions characterize the sea depths? What are thermoclines, diurnal migrations? What are the patterns of ocean currents? How do different oceans vary in (a) density, (b) salinity of water? What are the proportions of oceanic salts?

11. Review the essential physical differences between oceanic and freshwater habitats. What major types of organisms occur in fresh water, and in what general ways are they adapted to this habitat?

12. What are the main terrestrial habitats and what physical and biological conditions characterize each of them? In what way are latitudinal terrestrial habitats related to altitudinal habitats?

COLLATERAL READINGS

Bailey, H. S.: The Voyage of the "Challenger," *Sci. American,* May, 1953. A discussion of a classic marine expedition which laid the foundation for much of modern oceanography.

Bascom, W.: Ocean Waves, *Sci. American,* Aug., 1959. A pertinent supplement to a study of ocean ecology.

Bennett, H. H.: "Elements of Soil Conservation," 2d ed., McGraw-Hill, New York, 1955. Many useful data on agricultural and soil ecology may be found in this book.

Billings, W. D.: "Plants and the Ecosystem," Wadsworth, Belmont, Calif., 1964. A section on terrestrial biomes is included in this paperback.

Carson, R.: "The Sea around Us," Oxford, Fair Lawn, N.J., 1951. A classic nontechnical book on the physics, chemistry, and biology of the sea, written for popular consumption. Strongly recommended.

Cole, L. C.: The Ecosphere, *Sci. American,* Apr., 1958. The amount of life sustainable on earth is assessed by examining the relation of organisms and their environment.

Deevey, E. S.: The Human Population, *Sci. American,* Sept., 1960. An examination of the total amount of human life the earth may be able to support.

Ellison, W. D.: Erosion by Raindrop, *Sci. American,* Nov., 1948. A discussion of the physical and chemical effects of environmental water on the lithosphere generally and on soil conservation specifically.

Fairbridge, R. W.: The Changing Level of the Sea, *Sci. American,* May, 1960. This article discusses the effects of ice ages and of diastrophic movements of the ocean floor.

Gilbert, F. A.: "Mineral Nutrition and the Balance of Life," University of Oklahoma, Norman, Okla., 1957. A good account of the contribution of soil nutrients to the maintenance of ecological systems.

Henderson, L. J.: "The Fitness of the Environment," Macmillan, New York, 1913. A durable classic on the physical and chemical nature of the environment and its relation to organisms. Highly recommended.

Kellogg, C. E.: Soil, *Sci. American,* July, 1950. The development and the varieties of soil are discussed. Recommended.

Kuenen, P. H.: Sand, *Sci. American,* Apr., 1960. A discussion of the history and fate of sand grains, a good supplementary reference to the study of soil.

Munk, W.: The Circulation of the Oceans, *Sci. American,* Sept., 1955. An account of the pattern and the forces responsible for ocean currents.

Ommanney, F. D.: "The Oceans," Oxford, Fair Lawn, N.J., 1949. A recommended small book on the biology and ecology of the sea.

Opik, E. J.: Climate and the Changing Sun, *Sci. American,* June, 1958. Changes in the radiation rate of the sun may have contributed to the development of ice ages.

Plass, G. N.: Carbon Dioxide and Climate, *Sci.*

American, July, 1959. CO_2 contributes to the regulation of global temperature, and the gas therefore plays an important ecological role.

Stetson, H. C.: The Continental Shelf, *Sci. American,* Mar., 1955. A geologist assesses the importance of this part of the ocean floor.

Stommel, H.: The Anatomy of the Atlantic, *Sci. American,* Jan., 1955. The physical, geological, and chemical characteristics of this ocean are described.

Wexler, H.: Volcanoes and World Climate, *Sci. American,* Apr., 1952. An examination of the possible role of volcanoes in the causation of ice ages.

The readings below all have self-explanatory titles; they deal with the relation of the living to the non-living components of the biosphere and with the nature of various habitats:

Beebe, W.: "Edge of the Jungle," Little, Brown, Boston, 1950.

Berrill, N. J.: "The Living Tide," Dodd, Mead, New York, 1951.

Deevey, E. S.: Life in the Depths of a Pond, *Sci. American,* Apr., 1951

————: Bogs, *Sci. American,* Oct., 1958.

Ingle, R. M.: The Life of an Estuary, *Sci. American,* May, 1954.

Nicholas, G.: Life in Caves, *Sci. American,* May, 1955.

Pequegnat, W. E.: Whales, Plankton, and Man, *Sci. American,* Jan., 1958.

Ryther, F. H.: The Sargasso Sea, *Sci. American,* Jan., 1956.

Tiffany, L. H.: "Algae: The Grass of Many Waters," 2d ed., Charles C Thomas, Springfield, Ill., 1958.

Vevers, H. G.: Animals of the Bottom, *Sci. American,* July, 1952.

Walford, L. A.: The Deep-sea Layers of Life, *Sci. American,* Aug., 1951.

PART FOUR
THE WORLD OF LIFE

CHAPTER 11
PREMONERA AND MONERA

CHAPTER 12
PROTISTA

CHAPTER 13
METAPHYTA

CHAPTER 14
METAZOA

CHAPTER 15
METAZOA: PROTOSTOMIAL COELOMATES

CHAPTER 16
METAZOA: DEUTEROSTOMIAL COELOMATES

Following an introductory discussion of the origin of life, this part consists of an examination of the structural and evolutionary characteristics of all major groups and subgroups of organisms living today.

One main objective is to provide insight into the vast organizational diversity of the living creatures on earth. An appreciation of this diversity should show clearly that workable, successful solutions to the universal requirements of life have been found countless times, within innummerable evolutionary forms. A second main objective is to supply the essential background for the analysis of living functions following later. We know that these functions are metabolism and self-perpetuation and that they are performed in specific individual organisms. If therefore the functions are to be understood, it is clearly necessary that the performers themselves be understood.

CHAPTER 11
PREMONERA
AND
MONERA

As pointed out in Chap. 2, the living world today may be considered to consist of four large categories of organisms, namely, Monera, Protista, Metaphyta, and Metazoa. The first two of these presumably are the most ancient, and both probably evolved as descendants of some of the earliest organisms on earth. We may refer to these original ancestral forms collectively as the "Premonera," and we may properly ask how they originated. Indeed, we may ask how life itself originated. The first two sections of this chapter attempt to outline an answer.

We have reason to suspect, furthermore, that some premoneran group or groups probably evolved into Monera long before some other premoneran stocks gave rise to Protista. It is likely therefore that, of all organisms, the Monera now living represent the most ancient and most primitive branch of life still in existence. The detailed characteristics of these moneran organisms are examined in the last section below.

THE ORIGIN OF LIFE

It is thought today that life began as a result of a progressive series of chemical synthesis reactions which raised the organization of inanimate matter to successively higher levels. Atoms combined into simple compounds, these combined into more complex ones, and the most complex compounds so formed eventually became organized into living cells.

The details of these processes are at present known only partly. Some of the existing knowledge results from a backward projection of cellular types and activities encountered today. For example, one may deduce from viruses, bacteria, and other primitive existing forms what the earliest living systems might have been like. Other clues come from astronomy, physics, and geology, sciences which contribute information about the probable physical characteristics of the ancient earth. Important data are also provided by ingenious chemical experiments designed to duplicate in the laboratory some of the steps which many millennia ago may have led to the beginning of life.

What has been learned in this way indicates that living creatures on earth are a direct product of the earth. Moreover, there is every reason to believe that living things owe their origin entirely to certain physical and chemical properties of the ancient earth. Nothing supernatural appears to be involved—only time and natural physical and chemical laws operating within the peculiarly suitable earthly environment. Given such an environment, life probably *had* to happen. Put another way, once the earth had originated in its ancient form, with particular chemical and physical properties, it was then virtually inevitable that life would later originate on it also. The chemical and physical properties of the earth permitted certain chemical and physical reactions to occur, and one result of these reactions was something living. We may infer, moreover, that if other solar systems possess planets where chemical and physical conditions resemble those of the ancient earth, then life would originate on these other planets as well. Indeed, it is now believed strongly that life occurs not only on this earth but probably widely throughout the universe as well.

CHEMICAL EVOLUTION

The life-producing chemical and physical properties of the early earth were a result of the way the earth and our solar system as a whole came into being to begin with. Available evidence indicates that the solar system is anywhere from 5 to 10 billion years old. Several hypotheses have been proposed to explain how the sun and the planets were formed. According to one, now widely accepted, the whole solar system started out as a hot, rapidly rotating ball of gas. This gas was made up of free atoms. Hydrogen atoms probably were the most abundant, and other, heavier kinds were present in lesser quantities. The sun was formed when most of this atomic gas, hence most of the hydrogen, gravitated toward the center of the ball. Even today, the sun is composed largely of hydrogen atoms. A swirling belt of gas remained outside the new sun. Eddies formed in this belt and in time it broke up into a few smaller gas clouds. These spinning spheres of fiery matter were the early planets.

The earth thus probably began as a glowing mass of free hydrogen and other types of atoms. These eventually became sorted out according to weight. Heavy ones, such as iron and nickel, sank toward the center of the earth, where they are still present today. Lighter atoms, such as silicon and aluminum, formed a middle shell. The very lightest, such as hydrogen, nitrogen, oxygen, and carbon, collected in the outermost layers (Fig. 11.1).

At first, temperatures were probably too high for the formation of compounds—bonds would have been broken as fast as they might have formed. But under the influence of the cold of cosmic space, the earth began to cool down gradually. In time, temperatures became low enough to permit the formation of relatively stable bonds between atoms. Compounds then appeared in profusion and free atoms largely disappeared.

What simple compounds could have formed from hydrogen, carbon, oxygen, and nitrogen, the principal elements in the surface gas of the early earth? On the basis of their known chemical properties and their presumed relative abundance, H, C, O, and N should have joined into some half dozen different combina-

11 · 1 Elements composing the early earth became sorted out according to weight. Heavy elements like iron sank to the center; lighter ones like silicon formed a middle shell; and very light elements like hydrogen collected into an outer mantle.

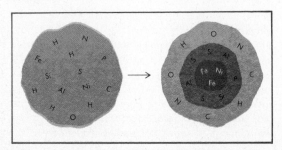

tions: water (H_2O); methane (CH_4); ammonia (NH_3); carbon dioxide (CO_2); hydrogen cyanide (HCN); and hydrogen molecules (H_2). We have evidence that at least the first three of these compounds actually came into being not only on the early earth but on other planets as well. For example, on the cold, distant planet Jupiter, water, methane, and ammonia are present today in the form of thick surface layers of permanently frozen solids. Apparently, these compounds must have formed there as on earth, but at that great distance from the sun the surface of the planet probably froze before much additional chemical change could occur. On the hot earth, by contrast, the early compounds could interact further and give rise to new compounds in the later course of time.

Moreover, there is every reason to believe that, under the conditions prevailing on the early earth, simple compounds that theoretically could have appeared actually did appear. On this basis, the formation of H_2, H_2O, CH_4, NH_3, CO_2, and HCN must have been a strong probability. Practically all the hydrogen molecules (and any free hydrogen atoms still present) must soon have boiled off the surface layers of the earth, for the gravitational attraction of the comparatively small planet could not have been great enough to hold these extremely light substances. The other compounds remained and constituted a hot, gaseous atmosphere.

In time, as the gas ball which was the earth continued to cool, temperatures become low enough to allow some of the gases to liquefy and some of the liquids in turn to solidify. Heavy substances near the center of the earth probably tended to liquefy and solidify first. But the heat of the materials prevented complete solidification, and to this day the earth contains a hot, thickly flowing, deformable center. On the other hand, the middle shell of lighter substances did congeal, and a solid, gradually thickening crust developed. As the crust thickened and cooled, it wrinkled and folded and gave rise to the first mountain ranges. Overlying this crust was the outer atmospheric mantle, which at temperatures then prevailing still remained gaseous.

Then the rains started. All the water on earth up to this stage was in the atmosphere, forming clouds probably hundreds of miles thick. The solidifying crust underneath at first was sufficiently hot for any liquid water to boil away instantly. But eventually the crust became cool enough to hold water in liquid form. Then rain began falling in unceasing, centuries-long downpours. Basins and shallows filled up and torrential rivers tore down from the mountains. The oceans formed in this way.

Dissolved in these seas were quantities of the atmospheric CH_4, NH_3, CO_2, and HCN, compounds which persist as gases at temperatures at which water is liquid. Also accumulating in the ocean were salts and minerals. At first there were none, but as the rivers eroded the mountainsides and dissolved them away and as violent tides battered the shores and reduced them to powder, salts and minerals came to be added to the ocean in increasing quantities. Moreover, massive submarine bursts of molten lava probably erupted frequently through the earth's crust, and they too added their substance to the mineral content of the world's waters. Thus the oceans acquired their saltiness relatively early and to a small extent they became saltier still during subsequent ages (Fig. 11.2).

The formation of large bodies of liquid water containing the early atmospheric gases and many minerals in solution was the key event which made the later origin of life possible. Water was and is now the most essential single component of living matter. We already know that water is virtually the best of all possible solvents, a property which makes it an excellent medium for chemical reactions. Moreover, water was originally the only good source of hydrogen and oxygen; as noted, free hydrogen and free oxygen became unavailable soon after the origin of the earth, and water molecules then came to serve as the principal suppliers. Water remains today virtually the only usable source of hydrogen and one of the important sources of oxygen.

Thus, oceanic water set the stage for the formation of living matter. The actors on this stage were the various gases and minerals dissolved in water, plus water itself. And the leading role was played by the carbon atoms present in gases such as methane; for from methane could be formed numerous kinds of *organic* compounds, that is, compounds containing *linked* carbon atoms and comparatively large amounts of chemical energy. The formation of organic compounds would have required external energy sources, but at least two such sources must actually have been available.

One of these was the sun. Although the dense cloud layers of water vapor at first must have prevented sunlight from reaching the earth's surface (which must have made the earth quite dark for long ages), the ultraviolet rays, X rays, and other high-energy radiations of the sun must have penetrated the clouds well. Some of the radiation could have provided the necessary energy for reactions among methane, ammonia, hydrogen cyanide, and water. Solar radiation certainly is known to support various chemical reactions today.

Moreover, a second energy source must have been the powerful electric discharges in lightning, which must have occurred almost continuously in the early

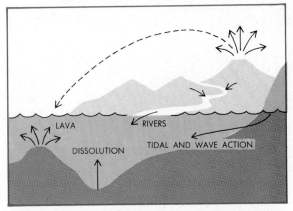

11 · 2 Original sources of oceanic salt. *Some came from volcanoes, both submarine and terrestrial; some was dissolved out of the sea bottom; some resulted from tidal action, which crumbled and dissolved the shore lines; and some came from the land surface, leached out by rain and rivers.*

cloud-laden, storm-lashed atmosphere. Like solar radiation, lightning is capable of activating and sustaining chemical reactions. Either lightning or solar energy (or also radioactive materials in the earth's crust) could have acted directly on the gas molecules of the atmosphere, as still happens today to some extent. The resulting aerial chemicals could then have been washed down into the seas by rain. Alternatively, reactions could have taken place directly in the waters of the ocean, where methane and all other necessary ingredients were dissolved.

That simple organic materials can indeed be created in such fashion was demonstrated in the early 1950s through dramatic and now classic laboratory experiments. In these experiments, the presumable environment of the early earth was duplicated in miniature. Into a flask were put inorganic mixtures containing water, methane gas, and ammonia gas, and electricity was discharged through these mixtures for several days to simulate the lightning discharges of the early earth. When the contents of the flask were then examined, many amino acids, fatty acids, and other simple organic compounds were actually found to be present.

Thus there is excellent reason to think that, under the impact of early energy sources, simple gases and other inorganic materials not only could but probably did react with one another. Such reactions must have given rise to a variety of simple organic compounds which accumulated in the ancient seas. These organic substances then constituted the biological "staples"

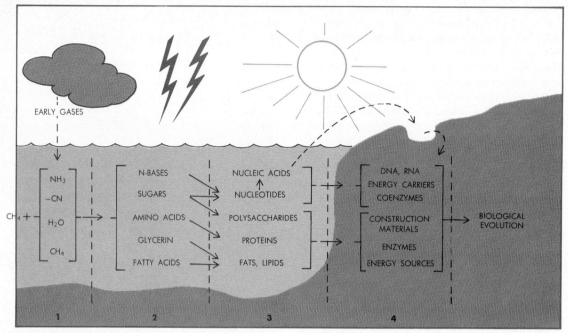

11 · 3 Chemical evolution. Summary of probable early synthesis reactions. At least three or four successive phases may have been involved. The original gaseous raw materials came from the early atmosphere, and with the aid of energy from lightning and the sun, key biological compounds were progressively synthesized in the ocean. The later, more complex synthesis reactions perhaps took place in sand pockets along the shore, where required ingredients could become highly concentrated by evaporation of water. After the origin of the first living units, the latter presumably were washed out to sea and further biological evolution then must have occurred in the sea.

out of which more complex organic materials could become synthesized (Fig. 11.3).

It now appears quite plausible from a chemical standpoint that proteins and nitrogen bases could have formed on the early earth from simpler biological staples already present. For example, recent experiments show that if concentrated mixtures of amino acids are heated under nearly dry conditions, proteinlike complexes are formed. Similarly, mixtures of other appropriate starting compounds heated under almost dry conditions can yield products having the characteristics of nitrogen bases (Fig. 11.4). Proteins would then have provided enzymatically active materials, and the chemical tempo on earth would henceforth have quickened substantially. Among

their other catalytic effects, the proteins might have promoted the combination of nitrogen bases, simple sugars, and phosphates into nucleotides; and the latter are only a simple chemical step away from energy carriers such as ATP. With enzymes and ATP then being available, a few further chemical steps lead to nucleotide derivatives such as coenzymes and to nucleic acids such as genetically active DNA and RNA. To be sure, direct laboratory demonstration of these last steps of synthesis is still lacking. Even so, there does not appear to be any basic chemical problem in envisaging that such syntheses can, and probably did, take place.

With the formation of proteins and nucleic acids, all the essential ingredients for the eventual origin of a living entity must have been in existence. Events up to this point may be referred to collectively as *chemical evolution:* the production and gradual accumulation in the early seas of all the various compounds that later came to function as components of living matter. The most fundamental of these compounds must have included at least seven categories of substances, namely, inorganic materials such as water and dissolved mineral substances, and organic materials such as adenosine phosphates, carbohydrates, fats, proteins, and nucleic acids.

The events that followed subsequently may be described as *biological evolution:* the actual putting together of the chemical components into the first living units, namely, cells. Note here that chemical evolution did not simply stop at one point, with biological evolution then taking over. On the contrary, chemical evolution continued and indeed goes on even now. Rather, at some stage of chemical evolution an additional kind of creation must have taken hold. Molecules no longer gave rise just to new molecules only, but some of the molecules also produced something entirely new, something hitherto completely nonexistent, namely, fully living cells. These in turn then produced more cells through processes of multiplication still going on today. In other words, the new dimension of biological evolution must have become superimposed on the still continuing older dimension of chemical evolution.

How did the first cell arise?

BIOLOGICAL EVOLUTION

The nature of the events which resulted in cell formation can be deduced in very general outline only; the details are considerably less clear than even those of chemical evolution. Conceivably, the same end result may have been achieved in several different ways. However, we might assume that, by one means or another, sets of all the key compounds already present in the early ocean must have collected together in tiny spaces; and each set of materials so accumulated must have remained aggregated in a cohesive drop. By virtue of the various properties of the aggregated materials, the drop would have been a metabolizing and self-perpetuating unit and so would have been alive.

If this describes the overall process, we may ask first whether or not such aggregates could actually have formed by known physical and chemical means. Certain possibilities which might appear reasonable theoretically must probably be regarded as unlikely in practice. For example, it is probably unlikely that aggregation of the necessary compounds could have occurred directly in the open ocean. The concentration of compounds must have been quite low, and the open water must therefore have been too dilute a solution to provide a reasonable chance for repeated aggregation of just the right sets of materials. Moreover, even if such aggregation could have occurred, it is difficult to imagine how the aggregated materials could have been kept together in open water for any length of time. After making chance contacts, the compounds most likely would have dispersed again.

It is physically and chemically more plausible to assume that the critical aggregations took place along the shores of the ocean. The solid ground available there would have provided appropriate surfaces to which oceanic molecules could have adhered. Many organic compounds are known to be readily *adsorbed* to various surfaces, a property which we often recognize as stickiness. For example, sugars, fats, and proteins stick very readily to many kinds of surfaces, and nucleic acids are extraordinarily adsorbable. Also, finely divided sand and clay particles are excellent adsorbing materials and such particles must have been abundant along the ocean shore. Accordingly, it is reasonable to think that some of the organic compounds formed in the ocean were washed to the shore, where some of them became adsorbed to various surfaces more or less at random. This process might have occurred progressively. The adsorbing surfaces could have trapped those molecules that did happen to make contact, and other molecules of the same or of different types might or might not have become added later. The concentrations of the molecules so could have increased slowly, a process which would have been reinforced by considerable evaporation of water in the tide zone.

Moreover, it is not necessary to assume that nucleic acids, proteins, complex polysaccharides, and large molecules generally first had to be formed in the open ocean and then had to become aggregated along the shore. On the contrary, it is physically and chemically more plausible that the first aggregations involved only the relatively simple organic compounds. Large molecules later could have become synthesized directly within, and indeed as a conse-

11 · 4 Thermal synthesis experiments in the test tube indicate that even under essentially simple conditions, amino acids can give rise to proteinlike complexes having a primitive gross structure (top), *and that nucleotide precursors such as ureidosuccinic acid can arise from relatively simple starting compounds* (bottom). *The basic pattern parallels that of biological synthesis in the living cell* (cf. Fig. 20.7).

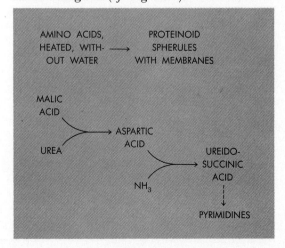

quence of, the simple accumulations. Thus, if microscopic organic pockets could become established along the shore, and if these accumulated high enough concentrations of biological staples, then such systems probably would have been adequate for the production of larger molecules within them. In line with the heating experiments cited earlier (see Fig. 11.4), evaporation of water and solar heat would actually have promoted the synthesis of more complex substances.

It is unlikely, therefore, that compounds as complex as proteins and nucleic acids could have formed by the chance accumulation of enough ATP, amino acids, and nucleotides in the open ocean. It is more likely that proteins and nucleic acids arose *after* the precursor compounds had already become collected together in a small enough space and in high enough concentrations to provide an adequate and perhaps fairly dry chemical environment for synthesis. And after genetically active nucleic acids had become synthesized, they themselves could then have directed the synthesis of specific, no longer randomly formed proteins, again right within the aggregations already present. Some of these proteins would subsequently have acted as specific enzymes and so would have facilitated the rapid formation of a wealth of new

compounds, for example, polysaccharides out of sugar raw materials.

Moreover, some of the proteins and also some of the fats and carbohydrates would have represented building materials. These could have become organized into a structural framework that ramified through and around the aggregated drop. Many proteins are known to precipitate out of solution and to form solid granules or threadlike fibrils, for example. Also, as has been shown in Chap. 4, mixtures containing proteins or protein-fat complexes may, as a consequence of their colloidal physical state, form membranous surface films. And the heating experiments mentioned above similarly show that proteinaceous aggregates form surface membranes quite readily. Moreover, polysaccharides, like cellulose, similarly may form fibrils or films. Thus, the aggregated drops on the ocean shore could well have developed external boundary membranes and some measure of internal scaffolding. They would henceforth have been distinctly individual units marked off from the surrounding ocean water, and they would have remained individualized even if they absorbed more water and were later washed back into the open ocean. Indeed, such units would have been primitive cells (Fig. 11.5).

They would also have been truly alive. Oceanic chemicals would have been nutrients and their absorption into the cells would have represented a simple form of nutrition. Internal exergonic decomposition reactions aided by protein enzymes and nucleotide coenzymes would have constituted respiration. The ATP generated through respiration would have supported endergonic syntheses. Nucleic acids would have functioned as genes, and by controlling synthesis they would have maintained steady states, growth, and cellular reproduction. Moreover, such genes would have mutated occasionally, would have been inherited by offspring cells, and would have become combined sexually if two cells happened to meet and fuse. Even the earliest cells must therefore have been

11 · 5 The possible origin of the first cells. *Appropriate chemical ingredients might have accumulated by adsorption in microscopic pockets along the seashore (1) and these ingredients could have become concentrated progressively (2). Under relatively dry conditions and perhaps with the aid of ATP, which might have been present, nucleic acids and proteins could have formed (3). The proteins then would have permitted the occurrence of enzymatically accelerated reactions and the formation of structural membranes and internal fibrils (4). Finally, primitive cellular compartments might have been washed out to sea (5).*

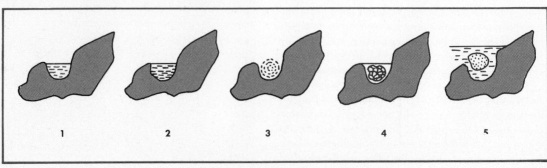

1   2   3   4   5

able to evolve and adapt. Evidently, such cells must have exhibited all the metabolic and self-perpetuative properties by which we define "life."

Undoubtedly, numerous trials and errors must have occurred before the first actual cells left their places of birth. Many and perhaps most of the aggregations on the shore probably were "unsuccessful." In given cases, for example, the right kinds of starting ingredients might never have come together; or the right amounts of ingredients might never have accumulated; or the mixture might have dried up completely; or it might have been washed out to sea prematurely and dispersed. Clearly, numerous hazards must have led to many false starts and to many incomplete endings. Yet when an appropriate constellation of materials did form a persisting aggregate, the formation of a living cell would have been a likely result.

A basic problem in tracing the possible origin of cells (and of later groups of organisms generally) is to decide whether they evolved *monophyletically,* from a single common ancestral stock, or *polyphyletically,* from several separate ancestral stocks (Fig. 11.6). Did early cells arise from a single first cell, an archancestor of all life, or did numerous "first" cells originate independently? The answer to this question (and to similar ones relating to many later groups) is simply not known. Nevertheless, biologists often try to arrive at a tentative answer on the basis of generalized arguments. For example, proponents of monophyletism invoke a *probability* argument: cells are so complex that multiple origins of such complexities are statistically quite unlikely. The argument leads logically to the view that all life started in a single place at a single time, from a single cell which formed by a "lucky accident."

Proponents of polyphyletism counter this line of reasoning with a probability argument of their own. They point out, first, that compared to their later complexities, the original cells could not really have been so complex. Initially they probably were little more than loose aggregates of chemicals surrounded by membranes, and structural complexity must have evolved subsequently, in gradual steps. Second, if the required conditions for original cell formation could actually have developed in one place at one time, it is statistically most likely that such conditions also developed in other places and at other times. In one sense, therefore, chance undoubtedly did play a role in cell formation: many aggregations never became cells, and those that did owed their existence to the chance accumulation of the right ingredients. But in another sense, cell formation was not simply an enormously "lucky accident," a one-time occurrence of very remote probability. On the contrary,

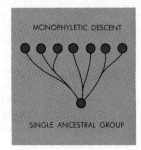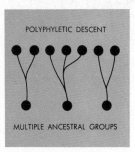

11 · 6   Monophyletism vs. polyphyletism.

given an early earth so constituted that certain compounds could form and given these compounds and their special properties, then cell formation *had* to take place sooner or later, inevitably and repeatedly. The only element of chance here was time; the uncertainty was not in the nature of "if," but in the nature of "when" and "how often." Accordingly, the origin of cells was as little an accident as is the eventual appearance of sevens and elevens in a succession of dice throws.

Monophyletists also invoke a *homology* argument: all cells are fundamentally so remarkably alike in chemical composition, in microscopic structure, and in function, that a common origin from a single ancestry seems clearly indicated. Polyphyletists here counter with an *analogy* argument: all aggregates that actually became living cells must necessarily have shared the same broad structural and functional characteristics; for those aggregates that did not exhibit such characteristics simply would never have remained "alive," by definition of this term. Thus, all living cells *must* have contained at least water, various mineral substances, adenosine phosphates, carbohydrates, fats, proteins, and nucleic acids. Only aggregates possessing these substances would have been able to metabolize and to self-perpetuate. The similarities among cells therefore are not necessarily an indication of common ancestry, but might merely reflect the universal attributes anything living must have regardless of origin.

Actual evidence is unavailable, and at present it is very difficult to decide whether a monophyletic or a polyphyletic view is more plausible. The problem of monophyletism versus polyphyletism recurs many times in tracing the evolutionary interrelations of organisms, and favoring one view in one instance does not require that the same view be favored in all other instances. Regardless of problems of this nature, best estimates at present suggest that the first cell or cells probably arose some 2 billion years after the origin of the earth, that is, perhaps 3 billion or more years ago.

It is not necessary to assume that cellular life originated exclusively by the processes just described or even that the above outline corresponds in detail to the actual events of the distant past. The important consideration at this stage of knowledge is mainly that we *can* envisage processes of cell formation plausible within the limits of the physics and chemistry of the earth. This in itself represents a major advance over knowledge available just two or three decades ago. In another two or three decades we are quite likely to have far surer knowledge, plus, perhaps, the ability to duplicate in the laboratory some of the key steps of these ancient events.

Note, incidentally, that no one point in the earth's early history really qualifies as a "beginning" of life. The cell is the major product of the first few billion years, and we regard this product as being alive. But the earlier organic compounds dissolved in the ocean already possessed the properties that eventually made life possible. Such compounds in turn did not originate their characteristic properties, but acquired them when they were formed from various simpler compounds. The potential of life clearly traces back to the original individual atoms, and the creation of life out of atoms was but a step-by-step exploitation of their properties. Evidently, life did not burst forth from the ocean finished and ready. Instead, it *developed*, and here is perhaps the most dramatic illustration that small beginnings may have surprisingly large endings. Development has been the hallmark of life ever since; life today is still unceasingly forming and molding. Indeed, it will never be finally "finished" until its last spark is extinguished.

PREMONERA

The original cells represented the first Premonera. Among them, abundant diversification must have occurred during subsequent ages and numerous new premoneran types must have arisen through evolution. We may surmise, moreover, that this evolutionary branching out must have been promoted and oriented by a powerful environmental stimulus, namely, the gradual disappearance of free molecular foods from the ocean.

For as more and more food molecules were withdrawn and used by more and more cells, the rate of global food utilization must eventually have become greater than the rate of food formation from methane, ammonia, and the other atmospheric constituents. In time, therefore, free molecular foods must have disappeared completely from the ocean, and that environment then became as exclusively inorganic as it still is today. Evidently, almost as soon as it

originated, living matter began to affect and to change the physical character of the earth. But it is clear that, unless new ways of procuring foods could have evolved, the ever-increasing multitude of reproducing, food-using cells would soon have nourished itself into extinction. Early cells did not succumb. On the contrary, they gave rise to the far-flung, richly diversified living world of today.

NUTRITIONAL EVOLUTION

One of the first evolutionary responses to dwindling food supplies probably was the development of *parasitism*. If foods could not be obtained from the open ocean, they still could be obtained within the bodies of living cells. Thus, a cell could solve its food-supply problem if it could manage to enter into a larger cell without being destroyed (compare Fig. 2.1). Methods of infecting cellular hosts could well have evolved almost as soon as cells themselves had evolved, and for many of the early premonerans parasitism must have been an effective new way of life.

Another new way that required relatively little evolutionary adjustment was *saprotrophism*. Here an organism drew food molecules not from the decreasing supply in the ocean but from the bodies of dead cells or disintegrated cellular material. Organic *decay* then was a result of the nutrient-gathering activities of these saprotrophs. Before the evolution of saprotrophism, decay was unknown on earth. Today, saprotrophic types are so abundant that virtually any substance begins to decay almost immediately after exposure to air or water.

A third new process which permitted survival despite dwindling food supplies was *holotrophism*, the process of "eating" other living cells whole. This method of feeding presumably originated through phagocytosis, that is, a generalized capacity of the cell surface to engulf microscopic particles. Pseudopodia and permanent cellular mouths (*gullets*) must have been later elaborations.

But all three of these new food-gathering procedures were ultimately self-limiting. Parasitism, saprotrophism, and holotrophism collectively constituted the *heterotrophic* forms of nutrition, and these merely changed the distribution of already existing organic matter; they did not add any new food to the global supply. Clearly, if totally new food sources had not become available, life would have had to cease sooner or later.

What was needed, fundamentally, was a new way of making organic substances, preferably right within cells. The original way, in which sun and lightning formed food compounds out of materials such as methane, ammonia, and water, was no longer adequate, if it occurred at all at that late period. But the raw materials for a new process were still available in abundance. Water was in inexhaustible supply and, in addition to methane or hydrogen cyanide, there now existed directly within cells an even better source of carbon: carbon dioxide, byproduct of respiration. Given CO_2 and water, organic molecules could be manufactured in cells, provided that new external sources of energy could be found. Internal energy in the form of ATP was still available, to be sure; but ATP was itself an organic compound and was therefore among the very substances that would have disappeared if new external energy had not made possible their continued manufacture. Premonera actually did evolve means of utilizing external energy in the production of organic compounds. Two broad categories of such *autotrophic* forms came into existence.

One group included organisms which found new external sources of energy in sulfur, iron, nitrogen, and a number of other metallic and nonmetallic materials obtainable from the environment. These *chemosynthetic* organisms must have evolved in such a way that they could absorb various inorganic molecules into their cells and there make them undergo various exergonic reactions. Chemical energy so obtained was then used within the cells to combine CO_2 and water into food molecules, specifically carbohydrates (compare Fig. 2.1).

Judging from the results some 2 or 3 billion years later, early chemosynthesis apparently was only a limited solution of the energy- and food-supply problem. Possibly it depended too much on particular inorganic materials available only in particular localities. A more generally useful solution required a steady, more nearly universal external energy source. Such a source was the sun. High-energy solar radiations like ultraviolet and X rays no longer were a sufficient energy source for the amount of food production required. Similarly, the earlier permanent cloud cover had disappeared by now and lightning too became inadequate as an energy source. But solar radiation of lower energy content, especially light, now beamed down to earth as predictably and dependably as could be desired. If sunlight could be used, the energy problem, hence the food problem, would be solved. Sunlight actually did become the ultimate energy supplier for the vast majority of organisms, and it has played that role ever since.

Utilization of light energy within cells requires a cellular light-trapping device. Many kinds of photosensitive compounds are known to be able to absorb light and to trap more or less of its energy. By chance reactions, such compounds may have formed very early in the open ocean, along with all the others we have discussed. And it is likely that some of these substances were among the many materials that collected together and formed cells. Alternatively, light-trapping compounds might have been manufactured directly within cells already in existence, as one of the new materials produced by cellular synthesis. In some such way, some of the premonerans came to possess substances that were more or less efficient in trapping the energy of sunlight. This energy could be then used to transform CO_2 and water into organic food compounds.

One group of such early light-trapping substances has been perpetuated to the very present. The members of this group are all related chemically; they are green and we call them *chlorophyll*. And the new process in which sunlight and chlorophyll promoted the transformation of CO_2 and water into foods was *photosynthesis* (compare Fig. 2.1).

With this new source of organic compounds assured, it did not matter that free molecular foods in the ocean finally disappeared. Photosynthesizing cells could make foods for themselves; holotrophic organisms could swallow such cells and then each other; parasites could invade photosynthesizers or holotrophs; and saprotrophs in turn could find foods in the dead bodies of any of these. Consequently, excepting only the chemosynthesizers, which made their own foods, all other organisms were saved from premature extinction by photosynthesis. Today, photosynthesis still supports all living creatures except the chemosynthesizers. We note that, sooner or later after the appearance of the first cells, five kinds of food-getting methods were evolved: parasitism, saprotrophism, holotrophism, chemosynthesis, and photosynthesis. Only the last two added to the net global supply of foods.

As photosynthesis occurred to an ever-increasing extent, it brought about far-reaching changes in the physical environment. A byproduct of photosynthesis is free molecular oxygen (O_2), a highly reactive gas which combines readily with other substances. Before the advent of photosynthesis, free oxygen had not existed since the early days of the earth, when oxygen atoms were still uncombined. Later, such small quantities of free oxygen as might occasionally have formed would have combined quickly with materials in the vicinity. Now, increasingly large amounts of free oxygen escaped from photosynthesizing cells into the ocean and from there into the atmosphere. The gas must have reacted promptly with everything it could, and this probably initiated a slow, profound "oxygen revolution" on earth (Fig. 11.7). This revolution ultimately transformed the ancient atmosphere into the modern one, which no longer contains methane, ammonia, and cyanide. Instead, it consists mainly of water vapor, carbon dioxide, and molecular nitrogen, plus large quantities of free molecular oxygen itself.

At higher altitudes, under the impact of high-energy radiation from space, oxygen molecules combined with one another and formed a layer of *ozone* (O_3). This layer, several miles up, has been in existence ever since. Ozone became an excellent screen against deep penetration of high-energy radiation. Consequently, organisms which evolved after the establishment of the ozone layer lived in an environment more or less completely free of high-energy radiation. This is why modern advanced plants and animals are comparatively unadapted to such radiation and are killed by even small doses of it. By contrast, the earliest organisms had evolved before the large-scale formation of ozone and had become more or less well adapted to space radiation. Some of their descendants among primitive forms now in existence still display this radiation resistance. They can withstand exposures to X rays and similar radiation that would kill an army of men.

Free oxygen also reacted with the solid crust of the earth and converted most pure metals and mineral substances into *oxides*—the familiar ores and rocks of which much of the land surface is now made. A few relatively unreactive metals like gold resisted the action of oxygen, but others could not. And if today we wish to obtain pure iron or aluminum, for example, we must smelt or otherwise process appropriate ores to separate out the firmly bound oxygen.

Free oxygen, finally, made possible a new, much more efficient form of respiration. The earliest cells respired without oxygen, and to a small extent all living organisms still do. But when free environmental oxygen began to accumulate in quantity, organisms newly evolving at that time additionally developed means of respiring with the aid of oxygen; and this method soon became the standard way of extracting energy from foods.

We note that the effects and activities of the early organisms greatly altered the physical character of the earth and also the biological character of the organisms themselves. So has it been ever since, even if never again so dramatically and incisively: the physical earth creates and influences the development of the biological earth, and the biological earth then reciprocates by influencing the development of the physical earth.

STRUCTURAL EVOLUTION

In parallel with the nutritional evolution of the Premonera, an internal structural evolution must have taken place as well. At first, the gene-forming nucleic acids probably were suspended free within the cell substance. It must have happened on occasion that such nucleic acids escaped from a cell into the open ocean, perhaps after an accidental rupture in the cellular boundary or after cell death. In this free state, the nucleic acids would have been simply lifeless chemicals. But it must have happened often that such inert components by accident encountered other early cells and entered them. Within these host cells, the inert nucleic acids could become active again, that is, the living machinery of the host could provide the means for nucleic acid control activities and reproduction.

Nucleic acids escaped from one cell, existing free for a time in an inert state, and then reentering and being reactivated by another cell, may have been the ancestors of the modern *viruses*. As outlined in Chap. 9, viruses today behave exactly that way.

Modern viruses are known to be highly complex in structure and behavior, and it is likely that their distant ancestors were far less complex. Indeed, such ancestors may have been naked nucleic acids. If so, formation of viruslike nucleic acid units and transfer from cell to cell could have occurred as soon as cells themselves were in existence.

Transfers of this kind must have had important consequences. For example, some cells would have lost certain properties and other cells would have gained them; the transferred nucleic acids were genes, and as they became shuffled among cells, so did the activities that these genes controlled. Therefore, in addition to mutations and sexual combinations of genes, transfer of viruslike nucleic acids

11 · 7 The oxygen revolution. Oxygen from photosynthesis reacted with other materials. A major result was the establishment of a new, modern atmosphere, containing N_2, CO_2, and H_2O in addition to O_2 itself.

$$CH_4 + 2\ O_2 \longrightarrow CO_2 + 2\ H_2O$$

$$4\ NH_3 + 3\ O_2 \longrightarrow 2\ N_2 + 6\ H_2O$$

$$O_2 + 2\ O_2 \longrightarrow 2\ O_3,\ OZONE$$

$$METALS,\ MINERALS + O_2 \longrightarrow ORES,\ ROCKS$$

$$ORGANISMS + O_2 \longrightarrow AEROBIC\ RESPIRATION$$

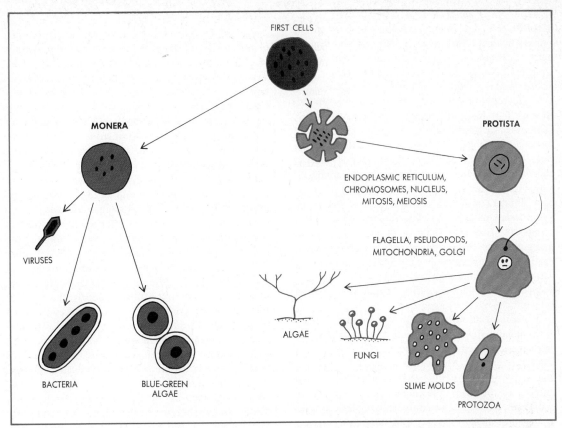

FIRST CELLS

MONERA

PROTISTA

ENDOPLASMIC RETICULUM,
CHROMOSOMES, NUCLEUS,
MITOSIS, MEIOSIS

FLAGELLA, PSEUDOPODS,
MITOCHONDRIA, GOLGI

VIRUSES

ALGAE

FUNGI

BACTERIA

BLUE-GREEN
ALGAE

SLIME MOLDS

PROTOZOA

11 · 8 Earliest cells (*with dispersed genetic material, as indicated*) *probably gave rise to two structural types, one without nuclear membrane and referred to as moneran cells, the other with nuclear membrane and referred to as protistan cells. The presumable later evolutionary history of these two cellular stocks is sketched above.*

would have constituted a third way in which the gene content of cells could have become altered. This process too must have promoted cellular evolution and must have contributed to the emergence of a great variety of different cell types. Certain kinds of modern viruses still transfer genes from one cell to another, a phenomenon known as *transduction* (see Chap. 20).

By hindsight, we know that among the premoneran organisms two main structural types came to have particular significance in later evolution (Fig. 11.8). As noted, early premoneran cells probably possessed freely suspended gene-forming nucleic acids. In some of the later descendants of these cells, the genes apparently aggregated together into threadlike filaments and formed loose clumps. In each cell, such a clump then remained embedded within the cell substance and in direct contact with it. The group of organisms descended from premoneran cells and characterized by this type of internal cellular arrangement collectively constitute the *Monera* (or *Procaryota*, organisms preceding the evolution of cell nuclei).

Representatives of this group are probably still in

existence today in the form of *bacteria* and *blue-green algae*. The exact ancestry of these modern organisms is uncertain. However, some of the present bacteria in particular are very close to our conception of what the first Monera might have been like. As judged from their living representatives, the early Monera must have developed four of the five methods of nutrition. Blue-green algae are largely photosynthetic, and bacteria are either photosynthetic, chemosynthetic, parasitic, or saprotrophic. Evidently, all methods except holotrophic eating evolved in the group.

In a second major type descended from premoneran ancestors, the gene-forming nucleic acids in each cell again condensed into threadlike filaments.

However, proteins became an integral part of the structure of such filaments, and these elaborately organized nucleoprotein organelles thus formed *chromosomes*. Furthermore, a membrane came to be present around all the chromosomes in a cell, setting off a distinct *nuclear* region surrounded by cytoplasm. And in the cytoplasm eventually evolved all the organelles we now find in a "modern" cell (see Fig. 11.8). Organisms originally descended from premoneran stocks and exhibiting such an internal cellular structure, sharply different from the moneran pattern, collectively form the *Protista* (or *Eucaryota*, organisms with distinct nuclei). Four descendant groups of the early Protista represent a major part of the living world today, namely, the *algae* (other than the blue-greens), the *fungi*, the *slime molds*, and the *protozoa*. Judging from these living representatives, early Protista must have developed four nutritional methods, namely, photosynthesis, holotrophism, saprotrophism, and parasitism. Chemosynthesis apparently did not evolve.

We cannot be sure whether Monera and Protista arose monophyletically from just one original group of premoneran cells or polyphyletically from two or more such groups. Although a monophyletic beginning is by no means ruled out, the many structural differences between the moneran and protistan cell types do suggest separate, polyphyletic origins as the more likely alternative. In any case, existing Monera appear to be more primitive in virtually all their characteristics than existing Protista.

11 · 9   Diagram of a moneran cell.

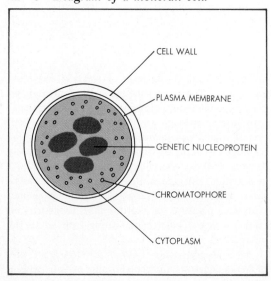

CELL WALL

PLASMA MEMBRANE

GENETIC NUCLEOPROTEIN

CHROMATOPHORE

CYTOPLASM

MONERA

As might be expected in view of their presumed evolutionary antiquity, Monera as a group are distinguished from all other living organisms largely by negative characteristics (Fig. 11.9). Thus, a moneran cell does *not* possess an organized nucleus with a distinct surrounding membrane. Although experiments indicate that the genetic DNA does form filamentous organelles, the ultrastructural and microscopic organization of these organelles does *not* correspond to that of chromosomes of the type found in other organisms. Instead, the moneran genetic material appears microscopically as one or more clumps exposed directly to the surrounding cytoplasm.

The cytoplasm itself does *not* appear to contain vacuoles, and it can *not* be observed to undergo the cyclosis and streaming movements typical of other cell types. Many Monera are photosynthetic, and these do *not* possess complexly organized chloroplasts like those found in all other photosynthetic cells. Instead, the structural unit of photosynthesis appears to be a disk of protein-containing material, 0.05 μ in diameter, greatly resembling a single layer of a single granum in a true chloroplast (see Chap. 7). Such a unit carries the photosynthetic pigments and it may therefore be called a *chromatophore*. Many chromatophores are distributed more or less uniformly throughout a photosynthetic moneran cell. Monera are also without endoplasmic reticula, mitochondria, or Golgi bodies, but they do possess an abundance of ribosomes, the only organelles present that appear to be equivalent structurally to those of other cell types. These many features of nonpossession clearly suggest that, at the time the Monera arose, the internal elaboration and specialization of cellular structure had not yet progressed very far.

Within the moneran category, the bacteria form the phylum *Schizophyta*, and the blue-green algae, the phylum *Cyanophyta*. The exact evolutionary relation of one phylum to the other is still relatively obscure. Some moneran groups exhibit traits intermediate between those of the schizophytes and the cyanophytes, and these groups could be, and often are, assigned to either phylum. Very probably, therefore, the existing Monera may constitute a polyphyletic assemblage of types and their subdivision into just two phyla may not represent a natural, ultimately correct classification.

PHYLUM SCHIZOPHTA: BACTERIA (2,000 SPECIES)

Although they include comparatively few described species, bacteria probably outnumber all other organisms many times over. They occur wherever life on earth is possible at all and, indeed, they are present in numerous places where no other organisms can exist. Bacteria thus play a major role in the economy of nature and of man. Moreover, they are eminently suitable test organisms in genetic and biochemical research. Much of our present understanding of the molecular basis of life has actually come from studies on bacteria.

As a group, schizophytes are the smallest cells known (Fig. 11.10). They average about 1 to 3 μ in length, as compared with about 10 μ for most cell types of other organisms. As in all Monera, a nuclear membrane is absent; genes occur in spherical or dumbbell-shaped clumps, one or more of which may be present. The cytoplasm is nonvacuolated, but in addition to ribosomes it may contain granules composed of, for example, lipids or polysaccharides. A rigid cell wall surrounds the cytoplasm of many bacteria. Such a wall consists of polysaccharides, proteins, and frequently also lipids. Very often, the cell wall in turn is surrounded by a gelatinous

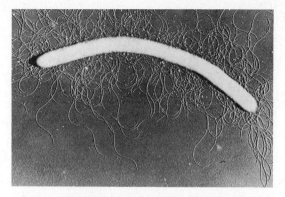

11 · 11 Electron micrograph *of* Proteus vulgaris, *a flagellate bacterium. Note the numerous locomotor flagella.*

11 · 10 Diagram of a bacterial cell.

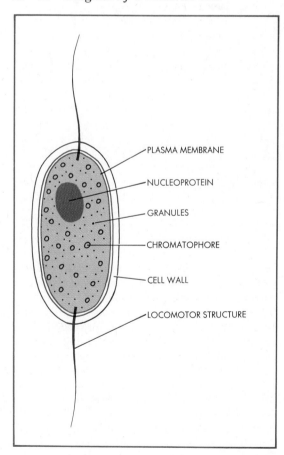

PLASMA MEMBRANE

NUCLEOPROTEIN

GRANULES

CHROMATOPHORE

CELL WALL

LOCOMOTOR STRUCTURE

capsule of different composition in different cases. Some of the usual constituents of such a capsule are polysaccharides, galactose, fructose, glucose, uronic acids, and amino acids. In many instances, it is the presence or absence of a capsule that determines whether a bacterium will be disease-producing or not.

Many bacteria are motile, flagella often being the locomotor organelles. However, bacterial flagella are structurally unique. Each is composed of just a single thin fibril, chemically different from the 11 flagellar fibrils present in other cell types (see Chap. 7). Given bacteria may possess one or more flagella at one end of the cell or a flagellum at each end or many flagella distributed over the entire cell surface (Fig. 11.11).

Bacterial cells have many different shapes. The three most common shapes are the spherical, or *coccus* type, the straight-rod, or *bacillus* type, and the curved-rod, or *spirillum* type (Fig. 11.12). Cells may occur singly, but in many cases two or more cells are aggregated together into *colonies,* which may be filamentous, disk-shaped, or three-dimensional. In each colonial species, the form of the colony is determined by the planes of cell division. Among cocci, for example, if a cell divides and the two resulting offspring cells remain in contact, the pair is said to be an aggregate of the *diplococcus* type. If further cell divisions in the same plane produce a filamentous chain of cells, the colony is of the *streptococcus* type. If, in a diplococcus, the plane of the next division in both cells occurs at right angles to the plane of the first division, then a disk of four cells results, designated as a colony of the *tetracoccus* type. Analogously, three divisions in the three planes

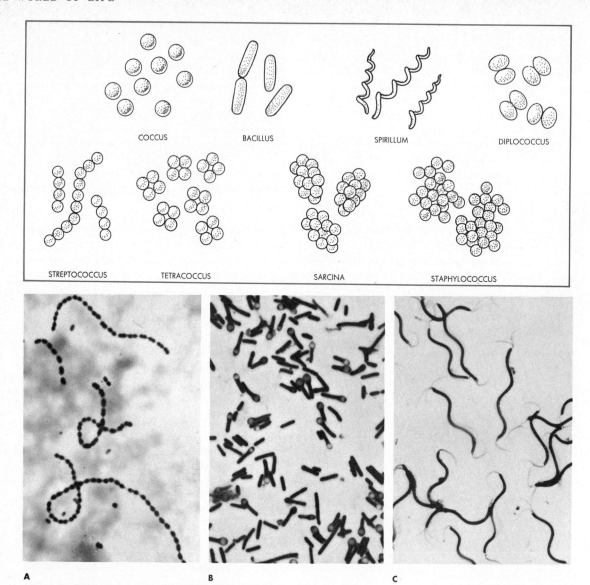

COCCUS   BACILLUS   SPIRILLUM   DIPLOCOCCUS

STREPTOCOCCUS   TETRACOCCUS   SARCINA   STAPHYLOCOCCUS

A   B   C

11 · 12 *Diagram: cell shapes and growth habits of bacteria. Photos: A, cocci, growing in chains. B, bacilli. C, spirilla.*

of space produce an eight-celled, cuboidal colony of the *sarcina* type. Successive divisions in random planes produce an irregular clump of cells known as a colony of the *micrococcus* or *staphylococcus* type.

In their usual state, bacterial cells are said to be in a *vegetative* condition. Some bacteria may also exist in an alternative state; they may transform into *endospores*. Development of an endospore begins with the formation of a membrane or wall within a bacterial cell. This wall encloses an oval or spherical portion of the cell substance, including genetic DNA

and some of the cytoplasm. The part of the cell outside the wall eventually degenerates, but the part within persists as the endospore. Such a structure represents a *dormant* cell; an endospore does not feed or multiply. The wall of the endospore is highly resistant to injurious physical and chemical agents, and bacteria so protected may survive in environments that would kill vegetative cells. Under favorable conditions an endospore may germinate: the wall breaks open and a normal vegetative cell emerges (Fig. 11.13).

With the exception of animallike eating, all possible forms of food procurement occur among the bacteria. Some species are autotrophic, that is, photo-

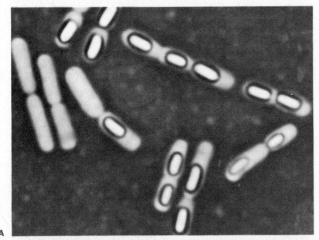

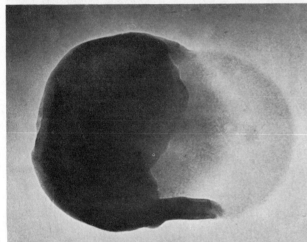

11 · 13 A, thick-walled endospores within rod-shaped bacterial cells. B, electron micrograph of a germinating spore of the bacterium Bacillus mycoides. Note the bacterial cell emerging from the coat of the endospore.

synthetic or chemosynthetic, and these produce their own food. The photosynthesizers possess unusual varieties of chlorophyll, and, as noted earlier, true chloroplasts are absent. Moreover, bacterial photosynthesis is chemically unique, different from photosynthesis in all other organisms. For example, bacterial photosynthesis never produces oxygen as a by-product (see Chap. 17).

Most bacteria are heterotrophic and depend on other organisms for food. Of these, some are free-living terrestrial or aquatic saprotrophs, and the rest are parasitic, commensalistic, or mutualistic symbionts. Also, some bacteria must have oxygen for respiration, others can respire without it, and still others may survive both with and without oxygen. In

most of these types, reserve foods are stored in the form of the polysaccharide *glycogen*. We may note, incidentally, that bioluminescence is fairly common among bacteria (Fig. 11.14).

Primarily as a result of their varied nutritional activities, bacteria as a whole have come to be of major significance to all other life on earth. Three general groups are of particular ecological importance: the saprotrophic *decay*-causing types; the chemosynthetic *nitrogen*-using types (nitrifiers, denitrifiers, and nitrogen fixers); and the parasitic *pathogenic*, or disease-producing, types.

Reflecting our still very limited knowledge of bacterial evolution, the classification of the bacteria is possibly the least stabilized of all the phyla of living organisms. Ten or so taxonomic subgroups can be distinguished, each equivalent in rank to an order. The following are most important.

Pseudomonadales: pseudomonads. These organisms are probably the most primitive bacteria now living (Fig. 11.15). Members of the group are generally flagellate, and cells of all three basic shapes are represented. In addition to numerous heterotrophic types, pseudomonads also include all the photosynthetic and chemosynthetic groups of bacteria. We shall have more to say about particular types among these in Chap. 17, in the context of nutritional patterns.

Eubacteriales: true bacteria. These constitute by far the largest and most studied group. Virtually all structural types are included, some with flagella; some without, some living as single cells, others in various colonial aggregations. Cell walls are generally rigid. The organisms are partly saprotrophs, living

11 · 14 Test-tube culture of bioluminescent bacteria. The continuous light they emit is strong enough to illuminate part of a printed page.

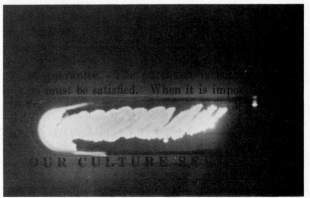

Courtesy Carolina Biological Supply Company.

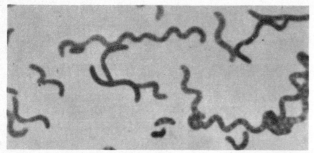

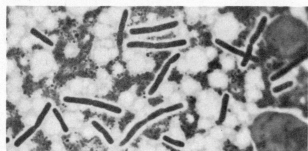

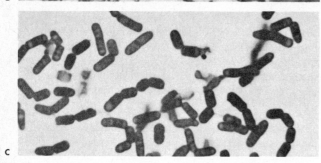

11 · 15 A, *Pseudomonadales:* Spirillum. *B, Eu-bacteriales:* Bacillus. *C, Eubacteriales:* Azotobacter.

free in almost all environments, and partly symbionts of all possible kinds. Among the latter are most of the pathogenic bacterial parasites, including many of particular concern to man. Certain indidivual species, for example, *Escherichia coli,* a commensal widely occurring in animal intestines, have been studied so extensively that, biologically, they are among the best-known organisms of all kinds (see Fig. 11.15).

Actinomycetales: branching bacteria. These microbes typically form branched filamentous colonies superficially resembling certain fungi. Motility is generally lacking. Some members of the group are quite familiar through their metabolic excretion products; the actinomycetes include the organisms that produce streptomycin, aureomycin, and similar antibiotics (Fig. 11.16).

Spirochaetales: spiral bacteria. Organisms of this

type are all unicellular and have the shape of spirals making at least one complete turn (see Fig. 11.16). In some cases the cells are veritable giants, reaching lengths of up to 0.5 mm. Tapered ends, often extended into very fine processes, are relatively common. The cells are quite flexible, and they may propel themselves by whirling and spinning around their long axes. The best-known spirochete is probably *Treponema pallidum,* causative agent of syphilis.

Myxobacteriales: gliding slime bacteria. These microorganisms are single cells, each a flexible motile rod. The cells are somehow able to creep or glide along a surface, leaving a layer of secreted slime behind them. At times the organisms *swarm,*

11 · 16 A, *a spirochete. B, filamentous branching growth of actinomycetous bacteria.*

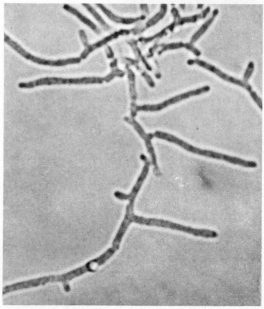

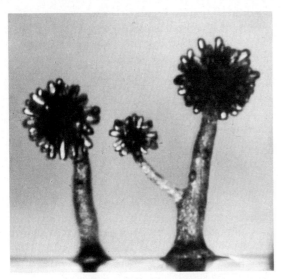

11 · 17   Fruiting body of a myxobacterium.

that is, they migrate into a mass and then stop moving. Such "resting" cells become embedded in secreted slime, and the whole aggregate forms a *fruiting body*. In some cases, fruiting bodies may be stalked and assume shapes of considerable complexity (Fig. 11.17). In this behavior the myxobacters greatly resemble certain of the protistan slime molds (see Chap. 12).

Beggiatoales: gliding bacteria. Like the myxobacters, the beggiatoas also are flexible, gliding cells, but they form filamentous colonies and do not aggregate into fruiting bodies (Fig. 11.18). Some beggiatoas (like some pseudomonads) use sulfur compounds in their metabolism. Propulsion of a colony is accomplished by slow rolls and by jerking or oscillating movements. These interesting, so far unexplainable motions are identical with the movements of certain blue-green algae. Moreover, in some gliding bacteria (for example, *Beggiatoa*) and some cyanophytes (for example, *Oscillatoria*), the structure of the cellular colonies and the manner in which they are formed are also quite indistinguishable. Indeed, the only essential difference between these types is that one is photosynthetic whereas the other is not. Thus, genera like *Beggiatoa* could be—and often are—regarded as colorless cyanophytes, perhaps evolved from pigmented cyanophyte ancestors by loss of pigments. Inclusion of beggiatoas among the bacteria must therefore be considered provisional.

Two additional groups are clearly not bacteria but may nevertheless be closely related. One comprises the *Rickettsiae*. These organisms are like bac-

teria in certain respects and like viruses in others. Beyond this, their evolutionary affinities are completely unknown. Moreover, considerable uncertainty still exists as to whether rickettsias are "organisms" at all, that is, cellular in nature. In a general way their spherical or rodlike structure does resemble that of bacteria. But rickettsias are far smaller than even small bacteria, being in the size range of large viruses. Rickettsias resemble viruses further in that they are obligate intracellular parasites, unable to carry out living functions outside the cells of specific hosts. Such hosts appear to be arthropods only, particularly ticks and lice. Several rickettsias are pathogenic. For example, one species is the causative agent of Rocky Mountain spotted fever and another of epidemic typhus fever, both diseases of man. Ticks in the first case and body lice in the second transfer the rickettsias to man.

The other group with possible affinities to bacteria includes the viruses themselves. They are definitely neither cells nor organisms but intracellular parasitic chemicals consisting of nucleic acids and proteins. At least some of the viruses now in existence may be descendants of nucleic acid fragments that broke away from the genetic material of early bacterial cells. If so, the cells of other organisms very possibly may have given rise to viruses too, in similar fashion. Indeed, virus creation of this sort may still be taking place today.

PHYLUM CYANOPHYTA:
BLUE-GREEN ALGAE (2,500 SPECIES)

The name of these organisms, "blue-green algae," is somewhat misleading, for some cyanophytes actually are not blue-green. Many are of black, purple, red,

11 · 18   Specimens of Beggiatoa.

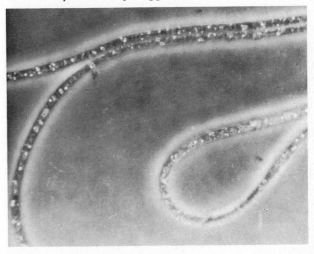

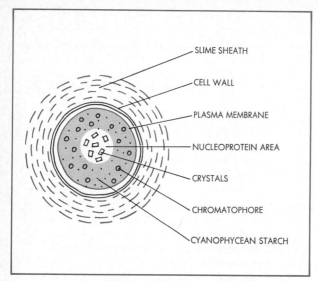

SLIME SHEATH

CELL WALL

PLASMA MEMBRANE

NUCLEOPROTEIN AREA

CRYSTALS

CHROMATOPHORE

CYANOPHYCEAN STARCH

11 · 19 Diagram of cell of blue-green algae.

yellow, green, blue, or various intermediate shades. These colors are produced by different proportions of several pigments present in different species. The pigments include a variety of chlorophyll called *chlorophyll a; carotene;* various *xanthophylls;* and two phycobilins, namely, blue *c-phycocyanin* and red *c-phycoerythrin.* These last two are unique to the cyanophytes, not being found in any other group of organisms.

Cyanophytes occur in virtually all environments containing water. The organisms range from the tropics to the poles and are present in soil, fresh water, and the ocean. In open aquatic habitats they often form part of the plankton. Extensive growths of blue-green algae frequently occur in areas which

11 · 20 Chroococcales. A, B, C, three stages in the growth of Chroococcus. D, two colonies of Gloeocapsa.

are wetted only intermittently, for example, tidal flats, stream banks, tree bark, and rocks sprayed with sea water. Some cyanophytes live in the icy waters of glaciers; others, in hot springs where temperatures reach 85°C or more. Apart from such free-living forms, some blue-green algae live in symbiotic association with other organisms.

The cell interior of a cyanophyte consists of a colorless central region and a surrounding pigmented region (Fig. 11.19). The central portion contains the genetic DNA as well as granules believed to be phosphate-containing crystals. This region is not separated from the surrounding parts by any membrane or other structure. In the outer cytoplasm are found the various pigments referred to above, as well as *cyanophycean starch.* This is the unique food-storage compound of the cyanophytes. It is not the same as the starch found in other organisms, and its chemistry is known only poorly.

The cytoplasm of a cyanophyte cell is enclosed in a wall which contains *cellulose* and frequently also *pectin.* In some cases the pectin may dissolve immediately after being secreted by the cell, but in others it may persist and form a thick gelatinous sheath around the cell wall. Flagella are entirely lacking in the phylum. Where locomotion occurs, it is of the gliding, jerky type described above for the beggiatoas.

If beggiatoas are considered to be bacteria, then all cyanophytes are photosynthetic. In their form of photosynthesis oxygen does become liberated as a byproduct, as is actually the case for all photosynthesizers except the bacterial ones. Like some of the bacteria, some of the blue-green algae may fix atmospheric nitrogen and incorporate this element into their bodies. Such cyanophytes thus play a role in the global nitrogen cycle. Like bacteria, furthermore, the cyanophytes are essentially unicellular. However, in many species the cells again do not separate after division but form colonies. These may consist of loosely grouped cellular aggregates or of cells tightly

A

B

C

D

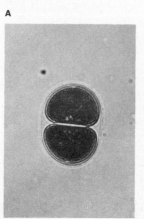
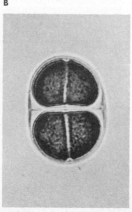
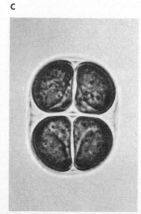
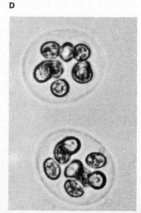

joined into distinct filaments. The arrangement of the cells in a colony and the way in which newly produced cells are added to the colony constitute the basis for cyanophyte classification. Three main subgroups (orders) are recognized: the *Chroococcales*, the *Chamaeosiphonales*, and the *Hormogonales*.

All the Chroococcales (Fig. 11.20) are unicellular, but the cells often form loose colonies held together by the gelatinous slime sheaths secreted by the organisms. *Chroococcus* and *Gloeocapsa*, frequently encountered in moist places, are two representative types. In both, the cells have conspicuous sheaths. After a cell divides, its sheath very often does not break and groups of associated offspring cells then retain a common sheath around them. The division planes are random in the two genera mentioned, but in other genera division takes place only in two or three planes. If divisions occur in two planes, a flat layer of cells results, as in *Merismopedia;* if divisions occur in three planes, the colony will be cuboidal, as in *Eucapsis.*

Chamaeosiphonales too are either solitary or colonial, but, unlike the Chroococcales, they regularly produce true spores (see Chap. 27). A representative type of this group is *Chamaeosiphon*, a freshwater epiphyte on green algae and other organisms (Fig. 11.21).

The Hormogonales are distinctly filamentous, cell divisions always being restricted to a single plane (see Fig. 11.21). The cells are joined so intimately that groups of them may be enclosed within a common wall. Such cell groups are called *hormogones*. In many cases, two neighboring hormogones in a multicellular filament may be joined by means of a unit known as a *heterocyst*. This structure, often larger than the cells on either side, appears to be a transparent cell with a double wall. A filament may break readily at these heterocysts, and their main function may be to make such breaks possible. The

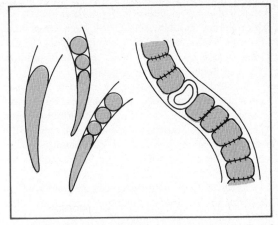

11 · 21   Blue-green algae. *Left, individuals of* Chamaeosiphon, *in two of which spores are cut off at one end of the cell. Right, portion of a* Nostoc *filament showing heterocyst (white hull).*

separated hormogones then may settle elsewhere and grow into new offspring filaments. In contrast with the other two groups, the Hormogonales are motile and display the jerky, rolling type of movement already mentioned.

Two common representatives of the Hormogonales are *Oscillatoria,* so named after its characteristic locomotion, and *Nostoc* (Color Plate IX, 19). The latter is found in clear fresh water, where it forms gelatinous balls of up to 50 cm in diameter. Such balls are composed of many filaments and their surrounding sheaths. When colonies of *Nostoc* are mature, the hormogones between heterocysts often enlarge, fill with reserve foods, and enter a dormant state. In this condition the organisms may survive through the winter season. *Nostoc* also lives mutualistically with fungi, the combinations representing some of the *lichens.*

REVIEW QUESTIONS

1. Which gases in the early atmosphere of the earth may have contributed to the formation of organic compounds? What were some of these compounds and what evidence do we have that they could actually have formed? Review the role of (*a*) temperature, (*b*) water, (*c*) organic compounds, and (*d*) enzymes in the origin of life.

2. Review the synthesis reactions through which compounds required for the origin of living systems might have occurred. Describe experiments duplicating some of these reactions. How are the first cells believed to have evolved? Distinguish between chemical and biological evolution.

3. What was the physical character of the earth (*a*) at the time it formed, (*b*) before living systems originated, and (*c*) after living systems originated? Review the principal events of the oxygen revolution and describe the consequence of this revolution.

4. How many years ago did (*a*) the earth form, (*b*) life originate? Distinguish between monophyletism and polyphyletism and cite arguments for and against each view as related to the origin of cells.

5. How are moneran and protistan cell types distinguished and how might both have arisen from the first cells? What living groups belong to the Monera and the Protista? What are viruses and how are they believed to have originated?

6. Through what processes of evolution may moneran and protistan nutritional patterns have arisen? What processes probably necessitated and promoted such nutritional evolution? Describe the principal chemical events of chemosynthesis and photosynthesis. In what groups of organisms do these occur?

7. Review the identifying characteristics of (a) Monera, (b) bacteria, and (c) blue-green algae. What features distinguish (b) and (c)?

8. Describe the general structure of a bacterial cell. How do bacteria (a) feed and (b) move? How are bacteria distinguished in shape and in growth patterns? What is an endospore?

9. Name some of the main subgroups of bacteria and review the characteristics of each. What are (a) Rickettsiae and (b) viruses?

10. Describe the general structure and the biochemical characteristics of a cyanophyte cell. How do cyanophytes (a) feed and (b) move?

11. Name the three main subgroups of blue-green algae and review the characteristics of each. What are the names of representative genera?

12. Define hormogone, heterocyst. Where do cyanophytes occur in nature?

COLLATERAL READINGS

Brown, H.: The Age of the Solar System, *Sci. American,* Apr., 1957. Estimations are based on the radioactivity of meteorites and rocks.

Calvin, M.: Round Trip from Space, *Evolution,* vol. 13, 1959. A brief examination of problems pertaining to the question of the origin of life.

Ehrlich, P. R., and R. W. Holm: "Process of Evolution," McGraw-Hill, New York, 1963. The first chapter of this book is a discussion of the origin of life.

Fox, S. W.: The Evolution of Protein Molecules and Thermal Synthesis of Biochemical Substances, *Am. Scientist,* vol. 44, 1956. The article relates some of the heating experiments referred to in this chapter.

Gamov, G.: The Origin and Evolution of the Universe, *Am. Scientist,* vol. 39, 1951. A physicist discusses the ways in which the universe may have arisen.

Kerkut, G. A.: "The Implications of Evolution," Pergamon, New York, 1960. This stimulating little book examines some of the assumptions underlying evolutionary thinking, including the problem of monophyletism versus polyphyletism.

Landsberg, H. E.: The Origin of the Atmosphere, *Sci. American,* Aug., 1953. The history of the atmosphere is traced on the basis of data from various sciences.

Miller, S. L.: The Origin of Life, in "This Is Life," Holt, New York, 1962. This article gives details on the atmosphere experiments referred to in this chapter

and also discusses the general problem of the origin of life. Moreover, the reference list at the end of the article cites all the pertinent original sources.

Oparin, A. I.: "Life: Its Nature, Origin, and Development," Academic, New York, 1961. The author fathered all modern thinking on the subject by a book published in 1936; the present volume is the latest revision of it.

Pelczar, M. J., Jr., and R. D. Reid: "Microbiology," 2d ed., McGraw-Hill, New York, 1965. An excellent basic text on bacteria.

Ross, H. H.: "A Synthesis of Evolutionary Theory," Prentice-Hall, Englewood Cliffs, N.J., 1962. This highly recommended book contains two early chapters on the origin of the universe and of life; the heating experiments by Fox (see entry above) are reviewed as well.

Smith, G. M.: "Cryptogamic Botany," 2d ed., vol. 1, "Algae and Fungi," McGraw-Hill, New York, 1955. A comprehensive treatise containing accounts of the blue-green algae.

Urey, H.: The Origin of the Earth, *Sci. American,* Oct., 1952. The probable development of the earth is analyzed by a noted chemist.

Wald, G.: The Origin of Life, *Sci. American,* Aug., 1954. A reexamination of the meaning of spontaneous generation in the light of modern thinking about the creation of life.

CHAPTER 12
PROTISTA

Of the four protistan groups now in existence, namely, algae, fungi, slime molds, and protozoa, the algae probably include the descendants of the most ancient protists. Indeed, the most primitive types among living algae are thought to resemble the original protistan ancestors to a considerable degree. From such primitive types we may therefore infer what traits the first protists must have exhibited.

GENERAL CHARACTERISTICS

In the course of probably millions of years, the cell type we now recognize as protistan gradually must have evolved innovations which set it off sharply from the moneran type (Fig. 12.1) Structurally, the protistan cell must have come to possess all the various specialized organelles examined in Chap. 7. Such organelles must have included, for example, chromosomes composed of nucleic acids conjugated to proteins and organized into microscopically clearly visible filaments; nucleoli; and a nuclear membrane bounding off a definite nucleus. The cytoplasm must have become equipped with an endoplasmic reticulum, mitochondria, Golgi bodies, chloroplasts, centrioles and kinetosomes, as well as flagella, cilia, and the capacity to form pseudopods. Ribosomes must have been inherited from their earlier premoneran ancestors, but protistan cells additionally evolved different kinds of vacuoles, granules, and fibrils. Moreover, the general size of the cell increased substantially over the moneran average and the cellular interior exhibited cyclosis.

Functionally, cell division came to be associated with new processes of chromosome duplication (*mitosis* and *meiosis*, see Chap. 26) not encountered as such among the Monera. As in the Monera, however, each protistan cell could by itself function as a reproductive unit directly, and offspring produced through cell division represented a new generation of "adults" immediately (that is, without intervening embryonic stages). Also like the Monera, early protists must have been capable of existing alternately as vegetative and dormant cells in response to given environmental conditions. Like many of its algal descendants today, for example, the ancient protist undoubtedly could secrete a thick, resistant wall over its surface and so become *encapsulated* or *encysted*. Or it could secrete a surrounding sheath of pectin-containing jelly and so enter a *palmelloid* state. In such a state the jelly is hygroscopic and holds water, hence the palmelloid condition becomes very advantageous during periods of drought (Fig. 12.2).

Above all, individual early protists must have been characterized by *multiple* means of nutrition. As already pointed out earlier, four methods of nutrition are in evidence among living Protista, namely, photosynthesis, holotrophism, saprotrophism, and parasitism. Some groups of primitive algal protists today have the capacity of obtaining food by two or more of these methods *simultaneously*. In all probability, therefore, nutrition by multiple means may have been a common characteristic of ancestral protists generally. Thus, it may have been quite usual for an early protist to engulf or absorb available ready-made food *as well as* to photosynthesize additional food internally. The adaptive advantage of such multiple nutrition can be appreciated readily. For example, at night or at the dimly lit bottoms of natural waters, an ancestral protist could hunt for food holotrophically, but in the presence of ample light it could save energy by photosynthesizing. In this respect, evidently, the ancient protists probably were *both* plantlike and animallike simultaneously.

From such a joint plant-animal starting point later must have evolved a purely photosynthetic, more nearly plantlike branch of protistan life and a purely heterotrophic, more nearly animallike branch (Fig. 12.3). Such a diversification would have occurred when groups of ancestral protists lost one or more of their forms of nutrition, different groups retaining a different form in each case. We can be fairly sure that these differential losses of nutritional capacities resulted from mutations, for it is possible today to induce just such loss-mutations in the laboratory. For

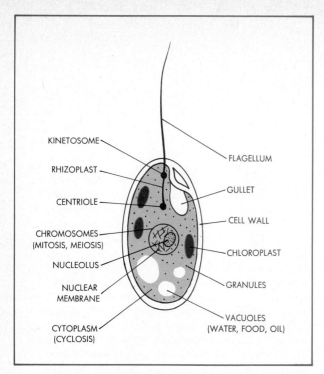

KINETOSOME

RHIZOPLAST

CENTRIOLE

CHROMOSOMES
(MITOSIS, MEIOSIS)

NUCLEOLUS

NUCLEAR
MEMBRANE

CYTOPLASM
(CYCLOSIS)

FLAGELLUM

GULLET

CELL WALL

CHLOROPLAST

GRANULES

VACUOLES
(WATER, FOOD, OIL)

12 · 1   *The basic protistan cell type.*

example, primitive living algae exhibiting multiple means of nutrition may be converted experimentally to either purely photosynthetic or purely heterotrophic organisms. Experiments of this kind undoubtedly duplicate the ancient natural process of nutritional evolution among protists. Among algae, most groups now no longer possess multiple means of nutrition. Instead, they have largely perfected the photosynthetic method, have lost the heterotrophic potential, and are rather plantlike. Analogously, there is little doubt that other early groups of protists which, on the contrary, had lost the photosynthetic capacity, came to be the ancestors of the exclusively heterotrophic protists of today, namely, the fungi, slime molds, and protozoa. Fungi are saprotrophic or parasitic, slime molds are saprotrophic for the most part, and protozoa are largely holotrophic though many are parasitic and a few are saprotrophic.

Another most significant characteristic of ancient protists must have been their capacity of existing in at least four alternative vegetative states, two of them motile and two nonmotile (Fig. 12.4). Cellular motility can be displayed in *flagellate* and *amoeboid* states. We know from living protists that, in a free-swimming flagellate condition, a parent cell can give rise by successive divisions to many, similarly flagellate offspring. An amoeboid state can then arise when a flagellate cell casts off its flagellum (but retains its kinetosome). Such a cell may now move along a surface and feed by means of pseudopodia. At some later time, even after offspring cells are produced by

division, new flagella can grow from the kinetosomes, creeping amoeboid activity may cease, and the free-swimming flagellate state may be resumed.

The two nonmotile states analogously develop by loss of flagella. One is a special type of multinucleate state which, for present purposes, we may refer to as the *coccine* condition. Here the cytoplasm of the nonmotile cell ceases to divide during the vegetative life of the cell, but the nucleus continues to divide. The result is a progressively more multinucleate yet still unicellular organism. At the time of reproduction, and only then, *multiple* cytoplasmic division takes place; the organism becomes partitioned into numerous cells simultaneously, each cell containing at least one nucleus. Such offspring cells, or *spores*, may disperse passively or develop flagella and disperse actively. In either case they soon settle and become new nonmotile cells that do not divide their cytoplasm except at the time of reproduction.

The second nonmotile condition we shall here call the *sporine* state. A cell in this case remains uninucleate and it does divide during its vegetative life. Since the cells do not carry out locomotion, offspring cells formed by division tend to remain in close proximity, a condition facilitating the development of multicellular aggregates. In these, individual cells may later redevelop flagella or become amoeboid and disengage from the aggregates.

Of these four different states of vegetative ex-

12 · 2   *Protective, or dormant, states of protistan cells.*

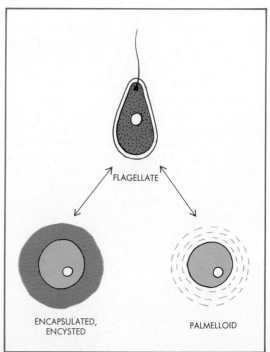

FLAGELLATE

ENCAPSULATED,
ENCYSTED

PALMELLOID

250

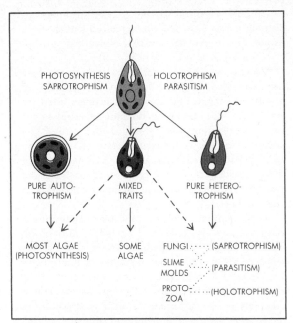

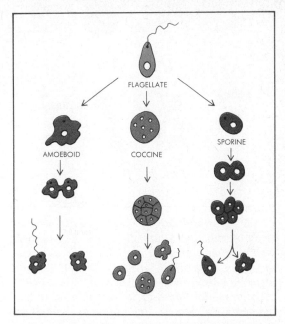

12 · 3 Ancestral protists (top) *presumably possessed chloroplasts as well as gullets and motility, hence their nutrition may have been both autotrophic and heterotrophic. From such stocks with joint plantlike and animallike traits probably evolved purely autotrophic and purely heterotrophic types, represented today by the groups indicated. Primitive groups which retained, and still retain, mixed traits may have contributed even later to the evolution of more nearly plantlike and animallike protists.*

12 · 4 Four basic vegetative states *of protistan existence. A flagellate cell may become amoeboid, and later that same cell or any of its offspring may revert to a flagellate state. Loss of flagella and development of multinuclearity lead to the nonmotile coccine state, in which, after cell-boundary formation during reproduction, the offspring cells may remain coccine or resume flagellate or amoeboid existence. Loss of flagella and successive vegetative divisions produce the sporine state. The resulting cells may separate or stay together as colonies, and any of the cells may also assume the flagellate or the amoeboid condition.*

istence, the flagellate condition is believed to be basic and primitive; all others may be derived from it. The adaptive advantage of such multiple alternative states must have been exceedingly important, particularly in conjunction with the multiple means of nutrition. Thus, by permitting cellular locomotion, the two motile states undoubtedly facilitated heterotrophic nutrition generally and made possible holotrophic food-hunting specifically; and the two sessile states became particularly economical when photosynthesis was under way, for they reduced the expenditure of locomotor energy to zero. Among some species of modern Protista, given individuals still can exist in two or more of these four alternative states. Most living species, however, exhibit one particular state more or less permanently.

We may infer, therefore, that ancestral types with the potential of multiple states gave rise to the separate flagellate, amoeboid, coccine, and sporine types of protists in existence today. We know also

that these four types produced not only unicellular members but, each independently, *multicellular* ones as well; as will become apparent presently, Protista today include *colonies* of motile flagellate types, motile amoeboid types, sessile coccine types, and sessile sporine types (Fig. 12.5).

Early sporine colonies in particular must have displayed rich evolutionary potentialities. Since they were sessile and their cells were joined directly and tightly, such colonies could hold together well and could grow to extremely large size, well beyond the microscopic range of the other types of colonies. Moreover, depending upon the planes of cell division, they could form one-dimensional filaments, or two-dimensional disks and sheets, or three-dimensional compact masses. All such sporine organizations are encountered today among modern protists. Indeed,

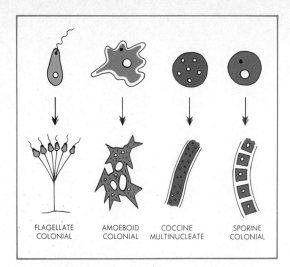

FLAGELLATE COLONIAL   AMOEBOID COLONIAL   COCCINE MULTINUCLEATE   SPORINE COLONIAL

12 · 5 *Multicellular (or multinucleate) derivatives of the four states of protistan existence. Note that multinucleate and filamentous coccine types (as exemplified by most fungi and some algae) are also called* siphonaceous *forms. Multicellular sporine types occur not only as simple filaments as shown, but also as complexly branched filaments, as sheets, and as three-dimensional aggregates.*

12 · 6 *Main aspects of protistan evolution. Note that the heterotrophic branch of evolution does not include sporine protists.*

structurally advanced sporine colonies are quite indistinguishable from and are actually identical with tissues. This level of organization evidently originated with the Protista.

We may note, incidentally, that any of the Protista, unicelled or multicelled, that have specialized in just one of the four states of existence often reveal, at the time of reproduction, the ancestral potential of developing other states. Thus, even if the organisms are sessile, the reproductive cells generally are flagellate or amoeboid. As we shall find, indeed, cells of both kinds are often formed at the same time; flagellate cells become sperms, amoeboid cells become eggs.

The evolution of Protista as a whole thus may be envisaged broadly as a series of branching lines of descent that began with unicellular ancestral stocks possessing both plantlike and animallike characteristics simultaneously (Fig. 12.6). From such stocks then emerged at least three kinds of groups. One remained relatively unchanged, and its algal representatives today still display joint plant and animal traits. A second group became exclusively photosynthetic. It is represented today by the majority of the algae, which, as we shall see, include flagellate, amoeboid, coccine, and sporine members. The third group became exclusively heterotrophic. Its present member-

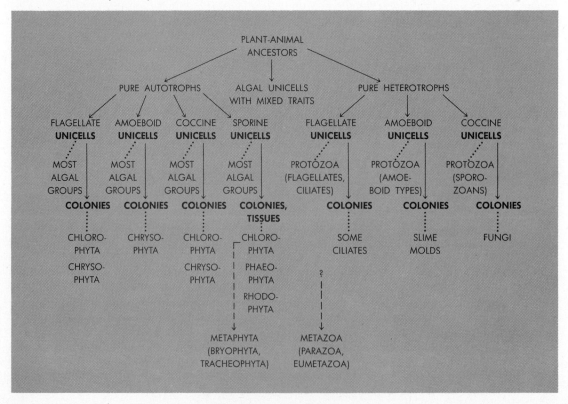

TABLE 11 COMPARATIVE BIOCHEMICAL CHARACTERISTICS OF ALGAE

GROUP	PHYLUM	CHLOROPHYLL	OTHER PIGMENTS	FOOD-STORAGE COMPOUNDS	CELL WALLS
green line	Chlorophyta	a, b	carotenes xanthophylls	starch	cellulose, pectins
	Charophyta	a, b		starch	cellulose, pectins
	Euglenophyta	a, b		paramylum, fats	usually none
brown line	Chrysophyta	a, c (e)	carotenes xanthophylls (lutein, fucoxanthin)	leucosin, fats	pectins, cellulose, silica, or none
	Pyrrophyta	a, c		starch, other polysaccharides, fats	cellulose or none
	Phaeophyta	a, c		laminarin, mannitol	cellulose, algin
red line	Rhodophyta	a, d	carotenes xanthophylls (lutein) r-phycocyanin r-phycoerythrin	floridean starch	cellulose, pectins

ship comprises the protozoa, which are primarily flagellate and amoeboid; the slime molds, which are basically amoeboid; and the fungi, which are distinctly coccine. In all of these groups and subgroups, moreover, multicellularity developed to different degrees of complexity.

ALGAE

In earlier classifications, algae, together with all Monera and fungi, were considered to constitute several phyla belonging to a subkingdom "Thallophyta" within the kingdom of plants. However, in line with the pertinent discussion in Chap. 2 and the evolutionary history just outlined above, we may now regard the algae as a superphylum or major subcategory within the category Protista. Although structural features provide useful distinctions between the algal phyla, the main differences are primarily chemical: types of chlorophyll and other pigments present, the chemical composition of the cell wall, and the chemical nature of stored foods.

Chlorophyll *a* is universally present in all algal groups. Since this pigment also occurs in the cyanophytes, it may represent an inheritance from the very earliest cells, shared alike by the blue-green and the protistan algae. This may also be true of carotenoid and xanthophyll pigments, some of which occur identically in cyanophytes and algae. However, whereas cyanophytes (and also the photosynthetic bacteria) possess only a single chemical variety of chlorophyll, protistan algae always possess at least two, namely, chlorophyll *a* plus one additional variant named *b*, *c*, *d*, or *e*. Indeed, on the basis of their specific chlorophyll content, three main groups of algae may be recognized. All three possess chlorophyll *a*, but in addition, one possesses chlorophyll *b*, the second chlorophyll *c* (or in some cases *e*), and the third chlorophyll *d*. In conjunction with other pigments present, these chlorophylls produce characteristic visible colors: some shade of green in the *a* plus *b* types, brown in the *a* plus *c* types, and red in the *a* plus *d* types. We may therefore distinguish a *green line*, a *brown line*, and a *red line* of algae (Table 11).

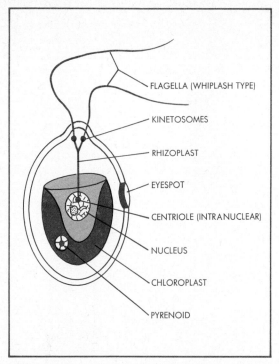

FLAGELLA (WHIPLASH TYPE)

KINETOSOMES

RHIZOPLAST

EYESPOT

CENTRIOLE (INTRANUCLEAR)

NUCLEUS

CHLOROPLAST

PYRENOID

12 · 7 *Diagram of* **Chlamydomonas,** *a unicellular flagellate green alga. The genus* Polytoma *is entirely similar except that chloroplast and pyrenoid are absent.*

PHYLUM CHLOROPHYTA:
GREEN ALGAE (6,000 SPECIES)

The phylum is identified by chlorophylls *a* and *b* and various carotenes and xanthophylls as noted; by comparatively rigid cell walls consisting usually of an inner cellulose layer and an outer pectic layer; by reserve foods stored as starch; and by flagellate cells or stages which, wherever present, bear two (or more rarely four) equally long anterior flagella, all of the whiplash type. These characteristics occur in precisely this combination only in the green algae and the Metaphyta. Early stocks of the former are therefore believed to have been in the specific ancestors of the latter.

The pigments of the green algae are contained in chloroplasts of various shapes and numbers. Typically present on the chloroplasts are small, often highly refractile bodies called *pyrenoids* (Fig. 12.7). These have a protein composition and around them accumulate deposits of starch. For this reason, pyrenoids are believed to be specific starch-synthesizing centers. Many flagellate algal cells possess an *eyespot, or stigma,* near the anterior end. This small organelle consists of a cup containing a photosensitive pigment, namely, a carotene derivative called *hematochrome,* chemically related to vitamin A; and of a "lens," a transparent, light-concentrating body lying in the pigmented cup. A functional connection, if not also a structural one, is believed to exist between the eyespot and the nearby kinetosomes of the flagella. By virtue of this complex of photosensory and locomotor structures, the cell may be able to distinguish regions of light and dark and may move accordingly.

Chlorophytes include three main evolutionary lines, distinguished by their principal vegetative states: a *flagellate* line, a *coccine* line, and a *sporine* line. Each is represented by both unicellular and

12 · 8 *Green algae of the coccine line of evolution.* A, Chlorella. *B,* Acetabularia. *C,* Bryopsis.

A B C

colonial forms. Given life cycles frequently include temporary encapsulated and palmelloid stages and, in a few cases, amoeboid stages.

The flagellate line is represented by single-celled types such as *Chlamydomonas*, which exhibits most of the characteristics of green algal cells in most nearly typical form (see Fig. 12.7). Different species of *Chlamydomonas* occur in soil, in freshwater ponds and pools, in quiet streams, and in the ocean. Very closely related to *Chlamydomonas* is *Polytoma*, a genus structurally nearly identical to *Chlamydomonas* except that it is colorless and nonphotosynthetic; it lives as a saprotroph. As we shall see, paired types of this sort are also encountered among most of the other algal phyla. Undoubtedly, such paired photosynthetic and colorless forms represent branch lines descended from a relatively recent common ancestor, one line having retained and the other lost the photosynthetic method of nutrition. As already noted, experiment in certain cases may duplicate such evolutionary processes.

Cells rather like *Chlamydomonas* form flagellate colonies in which the daughter cells remain joined after division. Among the green algae, such flagellate colonies usually consist of fixed numbers of cells—4, 8, 16, 32, 64, or larger multiples. If there are relatively few cells, they form disks or cup-shaped colonies; and if the cell number is comparatively large, the colony is usually a hollow sphere, as in *Volvox*. In this organism, the cells exhibit a high degree of coordination. A network of fibrils, presumably impulse-conducting, joins the kinetosomes of the many cells, and their flagella beat in a coordinated, locomotion-producing pattern (Color Plate IX, 20).

Chlorophytes in the coccine line of evolution include *Chlorella*, probably used more extensively in studies of photosynthesis than any other organism (Fig. 12.8). At the time of reproduction, the nucleus of *Chlorella* divides several times, and each offspring nucleus together with some of the surrounding cytoplasm becomes partitioned off as a *spore* cell. In *Chlorella* such spores are nonmotile, but in many close relatives of *Chlorella* the spores are flagellate and motile. Note in any case that division of the cell occurs only during spore formation, never during vegetative stages.

Many chlorophytic coccines attain extraordinary sizes and exhibit a remarkable internal specialization of their one nonmotile cell. For example, *Acetabularia*, growing in warm seas, may be 2 to 3 in. long (see Fig. 12.8). The alga consists of a stalk, an umbrella-like cap at the top, and fine outgrowths at the bottom of the stalk which anchor the organism on the sea floor. In this single cell, one nucleus is situated

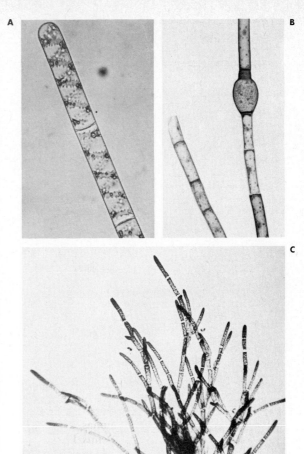

12 · 9   Green algae *of the sporine line of evolution. A, terminal cells of a* Spirogyra *filament. B,* Oedogonium. *C,* Cladophora.

in the base of the stalk. At the time of reproduction, the nucleus migrates into the cap, where it divides several times. Spores then form as in *Chlorella*. Other coccine algae become highly multinucleate in the mature state yet they too remain undivided single cells. Such algae usually have tubular bodies which may be branched in many different patterns. Tubular, or *siphonaceous,* algae of this sort are capable of indefinite extension in length. A good example is *Bryopsis* (see Fig. 12.8).

The sporine line of evolution is the most diversified of the chlorophytes. Unicellular types include the common *Protococcus*, which usually grows on perpetually moist tree bark in the form of loosely aggregated colonies. More highly organized colonies are produced by types in which cell divisions occur in one or more fixed planes. Divisions in one plane give rise to the many *filamentous* green algae (Fig. 12.9). In one group of these, exemplified by the common freshwater alga *Spirogyra*, the reproductive cells are either nonmotile altogether or amoeboid,

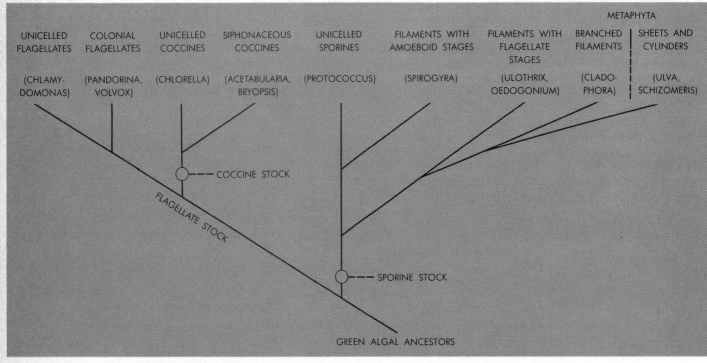

METAPHYTA			

UNICELLED FLAGELLATES

COLONIAL FLAGELLATES

UNICELLED COCCINES

SIPHONACEOUS COCCINES

UNICELLED SPORINES

FILAMENTS WITH AMOEBOID STAGES

FILAMENTS WITH FLAGELLATE STAGES

BRANCHED FILAMENTS

SHEETS AND CYLINDERS

(CHLAMY-DOMONAS)

(PANDORINA, VOLVOX)

(CHLORELLA)

(ACETABULARIA, BRYOPSIS)

(PROTOCOCCUS)

(SPIROGYRA)

(ULOTHRIX, OEDOGONIUM)

(CLADO-PHORA)

(ULVA, SCHIZOMERIS)

COCCINE STOCK

FLAGELLATE STOCK

SPORINE STOCK

GREEN ALGAL ANCESTORS

12 · 10 Probable evolutionary affinities of various groups of green algae.

but never flagellate. Another group of filamentous algae possesses flagellate reproductive cells. Representatives are *Ulothrix* and *Oedogonium*, both superficially rather like *Spirogyra*.

The group with flagellate stages has been the more progressive from an evolutionary standpoint, for from it arose not only filamentous types but also more complexly structured organisms. For example, cell divisions in two planes may produce a branched filament as in *Cladophora*, or a flat sheet of cells as in the common sea lettuce *Ulva* (see Fig. 12.10). Cell divisions occur in three planes in *Schizomeris*, which possesses a solid cylindrical body several cell layers thick. These algae have attained the tissue level of organization; and by virtue of their biochemical traits and their complex sporine construction, early stocks of such algae are believed to have been the specific ancestors of the Metaphyta (Fig. 12.10).

12 · 11 Stoneworts: Nitella.

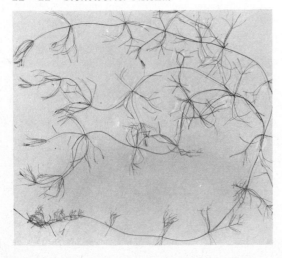

PHYLUM CHAROPHYTA:
STONEWORTS (250 SPECIES)

Because many of their characteristics, biochemical traits included, are similar to those of the green algae, the organisms in this group are often given the status of a class within the Chlorophyta. But the stoneworts probably warrant phylum rank inasmuch as at least four of their features are distinct from those of the chlorophytes.

As indicated by the representative genera *Chara* and *Nitella* (Fig. 12.11), the four diagnostic features are: a complex filamentous body organization, with rootlike, stemlike, and leaflike portions; a nodal arrangement of the branches; a pattern of body growth which is strictly terminal, or *apical*, rather than diffuse as in chlorophytes; and the presence of multicellular reproductive structures which in fact are true *organs*. In this last respect stoneworts are quite unlike other Protista but quite like Metaphyta; the organs consist of a core of sex cells and a surrounding layer of sterile cells. However, inasmuch as charophytes lack many important traits that Metaphyta possess, they cannot be readily grouped with the metaphytes. Stoneworts *are* protists, but highly advanced protists. They may conceivably have evolved in parallel with the ancestors of the Metaphyta from some complexly organized sporine stocks of green algae. But charophytes may not have gone as far in their evolution as the ancestral metaphytes.

PHYLUM EUGLENOPHYTA:
EUGLENOIDS (350 SPECIES)

By virtue of its pigments, this phylum belongs to the green-line algae. But the organisms differ in several important respects from other phyla of this line (Fig. 12.12). First, euglenoids are almost exclusively unicellular flagellates. Other vegetative states either have never developed or have been lost. Second, there may be a single anterior flagellum, or two flagella of equal length, or one long and one short flagellum, or even three flagella. In all cases the flagella are of the tinsel type and are therefore distinct both in number and structure from those of the green algae. Third, the cells are naked, without rigid cell walls, and very pliable and deformable. Lastly, the characteristic food-storage compound is not starch, but partly lipid material and partly a polysaccharide, called *paramylum,* chemically related to

starch. Euglenoids possess eyespots and pyrenoids like green algae, and they are also equipped with a *gullet,* an anterior funnel-shaped depression in the cell surface. The flagellum passes through this gullet.

Paired green and colorless euglenoids are common. For example, *Euglena* is a green photosynthesizer, interesting also in that it can and probably must occasionally feed as a saprotroph, whether light is present or not. *Astasia,* on the other hand, is a colorless saprotroph otherwise entirely similar to *Euglena.*

PHYLUM CHRYSOPHYTA:
GOLDEN-BROWN ALGAE (6,000 SPECIES)

> *Class Chrysophyceae:* yellow-brown algae
> *Class Xanthophyceae:* yellow-green algae
> *Class Bacillariophyceae:* diatoms

This is an enormously diversified phylum, including more different structural types than any other algal group. Moreover, early chrysophytes, particularly the early yellow-browns, may have been ancestral not only to all other chrysophytes but also to all other brown-line phyla, as well as to some of the slime molds, fungi, protozoa, and perhaps even sponges.

Chrysophytes are identified by various pigments of slightly different types in the different classes (see below). Foods are never stored as starch but partly as *oils* and partly as the polysaccharide *leucosin.* Cell

12 · 12 *Photo and diagram of* **Euglena.** *The genus* Astasia *is entirely similar except that chloroplasts are lacking.*

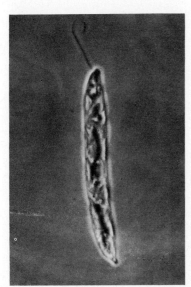
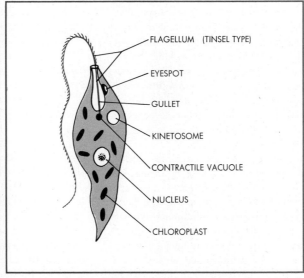

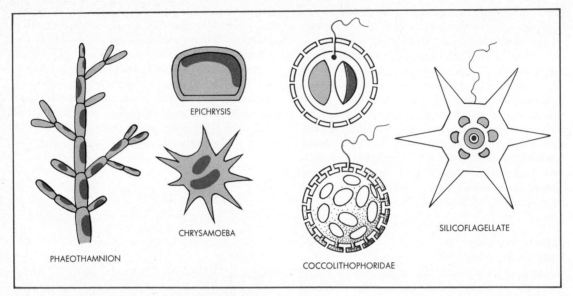

12 · 13 Diagrams of various Chrysophyceae. The silicoflagellate and coccolithophorids shown belong to the flagellate stock; Chrysamoeba *is amoeboid;* Epichrysis *is coccine; and* Phaeothamnion *is sporine.*

walls may be absent or present. In the latter case the wall is in two halves, the rim of one half tightly overlapping the rim of the other, like lid and box. Such walls are composed of pectic substances plus cellulose in some cases and silicon compounds in the majority of cases. Formation of encapsulated dormant stages, here called *statospores*, is further characteristic of the phylum.

Organisms in the class Chrysophyceae probably are the modern descendants of the original chrysophyte ancestors. Their pigments are chlorophyll *a* plus at least one other chlorophyll of still undetermined type; carotenes; and xanthophylls, which include the yellow *lutein* and the brown *fucoxanthin*. The last two endow these algae with a characteristic yellow-brown color. Four major evolutionary lines of yellow-browns are known, namely, flagellate, amoeboid, coccine, and sporine lines. Each of these has unicellular and colonial representatives (Fig. 12.13).

The flagellate forms display various kinds of flagellation patterns (see Fig. 12.17). These organisms, like the amoeboid forms, include many paired photosynthetic and colorless types. Some of the colorless flagellate chrysophyceans may have evolutionary affinities with certain of the primitive fungi. Analogously, colorless amoeboid chrysophyceans may have contributed to the evolution of slime molds and amoeboid protozoa; a colorless chrysophycean amoeba, for example, is virtually indistinguishable from a pro-

tozoan amoeba. Two groups of yellow-brown flagellates are partially enclosed within intricately sculptured external skeletons. In the *Coccolithophoridae* this skeleton is composed of calcium compounds, and in the *Silicoflagellidae*, of silicon compounds. These algae are marine and often form important components of plankton. They may be derived from ancestral stocks which, by loss of chlorophyll, may also have given rise to certain protozoa (namely, the foraminiferans and the radiolarians, respectively).

Organisms in the class Xanthophyceae are characterized by chlorophylls *a* and *e* (the latter quite similar to but not identical with chlorophyll *c*), by carotenes, and by xanthophylls of still undetermined nature. Paired photosynthetic and colorless types are again known. Moreover, the yellow-green algae display almost the same wide array of flagellate, amoeboid, coccine, and sporine types as the yellow-brown algae. Also, the xanthophyceans too have probably contributed to the evolution of other groups, notably the protozoa and slime molds.

Diatoms, forming the class Bacillariophyceae, possess chlorophylls *a* and *c*, carotenes, and xanthophylls that include the brown fucoxanthin. Whereas the other two classes are highly varied in vegetative types, the diatoms are relatively unvaried. They actually represent just one principal vegetative condition, namely, a sporine state which is mostly unicellular and occasionally primitively colonial. A diatom possesses a conspicuous rigid cell wall or shell, composed as in other chrysophytes of two tightly fitting halves and consisting of pectic and silicon-containing compounds. These shells are finely sculptured in a great variety of bilateral or radial patterns (Color Plate X, 21).

12 · 14 Cryptophyceae. Chilomonas *lacks chloroplasts but is otherwise entirely similar.*

In contrast to the other two classes, the diatoms are of major economic importance. As already noted in Chap. 10, diatoms are the most abundant single group of plankton organisms, and as such they support much of the flora and fauna of the ocean and the fresh water. The silica shells of dead diatoms make up large tracts of the ocean floor. Geologically uplifted parts of this floor are the source of *diatomaceous earth*, mined for its abrasive and various other properties. For example, it is a common component of tooth paste. Moreover, much of the petroleum used in industry today is probably derived from the oils synthesized and stored by diatoms of past ages.

PHYLUM PYRROPHYTA:

FIRE ALGAE (1,000 SPECIES)

    Class Cryptophyceae: cryptoflagellates
    Class Dinophyceae: dinoflagellates

The pigments in this phylum are chlorophylls *a* and *c*, carotenes, several xanthophylls which include at

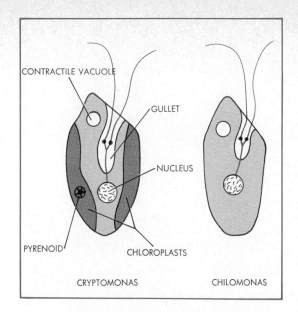

least three of unique composition. Foods are variously stored in the form of starch, starchlike carbohydrates, and fats and oils. Cell walls are absent in some of the Dinophyceae. In others, as well as in the Cryptophyceae, walls composed of cellulose are present.

The evolutionary affinities of the Cryptophyceae are uncertain and the group is included in the Pyrrophyta only provisionally. The organisms are very

12 · 15 Dinophyceae.

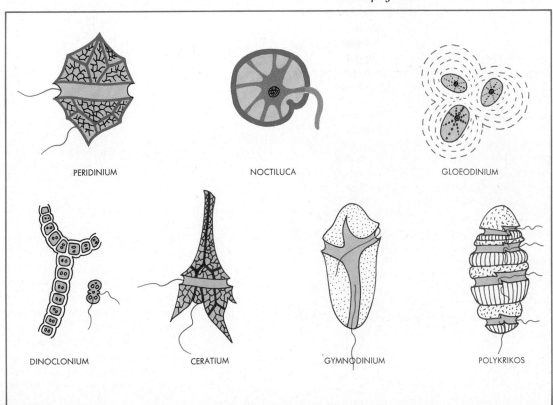

12 · 16 Brown algae. A, Fucus. B, Laminaria.
*In A, note reproductive receptacles at tips and
air bladders lower down. In B, note holdfast,
stipes (stalks), and leaflike blades.*

largely biflagellate unicells. A gullet is conspicuous near or at the base of the flagella. Paired photosynthetic and colorless types are represented, for example, by *Cryptomonas* and *Chilomonas,* respectively (Fig. 12.14).

The Dinophyceae (Fig. 12.15) are by far the more important class, for they constitute a major component of plankton. The vast majority of the Dinophyceae are dinoflagellates, that is, motile flagellate types. Most of them are unicellular, but some are colonial. All remaining Dinophyceae represent amoeboid, coccine, and sporine evolutionary lines, but in this class these types are not nearly so elaborately developed as in other algal groups.

Most of the dinoflagellates possess cellulose walls formed into distinct interlocking "armor" plates (for example, *Peridinium, Ceratium*). Two flagella are present, one directed backward in swimming, the other undulating within a transverse groove formed by the armor. Different nutritional variants are common. For example, *Ceratium* is photosynthetic, *Blastodinium* is a colorless parasite in animals, and *Noctiluca* either photosynthesizes or feeds like an animal. Paired photosynthetic and colorless types are known as well, and these have probably contributed to the evolution of other protistan groups. Many marine dinoflagellates are bioluminescent (for example, *Noctiluca*). On occasion, some dinoflagellates proliferate locally in fantastic numbers. For example, the reddish *Gymnodinium* often produces so-called red tides (hence the name of the phylum, which literally means "fire plants").

PHYLUM PHAEOPHYTA:
BROWN ALGAE (1,000 SPECIES)

The identifying pigments of these algae are chlorophylls *a* and *c*; carotenes; and several xanthophylls, of which three are unique to the phylum and one is the brown fucoxanthin, present in amounts sufficient to mask all other pigments. Foods are stored partly as *laminarin,* a unique polysaccharide, partly as *mannitol,* a sugar alcohol. The cell walls are composed of an inner layer of cellulose and an outer layer of *algin,* a pectic material unique to the brown algae.

Phaeophytes are exclusively multicellular and sessile. With the exception of three rare freshwater species, all are marine. Colorless forms are unknown and photosynthesis is the only food-procuring process. These plantlike organisms represent sporine filaments and more complex organizations of the tissue grade of construction (Fig. 12.16). In the filamentous forms (for example, *Ectocarpus*) and also in some of the tissue-level forms, growth proceeds from cells at the base of the body. In the remaining types, distinct apical cells present at the upper tip of the body give rise to all other cells by continual division.

Most of the seaweeds are brown algae. The majority of species live in shallow water and in the intertidal zone, attached to rocky bottoms by holdfasts. Ebb tides may expose the organisms to air for several hours, but their algin coating retains considerable amounts of water and protects the algae from desiccation. The most familiar of the brown algae is probably the rockweed *Fucus,* found along many shores. Undoubtedly the most spectacular of the seaweeds are the giant kelps, growing along the North American west coasts. For example, the kelp *Macrocystis* sometimes attains lengths of more than 100 yd, which makes it longer than a full-grown blue whale. *Laminaria,* the commonest of the kelps, is a cosmopolitan genus. Torn pieces of it may often be found washed up on beaches along with other algae, particularly after a storm.

Brown algae are the source of many substances useful to man, for example, iodine, which the algae concentrate, and algin, which finds wide use in many manufacturing processes (for example, ice cream). Because of this, extensive kelp beds in shallow waters are harvested regularly by special cutting and collecting machines.

PHYLUM RHODOPHYTA:
RED ALGAE (3,000 SPECIES)

The members of this phylum possess chlorophylls *a* and *d,* carotenes, xanthophylls (one of which is lutein), and the pigments *r-phycocyanin* and *r-phycoerythrin.* The last two occur uniquely in this phylum, and they are chemically not the same as similarly named pigments in the blue-green algae. Red algae store food in the form of *floridean starch,* chemically very much like glycogen but with somewhat different physical properties. The cell walls are composed of an inner layer of cellulose and an outer layer of pectin. Some rhodophytes, particularly the *stony coralline algae* (for example, *Corallina*), deposit calcium compounds on their outer surfaces. Such algae contribute importantly to the formation of coral reefs.

The cells of the simply constructed red algae typically are uninucleate, but in the larger forms they are usually multinucleate. Some red algae are parasitic and these are colorless or very nearly so, containing very few chloroplasts. All red algae are sessile. A few genera are unicellular (for example, *Porphyridium*), but most are multicellular. Like the brown algae, the red algae represent filamentous and more complex sporine organizations (Plate XI, 22). In some cases, growth by increase in cell number is accomplished by the division of virtually all cells of the organism. In other cases, distinct apical cells are alone specialized for continued division. The evolutionary origin of the red algae is difficult to trace. They are not obviously related to any of the other algal phyla and must have arisen, in ways unknown to us, from some early ancestral unicellular stocks.

Red algae are exclusively marine and they live in somewhat deeper water than the brown algae. The red pigment *r*-phycoerythrin appears to be an adaptation to this dimmer environment; *r*-phycoerythrin absorbs blue light particularly well, and the "blue" wavelengths of sunlight actually penetrate deeper into water than "red" wavelengths. Indeed, *r*-phycoerythrin has been found to play an important auxiliary role in the photosynthesis of these algae. Rhodophytes are lacier and more delicate than the sturdy brown algae. The latter are adapted to withstand pounding surf, but in deeper water the red algae are not so subject to wave action.

Some of the red algae are used commercially. The pectin of the genus *Gelidium* is the source of agar-agar, used as a medium for culturing microorganisms. *Porphyra, Rhodymenia,* and *Chondrus crispus,* the Irish moss, are among several types prized as vegetables in various parts of the world.

The probable evolutionary relationships of all the algal groups are outlined in Fig. 12.17.

FUNGI

PHYLUM MYCOPHYTA (90,000 SPECIES)

Class Phycomycetes (nonseptate fungi): water molds, downy mildews, blights, bread molds
Class Ascomycetes (sac fungi): yeasts, molds, powdery mildews, truffles, cup fungi
Class Basidiomycetes (club fungi): rusts, smuts, bracket fungi, mushrooms, toadstools, puffballs, stinkhorns
Class Fungi Imperfecti: provisional collection of types with incompletely known reproductive processes, not yet assignable to any of the above groups.

This huge phylum ranks fifth or sixth in numbers of described species among all phyla of organisms. As might be expected, therefore, fungi have representatives in almost every available habitat on earth, and many fungi are of major economic or medical significance to man. The organisms are partly free-living saprotrophs, partly symbionts of all possible types. They store foods in the form of glycogen and as lipids. Primitive members of the phylum are aquatic and produce flagellate reproductive cells. More ad-

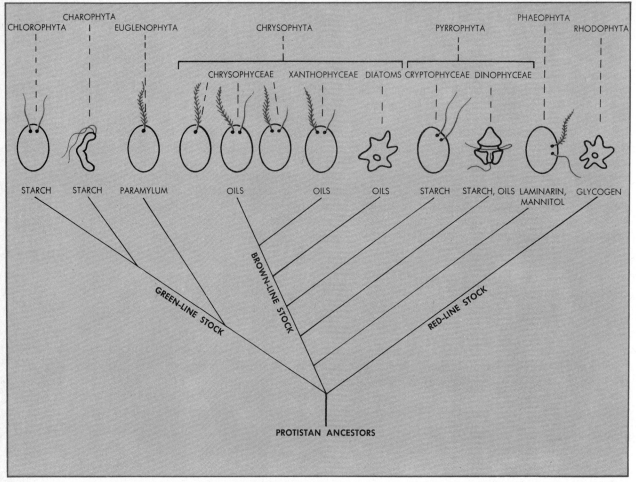

12 · 17 Probable evolutionary affinities *of all major algal phyla. Note that four basic flagellation patterns are exhibited, as exemplified by chloro-phytes and chrysophyceans. These four are, from left to right, above, the* chlamydomonad, chromulinid, isochrysid, *and* ochromonad *patterns.*

vanced fungi are terrestrial, with nonmotile reproductive cells dispersed passively by wind, water, and animals.

As a group, fungi may be regarded as a culmination of the sessile coccine state in protistan evolution. The vegetative body of a fungus is multinucleate, without internal cell boundaries. Phycomycetes are without internal partitions of any kind. In the other classes internal walls do develop, but these partitions, or *septa*, are incomplete, leaving pores through which the living substance may flow (Fig. 12.18). Thus the fungus body is always a continuous mass which may grow in size and in the number of nuclei. But cytoplasmic divisions do not occur in the vegetative state.

True cells, with complete individual boundaries and one nucleus each, are formed only during reproduction.

The living mass of a fungus is bounded externally by a rigid wall composed of cellulose in some of the primitive fungi and of chitin in others. Excepting only some of the primitive fungi, which are more or less spherical, the basic unit of the fungus body has the form of a tubular, often branched filament. Such a unit is called a *hypha*. As it grows, it may extend in length and branch increasingly. Numerous hyphae may be intermeshed into an irregular network, a so-called *mycelium* (Fig. 12.19). Hyphae may also pack together in more orderly patterns, producing, for example, bodies structured like mushrooms.

The evolutionary origin of fungi is obscure. Traditional hypotheses regard either protozoa or algae as the ancestral stocks, but there is really no reason why slime molds should not also be included as possible ancestors. Fungi share traits with protozoa, algae, and slime molds and such resemblances merely underscore the protistan character of all these groups. Actually,

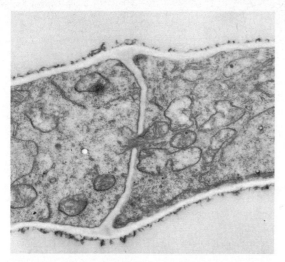

12 · 18 *The incomplete partitions in the hyphae of the ascomycete* Neurospora. *Note the continuity of the cytoplasm through the pore in the transverse partition.*

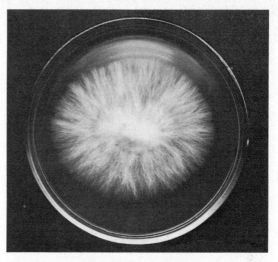

12 · 19 *A mycelium of a fungus.*

12 · 20 *Probable evolutionary interrelations of various fungal groups.*

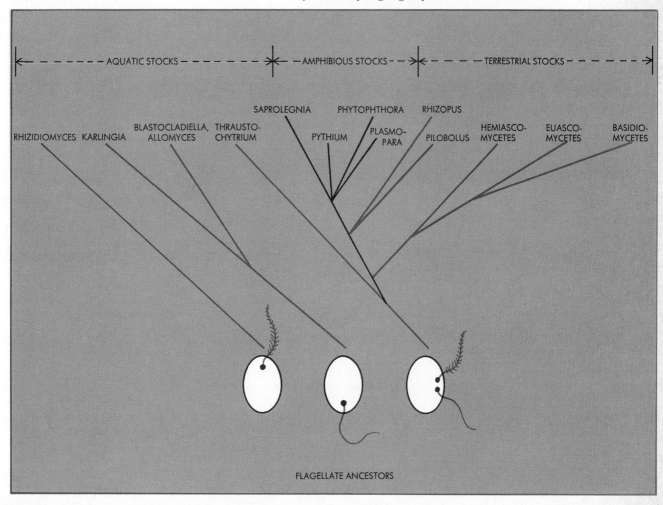

AQUATIC STOCKS — — — — — AMPHIBIOUS STOCKS — — — — — TERRESTRIAL STOCKS — — —

SAPROLEGNIA   PHYTOPHTHORA   RHIZOPUS

BLASTOCLADIELLA, THRAUSTO-   HEMIASCO-   EUASCO-   BASIDIO-
ALLOMYCES   CHYTRIUM   PLASMO-   MYCETES   MYCETES   MYCETES
RHIZIDIOMYCES KARLINGIA   PYTHIUM   PARA   PILOBOLUS

FLAGELLATE ANCESTORS

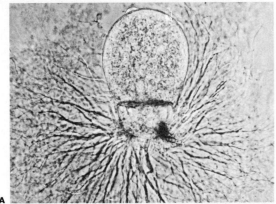

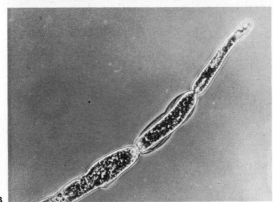

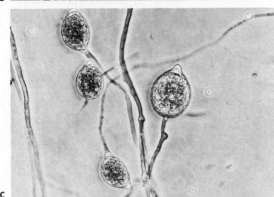

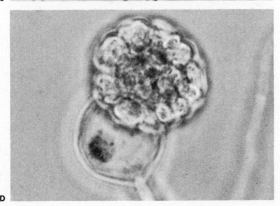

the flagellate stages of the primitive fungi strongly suggest a multiple origin of the phylum. Figure 12.20 outlines the probable evolutionary interrelations of groups within the phylum.

Class Phycomycetes

This is undoubtedly the most primitive fungal class. Within it, the most primitive fungi in turn are the aquatic Phycomycetes. Some of these are free-living, some are parasitic.

In the aquatic Phycomycetes (Fig. 12.21), the vegetative body is often microscopic and consists in many cases of little more than one multinucleate cell. In some instances such a body is drawn out at one point into fine branching extension, so-called *rhizoids,* which aid particularly in nutrient uptake. Cell walls are composed either of chitin only, or of chitin and cellulose, or of cellulose only. When such a fungus reproduces, its body becomes subdivided into numerous spore cells. These develop one or two flagella each and such *zoospores* then disperse by swimming actively in water.

Other members of the aquatic Phycomycetes are structurally more complex. In some (for example, *Blastocladiella*), the body consists of two multinucleate compartments, one vegetative and functioning in nutrient uptake, the other reproductive and producing zoospores. In still more advanced types, filamentous hyphae with branches are in evidence and in many cases such hyphae form mycelial meshworks.

Such structurally more complex Phycomycetes (see Fig. 12.21) illustrate a progressive transition from strictly aquatic to amphibious to strictly terrestrial ways of life. For example, *Saprolegnia* is a water mold growing saprotrophically in calm fresh waters. But this fungus may also live in well-irrigated soils. By contrast, *Pythium,* some species of which cause root rot in young vascular plants, is found in soil more often than in bodies of water. Regardless of where they are found, however, fungi like *Saprolegnia* and *Pythium* are still basically aquatic and they produce spores adapted to dispersal in water, that is, zoospores.

Distinctly amphibious types are represented, for example, by *Phytophthora,* best known as the causative agent of late blight in potatoes. Under favorable

12 · 21 Aquatic Phycomycetes. A, Karlingia; *note the rhizoids radiating out from the globular fungus body. B,* Saprolegnia; *a terminal portion of a hypha is shown. C,* Phytophthora; *note the globular sporangia on the hyphae. D,* Pythium; *note the mass of zoospores just escaped from the sporangium.*

PLATE XI

22. Red Algae.
A, *Antithamnion, a branched type.*
B, *Corallina, one of the stony*
coralline types.

A, B, *courtesy of Carolina Biological Supply Company*

PLATE XII

A, B, courtesy of Carolina Biological Supply Company

23. Euascomycetes.
A, fruiting bodies of the cup fungus Peziza.
B, fruiting bodies of the edible morel Morchella.

conditions, this fungus may develop *sporangia,* or spore sacs, which produce zoospores. But when lack of environmental water or too high a temperature prevents swimming zoospores from carrying out their dispersal function, the sporangia do not produce zoospores. Instead, they may become detached from the fungus and, after passive dispersion without the aid of external water, may later produce hyphae called *germ tubes.* Such germ tubes grow directly into new fungi. Evidently, the late blight fungus is adapted to either aquatic or terrestrial conditions. Purely terrestrial types are represented by species of *Plasmopara,* causative agent of downy mildew in onions. This fungus does not develop zoospores at all but forms sporangia growing via germ tubes only. It may therefore reproduce in the complete absence of free water.

The most advanced members of the Phycomycetes also are strictly terrestrial. They form neither zoospores nor germ tubes, however, but always produce non-motile encapsulated spores well adapted to passive dispersal on dry land. To this group belongs the bread mold *Rhizopus,* a familiar fungus growing on stale bread as a white, fuzzy-appearing mycelium.

Class Ascomycetes

In all probability this class arose from a relatively advanced ancestral stock of terrestrial Phycomycetes. Ascomycetes are similarly terrestrial, and motile stages are absent. The hyphae are incompletely septate; transverse partitions with central openings develop at intervals along a hyphal filament. The living mass between two consecutive septa most often contains one nucleus, but in many cases more than one is present.

Ascomycetes are so named because their characteristic spores, the *ascospores,* are manufactured within elongated or oval sacs called *asci* (Fig. 12.22). The members of the class are grouped into two subclasses on the basis of the number of asci produced. Fungi in which a single ascus develops are members of the subclass *Hemiascomycetes.* The best known of these are the *yeasts,* long important to man in the manufacture of bread and wine. Most yeasts are secondarily reduced, unicellular fungi. But some do develop the mycelial body, and nearly all produce the ascospores characteristic of the subclass.

In the second and large subclass, the *Euascomycetes,* an array of numerous asci develops, each borne at the tip of a special hypha. These hyphae and their asci are usually more or less packed together and are surrounded by supporting hyphae. The whole complex constitutes a *fruiting body.* Three general types of such fruiting bodies are known (Fig. 12.23). A

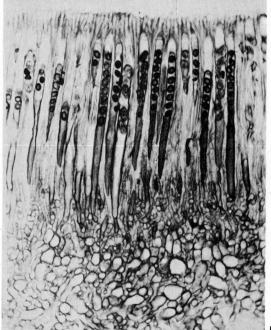

Courtesy of Carolina Biological Supply Company.

12 · 22 Asci of cup fungi. A, *section through a* Peziza *cup, showing the layer of asci lining the cavity of the cup. B, higher magnification of a portion of the ascus layer.*

cleistothecium is spherical, without external openings and with asci in the interior arranged either randomly or in some orderly pattern. A *perithecium* is a flask-shaped fruiting body with an opening at the neck of the flask. And an *apothecium* is a cup- or saucer-shaped fruiting body, the asci forming an orderly layer lining the inner surface (see Fig. 12.22).

Among the cleistothecial types is *Penicillium.* One species of this mold is the source of the antibiotic penicillin, other species produce the characteristic flavor of Roquefort, Camembert, and other kinds of

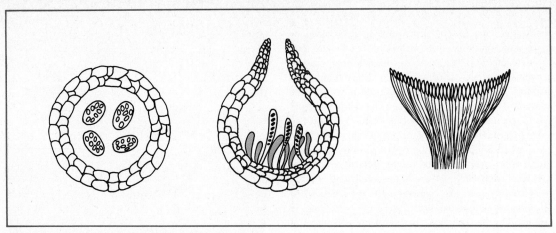

12 · 23 *Three types of fruiting bodies in Asco-mycetes.*

cheeses. Another cleistothecial group comprises the *powdery mildews,* all obligate parasites living in grapes, hops, grasses, roses, apples, and various cereal plants (Color Plate XII, 23). These fungi are not severely damaging, but by depriving the hosts of food they reduce crop yield, vigor, or both. Perithecial fruiting bodies are formed, for example, in the pink bread mold *Neurospora crassa,* an important organism in biological research. Of considerable economic

12 · 24 *A unicellular basidium, characteristic of the Homobasidiomycetes. Figure 27.22 diagrams basidia in Heterobasidiomycetes.*

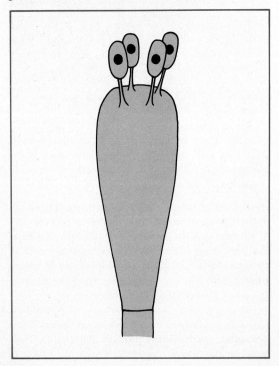

significance are perithecial types such as *Ceratocystis ulmi,* causative agent of the Dutch elm disease; *Venturia inaequalis,* causative agent of apple scab; *Endothia parasitica,* which has made chestnut trees extinct in North America; and *Claviceps purpurea,* the ergot fungus in rye. Apothecial fruiting bodies are characteristic of the cup fungi. Included in this group are *Monolinia fructicola,* which causes brown rot in peaches; the edible *morels* (Color Plate XII, 23); and the subterranean *truffles,* which are highly prized by gourmets and are hunted in France by specially smell-trained pigs and dogs. The fruiting bodies of truffles are rounded masses with irregular ascus-containing internal cavities.

Class Basidiomycetes

Available evidence suggests that this class of fungi has evolved from ascomycete ancestors, specifically from some early stock of the Euascomycetes. Basidio-mycetes too are incompletely septate, with filamentous hyphae forming mycelia and fruiting bodies. The identifying feature of the class is the formation of *basidiospores,* produced on often club-shaped bodies called *basidia* (Fig. 12.24). A basidium is considered by some to be a modified type of ascus.

The class contains two principal subclasses. In the *Heterobasidiomycetes,* a basidium is partitioned transversely or longitudinally into two, three, or four cells. Each such cell produces one basidiospore. In the *Homobasidiomycetes,* a basidium is one cell and produces four basidiospores in most cases. Both sub-classes are extremely large groups; together they comprise some 25,000 species.

Among the Heterobasidiomycetes are the *jelly fungi,* common saprotrophs on dead tree branches and decaying logs (Fig. 12.25). Much of the fungus body here is a hygroscopic gelatinous mass which swells considerably when wetted. Hyphae within the jelly produce the basidia. The most important Hetero-basidiomycetes from an economic standpoint are the *rusts* and *smuts*. Both groups are parasites of vascular plants (for example, black stem wheat rust, corn smut). The Homobasidiomycetes include the best known fungi of all, namely the *mushrooms* (Fig. 12.26). A typical mushroom of commerce is *Agaricus campestris*. The mycelium of this fungus, present in soil, develops stalked fruiting bodies with caps, on the underside of which are radially arranged *gills*. Club-shaped basidia are exposed along the surfaces of the gills. Mature basidiospores fall into the soil, where they germinate into new mycelia.

Not all mushrooms possess gills and not all are soil inhabitants. Very many are parasitic on woody plants, for example, the *bracket fungi,* and many others bring about decay of fallen trees. Apart from mushrooms, Homobasidiomycetes also include *puffballs, stinkhorns,* and *bird's-nest fungi* (Plate XIII, 24). All these are saprotrophs, and their basidia are formed within closed, rounded fruiting bodies. Spore release can take place only when the fruiting bodies decompose or when they break open. Such mechanical release is brought about by the spores themselves, for they are frequently so numerous that masses of them erupt right through the outer layers of a fruiting body.

Indeed, giant puffballs, which may reach diameters of several feet, probably have the distinction of being reproductively the most prolific of all living organisms. A single giant puffball may manufacture as many as 100 *trillion* spores. It has been estimated that if each of these spores were to grow into a mature fungus, a mass of living matter nearly 1,000 times the size of the earth would be produced.

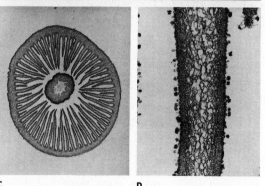

12 · 25 Heterobasidiomycetes. A, jelly fungus. B, wheat-rust lesion on stems.

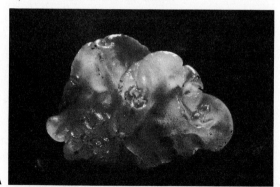

12 · 26 Homobasidiomycetes. A, mushroom with gills on the underside. B, bracket fungus. C, section through the cap of a mushroom, showing the arrangement of the gills. D, closeup of a gill, showing the mycelial meshwork in the interior and the spores, attached to basidia and projecting from the surface.

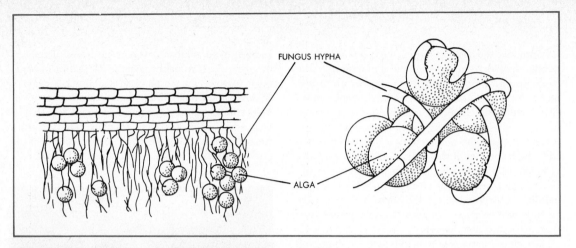

FUNGUS HYPHA

ALGA

12 · 27 Lichens. *Diagram: the interrelation between the algal cells and the fungal hyphae. Photo: a fruticose species. Lichens are also shown in Color Plate V, 12.*

Lichens, Fungi Imperfecti

Lichens are symbiotic associations of algae and fungi (see Chap. 9). The fungal members are Ascomycetes in the vast majority of cases. Among the algal members are *Nostoc, Gloeocapsa,* and other blue-green algae, as well as various coccine green algae. In a lichen, the fungus forms a mycelial framework within which the algae are held and supported. Some lichens are crustlike, or *crustose;* others are leaflike, or *foliose;* and still others are branching, or *fruticose* (Fig. 12.27). They are often epiphytic on trees, but more commonly they live independently on rock. Here they are important soil formers; they aid in the fragmentation of rock surfaces through acids produced by their

metabolism and also through acids formed when lichens decay.

Most of the Fungi Imperfecti are probably Ascomycetes too. Fungi in this artificial class are at present known only by their asexual stages. Whenever the sexual stages are discovered in a given species, that species may be assigned to one of the three other classes of fungi. In the past, such discoveries have increased the membership of the Ascomycetes most, that of the Basidiomycetes somewhat, and that of the Phycomycetes not at all. Correspondingly, the membership of the Fungi Imperfecti is steadily decreasing.

SLIME MOLDS

PHYLUM MYXOPHYTA

Class Myxomyceteae: multinucleate slime molds with flagellate swarmers
Class Acrasieae: multicellular slime molds with amoeboid swarmers
Class Labyrinthuleae: multicellular slime molds without fruiting bodies

This phylum represents the culmination of the colonial *amoeboid* state; the vegetative body of a slime mold is a naked, creeping, amoeboid mass, in some cases as much as 1 ft in diameter.

The evolutionary origin of the phylum remains obscure. Any ancestral group or groups, photosynthetic or not, that could have given rise to protozoan amoebae, or even to protozoan flagellates, or to primitive fungi, could qualify also as ancestral stocks of the slime molds. Inasmuch as the ones are unknown, the others are still unknown as well. From the nature of existing slime molds, it is highly probable that a multiple origin must be postulated for the phylum, with a different derivation for at least each class.

Adult slime molds of the class Myxomyceteae exist in the form of *plasmodia*, naked amoeboid sheets with irregular and slowly shifting contours (Fig. 12.28). Each such plasmodium contains hundreds or thousands of nuclei, but internal cell boundaries are absent and the whole organism is a continuous living mass. Some myxomycetes are parasitic in flowering plants, but most are free-living in moist wooded areas, where they creep over fallen leaves and rotting logs like supergiant amoebae (for example, *Physarum*).

When a myxomycete plasmodium reproduces, its amoeboid life ceases and for a time it becomes rather funguslike. More specifically, the plasmodial mass flows together into one or more heaped mounds or grows into one or more upright stalks each of which develops a bulbous upper tip. Such structures are *fruiting bodies,* or *sporangia* (Plate XIV, 25). Within a fruiting body spore cells then form, each typically containing one nucleus and its own wall. The spores secrete protective capsules and eventually escape from the fruiting bodies and scatter. In suitable environments they may germinate and produce *swarmers,* or single flagellate cells. Such cells greatly resemble colorless algal flagellates or protozoan flagellates. Swarm cells may undergo successive cell divisions, and eventually they fuse pairwise and undergo a sexual process. Thereafter the flagella are cast off and each cell becomes exclusively amoeboid. Such amoebae subsequently grow into vegetative, multinucleate plasmodia.

Slime molds in the class Acrasieae resemble the myxomycetes in many respects, but they exhibit several distinct characteristics. The adult vegetative body is a *pseudoplasmodium,* a true cellular colony

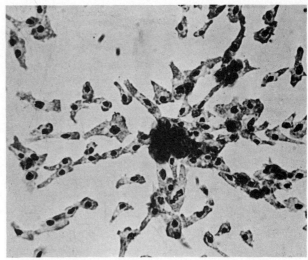

Courtesy of Dr. J. T. Bonner, and J. Exp. Zool., vol. 106, p. 7.

12 · 29 *The amoeboid cells of a slime mold,* Dictyostelium, *migrating together and eventually forming a compact aggregate. A reproductive structure will then develop from the aggregate.*

composed of hundreds or thousands of uninucleate amoeboid cells which do not lose their cell boundaries. Stalked fruiting bodies are again formed, and spores are produced as in myxomycetes. However, the products of spore germination are never flagellate, but are solitary uninucleate amoeboid cells. Such amoebae divide and increase in number. Eventually they all migrate into a common multicellular mass representing a new pseudoplasmodial generation (Fig. 12.29).

Organisms in the class Labyrinthuleae are poorly known. Multicellular pseudoplasmodia appear to be typical, but fruiting bodies are not. Motile unicellular swarmers are again a phase of the life cycle. These swarmers possess eyespots, suggesting algal affinities. On the other hand, the locomotion of the swarmers is neither flagellate nor amoeboid. Indeed, clearly identifiable locomotor structures are not visible at all and the cells appear to be sliding along a surface without noticeable change of shape. Just how their propulsion is accomplished is unknown (Fig. 12.30).

PROTOZOA

PHYLUM PROTOZOA (15,000+ SPECIES)

Subphylum MASTIGOPHORA: flagellate protozoa
Subphylum SARCODINA: amoeboid protozoa
Subphylum SPOROZOA: coccine protozoa
Subphylum CILIOPHORA: ciliate protozoa

12 · 28 *Plasmodium* of the myxomycete Physarella.

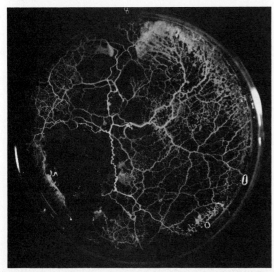

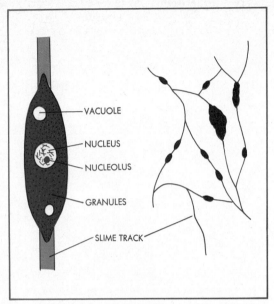

12·30 *Labyrinthula. Single cell on slime track on left; colony on right.*

Just as algae are the most nearly plantlike protists, so protozoa are the most nearly animallike. In the absence of group-identifying biochemical clues such as chlorophyll, it is difficult to pinpoint the detailed ancestry of these organisms. However, the characteristics of protozoa leave little doubt that they must be highly polyphyletic and that as a group they may be descended from possibly all the other unicellular stocks of Protista. By loss of chlorophyll, primitive algae in particular may have given rise to protozoa

12·31 *Possible interrelations among protozoan groups. Contributions to protozoan evolution by algae, slime molds, and fungi are suggested by colored lines.*

early and directly, or later and indirectly via other protistan types (Fig. 12.31).

Nutritionally, protozoa exhibit all known forms of heterotrophism. Free-living holotrophic types are most common. So-called "herbivorous" protozoa subsist largely on bacteria and microscopic algae, and "carnivorous" forms feed on minute Metazoa such as rotifers or on other protozoa (including fellow members of their own species in cannibalistic species). Some protozoa are saprotrophic and many are parasitic. Sporozoa are parasitic altogether and every other subphylum includes parasitic subgroups.

Although a few protozoan genera are colonial, the unicellular condition is almost universal in the phylum. Indeed, protozoa have exploited the unicellular way of life perhaps more diversely than any other organisms. The Mastigophora and Ciliophora are flagellate (though in the Ciliophora the flagella are shortened to cilia). Sarcodina are amoeboid and probably related closely to the Mastigophora. These two subphyla are sometimes actually classified as a single group. The coccine spore-forming Sporozoa are probably derived from flagellate and amoeboid stocks. We note that all but sporine states of existence are represented in the phylum as a whole. In all four subphyla, encapsulated or encysted states occur as temporary phases of given life cycles.

Although protozoa are classified traditionally as a single phylum, each subphylum might well be accorded independent phylum rank. On the cellular level of organization, the differences between, for example, an amoeba and a paramecium appear to be comparatively just as profound as those between single-celled green and golden-brown algae or the higher-level differences between mosses and grasses or between earthworms and caterpillars. If each of the latter pairs represents two different phyla, as is

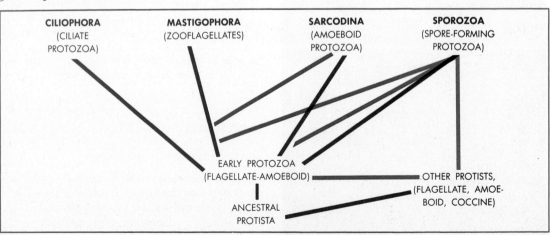

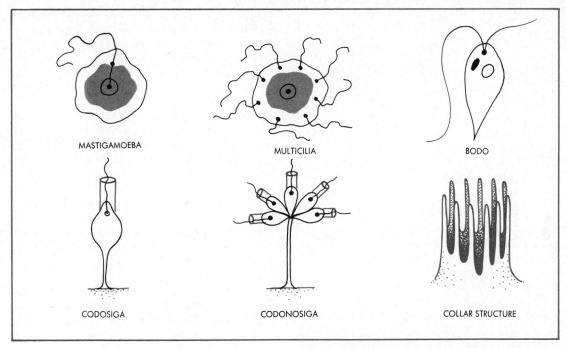

MASTIGAMOEBA

MULTICILIA

BODO

CODOSIGA

CODONOSIGA

COLLAR STRUCTURE

12 · 32 Free-living zooflagellates. Note the rhizoplast in Mastigamoeba *and the trichocyst in* Bodo. *The electron microscope shows that the collar of a collar flagellate like* Codosiga *is a circlet of long cytoplasmic extensions, as indicated at lower right.*

actually the case, then so probably should amoebae and paramecia. Protozoa could therefore constitute a superphylum, like algae.

Regardless of how they are classified, however, protozoa certainly are by any criterion among the most successful of all living creatures. They are components of all ecosystems in all aquatic habitats, in soils, and generally in any environment containing some moisture. The number of existing protozoan species has been underestimated fairly consistently. Figures often cited are in the order of 15,000, but there are known to be more than that many foraminiferan species alone. Moreover, very many animals harbor at least one unique parasitic protozoan species, which means that protozoa could well number in the hundreds of thousands of species. As a conservative figure, at least 100,000 species of protozoa may be presumed to exist.

The protozoan cell is either naked or is surrounded by a nonrigid *pellicle*, composed of a variety of organic and horny substances. Cellulose is not present. In many cases, shells of various inorganic compounds are secreted as external skeletons. Foods are stored as glycogen and fats. In free-living flagellate and ciliate types, gullets are usually well developed; amoeboid protozoa use pseudopodia for feeding. Underneath the cell surface in a number of protozoan groups are conductile neurofibrils, contractile myofibrils, and contractile vacuoles. The latter occur in

virtually all freshwater forms as well as in a few marine and parasitic types. Where present, such vacuoles serve primarily in maintaining an osmotic balance between the cell interior and the external medium, that is, they excrete excess water drawn into the cell osmotically. Centrioles are not present in ciliate protozoa. In the other groups such granules are either extranuclear or, more often, intranuclear. In many cases also, particularly among flagellates, the centriole and the kinetosome are interconnected by a fine rhizoplast, as in flagellate algae. Other cytoplasmic organelles serving a variety of specialized functions occur more or less uniquely in given protozoan groups. Protozoa are largely uninucleate, but all ciliates and many amoeboid types are multinucleate, often highly so. Sporozoa become multinucleate at particular life-cycle stages.

Though definite sensory structures can in most cases not be identified, protozoa are nevertheless exquisitely sensitive to their surroundings. They may "taste" food and refuse to ingest unsuitable materials; they give distinct avoidance responses to undue temperatures, light, electric charges, pH, mechanical stimuli, and chemicals in the water; they seek out

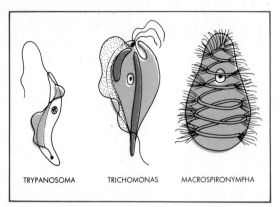

12 · 33 Three symbiotic zooflagellates. In Trypanosoma, *note the posterior kinetosome and the undulating membrane edged by the flagellum.* Trichomonas *has an axostyle, a parabasal body, a gullet, and an undulating membrane, in addition to a nucleus with intranuclear centriole and a kinetosome with additional flagella.* Macrospironympha *possesses a spiral, ribbonlike kinetosome and hundreds of flagella emanating from it.* Trichonympha (*not shown*) *is similarly hyperflagellate.*

12 · 34 Actinopod Sarcodina. *At left is a sketch of an axopodium, showing the stiff supporting flagellum (axoneme) emanating from a kinetosome and the layer of cytoplasm covering it. Near the tip is a food vacuole. Numerous axopodia radiate out from an intranuclear centriole in the heliozoid Actinophrys, sketched at center. Photo: a variety of radiolarian shells. Note the latticelike construction of all. In the living organisms, axonemes and silica spicules project through the openings.*

optimum environments by trial-and-error behavior; and many of them have been trained through conditioning and have been made to give "learned" responses to specific stimuli.

Mastigophora

Also called *zooflagellates*, these organisms are probably the most primitive protozoa. The ancestors of the group may have been close kin to the early photosynthesizing premonerans from which the algae arose. Moreover, numerous zooflagellates may have evolved later from some of the Chrysophyta and other established algal groups. In any of these possible derivations loss of chlorophyll would have been a first step, and holotrophic, saprotrophic, or symbiotic ways of life must have been adopted subsequently. Parasitic zooflagellates are particularly common today.

The most primitive zooflagellates now in existence are generally free-living and holotrophic, and they greatly resemble colorless flagellate algae. In many of them, the flagella may be lost temporarily and the protozoa then become amoeboid. In some cases, moreover, the flagellate and amoeboid conditions are associated so intimately that an organism is flagellate and amoeboid simultaneously; the front end of the cell bears a flagellum and the hind end produces pseudopodia (Fig. 12.32). Such interrelations between the two motile states support the generally accepted conclusion that at least some flagellate and amoeboid protozoa may be related very closely.

Free-living zooflagellates also include *collar flagellates*, which resemble certain flagellate chryosophytes. For example, *Codosiga* is a collar flagellate subsisting on debris and microorganisms. Food is trapped

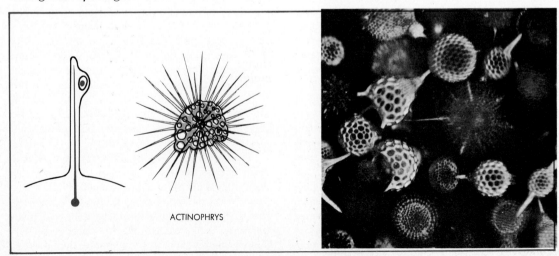

ACTINOPHRYS

within the collar of the organism, and the flagellum then creates a current sweeping the food toward the cell body, where it is engulfed. Some collar flagellates form colonies of various types (see Fig. 12.32). Because collar flagellates bear considerable resemblance to certain cell types present in sponges, it is thought that the evolutionary history of sponges may trace back to zooflagellate ancestors.

Early free-living zooflagellates undoubtedly gave rise to the many symbiotic forms living today (Fig. 12.33). These are highly specialized and adapted to specific hosts. For example, *Trichonympha* is a wood-digesting symbiont in the gut of termites. This zooflagellate possesses hundreds of flagella inserted in enlarged, ribbon-shaped kinetosomes. (Interestingly, superflagellation of this sort has developed also in the motile sperm cells of primitive coniferous plants, for example, cycads and ginkgoes. The same adaptive forces may have oriented this parallel evolution. Zooflagellates like *Trichonympha* must move through the thick, viscous contents of a termite gut and the plant sperms, analogously, move through the thick, viscous living substance of female reproductive organs. In both cases, numerous "paddles" in the form of flagella are adaptively useful.) Other specialized symbiotic zooflagellates include, for example, *Trichomonas*, a commensal in the gut of man and other vertebrates, and *Trypanosoma*, different species of which live parasitically in the bloods of various vertebrates. One such species causes sleeping sickness in man.

Sarcodina

These organisms are almost certainly derived from quite a number of evolutionary sources (see Fig. 12.31). Likely ancestors include, for example, free-living zooflagellates as well as amoeboid (or indeed flagellate) groups among any of the algal phyla. An algal amoeba that loses its chlorophyll will be hardly distinguishable from a protozoan amoeba.

The subphylum is divided into two classes according to the nature of the pseudopodia. In the class *Actinopodea*, pseudopods have the form of *axopodia* (Fig. 12.34). The pseudopodial cytoplasm here is supported internally by a flagellum that has become nonmotile and forms a stiff, straight spike. Each such spike, or *axoneme*, emanates from a kinetosome or centriole within the cell body. Microorganisms trapped on an axopodium are engulfed at the point of contact and a food vacuole then passes through the axopodium into the cell body. To this class belong, for example, the predominantly freshwater Heliozoa, or "sun animalcules," globular organ-

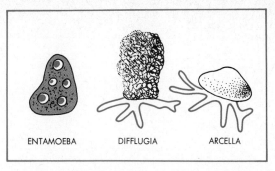

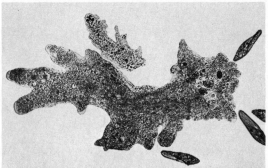

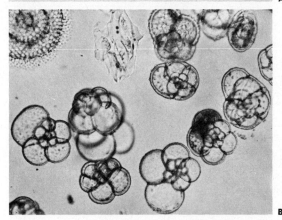

A, courtesy of Carolina Biological Supply Company.

12 · 35 Rhizopod Sarcodina. Entamoeba histolytica *is shown with ingested blood corpuscles in food vacuoles. The shell of* Difflugia *is made of sand grains; that of* Arcella, *of chitinous substances. Photos: A, Pelomyxa, one of the naked, multinucleate amoeboid types (with paramecia around it and* Amoeba proteus *near top, for comparison). An amoeba is also illustrated in Fig. 2.8. B, Globigerina, a common foraminiferan. The helically coiled shells have minute openings through which the pseudopodia project.*

isms in which the numerous axopodia radiate out from the cell like sun rays. *Radiolaria* are marine Actinopodea equipped externally with intricately sculptured, latticelike silica shells. The axopodia here project through the spaces in the skeletal lattices.

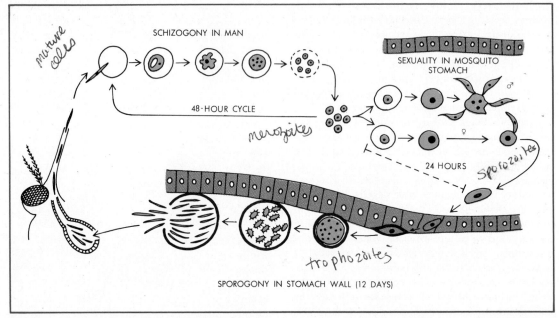

SCHIZOGONY IN MAN

mature cells

48-HOUR CYCLE

merozoites

SEXUALITY IN MOSQUITO STOMACH

♂

♀

24 HOURS

sporozoites

trophozoites

SPOROGONY IN STOMACH WALL (12 DAYS)

12 · 36 *The life cycle of the malarial parasite* **Plasmodium vivax.** *Mature cells invading human red blood corpuscles* (top left) *undergo multiple fission* (schizogony). *Production of offspring cells* (merozoites) *destroys a corpuscle and free merozoites* (which at this point cause an attack of fever) *then reinfect new corpuscles and lead to repetition of a 48-hr fever cycle. Merozoites entering red corpuscles also function as gamonts, and if human blood is sucked up by an Anopheles mosquito, the gamonts break free in the mosquito stomach, transform into male and female gametes, and effect fertilization. The zygote then encysts in the stomach wall and undergoes meiotic multiple fission* (sporogony). *The resulting free spore cells* (sporozoites) *subsequently migrate through the body cavities and organs of the insect, including the salivary glands. From there the sporozoites are injected into the human circulation when the mosquito bites a man. Sporozoites mature in human liver cells into trophozoites, and the latter begin a new life cycle.*

The second class comprises the *Rhizopodea*, characterized by pseudopodia without axonemes (Fig. 12.35). Being unsupported internally, such pseudopodia flow freely and change their contours continually. Many members of this class are naked cells, and among these the most familiar is undoubtedly the common amoeba, *Amoeba proteus.* Closely related is the parasitic *Entamoeba histolytica,* which causes amoebic dysentery in man, and *Pelomyxa,* a large, free-living, highly multinucleate amoeba. Other Rhizopodea encase their bodies in various types of shells. For example, *Arcella* secretes a chitinous housing and extrudes pseudopodia through an opening in this shell. *Difflugia* cements tiny sand grains to a chitinous envelope. Most widespread are the *Foraminifera,* marine Rhizopodea manufacturing calcareous shells of many different forms, all resembling minute snail shells. Pseudopods are extruded through holes in these shells, hence the name of the group (signifying "hole bearers"). Fo-

raminiferan shells may accumulate in given tracts of ocean floor in such numbers that they form the predominant bottom deposit in these regions. This is true also of the silica shells of the Radiolaria. Foraminiferan deposits may become transformed into chalk, radiolarian deposits, into flint. When either of these is uplifted geologically, it may contribute massively to the formation of land (for example, the chalk cliffs of Dover).

Sporozoa

As indicated by their name, these protozoa pass through life cycles that include spore-forming stages; a single cell may undergo *multiple fission* and become divided up into numerous smaller cells simultaneously. Each such spore cell is uninucleate, and after it has become established in a given host as a mature parasite it eventually becomes multinucleate in preparation for the next multiple fission. In certain sporozoans as many as three successive spore-forming generations occur in a single life cycle. Such life cycles may also require one or more intermediate hosts in addition to a main host. We note that Sporozoa represent coccine forms; cell division takes place primarily during the reproduction of the organisms. The cells produced by multiple fission are amoeboid in many cases, flagellate in others. Accordingly, it is generally believed that Sporozoa may have evolved from flagellate-amoeboid stocks among ancestral free-living protozoa and other Protista. The subphylum also appears to be highly polyphyletic.

Many sporozoan parasites are relatively harmless but many others are not. For example, *Eimeria* is the causative agent of coccidiosis, a disease common in domesticated and other mammals and characterized by severe digestive disturbances. The best known and most studied sporozoan is *Plasmodium*, various species of which cause malaria in mammals, birds, and occasionally in lizards. Man is subject to infection by three species, each responsible for a different type of malaria. Repeated cycles of multiple fission and spore release from red blood corpuscles result in successive attacks of fever, the time interval between attacks being a main diagnostic feature of each of the three types of malaria. Completion of the plasmodial life cycle requires a specific blood-sucking intermediate host, namely, the *Anopheles* mosquito in man, the *Culex* mosquito in birds. In the intestinal tissues of such insects sexual processes and additional multiple fissions take place without apparent harm to the hosts. The cells so formed then invade the salivary glands of the insects, and from there the parasites are injected into the blood streams of new main hosts through mosquito bites (Fig. 12.36).

Ciliophora

These organisms are the most complexly elaborated protozoa and they also represent the most diversely specialized of all known cell types. Ciliates probably constitute a monophyletic assemblage, with an ancestry tracing back presumably to zooflagellates or to other protistan flagellates; organisms with traits intermediate between those of flagellates and ciliates are known.

The cilia of these organisms typically are arranged in orderly rows and they beat in a coordinated, *metachronous* rhythm, that is, in wavelike sequence. The rows of cilia are attached internally to corresponding rows of kinetosomes, the latter being joined to one another by complex systems of fibrils (Fig. 12.37). Also present just underneath the surface pellicle is a system of conductile neurofibrils as well

as, in many species, contractile myofibrils paralleling the rows of kinetosomes. Rows of dischargeable *trichocysts* may also be found in given ciliates. Cilia often occur as modified compound organelles. For example, if cilia in a row are fused into a sheet, an *undulating membrane* is formed. Such a membrane may serve, like cilia themselves, in locomotion or in producing food-bearing currents. Tapered tufts of fused cilia are *cirri*, strong bristlelike organelles functioning as locomotor legs. Fused cilia from several rows form *membranelles*, tiny paddles which create an extra-strong beat.

12 · 37 Surface organelles and cilia *in ciliate protozoa, diagrammatic. A, cross section through portion of* Paramecium *surface; in surface view the pellicle has a hexagonal pattern, with a depression in each hexagon. B, surface view of* Stentor, *showing portions of two adjacent ciliary rows, each accompanied by a myofibril. The cilia are drawn to illustrate their wavelike, metachronous beat. In C, the triangular basal portion of each membranelle is an anchor lying in the surface cytoplasm of the organism. D and E show the organelle portions projecting beyond the cell surfaces.*

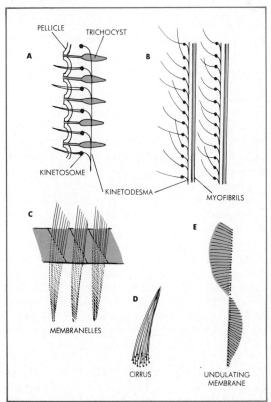

PELLICLE   TRICHOCYST

A

KINETOSOME

KINETODESMA

B

MYOFIBRILS

C

MEMBRANELLES

D

CIRRUS

E

UNDULATING MEMBRANE

276

THE WORLD OF LIFE

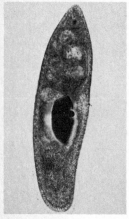
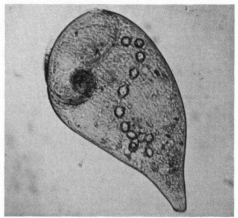

A, courtesy of Carolina Biological Supply Company.

12 · 38 Ciliates. *A, Paramecium caudatum, stained to reveal the macronucleus (large dark central body) and the micronucleus (small dark body partly overlapping the macronucleus on one side). B, Stentor coeruleus, from life. Note gullet region (dark spiral), peristome area ringed by membranelles (large ciliary ring curving into gullet), macronuclear chain, and holdfast (partly contracted at end opposite gullet). Faint rows of body cilia are also visible.*

Most ciliates possess a permanent gullet, and this mouth area is often equipped with variously complex systems of membranelles (Fig. 12.38). Food vacuoles migrate over a more or less definite path within the ciliate body, and digestive remains are egested at a fixed point, the *cytopyge*, often located in or near the gullet. Contractile vacuoles occur at fixed positions near the body surface, and in many cases definite cytoplasmic channels form an internal drainage system leading to the contractile vacuoles.

Ciliates are always multinucleate. They possess at least one and often many (up to several hundred) *micronuclei*, and at least one or many (up to several dozen) *macronuclei* (see Fig. 12.38). The micronuclei contain typical chromosomes but the macronuclei do not, at least not in the usual identifiable form. In the microscope the genetic substance of a macronucleus appears as a homogeneous clump of material. Micronuclei produce and exert long-range control over the macronuclei, and they are also the principal controllers of sexual processes. Macronuclei govern all metabolic and developmental functions, and they are directly responsible for the maintenance of the visible traits of the organism. Micronuclei may be lost or removed and a ciliate may survive without difficulty as a vegetative individual, which may even

continue to divide vegetatively. However, if the macronuclei are removed or lost, even if the micronuclei are still present, all structures such as gullet, membranelles, cirri, contractile vacuoles, and body cilia degenerate and the organism dies. Even so, it can be shown that all macronuclear functions are ultimately determined by the genes in the micronuclear chromosomes.

The evolution of ciliates appears to have been characterized by a progressive increase in the complexity of the ciliary apparatus and the mouth structures. For example, primitive forms such as *Prorodon* possess only simple cilia distributed uniformly over the whole body, and the mouth is a small, shallow depression at one end (Fig. 12.39). The mouth in

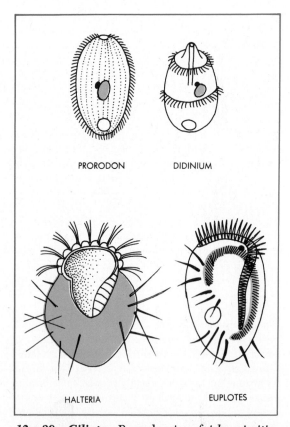

12 · 39 Ciliates. Prorodon *is a fairly primitive ciliate, with uniform body cilia and a simple mouth. In Didinium the mouth is at the tip of a proboscis; in addition to the rings of cilia shown here, an otherwise uniform body ciliation is also present (but not indicated). Halteria and Euplotes are advanced types; simple cilia are absent, but various kinds of membranelles and cirri are situated in specific regions.*

Didinium is more specialized, being equipped with an extensible proboscis by means of which the organism may swallow a paramecium whole. *Paramecium* itself is a somewhat more advanced type. In this best known of all ciliates the body ciliation is still simple and uniform, but it possesses a deep, funnel-shaped gullet with a wall lined by sets of membranelles and an undulating membrane (see Fig. 12.38). A complex gullet as well as a more elaborate ciliation is in evidence in types such as *Stentor*. This large, trumpet-shaped, and beautifully pigmented form possesses a conspicuous band of membranelles ringing the gullet area, in addition to simple, uniformly distributed body cilia. In the most advanced ciliates the general body ciliation is reduced or even absent altogether, but specialized membranelles, cirri, or other compound ciliary organelles are present in various surface regions. For example, *Euplotes* uses cirri on the underside of its flattened body as miniature legs, and *Halteria* uses long surface bristles as tiny stilts in a jumping form of locomotion (see Fig. 12.39).

Among the most complex of all ciliates, and thus among the most elaborately organized of all known cells, are forms such as *Cycloposthium* (Fig. 12.40). This intestinal commensal of mammals again lacks general body ciliation but possesses complex groups of membranelles in several surface regions. Moreover, its interior organelles include skeletal supports, virtually a complete alimentary "system" with a permanent rectal tube, a "neuromuscular system" composed of numerous sets of neurofibrils and myofibrils, and an "excretory system" of several contractile vacuoles.

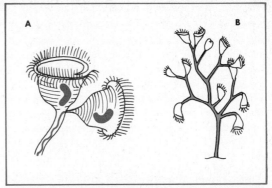

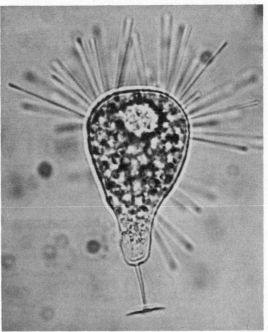

12 · 41 Sessile ciliates. *A, daughter individuals of* Vorticella *just after fission. One daughter inherits the stalk of the parent (with spiral myoneme); the other develops a posterior ciliary girdle and will migrate away and settle elsewhere via a newly formed stalk. B, Sketch of the colonial ciliate* Epistylis. *C, photo of a suctorian. Note attached cell body and the sucking tentacles.*

12 · 40 Cycloposthium, *one of the most complex ciliates and most complex type of cell of all kinds. The whole structural complexity of this ciliate cannot become apparent, however, in a sketch such as this.*

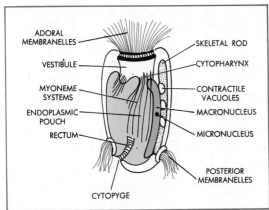

ADORAL MEMBRANELLES
VESTIBULE
MYONEME SYSTEMS
ENDOPLASMIC POUCH
RECTUM
CYTOPYGE
SKELETAL ROD
CYTOPHARYNX
CONTRACTILE VACUOLES
MACRONUCLEUS
MICRONUCLEUS
POSTERIOR MEMBRANELLES

Although most ciliates are motile, some are solitary or colonial sessile forms (Fig. 12.41). For example, *Vorticella* is a stalked solitary type, with a myofibrillike contractile organelle in its stalk. Branched colonies are produced by *Epistylis* and related genera. Sessile ciliates also include the *suctorians*. These trap prey by means of tentacles and, by some still poorly understood process, they suck the contents of the prey through the tentacles into their bodies. Mature suctorians lack body cilia but such cilia do appear in the offspring, which are budded off the parent cells. The buds then swim about for a time with the aid of their cilia, then settle and transform into new sessile adults without cilia.

The foregoing account clearly suggests that protozoa specifically and Protista generally are far from "simple." Their evolutionary histories are long and they may thus be primitive, and many of them have remained microscopic in size. Yet in this very primitiveness and smallness lies perhaps their most remarkable attribute; namely, that despite being limited to the confines of single cells they can be as diverse, varied, and complex in the microsphere of life as only very few groups of far larger organisms can be in the macrosphere.

REVIEW QUESTIONS

1. What are the unifying features of the Protista? Why should the various protistan groups no longer be classified simply as "plants" and "animals"? Describe the probable ancestral type from which Protista are believed to have evolved.

2. On what basis may it be assumed that ancestral protists probably could obtain nutrients by more than one method? What states of existence could early protists probably exhibit? Define each of these states and give specific examples of each.

3. List specific examples of unicellular and multicellular algae exhibiting each of the states of existence. Which protistan group probably gave rise to the Metaphyta? What is the basis for such an assumption?

4. What are the group characteristics of the algae? What are the special characteristics of the green-line, brown-line, and red-line algal groups? Review here the (a) pigments, (b) food-storage compounds, and (c) cell-wall compounds of these organisms.

5. What is the probable evolutionary significance of pairs of algae where one is photosynthetic and the other not? Give specific examples of such pairs for three or four algal phyla.

6. In what ways are (a) charophytes and (b) euglenophytes similar to chlorophytes and in what ways are they different?

7. Describe the characteristics of chrysophytes generally and of each chrysophyte class specifically. What groups are included among the Pyrrophyta and what features identify each of these groups?

8. Review the identifying features of brown algae and of red algae.

9. Review the structural characteristics of fungi generally. What are the possible evolutionary relations of this phylum to other Protista? Name the main groups within the fungi and the possible evolutionary relations of these groups to one another.

10. Describe the general characteristics of the various fungal classes. What different types of fruiting bodies are encountered among the Euascomycetes? What are Fungi Imperfecti? Lichens?

11. What differentiates the classes of slime molds? Review the life cycles of these organisms. What justifies the inclusion of slime molds within the Protista? Which features of slime molds are protozoalike and which are funguslike?

12. Define protozoa taxonomically and give analogous definitions for each of the four main subgroups. Distinguish protozoa and (a) other protists, (b) Metazoa. What states of existence are exhibited by (a) fungi, (b) slime molds, (c) protozoa?

13. Review the possible evolutionary relations of protozoan groups to one another and to other organisms. Describe the general structural characteristics of protozoan cells. What cytoplasmic and nuclear organelles are typical of such cells?

14. Describe the characteristics of various representatives of the Mastigophora and the Sarcodina. Describe the life cycle of the malarial parasite *Plasmodium*.

15. What is the general structure of a ciliate? What are cirri, membranelles, and undulating membranes? How does gullet structure vary in different ciliate groups? Distinguish micronuclei and macronuclei (a) structurally, (b) functionally.

COLLATERAL READINGS

Alexopoulos, C. J.: "Introductory Mycology," Wiley, New York, 1952. Recommended for further background reading on fungi.

Bonner, J. T.: A Colony of Cells, *Sci. American*, May, 1950. A study of the green alga *Volvox*.

————: "The Cellular Slime Molds," Princeton, Princeton, N.J. 1959. This book reviews the extensive research done on these interesting organisms, much of it by the author himself.

————: How Slime Molds Communicate, *Sci.*

American, Aug., 1963. An examination of the mechanism by which solitary amoebae of slime molds aggregate into pseudoplasmodia.

Brook, A. J.: Water Blooms, *New Biol.*, vol. 13, 1957. An article on the waxing and waning of algal life in water.

Doyle, W. T.: "Nonvascular Plants: Form and Function," Wadsworth, Belmont, Calif., 1964. This paperback reviews the biology of all protistan groups except the protozoa. Recommended.

Emerson, R.: Molds and Man, *Sci. American*, Jan., 1952. The importance of harmful and beneficial fungi for man is discussed by a noted mycologist.

Fogg, G. E.: Famous Plants—Chlorella, *New Biol.*, vol. 15, 1953. An alga used widely in biological research is dealt with in detail.

Gray, W. D.: "The Relation of Fungi to Human Affairs," Holt, New York, 1959. A more extensive coverage of roughly the same topic dealt with in the article by Emerson, above.

Hall, R. P.: "Protozoology," Prentice-Hall, Englewood Cliffs, N.J., 1953. An introductory text on protozoa.

Hyman, L.: "The Invertebrates," vol. 1, "Protozoa through Ctenophora," McGraw-Hill, New York, 1940. A detailed, advanced-level account of Protozoa is given in the third chapter of this important treatise.

Ingold, C. T.: Famous Plants—The Mushroom, *New Biol.*, vol. 18, 1955. An interesting article dealing with the most important of all fungi.

Jahn, T. L., and F. F. Jahn: "How to Know the Protozoa," William C. Brown, Dubuque, Iowa, 1949.

This book greatly facilitates the identification and characterization of these protists.

Jane, F. W.: Famous Plant-Animal—Euglena, *New Biol.*, vol. 19, 1955. A short biology of a commonly used laboratory alga.

Lamb, I. M.: Lichens, *Sci. American*, Oct., 1959. The biology and ecology of these symbiotic alga-fungus combinations are examined.

Milne, L. J., and M. J. Milne: The Eelgrass Catastrophe, *Sci. American*, Jan., 1951. An account of an epidemic of labyrinthulae among eelgrasses.

Milner, H. W.: Algae as Food, *Sci. American*, Oct., 1953. The title gives an adequate description of the subject matter.

Newton, L.: Famous Plants—Fucus, *New Biol.*, vol. 17, 1954. A study of the most common of the coastal brown algae.

Niederhauser, J. S., and W. C. Cobb: The Late Blight of Potatoes, *Sci. American*, May, 1959. The nature and control of a serious fungus pest are discussed.

Russell, P. F.: The Eradication of Malaria, *Sci. American*, June, 1952. Problems in the control of this widespread sporozoan parasite are examined.

Smith, G. M.: "Cryptogamic Botany," 2d ed., vol. 1, "Algae and Fungi," McGraw-Hill, New York, 1955. All Protista except the protozoa are described in detail in this comprehensive volume.

Wichterman, R.: "The Biology of Paramecium," McGraw-Hill, New York, 1953. Highly recommended not only for further data on this ciliate but also for additional background on protozoa generally.

CHAPTER 13
METAPHYTA

At some points during their evolutionary history, the Protista gave rise to the two largest groups of organisms now in existence, the *Metaphyta* and the *Metazoa*. There can be little doubt that both groups have had protistan, not moneran origins. The cell structure is typically protistan, and flagellate, amoeboid, and sporine states of existence are common. Sperms and many integumentary and sensory cells are flagellate (or ciliate); eggs, mesenchyme cells, and blood and connective tissue cells are actually or potentially amoeboid; and the vast bulk of the metaphytan and metazoan body is sporine, that is, composed of nonmotile cells which divide during their vegetative life.

Metaphyta and Metazoa are distinguished from Protista in their organ and organ-system levels of organization, in possessing reproductive structures that are at least tissues and in most cases organs, and in developing via distinct embryonic stages. Additional differences are reproductive and will be discussed in Chap. 27. The two groups are distinguished from each other in that Metaphyta do not but Metazoa typically do possess larval stages. Also, Metaphyta are photosynthetic and sessile, whereas Metazoa are heterotrophic and motile either in the larval or the adult stage or in both.

Metazoa certainly evolved very much earlier than the Metaphyta. The latter arose only some 350 million years ago and thus represent the newest major branch of life.

GENERAL CHARACTERISTICS

The category Metaphyta comprises two phyla, the *Bryophyta,* or moss plants, and the *Tracheophyta,* or vascular plants. In rather general terms, the probable protistan ancestors of the category as a whole can be pinpointed comparatively well. Metaphyta appear to be descended from early sporine green algae which also gave rise to the complex sporine green algae of today. The tissue-level construction of these advanced green algae is repeated in the Metaphyta, and the latter subsequently have added the organ and organ-system levels as well. Moreover, like such algae, metaphytes possess *chlorophylls a* and *b, carotenoid* and *xanthophyll* pigments of nearly identical type, cell walls made of *cellulose* and *pectic substances,* food stores in the form of *starch,* and two *flagella* of the whiplash type in motile cells (or multiples of two in certain advanced metaphytes).

Directly or indirectly, most characteristics distinguishing the Metaphyta uniquely from the Protista are adaptations to terrestrial ways of life. For example, in the absence of support against gravity by the buoyant action of water, Metaphyta possess specialized *skeletal tissues* not present in any of the Protista. Such tissues reach their most advanced form in the sclerenchymas and woods of the tracheophytes. The requirement of mechanical support is met additionally by the generally *upright, radial* construction of metaphytes, though this is not an invariable feature. Such a design distributes the weight equally around the vertical axis and permits lower body portions to support upper ones directly.

In the absence of open water around all surfaces, Metaphyta possess specialized *absorbing tissues* projecting into soil. These are either *rhizoids* or more elaborate *roots*. Since such structures are present only in specific regions of the plants, metaphytes possess more or less specialized nutrient-distributing or *conducting tissues,* the most highly developed being the *vascular* tissues.

Permanent exposure to air introduces the problem of desiccation. Metaphytes minimize this problem through *waxy cuticles* on exposed surfaces, which let light pass but not water or atmospheric gases. But since gases must be exchanged with the environment, impervious cuticles cannot form a complete, unbroken coating over the external surfaces. Metaphyta actually possess gas-transmitting surface pores, or *stomata* (see Chap. 7).

Adaptive responses to the dangers of desiccation are in evidence also in the structures and processes of reproduction and in the life cycles. The reproductive structures arise from single cells, but at maturity they are always *organs* composed of at least two specialized tissues. One is an external sterile tissue, one or more cell layers thick, which protects against desiccation, and the other is an internal spore- or sex-cell-producing tissue. Mature spores are nonmotile and encapsulated in all Metaphyta. Female sex cells, eggs, are equally nonmotile. Male sex cells, sperms, are naked and motile in primitive metaphytes, and release of such cells is timed to coincide with wet or rainy conditions. In advanced metaphytes even the male sex cells are nonmotile and their release has become independent of external water. The general sessilism of metaphytes has been accompanied by a loss of kinetosomes from all cells excepting only those sperm cells that are motile. Centrioles are absent as well in the cells of most metaphytes.

The life cycle of metaphytes always includes a distinct *embryonic phase,* a characteristic not generally encountered in any of the Protista. (In earlier classifications the Metaphyta have actually been regarded as a subkingdom "Embryophyta" within the kingdom of plants, with Thallophyta as the other subkingdom; see Table 1, Chap. 2). The embryo introduces a *developmental* phase into the life cycle and thereby provides the time necessary for the elaboration of the many specialized tissues of the mature metaphyte. Since such internal elaboration is an adaptation to terrestrial conditions, the plant embryo too may be considered to be an evolutionary response to the requirements of life on land.

Finally, Metaphyta invariably undergo a life cycle consisting of two different, successive adult generations. One produces sex cells only, and it is called the *gametophyte generation.* The sex cells participate in fertilization and a new adult develops thereafter. This adult produces spores only, and it is therefore called the *sporophyte generation.* Spores subsequently grow into new gametophytes. The mature plants of these two generations are structured quite differently, both externally and internally; they represent excellent examples of polymorphism. As will become apparent in later contexts, life cycles characterized in this manner by an *alternation of generations* originated among the Protista, in adaptation to their own problems of aquatic life. Metaphyta then inherited such life cycles and made them one of the foundations of their signal success as terrestrial plants.

There are excellent reasons to believe that Metaphyta actually became terrestrial not because their ancestors might have "preferred" to live on land but because the ancestors had to become adapted to terrestrial conditions if they were to survive as aquatic

forms. Undoubtedly, the algal ancestors occasionally experienced prolonged droughts, not an unusual hazard in freshwater habitats. Various evolutionary responses to these hazards then permitted them to survive through periods of drought and thus allowed them to persist as basically aquatic organisms. Almost incidentally, however, gradual perfection of the adaptations to *temporary* terrestrial living must eventually have produced plants able to survive without open water altogether. Such plants could then be *permanently* terrestrial.

At least two terrestrial groups must have evolved from the green algae separately and independently. One culminated in the bryophytes, the other in the tracheophytes.

BRYOPHYTES

PHYLUM BRYOPHYTA:
MOSS PLANTS (25,000 SPECIES)

> *Class Bryopsida:* mosses
> *Class Hepaticopsida:* liverworts
> *Class Anthoceropsida:* hornworts

The members of this cosmopolitan phylum generally live in more or less shady, perpetually moist places, where the danger of drying out is minimized and where rain water is amply available as a medium for the flagellate sperms. Bryophytes often inhabit bogs and swamps, the peat moss *Sphagnum* being particularly common in such areas. Some bryophytes grow in the cold regions of the world, high on mountains and in the tundra; others grow in deserts, near hot springs, and in the tropics. In tropical rain forests, bryophytes occur abundantly as epiphytes on the leaves, branches, and trunks of trees. Several species of bryophytes are completely aquatic, being adapted secondarily to a floating or submerged life in fresh water. But bryophytes do not include any marine forms.

Terrestrial bryophytes frequently are important soil formers and soil protectors. They may settle where lichens have begun to convert bare rock surfaces into small patches of soil and, by their metabolism and decay after death, bryophytes then contribute to a further transformation of rock into soil. Moreover, many bryophytes form dense, soil-covering carpets rather rapidly. Such carpets not only prevent erosion of soil but also aid in maintaining its water content; water is retained well between the closely spaced plants. In addition, many bryophytes absorb water directly through their leaves, which spares the water supplies of soil. In their own

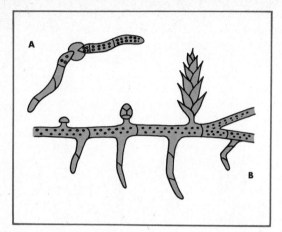

13 · 1 Germinating spore *of a moss* (A), *showing rhizoid and growing protonema; B, protonema of a moss, showing rhizoids, buds, and young shoots.*

way, therefore, bryophytes play an important role in the small-scale economy of nature.

As a group, bryophytes are distinguished from tracheophytes by a life cycle in which the gametophyte generation is always *dominant*. This generation lasts longer, is physically larger and more conspicuous, is nutritionally independent, and in general represents the "main" plant. Casual reference to a "moss," for example, is a reference to the gametophyte generation. By contrast, the sporophyte generation is small and short-lived, and this plant is invariably *attached* to the gametophyte. Moreover, it is nutritionally dependent on the gametophyte, drawing many or all required inorganic and some required organic nutrients from it. Thus the sporophyte is essentially a parasite.

Class Bryopsida

This class is probably the most primitive, and early mosses may have been ancestral to the other bryophyte classes.

The gametophyte body of a moss generally consists of two parts (Fig. 13.1). One is a branched network of green filaments lying on or close to the ground. Each such filament, rather reminiscent of some of the filamentous green algae, is a *protonema*. Extending from it in places into the soil are filamentous, nongreen *rhizoids*. The second and structurally quite different part of the body consists of one or more upright green *shoots*, which develop from buds growing upward on the protonema. A shoot is composed of a *stem* to which are attached radially

arranged *leaves*. At maturity, a shoot also bears terminal *sex organs*. The common moss *Funaria* illustrates this typical organization rather well. From the protonema of *Funaria* extend numerous branched, multicellular rhizoids. Upright shoots, from 1 to 3 cm high, grow from the protonema where the rhizoids join it.

The stem of the shoot is composed of an outer *epidermis*, one cell layer thick, green, and without stomata (Fig. 13.2). Underlying this covering tissue is a *cortex* consisting of several layers of parenchyma cells. These contain chlorophyll only during the early stages of shoot development. The center of the

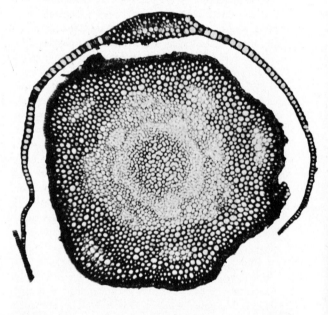

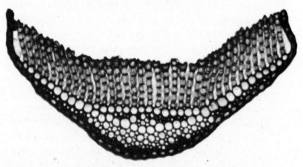

13 · 2 The moss Polytrichum. *Top, cross section through a stem. Note the thick-walled cortex cells and the thin-walled inner cells. Bottom, cross section through a leaf. Note the columns of cells along the upper surface and the air spaces between the columns.*

stem is filled with elongated, thin-walled cells in which the cell substance degenerates during development. Such cells, reminiscent of the vascular elements of tracheophytes, undoubtedly function in water and nutrient transport. The leaves of *Funaria* have a well-defined midrib which contains several layers of sclerenchymatous supporting cells. A single layer of green cells on each side of the midrib forms the leaf blade. Other mosses possess considerably more complex leaves. In the pigeon-wheat moss *Polytrichum*, for example, a leaf consists of many layers of differently specialized cells. As indicated in Fig. 13.2, such a leaf also contains air spaces near the upper surface which permit even deep-lying green cells to exchange gases directly with the external atmosphere.

As a shoot matures, sex organs develop at its tip. Male organs are *antheridia*, female organs, *archegonia*. In *Funaria* and many other mosses, a single plant may form both types of sex organs. In another group of mosses (for example, *Polytrichum*), male and female organs develop on different plants. An egg is produced, fertilized, and then retained within an archegonium. By repeated division such a fertilized egg develops into the *embryo* of the sporophyte generation. The sporophyte thus grows atop the shoot of the gametophyte (Fig. 13.3).

A mature sporophyte consists of an expanded *foot*, which anchors the base of the sporophyte to the tip of the gametophyte; a *stalk;* and a terminal spore-producing organ, or *sporangium*. The external tissue of a sporophyte is an epidermis which usually contains stomata. Parenchymatous cells make up the interior of the stalk, and the column of such cells also continues into the sporangium, where it forms a central *columella*. Between it and the sporangial epidermis is the spore-producing tissue. During its early development, the sporophyte is green and depends on the gametophyte mainly for water and mineral nutrients. But as the sporangium matures, chlorophyll largely disintegrates and the sporophyte is then nutritionally dependent completely on the gametophyte.

A ripe sporangium consists of an outer cup-shaped *capsule* covered by a *lid*. The rim of the capsule under the lid is studded with flexible *teeth*. When the sporangium is dry and brittle, the lid falls away and the mature spores within the capsule become exposed. Spore dispersal is accomplished partly by wind and partly by the teeth around the rim of the capsule. These teeth are hygroscopic, and they flex into and out of the capsule with changes in humidity. Thus they may flip spores out of the capsule (see Fig. 13.3).

Among mosses of more than small-scale significance ecologically are the peat mosses, all members of the genus *Sphagnum*. These plants live in swamps and

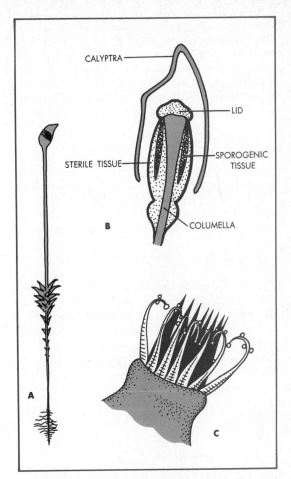

13 · 3 **Moss gametophyte** *with attached sporophyte (A). Note spore capsule at upper tip. B, detail of spore capsule. C, the teeth along the rim of the spore capsule at a stage of spore dispersal. The calyptra has fallen away at this stage.*

bogs all over the world, but particularly in the tundra and in colder regions generally. Metabolic activities make the plants and the water in which they grow quite acid (pH 3.7 to 4.9), too acid actually for most decay bacteria. Thus, old plants pile up in beds of considerable thickness, filling in swamp areas and forming the main organic component of peat. The gametophyte body of these plants is specialized particularly for water storage. The protonema is a flat, broad sheet bearing a highly branched system of long shoots (Fig. 13.4). In the cortex of the shoots are thick-walled cells in which the living substance disintegrates during cell development. At maturity, therefore, only water-storing hulls remain. The leaves analogously contain large cells of which only the walls remain in the mature plant. Water again fills the interior spaces (and these communicate with the external environment via a pore in each cell wall). This spongy, water-holding property has made peat mosses useful commercially, for example, as packing material for goods that must be kept moist.

Class Hepaticopsida

Whereas mosses are characteristically vertical and radially symmetrical, liverworts are prostrate, horizontal plants with clearly differentiated dorsal and ventral surfaces. On the basis of their body organization, two groups of liverworts may be distinguished.

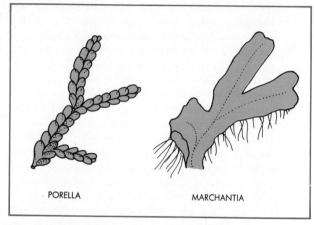

13 · 5 *Comparison of general body shapes of a foliose liverwort* (Porella) *and a thallose liverwort* (Marchantia).

13 · 4 *Branched shoot of the peat moss* Sphagnum (A). *The protonema is not shown. Note the pendant branches and the attached sporophytes. B, C, whole view and detail of a* Sphagnum *leaf. Note the thin, living, chloroplast-containing cells and, between rows of these, the nonliving, boxlike, air- and water-containing hulls of cells.*

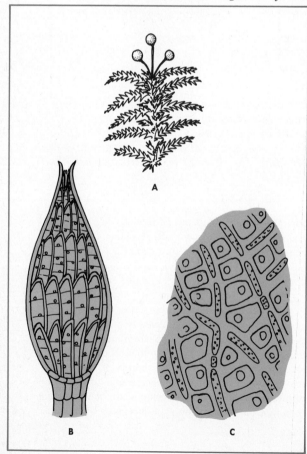

One is said to be *foliose;* that is, the body is leafy as in mosses. The leaves here are almost always without midribs. The other group is said to be *thallose;* that is, the body forms a sheet, or *thallus,* flat on the ground (Fig. 13.5).

Foliose liverworts are rather elaborate externally but relatively uncomplicated internally. For example, *Porella* is a leafy liverwort often epiphytic on trees. The plant possesses a horizontal stem which usually bears three rows of leaves, one row ventral and two rows dorsolateral. The stem is composed of a central cylinder of large, thin-walled cells and of an outer cortical tissue containing smaller cells with somewhat thicker walls. A leaf consists of a single layer of polygonal, parenchymatous cells. The sex organs of *Porella* arise on the dorsal surfaces. Antheridia form where leaves join the stem, and archegonia are usually terminal.

In contrast to foliose types like *Porella,* thallose liverworts are relatively simple externally but are organized quite elaborately internally. *Riccia* and *Marchantia* are good illustrations. The thallus of these plants is characteristically ribbon-shaped and lobed, with a median furrow along the upper surface (see Fig. 13.5). From the underside project numerous rhizoids. At the forward margin of a thallus is a *growing point,* consisting of a cluster of a few apical cells. As these divide off new cells to both sides, two lobes are formed. And as these lobes continue to enlarge, the growing point comes to be located in a notch between the lobes. Later the cells of the growing point may become separated into two groups, each of which may then initiate the formation of a thallus branch. A growth pattern of this sort is said to be *dichotomous;* it leads to the formation of two equal branches from one main branch.

Internally, a thallus is stratified dorsoventrally into three distinct zones, each composed of one or more tissues (Fig. 13.6). The bottom zone is largely absorptive and consists mainly of nongreen rhizoids. The middle zone is formed from nongreen parenchyma and it functions in storage and conduction of nutrients. The upper zone is photosynthetic and includes elaborate air chambers and air pores. In types like *Marchantia,* the location of the internal air chambers is marked externally by fine diamond-shaped lines on the surface of the thallus. Some thallose liverworts have become simplified secondarily in their internal organization. In forms like *Sphaerocarpos,* for example, the thallus is membranous and only one cell layer thick.

Sex organs develop in various ways and locations in different thallose liverworts (see Chap. 27). However, in all liverworts, foliose or thallose, the sporophytes formed after fertilization again remain attached to the archegonia, as in mosses. Such sporophytes similarly consist of foot, stalk, and sporangium, though the stalk is quite short and the whole sporophyte is therefore smaller than in mosses (Fig. 13.7). Embryo sporophytes are green but later they lose most of their chlorophyll. Mature sporophytes then depend on the gametophytes for nutrients. When a sporangium becomes ripe, it breaks open, exposing the spores. These are scattered partly by wind, partly by *elaters,* characteristic of liverworts and hornworts. Elaters

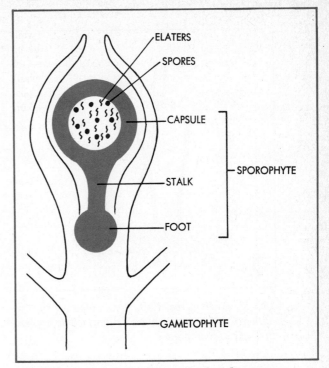

13·7 *Sporophyte* (color) *of the liverwort* Porella.

are thin, elongated, hygroscopic filaments possessing spirally thickened inner walls. Interspersed among the spores, elaters twist and coil as they dry and such jerky motions flip spores out of a sporangium.

Class Anthoceropsida

The hornworts are characterized by thallose gametophytes. These are irregularly scalloped along the margins, but they are without notches and without surface furrows or midribs. Rhizoids are present on the underside (Fig. 13.8). Internally, the tissues of the thallus are not highly specialized. The cells are parenchymatous, and each possesses a single large chloroplast with a conspicuous pyrenoid (as in green algae). In this respect hornworts differ sharply from the other bryophyte classes, in which the cells possess numerous chloroplasts each and do not contain pyrenoids. The central portions of a hornwort thallus are usually several cell layers thick, but there are no air chambers or air pores.

The best known hornwort is probably *Anthoceros,* fairly common on damp soils. Sex organs of both types are formed within the same individual of *Anthoceros,* embedded deep in the thallus. In contrast to the simply constructed gametophyte, the sporophyte of *Anthoceros* is differentiated to a remarkably high degree. The foot is anchored within the thallus. A

13·6 *Internal structure of a thallus of* Marchantia.

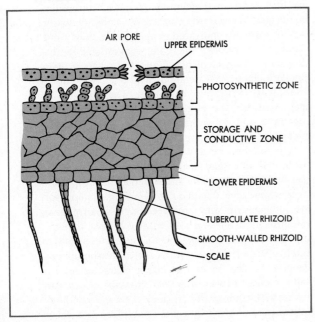

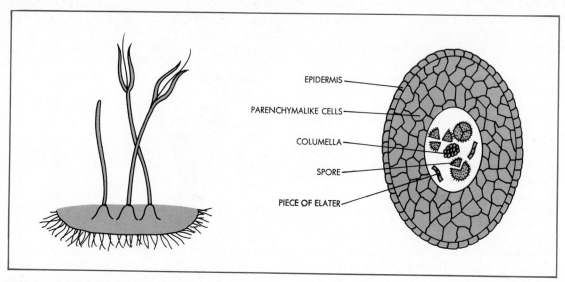

EPIDERMIS

PARENCHYMALIKE CELLS

COLUMELLA

SPORE

PIECE OF ELATER

13 · 8 Anthoceros. *Left, whole view of thallus with attached sporophytes. Right, cross section through a sporophyte.*

stalk connects the foot with a rod-shaped sporangium, which projects upward from the thallus to a height of several inches (see Fig. 13.8). This sporangium contains a central cylindrical columella and surrounding spore-forming tissue with elaters. Surrounding this tissue in turn is a green parenchymatous cortex, and covering the whole on the outside is an epidermis. The cells in this layer secrete conspicuous waxy cuticles on their outer surfaces. Also present in the epidermis are stomata, formed by pairs of guard cells as in vascular plants. These stomatal pores lead into air spaces between the cells of the underlying cortex.

A sporophyte retains its chlorophyll throughout its existence and therefore requires only inorganic supplies from the gametophyte. Mature sporophytes split open lengthwise from their upper ends down, and spores may then escape with the aid of the elaters.

TRACHEOPHYTES: GENERAL CHARACTERISTICS

PHYLUM TRACHEOPHYTA: VASCULAR PLANTS (260,000 + SPECIES)

Subphylum PSILOPSIDA: psilopsids (3 species)
Subphylum LYCOPSIDA: club mosses (900 species)
Subphylum SPHENOPSIDA: horsetails (25 species)
Subphylum PTEROPSIDA

Class Filicineae: ferns (10,000 species)
Class Gymnospermae: coniferous plants (700 species)

Class Angiospermae: flowering plants (250,000 species)

Internal evidence from living tracheophytes as well as fossil data (see Chap. 32) indicate that ancestral Psilopsida probably were the first members of the phylum, evolved in some independent way from an unknown green algal stock. Early psilopsids in turn appear to have given rise to four separate branch lines, represented today by the four subphyla listed above. Of these, the first three came to flourish soon after they evolved but then they declined. Today they are little more than evolutionary relics. Pteropsida, on the contrary, started out relatively inconspicuously but subsequently increased in importance slowly and steadily. At present they are unquestionably the dominant group of plants. Flowering plants in particular include more species than all other Metaphyta and plantlike Protista combined. These plants in fact constitute the largest group of photosynthetic organisms and, after the insects, the second largest group of all types of organisms.

The phylum as a whole is identified uniquely by independent and *dominant sporophytes,* and by gametophytes that are either independent or dependent but never dominant. Where the gametophytes are independent they are exceedingly small plants, reminiscent in general structure of simple thallose bryophytes such as *Anthoceros.* Casual reference to a tracheophyte is always a reference to the sporophyte generation. The phylum is further characterized by the presence of two distinct and specialized vascular tissues in the sporophytes, namely, the water-conducting *xylem* and the food-conducting *phloem.* A third unique feature of the phylum is that the body of virtually all sporophytes is clearly subdivided into *roots, stems,* and *leaves,* each such body part representing a true organ.

Tracheophytes possess a vertical main axis and a conspicuous radial symmetry around this axis. Such an organization makes possible efficient nutrient absorption from all sides around the plant, and it also provides a mechanically balanced body construction; the plant can be anchored safely and can obtain maximum internal support along the vertical axis. Many tracheophytes taper upward, which allows the greatest weight to rest on the broadest foundation. In addition, specially developed supporting structures are present: collenchyma, sclerenchyma, and the cellulose and lignin of wood. In effect, the size of the plant need be limited only by the inherent strength of its supporting materials. This strength is comparatively much greater than that of animal skeletons; woody plants include the largest living things of all, living and extinct animals not excepted. Thus, tracheophytes have solved the gravity problem far more efficiently than bryophytes, which solve it mainly by staying small and close to the ground. This solution serves well enough, to be sure, but the cost of such conservatism is lack of spectacular success on land.

Large size necessitates long-distance nutrient conduction. Moreover, because the plant is surrounded partly by air and partly by soil, the aerial and subterranean portions of the plant must differ in function if not also in structure. The characteristic root-stem-leaf organization of the tracheophyte is a specific adaptation to these requirements. Roots absorb from the ground; leaves photosynthesize; and stems interconnect, conduct, and support.

Surfaces are necessary for the absorption of raw materials. For a given mass of absorbing tissue, the best architectural arrangement is consequently that which offers the largest area. Indeed, roots are most often highly branched rather than thick and compact; and leaves, similarly, are flat and thin or needle-shaped. A large surface is also required for illumination by sunlight. However, the sun is not stationary but arcs across the sky every day. A given mass of stationary light-receiving tissue will therefore be illuminated most if it is subdivided into numerous flat, thin plates, and if these are set at many different angles. Leaves are actually spaced in this manner. In many plants, moreover, the leaves turn toward the sun if the heat is not too great and turn away from the sun if it is. Another well-known adaptation is the ability of tracheophytes to grow toward the light even if they are planted away from it (see Chap. 22).

Large surfaces for illumination and absorption also constitute large surfaces for evaporation, a potential disadvantage. However, the exposed aerial surfaces are coated with waxy cuticles which let sunlight through readily and prevent the escape of internal water. They also bar the entry or exit of gases from and to the atmosphere. Yet gas exchange must occur. The dilemma is resolved by the stomata, which permit gas exchange and therefore also a certain amount of evaporation. Nevertheless, the greater part of the exposed portions of the plant body is protected by wax and a large surface is still available for illumination. Waxy surfaces are additionally advantageous in that they allow rain or dew to run off.

In the stationary plant, in which water is vital and in which food cannot be produced during the night and often not during the winter either, storage of water and food is likely to be of major importance. Indeed, water storage is a function of every living tracheophyte cell. Every such cell is *succulent;* it contains a large amount of water, much of it in vacuoles. This condition also makes the cells highly *turgid.* The comparatively large amounts of water are confined by rigid cell walls and this constraint puts the water under considerable pressure. Such cellular turgor gives tissues additional mechanical support and permits even "soft" plant parts like leaves to maintain their shape well. But if water is in insufficient supply, succulence, turgor, and mechanical support may all become reduced and the plant may wilt.

To some extent, food storage too is a function of every living plant cell, parenchymatous cells most particularly. Moreover, many tracheophytes possess enlarged body parts with greatly proliferated parenchymatous tissues and adapted especially for food storage. Stems and roots are modified more frequently for this function than leaves, probably partly because leaves must produce food and cannot be spared for storing much of it; partly because massive food stores can be supported physically far better in the ground than in the air; and partly because leaves are temporary, relatively short-lived organs. Indeed, storage stems in many cases are underground, a location in which they may also aid in protecting the plant against drastic temperature fluctuations and in easing the problem of mechanical support.

Some of the principal types of modified stems are (Fig. 13.9): *rhizomes,* horizontal underground stems common particularly in primitive tracheophytes; *tubers,* locally expanded ends of rhizomes, often adapted for food storage, as in potatoes; *bulbs,* shortened, usually underground stems to which thickened storage leaves are attached, as in onions; *corms,* shortened, bulky, underground storage stems which

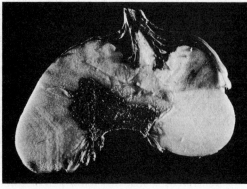

A   B   C   D

13 · 9   **Some types of stems.** *A, a bulb. The central vertical stem is surrounded by leaves, which form the bulk of the bulb. B, a corm. Leaves are borne at the top. C, a tuber. D, a runner.*

superficially resemble bulbs but which possess scalelike leaves on the outer surfaces, as in gladioli; *runners,* horizontal stems flat on the ground and supported by the ground, as in strawberries; and *twining stems,* which wind around upright or other objects and obtain support from them, as in beans.

Variant types of roots include (Fig. 13.10): *fibrous roots,* in which numerous branch roots lead off from the stem base into soil in all directions, as in grasses; *taproots,* single, thick, vertical storage roots from which small branch roots may lead off, as in carrots; *adventitious roots,* which sprout from any region of the plant (except a root), even from regions near the tip of the stem; *prop roots,* which are adventitious roots specially adapted to provide mechanical support, as in banyan trees and older corn plants; and *aerial roots,* not in contact with the ground at all but absorbing water from sources available above ground, as in the epiphytic orchids. Such roots have a many-layered epidermis composed of cells without living interior substance. The remaining walls are specialized for water uptake, prevention of water loss, and protection against mechanical injury.

These various examples suggest, and the prodigious success of tracheophytes clearly proves, that the basic structure of these plants is adapted very adequately to both the general and the specific character of their particular terrestrial environment. But a suitable body construction is only one requirement for a successful sessile way of terrestrial life. Another requirement is adaptability to potentially lethal changes in local weather, for a plant rooted to the ground cannot escape climatic extremes. It can only attempt to protect against them. Water poses the key problem here. In summer heat and in deserts, the plant is in danger of having too little internal water; and in winter or at high latitudes and altitudes there is

likely to be too much water, for water freezes and kills.

The heat problem is one of internal *water conservation,* and it affects the exposed stems and leaves far more than the underground roots. Tracheophytes living in dry, warm or hot climates are *xerophytes;* they are protected in various ways against excessive water loss by evaporation. For example, waxy cuticles over exposed surfaces are greatly thickened, sometimes becoming even thicker than the epidermal cells which secrete them. Stomata are often reduced in number and they may be located mostly or entirely on the underside of leaves, away from the direct sunlight. These undersurfaces are thus shaded and somewhat cooler, and the stomata are not so likely to become clogged by settling dust. Further, stomata may be sunk deep into microscopic epidermal pits, which provide shade except when the sun shines straight into them and again protect against clogging by dust (Fig. 13.11).

Under near-desert conditions, the rate of evaporation may nevertheless be too high. Water vaporization can be held down, however, by reduction of the *area* of exposed parts in proportion to their volume. Thus, plants may possess but a few large leaves (for example, ferns) or small scalelike or needle-shaped leaves. In the extreme case, well exemplified by cacti, leaves may be reduced to thorny spines and the function of food manufacture may be taken on largely by thick, massive stems. Exposure may also be reduced if the stems are underground, and we may note that horizontal rhizomes are particularly common in xerophytes. Water-storing capacity may be increased through bulky, succulent leaves, as in many ornamental house plants. Through adaptations such as these, tracheophytes are able to survive even in the hottest, driest regions provided that at least *some* water is available at *some* time. Quite a number of tracheophytes have overcome the water-conservation problem altogether by adapting secondarily to

PLATE XIII

B, courtesy of Carolina Biological Supply Company

24. Homobasidiomycetes.
A, puffball. B, stinkhorns.
C, bird's-nest fungi.
*The globular bodies within
the latter are reproductive
dispersal units.*

PLATE XIV

A, B, courtesy of Carolina Biological Supply Company

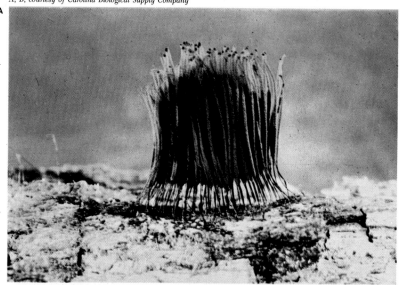

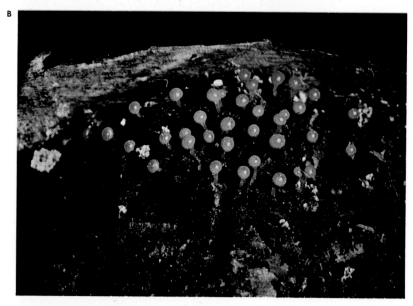

25. Fruiting bodies
of two types of slime molds.

PLATE XV

26. Cross section through a leaf.
*Note the upper and lower epidermis
(each with stomata); the densely packed
cells of the palisade mesophyll,
just underneath each epidermal layer;
the spongy mesophyll, filling
up most of the remaining interior space;
and the conspicuous main vein,
with xylem (red) and phloem (dark green)
forming a semicircular band
and with a layer of fiber tissue
(dark red) lying underneath this bank.*

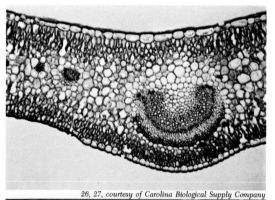

26, 27, courtesy of Carolina Biological Supply Company

27. Lycopodium.
*View of whole club mosses. Many of the plants
bear terminal, spore-sac-containing cones.*

PLATE XVI

28. Selaginella.
The leafy parts of Selaginella.

29. Equisetum.
A view of aerial portions. Note nodal and whorled arrangement of the green branches.

A   B   C

13 · 10 Some types of roots. *A, fibrous roots. B, taproots. C, prop roots.*

an aquatic habitat and living as *hydrophytes* (see Fig. 10.26).

Where water supplies are neither overly abundant nor overly sparse, as in much of the temperate zone, the plants are said to be *mesophytes*. Such plants must nevertheless cope with considerable fluctuations of climatic conditions. Thus, a summer day may be excessively hot and dry, and the mesophytic tracheophyte may droop and begin to wilt. But if water becomes available within a few days, conditions within the plant are soon restored to normal. In winter, by contrast, frost for even an hour is likely to kill; below the freezing point, free water not firmly bound in colloidal gels is transformed into ice crystals. Such crystals may tear and disrupt the structural framework of cells and this is why very low temperatures are potentially lethal.

Probably in response to yearly cold seasons or outright winters, tracheophytes have evolved major adaptations profoundly affecting their whole way of life. On the basis of these adaptations, we may distinguish three groups of vascular plants, namely, *perennials, biennials,* and *annuals.*

In perennials, major or all portions of the plant body persist through successive winters. At the approach of winter, such plants may manufacture large quantities of colloidal materials within their cells. Much of the living substance of cells may thereby become converted into a gel state. As a result, little water remains free inside cells and ice formation is forestalled successfully. In evergreen plant groups, such *winter hardening* is particularly effective. Even leaves can be retained, and vital processes carry on as in summer though at a slower pace (provided water replacement is not made impossible by frozen

conditions in other parts of the plant). Conifers like pines are good examples of evergreen perennials.

Other perennials are *deciduous* plants; they cannot protect their foliage against the cold and they shed leaves in the fall. But the rest of the plant

13 · 11 Adaptations to dry conditions. *Section of pine leaf showing sunken stoma (top center) and lobed parenchyma cells in interior. See also Plate I, 1 and Fig. 7.10, the latter showing section through leaf with thick waxy cuticle over epidermis.*

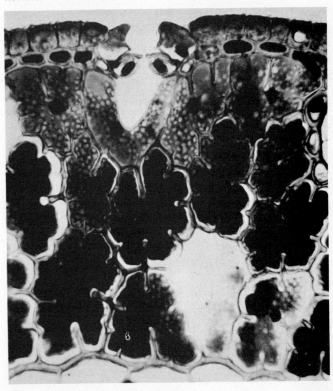

lives on. Buds and embryonic leaves have developed during the preceding summer, and these sprout the next spring into new foliage. In the absence of mature leaves during the cold season, little or no food can be produced. However, such plants accumulate food reserves at other seasons and store them in roots and stems. Flowering trees living in the temperate zone are familiar examples of deciduous perennials.

Still other perennials are soft-bodied and *herbaceous* (for example, asparagus, dandelions). In such plants, the leaves as well as the aerial parts of the stem die off in the fall. But the roots and a short underground piece of stem survive. Reserve foods in these underground body parts last through the winter and suffice in spring for the development of a new aerial shoot. Leaves and a mature stem then grow

from this shoot. Since the aerial portions of these plants persist only through a relatively short growing season, they never become very extensive; bulky wood is neither required nor formed and the plants remain nonwoody herbs.

The above patterns (Fig. 13.12) give evidence of an adaptive trend in perennials: it is more economical to retrench when life becomes difficult than to maintain elaborate aerial structures against heavy odds. This trend does not halt here, however. Winter retrenchment goes even further in biennial and annual herbaceous plants.

In biennials (for example, carrots), leaves die off in a first winter after they have manufactured extensive food reserves which are stored in bulky roots. The roots and portions of the shoot survive that winter, and from them a new plant develops the following spring. This second-year plant flowers and forms seeds. At the approach of the second winter the entire plant dies, roots included. Only the seeds survive, and these subsequently initiate a new two-year cycle. The annual plant (for example, wheat) flowers and produces seeds every year. The whole plant dies in the fall, and its seeds give rise to a new generation the following spring (see Fig. 13.12).

Evidently, vascular plants have found several workable solutions to the problem of cold. They may winterproof the whole body or some part of the

13 · 12 Survival patterns of plants. *In perennials such as conifers, the whole plant survives the winter. In deciduous perennials, foliage is shed in the cold season but the rest of the plant survives. In herbaceous perennials, only the roots and a small piece of stem survive the winter. Biennial plants retain only the roots and a small piece of stem during a first winter, and only seeds survive the second winter. In an annual, the whole plant dies every year and is perpetuated only by seeds.*

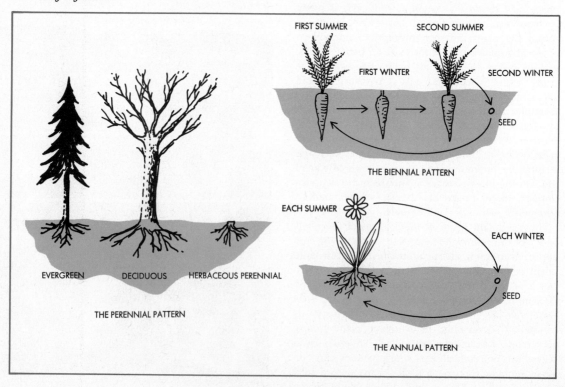

FIRST SUMMER   SECOND SUMMER

FIRST WINTER   SECOND WINTER

SEED

THE BIENNIAL PATTERN

EACH SUMMER   EACH WINTER

SEED

THE ANNUAL PATTERN

EVERGREEN   DECIDUOUS   HERBACEOUS PERENNIAL

THE PERENNIAL PATTERN

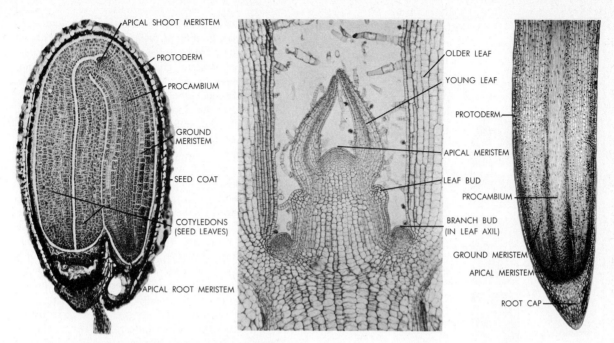

13 · 13   Meristems, *apical and primary. Left, longitudinal section through a seed, showing the embryo within. Middle, longitudinal section through a shoot apex. Right, longitudinal section through a root apex. In all cases, note the basic meristematic tissues and their position.*

body, or they may rely entirely and most economically on a handful of hardy cells, namely, seeds. These often contain as little as 5 per cent water and are therefore adapted excellently to withstand the rigors of winter.

Thus, in numerous and very elegant ways, tracheophytes have made the most of their difficult terrestrial habitat. Actually there are only two types of land environments in which a tracheophyte cannot live: the glacial regions, as at very high altitudes and latitudes, and the permanently arid regions, as in some deserts.

TRACHEOPHYTES: GROWTH AND STRUCTURE

PRIMARY GROWTH: STEM AND ROOT

A tracheophytic sporophyte begins its life history as a fertilized egg which divides and becomes a multicellular *embryo*. Such an embryo has the form of a tiny rod, with a *shoot apex* at one tip and a *root apex*

at the other (Fig. 13.13). At these apices, specific cells called *apical meristems* remain permanently embryonic. They continue to divide, and new cells formed by them are added behind each tip to the embryonic tissues already present. The whole embryo so continues to elongate.

New cells produced by the apical meristems soon become organized into three fundamental embryonic tissues, the *primary meristems*. These are the *protoderm* on the outside, the *procambium* in the center, and the *ground meristem* between the protoderm and procambium. As the embryo continues to lengthen, new primary meristems form just behind the tips and somewhat older primary meristems gradually come to be situated farther away from the tips. Such older primary meristems soon begin to specialize as adult stem and root tissues. A small zone immediately behind each apex is therefore always meristematic, and behind this zone the three embryonic tissues are always in process of developing into adult tissues. Thus, a lengthwise view of a shoot or a root exhibits an orderly sequence of zones corresponding to the stages each adult stem or root tissue has passed through during its development (Fig. 13.14).

The nature of the adult tissues formed from the three primary meristems has already been described in Chap. 7. Figure 13.15 shows which adult tissues are produced by which of the primary meristems.

In the stem region, the protoderm-derived epider-

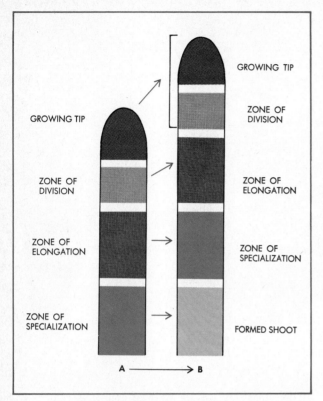

13 · 14 Lengthwise development of a growing shoot. *The condition depicted in A changes to that of B after a period of growth. Note how any given zone transforms into that originally below it. The growth pattern is comparable in a growing root.*

mis is cutinized and contains paired, green, stomata-enclosing guard cells. Wax cuticles and stomata are absent in the root, but present there are root-hair cells, usually in a distinct zone some distance behind the root apex. Root hairs are temporary structures. Ahead of the root-hair zone, hairs have not yet developed; behind it, they have already disappeared. In other words, the root-hair zone advances as the root apex advances. Also present in the root is a *root cap*, several layers of cells which envelop the root tip externally (Fig. 13.16). A root cap is formed by the apical root meristem. Such a cap is an important adaptive device, for as the root tip grows forward, hard soil grains would soon macerate unprotected meristem tissue. In the presence of a root cap, however, cap cells wear off instead and the growing tip is shielded effectively. New cap cells continue to be formed by the root meristem.

The adult cortex and the endodermis are formed from the embryonic ground meristem. In many tracheophytes the stem cortex is photosynthetic. The

endodermis may be reduced or absent in stems, but it is always present in roots. Passage cells without suberin coats are conspicuous here.

The procambium gives rise to three of the four adult tissues of the stele, namely, the pericycle (frequently reduced or absent in stems), the primary phloem, and the primary xylem (or primary wood). The fourth adult stelar tissue, pith, is a derivative of the ground meristem, not the procambium. These stelar tissues come to be arranged in different ways in the roots and stems of different tracheophytes (Fig. 13.17).

The most primitive type of stele is a *protostele*, characterized by the absence of pith. Three variant forms of it are known. A *haplostele* is the simplest type. In it, xylem develops as a central cylinder, phloem forms a sleeve surrounding the xylem, and the pericycle in turn surrounds the phloem. An *actinostele* is quite similar, except that the central xylem column is alternately grooved and ridged in a vertical direction, which gives a cross-sectional view a somewhat starlike appearance. The number of "arms" varies from about two to six. The third type of protostele is a *plectostele*. Here the xylem is organized as several separate lengthwise ribbons or plates embedded in phloem.

With only a few exceptions, the roots of almost all tracheophytes are actinostelic. The stems of various primitive tracheophytes contain protosteles of all three types. However, the stems of most tracheophytes do not contain protosteles at all but contain steles with pith.

One stele type with pith is a *siphonostele*. Several variants of it are known, but all are characterized by a central column of pith and by sleeves of vascular tissues surrounding the pith completely. Re-

13 · 15 Primary meristems *and the principal adult tissues derived from them.*

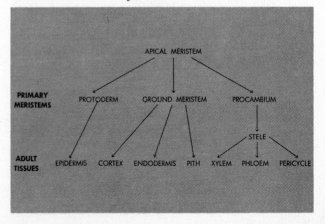

lated to siphonosteles are stele types collectively called *dictyosteles*. In these, the xylem and phloem tissues are arranged as distinct and separate *vascular bundles* grouped in more or less circular patterns within the stem. Such a circle of bundles surrounds the pith incompletely, the latter being continuous with the stem cortex outside the ring of bundles. Within a vascular bundle, phloem often lies toward the outside, xylem toward the inside (*eustelic* dictyostele, see Fig. 13.17). In other cases, a vascular bundle consists of a complete tube of phloem surrounding a core of xylem (*meristelic* dictyostele). A third stele

13 · 16 *The root-hair zone of a root. At lower tip note thickening formed by the root cap. See Fig. 7.16 for close-up of individual root hairs growing out from epidermal cells.*

13 · 17 *Steles of vascular plants: white areas, cortex; solid green areas, pericycle; light-green areas, phloem; gray-green areas, xylem; stippled areas, pith. The top three stele types shown are collectively known as protosteles, or steles without pith. Of the steles with pith, the dictyòstele shown is a variant called a eustele; it contains phloem on the outside and xylem on the inside of each vascular bundle.*

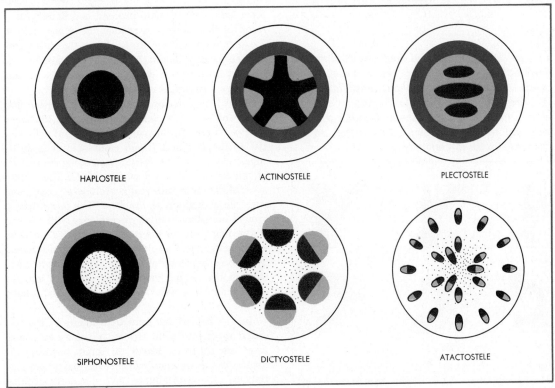

| HAPLOSTELE | ACTINOSTELE | PLECTOSTELE |
| SIPHONOSTELE | DICTYOSTELE | ATACTOSTELE |

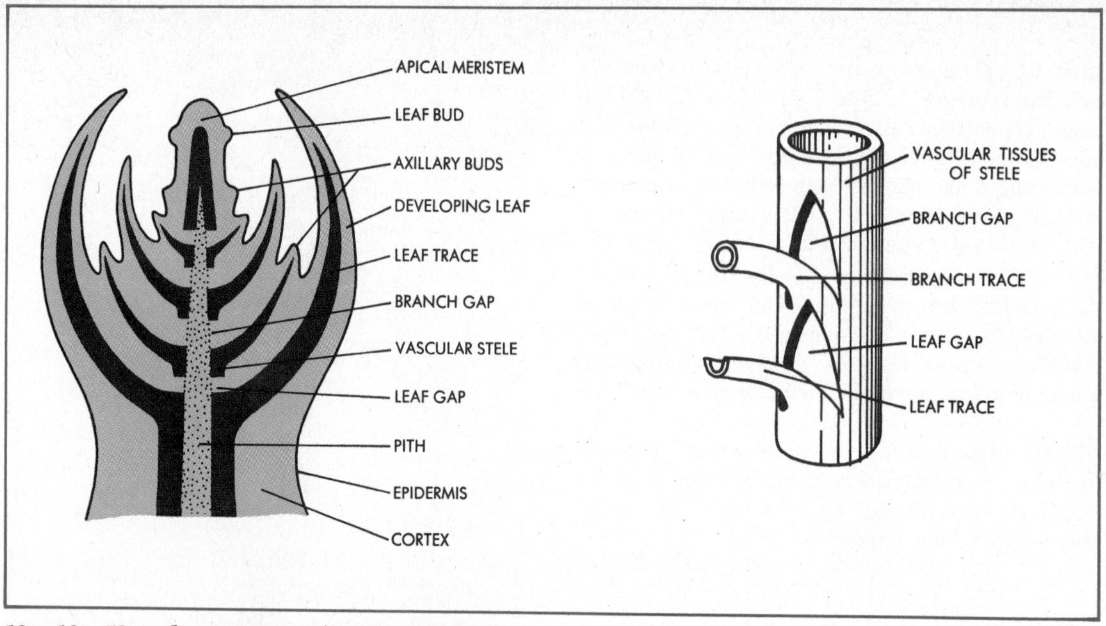
APICAL MERISTEM
LEAF BUD
AXILLARY BUDS
DEVELOPING LEAF
LEAF TRACE
BRANCH GAP
VASCULAR STELE
LEAF GAP
PITH
EPIDERMIS
CORTEX
VASCULAR TISSUES OF STELE
BRANCH GAP
BRANCH TRACE
LEAF GAP
LEAF TRACE

13 · 18 Vascular tissues. *Left, the distribution of vascular tissues in the apex of a shoot (compare with Fig. 13.13). The external boundary line corresponds to the protoderm and the light-colored areas to ground meristem. Right, three-dimensional view of a section of a vascular cylinder in a region where leaf and branch traces emerge. Note that the vascular tissues of both leaves and branches leave gaps in the stele.*

13 · 19 Microphylls and megaphylls. *Top row, longitudinal views; bottom row, cross-sectional views. A, microphyll without vascular trace. B, microphyll with vascular bundle. C, megaphyll. Note the many vascular bundles and the leaf gap in the megaphyll. Leaf gaps are not associated with microphylls.*

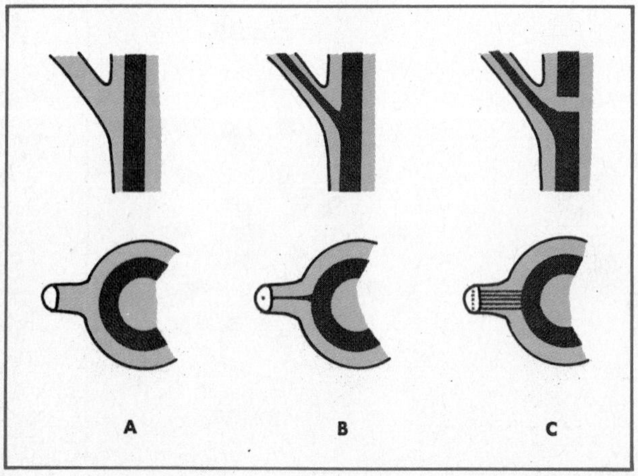
A
B
C

type with pith is an *atactostele.* Vascular bundles are present here as well, scattered randomly throughout the stem. In such stems it is difficult to differentiate precisely between pith and cortex.

PRIMARY GROWTH: LEAVES AND BRANCHES

Stem and root growth proceed indefinitely as a result of the continuous production of new cells at the shoot and root apices. Leaf growth, on the contrary, is usually limited. A leaf may be considered to be a *modified branch stem* which in most cases does not possess an apical meristem of its own.

A *leaf bud* forms from embryonic tissue just below and lateral to the shoot apex (Fig. 13.18). Sometimes a single cell but more often several cells give rise to the leaf bud. These embryonic cells divide repeatedly, most divisions occurring along the margins of the expanding and flattening blade. The surface layer of the embryonic leaf is protoderm, continuous with the protoderm of the stem. The inner mass is ground meristem, similarly continuous with the corresponding tissue of the stem. During this early developmental phase, a column of procambium branches away from the center of the stem and grows laterally through the ground meristem of the stem into the ground meristem of the leaf. This procambial column is a *leaf trace.*

In due course the embryonic tissues of the leaf differentiate into adult tissues. In some exceptional cases among ferns, leaves do retain meristematic tissues at the tips and such leaves may grow continuously, like stems. But in the vast majority of cases, *all* leaf tissues soon become adult. At such a stage the leaf has attained its final size and does not grow thereafter (Color Plate XV, 26).

Leaf protoderm develops into epidermis. As in the stem, leaf epidermis is cutinized and contains green guard cells enclosing stomata. The interior ground meristem gives rise to adult parenchymatous *mesophyll* tissue. This is usually the chief food-producing tissue of the plant; all mesophyll cells contain chlorophyll. In leaves of some primitive tracheophytes, mesophyll cells may be packed more or less close together, with or without occasional air spaces between cells. In most tracheophytes, however, leaf mesophyll is organized into two distinct zones. Just underneath the upper epidermis in horizontally placed leaves and underneath the whole epidermis in most upright and needle-shaped leaves, mesophyll cells are arranged in compact layers, or *palisades*. Elsewhere, mesophyll is *spongy* and organized into loose cellular strands and layers honeycombed extensively with air spaces. These connect with one another and lead to the exterior of the leaf through open passages in the palisade tissue and the stomata. Such a structural arrangement permits the greater part of every mesophyll cell to come into direct contact with fresh external air.

The procambial leaf traces develop into vascular xylem and phloem. Two fundamental leaf types may be distinguished on the basis of the amount of vascular tissue formed. In a so-called *microphyll,* the vascular tissue is equivalent to a single vascular bundle. In a *megaphyll,* by contrast, the vascular tissue is equivalent to numerous vascular bundles. Microphylls occur only in primitive tracheophytes; megaphylls are characteristic of most vascular plants (Fig. 13.19).

Megaphylls leave distinct *leaf gaps* in the stele of the stem. Such a gap forms during the early development of a leaf. When a stem elongates beyond the base of a leaf trace, new stem procambium formed above this base does not connect directly with it. Instead, a small discontinuity is left in the stem procambium just above the base of the leaf trace (see Figs. 13.18 and 13.19). This discontinuity becomes the leaf gap, and in the adult condition it is usually filled with parenchymatous tissue. Microphylls do not produce leaf gaps.

A microphyll is composed of a leaf blade only. But a mature megaphyll usually consists of a *petiole,* a thin basal stalk which attaches the whole leaf to the stem; two *stipules,* small appendages which grow out near the base of the petiole in many species; and a *lamina,* the leaf blade itself (Fig. 13.20). In the lamina, the vascular tissues together with greater

13 · 20   Leaf types *and leaf arrangements.*

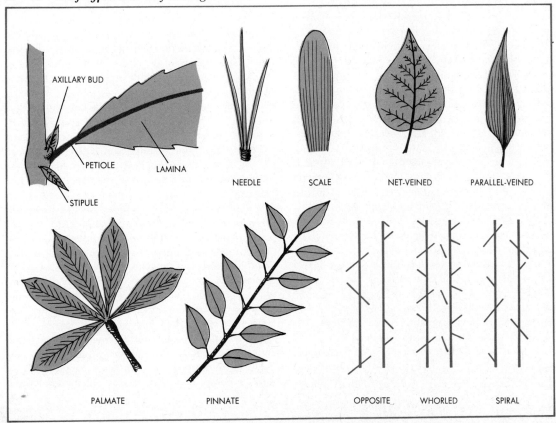

AXILLARY BUD

PETIOLE   LAMINA

STIPULE

NEEDLE   SCALE   NET-VEINED   PARALLEL-VEINED

PALMATE   PINNATE   OPPOSITE   WHORLED   SPIRAL

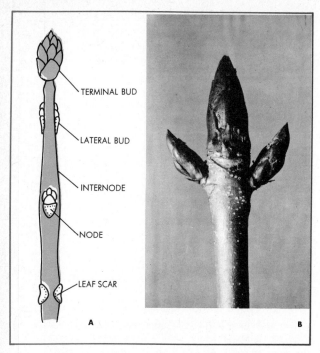

TERMINAL BUD

LATERAL BUD

INTERNODE

NODE

LEAF SCAR

A   B

13 · 21 *Diagram: stem with dormant buds. Photo: terminal dormant bud of the horse chestnut.*

or lesser amounts of supporting fiber tissues form *veins*. These may be either *parallel* to one another or *reticulate*, that is, arranged in the form of a network. In external form, a lamina may be *flattened*, *needle-shaped*, or *scalelike*. A leaf is *simple* if it contains only a single lamina. Multilaminate leaves are said to be *compound*. If the blades of a compound leaf join the petiole at a single point, the leaf is *palmate*; and if they are attached at several points, the leaf is *pinnate*.

The geometric arrangement of leaves on a stem is known as *phyllotaxis*. Several different phyllotactic patterns may be distinguished (see Fig. 13.20). In an *alternate* pattern, single leaves grow out at successive levels of the stem. In such cases the leaf bases mark out a spiral winding up along a stem. The geometric characteristics of such spirals are quite distinct for given species. Leaves are *opposite* if two leaves grow out at the same level of the stem, and they are *whorled* if more than two arise at the same level. In these instances, the regions of the stem where leaves are attached are called *nodes*, and the leaf-free regions between nodes are *internodes*.

In many tracheophyte species living in the temperate zone, the plant body becomes *dormant* during the winter. Growth ceases and the leaves of deciduous

types are shed. A fallen leaf leaves a permanent leaf scar on the stem (Fig. 13.21). In such species also, the apical shoot meristems are protected during the winter by *bud scales*. These are modified leaves or leaf parts developing at the approach of winter around an apical meristem. The scales are close together and form an apical bud, or *terminal bud*, on a dormant stem in winter condition. When apical growth resumes the following spring, bud scales fall off and leave densely placed *bud-scale scars* on the stem. By counting the number of stem regions where such scars occur, it is often possible to determine the age of a plant.

In some tracheophytes, particularly primitive types, stems branch *dichotomously*, a given stem splitting terminally into two equal branches. Such a pattern of branching results from a vertical subdivision of the shoot apex, each branch thereby acquiring its own apical meristem. More commonly, however, the branching pattern is *monopodial*, in which a given stem produces one or more subordinate *lateral branches* (Fig. 13.22). A lateral branch arises from a *branch bud*, developed at the apical shoot meristem in the *leaf axil*. This is the region where a leaf joins the stem, specifically the angle between the upper leaf or petiole surface and the stem. Wherever a leaf bud is formed, a branch bud forms in the leaf axil as well. Such branch buds always produce their own *branch gaps* in the stele of the parent stem (see Fig. 13.18).

Branch buds often do not mature immediately. Some may remain dormant for many years and some may not develop at all. Accordingly, a leaf may or may not be accompanied by a branch stem. Dormant branch buds are usually clearly visible in wintering stems just above leaf scars. When a branch bud does mature, it develops an active apical meristem of its own and grows in every respect like the parent stem. We note again that an important difference between a leaf and a branch is that one does not and the other does acquire an apical meristem in the bud stage.

Roots too may form branches, but the process of development differs here from that of stem branches. At varying distances behind the apex of the main or primary root, *lateral roots* may be formed (Fig. 13.23). Such branch roots originate in the pericycle. Cells in localized regions of the pericycle divide and form a pad of tissue, a so-called *root primordium*. During the later development of such a primordium, it pushes out through the peripheral tissues of the primary root. By the time it emerges through the epidermis, a root cap and the primary meristems have been formed. A stele with vascular tissues then matures, and these tissues become continuous

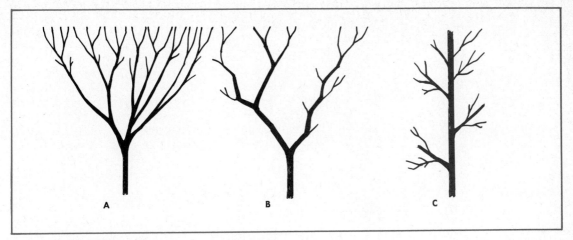

13 · 22 Branching patterns. A, dichotomous.
B, transitional between A and C. C, monopodial.

with the corresponding tissues of the primary root.
At this stage the lateral root is fully established and
continues to grow like a primary root.

SECONDARY GROWTH

The whole organization of the tracheophyte body
described up to this point represents the product of
primary growth: all body parts are direct derivatives
of the apical meristems and the three primary meristems of the embryo. Essentially, primary growth makes
possible extension in *length,* and any increase in the
thickness of stems and roots is due mainly to enlargement of cells in a lateral direction. In many
tracheophytes, primary growth is basically the only
means of increasing body size. However, numerous
tracheophytes are capable of growing not only in
length but also in thickness, through lateral increase
of cell *number.* These plants undergo processes of
secondary growth, superimposed on continuing processes of primary growth. Apart from comparatively
enormous increases in stem and root girth, the
large-scale result of such secondary growth is the
development of *bark* and of secondary *wood.*

Secondary wood tends to be formed in relatively
large quantities and new layers are added each year
to those accumulated previously. Plants of this type
develop into shrubs and trees and become recognizably *woody* in appearance. To be sure, primary
growth gives rise to wood too, namely, primary xylem.
But in the vast majority of cases primary wood is
formed in such small amounts that the plant is left in
a *herbaceous* condition; and if a distinctly woody
plant is to develop, secondary wood must be formed
by secondary growth. Thus, the term "woody plants"

refers largely to plants in which secondary growth
occurs.

In woody plants, young shoots and roots develop
as in all other cases through primary growth. Moreover, the plant later continues to elongate through
primary growth at each apex, and the regions
immediately behind each apex maintain the characteristic primary organization of nonwoody roots
and stems. More specifically, the primary root pattern in such cases is always actinostelic and the

13 · 23 Cross section of a root with outgrowing
*lateral root. Note that the lateral root originates
in the pericycle region of the primary root.*

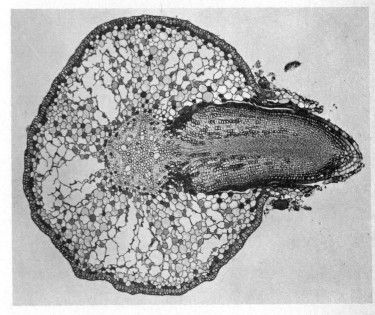

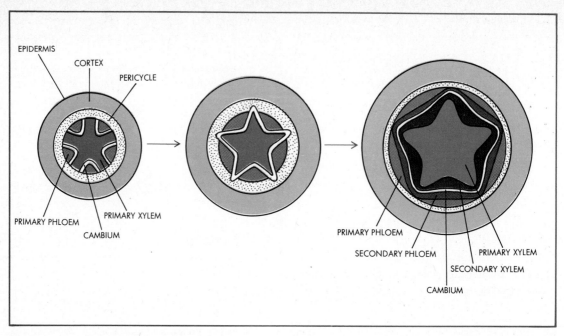

13 · 24   Development of cambium *and of cam-bium-derived tissues in the root. In some roots, pith is in the center (not shown here).*

primary stem pattern is typically dictyostelic. Subsequently, in older regions well behind each apex, these primary patterns become transformed into secondary ones. And as a result, even woody plants always possess early shoots and later growing tips which remain "green." Since leaves bud off near the shoot apex and do not possess apices of their own,

13 · 25   Development of cambium *and of cam-bium-derived tissues in a dictyostelic stem.*

they do not participate in secondary development at all.

The transformation of roots and stems from primary to secondary states is brought about by *secondary meristems,* or *cambia.* Two kinds of cambia develop, a *vascular cambium* and a *cork cambium.* Each arises from different primary tissues, and the process of formation differs somewhat in root and stem.

In a root, the vascular cambium forms between the primary xylem and phloem in the stele (Fig. 13.24). As noted earlier, if only primary growth occurs in a root, the entire embryonic procambium eventually matures into adult actinostelic tissues. But if

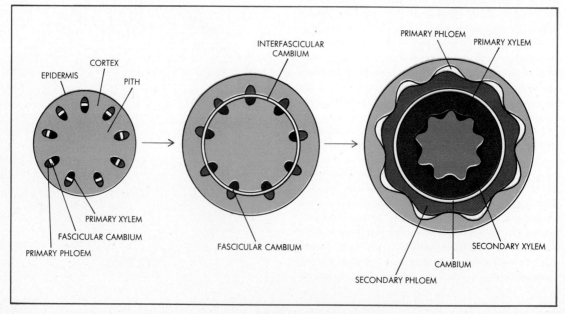

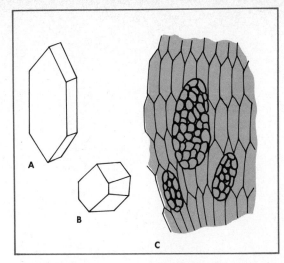

13 · 26 Cell types of cambium. A, fusiform initial. B, ray initial. C, tangential view of cambium layer, showing arrangement of fusiform initials and islands of ray initials.

secondary growth takes place as well, then a layer of procambium between the primary xylem and phloem remains permanently embryonic and relatively unspecialized. This layer then becomes the vascular root cambium, which ultimately surrounds the primary root xylem completely.

In a stem, part of the vascular cambium again forms between primary xylem and phloem, from procambium that has remained embryonic (Fig. 13.25). Since the dictyostelic stem contains circularly arranged vascular bundles, with xylem toward the inside and phloem toward the outside, procambium between these xylem and phloem areas represents an incomplete tube, interrupted between neighboring bundles. This discontinuous tube soon becomes continuous, however, for layers of parenchyma between neighboring bundles acquire the properties of a cambium. The complete tube of vascular cambium so formed is continuous with the corresponding tube in the root; and as the stem-root axis continues to elongate through primary growth at the apices, the open-ended cambial tube lengthens apace as progressively more cambium develops behind the apices.

Vascular cambium in both root and stem contains two types of meristematic cells (Fig. 13.26). The less abundant type comprises so-called *ray initials*. As these continue to divide, they bud off new cells toward both the inside and the outside of the cambial layer. The new cells on the inside form lengthening strands of tissue extending toward the center of the stem. Such strands are *xylem rays*. Analogously, new cells deposited toward the outside of the cambial layer become tissue strands called *phloem rays*. Both

kinds of rays function in lateral transport of nutrients within stem and root.

All other cells of the cambium, far more numerous than the ray initials, are known as *fusiform initials*. They too continue to bud off new cells toward both the inside and the outside. Indeed, the combined activity of all the fusiform initials generates whole *layers* of new cells at both sides of the cambium. Layers produced toward the inside soon mature into all the various cellular components of xylem tissue; and layers budded off toward the outside form all the components of phloem tissue (see Chap. 7). Vascular tissue so generated by cambium constitutes *secondary xylem* (or *secondary wood*) and *secondary phloem*. These tissues are traversed in places by the xylem and phloem rays (Fig. 13.27).

As secondary xylem continues to be formed in successive concentric layers within the cambial tube, it cannot push toward the center of the stem to any great extent for this space is already occupied by the primary xylem and the pith. The accumulating secondary xylem must therefore expand outward and increase the net thickness of the stem or the root. Furthermore, as secondary phloem develops in concentric tubes from the cambial tube outward, it increases the thickness of stem or root still more. Indeed, as secondary phloem presses increasingly against primary phloem, cortex, and epidermis, these primary tissues must ultimately rupture; for being adult and thus no longer able to grow, these tissues

13 · 27 Cross section of a three-year-old woody stem.

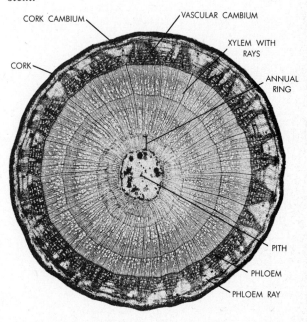

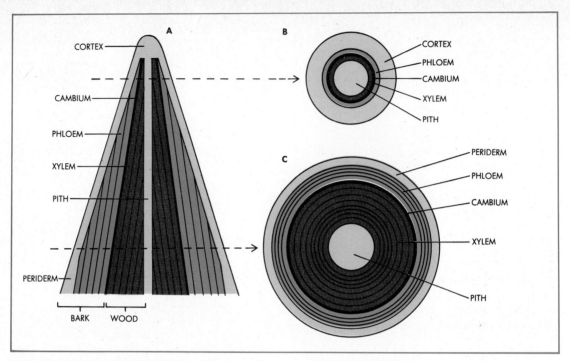

13 · 28 Tissue arrangements in a shoot. *A, diagrammatic longitudinal view, showing the formation of successive tissue layers to the outside and inside of the cambium. A cross section at the level of the upper broken line would appear as in B; at the level of the lower broken line, as in C.*

13 · 29 *Diagram: the position of the cork cambium and its products in a woody stem. Photo: the structure of the periderm.*

cannot keep pace with the ever-expanding girth of the stem or the root.

Note that successive concentric tubes of secondary xylem and phloem become progressively longer, inasmuch as the cambial tube that generates them becomes longer itself as the stem-root axis gradually elongates. Also, the secondary tissues are least extensive near the apices, where cambial activity is just beginning; and the largest amounts are present

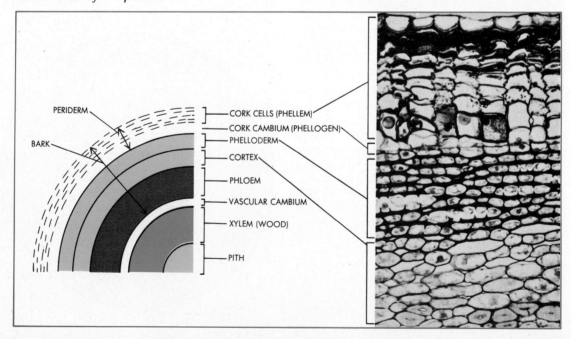

at the stem-root juncture, the region which has grown for the longest period and is the oldest. This juncture is therefore the region of greatest girth, and from here the stem *tapers* upward and the root tapers downward (Fig. 13.28).

The second of the cambial tissues is the cork cambium, or *phellogen*. In a stem, this tissue usually originates in the cortex, just underneath the epidermis (Fig. 13.29). In a root, cork cambium arises from outer layers of the pericycle. Such layers proliferate by cell division, a process which pushes the endodermis, the cortex, and the epidermis outward. As a result, these primary tissues are usually lost from the root and an outer layer of the enlarged pericycle then develops into cork cambium.

The cork cambium of both stem and root, like the vascular cambium, produces new cell layers toward the inside and outside. Layers budded off toward the inside, called *phelloderm,* become parenchyma. Layers generated toward the outside form *phellem,* or *cork.* During their maturation, cork cells deposit heavy suberin coats on their walls and accumulate many tannin compounds in their interior. The living substance of these cells then disintegrates, and mature cork consequently is wholly nonliving. Cork, cork cambium, and the inner phelloderm collectively constitute the *periderm.*

Cork cells are usually packed close together and intercellular spaces are absent. This arrangement and the chemical nature of cork cells make the outer covering of a woody plant quite impervious to water and air. At various places, however, the cork cambium does retain loosely arranged cork cells separated by intercellular spaces. Such spongy regions are known as *lenticels.* They permit gas exchange between the interior living tissues of the root or stem and the atmosphere (Fig. 13.30).

As root and stem girth continues to increase through secondary growth, vascular growth in particular, the original epidermal and cortical tissues tear and soon flake off. Periderm first develops in the fissures, and eventually a continuous layer of periderm comes to surround the entire circumference of stem or root. Further increases in diameter then cause rupturing and flaking off in this original periderm. But new cork cambium continues to form and new cork is laid down. This tissue later ruptures and flakes off in turn, and the cycle of new formation and flaking off repeats indefinitely. The pericycle of roots itself disappears eventually, and secondary phloem in both root and stem ultimately becomes the chief source for the regeneration of cork cambium.

We note that, in a mature woody stem or root, *wood* fills most of the space inside the tube of vascular cambium. All tissues outside the vascular cambium are collectively called *bark.* In a section of woody stem, therefore, nothing is left of the original primary tissues except the central pith, possibly some primary xylem around the pith, and the microscopically thin layer of vascular cambium at the line of juncture between wood and bark. In a mature woody root the pattern is similar, except that pith is usually absent from the beginning. Thus the concentric components of a woody section are, from the outside inward: periderm, secondary phloem, vascular cambium, secondary xylem, and possibly pith.

Secondary phloem is produced less abundantly than secondary xylem. Moreover, older xylem accumulates and persists in the core of a tree trunk, whereas older phloem near the surface continually flakes off as the trunk thickens. Therefore, only a thin rind of young phloem is present within bark at any given time. As a further result, the vast bulk of a trunk is

13 · 30 Lenticels, external and cross-sectional views.

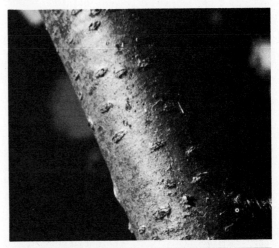

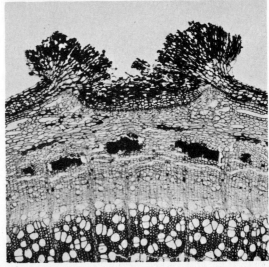

13 · 31 Portion of a 12-year old tree trunk, showing annual rings.

nonliving; all the tracheids and vessels in wood as well as the cork layers in bark are devoid of living substance.

Just as only *young* phloem is functional, so also only *young* xylem is functional. Though it is present, older xylem in time gradually blocks up with resins and gums, and water conduction through these channels is then no longer possible. Such central regions of a trunk represent *heartwood* (Fig. 13.31). The core of a tree may therefore be hollowed out without interfering with xylem conduction. But the outer, young wood of a tree, called the *sapwood*, must remain intact if a tree is to remain alive.

In an older tree growing in the temperate zone, the xylem vessels laid down during spring generally have a larger diameter than those formed in summer. In spring, melting snow provides the tree with much water and, under the influence of hormones (see Chap. 22), wider conducting channels are then formed which accommodate the greater flow. This alternation of narrow summer and fall xylem and wider spring xylem is recognizable with the naked eye as a concentric series of dark and light bands, or *annual rings*. The number of rings indicates the age of a tree. Moreover, from the comparative widths of spring and summer rings it is also possible to estimate the amount of rainfall, hence general climatic conditions, during past seasons as far back in time as the tree has lived.

Through the secondary growth processes described, a young, green sporophyte is slowly transformed into a tall, thick, tapering woody tree. Note that such a plant can become really tall only because secondary tissues do displace primary ones everywhere except near the apices. For although a plant can elongate through primary growth, such elongation will be greatly limited, for obvious mechanical reasons, if a corresponding increase in thickness cannot take place at the same time.

TRACHEOPHYTES: REPRESENTATIVE TYPES

SUBPHYLUM PSILOPSIDA

Leaves are microphylls; roots absent, absorption through rhizoids. *Psilotum, Tmesipteris.*

These most primitive of all living vascular plants are xerophytes. Two species of *Psilotum* grow in tropical and subtropical regions of the Americas, either in soil pockets rich in humus or epiphytically on trees. One species of *Tmesipteris* is found in Australia, New Zealand, and New Caledonia as a hanging epiphyte on fern and other trees (Fig. 13.32).

The sporophyte body of a psilopsid is based on a horizontal rhizome, underground in the nonepiphytic plants. A unique distinguishing feature of the subphylum and unquestionably a highly primitive trait is the absence of true roots. The only absorptive structures present are *unicellular rhizoids*. Erect aerial stems grow upward from the rhizome. Such stems are about 1 ft or more high and branch dichotomously. In adaptation to xeric habitats, the aerial stems possess a heavily cutinized epidermis with sunken stomata.

Internally, a psilopsid stem (Fig. 13.33) contains a parenchymatous cortex with chloroplast-containing layers near the surface and sclerenchymatous strengthening layers more interiorly. An endodermis with passage cells is present. The steles of the rhizomes are usually actinosteles. Aerial stems may possess siphonosteles, in which case thick-walled sclerenchyma functions as pith. Secondary growth does not occur, and xylem contains tracheids only, not vessels. The leaves are always microphylls. In *Psilotum* such leaves contain neither vascular tissue nor stomata. The microphylls of *Tmesipteris* do contain a single strand of vascular tissue as well as stomata.

Sporangia of psilopsids develop in bulbous cases on the aerial stems (see Fig. 13.33). Spores develop into gametophytes which are tiny independent plantlets. They consist largely of nongreen parenchymatous cells and they are covered with rhizoids.

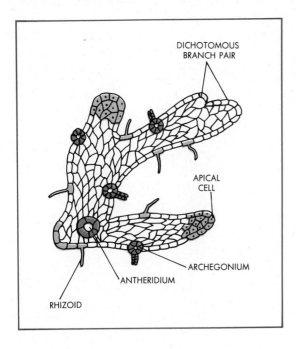

13 · 32 Psilopsida. *Diagram: the gametophyte of* Psilotum. *Photo: the sporophyte of* Psilotum. *Note spore sacs.*

These plants live saprotrophically on tree trunks, in rocky crevices, and occasionally in soil. The sex organs of the gametophytes produce eggs and swimming, multiflagellate sperms. As in bryophytes, wet periods are required for fertilization.

SUBPHYLUM LYCOPSIDA

Leaves are microphylls; roots present. *Lycopodium*, club mosses, ground pines; *Selaginella*, spike mosses, resurrection plants; *Isoetes*, quillworts.

Lycopsids are comparatively the most abundant of the three relic subphyla of tracheophytes. The plants still range in respectable numbers from the tropics to north temperate regions. Many ancestral lycopsids were large woody trees, but their present-day relatives are invariably small and nonwoody. Many lycopsids are creepers with prostrate rhizomes, others are erect, and some are epiphytes. In all cases, true roots are present and leaves are always microphylls.

Horizontal as well as erect, dichotomously branched stems are encountered in the genus *Lycopodium*

13 · 33 Cross section of a stem of Psilotum. *Note the epidermis with cuticle and stomata, the thick underlying cortex with a layer of sclerenchymatous cells, and the central actinostelic protostele with xylem in the core and surrounding phloem.*

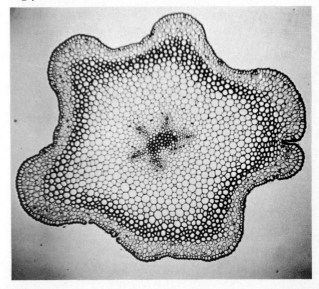

(Fig. 13.34). The roots of these plants are frequently adventitious, the pericycle of the stem being the tissue from which such roots arise. In erect forms, adventitious roots sometimes originate near the shoot apex and grow down right *through* the stem cortex. All growth is primary. Roots are usually actinostelic; stems are actinostelic and plectostelic. Leaves contain air spaces in the mesophyll and stomata on both surfaces.

The sporangia of *Lycopodium* develop terminally on erect stems. Leaves bearing sporangia are called *sporophylls,* and a whole group of sporophylls at the tip of a stem forms a *cone,* or *strobilus.* Gametophytes are small, independent, soil-inhabiting plantlets, ovoid or cylindrical in shape (Fig. 13.35). Their base is colorless and bears many rhizoids. Lobes containing green parenchyma project upward into the air. The gametophytes of many species are perennial, persisting for as long as 10 to 25 years. Such plants possess marginal meristems and may therefore grow continuously. Sperms are flagellate and swimming, and wet conditions are required for fertilization.

The genus *Selaginella* includes a most interesting group of lycopsids; unusual or noteworthy features are exhibited by all body parts of the sporophytes and by the gametophytes as well. Living largely in damp, shady places in the tropics, the sporophytes are small and delicate, some of them erect and shrubby, others rhizomatous with erect branches (Fig. 13.36

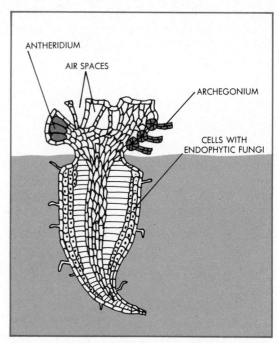

13 · 35 **The gametophyte of Lycopodium.** *Note the sex organs in the aerial portions and the rhizoids in the subterranean portions of the plant.*

and Color Plate XV, 27). Growth is primary. The stem epidermis is cutinized and lacks stomata. Stems are haplostelic, but upright branch stems often contain *several* haplosteles *each.* If such branches are put into horizontal positions, all newly formed procambial tissues mature as a single stele, as in originally horizontal stems. Each haplostele is surrounded by a large air space, and the stele is held in place only by a thin membrane of endodermis cells which traverses the air space and interconnects cortex and stele.

Very young sporophytes develop roots like other lycopsids, but virtually all later roots form from so-called *rhizophores.* These are stemlike outgrowths produced from *axial meristems,* located where an upright stem forks into branches. A rhizophore arcs from such an axial meristem into the ground, and the part which enters the ground reorganizes structurally and functionally into a root.

The leaves are microphylls, with stomata usually only in the lower epidermis. Internally, the mesophyll is organized into distinct palisade and spongy layers. Each leaf bears a *ligule,* a small tuft of tissue attached to the upper leaf surface near the juncture with the stem (see Fig. 13.36). Ligules are characteristic of lycopsids generally, but they are not present in *Lycopodium.* Neither the function nor the evolutionary history of ligules is known.

Selaginella is *heterosporous;* it produces *two* types

13 · 34 **Cross section through the stem of Lycopodium.** *The stele here combines actinostelic and plectostelic features.*

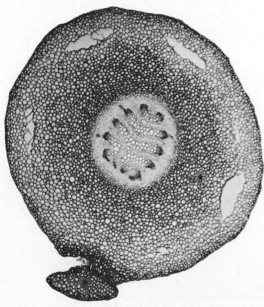

of spores, namely, small *microspores* and larger *megaspores*. Among tracheophytes now living, this phenomenon is otherwise encountered only in seed plants (see below). *Microsporangia* form microspores, and these grow into *microgametophytes*. The latter produce only swimming, flagellate sperms. Analogously, *megasporangia* form megaspores, and these develop into exclusively egg-producing *megagametophytes*. Both types of gametophytes are microscopic,

13 · 36   A, cross section through the stem of **Selaginella;** *note the two haplosteles situated in the large central air space. B, cross section through a rhizophore; note similarity to A. C, the position of a ligule on a microphyll.*

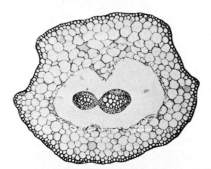

A

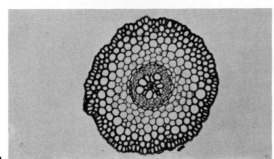

B

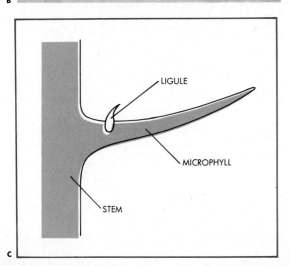

C

13 · 37   Isoetes, aerial portions.

consisting of but a few cells. They are nongreen and are retained within their respective sporangia, nourished by food previously supplied by the parent sporophytes. Sperms must swim from microgametophytes to eggs within megagametophytes, and fertilization and development of new sporophytes then take place there.

Quillworts of the genus *Isoetes* are the only surviving lycopsids still capable of secondary growth (Fig. 13.37). They do not become woody, however, and their secondary growth results from the activities of a cambium developed in the cortex of the plants. Quillworts are deciduous perennials. They live in marshy areas, with stems embedded in the ground. The stems are *corms*. Numerous roots project from the lower part of the corm, and the upper part bears dense clusters of erect microphylls which project into the air. These leaves give the quillwort part of its English name as well as a superficial resemblance to a patch of lawn grass.

SUBPHYLUM SPHENOPSIDA

Leaves are microphylls; stems with nodes bearing whorls of leaves; roots present. *Equisetum,* horsetails, scouring rushes.

Like the lycopsids, the sphenopsids attained their evolutionary peak in past ages. The only surviving genus is *Equisetum,* and all living sphenopsids are members of it (Color Plate XVI, 29). The plants range from the tropics to the temperate zone. They are characterized by underground rhizomes which bear erect aerial branches with microphylls. Both the rhizomes and the aerial stems possess nodes, and on the exposed nodes the leaves are present in whorls. Roots are largely adventitious, growing out along the rhizome. The underground portions are perennial, but the aerial structures of plants in the temperate zone are regrown each year.

Growth is exclusively primary. Roots are actinostelic; stems are largely dictyostelic. The stems are conspicuously ribbed longitudinally, and the epidermal cells are not only cutinized but also coated with thick deposits of silica. Stomata occur between the ridges of the stem. The cortex consists of outer layers of sclerenchyma and inner layers of photosynthetic parenchyma. Vertical air spaces and wide air canals pass through both cortex and pith. Vascular bundles are located under the ridges of the stem and each is enveloped by endodermis (Fig. 13.38). Leaves have stomata on both surfaces, and numerous air spaces ramify through the inner mesophyll.

In many forms the rhizome produces not only highly branched, green aerial shoots but also unbranched, nongreen, sporangial shoots. In all sphenopsids the sporangia are in cones, as in lycopsids. The

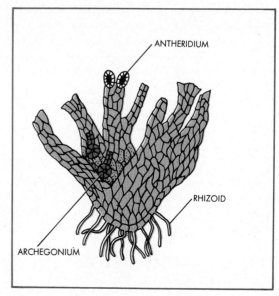

13 · 39   *The gametophyte of* Equisetum. *Note the sex organs.*

gametophytes are small, independent plantlets. They have the appearance of miniature pincushions, with tiny wings or lobes projecting upward (Fig. 13.39). The lobes are green; the base usually is not. Rhizoids grow from the underside of the base. Sperms are flagellate and swimming, and water is required for fertilization.

SUBPHYLUM PTEROPSIDA

Leaves are megaphylls; stems largely with pith; roots largely actinostelic. *Filicineae, Gymnospermae, Angiospermae.*

This largest subphylum of vascular plants probably evolved from early psilopsid stock as a fourth independent line of descent. Ferns were undoubtedly primitive, and an ancestral group of ferns then gave rise to the seed plants. Among these in turn, cone-bearing types appear to have evolved first and some of these were probably ancestral to the flowering types (see Chap. 32).

The subphylum as a whole is distinguished from the three others primarily by the presence of *megaphylls,* large leaves with multiple vascular bundles which always leave leaf gaps where they branch off from the stele.

Class Filicineae (ferns)

Growth primary only; xylem with tracheids but without vessels; gametophytes green and independent; seeds not formed.

13 · 38   Equisetum. *Cross section through a portion of the stem.*

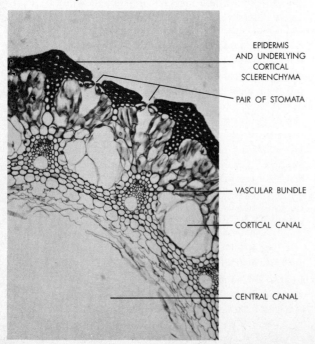

EPIDERMIS AND UNDERLYING CORTICAL SCLERENCHYMA

PAIR OF STOMATA

VASCULAR BUNDLE

CORTICAL CANAL

CENTRAL CANAL

Ferns are possibly even more abundant today than in the past. They range from temperate regions to the tropics, where they reach their greatest development. Tree ferns in such localities may attain heights of 50 to 60 ft, with leaves 10 to 15 ft long. But note that, despite their size, tree ferns are not woody plants; secondary growth is absent from the entire class. Other ferns are shrubby, and many are hanging epiphytes in rain forests. Deciduous forests and other well-watered temperate-zone areas harbor many fern species as abundant ground cover. Some few ferns are secondarily aquatic.

Most ferns are characterized by underground perennial rhizomes, with large, upright, complexly shaped leaves. These are regrown every year in most species of the temperate zone, but in some species the leaves last several seasons and are perennial. Leaves commonly exhibit *circinate vernation;* young leaves form tight coils, and as they grow by division of meristematic cells at the leaf tip they unroll and straighten up (Fig. 13.40).

The stem is frequently covered with fibrous remnants of leaf bases, giving it a somewhat "hairy" appearance. An epidermis is underlain by a thick, highly sclerenchymatous cortex, which endows the stem with a strength equivalent to that of wood and

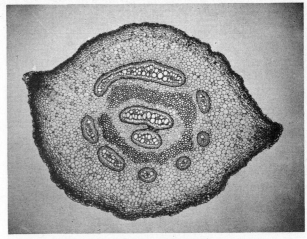

13 · 41 Fern stele, *partly dictyostelic and partly plectostelic.*

permits some ferns to attain the proportions of trees. The vascular tissue can have variously protostelic, siphonostelic, or dictyostelic arrangements (Fig. 13.41). All variant types of these steles are encountered among ferns, as well as some additional variants not in existence in other plants. Xylem contains tracheids only. In some species, a loss of pit membranes at the end walls of adjacent tracheids leads to the establishment of continuous longitudinal channels. These are rather like primitive kinds of vessels.

Sporangia develop on the undersides of leaves, frequently in groups projecting from the lower leaf surface. Such groups may be covered by a cap of sterile tissue, the *indusium.* A multisporangial structure of this kind is known as a *sorus.* Numerous sori may form in rows of a leaf (Plate XVII, 30). Spores give rise to gametophytes which are independent, green, and up to 1 cm in size. The body of these plantlets is a prostrate heart-shaped thallus, with rhizoids on the underside. This side also bears the sex organs. Sperms are flagellate and require wet conditions for distribution.

13 · 40 Ferns. A, *circinate vernation of developing fern leaves.* B, *tree ferns.*

A

B

Class Gymnospermae
(cone-bearing seed plants)

Growth primary and secondary; xylem with tracheids but without vessels in most cases; reproductive organs in cones; seeds formed, not enclosed.

> *Subclass Cycadophytae:* wood not extensive
> > Order Cycadales: cycads, "sago palms"; 100 species
>
> *Subclass Coniferophytae:* wood extensive
> > Order Ginkgoales: maidenhair trees; 1 species
> > Order Coniferales: conifers; 600 species
> > Order Gnetales: 70 species

13 · 42   Cycads.

The most distinctive features of this class are reproductive, and we shall discuss them in detail in Chap. 27. We may note here that gymnosperms are *heterosporous* (like *Selaginella*), with microspores and megaspores developed in microsporangia and megasporangia, respectively. Such sporangia are borne on sporophylls in cones. Reproduction also includes a process of *pollination*, which circumvents the requirement of free water for sperms. After fertilization, embryos develop within *seeds* and these remain exposed on the sporophylls of the cones; hence the name of the class, "naked-seed formers." Through the evolution of pollination, gymnosperms were the first Metaphyta to become reproductively quite independent of free water. This independence contributed immeasurably to their success as terrestrial plants. Gymnosperms reached their greatest abundance in earlier ages; groups now in existence are remnants of a long evolutionary decline.

Most of the present gymnosperms are perennial evergreens. Primary growth produces actinostelic roots and dictyostelic stems. Active secondary growth occurs thereafter, however, and the woody habit is virtually universal in the class.

In the subclass Cycadophytae, the cycads are the only living order. These plants are limited today to isolated areas in tropical and subtropical regions. Many cycads are grown as ornamental plants in California, Florida, and some other states. As a group, cycads are generally rather small plants, averaging about 5 ft in height (Fig. 13.42). However, some species may become as tall as 60 ft. The stems are unbranched and bear large leaves at the top. This external structure gives cycads a superficial resemblance to tree ferns. Internally, the stem contains a wide pith, an extensive starch-storing cortex, and very little wood.

Members of the subclass Coniferophytae are generally much more massive than the cycads, and their other characteristics are largely opposite as well. For example, Coniferophytae possess small simple leaves, narrow pith, narrow cortex, and a very active cambium which deposits extensive accumulations of wood.

The order Ginkgoales consists of the single relic species *Ginkgo biloba* (Fig. 13.43). It is native to eastern Asia, but it is grown throughout the world as a shade tree. It reaches heights of some 90 to 100 ft, and its trunk may have a diameter of 3 to 4 ft at the base. The tree is highly branched and possesses two types of branches. On one type, the *long shoots*, very little foliage is present. From such long branches grows the other type, the short *spur shoots*, which bear terminal groups of wedge-shaped leaves and sporangia.

The Coniferales, or conifers proper, today are the dominant, most abundant, and most conspicuous

13 · 43   The maidenhair tree Ginkgo. The end of a long shoot with leaf-bearing spur shoots is shown.

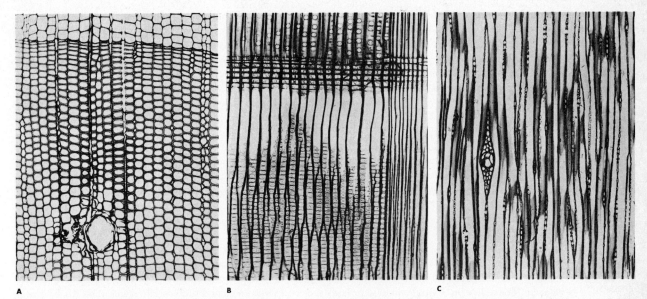

A B C

13 · 44 Pine wood. A, *transverse section; note resin canal near botton. B, radial section; note pits in tracheids and xylem ray traversing upper part of photo. C, tangential section; note pits in tracheid walls and end view of a xylem ray in mid-region of photo.*

gymnosperms. Although they are cosmopolitan, they are concentrated particularly in the temperate zone and the taiga of western North America and northeast Asia. The order includes pines, spruces, firs, cedars, yews, and redwoods, all of which are evergreens; and larches and bald cypresses, which are deciduous. All are relatively tall trees, with straight main stems and many branches. Giant redwood sequoias reach heights of some 400 ft, which makes them the largest and most massive living things on earth. Because conifers develop very much wood in proportion to other tissues, they are used widely as lumber and in paper manufacture. The vascular tissues of conifers are characterized by the presence of *resin canals,* ducts formed by the activity of the vascular cambium. These channels secrete the aromatic gums and resins so characteristic of conifer wood. Gum and resin compounds are largely excretion products, and they may play a role in the process of winter hardening (Fig. 13.44).

As in ginkgoes, pines and some other conifer species develop both long shoots and spur shoots, the latter bearing most of the leaves and the sporangial cones. But most species form long shoots only, with leaves and cones attached directly to them. Leaves are familiarly needlelike in many conifers, but scalelike leaves are formed by, for example, cypresses and incense cedars.

The order Gnetales consists of three genera (*Ephedra, Gnetum, Welwitschia*) which may not be very closely related to one another or even to other gymnosperms (Fig. 13.45). One of the principal distinguishing features of the group is the presence of true xylem vessels, a trait not otherwise encountered among gymnosperms but typical generally of angiosperms. Gnetales may possibly represent remnants of one or more quite independent lines of pteropsid evolution.

Class Angiospermae
(flowering seed plants)

Growth primary and secondary or primary only; xylem with tracheids as well as vessels; seeds formed in flowers, enclosed within fruits.

13 · 45 Welwitschia.

Subclass Dicotyledoneae (dicots): leaves net-veined; stems dictyostelic; flower parts in fours, fives, or multiples; two cotyledons in seed; 200,000 species.

Subclass Monocotyledoneae (monocots): leaves parallel-veined; stems atactostelic; flower parts in threes or multiples; one cotyledon in seed; 50,000 species.

Flowering plants today inhabit virtually all environments except the open ocean. They include annuals, biennials, and virtually all possible kinds of perennials; herbaceous types, semiherbaceous types, and woody types; aquatic types, parasitic types, saprotrophic types, and partly carnivorous types. They enrich the world with unmatched beauty, color, and scent, but they also exude poison and stench. Some survive only for a few days; others live for centuries. Some are near-microscopic; others are gigantic. Some live in solitude in dusty deserts or wind-blown tundras; others form impenetrable jungles. They provide man and other animals with practically all of their food and most of their shelter, and in addition they provide man with much of his clothing, many of his drugs, and numerous of the other vital necessities which maintain his civilization. Angiosperms as a group display more adaptive plasticity and variety than any other group of plants, major

13 · 46 Oak wood. Left, transverse section. Center, radial section. Right, tangential section. In left photograph, note the large vessels into which parenchyma has grown. Such vessels appear in longitudinal section toward the left of the middle and the right photographs. Groups of xylem ray cells appear in longitudinal section in the middle photograph and in cross section in the right photograph.

or minor; and far more so than in any other case, an unqualified reference to "plants" implies a reference to the flowering plants.

The class is distinguished from gymnosperms by the presence of xylem which contains tracheids as well as, in virtually all cases, true *vessels*. In sclerenchyma tissue, the components are not only sclereids as in other tracheophytes, but also *fibers*. Reproductively, angiosperms are heterosporous, pollen-producing, and seed-forming. However, angiosperm sporangia are in *flowers*, not cones. Seeds are not exposed on sporophylls as in gymnosperms, but groups of them are developed and retained within an *ovary*. After seed formation the ovary expands into a *fruit*, hence the name of the class, "hidden-seed formers." Details of these and other reproductive characteristics will be discussed in Chap. 27.

Evidence from living angiosperms indicates that their unknown ancestors probably possessed actinostelic roots and dictyostelic stems. The stems appear to have lacked an endodermis and pericycles were reduced or absent. The plants also must have had the capacity of secondary growth. From such an ancestral stock, two independent evolutionary lines probably led to the two present subclasses, the dicots and monocots. Each retained most of the ancestral traits but changed or added others.

Among the dicots, many today retain the capacity of extensive secondary growth. These constitute the *woody* dicots (for example, oak, Fig. 13.46). Others exhibit secondary growth only to a reduced degree; they become woody only in old, basal portions of the stem and root. Such plants represent the *semiherbaceous* dicots (for example, sunflower, Fig. 13.47). A third group is incapable of secondary growth altogether, and these dicots are fully *herbaceous* (for example, buttercup, Fig. 13.47).

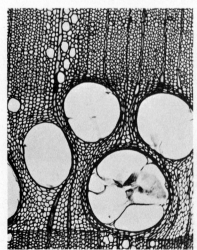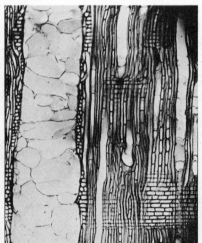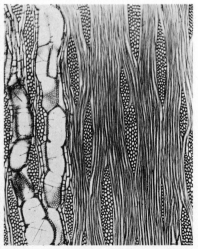

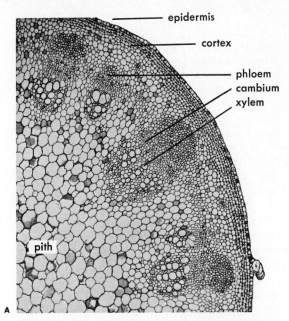

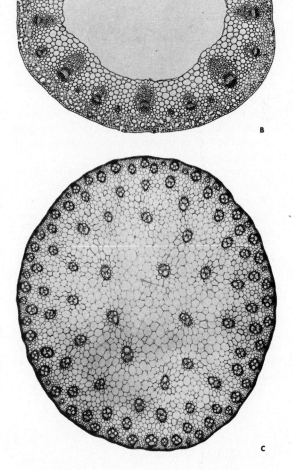

13 · 47 Stems. *A, cross section through the stem of a sunflower. Note the circular arrangement of the vascular bundles. B, cross section through the stem of a buttercup. Note the spacing of the vascular bundles and the hollow nature of the stem. C, cross section through the stem of a corn plant. Note the scattered arrangement of the vascular bundles.*

The monocot subclass has changed rather more drastically from the presumed ancestral condition. First, the primary stem has not remained dictyostelic as in the dicots, but has become atactostelic (for example, corn, Fig. 13.47). Second, monocots almost never exhibit secondary growth and virtually all are herbaceous. The main exceptions are palms, in which a complex and rather atypical form of secondary growth is encountered.

Several other differences distinguish dicots and monocots. Leaves are characteristically net-veined in dicots, parallel-veined in monocots. Flower parts and seed chambers in the ovary occur in fours, fives, or multiples of these numbers in dicots, but in threes or multiples in monocots. In most dicots the early sporophyte embryo within the seed develops two embryonic seed leaves; in most monocots, only one such leaf is formed. These leaves nourish the embryo and the later seedling through stored food or through photosynthesis, until the first adult leaves are mature. Seed leaves are called *cotyledons,* and their number gives each subclass its name.

Each subclass contains numerous orders. Dicots are the more abundant and presumably the more primi-tive group. They include all the flowering trees and shrubs, including apple, peach, cherry, oak, chestnut, walnut, elm, and rubber trees, and many others; as well as strawberry, bean, cabbage, turnip, cotton, cocoa, coffee, avocado, celery, carrot, parsley, spinach, citrus, lilac, blueberry, cranberry, potato, tomato, to-bacco, pepper, melon, cucumber, lettuce, goldenrod, rhubarb, and artichoke plants, and thousands more. Monocots have at least equal economic importance, for in this subclass are wheat, corn, rye, rice, oat, barley, bamboo, sugar cane, and all other grasses; as well as palms, lilies, irises, pineapples, bananas, and orchids.

REVIEW QUESTIONS

1. How are Metaphyta and Metazoa distinguished from each other and how are both distinguished from Protista? Review the identifying characteristics of Metaphyta. What is a gametophyte? A sporophyte?

2. Describe the group characteristics and the basic structure of all bryophytes. Name the classes of bryophytes and their identifying features. Define elater, thallus, rhizoid, protonema.

3. State the identifying characteristics of tracheophytes. How is this phylum classified into subphyla and classes? What is the probable evolutionary relation of (a) tracheophytes as a whole to bryophytes and Protista and (b) the subcategories within the tracheophyte phylum?

4. Review the architectural adaptations of tracheophytes to life on land. Name different modifications of (a) stems and (b) roots, and state the adaptive role of each such modification.

5. How do tracheophytes conserve water? How do they protect against (a) heat and (b) cold? What different groups of tracheophytes are perennial, biennial, and annual, and what are the life cycles of such plants?

6. Show how the sporophyte embryo of a tracheophyte develops into a mature plant by primary growth. Name specific tissues and indicate how they differentiate. Describe the organization of different types of steles.

7. Define leaf trace, leaf gap, mesophyll. What is the difference between a microphyll and a megaphyll? Describe the structure of a leaf. What types of leaves and leaf arrangements may be distinguished? How does a leaf develop?

8. Describe how a stem or a root grows in length. What is secondary growth? Show how a vascular cambium forms secondary xylem and phloem. Describe the activities of a cork cambium.

9. Define lenticel, ray initial, phellogen, periderm, fusiform initial, phloem ray, phellem, annual ring, heartwood, bark, wood.

10. Describe the complete structural organization of a mature woody plant in (a) the woody part of the stem, (b) the woody part of the root, (c) the nonwoody apical part of the stem, and (d) the nonwoody apical part of the root.

11. Describe the structure of the sporophytes of (a) psilopsids, (b) lycopsids, and (c) sphenopsids. In what aspects of the life cycle does *Lycopodium* differ from *Selaginella*?

12. Define the terms sporophyll, ligule, heterospory, rhizophore, circinate vernation, sorus, spur shoot, atactostele.

13. Review the identifying features of pteropsids. Describe the structural organization of a fern sporophyte. Show how the general life cycle of a seed plant differs from that of other tracheophytes.

14. How are gymnosperms subclassified? Describe the structural characteristics of gymnosperms. What are the identifying features of angiosperms? Name the subclasses of angiosperms and their identifying features. Name representative plants of each subclass.

15. Describe the internal structure of (a) a woody angiosperm, (b) a semiherbaceous angiosperm, and (c) a herbaceous angiosperm.

COLLATERAL READINGS

Carlquist, S.: "Comparative Plant Anatomy," Holt, New York, 1961. A small advanced book containing very detailed descriptions of the structure of angiosperms. The references to the original literature may be useful in addition.

Doyle, W. T.: "Nonvascular Plants: Form and Function," Wadsworth, Belmont, Calif., 1964. The last chapter contains a concise account of the biology of bryophytes.

Esau, K.: "Anatomy of Seed Plants," Wiley, New York, 1960. One of the best texts on gymnosperms and angiosperms.

Foster, A. S., and E. M. Gifford: "Comparative Morphology of Vascular Plants," Freeman, San Francisco, 1959. A more advanced text on the structure of tracheophytes of all types.

Galston, A. W.: "The Life of the Green Plant," 2d ed., Prentice-Hall, Englewood Cliffs, N.J., 1964. This paperback contains chapters on the structure, nutrition, growth, and development of plants.

James, W. O.: Succulent Plants, *Endeavor,* vol. 17, 1958. This article shows how xerophytic plants may conserve water and protect against heat.

Mangelsdorf, P. C.: The Mystery of Corn, *Sci. American,* July, 1950. An interesting account of the search for the evolutionary ancestor of domesticated corn.

————: Wheat, *Sci. American,* July, 1953. The

article describes the origin of domesticated wheat and the basis of the usefulness of this plant to man.

Richards, P. W.: Famous Plants—The Liverwort Marchantia, *New Biol.*, vol. 27, 1958. One of the best-known bryophytes is examined in this article.

Salisbury, F. B., and R. V. Parke: "Vascular Plants: Form and Function," Wadsworth, Belmont, Calif., 1964. This paperback deals in introductory fashion with the anatomy and the functional processes of tracheophytes.

Wardlaw, C. W.: The Banana, *New Biol.*, vol. 11, 1951. An economically important monocot is examined in some detail.

Watson, E. V.: Famous Plants—Funaria, *New Biol.*, vol. 22, 1957. The biology of one of the mosses is given special attention.

White, D. J. B.: The Stem Apex of a Dicotyledon, *New Biol.*, vol. 16, 1954. Recommended for further data on apical organization and growth.

Williams, S.: Wood Structure, *Sci. American*, Jan., 1953. A better appreciation of the anatomy of woody plants may be obtained through this article.

CHAPTER 14
METAZOA

Whereas the protistan source of the Metaphyta can be ascertained reasonably well, that of the Metazoa cannot. Metaphyte structure happens to include useful chemical clues such as chlorophyll and other pigments, and plants also arose at a comparatively late period in the earth's history, when fossils were already abundant and can aid us now in tracing ancestries (see Chap. 32). By contrast, metazoan origins must be determined without special chemical indicators and also without fossil evidence, for Metazoa evolved much earlier than the Metaphyta, well before fossils began to leave a record of the past. Consequently, although we can be reasonably certain that Metazoa did originate among the Protista, it is at present quite impossible to decide which of the protistan groups or how many of them might actually have been ancestral.

According to early classical hypotheses, Metazoa are assumed to have evolved from protozoa. But there is actually very little evidence for such a view. *Any* of the early protistan stocks could have given rise to Metazoa, and this descent could in fact have taken place long before protozoa as such had originated. Moreover, *numerous* early protistan types could have contributed independently and at different times to the evolution of the Metazoa, for this assemblage of organisms does appear to be considerably polyphyletic.

Regardless of the problem of origins, however, it is fairly clear that Metazoa form a well-defined group of organisms sharing their most fundamental structural and functional features in common.

GENERAL CHARACTERISTICS

Like the Metaphyta, Metazoa exhibit a complex multicellular construction encompassing the organ and organ-system levels of organization. Most cells of the body are sporine; flagellate (ciliate) and amoeboid potentials are in evidence in various cell types, either permanently or at specific stages. Metazoa differ from Metaphyta in that all cells usually possess centrioles, and that the cells not in direct contact with the external environment are all naked, without walls or cuticles. Further, metazoan development passes not only through embryonic but typically also through larval stages. Most obviously, metazoan nutrition is exclusively heterotrophic and, with but few exceptions, specifically holotrophic. Virtually all animals, free-living as well as parasitic ones, ingest bulk foods, digest them thereafter, and then egest unusable remains. This collective function of *alimentation* thus constitutes a nearly universal characteristic of animal nature.

Indeed, the two traits of elaborate body construction and alimentation jointly can be shown to prescribe practically every other aspect of animal nature as well. For example, the two traits almost automatically necessitate the further trait of *motility*, or active motion. To be sure, many nonanimal organisms (for example, most bacteria and all fungi) are likewise heterotrophic, yet most of these are incapable of active movement. However, the body of these organisms is not structured elaborately and indeed is in many cases unicellular and microscopic. As a result, the correspondingly small amounts of food required can usually be obtained at the spot where the organism happens to be located, or where wind, water currents, and other such agencies of passive dispersal may have chanced to carry the organism. In animals, on the contrary, movement by passive means would be quite inadequate. Being complexly structured and on the whole therefore bulkier, animals require commensurately larger quantities of food; and random passive dispersion by environmental agencies in most cases is not likely to carry animals to adequate amounts or kinds of food organisms. Active, self-powered motion consequently becomes a necessary, and rather familiar, characteristic of animals.

Flagella, cilia, pseudopodia, and muscles are the means of animal motion, and this motor capacity is used in two major ways to obtain food. In the more common case, an animal carries out some form of *locomotion;* it propels its whole body toward the location of a likely food source. In the second case, the animal remains stationary and *sessile,* and lets the food source move toward it. All sessile animals are aquatic; they employ their motion-producing equipment either to create water currents that carry food organisms to them or to trap food organisms that happen to pass close by.

Once the capacity of motion is given, it may serve not only in the search for food but also secondarily in other vital activities. As is well known, for example, locomotion aids animals significantly in protecting them from potential environmental dangers, both biological ones occasioned by other organisms and physical ones such as climatic changes. The latter affect all animals daily and seasonally, as they affect plants. But animals respond primarily by moving, either to sheltering sites nearby or to more suitable territory farther away. Locomotion also plays an important role in mate selection and in reproduction generally. Yet in virtually all cases, the most consistent and continual locomotor effort made by animals probably is the search for food.

Before an animal can effectively move toward food or vice versa, it is clearly essential for the animal to recognize that, at such and such a spot in the environment, an object is located that is or appears to be a usable food. Moreover, after such identification and localization have been accomplished, it is equally essential to *control* the ensuing motion, that is, to set and adjust course and speed, and to determine when movement is to begin and to terminate. What is needed, evidently, is a complete guidance apparatus. Most animals actually possess it in the form of a *nervous system.* In it, sense organs of various kinds permit recognition of environmental detail, impulse signals via nerves produce control over motion, and a brain or brainlike organ correlates and coordinates; it fits a given set of recognitions to an appropriate set of motions. In exercising these functions, nervous systems actually must regulate more than motion as such; for if muscles, for example, are to function at all, any structure or process that contributes to the maintenance of proper operating conditions within muscles requires regulation as well. It happens that virtually all internal components of animals play at least some role in maintaining the fitness of muscles. Correspondingly, nervous systems coordinate almost all internal operations of the body, and in effect the systems so become major controllers of steady states.

Indeed, steady-state control is essential not only in achieving proper motion but also in performing any other function. The general importance of such control is underscored by the existence, in most animals, of *chemical* coordinating systems in addition

to the neural ones. In different animal groups the chemical regulators differ greatly in form and specific activity, and in many instances chemical control is exercised by components of other organ systems (for example, blood, kidneys, gills). In some groups, notably in insects and vertebrates, various processes of chemical control are governed by specialized hormone-producing *endocrine systems.* These, and internal chemical coordinators in general, operate in conjunction with the neural coordinators. Both kinds basically serve in making the overt actions of an animal dovetail sensibly with the requirements imposed by given environmental situations. Motion is a major one of these overt actions. Thus, inasmuch as internal coordination is a prerequisite to effective motion and inasmuch as motility is itself necessitated by holotrophism, we may regard the presence of nervous and other steady-state controllers as a direct consequence of the mode of animal nutrition.

The requirement of motility has a significant effect on the architecture of animals. Motion must take place in water or air, and movement clearly will be most efficient if the external medium offers the least possible resistance. Unlike a tree, therefore, which is constructed in a ramified shape for *maximum* exposure to light, air, and soil, an animal is built as compactly as is feasible, for *minimum* surface exposure. Indeed, most motile animals also tend to be *bilaterally symmetrical* and *elongated* in the direction of motion, a shape which aids in reducing resistance to movement and provides stable mechanical balance between mirror-image right and left sides. Moreover, since one end of an elongated animal necessarily enters new environments first, that end will serve best as the place for the chief sense organs and nerve centers and for the food-catching apparatus. The leading part of the body so becomes a *head.* At the same time, elimination products of all kinds are best released at the hind end, where they do not impede forward progression. A general build of this sort is actually standard and nearly universal among moving animals (Fig. 14.1).

By contrast, sessile animals, and also many of the slow and sluggish types, face their environment more or less equally from all sides, like plants, and their architecture reflects this. They are or tend to be *radially symmetrical,* and a distinct head is usually not present (see, for example, Color Plate XVIII, 31). Also, sense organs and other components of nervous systems tend to be greatly reduced, an observation which underscores clearly that the primary function of such systems is to control movement.

The physical problem of locomotion undoubtedly contributes to the preponderance of aquatic types among animals. Actually only relatively few groups

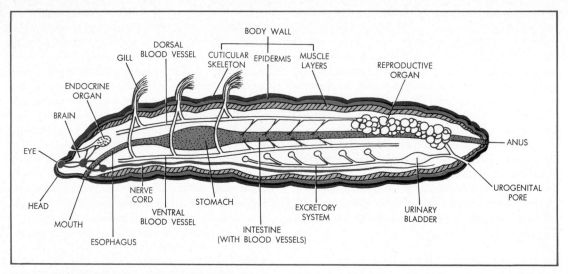

14 · 1   Diagrammatic representation of a moving animal. *This is a hypothetical animal, showing the general position of the organ systems. Note that the integumentary and nervous systems are at or near the surface, that the alimentary, breathing, excretory, and reproductive systems communicate with the surface, and that the circulatory and muscular systems extend throughout the body. If present, endocrine and skeletal systems often range throughout the body as well, and the skeletal components may be located exteriorly or interiorly.*

are terrestrial: some snails, some worms, arthropods such as insects and spiders, and vertebrates such as reptiles, birds, and mammals. All other animal groups are primarily aquatic, and this is probably correlated with the requirement of locomotion. Propulsion can be accomplished with less effort in water than on land or in air; friction is greatest on land, support against gravity is least in the air. In water, however, an animal is buoyed up and comparatively little energy need be expended for locomotion. Moreover, food is abundant in water and a water environment is biologically beneficial in other respects as well.

Once animal and food source are near each other, the animal must then make actual use of food. Here again the condition of holotrophism imposes characteristically animal traits. We already know that two basic "strategies" of handling foods are encountered. In one, the animal is free-living and the food source enters the animal. In the other, the animal is parasitic and it enters the food source. Like free-living animals, most parasitic ones still possess complete alimentary systems, inherited from their originally free-living ancestors. In many animal parasites alimentary structures are secondarily reduced, however, and in some cases they are no longer present at all. Not bulk foods but individual food molecules then enter the parasite directly through its surface, as in all nonanimal parasites.

The necessity of holotrophic feeding also has a major effect on the basic animal way of life. Because the supply of appropriate food organisms is limited, animals tend to compete openly for whatever foods are available. As a result, some animals become predators, some become prey. Numerous adaptations in structure and function aid either the hunter or the hunted: brute strength, speed, body colors and shapes which protect by camouflage, colors and sounds which warn or lure, and many others. Significantly also, predator and prey are often characterized by distinct modes of *behavior*, as expressed, for example, through furtiveness, stealth, cunning, aggressiveness, timidity, and other manifestations of "mentality" and "personality."

In addition to channeling animal life into patterns of offense and defense, competitive holotrophism is correlated with specializations in animal eating habits. Thus, *herbivores* are specialized to eat only plant foods, *carnivores* subsist only on other animals, and *omnivores* may eat both animal and plant foods, living or dead. In view of its abundance, plant food is easily come by. As a result, more herbivorous animal types exist than any other. Also, since plants do not put up a fight before being eaten, herbivores generally are of more or less gentle disposition and are more adept in defense than in offense.

A plant diet presents its own special problems.

The large quantities of cellulose present make plant tissues tough and difficult to tear. Animals must therefore scrape or grind or chew plant foods or suck the juices out of them. Correspondingly, rasping, crushing, grinding, and sucking structures are particularly common among the ingestive devices of herbivores. Such animals also tend to possess comparatively long digestive tracts, which offer more surface and more time for the digestion of plant foods. A pound of fresh plant material consists largely of water and cellulose and of correspondingly less usable food. Accordingly, herbivores generally eat more, and more often, than other animal types.

Carnivores are specialized to overcome not only herbivores but also smaller carnivores and omnivores. Speed, strength, and varied prey-killing equipment in mouth or body appendage are familiar adaptations to a carnivorous way of life. Note, however, that virtually none of the carnivores kills wantonly, but only when hungry or threatened; it is to the carnivore's advantage to live in a thriving population of herbivores. Animal tissue is softer than that of plants and tears fairly easily. Correspondingly, sharply pointed ingestive aids adapted for tearing are predominant among carnivores. Absence of cellulose in animal foods also tends to reduce chewing time and makes for easier digestion and relatively shorter alimentary tracts. Nutritive values per pound of animal tissues are greater than in plant foods. Therefore, carnivores generally eat fewer, smaller meals.

Omnivores subsist on whatever nourishment they can find or catch. Many omnivores wait on the scene of battle between carnivore and herbivore, to scavenge among the remains. Others live on minute plant and animal debris in soil or water. The food-trapping and other alimentary structures of omnivores usually combine herbivorous and carnivorous features, as might be expected.

Numerous important animal characteristics derive from the bulkiness and compactness of the animal body. Since animal cells possess comparatively little inherent rigidity, a bulky collection of cells cannot readily maintain shape and is likely to sag into a formless mass under the influence of gravity. Animals therefore require antigravity supports, and they actually possess them in the form of *muscular* and *skeletal systems*. That muscles function not only in motion but also in support is well illustrated in animals such as earthworms, which do not possess a skeleton. The same muscles that move such animals also contribute to holding them together and to maintaining their shapes. Moreover, even an animal with a skeleton would sag into a formless mass if muscles did not maintain a taut, firm organization. Conversely, that skeletons function in support as well as in locomotion is also clear. A large, heavy animal could neither hold its shape nor propel itself forward by muscles alone, without rigid supports.

Animal skeletons are either calcium-containing (*calcareous*), silicon-containing (*silicaceous*), or variously *horny*. Such supports are organized either as *exoskeletons* or as *endoskeletons*. In an exoskeleton, the supporting material is on the outside of the animal and envelops it partly or wholly. Mollusks and arthropods are among groups with exoskeletons. In an endoskeleton, the supports are internal and soft tissues are draped over them. The main animal groups characterized by this type of skeleton are the echinoderms and the chordates, the latter including the cartilage- and bone-possessing vertebrates. Endoskeletons permit animals to become far larger than do exoskeletons. With increasing body size, an exterior skeletal envelope rapidly becomes inadequate to support deep-lying body parts. Interior supports, by contrast, can buttress all parts of even a large animal. It is not an accident, therefore, that the largest animals are the vertebrates, and that animals with exoskeletons or without skeletons of any kind are comparatively small (Fig. 14.2).

The bulky construction of animals also creates problems of internal logistics. For example, after food is eaten and digested, the usable nutrients must be distributed to all parts of the animal body. If the distances between the alimentary system and the farthest body parts range over only a few cell layers, as is the case of several groups of relatively simply constructed animals, then internal food distribution can be achieved adequately by ordinary physical diffusion. But if food substances must traverse very many cell layers before reaching distant body parts, as in the majority of animals, then distribution by diffusion no longer suffices. Some sort of internal transport system becomes essential, and the *circulatory systems* of animals meet this requirement (Fig. 14.3). In such networks of vessels, the transport vehicle of food is blood, more specifically, the water component of blood, in which nutrients are carried in solution. One or more muscular pumping organs, or hearts, maintain a circulation of blood throughout the body. Blood is not red in all animals, but is blue or green in some and colorless in many others. Where blood is pigmented, the pigment functions specifically in transport of oxygen, not food, a circumstance which points up another problem of internal logistics.

Because of the compact construction of an animal, most of the cells are not in immediate contact with the external environment. Yet all cells require environmental oxygen for respiration, and every cell also must release to the environment any waste sub-

A

B

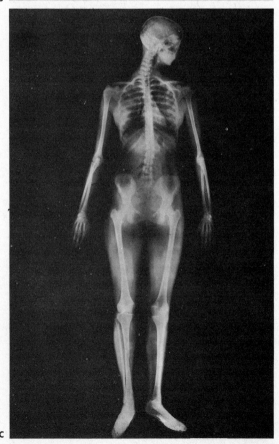

C

14 · 2 Skeletal types. A, the calcareous exoskeleton of a snail. B, the horny exoskeleton of a stag beetle. C, X-ray photograph of a girl, showing the human endoskeleton.

stance resulting from metabolism. Direct diffusion again suffices for these functions in several groups of simply constructed animals, where the thickness of the body does not exceed a few cell layers. In the majority of animals, however, the structural complexity is such that at best only the cells within diffusion distance from the body surface could exchange materials with the environment directly. Transport channels are therefore required, and in most animals the circulatory system serves as the principal link between the environment and the interior of the body; blood serves as traffic vehicle to and from the body surface.

In some instances (for example, earthworms, frogs), the entire body surface is adapted to absorb oxygen from the environment into the blood vessels of the skin, and the entire skin, similarly, may release waste substances from the blood into the environment. In such cases the skin must remain relatively thin and permeable and can afford only limited protection. In most animals, however, the integumentary system is elaborated more complexly and is composed of skin, skin glands, and a large variety of different skin-covering structures such as shells, scales, hair, or horn. A system of this kind protects, supports, and is relatively impermeable to the environmental medium. Animals so covered may exchange materials with the environment only at restricted areas, where surface thinness and permeability are preserved and where the blood supply is particularly abundant. For protection, such thin and sensitive areas are frequently tucked well into the body, away from the general body surface yet still in direct communication with the environment. These areas represent organs making up two systems, the *breathing* and the *excretory systems*. Gills and lungs are the principal types of oxygen collectors, but these organs also contribute importantly to waste excretion. Serving in excretion primarily are kidneys as well as other, functionally equivalent types of organs.

Bulk and complex organization affect yet another aspect of animal nature, namely, the pattern and process of reproduction. Like plants, animals too possess *reproductive systems* which manufacture sperms and eggs and thereby contribute to the formation of fertilized eggs. But again like the adult plant, the adult animal is so elaborately multicellular that successive cell divisions by themselves are quite insufficient to transform the fertilized egg, a single cell, into the intricately organized adult. In addition to mere increase in cell number, therefore, a specialized, lengthy course of development must take place. Indeed, animal development must lead to the formation of highly complex body parts without equivalents in plants: nervous systems, muscular systems, skeletal supports with jointed components, and in general all parts functioning more or less directly in locomotion.

As already noted, animal development actually does occur in uniquely characteristic manner, two major distinguishing features being the *embryo* and, generally, the *larva*. The embryonic phase of development starts with the fertilized egg and usually terminates in a process of *hatching*. The ensuing larval phase then continues to *metamorphosis,* or transformation into the adult. Both embryo and larva are most often unlike the adult in structure or function. And both developmental phases may be regarded as specifically animal devices that provide the necessary time, and the means, for the production of a complexly structured adult out of a single cell (see Color Plate XIX, 32).

We find, therefore, that if we take the basic animal attributes of holotrophism and high level of structural complexity as a starting point, we may deduce all other principal facets of animal nature as contingent requirements. As we have seen, the two basic attributes at once necessitate the presence of nervous, muscular skeletal, alimentary, circulatory, excretory, breathing, and integumentary systems. And if to these we add a reproductive system and in some cases also an endocrine system, we have a complete maximum list of all the major architectural ingredients composing an animal. Implied also is a good deal about how an animal moves, behaves, feeds, develops, copes with its environment—in short, pursues life. Moreover, we also know in broad outline how the structural ingredients of the animal must be put together to form a sensibly functioning whole. As suggested in Fig. 14.1, some of the organ systems must be in surface positions in whole or in part (for example, integumentary, nervous); others may lie deep but must at least communicate with the surface (for example, alimentary, breathing, excretory, and also reproductive); and still others must range over and through the whole body (for example, skeletal, circulatory, nervous, endocrine).

Based on such a preliminary sketch, the fundamental anatomy of a motile, elongated animal may readily be envisaged to resemble a complex tube having a triple-layered construction. The outermost layer of the tube is the body wall, the most conspicuous component here being the integumentary system. The innermost layer, which encloses the

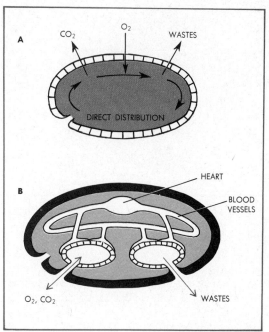

14 · 3 Contrasts between large and small animals. *If an animal is small and its surface is thin and permeable* (A), *then breathing and excretion may occur directly through the body surface, and the internal transport of materials may be accomplished without special structures. But if an animal is larger and its surface is thick and impermeable* (B), *then the breathing and excretory surfaces usually are parts of specialized, interiorized organ systems and internal transport of materials is accomplished by distinct circulatory systems.*

open channel through the tube, is represented principally by the alimentary system. And the bulky middle layer contains all other organs and systems. Such a triple-layered picture of animal architecture is actually more than a rough analogy; for at an early stage of development most animal embryos do consist of just three layers, one inside the other and each originally not more than one cell thick. From the outside inward, these so-called *primary germ layers* are known as the *ectoderm,* the *mesoderm,* and the *endoderm* (Fig. 14.4). Subsequently they each proliferate greatly and give rise to the triple-layered adult "tube." Ectoderm forms, for example, the integumentary and the nervous systems. Mesoderm develops in part into the muscular, circulatory, and reproductive systems. Endoderm produces the alimentary system. Other systems arise from different germ layers in different animal groups.

Indeed, the specific patterns of embryonic growth

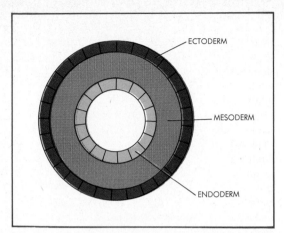

14 · 4 The three germ layers of an animal embryo. *These layers will give rise to the triple-layered "tube" of the adult body, as in Fig. 14.1. Ectoderm generally forms epidermis and nervous system, endoderm forms the alimentary system, and mesoderm develops into muscular, circulatory, and reproductive systems. The other systems arise from different germ layers in different animal groups.*

and the degrees of anatomic complexity they come to attain are major criteria by which we distinguish taxonomically between actual animal types.

GROWTH AND STRUCTURE

It can be shown that, in any organism, generalized traits appear earlier during development than specialized traits (see also Chap. 2); the more generalized a trait, the sooner it develops. For example, a human embryo develops vertebrate characteristics (for example, rudiments of a vertebral column) before mammalian characteristics (for example, rudiments of hair); mammalian characteristics before human characteristics (for example, rudiments of a chin); and only at the very last moment does the embryo acquire the specific personal traits that will distinguish the adult uniquely from all other human adults (see Fig. 28.20). Analogous successions of progressively less general, hence more specific, developmental stages characterize the embryonic histories of all animals.

We know also that general traits are shared by more organisms than special traits. Indeed, this correlation is a universal basis of classifying organisms; the higher a taxonomic rank, the more generalized are the traits that define the organisms at this rank. For example, the general trait of having a vertebral column defines a higher taxonomic level (namely, a subphylum) than the more specialized trait of having

hair (namely, a class). Since therefore animal development produces a sequence of progressively less generalized traits, and since such traits can be used to establish taxonomic position, it follows that developmental patterns can be used to subclassify the Metazoa. Developmental patterns actually have been used in this way, and Metazoa are arranged into a hierarchy of large taxonomic subunits. Representing ranks higher than phyla, these subcategories are without equivalents among Metaphyta.

Developmentally the first and thus the most generalized trait of animals is their *level of organization.* All animals typically begin life as single cells, and some then develop no farther than to a tissue level of complexity. But others do pass beyond this level during their embryonic phase and become predominantly more complex. Accordingly, the metazoan category is said to include two taxonomic *branches* (Fig. 14.5). In the branch *Parazoa,* the highest level of organization is the tissue. This branch happens to encompass just one phylum, the *sponges* (Porifera). The second metazoan branch comprises the *Eumetazoa,* and these animals are defined by the presence of permanent organs and particularly also of organ systems. The organ level is the highest principally in two phyla, the *coelenterates* and the *ctenophores.* All other Eumetazoa pass beyond the organ level during their development and come to exhibit a conspicuous organ-system level of construction. This structural difference between organ and organ-system levels serves as a basis for further taxonomic distinction. Indeed, the distinction is reinforced by an additional one, namely, different *symmetries* of the body.

The trait of symmetry has a very high degree of generality; it appears in animal development very soon after levels of organization are established. At very early stages, the embryos of all animals are radially symmetrical; they are solid or hollow balls composed of a few cells. Sponge embryos subsequently form adults exhibiting a variety of symmetries, asymmetries most particularly. This change from the original embryonic radiality appears to be correlated with a change in way of life: sponge embryos (and larvae) are actively motile, whereas the adults are exclusively sessile. Among the Eumetazoa, some groups retain the initial radiality throughout embryonic and larval life, and this symmetry then carries over more or less unchanged into the adult stage as well. In all other Eumetazoa, the initial radiality very rapidly changes to an embryonic bilaterality, and the remaining embryonic period as well as the larval and adult stages then usually remain bilateral.

On this basis, we may subclassify the branch Eumetazoa into two taxonomic *grades* (see Fig. 14.5).

The grade *Radiata* includes the coelenterates and the ctenophores. These animals are identified both by an organ level of construction and by a pronouncedly radial symmetry in the embryos, larvae, and adults. All other Eumetazoa exhibit a system level of construction and they are primarily bilateral. These constitute the grade *Bilateria*. In most Bilateria not only the embryos but also the larvae and adults are bilateral. Such adults characteristically are motile and elongated, and they typically possess a head. In numerous Bilateria, however, the adult is specialized to pursue a sluggish or sessile way of life and, as pointed out earlier, a secondary tendency toward radiality or some form of asym-

14 · 5 Taxonomy, level of organization, and symmetry. *The grade Radiata is identified by primary as well as secondary radial symmetry, regardless of whether the adults are sessile or motile. The grade Bilateria is identified by primary bilateral symmetry and by adults which are bilateral if motile or often secondarily radial if sessile.*

metry is then usually manifest and a head is absent as well (for example, starfishes). Apparently, adult symmetries and ways of life tend to be correlated; adult bilaterality and motility go together, as do adult radiality or asymmetry and sessilism or sluggishness. Note, however, that whereas this generalization holds fairly well for the Bilateria, it does not hold for the Radiata. For example, the pronounced adult radiality of jellyfishes might be construed as an adaptation to sessilism; yet jellyfishes are highly motile. Adult radiates actually include sessile attached types as well as creeping and swimming motile types, and all are basically radial. We may conclude, therefore, that the division of Eumetazoa into Radiata and Bilateria is based wholly on *primary*, or embryonic, symmetries; *secondary*, or adult, symmetries then may or may not be the same and may or may not be correlated with ways of life.

After symmetry, the next most generalized trait is the form of the *alimentary structures;* once symmetry is established in the embryo, the pattern of the alimentary system is among the first to become elab-

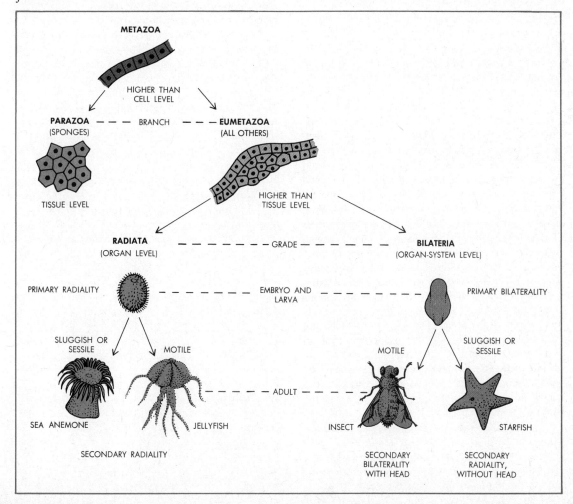

METAZOA

HIGHER THAN
CELL LEVEL

PARAZOA — — — BRANCH — — — EUMETAZOA
(SPONGES)   (ALL OTHERS)

TISSUE LEVEL

HIGHER THAN
TISSUE LEVEL

RADIATA — — — — — GRADE — — — — — BILATERIA
(ORGAN LEVEL)   (ORGAN-SYSTEM LEVEL)

PRIMARY RADIALITY — — — — EMBRYO AND — — — — PRIMARY BILATERALITY
LARVA

SLUGGISH OR   MOTILE   MOTILE   SLUGGISH OR
SESSILE   SESSILE

SEA ANEMONE   JELLYFISH — — — ADULT   INSECT   STARFISH

SECONDARY RADIALITY   SECONDARY   SECONDARY
BILATERALITY   RADIALITY,
WITH HEAD   WITHOUT HEAD

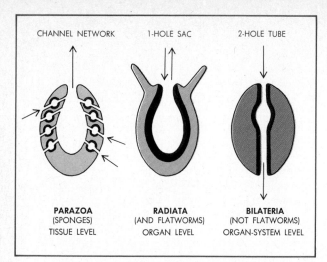

14 · 6 Alimentary patterns of Metazoa. *The positions of the alimentary cells are shown as dark layers. In Radiata and Bilateria, the alimentary portions are endodermal; the outer body parts are principally ectodermal in radiates, and both ectodermal and mesodermal in bilateral animals.*

orated. Three major alimentary patterns are encountered among Metazoa (Fig. 14.6). One, unique to the sponges, may be described as a *channel network* pattern. Alimentary channels here ramify extensively throughout the body and communicate with the exterior via openings in the body wall. The channels are lined by flagellate cells which function in cooperative groups and which are specialized particularly for alimentation. Thus, as would be expected in a sponge, the alimentary apparatus exhibits a primitive tissue level of construction.

The second type of alimentary architecture may be considered to have a *one-hole sac* pattern. A single opening in the sac functions as both mouth and anus, and the lining of the sac is a single tissue layer which includes digestive cells. This lining represents one of the primary germ layers, namely, the endoderm. It becomes identifiable after the early embryo acquires an internal cavity with an opening communicating with the exterior—the cavity of the later alimentary sac. At such a stage one other of the three primary germ layers is already present as well, namely, the integumentary ectoderm. The third germ layer, mesoderm, may not have formed at all as yet or may be indistinct as a few cells between ectoderm and endoderm. A one-hole sac alimentary system is encountered in all Radiata and in one phylum of the Bilateria, namely, the flatworms.

The third alimentary pattern characterizes all other Bilateria and may be described as a *two-hole tube* system. Developmentally, such a tube arises from a sac. The embryos of the Bilateria first develop a one-hole endoderm-lined sac as do the embryos of the

radiates and flatworms. But whereas the latter then retain the sac design permanently, the bilateral embryos do not: a second opening soon develops in the sac, typically at the end of the body opposite to the first opening. One opening then specializes as a mouth, the other as an anus, and the tube interconnecting them becomes the alimentary tract in which food passes only one way, from mouth to anus.

Of the two openings formed in the embryo, which becomes the mouth and which the anus? The answer varies for different bilateral groups (Fig. 14.7). In one group, the original opening of the one-hole sac forms the mouth, and the second opening developed later becomes the anus. In the other group the pattern is reversed, the first opening forming the anus, the second the mouth. We may use this distinction to define two general, descriptive categories among the Bilateria. In the *Protostomia*, the first opening is the mouth, and in the *Deuterostomia*, the second opening is the mouth. Protostomia include most of the phyla of worms, as well as mollusks, arthropods, and numerous other phyla. There are fewer phyla among the Deuterostomia, their best-known members being the echinoderms and the chordates.

Taken together, the level of organization, the symmetry, and the alimentary pattern provide a broad outline of the fundamental body form of any animal. Alimentary pattern and symmetry specify

14 · 7 Taxonomy and alimentary patterns. *Among radiate animals, the single alimentary opening develops in the embryo and serves as both mouth and anus in the adult. Among Bilateria, the original alimentary opening of the embryo becomes the mouth in Protostomia, the anus in Deuterostomia. In each case a second alimentary opening develops later at the opposite end of the animal.*

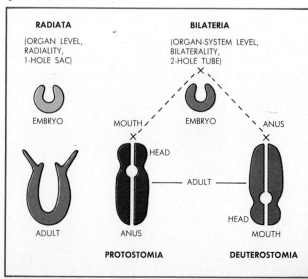

the basic interior and exterior architecture, respectively, and the organizational level specifies the complexity of the architectural building blocks. More detailed characterizations may now be obtained by studying the interior structure of animals, that is, the *mesodermal* portions developing between the alimentary endoderm and the integumentary ectoderm.

In the Radiata, mesoderm arises by the migration of a few cells from the ectoderm. Such cells are *mesenchymal* and this middle layer does not become elaborated much further even in the adults. In many cases it becomes quite bulky as a result of jelly secretion by the cells of the mesenchyme. In any event, the mesoderm of the Radiata adds little toward a taxonomic subclassification of the group.

In the Bilateria, however, the mesoderm does provide important further distinctions. In these animals mesoderm cells accumulate far more extensively than in the Radiata, and the cells also become organized into numerous tissues, organs, and systems. Indeed, the bulk of the adult body comes to have a mesodermal origin. In different bilateral embryos the mesoderm arises either from the ectoderm or from the endoderm or from both of these primary layers. Accordingly, we may distinguish between *ectomesoderm* and *endomesoderm* (Fig. 14.8). In only comparatively few cases does mesoderm arise purely from ectoderm or purely from endoderm. Most Bilateria develop their middle layer from both of the other layers. Frequently, the mesoderm of the larva tends to be partly or largely ectomesodermal, and the mesoderm of the adult then is predominantly endomesodermal.

In some Bilateria, for example, the flatworms, the mesoderm of the adult fills completely the region between the ectodermal integument and the endodermal alimentary system. In parts of this middle layer the mesoderm cells may remain loose, jelly-secreting mesenchyme, as in the Radiata, but in other

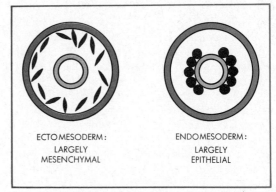

ECTOMESODERM: LARGELY MESENCHYMAL

ENDOMESODERM: LARGELY EPITHELIAL

14 · 8 Mesoderm derivations. *The colored layers represent embryonic ectoderm (darker color) and endoderm (gray); the lighter-colored cells are mesoderm. Mesenchymal ectomesoderm, characteristic of Radiata and many Bilateria, typically originates as a series of loose cells. Epithelial endomesoderm, as in most Bilateria, usually forms as cohesive layers of cells from the start. Both kinds of mesoderm often develop in bilateral animals.*

parts the cells develop into the components of specialized organ systems. Animals so constructed may be considered to form a *subgrade* within the grade Bilateria, namely, the subgrade *Acoelomata*. The significance of this term will become apparent presently (Fig. 14.9).

14 · 9 Mesoderm and coelom localizations in the subgrades of the Bilateria. *The principal body cavity in the Pseudocoelomata is a pseudocoel, and in the Coelomata, a true, peritoneum-lined coelom. In coelomates a dorsal and ventral mesentery (formed by two mesodermal layers) supports the alimentary tract.*

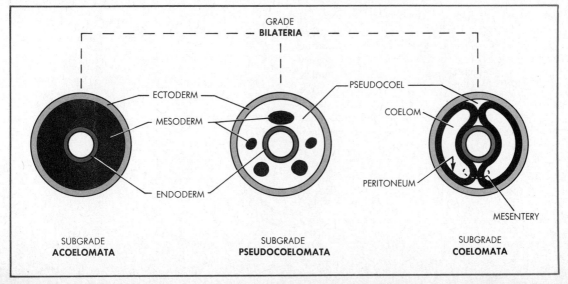

GRADE
BILATERIA

ECTODERM

MESODERM

ENDODERM

PSEUDOCOEL

COELOM

PERITONEUM

MESENTERY

SUBGRADE
ACOELOMATA

SUBGRADE
PSEUDOCOELOMATA

SUBGRADE
COELOMATA

In all other Bilateria, the middle body layer does not form a solid accumulation of body parts. Instead, as the mesoderm develops in the embryo, a more or less extensive free space is left between the ectoderm and the endoderm. This space later becomes the *principal body cavity* of the adult. Such a cavity is advantageous adaptively in several ways. For example, it makes the activities of the body wall mechanically independent of those of the alimentary tract. Moreover, the cavity permits an animal to attain considerable size, for fluid filling such a cavity may serve as a hydraulic "skeleton." In many cases, also, the fluid may aid in transporting food, wastes, and gases to and from deep-lying body parts, which in a large animal would otherwise be beyond the effective range of direct diffusion from integument and alimentary tract.

In many Bilateria, for example, the rotifers, the roundworms, and the hairworms, the principal body cavity is bounded on the outside directly by the body wall and on the inside directly by the alimentary system. The mesoderm in such cases is aggregated only in specific circumscribed regions within the body cavity, and this cavity is not lined by any membranes. Animals so characterized constitute another subgrade of Bilateria, the *Pseudocoelomata* (see Fig. 14.9).

In all remaining Bilateria, the body cavity arises in a different way. During the embryonic development of mesoderm, part of it becomes applied against the inner surface of the ectoderm, and another part comes to surround the alimentary tract. In such animals, therefore, the body wall comprises both ectodermal and mesodermal layers, and the alimentary wall comprises both mesodermal and endodermal layers. The mesoderm later give rise to various tissues and organs, and particularly also to a membrane which comes to enclose the free space between the outer and inner mesodermal parts. This mesodermal membrane is a *peritoneum*. Vertical portions of it known as *mesenteries* suspend the alimentary tract from the body wall. The free space enclosed within the peritoneum now represents the principal body cavity. We may note that any cavity bounded completely by mesodermal components, especially by a peritoneal membrane, is known as a *coelom*. Accordingly, animals possessing a coelom may be said to constitute a bilaterial subgrade of *Coelomata* (see Fig. 14.9). The meaning of the terms "acoelomate" and "pseudocoelomate" then becomes clear. Acoelomates are animals without

14 · 10 Patterns of coelom-formation in the subgrade Coelomata. *The pattern shown for lophophorates is but one of several known to occur in that group.*

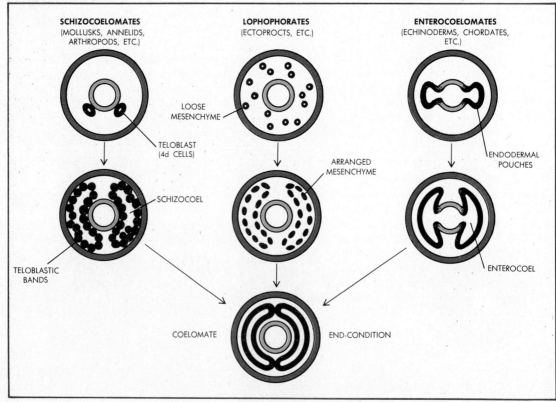

SCHIZOCOELOMATES
(MOLLUSKS, ANNELIDS, ARTHROPODS, ETC.)

LOPHOPHORATES
(ECTOPROCTS, ETC.)

ENTEROCOELOMATES
(ECHINODERMS, CHORDATES, ETC.)

LOOSE MESENCHYME

TELOBLAST (4d CELLS)

ENDODERMAL POUCHES

SCHIZOCOEL

ARRANGED MESENCHYME

TELOBLASTIC BANDS

ENTEROCOEL

COELOMATE   END-CONDITION

coelom and indeed without body cavity of any kind. Pseudocoelomates possess a *pseudocoel*, or "false" coelom, that is, a body cavity lined by ectoderm, endoderm, perhaps partly by mesoderm, but in any event not by a peritoneum. The cavity thus resembles a true coelom superficially.

Among the coelomate Bilateria, further subgroups may be distinguished on the basis of *how* the coelomic cavities develop (Fig. 14.10). In one such subgroup, comprising among others the phyla of mollusks, annelids, and arthropods, the adult mesoderm arises in the embryo from two endoderm-derived cells, one on each side of the future gut. These so-called *teloblast* cells then proliferate into a pair of *teloblastic bands* of tissue. At first the bands are solid cellular aggregates, but later each splits into outer and inner mesodermal sublayers. Thus, because the coelom forms by a splitting of mesoderm, it is called a *schizocoel*. Animals characterized by body cavities of this type may be designated as *schizocoelomates*, taxonomically roughly equivalent to a superphylum.

In another coelomate subgroup, represented principally by echinoderms and chordates and again constituting a superphylum, the mesoderm arises in the embryo as paired lateral pouches growing out from the endoderm (see Fig. 14.10). The pouches subsequently lose continuity with the endoderm, though their inner portions remain applied against the developing alimentary system and their outer portions become applied against the developing body wall. The final condition is essentially quite similar to that in schizocoelomates. However, since the mesoderm and the coelom here are derivatives of the future gut, or *enteron*, the body cavity is called an *enterocoel*. Animals possessing such cavities are therefore known as *enterocoelomates*.

In a third subgroup or superphylum, various other patterns of coelom formation are encountered. In one, for example, loose mesoderm cells of the embryo later migrate in amoeboid fashion and simply arrange themselves into a continuous peritoneal layer (see Fig. 14.10). Coeloms developed in this and various similar ways have not been given any special technical names. Animals in this subgroup also include types in which coeloms form in unique schizocoelic and enterocoelic fashion as well. The whole assemblage of animals may be referred to as the *lophophorates*, to which belong the phyla of phoronids, ectoprocts (moss animals), and brachiopods (lamp shells). They are not particularly abundant today, but their ancestors may have been among the most ancient coelomate animals from which both the schizocoelomate and the enterocoelomate superphyla later evolved.

We may therefore characterize the Bilateria broadly

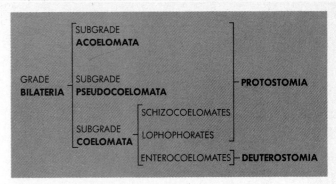

14 · 11 *Interrelations of the major bilaterial groups.*

both from the standpoint of mesoderm and coelom formation and from that of alimentary development, that is, whether the mouth or the anus forms first in the embryo. The subgrades Acoelomata and Pseudocoelomata happen to be protostomial, the mouth here being formed first. In the subgrade Coelomata, protostomial types include the lophophorate and schizocoelomate superphyla, whereas deuterostomial types are represented by the enterocoelomate superphylum (Fig. 14.11).

A trait of considerable anatomical and functional significance is the presence or absence of body *segmentation*. A segmented body is one that is marked by transverse constrictions into an anteroposterior succession of segments. Two fundamentally different types of segmentation may be recognized. One type, *superficial* segmentation, originates in the ectoderm and by and large affects only the body wall. The result is a series of ringlike creases in the cuticle and the body wall, which may facilitate the bending or telescoping of the body. Superficial segmentation has little additional significance; it occurs fairly haphazardly among acoelomate and pseudocoelomate animals (Fig. 14.12).

Of greater importance is the second type, *metameric* segmentation, which originates in the mesoderm and affects most mesodermal as well as most ectodermal body parts. Here the developing mesoderm of the embryo becomes constricted transversely into segmental portions, usually in anteroposterior sequence. Each such portion then typically acquires its own coelomic body cavity and peritoneum. The most anterior segments thus are the oldest. Soon after such mesodermal segments have formed, the ectoderm overlying them comes to develop in a correspondingly segmental fashion. As a result, the whole thickness of the body with the exception of the endoderm becomes marked off into segments, or *metameres*. The metameric arrangement subsequently persists in later development, and most ectodermal and mesodermal organ systems form as segmented series of parts. For example, the muscular system arises in segmental blocks called *somites*. Each metamere may also have its own excretory, reproductive, skeletal, locomotor, and nervous organs. However, the metameres are not completely independent, for each organ system usually includes components which interconnect the organs in adjacent segments (see Fig. 14.12).

Metameric segmentation occurs only in the coelomate animals, more specifically, in the annelids, the

14 · 12 Segmentation. A, superficial segmentation; only the integument exhibits ringlike creases. B, metameric segmentation; both ectodermal and mesodermal derivatives are arranged segmentally, and the coelom is subdivided into metameric anteroposterior compartments. C, diagram of the segmental arrangement of organ systems in metameric animals. The excretory organs shown are so-called metanephridia, essentially tubes leading from the coelomic body cavity to the outside.

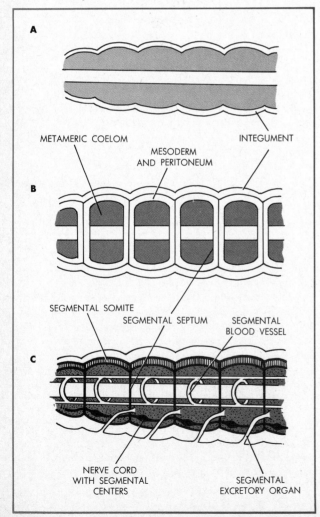

A

METAMERIC COELOM   INTEGUMENT

MESODERM
AND PERITONEUM

B

SEGMENTAL SOMITE

SEGMENTAL SEPTUM   SEGMENTAL
                       BLOOD VESSEL

C

NERVE CORD
WITH SEGMENTAL   SEGMENTAL
CENTERS   EXCRETORY ORGAN

arthropods, and the vertebrates. We know that annelids are related fairly closely to arthropods, but that these two groups are not closely related to the vertebrates. It appears therefore that metamerism evolved at least twice independently, once in the schizocoelomate superphylum and once in the enterocoelomate superphylum. In arthropods and vertebrates the metameric pattern is particularly evident in the embryos and larvae, but becomes obscured to a greater or lesser extent in the adults. It is probably not an accident that arthropods and vertebrates also happen to be the most advanced and most successful animals, and it is fair to say that this success is in large part due to the segmental construction. For metamerism entails two basic adaptive advantages. First, the mere repetition of a pattern is itself often exceedingly useful, on the principle that there is safety in numbers. In a sense, simple metameric segmentation as in annelids provides the same kinds of advantages on an organ-system level that simple multicellularity provides on a cellular level. Second, once a repeat pattern is available, the units of the pattern can become elaborated and specialized in different ways. This is exemplified in arthropods and vertebrates, which have become far more diversified structurally and functionally than any other animals primarily through diversification of their segments. Here again we find an organ-system level parallel to the different specializations possible among the cells of a multicellular aggregate. The recipe for biological success thus appears to be described well by the classic phrase "repeat, then vary."

At this point, our classification of metazoan growth and structure has reached a fairly substantial level of detail; the next level of detail describes the individual phylum and its smaller taxonomic subunits. Indeed, the phylum of sponges is uniquely characterized already, by structural details outlined above. To distinguish the two radiate phyla, coelenterates and ctenophores, we must specify at least one more structural difference; and to distinguish among the several phyla within each subgrade or superphylum of the Bilateria, we must likewise specify one and in most cases more than one additional architectural difference. It is one of the functions of the remainder of this and the following chapters to provide just such specifications.

Based on the developmental and structural characteristics of living animals, inferences may be made about the presumable evolutionary interrelations of the principal animal groups. Because of the inferential nature of such interrelations, many of them are still far from certain or universally agreed on even in a tentative way. Nevertheless, reasonable hypotheses of the likely major interrelations have been made; they are summarized in Fig. 14.13.

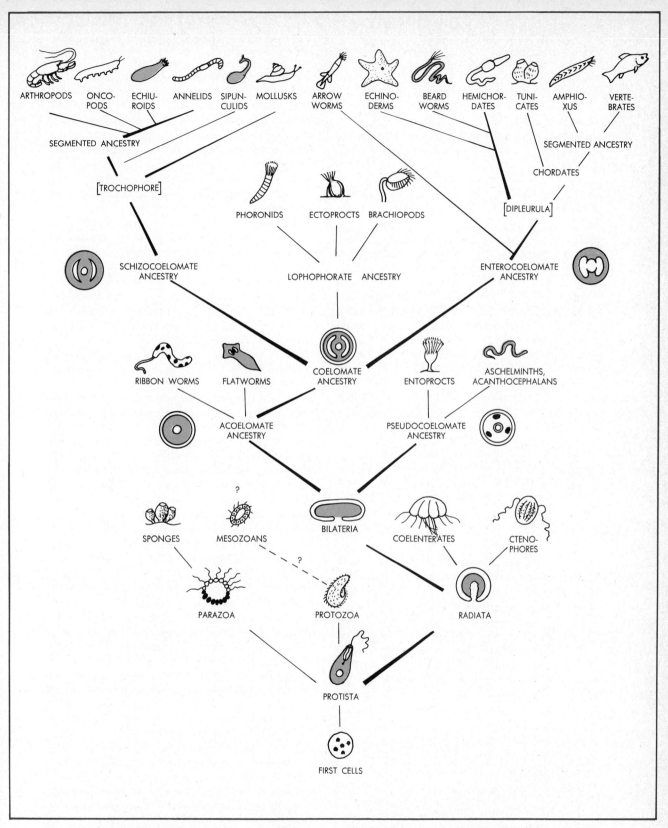

14 · 13 Probable and possible evolutionary interrelations of animals. *Read from bottom up. The presumable main paths of interconnection are marked by heavier lines. The terms trocho-phore and dipleurula in square brackets near top of figure refer to larval types that may have represented ancestral evolutionary stages.*

REPRESENTATIVE TYPES: NONCOELOMATES

BRANCH PARAZOA

Animals at tissue level of organization; body tissues not homologous to primary germ layers of other animals.

Phylum Porifera (sponges)

"Pore-bearing" animals; mostly marine, some in fresh water; adults sessile, often in colonies; body radial to asymmetrical; alimentation via channel system with flagellate collar cells; nerve cells absent; 5,000 species.

> *Class Calcarea* (chalk sponges): spicules calcareous with one, three, or four rays. *Leucosolenia, Sycon, Leuconia*
> *Class Hexactinellida* (glass sponges): spicules silicaceous with six rays, often fused into continuous networks. *Hexactinella, Euplectella*
> *Class Demospongiae* (horny sponges): spicules of horny spongin, silica, or both, sometimes none; if present, silica spicules with one to four rays. *Halisarca, Spongia*

The late embryos and the larvae of sponges are flagellate externally and free-swimming. They are globular in shape and consist essentially of two cell layers. When they settle and metamorphose into the

14 · 14 Sponge development. *1, blastulalike embryo underneath maternal collar cell layer; 2, inversion (embryo turns inside out through opening in nonflagellated half, resulting in exteriorized flagella); 3, amphiblastula larva; 4, invagination of flagellated half into nonflagellated half; 5, larva settles; 6, open end of embryo closes over and an osculum breaks through at the free side, establishing the basic adult structure.*

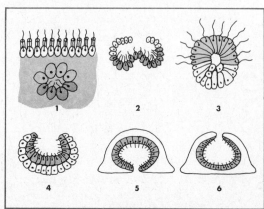

sessile adults, the larvae undergo a curious *inversion:* the flagellate cells of the outer layer eventually come to lie in the interior, and the cells of the originally interior layer come to lie on the outside (Fig. 14.14). Jelly-secreting cells later migrate in between the outer and inner layers, hence an adult sponge exhibits a basically three-layered construction. In view of the earlier inversion, however, the layers are not equivalent to ectoderm, mesoderm, and endoderm.

The outer layer of a mature sponge typically forms a covering epithelium (Fig. 14.15). In it, some of the cells contain contractile myofibrils. At numerous places in the epithelium, small pores, or *ostia,* lead into the interior of the body and admit food-bearing water currents. The middle layer contains in addition to jelly-secreting cells also a variety of other cells which form, for example, reproductive cells and skeletal *spicules.* These are needle-shaped secretions consisting of from one to six rays. The classes of sponges are defined on the basis of the characteristic numbers of rays present and the different chemical compositions of the spicules. In the interior layer of a sponge, the flagellate cells, or *choanocytes,* acquire collars and become remarkably similar to the protozoan collar flagellates. The flagella of the choanocytes are directed into the central cavity of the sponge, the *spongocoel,* which communicates with the ostia on the surface. Water is drawn through the ostia into the spongocoel by the beat of the flagella, and a common stream of water then leaves the sponge through an *osculum,* a larger opening from the spongocoel. Food present in the water flowing past the choanocytes is trapped by them and digested intracellularly in food vacuoles.

Three degrees of structural complexity may be recognized among sponges, according to how intricately the water channels are arranged (Fig. 14.16). In the simplest, or *asconoid,* sponges, the spongocoel is a wide, straight-walled chamber, with choanocytes lining the entire wall. The sponge *Leucosolenia* exemplifies this pattern. More complexly constructed are the *syconoid* sponges, represented by *Sycon,* for example. In this pattern the spongocoel is extended into numerous deep side chambers, and only the latter contain choanocytes. Architecturally most elaborate are the *leuconoid* sponges, exemplified by *Leuconia.* Here the spongocoel forms a highly branched network of narrow channels ramifying extensively throughout the sponge. Choanocytes are present only in small chambers spaced out along the course of the channels.

All three degrees of structural complexity are encountered in the calcareous sponges, but glass and horny sponges are predominantly leuconoid. Glass

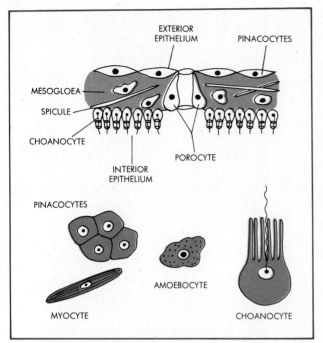

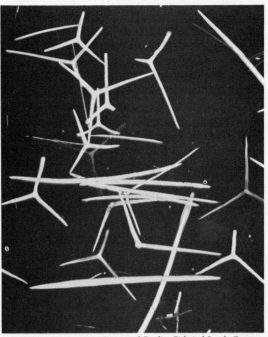

Courtesy of Carolina Biological Supply Company.

14 · 15 Tissues and cells of a sponge. *Diagrams: top, the three basic tissue layers. In the mesogloea, free skeletal spicules and amoebocytes are indicated. A porocyte is a tubular cell with a water canal into the sponge. Bottom, some of the cell types. Note the larger nucleolus in an amoe-* bocyte. *Myocytes are modified pinacocytes with contractile myofibrils. The choanocyte collar consists of a circlet of cytoplasmic extensions, as shown (see also Fig. 12.32). Variants of amoebocytes form numerous other cell types with different functions. Photo: sponge spicules.*

14 · 16 Three levels *of structural complexity in sponges. The black indicates the position of the layers of collar cells.*

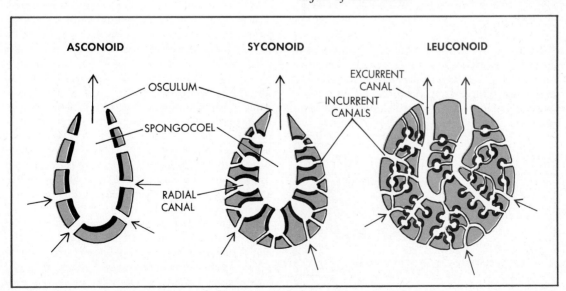

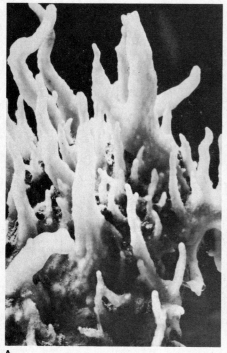  

A   B   C

14 · 17   Sponges. A, *a calcareous type.* B, *a glass sponge; the ropy tuft anchors the animal to the sea floor.* C, *a horny sponge; to this group also belong the bath sponges.*

sponges are characterized further by their syncytial nature and by the absence of a definite surface epithelium. Many of these marine sponges occur in deep water, where conspicuous tufts of skeletal material anchor them to the sea floor. The horny sponges

14 · 18   Vegetative reproduction in sponges. In budding, a bud may form either a separate (left) or an attached (right) individual. In a gemmule, elongated spicules and pinacocytes form exterior layers; amoebocytes fill the interior.

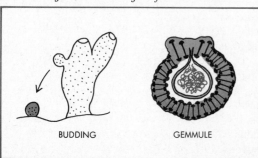

BUDDING   GEMMULE

include all the known freshwater species, in addition to numerous marine types (Fig. 14.17).

Apart from propagating via sex cells, sponges may also reproduce by *budding,* a process in which small aggregates of cells collect at some region of the body surface of a parent sponge (Fig. 14.18). Such aggregates may then fall off and develop into independent sponges or may retain continuity with the parent and form extensive colonies of sponges. The animals may also be fragmented into pieces, and each piece usually reconstitutes a whole individual. Indeed, it has long been known that a sponge may be dissociated completely into a suspension of loose cells (for example, by pressing the animal through fine-meshed cheesecloth). The separated cells then migrate in amoeboid fashion into an aggregated mound and reconstitute an intact, normally structured whole. All freshwater and some marine sponges produce *gemmules* under conditions of drought or low temperature. A gemmule consists of an external layer of cells with spicules and a variety of internal cells. When environmental conditions become favorable again a gemmule "germinates" and forms a new whole sponge.

Because of their unusual developmental patterns, their choanocytes and alimentary water channels, and their primitive tissue level of organization generally, sponges are regarded almost universally as an independent branch of metazoan evolution. The animals may well have arisen from protozoan stocks, and in any case their line of descent appears to have been terminal; sponges have probably produced nothing but other sponges.

BRANCH EUMETAZOA

Animals above tissue level of organization; adult body formed from embryonic ectoderm, mesoderm, and endoderm.

GRADE RADIATA

Animals attaining organ level of complexity; with primary and typically also secondary radial symmetry. *Cnidaria* (coelenterates); *Ctenophora* (comb jellies).

Phylum Cnidaria (coelenterates)

Tentacle-bearing radiates with *cnidoblasts* containing *nematocysts;* alimentary cavity with single opening; polymorphic, with medusae and/or polyps; solitary or colonial, largely marine; development via *planula* larvae; 10,000 species.

Class Hydrozoa: polyp and medusa phases alternating or either phase reduced or omitted; alimentary cavity not partitioned; solitary and colonial, some as floating colonies, some as coral colonies. *Obelia, Hydra, Gonionemus, Millepora, Physalia*
Class Scyphozoa: medusae dominant; alimentary cavity typically partitioned by four gastric septa; jellyfishes. *Aurelia*
Class Anthozoa: polyps only; alimentary cavity partitioned by six, eight, or multiple numbers

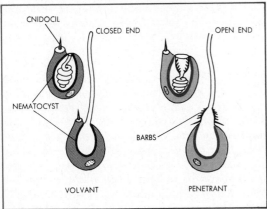

14 · 19 Two basic types of cnidoblasts, undischarged and discharged (schematic). Numerous variants of each type are known.

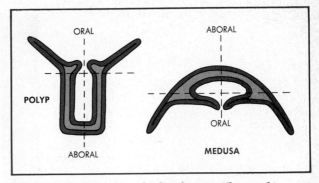

14 · 20 Coelenterate body forms. *The oral-aboral axis is long compared with the body diameter in a polyp, whereas the reverse holds true in a medusa. Both polyp and medusa are variants of a single common body pattern.*

of gastric septa; corals, sea anemones, sea fans, sea pens, sea feathers, sea pansies.

The phylum is identified by the presence of stinging cells, or *cnidoblasts,* found singly or in grouped "batteries" around the mouth, on the tentacles, and elsewhere on and within the body. Each cnidoblast contains a horny *nematocyst,* a stinging capsule with a coiled, hollow filament inside, which may have a closed or open free end (Fig. 14.19). Appropriate mechanical or chemical stimuli cause explosive discharge of a nematocyst filament, a process in which the filament turns inside out. Filaments with closed ends (*volvants*) function in trapping and holding prey. Those with open ends (*penetrants*) pierce through the body surface of prey and secrete a paralyzing toxin. A massive injection of coelenterate toxin is powerful enough to kill a man.

Coelenterates are basically dimorphic, the two structural forms being the *polyp* and the *medusa* (Fig. 14.20). If the main axis of the body is long relative to the diameter, the animal represents a cylindrical polyp; and if the main axis is short relative to the diameter, the animal is an umbrella- or bell-shaped medusa. Polyps are sessile vegetative individuals; medusae are free-swimming, sexual individuals. Both types bear tentacles and both or either one only may occur in a given life cycle.

The body wall of any coelenterate, polyp or medusa, is fundamentally three-layered (Fig. 14.21). The outside layer is an ectodermal *epidermis* which, in many polyps, secretes an exoskeleton. The latter may be little more than a thin, transparent layer of chitin or it may be a massive accumulation of calcareous stone, as in the reef-forming coelenterates.

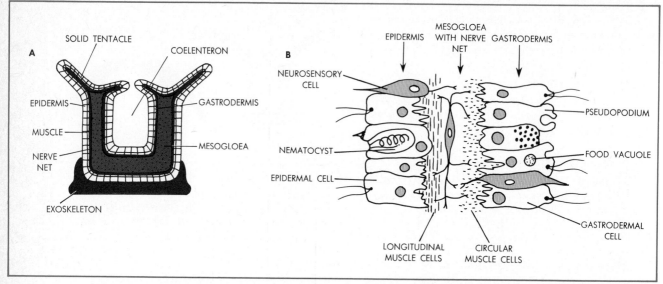

A

SOLID TENTACLE

COELENTERON

EPIDERMIS

MUSCLE

NERVE NET

GASTRODERMIS

MESOGLOEA

EXOSKELETON

B

EPIDERMIS

MESOGLOEA WITH NERVE NET

GASTRODERMIS

NEUROSENSORY CELL

NEMATOCYST

EPIDERMAL CELL

PSEUDOPODIUM

FOOD VACUOLE

GASTRODERMAL CELL

LONGITUDINAL MUSCLE CELLS

CIRCULAR MUSCLE CELLS

The inside layer is an endodermal *gastrodermis*, which lines the alimentary cavity and contains flagellate and amoeboid digestive cells. Between epidermis and gastrodermis is a mesodermal *mesogloea*, a layer containing mesenchyme cells. These secrete varying amounts of connective tissue fibers and also jelly. In polyps the amount of jelly is generally small and is absent altogether in exceptional cases (particularly *Hydra*). But in medusae the jelly becomes extensive and forms the bulk of the animal. Embedded in the mesogloea is a simple nerve net which innervates sensory cells present in both the epidermis and the gastrodermis. Scyphozoa and Anthozoa also possess distinct muscle cells. Hydrozoa are without them, however, but contain myofibrils in most of the cells of the epidermis and gastrodermis. All three body

14 · 21 Coelenterate structure. A, sectional diagram of a polyp showing the three layers of the body. B, cell types in the three body layers, as in jellyfishes and sea anemones. Note that the epidermal and gastrodermal cells have pseudopodial bases here; these bases are T-shaped in Hydrozoa. Note also that true muscle cells as shown here are absent in Hydrozoa, myofibrils being present within the T-shaped epidermal and gastrodermal cells in these animals.

layers or only the outer two contribute to the formation of tentacles.

All coelenterates develop via a *planula*, an ovoid larva consisting of an external ciliated ectoderm and an inner cell mass representing both mesoderm and endoderm (Fig. 14.22 and Plate XX, 33). The planula later acquires an interior cavity and an opening at one end, the beginnings of the alimentary system. After a planula swims about for a time it settles and gives rise to the polyp phase of a life cycle. In many

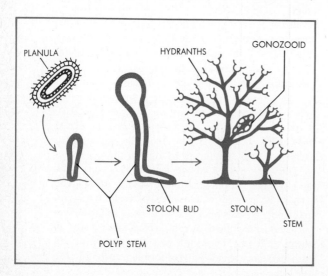

PLANULA

HYDRANTHS

GONOZOOID

STOLON BUD

STOLON

STEM

POLYP STEM

14 · 22 Hydrozoan colonies. The planula larva acquires a thin mesogloea and a hollowed-out center which represents the early coelenteron. The larva eventually settles at its anterior end and proliferates into the stem of the first polyp. Branching growth from both upright stems and stems along the ground (stolons) then gives rise to a colony of polyps. Most of the polyps are tentacled feeding individuals (gastrozooids, or hydranths); some are medusa-forming gonozooids.

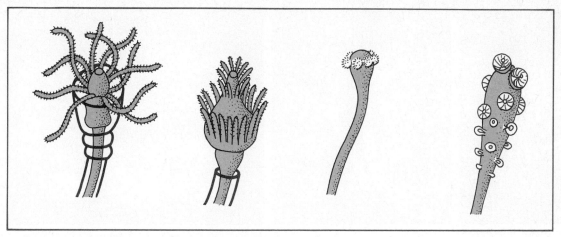

14 · 23 *Polymorphism of hydrozoan polyps. Left, gastrozooid (hydranth) as in* Obelia, *with mouth at tip of conical manubrium. A cuplike chitinous protective layer, the perisarc, surrounds the lower part of the hydranth. Left center, gastrozooid as in* Tubularia, *with double wreath of tentacles and perisarc terminating below hydranth. Right center, protective dactylozooid, with batteries of stinging cells and without mouth or tentacles. Right, gonozooid, studded with medusa-producing buds. In types such as* Obelia, *a perisarc envelops the gonozooid.*

Hydrozoa, the planula grows into a highly branched colony of polyps possessing a continuous, interconnecting alimentary cavity. Each polyp here consists of a stalk, constructed from the three body layers and usually covered by a thin chitinous exoskeleton, and a terminal *hydranth*, a tentacled feeding individual (Fig. 14.23). Several other polymorphic variants of polyps usually form as well. For example, many hydrozoan colonies include protective individuals, stalked non-feeding knobs of tissue studded with batteries of stinging cells. At various locations within a colony reproductive individuals also arise sooner or later. In these the stalks carry neither hydranths nor protective bodies but medusa buds. The latter eventually detach from the colony and begin the free-swimming medusa phase of the life cycle.

A hydrozoan medusa (Fig. 14.24 and Plate XXI, 34) possesses tentacles around the bell margin, eyespots and balancing organs at the tentacle bases, and the mouth, or *manubrium*, is often equipped with long, trailing tentacles as well. From the alimentary cavity emanate four *radial canals* at right angles to each other. At the bell rim these canals are continuous with a *ring canal* circling the bell margin.

A nerve cord runs alongside the ring canal. Hydrozoan medusae usually possess a *velum*, a thin, contractile extension of the bell projecting underneath the bell like a shelf. Mature medusae also possess sex organs, one along each of the radial canals. Fertilized eggs give rise to planulae which start a new life cycle.

In many Hydrozoa (for example, *Obelia*), the polyp and medusa phases play a roughly equally important role. In other groups, however, one or the other phase is reduced or omitted altogether. For example, in types such as *Gonionemus* the planula produces a single, solitary polyp. This individual is comparatively short-lived and soon transforms into a medusa, the dominant phase in this genus (Fig. 14.25). By contrast, *Hydra* does not develop medusae at all. Instead, the solitary parent polyp develops sex organs itself and gives rise to new polyps directly. Polyps are analogously dominant in the Portuguese man-of-war, *Physalia*, in which several polymorphic types of polyps collectively form a floating colony (Plate III, 7). Sessile polyp colonies with highly reduced medusa stages are characteristic of *Millepora*, the reef-forming

14 · 24 *Hydrozoan medusae: sectional view.*

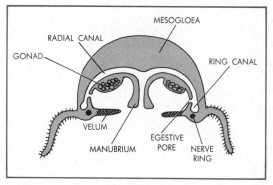

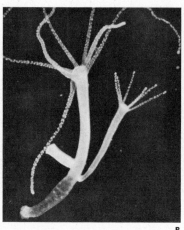

A B C

14 · 25 Various Hydrozoa. *A,* Gonionemus *medusa, from life. B,* Hydra, *from life; note the two budded offspring on parental animal. C, portion of skeleton of* Millepora, *the millepore coral.*

14 · 26 Development of Scyphozoa. *Diagram: the planula settles and becomes a scyphistoma larva. The larva may then bud via stolons and eventually via strobilation, a segmentation process resulting in free ephyra larvae. Photo: scyphistoma larvae of* Aurelia, *hanging from underside of rock; young larva at right, strobilating older larvae in middle and at left. Note ephyrae being cut off at left.*

millepore corals. Individual polyps here sit in depressions in the calcareous exoskeleton they themselves have secreted. The polyps interconnect via tunnels left in the surface layers of the stony mass.

In the class Scyphozoa, the planula settles and forms a *scyphistoma* larva, a solitary polyp form (Fig. 14.26). By a process of budding known as *strobilation,* a scyphistoma then cuts off from its free end a succession of free-swimming larval medusae, so-called *ephyrae.* Each ephyra ultimately matures as a sex-organ-possessing medusa, the adult jellyfish. Such medusae (Fig. 14.27 and Plate XXI, 35) resemble their hydrozoan counterparts in most respects, except that the margin of the umbrella is scalloped into four (or more often a multiple of four) lappets, and a velum and a marginal nerve ring are most often lacking. In some jellyfishes radial canals do

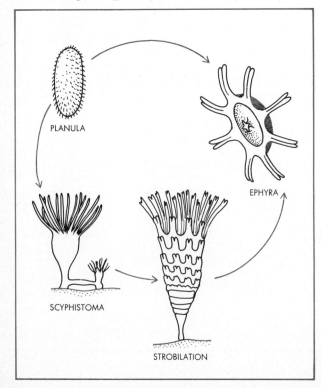

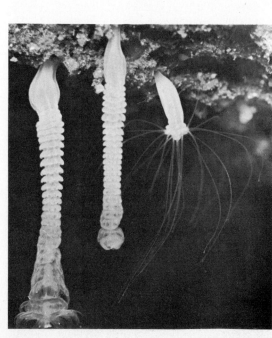

occur; in *Aurelia* even a ring canal is present. However, most Scyphomedusae are without a canal system. Instead, the alimentary cavity is quite large and is partitioned by four gastrodermal folds, or *gastric septa*, extending into the cavity. The free edges of the septa are studded with stinging cells and enzyme-secreting digestive cells. Sex organs form in sets of four.

In the Anthozoa, medusae are not formed at all; polyps are sexual and give rise to planulae that develop into new polyps directly. In such polyps (Fig. 14.28), the mouth is an elongated slitlike opening. At one or at both ends of it is a band of flagellated cells, the *siphonoglyphs*, which aid in circulating water into and out of the alimentary cavity. The latter is always partitioned by gastric septa. Each of these septa bears a longitudinal band of muscles on one side. The anthozoan mesogloea is a true connective tissue, with numerous cells and fibers and very little jelly. Tentacles and gastric septa number eight or multiples of eight in one anthozoan subclass, the Octocorallia. All members of it are colonial, and many colonies contain several polymorphic variants of polyps. The subclass includes, for example, the sea fans (*Gorgonia*), the sea pens (*Pennatula*), the red precious corals (*Corallium*), the blue corals (*Heliopora*), the soft corals (*Alcyonium*), and the organ-pipe corals (*Tubipora*). In a second subclass, the Hexacorallia, tentacles and gastric septa occur in sets of six or multiples of six. To this group belong the solitary sea anemones (for example, *Metridium*), and the colonial stony corals (for example, *Meandra*, the brain corals). Stony corals are the most important and abundant reef formers (see Color Plates XXII–XXIII).

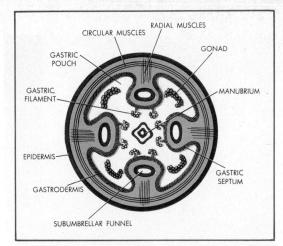

14 · 27   Jellyfish. *Horizontal section of medusae indicating the structure of most types of medusae in this class (*Aurelia *does not possess gastric pouches and septa as shown here*).

Many biologists consider the hydrozoan medusae to represent the most primitive living coelenterates, and polyps are regarded as precociously prolonged and elaborated larval forms. Moreover, coelenterates as a whole are widely believed to represent the most primitive living Eumetazoa. If this view is correct,

14 · 28   Anthozoan structure. *A, cutaway section through a sea anemone, to show the gastric partitions. B and C, the symmetries and ground plans of Octocorallia and Hexacorallia, with longitudinal muscles on the ventral surfaces of the gastric septa and with one or two siphonoglyphs.*

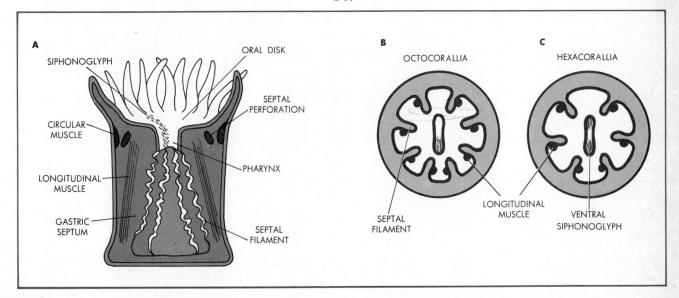

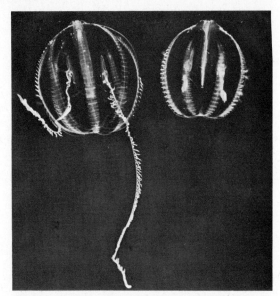

14 · 29 The ctenophore Pleurobrachia, *from life. Note comb plates in comb rows, fringed tentacles, and position of sensory balancing organ at top of animals.*

14 · 30 Ctenophore structure *is illustrated by this diagram of Pleurobrachia.*

the Bilateria would all be descended from ancestral coelenterates. The pertinent evidence is inconclusive, however. It is equally possible that coelenterates, and radiates generally, constitute an independent branch of eumetazoan evolution. In that case the Bilateria must have arisen separately from an early protistan source. This important issue cannot be resolved from the data now available.

Phylum Ctenophora (comb jellies)

Medusalike construction; locomotion by eight meridian *comb plates;* tentacles if present with *colloblasts;* development via *cydippid* larvae; exclusively marine; 80 species. *Pleurobrachia, Cestum, Beroë.*

This small but cosmopolitan phylum includes only solitary members. Most comb jellies are glassily transparent, globular in shape, and part of the zooplankton. Some (for example, the Venus's-girdle *Cestum*) are compressed laterally into a ribbonlike form, and others (for example, *Beroë*) are flattened and adapted secondarily to a creeping existence (Fig. 14.29).

The epidermis bears eight rows of *comb plates,* each plate being a short band of cilia. In globular types (for example, *Pleurobrachia*), the eight comb rows converge toward one point of the body where a

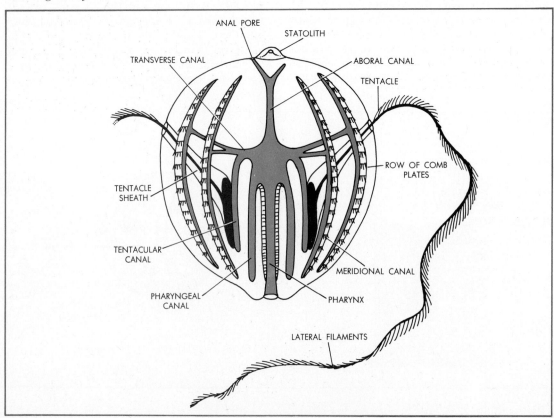

PLATE XVII

30. Ferns.
*A, sori on underside of fern leaf.
Indusia are not present in this type.
B, a fern gametophyte.*

A

B

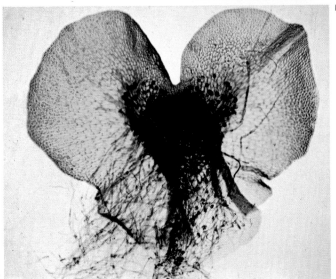

B, courtesy of Carolina Biological Supply Company

31. Motion and feeding.
Animals obtain food either by active locomotion or by trapping small moving food organisms, as among the sessile featherduster worms illustrated here. These worms, named Sabella and related distantly to earthworms, live in attached tubular housings and project their feathery food-trapping crowns from the open ends of the tubes.

32. Stages in the life cycle of amphibia
*symbolize the main stages in the sexual
development of animals generally.
A, eggs; B, embryo; C, larva; D, adult.
The transition from embryo to larva is achieved
by hatching; that from larva to adult,
by metamorphosis. The photographs
are not reproduced to
the same scale.*

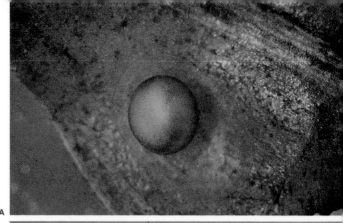

A

B

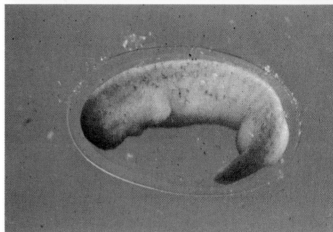

C

D

PLATE XX

33. *Tubularia*
*(**A**) and **Clava** (**B**). In both photos, note the tentacle-equipped hydranths.*

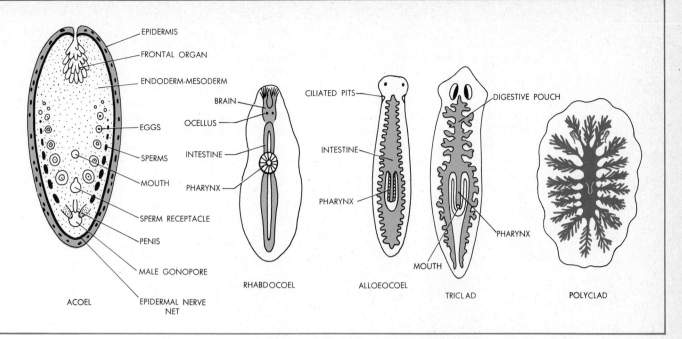

Labels on figure:
EPIDERMIS
FRONTAL ORGAN
ENDODERM-MESODERM
BRAIN
OCELLUS
EGGS
INTESTINE
SPERMS
PHARYNX
MOUTH
SPERM RECEPTACLE
PENIS
MALE GONOPORE
EPIDERMAL NERVE NET
ACOEL
RHABDOCOEL
CILIATED PITS
INTESTINE
PHARYNX
ALLOEOCOEL
MOUTH
PHARYNX
TRICLAD
DIGESTIVE POUCH
POLYCLAD

14 · 31   Free-living flatworms. *Diagram depicts types from each of the major orders. Acoel structure is shown in greatest detail, and although this diagram is larger than the others the actual animal is far smaller than the others (animals are not drawn to the same scale). Note the variations in the architecture of the alimentary system.*

complexly organized balancing organ is present (Fig. 14.30). Most comb jellies possess two long, feathery tentacles, each anchored in an epidermal pouch extending deep into the body. The tentacles are equipped with muscles and may be withdrawn completely into their pouches. On the feathery fringes of a tentacle are numerous *colloblasts*, adhesive cells which aid in trapping microscopic food. The single alimentary opening, located at a point of the body opposite the balancing organ, leads into a series of gastrodermis-lined chambers and canals. A jelly mesogloea fills the space between epidermis and gastrodermis and, as in coelenterates, a nerve net is embedded in the jelly. All ctenophores are hermaphrodites, that is, a single individual develops both male and female sex organs. Fertilized eggs form larvae which come to resemble the adults more and more as they mature.

Ctenophores are generally believed to have evolved from coelenterates, as an offshoot line from early stocks of hydrozoan medusae.

BRANCH EUMETAZOA

    GRADE BILATERIA. Animals at organ-system level of complexity; with primary and typically also secondary bilateral symmetry

        SUBGRADE ACOELOMATA. Protostomial, that is, adult mouth formed from first embryonic opening; mesoderm from ectoderm and endoderm, filling space between body surface and alimentary system, hence internal body cavities not present; skeletal or breathing systems absent; nervous system basically a nerve net, with localized thickenings. *Platyhelminthes, Nemertina*

Phylum Platyhelminthes (flatworms)

Body flattened dorsoventrally, alimentary system with single opening; without circulatory system; 10,000 species.

    Class Turbellaria: free-living flatworms; epidermis cellular or syncytial, without cuticle. *Dugesia,* planarians
    Class Trematoda: flukes; holotrophic parasites; epidermis absent; exterior with cuticle and one or more suckers. *Clonorchis,* liver flukes; *Schistosoma,* blood flukes
    Class Cestoidea: tapeworms; fluid-feeding parasites; epidermis absent, exterior with cuticle; without alimentary system. *Taenia*

Free-living flatworms of the order Acoela are believed to be the most primitive Bilateria and, according to a widely held view, to be descended more or less directly from ancestral coelenterates. Indeed, acoel structure is rather planulalike. An acoel worm consists of a single-layered epidermis and an inner cell mass representing both mesoderm and endoderm (Fig. 14.31). A single opening in the epidermis on the underside of the flattened body is the sole component of an alimentary system; the endo-

14 · 32 Planaria. *Photo: the free-living planar-ian* Dugesia. *Note eyes, pointed lateral lobes (auricles) at level of eyes, pharynx in middle of underside, and darkly stained branches of digestive tract. Diagram: cross section through the anterior portion of a planarian. The epidermis is wholly or partly ciliated as shown here. Mesenchyme makes up the parenchyma.*

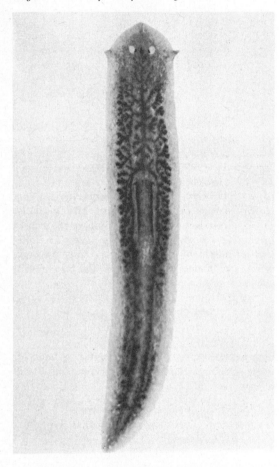

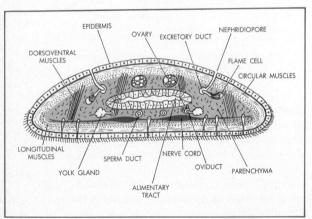

derm mass within the body digests food intracellularly. All other orders are organized more complexly and possess a definite alimentary system composed of mouth, pharynx, and blind-ended intestine. These organs form a straight saclike tube in one order (Rhabdocoela), a straight tube with lateral pouches in another (Alloeocoela), a three-branched system with lateral pouches in a third (Tricladida), and a many-branched system in a fourth (Polycladida).

The triclad planarians (for example, *Dugesia*) are the best-known turbellarians and their organization typifies that of the class as a whole. A planarian is up to ½ in. long and possesses a roughly triangular front end with a pair of conspicuous dorsal eyes (Fig. 14.32). The epidermis of such a worm is glandular and ciliated ventrally, and secretes a mucus track on which the ventral cilia propel the animal in a gliding form of locomotion. A planarian may also move and swim by muscular undulations of its body; two or more layers of muscle underlie the epidermis. Underneath the muscles is the nervous system. Its main components are a brain ganglion anteriorly and a pair of ventral nerve cords passing from this ganglion posteriorly. Transverse nerve connections between the longitudinal cords give the system a ladderlike appearance (Fig. 14.33).

Mid-ventrally, the worm possesses a muscular, tubular pharynx which can be protruded and retracted. The mouth at the tip of the pharynx grasps small food particles. The pharynx leads into three interconnected intestinal pouches, one pouch pointing anteriorly, the other two, posteriorly. Each pouch bears numerous lateral branches which increase the digestive surface. The intestinal lining contains flagellate and amoeboid cells and, as in coelenterates, food is digested intracellularly. The space between the body wall and the intestine is filled solidly with mesenchyme, connective tissue fibers, muscle strands, and some amount of jelly. Also present here are the excretory and reproductive systems.

Excretion is accomplished by a so-called *flame-bulb* system (see Fig. 14.33). A flame bulb is a single cup-shaped cell with a tuft of flagella pointing into the cavity of the cup. On its outside surface the cell filters the body fluids, and the filtrate is then propelled by the flagella into a duct with which the flame bulb connects. Numerous flame bulbs are present throughout the mesenchyme, and their ducts join and eventually lead to the exterior through several excretory pores. The reproductive system includes both male and female systems in the same worm, that is, the animals are hermaphrodites. The male system contains an anteroposterior series of pairs of testes, with ducts leading to a copulatory organ just behind the pharynx. The female system anal-

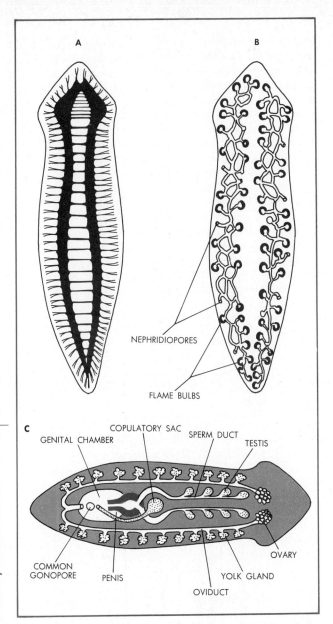

NEPHRIDIOPORES

FLAME BULBS

C

GENITAL CHAMBER

COPULATORY SAC   SPERM DUCT

TESTIS

COMMON
GONOPORE

PENIS

OVARY

YOLK GLAND

OVIDUCT

14 · 33 Planarian structure. A, scheme of the ladder-type nervous system. B, the excretory system. Flame bulbs are the cup-shaped filtering cells, and nephridiopores are the exterior openings of the duct system. C, the reproductive system. Both male and female systems are present in these hermaphrodites.

planarians, encysted fertilized eggs develop directly into miniature offspring worms, but in the marine orders Acoela and Polycladida free-swimming ciliated larvae are formed. These transform gradually into adult worms.

Flukes of the class Trematoda differ from free-living flatworms in three principal respects, all correlated with the parasitic way of life of these animals (Fig. 14.34). First, flukes are without epidermis, the exterior layer being a tough and resistant horny cuticle secreted by mesenchyme cells. Second, eyes and other sense organs are reduced or lacking altogether. And third, flukes possess one or more muscular suckers, hooks, or other adhesive devices with which they hang on to host tissues. In their internal structure flukes are otherwise like free-living flatworms, rhabdocoels most particularly. Their life cycles are complex and usually require one or more intermediate hosts. An illustrative example is the cycle of the Chinese liver fluke, *Clonorchis sinensis*, described in Chap. 9 (see Fig. 9.18).

The cestodes, or tapeworms, are intestinal parasites lacking an alimentary system of their own; they absorb molecular nutrients directly through the body surface. These worms likewise possess an exterior cuticle instead of an epidermis. The body consists of a head, equipped with hooks and suckers, a neck, and a segmental series of *proglottids* formed continuously behind the neck (see Fig. 9.15). The oldest proglottids are at the hind end of these often extremely long (up to 50 ft) worms. Nerve cords and excretory ducts run the entire length of a worm, but each proglottid contains a complete male and female reproductive system. The male system matures earlier, hence proglottids near the middle of the worm contain ripe sperms, whereas proglottids nearer the hind end contain ripe eggs. Fertilization most often takes place between two proglottids of the same worm. The life history of the beef tapeworm, *Taenia saginata*, has been outlined in Chap. 9 (see Fig. 9.17).

Both flukes and tapeworms are believed to have evolved from ancestral rhabdocoel turbellarians. Rhabdocoels also appear to have given rise to the second acoelomate phylum, the nemertines.

Phylum Nemertina (proboscis worms)

Alimentary system with separate mouth and anus; circulatory system present; eversible proboscis within rhynchocoel; 600 species. *Cerebratulus, Lineus*

These animals, often also called "ribbon worms," range in length from less than 1 in. to under 2 ft, but one species of *Lineus* may attain a length of

ogously consists of numerous pairs of ovaries and ducts leading into a genital chamber. The copulatory organ of the male projects into this chamber, and during mating the copulatory organ of one worm is inserted into the genital chamber of another. In

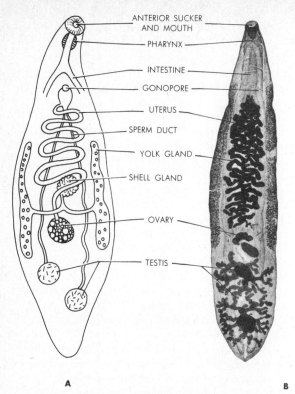

ANTERIOR SUCKER AND MOUTH
PHARYNX
INTESTINE
GONOPORE
UTERUS
SPERM DUCT
YOLK GLAND
SHELL GLAND
OVARY
TESTIS

A   B

14 · 34   *The structure of a trematode* (Clonorchis sinensis, *the Chinese liver fluke*).

some 100 ft. The phylum is the first in which we encounter an alimentary system with a one-way tube construction (Fig. 14.35). Mouth, fore-gut, intestine, and anus are the principal components. The wall of the system is a single layer of ciliated cells, and digestion occurs *extracellularly,* that is, right in the space of the alimentary tract. In this respect nemertines are again different from all previous phyla. Food is moved through the tract by the muscular contractions of the body wall, and a solution of nutrient molecules in water is absorbed into the tract lining.

The nemertines are also the first phylum in which we encounter a circulatory system with blood. The system lies in the mesenchyme and consists basically of two lateral vessels joined anteriorly and posteriorly. In many cases a dorsal vessel or cross-connecting transverse vessels are also present. The blood of most nemertines is colorless but in some forms it contains hemoglobin within blood cells. Excretion is accomplished by a flame-bulb system similar to that in flatworms. Also similar is the nervous system, which contains anterior brain ganglia and a pair of lateral nerve cords in the body wall.

The most distinctive trait of a nemertine is its *proboscis,* an anterior muscular tube which in the rest state lies in a chamber, the *rhynchocoel,* dorsal to the intestine (Fig. 14.36). The tip of the proboscis is attached by a retractor muscle to the wall of the rhynchocoel. Muscular contraction of this wall exerts pressure on the fluid within the chamber, resulting in an explosive eversion of the proboscis to the exterior. The animal uses this organ in locomotion, in burrowing, and principally in trapping food animals, which become encoiled by the proboscis. In many cases the tip of the proboscis is armed with a *stylet,* a sharp-pointed spike, and with glands which secrete poison into a wound made by the stylet.

Like the flatworms, nemertines possess anteroposterior pairs of sex organs, with ducts leading to the outside. Fertilized eggs typically develop into ciliated, helmet-shaped larvae (for example, *pilidium* larvae), and these become adult worms through a drastic metamorphosis in which most body parts become reorganized greatly.

14 · 35   *Nemertine structure. The diagram depicts the alimentary, circulatory, and excretory systems. The circulatory cross vessels are continuous and not actually interrupted by the alimentary tract.*

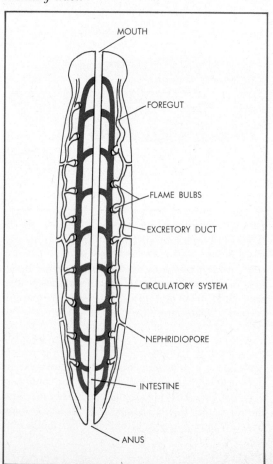

MOUTH
FOREGUT
FLAME BULBS
EXCRETORY DUCT
CIRCULATORY SYSTEM
NEPHRIDIOPORE
INTESTINE
ANUS

SUBGRADE PSEUDOCOELOMATA

Protostomial, first embryonic opening becoming mouth; mesoderm from ectoderm and endoderm, aggregated locally between body surface and alimentary system, hence leaving pseudocoelic body cavity lined by ectoderm and endoderm; nervous system not a nerve net; skeletal, circulatory, or breathing systems absent; excretion largely by flame-bulb systems. *Aschelminthes, Acanthocephala, Entoprocta*

Phylum Aschelminthes (sac worms)

Body often segmented superficially; cells or nuclei constant in number and arrangement for each species; musculature typically not as circular and longitudinal layers; pharynx usually highly differentiated.

Class Rotifera: microscopic aquatic animals with anterior wheel organ; 1,500 species. *Philodina*
Class Gastrotricha: microscopic aquatic animals with cilia and cuticular spines; 200 species. *Chaetonotus*
Class Kinorhyncha: microscopic marine animals without cilia; 100 species. *Echinoderella*
Class Priapulida: marine animals up to 3 or 4 in. long; body with prosoma and trunk; 5 species. *Priapulus*
Class Nematoda: roundworms; cylindrical, elongated worms without cilia; 12,000+ species. *Ascaris, Trichinella, Necator*
Class Nematomorpha: hairworms; highly elongated animals with reduced alimentary system; parasitic young; 80 species. *Gordius*

This phylum encompasses a heterogeneous collection of types usually grouped into classes as above, but which may equally well be regarded as separate phyla. The phylum as a whole exhibits some very distant evolutionary affinities to the flatworms, and early rhabdocoel flatworms in particular are often hypothesized to have been the specific ancestors. If so, rotifers may possibly provide an evolutionary bridge between flatworms and gastrotrichs, and the latter in turn may form a link to the other aschelminth classes. Only the rotifers and the nematode roundworms are sufficiently abundant to warrant more than passing attention here.

Rotifers are syncytial animals, and each member of a given species is constructed from exactly the same number of embryonic cells. Thus, any two members of a species are structurally identical and the architecture of each species can be mapped out precisely, nucleus for nucleus. Such cell and nuclear constancies also characterized virtually all other groups of the sac worms.

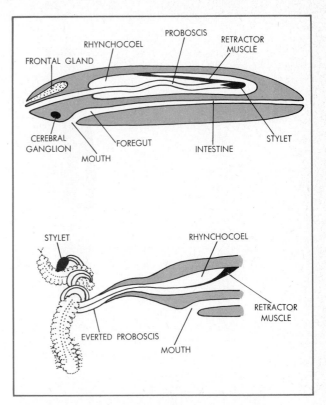

14 · 36 The proboscis apparatus. Top, position of rhynchocoel and proboscis in rest condition. Bottom, everted proboscis entangling and capturing a clam worm.

The body of a rotifer is usually organized into a *head*, a *trunk*, and a tapered *foot* (Fig. 14.37). The head bears an anterior *wheel organ*, a wreath of cilia used in swimming locomotion and in the creation of food-bearing water currents. The end of the foot is typically bifurcated into two *toes*, each containing a *cement organ*. The exterior of the body is a tough scleroprotein cuticle, secreted by the thin epidermis underneath. Transverse ringlike grooves scored into the cuticle give the animal a segmented appearance. The epidermis bounds the pseudocoelic body cavity in which mesenchymal cells are present. Muscle cells are not arranged as distinct layers, but crisscross in specific patterns through the pseudocoel. The alimentary tract is a straight syncytial tube. It begins at the mouth ventral to the wheel organ and leads into a pharynx. Here called *mastax*, the pharynx is a complex muscular chewing organ containing cuticular jaws studded with teeth. The detailed construction of the mastax differs for different species. Behind the mastax, the remainder of the alimentary tract has a ciliated inner surface. The tract terminates at the

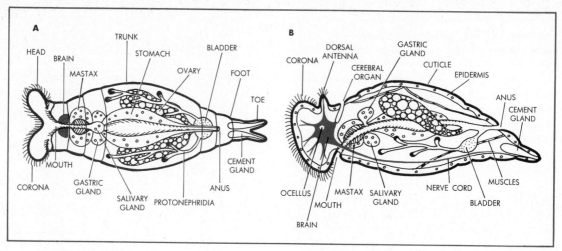

14 · 37 Rotifer structure. A, ventral view. B, side view.

anus, located in the region between the toes of the foot.

From a brain ganglion dorsal to the pharynx lead two main ventral nerve cords (see Fig. 14.37). Most rotifers possess an eyespot directly on the dorsal surface of the brain ganglion. Particularly characteristic of these animals is a *dorsal antenna,* a small surface projection dorsal to the brain ganglion. The precise function of this innervated and ciliated organ is obscure. The excretory system consists of a single pair of flame-bulb clusters in the pseudocoel. At their posterior ends the ducts from the flame bulbs form a urinary bladder, which opens into the hind part of the intestine.

During spring and summer, female rotifers produce eggs which develop into new females without being fertilized. These females in turn reproduce without fertilization and many generations of females succeed one another in this manner. In the fall, the females lay some eggs which are smaller than the rest. These hatch into small males, structurally simplified individuals lacking digestive systems but capable of producing sperms. The fertilized eggs then formed possess thick, hard shells and may resist unfavorable environments for very long periods. Under suitably favorable conditions, for example, in the following spring, the shelled eggs develop into females (Fig. 14.38). In some types of rotifers males are unknown altogether, the species being propagated exclusively by unfertilized eggs. This phenomenon of egg development without fertilization is called *parthenogenesis.* We have already encountered it in the discussion on social insects (Chap. 8).

Nematodes may possibly be the most abundant

of all animals, both in numbers of individuals and numbers of species. Named species total only about 12,000 at present, but new ones are being described at an average rate of one per day. Virtually every other animal may harbor at least one and often more than one type of parasitic nematode. In addition,

14 · 38 Life cycle of rotifers. Amictic eggs produced by females develop parthenogenetically into new generations of females. Mictic eggs develop parthenogenetically into simplified males (bottom), which produce sperms. If sperms then fertilize mictic eggs, encysted winter eggs are formed. These produce new generations of females the following spring.

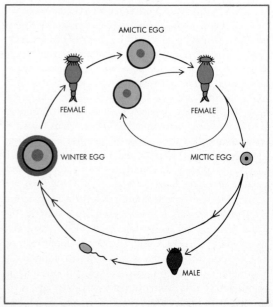

roundworms also parasitize plants, and free-living nematodes are so abundant that a spadeful of garden earth is likely to contain up to a million worms. Informed guesses place the number of existing nematode species at about 500,000 which would make the class the second largest group of animals after the insects.

The mouth and anus of a nematode are at the tapered ends of the cylindrical body (Fig. 14.39). A resistant exterior cuticle is produced by a usually syncytial epidermis, which is thickened on its inner surface into four longitudinal *chords*, one dorsal, one ventral, and one on each side of the body. Epidermal nuclei are usually present only in these chords, of which the lateral ones are visible externally as faint lines. In each body quadrant between the chords, the epidermis is underlain by a layer of muscles the cells of which are aligned longitudinally only; the worm can bend but not stretch. The nervous system consists of a nerve ring around the pharynx, a dorsal and a ventral nerve cord, and from one to three pairs of lateral cords. Sensory bristles on the surface and often also eyes are present in free-living worms, but sense organs are reduced in parasitic types. The well-developed pharynx is a long muscular tube, often expanded along its length into one or more bulbous enlargements. The interior canal of the pharynx has a highly characteristic, three-cornered cross section. The excretory system is unique and does not resemble that of any other type of animal. It consists of a pair of large cells, the *ventral glands*, situated under the pharynx. The necks of these cells lead forward to excretory pores.

Male nematodes are usually smaller than female ones and are identifiable by their curled posterior ends. Single or paired testes communicate via ducts with the hindgut. Sperms of nematodes are unique in being amoeboid, not flagellate (and we may note that cilia or flagella are lacking entirely in the class). Ovaries similarly connect with ducts leading to the exterior. Fertilization takes place by copulation. During their larval development nematodes typically molt their cuticles, and enlargement of the larvae takes place at these molting stages. The life cycles of the worms are more varied than those of almost any other animal. In the free-living types, the larvae develop directly into new free-living adults. In parasitic types, an infective stage is reached at a given point in development or during the adult phase. Up to that point the worms are free-living, and when they become infective, they must enter a specific plant or animal host within a short time or perish. Numerous nematodes require one or more intermediate hosts for the completion of their life cycles.

Among the serious nematode pests of man (Fig.

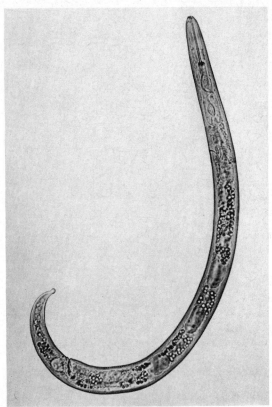

A

B

B, courtesy of Carolina Biological Supply Company.

14 · 39 Nematodes. A, *whole view of a mature female of the nematode* Paratylenchus, *which causes disease in plants.* B, *cross section through the pharyngeal region of* Ascaris. *Note exterior cuticle, longitudinal chords, muscle quadrants, and thick central pharynx with triangular interior canal.*

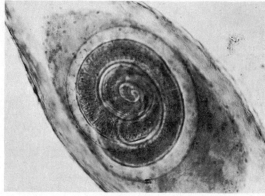

14 · 40 A larva of a trichina worm, *encapsulated in pig muscle. If infected pork is cooked improperly, the larvae are digested out in the intestine of the host and the worms then invade the host tissues.*

14 · 41 Aschelminths. *A, photo of a gastrotrich. B, diagram of kinorhynch structure. C, diagram of a priapulid. D, outline of a hairworm.*

14.40) are the *trichina* worms (*Trichinella spiralis*), introduced into the human body via insufficiently cooked pork; the *hookworms* (for example, *Necator americanus*), which live in soil and infect man by boring through his skin; the *guinea* worms (for example, *Dracunculus medinensis*), which develop as larvae in copepods, enter man via copepod-containing drinking water, and form ulcerating blisters in the skin of man from which the larvae of the next generation are released; and the *filaria* worms (for example, *Wuchereria bancrofti*), transmitted by mosquitos and causing blocks in human lymph vessels. The disease resulting from filarial infections is characterized by immense swellings and is known as *elephantiasis*. One of the relatively less dangerous roundworms is *Ascaris lumbricoides*, a species which lives in the intestine of man and other mammals.

The remaining aschelminth groups display many basic organizational features encountered also in rotifers, nematodes, or both (Fig. 14.41). For example, gastrotrichs resemble rotifers in the organization of the body wall, and hairworms are generally rather like nematodes, though they are exceedingly elongated and thin. Gastrotrichs and kinorhynchs possess rotifer-

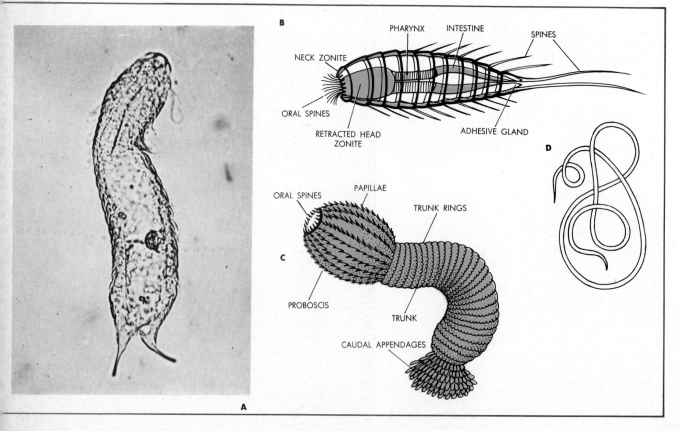

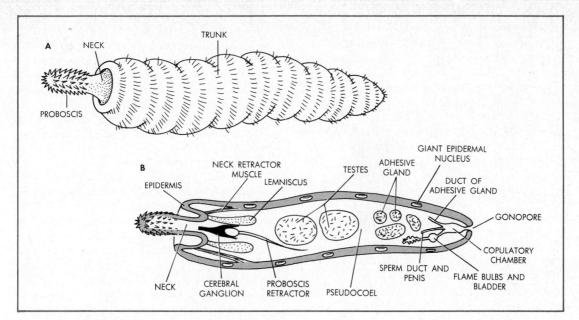

14 · 42 Acanthocephala. *A, external appearance of an acanthocephalan, proboscis extended. B, longitudinal section through A, proboscis retracted, body-wall muscles and female reproductive system not shown. Note the giant nuclei of the epidermis.*

like flame-bulb systems, and in both classes as well as in the priapulids the pharynx is structured remarkably like that of nematodes. Kinorhynchs further contain roundwormlike epidermal chords, molt their larval cuticles, and possess an adult nervous system nearly identical with that of priapulids. But each group also exhibits its own special features; for example, surface spines and bristles in gastrotrichs, conspicuous superficial segmentation in kinorhynchs, a body characterized by a bulbous, warty *prosoma* portion in the anterior region of priapulids, and a reduced or absent alimentary system in the parasitic adults of hairworms. Evidently, a sufficient number of shared traits suggests reasonably close interrelation of these animal groups, yet a sufficient number of unshared traits also suggests that the interrelation probably is not too close.

Phylum Acanthocephala
(spiny-headed worms)

Parasitic, with arthropod intermediate hosts and vertebrate final hosts; nuclear constancy in adult; with armed proboscis; alimentary system absent; excretory system of flame bulbs or absent; 600 species. *Moniliformis*

These worms are similar in some respects to the parasitic flatworms, and they have often been classified with the acoelomates. However, the organization of the animals is clearly pseudocoelomate, and their structure actually relates them to the Aschelminthes; the worms could well be regarded as a class within the Aschelminthes, as indeed they have been by some biologists.

Spiny-headed worms are identified by an anterior, comparatively short proboscis, armed with numerous recurved spines or hooks (Fig. 14.42). This organ of attachment can be withdrawn into the anterior portion of the spiny or warty *trunk*. Like most of the aschelminths, the Acanthocephala exhibit a syncytial structure as adults and the nuclear number is constant for each species. In many cases the external cuticle is superficially segmented, very conspicuously so in types like *Moniliformis*. In the epidermis, a unique *lacunar system* consisting of fluid-filled channels is formed by unlined spaces in the epidermal cytoplasm. This system does not communicate with any other parts or cavities of the body and is believed to function in food transport; the worms are fluid feeders without alimentary systems, and food absorbed through the body surface is thought to be distributed by the lacunar system. At the juncture of proboscis and trunk, the epidermis is extended into the pseudocoel in the form of two elongated bodies, the *lemnisci*, which are thought to serve as reservoirs for the lacunar fluid when the proboscis is retracted.

The epidermis is underlain by an outer circular and an inner longitudinal layer of syncytial muscle fibers. The nervous system consists of an anterior brain ganglion in the proboscis and two longitudinal lateral cords. A pair of reproductive organs lies in

345

ligament sacs, longitudinal membranous chambers within the pseudocoel. Males are equipped with copulatory organs, and the females retain the fertilized eggs within their ligament sacs until larvae have formed. Upon release, the larvae must enter the body cavity of intermediate hosts, which are always insects. If an infected insect is then eaten by a final vertebrate host, the larvae attach to the intestinal lining of the vertebrate and mature into adults.

Phylum Entoprocta

Adults stalked and sessile, solitary and colonial; with mouth and anus inside a circlet of ciliated tentacles; development via unique larvae; 60 species. *Loxosoma, Pedicellina, Urnatella*

Entoprocts are the only pseudocoelomates that are not wormlike. All but the freshwater genus *Urnatella* are marine. Types like *Loxosoma* are solitary, and others, for example, *Pedicellina,* form colonies encrusting rocks, shells, and algae in shallow water. The individual animals are largely microscopic. Each entoproct is attached by a stalk, a continuation of the body wall (Fig. 14.43). The remainder of the body is organized around a U-shaped alimentary system, mouth and anus opening away from the

attachment surface. This oral side is ringed by tentacles which, unlike those of coelenterates, are ciliated. Entoprocts are *filter feeders;* microscopic food organisms are strained out by the tentacles from water currents created by the cilia.

A cuticle covers the body and the stalk but not the tentacles. The epidermis is underlain by a layer of longitudinal muscles. These continue into the tentacles and permit the latter to be curved inward. A gelatinous, mesenchyme-containing pseudocoel extends into the hollow tentacles. In the curve of the alimentary U lies the main nervous ganglion, and near it is a pair of sex organs. Nerves from the main ganglion lead to subsidiary ones near the tentacle crown. The excretory system consists of a single pair of flame bulbs and of ducts opening between mouth and anus.

Some entoprocts are hermaphroditic, but most are not. Eggs develop in a "brood chamber," a depression between mouth and anus (Fig. 14.44). Early embryos just entering the chamber push aside older embryos already there. A brood chamber is therefore likely to contain a series of embryos at all stages of development. A free-swimming, conical larva then forms, of a type quite unique to entoprocts. A remarkable metamorphosis eventually ensues. The larva settles with its mouth-anus side directed downward, and then the whole alimentary system undergoes an internal rotation of 180°, which brings the mouth and anus away from the attached side and into the adult position. A crown of tentacles

14 · 43 An entoproct in sagittal section. Anterior is toward left, dorsal toward bottom. Right diagram shows individual with tentacles tucked in.

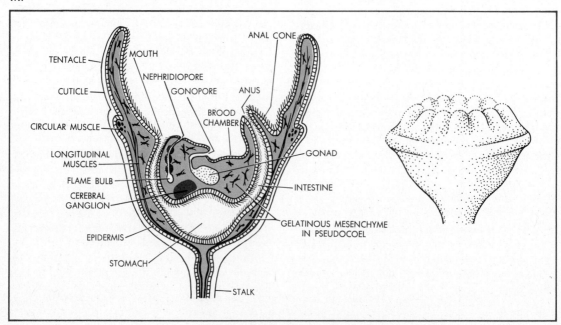

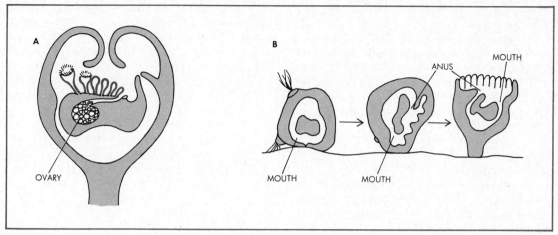

14 · 44 Entoproct development and metamorphosis. A, schematic section through an adult, showing series of progressively older embryos (heavy colored lines) in brood pouch. B, the free larva settles at the oral side, the internal organs then rotate through 180°, and growth of stalk and tentacles subsequently establish the adult organization.

develops, and a colony may arise subsequently by budding from the stalk.

The evolutionary affinities of entoprocts are obscure. The phylum probably represents an independent branch of pseudocoelomate animals, presumably stemming from very distant acoelomate stocks that also produced the coelomates.

REVIEW QUESTIONS

1. What structural and functional features distinguish most Metazoa from most Metaphyta? In what architectural respects are moving animals generally different from sessile ones? What are the chief nutritional patterns among animals? How does alimentation influence the general structural and functional organization of animals?

2. Show in some detail how the basic traits of animals determine and influence the characteristics of all other aspects of animal nature. As far as you can, contrast such typically animal attributes with those generally considered to be characteristic of plants. How does the requirement of locomotion influence the general architecture of an animal?

3. Name the branches, grades, and subgrades of animals. What criteria define each of these ranks? What animals are included in each? Draw up a comprehensive diagram indicating the presumable evolutionary interrelations of all major animal groups.

4. Define Protostomia, Deuterostomia, Bilateria, Parazoa, coelom, schizocoel, enterocoel, mesoderm, ectomesoderm, germ layer, peritoneum, mesentery, metamerism, somite, teloblast, mesenchyme.

5. Show how Bilateria are subdivided taxonomically on the basis of mesoderm and coelom forma-

tion, and show how coeloms arise in different ways in different groups. What is the adaptive advantage of a coelom? Does a pseudocoel offer analogous advantages?

6. Define the phylum Porifera taxonomically. Describe the cell types and principal tissues of sponges. What structures does each cell type produce? Describe the three architectural variants of sponges and indicate classes and genera in which each variant is encountered.

7. Which phyla are included among the Radiata, and what diagnostic features distinguish these phyla? Name the classes of coelenterates and describe the life cycles characteristic of each. Distinguish between polyps and medusae.

8. Describe the structural and functional characteristics of cnidoblasts. What cell types occur in the coelenterate epidermis, gastrodermis, and mesogloea? Describe the structure of a hydrozoan polyp colony. How do polyps of *Obelia* form medusae? Describe the structure of a hydrozoan medusa.

9. Define Scyphozoa taxonomically and describe the structure of a medusa in that class. Define Anthozoa taxonomically and distinguish between the subclasses. Describe the structure of a sea anemone.

Characterize the ctenophores taxonomically and describe the structure of these animals.

10. Which phyla are included among acoelomates? Name the classes of flatworms and describe the main structural features of Turbellaria. Review the life cycles of flukes and tapeworms. Describe the structure of the Acoela and contrast it with that of a planula. What is the specific organization of the reproductive system of planarians?

11. Define the nemertines taxonomically. Describe the structure and function of the proboscis apparatus. Review the sequence of body tissues from the epidermis inward. By what means is food (a) moved through the gut, (b) digested? What is the organization of the nemertine (a) nervous system, (b) circulatory system, (c) excretory system?

12. Give taxonomic definitions of pseudocoelomates, aschelminths, acanthocephalans, and entoprocts. Name the classes of aschelminths and indicate characteristics that justify inclusion of these animals within a single phylum.

13. Describe the structure of a rotifer. What is the phenomenon of cell constancy and in which animal groups is it encountered? Describe the life cycle of a rotifer. What is the structure of a nematode? What are longitudinal chords? Name nematodes found in man.

14. Describe the structure of a spiny-headed worm. What are lemnisci, the lacunar system, ligament sacs? How does the proboscis of an acanthocephalan differ from that of a nemertine? Describe the structure of an entoproct. How does such an animal feed? In what respects are entoprocts different from all other pseudocoelomates?

15. Make a diagram indicating possible evolutionary interrelations among the various pseudocoelomate and acoelomate phyla and classes. On what structural evidence can you base such a diagram?

COLLATERAL READINGS

Berrill, N. J.: "Growth, Development, and Pattern," Freeman, San Francisco, 1961. Several chapters of this valuable book (particularly chaps. 8 and 9) deal specifically with the growth and development of coelenterates (including the formation of polymorphic variants). Other sections analyze growth processes in various invertebrate groups.

Best, J. B.: Protopsychology, Sci. American, Feb., 1963. A review of the interesting research on learning and memory in whole and regenerating planarians.

Brien, P.: The Fresh-water Hydra, Am. Scientist, vol. 48, 1960. A detailed examination of this common but atypical coelenterate.

Buchsbaum, R.: "Animals without Backbones," University of Chicago, Chicago, 1948. A beautifully illustrated introductory account of invertebrates, including types studied in the present chapter.

Cameron, T. W. M.: "Parasites and Parasitism," Wiley, New York, 1956. Among many other parasitic types discussed in this book, flukes, tapeworms, and roundworms receive prominent attention.

Chitwood, B. G.: Nematoda, in "McGraw-Hill Encyclopedia of Science and Technology," vol. 9, 1960. A concise, informative article by one of the foremost students of roundworms.

Griffin, D. R.: "Animal Structure and Function," Holt, New York, 1962. The second chapter of this paperback contains a brief description of the body plans of selected animals.

Hyman, L: "The Invertebrates," vols. 1–5, McGraw-Hill, New York, 1940–1959. The most comprehensive English-language treatise on invertebrate animals. Accounts of the phyla studied in this chapter are in the first three volumes. The first also includes discussions of general animal characteristics.

Lane, C. E.: Man-of-war, the Deadly Fisher, Nat. Geographic, Mar., 1963. A well-illustrated article on Physalia.

Lansing, A.: Experiments in Aging, Sci. American, Apr., 1953. A review of experiments showing that the longevity of a rotifer is determined by how old its parent was when the latter produced the egg that gave rise to the animal.

Moore, D. V.: Acanthocephala, in "McGraw-Hill Encyclopedia of Science and Technology," vol. 1, 1960. A good, short description of the biology of these worms.

Wilson, H. V., and J. T. Penney: Regeneration of Sponges from Dissociated Cells, J. Exp. Zool., vol. 56, 1930. An account of the original experiments mentioned in this chapter.

CHAPTER 15 METAZOA: PROTO- STOMIAL COELOMATES

GRADE BILATERIA

SUBGRADE COELOMATA. Mesoderm in part from ectoderm but primarily from endoderm; with true coelom, formed in various ways as a body cavity lined entirely by mesoderm. *Lophophorates, schizocoelomates, enterocoelomates.*

An original stock of coelom-possessing animals is generally assumed to have evolved from presently unspecificable acoelomate ancestors and to have given rise to a variety of coelomate types. As outlined in the preceding chapter (see Fig. 14.13), we may group these into three general categories. One group, probably the most primitive, develops a coelom in various different and largely unique ways, and the animals additionally possess a rather similar food-catching apparatus, namely, a lophophore. We may refer to these types as the *lophophorates.* In a second group the coelom arises by a splitting of mesoderm into outer and inner portions. Animals exhibiting such schizocoels comprise the *schizocoelomates.* In a last group, the coelom appears in the form of cavities within mesoderm pouches growing out from the endoderm. Types so characterized by enterocoels are the *enterocoelomates.* The lopho-phorates and schizocoelomates are also protostomial, that is, the first embryonic opening forms the adult mouth, as in the Bilateria discussed in Chap. 14. These protostomial coelomates are the subject of the present chapter.

LOPHOPHORATES

Three phyla are included in this group, the *Phoronida,* the *Ectoprocta,* and the *Brachiopoda.* All are sessile or sedentary *filter feeders;* the animals strain micro-scopic food organisms from their aquatic environment by means of ciliated tentacles. The latter are com-ponents of a *lophophore,* a body part in which the mouth is located. The alimentary tract is U-shaped, as is common in sedentary animals, and the anus opens outside the lophophore region. None of these animals possesses a head or a clearly distinct head region. The body is simply marked into a lophophore-bearing forepart and a trunk, each enclosing a por-tion of the coelom. Lophophorates are without breathing systems, and all are endowed with a poten-tial of forming an exoskeleton, expressed differently in the three phyla. From an evolutionary standpoint each of these phyla probably represents a distinct group in its own right, and lophophorates as whole do not appear to be obviously or closely allied to any other existing coelomates.

PHYLUM PHORONIDA

Marine, wormlike, tube-dwelling; with horseshoe-shaped lophophore; excretion through metanephridia; circulatory system present; development via *actino-troch* larvae; 16 species. *Phoronis*

These animals live in upright tubes found in shal-low water along sandy or muddy shores (Fig. 15.1). Representing the exoskeleton of phoronids, the tubes are chitinous, parchmentlike secretions in which the animals may move freely. From the upper end of the tube a phoronid may project its lophophore, which consists of a double row of ciliated tentacles set on a double ridge of the body wall. The mouth is a slit-like, crescent-shaped funnel between the two ridges, centered in the middle between the left and right *arms* of the lophophore. This mid-region is also the place where new tentacles are developed; the oldest tentacles are at the outer extremities of the lophophore arms.

The body wall of a phoronid contains a cuticle-covered glandular epidermis underlain by muscle layers. In the mid-trunk region (Fig. 15.2), the longi-tudinal muscles usually form radial, ribbonlike bundles projecting into the coelom. The innermost layer of the body wall, lining the coelom, is a syncytial peritoneum. This membrane also traverses the coelom as mesenteries and is applied against the outer surface of the U-shaped alimentary tract. The mesenteries divide the trunk coelom into four longitudinal compartments, and the trunk coelom as a whole is divided off from the lophophore-coelom by a transverse *peritoneal septum.*

The nervous system of phoronids is an integral part of the epidermis; neural elements are said to be *intraepidermal.* The main components are an epidermal nerve ring along the outer edge of the lophophore, and a median ganglionic enlargement in this ring represents the main neural center. Also present is a single longitudinal cord in the trunk epidermis along the left side of the body. The alimentary tract is regionated into esophagus, stomach, and intestine, and the inner mucosal lining is ciliated throughout. The anus opens anteriorly between the lophophore arms. Digestion is mainly intracellular, a primitive trait. The circulatory system (see Fig. 15.2) consists of two longitudinal trunk vessels interconnected posteriorly and opening anteriorly into a pair of ring vessels in the lophophore base. From each ring ves-

15 · 1 Phoronids. *A, general appearance of a phoronid in straight tube. B, the anterior, lophophoral end of a phoronid.*

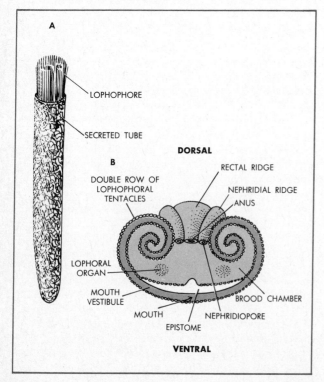

15 · 2 Phoronid structure. *A, the alimentary, nervous, circulatory, and reproductive systems; schematic. Peritoneal membranes enveloping alimentary tract and blood vessels not shown. B, cross section through trunk. Note ridges of longitudinal body-wall muscles, overlain by peritoneum. The basic structure of a metanephridium is sketched in Figs. 14.12 and 15.25.*

sel emanate branches into the tentacles. Blood contains hemoglobin-carrying red corpuscles.

Excretion is carried out by *metanephridia,* encountered widely among coelomate animals. A metanephridium is essentially a duct leading from the coelom to the body exterior. A ciliated funnel leads coelomic fluid into the duct, and the cells of this duct then filter and absorb materials from the fluid. The remainder passes outside as urine. In phoronids a pair of metanephridia is present, with exits to either side of the anus. The sex organs are loose masses along the peritoneum. Sperms and eggs are released into the coelom, and from there they leave the animal through the metanephridia. These excretory organs provide the only exit from the body cavity.

Development occurs via free-swimming, elongated *actinotroch* larvae, which, when mature, carry tentacles and conspicuous ciliary bands girdling the body (Fig. 15.3). In the mid-region of such a larva, between mouth and anus, a progressively deepening pouch forms in the body wall. This *metasome pouch* plays a key role during metamorphosis, the main events of which are completed in the span of a few minutes. The larva undergoes spasmic contractions resulting in the sudden eversion of the metasome pouch. Body-wall muscles and a loop of the alimentary tract are carried along into the everted part, which now constitutes the adult trunk. Most of the other larval components then degenerate and are

15 · 3 Phoronoid development. *Photo: actinotroch larva, from life. Note larval tentacles, digestive tract, metasome pouch at midbody, and posterior ciliary girdle. Diagram: metamorphosis. The metasome pouch has everted, carrying a loop of the alimentary tract with it. Adult lophophoral tentacles have already begun to form along the band of degenerating larval tentacles. The small figure outlines the establishment of an adult by continued elongation of everted metasome pouch and degeneration of other larval parts.*

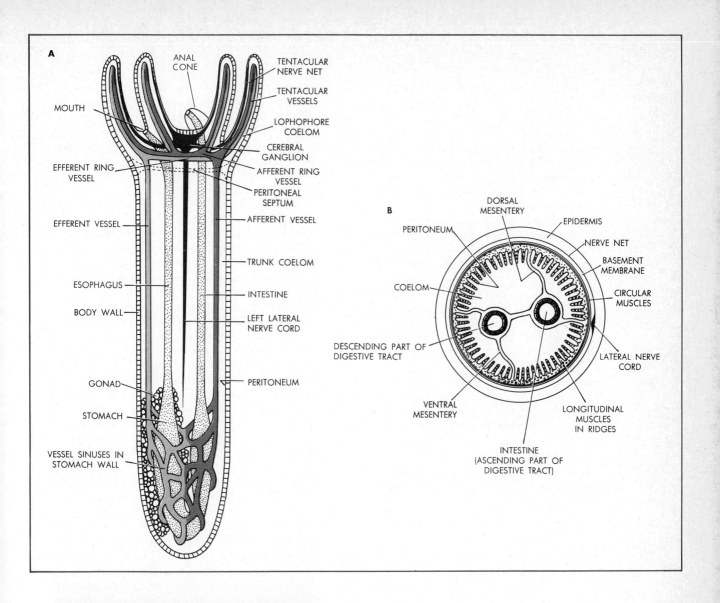

A

ANAL CONE

TENTACULAR NERVE NET

TENTACULAR VESSELS

MOUTH

LOPHOPHORE COELOM

CEREBRAL GANGLION

EFFERENT RING VESSEL

AFFERENT RING VESSEL

PERITONEAL SEPTUM

EFFERENT VESSEL

AFFERENT VESSEL

TRUNK COELOM

ESOPHAGUS

INTESTINE

BODY WALL

LEFT LATERAL NERVE CORD

GONAD

PERITONEUM

STOMACH

VESSEL SINUSES IN STOMACH WALL

B

DORSAL MESENTERY

PERITONEUM

EPIDERMIS

NERVE NET

BASEMENT MEMBRANE

COELOM

CIRCULAR MUSCLES

DESCENDING PART OF DIGESTIVE TRACT

LATERAL NERVE CORD

VENTRAL MESENTERY

LONGITUDINAL MUSCLES IN RIDGES

INTESTINE (ASCENDING PART OF DIGESTIVE TRACT)

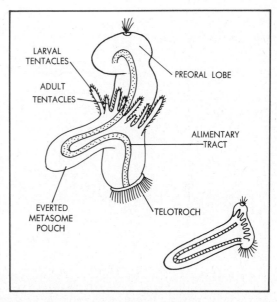

LARVAL TENTACLES

PREORAL LOBE

ADULT TENTACLES

ALIMENTARY TRACT

EVERTED METASOME POUCH

TELOTROCH

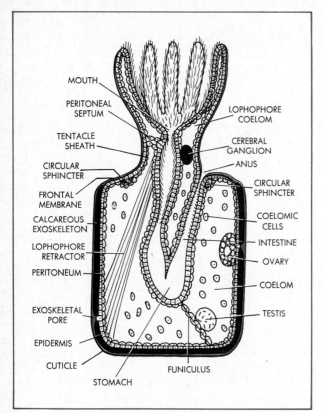

MOUTH

PERITONEAL
SEPTUM

TENTACLE
SHEATH

CIRCULAR
SPHINCTER

FRONTAL
MEMBRANE

CALCAREOUS
EXOSKELETON

LOPHOPHORE
RETRACTOR

PERITONEUM

EXOSKELETAL
PORE

EPIDERMIS

CUTICLE

STOMACH

FUNICULUS

LOPHOPHORE
COELOM

CEREBRAL
GANGLION

ANUS

CIRCULAR
SPHINCTER

COELOMIC
CELLS

INTESTINE

OVARY

COELOM

TESTIS

15 · 4 *A marine ectoproct with extended lophophore in section. Freshwater types possess body-wall muscles and the exoskeleton is a gelatinous secretion (see also Fig. 15.6).*

cast off. The adult lophophore grows in the region of the larval tentacles, and it later acquires its own coelom developed from mesenchymal cells.

PHYLUM ECTOPROCTA

Moss animals, also called *Bryozoa* or *Polyzoa*: marine and freshwater; always sessile in colonies, formed by budding from single microscopic individuals; often polymorphic; with lophophore and U-shaped alimentary tract, the anus opening outside the tentacle crown; without circulatory or excretory systems; exoskeleton membranous, calcareous, or gelatinous; development via various larval types; 5,000 species. *Bugula, Plumatella.*

Ectoprocts have a remarkably close though nevertheless superficial resemblance to the entoprocts. The individual ectoproct is of microscopic dimensions, encased in a secreted exoskeleton which is part of its body wall (Fig. 15.4). In the marine forms, the exoskeleton is essentially a calcareous box open at the unattached side, where the lophophore may be protruded. In freshwater types the casing is massively gelatinous. The peritoneum directly lines the epidermis interiorly in marine ectoprocts; a body-wall musculature between epidermis and peritoneum is present only in freshwater forms.

The lophophore is structured essentially as in phoronids. A single row of tentacles is set on a *tentacle sheath*, which inverts when the lophophore is withdrawn and then forms a tube enclosing the tentacles. The alimentary tract consists of esophagus, stomach, and intestine, the latter passing to the anus located on the tentacle sheath, that is, outside the lophophore. As in phoronids, the coelom is subdivided by a peritoneal membrane into a lophophore coelom and a trunk coelom. The nervous system consists of a main ganglion between mouth and anus, a nerve ring around the lophophore base, and a nerve

15 · 5 *Metamorphosis in marine ectoprocts. A, cyphonautes larva with everted adhesive sac, just before settling. B, attached larva with disintegrating interior tissues. C, formation of primary vesicle from larval ectoderm. D, growth of the primary vesicle leads to establishment of adult organization in essential features. Mesodermal mesenchyme cells (color) are arranged into a peritoneum.*

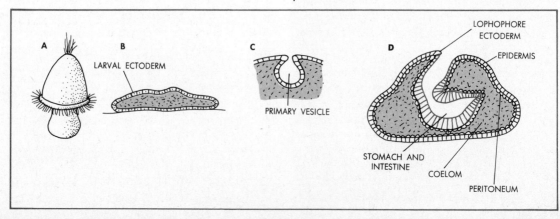

A   B   LARVAL ECTODERM

C   PRIMARY VESICLE

D   LOPHOPHORE
ECTODERM

EPIDERMIS

STOMACH AND
INTESTINE   COELOM

PERITONEUM

net in the body wall. Sex organs without ducts are attached to the peritoneum. Inasmuch as metanephridia are absent, reproductive cells probably leave the coelom through temporary openings in the lophophore region.

Marine ectoprocts form ciliated, free-swimming larvae which metamorphose through very drastic transformations. The larva settles and then disintegrates, becoming little more than a mound of loose cells covered by a layer of larval ectoderm (Fig. 15.5). The latter subsequently pouches in, and from this pouch all components of the adult later arise. Evidently, the structure of the adult is in no way related to the structure of the larva, and larval ectoderm gives rise not only to the ectodermal but also to the mesodermal and endodermal body parts of the adult. From such an adult a colony later develops by budding. Buds form by an ingrowth of epidermis from the body wall, leading to a partitioning of the parent (Fig. 15.6). In the budded compartment all structures then develop directly from the epidermis. Marine ectoprocts often are polymorphic. Among several types of polymorphic variants produced are protective individuals called *avicularia*. In these, the interior organs are underdeveloped but parts of the body wall are elaborated into the form of bird's beaks. Operated by muscles, snapping beaks of this sort may prevent other organisms from settling on a colony.

Freshwater ectoprocts develop directly, without larval stages. Moreover, these animals also may propagate by means of *statoblasts*, reproductive bodies reminiscent of the gemmules of sponges (see Fig. 15.6). Statoblasts are produced in the peritoneal mesenteries of the animals, and each consists of an internal mass of cells and an exterior protective shell. These bodies withstand dry conditions and low winter temperatures, and they germinate in spring into individuals that give rise to new colonies.

PHYLUM BRACHIOPODA (LAMP SHELLS)

Marine; with dorsal and ventral bivalve shells, often with stalk; shells lined by mantle lobes of body wall; circulatory system and metanephridia present; development via free-swimming larvae; 300 species. *Lingula*.

By virtue of their two-shelled, or *bivalve*, calcareous exoskeletons, brachiopods resemble clams superficially (Fig. 15.7). However, whereas the valves are lateral in clams, they are dorsal and ventral in brachiopods. The ventral valve (often borne uppermost in the living animal) is usually the larger one. Leading away from its inner surface is a stalk by which many brachiopods are anchored to a solid sur-

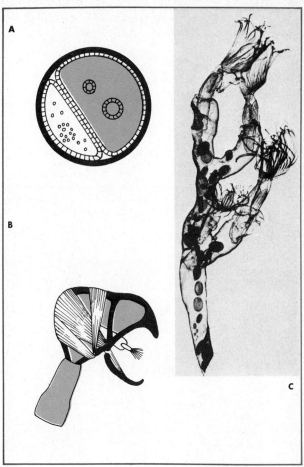

C, courtesy of Carolina Biological Supply Company.

15 · 6 Variants of ectoprocts. A, *budding. A parent individual (colored area) forms an epidermal partition which divides off a budded rudiment (white area). Cells in the latter then give rise to a whole offspring. B, a stalked avicularium. Note muscles attached to the skeletal parts, and the hinged lower operculum, a beaklike portion of the exoskeleton opened and closed by the muscles. The reduced organs of this ectoproct polymorph form a tuft of tissue projecting from the "mouth" of the beak. C, photo of portion of a colony of freshwater ectoprocts, showing numerous statoblasts (dark oval bodies) in the interior. Note the gelatinous housing.*

face. The stalk passes through a perforation in the ventral valve (hence the name "lamp shell," from the resemblance of the empty exoskeleton to an ancient oil lamp). Most stalked brachiopods are attached permanently, but *Lingula* is not. Its stalk merely sticks in the bottom of a vertical mud burrow along tidal flats, and by using its stalk as a locomotor organ the animal may change locations.

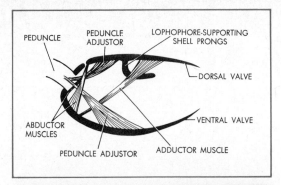

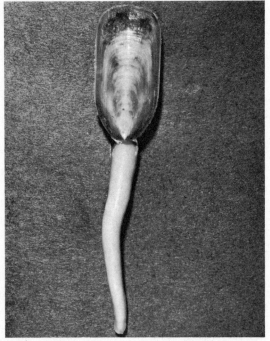

15 · 7 Brachiopods. *Diagram: sectional view of a brachiopod to show the valves and some of the valve muscles. The peduncle is the stalk by which the animal is attached. Photo:* Lingula.

A brachiopod occupies only the posterior space between its valves, the anterior portion being filled by the large lophophore (Fig. 15.8). In this anterior *mantle cavity,* the inner lining of a valve is a double-layered flap of body wall, forming a *mantle lobe.* The body wall consists of epidermis, mesenchymal (and often cartilagelike) connective tissue, and peritoneum. Between the last two layers, muscles are present in the lateral body wall, that is, the portion of the wall not in contact with the valves. The stalk is an extension of the ventral body wall and has the same tissue construction. Interior muscles close and open the valves.

A single row of tentacles emanates from the coiled lophophore arms. The mouth leads from the lophophore base into an alimentary system which is complete only in some of the brachiopods, for example, *Lingula.* The system here is U-shaped and the anus opens into the mantle cavity. In another group of brachiopods the intestine is a blind-ended tube. A nerve ring around the esophagus constitutes the main nervous center. Dorsal to the stomach lies a simply constructed contractile vesicle, or *heart.* Leading away from it in both directions are branched, open-ended vessels. Metanephridia connect the trunk coelom and the mantle cavity. These excretory tubules also serve as reproductive ducts. Sex organs without ducts are attached to the peritoneum.

The development of brachiopods includes free-swimming ciliated larvae which transform into adults gradually. The early embryonic stages are interesting in that the coelom of some brachiopods develops by a splitting of early mesoderm, whereas in other cases the coelom arises as a sac separated off the early endoderm. Technically these body cavities may therefore be called schizocoels and enterocoels, respectively, but the actual patterns of formation are not equivalent to those encountered in the schizocoelomate and enterocoelomate animals yet to be discussed. Even so, the very occurrence of schizocoels and enterocoels could suggest that brachiopods may possibly represent a living remnant of an ancient evolutionary link between the schizocoelomates and enterocoelomates proper.

SCHIZOCOELOMATES

Although they include adult types as diverse as clams, earthworms, and houseflies, the schizocoelomates are characterized fairly uniformly by almost identical basic patterns of development. Thus, the early embryonic phases are quite alike, and mesoderm typically arises from endoderm-derived *teloblast* cells. These cells proliferate, form outer and inner tissue layers, and so leave a schizocoel as a body cavity. Larvae are further characteristic of schizocoelomate development, and the basic larval form in all cases is a *trochophore* (Fig. 15.9). This form may occur as a ciliated, free-swimming larva or as a late stage in the development of the embryo, and in many cases other larval forms may succeed the trochophore phase before the adult is produced.

Ancestral coelomate stocks presumably gave rise to two main series of schizocoelomate animals, namely, an earlier one that remained unsegmented and a later one in which metameric segmentation became highly elaborated (see Fig. 14.13). The unsegmented types are represented today by the Mollusca and Sipunculida, the segmented types, by the Annelida,

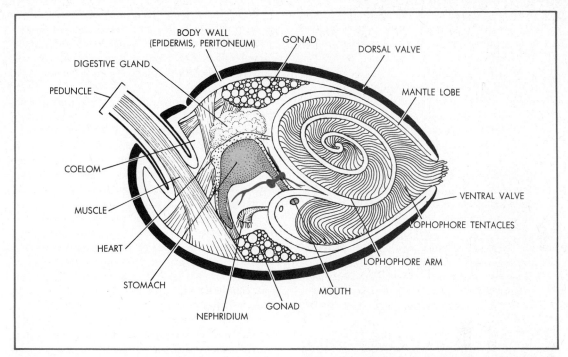

Echiuroida, Oncopoda, and Arthropoda. Of these six phyla, the mollusks, annelids, and arthropods are among the most successful of all animal types.

PHYLUM MOLLUSCA (MOLLUSKS)

Soft-bodied animals; body bilateral, usually composed of *head,* ventral *foot,* and dorsal *visceral hump,* the latter covered by *mantle* which typically secretes an *exoskeleton;* alimentary system with *radula* and *hepatopancreas;* breathing via gills; circulatory sys-

15 · 8 *Longitudinal section through a brachiopod. Note nerve ring around esophagus and blind-ended intestine.*

15 · 9 *The trochophore larva. Diagram: sagittal section. Mesodermal structures in color. The prototroch and metatroch circlets of long cilia are indicated by broken lines. A metatroch or telotroch is not necessarily present in all types of trochophores. Photo: late trochophore, from life; the mouth is toward the right.*

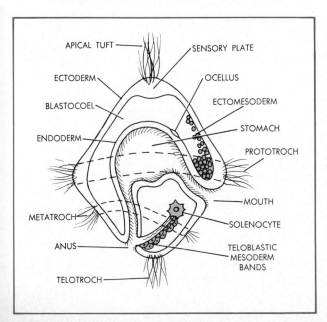

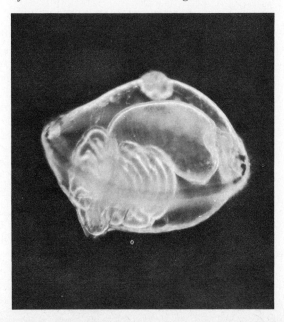

tem with chambered heart and extensive blood sinuses; excretion through renal organs; larvae *trochophores* followed in many cases by *veliger* stages; 100,000 species.

Class Amphineura (chitons): marine; head reduced, without eyes or tentacles; nervous system without ganglia.
Class Gastropoda (snails): marine, freshwater, and terrestrial; visceral hump typically coiled, with torsion or various degrees of detorsion; usually with shell; head with eyes and one or two pairs of tentacles.
Class Scaphopoda (tusk shells): marine; shell tubular, open at both ends; foot a burrowing organ.
Class Pelecypoda (clams): mostly marine; laterally compressed, with dorsally hinged valves; head rudimentary, foot usually tongue-shaped and used in burrowing; mouth with labial palps; radula absent; gills usually expanded into ciliary feeding organs.

15 · 10 *Left, presumable structure of hypothetical ancestral mollusk in sagittal section. Of paired organs, only those on one side are indicated. Arteries from the ventricle lead into the blood sinuses in all parts of the body, and blood from there returns to the heart via the two nephridia, the two gills, and the two atria. Right, diagram of the molluscan radula, as in a squid. The radula is a horny band with recurved teeth and is moved back and forth by muscles around a cartilaginous supporting prop (dark color). Unlike most mollusks, a squid also has horny jaws, as shown here.*

Class Cephalopoda (squids, octopuses): marine; head with tentacles; foot formed into a funnel; shell either external and chambered or internal and reduced; nervous system exceedingly well developed; with cartilaginous endoskeleton.

The mollusks constitute the second largest animal phylum; only the arthropods include more known species (and nematodes probably include more existing but so far undescribed species). Most mollusks have a length in the order of an inch or two, but the phylum also includes the largest and most highly elaborated of all invertebrates, namely, the squids, some of which are 50 to 60 ft long.

Although the molluscan phylum includes such seemingly unrelated animals as snails, clams, and squids, the construction of all of them nevertheless can be derived from a single ancestral structural pattern. The original mollusks which exhibited this pattern can be hypothesized to have had the following characteristics (Fig. 15.10).

The body consisted of a *head*, which may have borne a pair of sensory tentacles; a broad, ventral muscular *foot*, serving in a creeping form of locomotion, and a dome-shaped, dorsal *visceral hump*, which contained the principal organ systems. The body wall of the dome was a *mantle* which secreted calcareous spicules in the epidermal layer and was extended into an overhanging rim around the sides of the body, particularly at the posterior end. The space under this posterior rim represented a *mantle cavity*. Projecting into it were a pair of feathery or leaflike gills, the *ctenidia*. The mouth led into a pharynx equipped with a *radula*, a horny band studded with recurved teeth arranged in a variety of patterns.

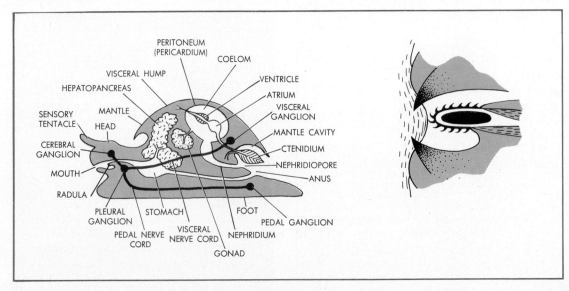

Muscles moved this band back and forth over a carti-laginous supporting rod in the ventral wall of the pharynx. Protruded through the mouth, the radular apparatus served in rasping pieces of tissue from plant or animal food organisms. From the pharynx, food passed through an esophagus into a stomach, which connected with a conspicuous *hepatopancreas,* or "liver." In the latter, a substantial amount of digestion occurred intracellularly. Extracellular diges-tion took place in the intestine, which opened pos-teriorly into the mantle cavity.

The nervous system consisted of a nerve ring around the esophagus, thickened dorsally into a pair of *brain ganglia* and ventrally into a pair of *pleural ganglia.* From the latter emanated two pairs of longi-tudinal nerve cords; the *pedal cords* traveled pos-teriorly into the foot, where they thickened into a pair of *pedal ganglia,* and the *visceral cords* passed posteriorly into the dorsal hump, where they formed a pair of *visceral ganglia.* A transverse connection between the visceral ganglia established a *visceral loop.* The ancestral mollusk also possessed a circula-tory system containing a heart with one ventricle and two posterior atria, as well as systems of arterial and venous vessels from and to the gills. Additional vessels passed into all other body regions and opened into extensive *blood sinuses,* that is, free spaces which permeated all organs. Such a system was an *open* circulation, blood not having been confined entirely to the space within vessels. The coelom was com-paratively reduced. Its principal component was a *pericardial cavity* around the heart. Leading into this coelomic space were the ducts of the sex organs, located anteriorly, and passing posteriorly were a pair of excretory tubules. The latter were essentially metanephridial; they connected the pericardial coe-lom with the exterior, via excretory pores in the mantle cavity near the anus. Sex cells were shed into the pericardial coelom and they then left through the excretory ducts. Development included trocho-phore larvae.

This ancestral organization is still preserved to varying degrees in the mollusks now living.

Amphineura

Chitons have deviated least from the ancestral con-struction. The head has become reduced, and ten-tacles and eyes are absent (Fig. 15.11). The exo-skeleton is more elaborate, being composed of eight overlapping shell plates. The mantle cavity is a nar-row groove circling the entire animal under the mantle rim. Numerous pairs of small gills project into this mantle cavity. In parallel with the reduc-tion of the head the nervous system has become

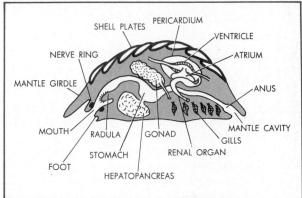

15 · 11   Chitons. *Photo: a representative chiton, seen from dorsal side; note the eight shell plates set into the mantle. Diagram: sagittal section, showing some of the internal structures.*

simplified. Thus, definite ganglionic thickenings are usually absent, and a nerve ring around the esophagus merely extends posteriorly as two pairs of cords. The visceral cords typically are joined posteriorly and form a loop. The only other principal deviation from the ancestral molluscan pattern is the presence of separate reproductive ducts to the outside, a con-dition characteristic also of all other mollusks. A pair of tubular excretory ducts still emanates from the pericardial coelom, but these ducts have become complex *renal organs,* again as in all other mollusks.

Chiton larvae are typical free-swimming tro-chophores. They eventually develop a foot in the region between mouth and anus, and shell plates at

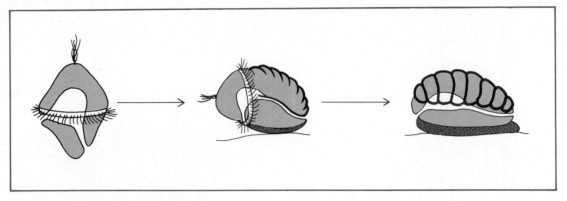

15 · 12 Chiton development. *Left to right, the trochophore settles on the ventral side and develops shell plates (heavy black lines) and a foot (dark shaded area).*

the opposite side. A larva then settles with the foot directed downward (Fig. 15.12).

Gastropoda

In snails the ancestral construction is again largely preserved, but the early evolution of mollusks has included two developmental innovations that give a snail its characteristic organization. These new processes take place during the larval stages.

A trochophore develops in the usual manner and this larva subsequently becomes a *veliger,* a larval form possessing a *velum,* an elaborate ciliary girdle used as a swimming organ (Fig. 15.13). A foot develops as in chitons, between mouth and anus. But

15 · 13 Snail development. *A, mature veliger, before torsion. The dorsal visceral hump has enlarged greatly, producing a U-loop in the alimentary tract. B, veliger after torsion. The alimentary tract is now coiled, with the anus shifted to same (anterior) side as the mouth.*

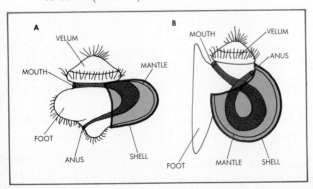

then the opposite, dorsal side undergoes a pronounced enlargement, which pushes the developing visceral hump up in a dorsal direction. This upward growth occurs unequally on the left and right sides, resulting in a spiral coiling of the visceral hump and the shell covering it. Moreover, the upward growth also has the effect of pulling the alimentary tract into a U shape, until the anus comes to lie quite close to the mouth.

A distinct and separate event then takes place as well; referred to as *torsion,* it is achieved in the course of a few minutes: the whole visceral hump of the veliger rotates 180° relative to the rest of the body, usually in a counterclockwise direction. The results of torsion are that the mantle cavity comes to lie anteriorly, above the head; the gills are anterior; the anus, excretory pores, and reproductive openings all are anterior, in the mantle cavity; the alimentary tract is twisted from a U shape into a loop; the visceral nerve loop becomes twisted into a figure of eight; and the heart is turned around, the atria coming to lie anterior to the ventricle.

In many snails (for example, limpets, abalones), the left-right inequality of early growth is not too great and the internal organs then develop in pairs despite the coiling and subsequent torsion. In another group, however (for example, periwinkles, whelks), growth on the left side is suppressed to such an extent that the left organs fail to develop. The right organs then come to lie on the left side after torsion, and such snails possess only one gill, one atrium, and one kidney. In still another group, shells are reduced or absent altogether, and the torsion then also fails to persist. Thus, many sea slugs first undergo 180° torsion and left organs do not develop. But then a 90° or 180° *detorsion* takes place, which brings the visceral hump back partly or wholly to its original larval position (Fig. 15.14).

In the land snails (for example, the edible snail *Helix*), the mantle cavity is modified from a gill chamber to a lung chamber and such snails breathe

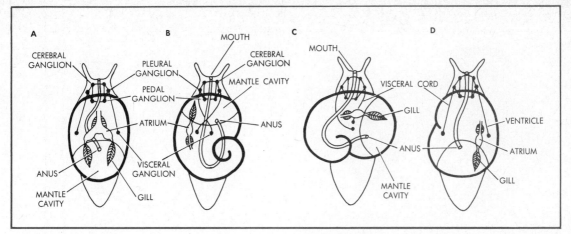

air. Some of these types have adapted secondarily to aquatic life, but they are still lung breathers and must surface periodically for air (Color Plate XXIV, 37).

Scaphopoda

Like snails, the tusk shells have similarly elongated in a dorsal direction but a coiling has not taken place. The scaphopod shell is tapered and tubular, giving the animals a tusklike appearance (Fig. 15.15). From the wider, ventral end of the shell projects a muscular, conical foot, which serves as a digging organ. Also protruding from the ventral end is a reduced proboscislike head, to which are attached numerous

15 · 14 Torsion and detorsion. *A, original condition, paired organs present, anus posterior. B, after torsion. Only right members of paired organs present, lying on left side, anus anterior, visceral cords form figure-eight. C, 90° detorsion. Mantle cavity, gill, and anus lie on right side, heart lies transversely, visceral cords partially untwisted. D, complete 180° detorsion. Pattern resembles A, but only right members of paired organs present.*

15 · 15 Scaphopoda. *A, sagittal section through Dentalium. B, body proportions and position of animal in its sand burrow.*

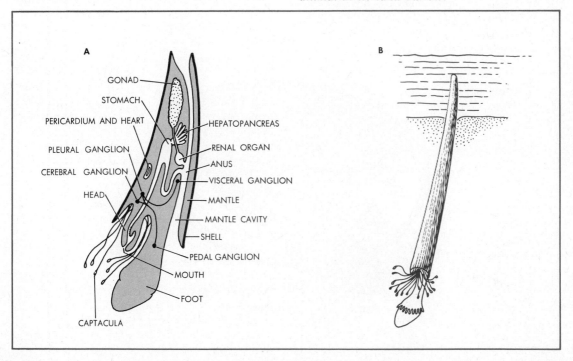

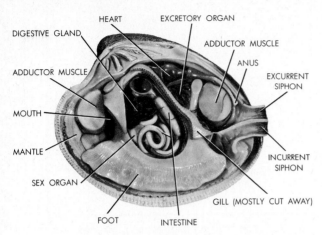

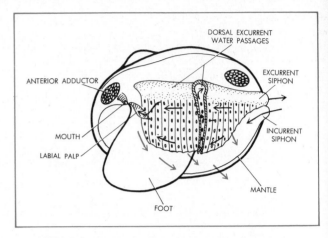

15 · 16 Clam structure. *Photo: model indicating general anatomy. Diagram: the gills of the left side, the outer gill shown as a cutaway. Black arrows indicate ciliary paths of food particles toward mouth and of water into excurrent siphon via dorsal gill passage; colored arrows show paths of heavy particles not adhering to gill.*

15 · 17 Clam structure: *some of the internal organs in sagittal view. The excretory and reproductive openings exit into the excurrent water passages.*

prehensile tentacles. From one end of the animal to the other passes a channellike mantle cavity. Water circulates in and out of it via the dorsal shell opening, which projects beyond the burrow of the animal into clear water.

Scaphopods appear to represent a separate line of molluscan evolution, on a level of specialization intermediate between that of gastropods and that of pelecypods.

Pelecypoda

Clams are adapted to a sedentary filter-feeding existence. In these animals the ancestral body has

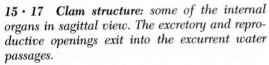

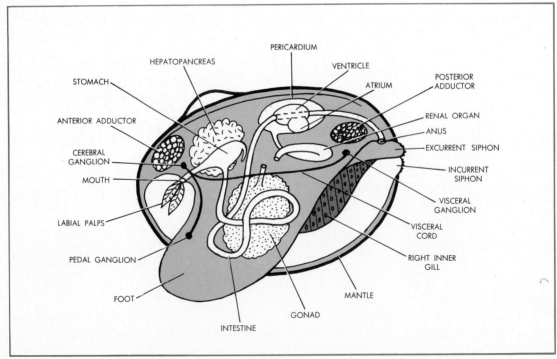

become flattened from side to side, the head has disappeared, and the gills have expanded into ciliary food-collecting organs which also retain a breathing function.

The visceral mass of a clam is suspended from the dorsal mid-line (Fig. 15.16). Continuous ventrally with the visceral mass is the foot, which in many cases may be protruded between the valves. Two pairs of large gill plates project into the mantle cavity, one member of each pair on the left side of the foot, the other member on the right. The gills continue posteriorly as a horizontal partition which divides the posterior region of the mantle cavity into a dorsal compartment and a ventral main compartment. Both compartments open to the outside along the posterior valve edges, the dorsal chamber forming an *excurrent siphon*, the ventral one an *incurrent siphon*. In some clams these siphons are extended into long retractile tubes projecting beyond the valves.

Cilia on the gills draw food-bearing water through the incurrent siphon into the ventral mantle compartment. Food caught up in mucus on the gills then passes forward to the *labial palps*, which conduct food into the mouth. Water passes through the gills, where it contributes to oxygenating the blood, then leaves via the dorsal mantle compartment and the excurrent siphon. Clams are without a radula, a superfluous structure in a filter-feeding animal. The alimentary tract passes through the pericardial coelom, coils through the visceral mass, and opens into the excurrent siphon (Fig. 15.17).

Paralleling the reduction of the head, the nervous system is to some extent reduced. A pair of fused cerebral-pleural ganglia lies anteriorly in a nerve ring around the esophagus. Nerve cords from there connect with a pair of pedal ganglia in the foot and a pair of visceral ganglia near the anus. The renal organs are paired and lead from the pericardial coelom to the outgoing water current. The circulation is open. A ventricle in the pericardial coelom surrounds the intestine, and arteries from the ventricle pass into open blood sinuses in all body parts. Blood from there collects in veins, which carry it through the kidneys, then through the gills, and oxygenated blood ultimately returns to the heart via two atria.

The sex organs are formless masses around the intestinal coils. Reproductive ducts discharge into the outgoing water current. In marine forms fertilization usually occurs in open water and the trochophores and veligers are free-swimming. Freshwater clams typically discharge eggs into the spaces within the gill plates. Fertilization occurs there, the sperms entering with the incurrent water. Highly

modified veligers, so-called *glochidia* larvae, are then formed, which are expelled through the excurrent siphon; and if they are not to perish, they must attach themselves within a short time to the gills or fins of fishes. At such sites the glochidia live parasitically until they are mature and become independent adults (Fig. 15.18).

15 · 18 Various clams. A, glochidia larvae of a freshwater mussel. B, an adult freshwater clam (Anodonta); note conspicuous burrowing foot. C, a razor clam (Solen); note foot at left, siphon at right. D, a giant clam (Tridacna).

A, courtesy of Carolina Biological Supply Company.

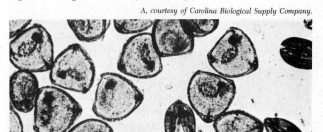

Clams lead a semisedentary, burrowing life. They may change station by digging the foot into sand or mud, distending it with blood to form an anchor, and then pulling the rest of the body after it. Otherwise clams remain partly or wholly buried, with the siphon protruding up into clear water. Some clams, notably oysters, are permanently attached, their larger, left valve being cemented to the ground. Similarly attached is the giant clam *Tridacna,* which may be 2 yd wide and weigh ¼ ton.

Cephalopoda

These animals are the most advanced mollusks and have evolved the most pronounced departures from the ancestral construction. As in snails, early cephalopods elongated the visceral hump in a dorsal direction. But growth remained equal on the left and right sides, hence the hump came to form a flat coil. Also, the covering shell became partitioned into progressively larger compartments as the animal grew, and only the last, largest compartment was occupied by the animal. All earlier compartments were filled with air (Fig. 15.19). This organization of the shell gave the early cephalopods considerable buoyancy and permitted them to adopt a free-swimming existence. In correlation with this newly developed mode of life, the foot became modified partly into muscular prehensile tentacles, which also equipped the animals as predatory, carnivorous types. The chambered nautilus today still exemplifies this early stage of cephalopod evolution. In other lines of the cephalopod group, the shells became reduced greatly or were lost altogether, and the nervous and sensory systems became highly developed in conjunction with rapid, swimming locomotion. The result was the emergence of modern squids and octopuses.

In a squid (Fig. 15.20), a thick muscular mantle surrounds the visceral mass. Underneath the mantle on the upper side lies the remnant of the shell, which in squids is a horny, leaf-shaped *pen.* Anteriorly the mantle terminates at a free edge, the *collar,* which fits over a mid-ventral muscular tube, the *funnel.* The channel within the funnel leads into the mantle cavity. When the mantle musculature is relaxed, water passes between the collar and the funnel into and out of the mantle cavity. On contraction of the mantle muscles, the collar clamps tightly around the funnel and water is forced out through the funnel tube. The funnel may be bent backward and in other directions, enabling a squid to change swimming direction. Jet propulsion of this kind places squids among the fastest swimmers.

A squid possesses 10 tentacles. One pair is long and equipped with suckers at the tips. These tentacles catch prey. All remaining tentacles are shorter, sucker-equipped, and serve to hold prey while powerful horny beaked *jaws* in the mouth bite chunks out of it. A radula is present but is probably used little, food being swallowed rapidly. The alimentary tract is U-shaped (Fig. 15.21) and includes a stomach which

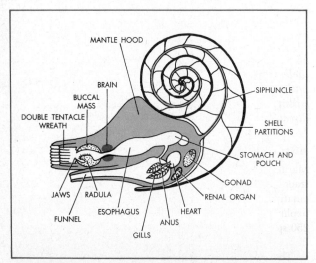

15 · 19 The chambered nautilus. *Diagram: sectional longitudinal view, showing position of some of the organs. Note double circlet of tentacles and absence of ink sac. Gills shown on one side only. Photo: section through shell; note compartments partitioned off by septa and the siphuncle.*

connects with a large digestive gland. The anus opens anteriorly into the mantle cavity. An *ink sac* discharges into the mantle cavity via the anus. Expelled through the funnel, a cloud of ink probably distracts an enemy while the squid makes its escape.

A highly developed nervous system is particularly characteristic of cephalopods. Several fused pairs of ganglia form a complex brain, which is surrounded by a cartilage capsule. Located between the eyes, the brain represents the dorsal part of a nerve ring circling the esophagus. From the ring elaborate tracts of nerves ramify throughout the body. The eyes of squids are as complex as those of vertebrates. Breathing is accomplished by a pair of feathery gills in the mantle cavity. The circulation is closed, that is, blood is confined entirely to vessels. A heart ventricle pumps blood throughout the body and returning blood passes first through the kidneys and then via *gill hearts* into the gills. Oxygenated blood subsequently circulates back to the main heart. The coelom is spacious and occupies the hind part of the visceral mass. A single sex organ and a pair of kidneys in the coelom open via separate ducts into the mantle cavity. Larvae are not formed. Instead, fertilized eggs within protective capsules are laid and develop directly into miniature adults.

Whereas squids are active swimmers, octopuses lead a semisedentary life. These animals have saclike shapes, and an internal shell is in many cases absent altogether. Most octopuses are quite small, but the largest known specimens have an arm spread of about 30 ft.

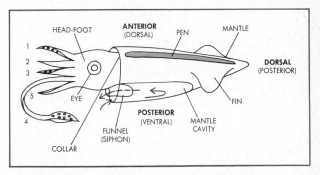

15 · 20 The general structure of a squid. *Tentacles shown on left side only. Arrows indicate path of water into and out of mantle cavity, resulting in jet propulsion in posterior (dorsal) direction.*

PHYLUM SIPUNCULIDA (PEANUT WORMS)

Marine; body with introvert and trunk; alimentary tract recurved and coiled, anus anterodorsal; circulation rudimentary or absent; excretion metanephridial; development via trochophore larvae; 250 species. *Sipunculus*

The evolutionary change from unsegmented to wormlike, segmented schizocoelomates appears to have left living evidence of at least one intermediate transitional stage in the form of the sipunculids. These animals are identified readily by their long, slender *introvert*, a proboscislike anterior tube which

15 · 21 A squid in sagittal section.

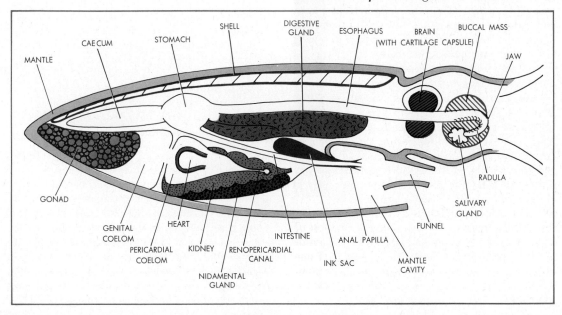

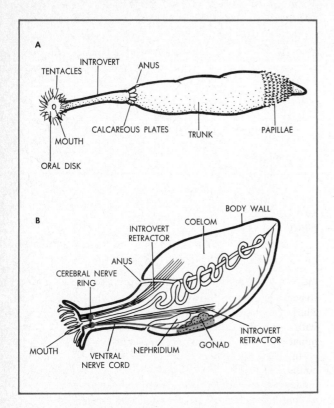

15 · 22 Sipunculids. *A, external features. B, sagittal section, showing position of various organs.*

may be invaginated and retracted into the plump *trunk* (Fig. 15.22). At the tip of the introvert is an *oral disk* with a mouth and a wreath of tentacular outgrowths. Peanut worms lead a sedentary, burrowing life in sandy and muddy tidal flats.

The body wall of a sipunculid consists of a cuticle-covered epidermis, two layers of muscle, some connective tissue, and a peritoneum. Mesenteries in the large, spacious coelom are poorly developed, and the alimentary tract is held in place largely by muscles. This tract passes from the mouth through the introvert into the intestine, which then recurves in the posterior part of the trunk and coils forward to an anus. The latter lies dorsally, in the front part of the trunk. The nervous center is a nerve ring in the anterior portion of the introvert, thickened dorsally into a brain ganglion. A ventral cord with lateral branches passes from the ring posteriorly. Embedded in the brain ganglion is a pair of eyecups. Sipunculids possess a pair of anteriorly located metanephridia, and a circulatory system is usually absent. However, the coelomic fluid contains red blood cells as well as interesting microscopic cellular aggregates called

urns. Some of these are fixed to the peritoneal lining, others swim free in the coelomic fluid by means of their cilia. The function of these bodies is obscure. Sex organs form along the peritoneum and reproductive cells pass outside via coelom and metanephridia. A trochophore larva elongates greatly in the region between mouth and anus, a process which leaves the anus at a progressively more anterodorsal position.

The close evolutionary relation of sipunculids to annelids is indicated by their entire embryonic and larval development, their annelidlike nervous systems, and their wormlike and coelomate structure generally. However, sipunculids are completely unsegmented, and thus they may represent a preannelid line of wormlike schizocoelomates.

PHYLUM ANNELIDA

Metamerically segmented worms, typically with chitinous bristles; coelom partitioned, organ systems arranged on segmental basis; circulatory system usually closed; larvae trochophores or absent; 15,000 species.

Class Polychaeta: largely marine; with segmental parapodia and numerous bristles; with free-swimming trochophore larvae. *Nereis,* clamworms; *Sabella,* feather-duster worms; *Arenicola,* lugworms.
Class Archiannelida: marine, some parasitic; structurally simplified; without external segmentation; parapodia and bristles generally absent; with epidermal ciliation and nerve cords within epidermis. *Polygordius*
Class Oligochaeta (earthworms): mostly terrestrial and freshwater; head reduced, without appendages; parapodia absent, bristles few; hermaphroditic; development without larvae. *Lumbricus,* terrestrial earthworms; *Tubifex,* aquatic earthworms.
Class Hirudinea (leeches): mostly freshwater parasites, some carnivorous; with terminal suckers; parapodia and bristles absent; number of segments, fixed throughout life; coelom packed with mesenchyme; hermaphroditic; development as in oligochaetes. *Hirudo*

In these worms metamerism has become evolved in fully elaborated form, presumably for the first time among coelomates. Characteristically, the first anterior segment forms the head, and all others except the last, anus-bearing segment are alike developmentally. In given species up to 800 trunk segments may be produced. They often remain more or less alike even in the adult worm, but in numerous instances considerable segmental specialization is in evidence.

Polychaetes undoubtedly represent the primitive annelids. Segmental development here begins with a pronounced posterior elongation of the trochophore (Fig. 15.23). This posterior growth is accompanied by a forward proliferation of the mesodermal teloblast bands on each side of the larval body. These bands give rise to anteroposterior pairs of cellular aggregations, the *somites*, which later hollow out and so form paired schizocoelic coelom sacs. Segments mature in anteroposterior succession, the anterior segments being the oldest. In each larval segment, the ectoderm pouches in on the ventral side and produces a segmental portion of the nervous system as well as a pair of metanephridia. Laterally the ectoderm and mesoderm fold out on each side into a *parapodium*, a flap of body wall. Within epidermal pits of a parapodium later develop stiff chitinous bristles, the *setae* characteristic of annelids generally. The peritoneal mesoderm will give rise to the blood vessels, the muscular system, and the sex organs.

An adult polychaete such as the clamworm *Nereis* then has the following segmental organization (Fig. 15.24). The first segment is a preoral head segment, or *prostomium*, which bears one or two pairs of dorsal, lens-containing *eyes*, a pair of anterodorsal sensory *tentacles*, and a pair of anteroventral sensory *palps*. Behind the head is a *peristomium*, in which the mouth is located anteroventrally and which also bears four pairs of tentacular palps. The mouth leads into an eversible pharynx, armed with chitinous jaws. Posteriorly, the trunk is marked conspicuously

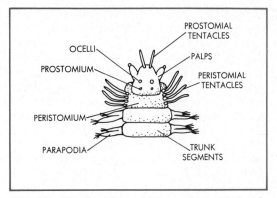

15 · 24 Head region *of* Nereis *(top view). The pharynx is retracted and not visible.*

into segments, and the only internal system not structured metamerically is the alimentary tract. The latter consists, behind the pharynx, of an esophagus with digestive glands and a straight intestine terminating at the anus in the last segment.

In each trunk segment (Fig. 15.25), the body wall consists of a thin, horny (nonchitinous) cuticle, an epidermal layer, an outer (segmental) circular and an inner longitudinal muscle layer, and the peritoneum. On each side of the segment is a parapodium consisting of one or two flaps and containing bundles of chitinous setae set into epidermal pits. These bristles serve partly in protection but more particularly as locomotor levers and holdfast spikes. On the ventral side, each trunk segment contains a pair of ganglia with transverse connectives and lateral branches, as well as longitudinal cords passing into adjacent segments. In the peristomium the cords form a ring around the pharynx. Dorsally this ring contains a pair of large brain ganglia, located in the prostomium. The circulatory system consists of a longitudinal dorsal and ventral trunk vessel, interconnected in each segment by transverse systems that include capillary nets in the alimentary tract, in the parapodia, and in the other segmental organs. Blood flows forward dorsally by wavelike contractions of the dorsal vessel, backward ventrally. Breathing is accomplished principally through the epidermis, particularly in the parapodia, which wave back and forth and thereby circulate water around the body. The metanephridia open near the bases of the parapodia.

During the breeding season, *Nereis* and polychaetes generally undergo characteristic structural changes. Thus, body colors and textures become altered, the parapodia enlarge, and long swimming setae are developed. In *Nereis*, such dimorphic changes occur in each sex in the posterior half of the body, where

15 · 23 Segmental development *of annelids. 1, trochophore; 2, posterior elongation, proliferation of teloblastic mesoderm bands; 3, mesodermal somites forming; 4, later stage in segmental development, reduction of larval head structures.*

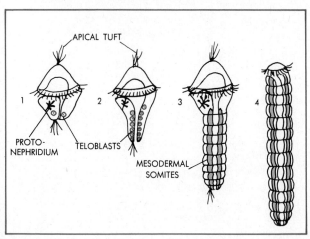

the segmental coeloms concurrently fill with sperms or eggs. At certain fixed nights, determined in part by environmental factors such as the amount of moon-light in a particular month of the year, the posterior sexual parts of the worms become detached and swarm separately to the surface of the sea. In this form, called *heteronereis*, these worm sections then burst and disintegrate, and the released sex cells effect fertilization. The nonswarming body parts subsequently regenerate the lost heteronereis regions. These regenerated sections fill up again with reproductive cells by the following year, becoming ripe in the same calendar period.

Many polychaetes swim freely only when locomotion is actually unavoidable, the worms preferring to spend most of their time in burrows. *Nereis* is among numerous types that dig simple burrows in sand. More complex tunnel systems are formed by the lugworm *Arenicola* (Fig. 15.26), whose coiled earth

castings are familiar sights along beaches. Other polychaetes line their burrows with secreted tubes and still others live in tubes altogether. For example, the feather-duster worms possess a crown of tentacles which may be protruded from or retracted into permanent upright tubes. The tentacles trap food organisms (see Color Plate XVIII, 31).

Archiannelids are a small group of simplified worms in which many larval traits have been retained into the adult phase. Such permanently trochophoral traits include the absence of external segmentation, the presence of ciliation on the ventral side of the body, the persistence of the nervous system as part of the epidermis, the frequent development of larva-like excretory organs (that is, not metanephridia), and the general absence of parapodia and setae (see Fig. 15.26 and Color Plate XXV, 38). Internal segmentation is well developed, however. There can be little question that the group represents an offshoot from polychaete ancestors.

Analogously derived from polychaete stocks are the earthworms, of the class Oligochaeta. These burrowing animals are detritus feeders. They possess a reduced prostomium without appendages (Fig. 15.27). In the trunk segments parapodia are absent, but each segment bears four pairs of retractile setae, two pairs on each side, corresponding to the setae of polychaetes. Internally the pharynx is neither armed nor eversible, and the remainder of alimentary tract

15 · 25 *Adult segmental structure of polychaetes. A, cross section through trunk segment of* Nereis. *B, schematic side view of polychaete segments showing position of various internal organs. C, schematic cross section of* Nereis *trunk segment, showing pattern of circulation. Blood flows from dorsal vessels to ventral ones in the anterior body segments. D, scheme of anterior portion of nervous system, as in* Nereis.

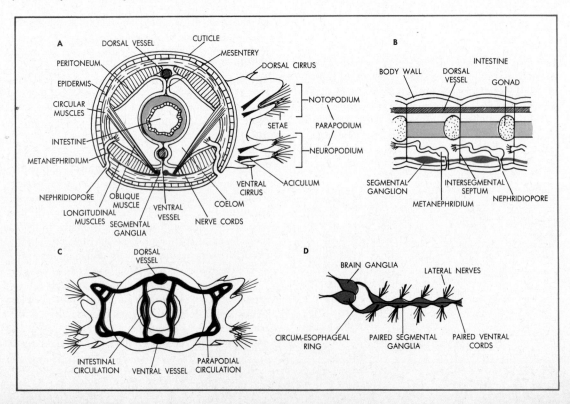

A

C

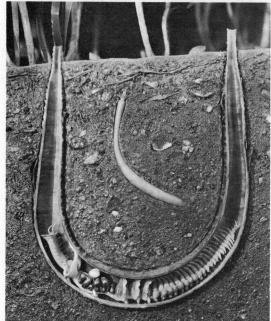

B

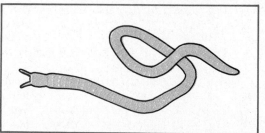

D

15 · 26   Polychaetes. *A, the clamworm* Nereis, *from life. B, model of a section through the tube of the parchment worm* Chaetopterus. *The head of the animal is at left. Note the greatly elaborated parapodia. Between the arms of the U tube is a sipunculid. C, the burrowing lugworm* Arenicola. *Another polychaete is illustrated in Color Plate XVIII, 31. D, diagram of the archiannelid* Polygordius, *closely related to polychaetes. External segmentation is lacking, and the internal segments are suggested by cross lines.*

15 · 27   Earthworm structure. *A, cutaway diagram of anterior body region, segments numbered. Segment 12 and all segments behind it contain, on each side, a transverse vessel (shown in cutaway view) interconnecting the dorsal and subneural longitudinal blood vessels. B, scheme of dorsoventral blood-circulation pattern in each trunk segment. Blood vessels form extensive capillary beds (not shown) in the body wall, the ne-* *phridia, and the gut wall. See Fig. 2.12 for a photographic cross section through an earthworm. This figure shows the epidermis, the body wall muscles, the intestine with the deep, dorsal typhlosole fold, the dorsal blood vessel just above it and the ventral vessel below it, and portions of the metanephridial tubes in the coelom to each side of the intestine.*

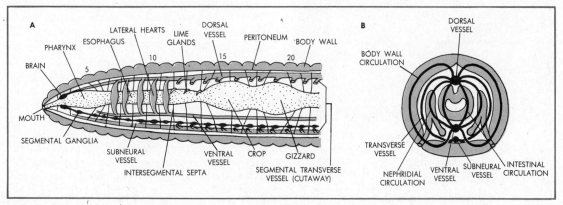

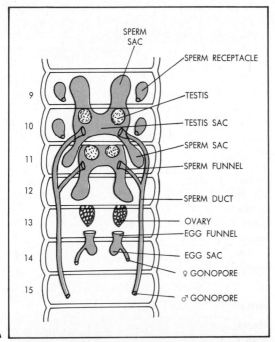

15 · 28 Earthworm reproduction. A, *ventral view of reproductive system, segments numbered. B, photo showing position and extent of clitellum. C, copulating earthworms.*

consists of esophagus, crop, gizzard, and intestine. The esophagus bears paired *lime glands,* which secrete calcium ions from the blood into the alimentary tract. The crop is a storage compartment, and the strongly muscled gizzard grinds swallowed earth. Soil particles here aid in macerating food organisms present. Along the dorsal side of the intestine runs a fold, the *typhlosole,* which projects into the intestinal cavity and increases the absorptive area.

The nervous and circulatory systems are similar to those of polychaetes, except that the dorsal circulatory vessel is not contractile. Circulation is maintained instead by five pairs of contractile "hearts," connective vessels joining the dorsal and ventral main channels in segments 7 to 11. The metanephridia are as in polychaetes, and oligochaetes in addition possess excretory *chloragogue* cells in the peritoneum surrounding the gut and the main blood vessels. These cells absorb wastes and then detach and float free in the coelomic fluid. Cells in the coelom may then engulf the chloragogues, migrate into the body wall, and there deposit the excretion products as pigments.

The most pronounced differences between polychaetes and oligochaetes are reproductive. Oligochaetes are hermaphrodites, with male and female systems developed in specific segments (Fig. 15.28). An important reproductive role is played by a conspicuous *clitellum,* a thickened glandular band around the epidermis in which the segmental divisions are obscured. In an earthworm the clitellum extends over segments 31 to 37. A pair of ventral mucus-forming grooves connects the male openings in segment 15 with the clitellum.

In mating, two worms come into contact with their heads pointing in opposite directions. The region of closest contact ranges from segment 9 to the posterior end of the clitellum, and in this region each worm secretes a mucus sheath around itself. Sperms are then released by both worms, and these cells are propelled in the mucus grooves from segment 15 of one worm to segments 9 and 10 of the other. There the sperms enter the sperm receptacles and are stored, whereupon the worms separate. Subsequently, the clitellum of each worm secretes a mucus sheath which is propelled anteriorly by muscular movements of the body wall. As this sheath passes segment 14, several eggs are shed into it; and as it continues past segments 9 and 10, sperms from the other worm are deposited into it. Fertilization then takes place within the mucus sheath, and after the sheath slips over the head of the worm the open ends seal up and an egg *cocoon* is so formed. Development follows the typical annelid pattern but the trochophore stage is greatly abbreviated and a free larval phase is absent.

There is little doubt that Hirudinea represent evolutionary offshoots of oligochaetes that have become ectoparasitic. In most leeches setae are entirely absent, the number of internal segments is fixed at 34, and suckers are typically present at both ends of the body (Fig. 15.29). A "segment" in a leech refers to an *internal* metamere only; each such segment is annulated externally into 2 to 16 superficial cuticular rings, the exact number being fixed for each species. Thus there are always more external "segments" than true internal ones.

15 · 29 Leeches. *A, specimen showing exterior annulation, terminal suckers, and clitellum (just above constriction on body). B, diagram of ingestive saw apparatus in anterior sucker. The muscular pharynx behind the saws provides suction for ingestion of blood through an incision made by the saws.*

A, courtesy of Carolina Biological Supply Company.

A

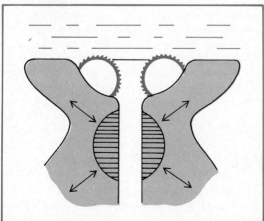

B

Most leeches are blood suckers. They contain a pharynx armed with three sawlike chitinous jaws. With these a leech may cut a Y-shaped incision through even tough skin or armor such as fish scales. Also present are salivary glands that secrete the anticoagulant *hirudin* into a wound cut by the pharyngeal saws. The alimentary tract includes a crop and numerous intestinal side branches, which may hold up to 10 times as much blood as the weight of the leech itself and enable the animal to survive as long as 9 months from a single feeding. The usual hosts of leeches are fishes and other vertebrates, including on occasion man. But note that many of the leeches are not obligatory blood feeders; they normally survive as carnivores, catching worms and other invertebrates. And some leeches are actually nonparasitic altogether.

Leeches reproduce like oligochaetes, and a clitellum usually performs a similar cocoon-forming function.

PHYLUM ECHIUROIDA (SPOON WORMS)

Marine; somites in larva but unsegmented as adults; with proboscislike prostomium; one pair of anteroventral setae; coelom not partitioned; one to three pairs of metanephridia; development via trochophore larva; 60 species. *Echiurus, Bonellia.*

This small phylum comprises plankton feeders living in sand or mud burrows. The plump trunk of such a worm bears an extended, tubular prostomium anteriorly. The tip of this prostomium is roughly spoon-shaped in forms like *Echiurus* but is bifurcated into two tissue flaps in *Bonellia* (Fig. 15.30). A highly mobile organ, the prostomium may be contracted, but it does not introvert or retract into the trunk. At the base of the prostomium lies the mouth. A pair of setae is set into the ventral surface and *Echiurus* also bears a circlet of setae around the anus.

Internally, spoon worms possess a coiled alimentary tract, a simplified nervous system consisting of anterior nerve ring and longitudinal nerve cords, a circulatory system composed mainly of a dorsal and a ventral vessel, and metanephridia opening anteroventrally on the trunk. Sex organs discharge via the spacious coelom and the metanephridia. *Bonellia* exhibits sexual dimorphism, the dwarfed males being parasitic in the females.

The early echiuroid larva is a typical trochophore. In later stages it also exhibits rudimentary segmentation: 15 mesodermal somites arise, and the developing ventral nerve cord acquires a corresponding number of segmental swellings and paired lateral branches. But these beginnings of metamerism never

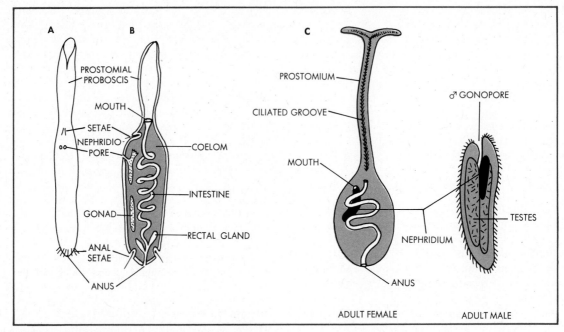

15 · 30 Echiuroids. *A and B, external ventral features and sagittal section of* Urechis. *C, some structural details of* Bonellia. *The reduced and parasitic male is very small and lives permanently within the excretory organ of the female.*

become further elaborated. Indeed they become obscured later, and they eventually disappear altogether as the adult stage is reached. In view of this developmental pattern, echiuroids may represent a postannelid stage of evolution in which segmentation and other annelid traits have been reduced or lost.

PHYLUM ONCOPODA

Claw-bearing animals, fundamentally segmented; usually with unjointed legs; 500 species.

Subphylum PENTASTOMIDA: blood-sucking endoparasites in vertebrates; larvae with claw-bearing legs; adults wormlike, with two pairs of claws on side of mouth; circulatory, excretory, breathing systems absent. *Linguatula*
Subphylum TARDIGRADA (water bears): microscopic, mostly terrestrial; with six segments and four pairs of claw-bearing legs; cell numbers constant; without circulatory, excretory, or breathing systems; development without larvae. *Milnesium*
Subphylum ONYCHOPHORA: terrestrial, wormlike; with many pairs of claw-bearing legs and

corresponding internal segments; external segmentation absent; annelid and arthropod traits mixed. *Peripatus*

The Oncopoda represent a "phylum of convenience," an assemblage of three small groups perhaps interrelated very distantly. These groups may constitute the surviving remnants of three separate and independent lines, all offshoots of a main evolutionary line leading from polychaete ancestors to arthropod descendants (see Fig. 14.13).

The affinities of the pentastomids (also known as *linguatulids*, Fig. 15.31) are particularly obscure, in part because of the parasitic nature of the animals. They are wormlike, superficially annulated, and possess air pores scattered over the surface. They live in the breathing organs of various vertebrates. Claws lateral to the mouth enable them to remain attached. Fertilized eggs reach water environments via the mouth of the hosts. Larvae typically develop in intermediate hosts, and the arthropod affinities of the group are suggested principally by these larvae. They have the general appearance of mites, and they are equipped with four to six pairs of stumpy legs, each with two terminal claws. Moreover, the larvae also molt their cuticles at intervals.

Traits intermediate between those of annelids and arthropods are exhibited more clearly by the tardigrades (see Fig. 15.31), microscopic animals existing on land and in fresh water. The barrel-shaped body of a water bear consists of a prostomium and five trunk seg-

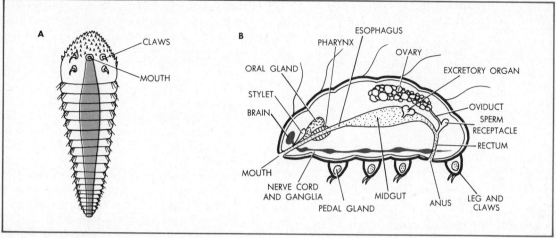

15 · 31   Oncopods. *A, ventral view of a lingua-tulid. B, sagittal section of a tardigrade.*

ments. The first four trunk segments bear short, stumpy legs with claws. On the head segment are the openings of a pair of *oral glands,* and also horny, partly chitinous *stylets,* used in piercing the walls of food organisms. The mouth leads into a straight alimentary tract which terminates at the anus in the last segment. The epidermis is covered by a cuticle which is molted several times during the life of the animal. A segmentally arranged body musculature underlies the epidermis. The nervous system is annelidlike and contains four segmental ganglia. A pair of eyecups is embedded on each side of the brain ganglion. The body cavity lacks a peritoneum in the adult, the cavity being a blood sinus as in arthropods. Excretion

takes place through the oral glands, the alimentary tract, and the body surface. The epidermis also serves as the principal breathing structure. A single gonad lies in the dorsal part of the animal. The embryonic development of tardigrades is of interest in that the coelom sacs do not form schizocoelically by splitting of mesoderm, but *enterocoelically* by outgrowth of pouches directly from the endoderm. Larvae are not formed, and adults arise directly.

Of all the Oncopoda, the Onychophora are most clearly intermediate between annelids and arthropods, and their very existence provides one of the best proofs that annelids and arthropods are closely related. *Peripatus* and allied types possess a caterpillarlike body that is covered with a thin, nonchitinous, velvet-textured cuticle. Under the epidermis are two muscle layers as in annelids. The head consists of three segments. The first bears a pair of annelidlike eyes and a pair of nonretractile tentacles. A pair of *oral papillae* on the second seg-

15 · 32   Peripatus. *Sagittal section showing position of principal organs.*

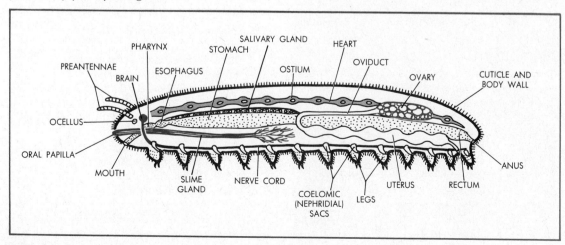

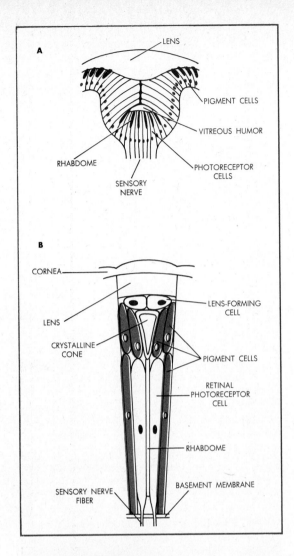

A

LENS

PIGMENT CELLS

VITREOUS HUMOR

RHABDOME

PHOTORECEPTOR CELLS

SENSORY NERVE

B

CORNEA

LENS-FORMING CELL

LENS

CRYSTALLINE CONE

PIGMENT CELLS

RETINAL PHOTORECEPTOR CELL

RHABDOME

SENSORY NERVE FIBER

BASEMENT MEMBRANE

15 · 33 *Arthropod eyes.* A, *simple eye* (ocellus), *as in insects.* B, *longitudinal section through a single visual unit* (ommatidium) *of a compound eye.* C, *photo of compound eye in insect.*

ment contains the openings of elongated *slime glands.* The secretion of these glands may be shot out explosively and is used to entangle prey or enemy. The third segment contains the mouth, equipped with a pair of horny biting *jaws.* (See Fig. 15.32 and Color Plate XXV, 39.)

Along the trunk, the stumpy paired legs each carry two recurved claws. The legs mark the position of internal segments and of segmentally arranged organs. The nervous system is annelidlike, though distinct ganglia are absent. Also annelidlike are the multiple pairs of metanephridia which open ventrally at the bases of the legs. The coeloms are greatly reduced in size and segmental septa are absent, as in arthropods. Again as in arthropods, the blood circulation is open; the only vessel present is a single dorsal *heart* with lateral segmental openings, or *ostia.* Another very arthropodlike feature is the breathing system, which consists of *tracheal tubes.* The reproductive organs are paired, with a duct opening just in front of the anus. These ducts are ciliated internally, as in annelids and in contrast to arthropods, in which cilia are absent altogether. Fertilized eggs are retained within the female body and miniature young are formed without larval stages. Development is generally rather arthropodlike. But onychophorans as a group represent as perfect a "missing link" between two other types of organisms as is known in biology.

PHYLUM ARTHROPODA

Metamerically segmented; with jointed legs and chitinous exoskeleton; characteristically with compound eyes; larvae various or absent; 1 million species.

Subphylum CHELICERATA: without jaws or antennae
Class *Xiphosurida*: horseshoe crabs
Class *Pantopoda*: sea spiders
Class *Arachnida*: scorpions, spiders, ticks, mites
Subphylum MANDIBULATA: with jaws and antennae
Class *Crustacea*: crustaceans
Class *Chilopoda*: centipedes
Class *Diplopoda*: millipedes
Class *Hexapoda*: insects

Arthropods form the largest phylum not only among animals but among all living organisms; more

C

arthropod types are known than all other living types combined. About 75 per cent of the described species comprise the insects, but according to one estimate some 10 million insect species may actually exist. One of the orders of insects, the beetles, includes 300,000 species alone, which makes this order larger than any other *phylum* of organisms.

The unrivaled success of the phylum is a consequence of the basic arthropod construction, the essential features of which are the metameric organization and the exoskeletal armor. We do not have a record of the original schizocoelomate ancestor from which arthropods evolved, but we are well justified in assuming that this ancestor was primitively polychaetelike, with metameric segments and paired segmental appendages. Such a stock then must have adopted a crawling existence, the parapodial appendages serving as legs. Later, the epidermal potential of forming chitin, restricted at first (and in annelids even today) to the production of setae, evidently became general and led to development of a chitinous cover over the whole body. This exoskeleton not only protected but also strengthened and supported mechanically; it must have permitted the legs to become more elongated and jointed into segments, hence more efficient.

Furthermore, far more so than in the annelid group, the parapodial appendages could become structurally and functionally different in different segments, for the chitinous cover could become molded and elaborated into diverse permanent shapes. As a result, the segmental appendages of the evolving arthropods became not only walking legs, but also structures adapted to biting, cutting, sucking, piercing, cleaning, grasping, carrying, breathing, swimming, flying, egg laying, sperm-transferring, sensing, and even silk spinning. In effect, the possibilities of diversification inherent in a segmental repetition of parts became exploited in an almost infinite variety of ways. Moreover, a chitin cover also served well in the elaboration of complex sensory receptors, including most particularly the unique compound eyes. Arthropods possess two types of eyes, namely, *simple* ones, also called *ocelli*, and *compound* ones (Fig. 15.33). In an ocellus, a single lens covers several light-sensitive cells. In a compound eye, numerous complete visual units (or *ommatidia*) are grouped together into a large composite structure. Each ommatidium contains a separate lens and light-sensitive cells.

The fundamental body divisions of an adult arthropod are *head, thorax,* and *abdomen* (Fig. 15.34). These may or may not be marked off sharply, and in many cases the head and thorax are fused together into a *cephalothorax.* Any of the body divisions may be unsegmented externally as a result of fusion of

15 · 34 Arthropod structure. A, lateral view of a grasshopper larva, showing segmental structure generally. Head, at right, is externally unsegmented and bears antennae, eyes, and mouth parts. The thorax, consisting of three segments in insects, bears three pairs of legs (one per segment) as well as two pairs of wings in adults (on the second and third thoracic segments). The abdomen in insects typically consists of 11 segments and is without appendages. Numbers of segments and types of appendages vary considerably for different arthropod groups, but sets of mutually different segments are present in all. B, segmental exoskeletal parts and basic appendage structure. Epipodites typically are gills. Endopodites typically terminate in claws or pincers. Only a few of the trunk and appendageal muscles are shown.

A

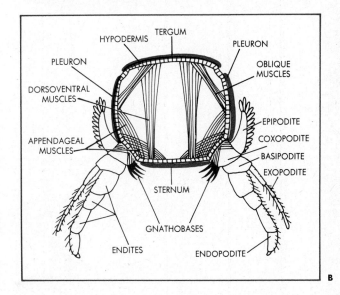

B

segments during embryonic stages. Fused or unfused segments of head, thorax, or cephalothorax are often covered by a *carapace,* a continuous exoskeletal shield. In the head, the appendages are largely sensory and ingestive. The segmental appendages of thorax and abdomen are to some extent ingestive, reproductive, and respiratory, and to a large and conspicuous extent locomotor. Typically, the most posterior part of the abdomen is a *telson,* a terminal nonsegmental section of the body.

Segments and appendages are covered by a continuous chitinous cuticle, secreted by the underlying epidermis and molted periodically during larval growth or throughout life. This cuticle is basically thin and pliable. It forms the joint membranes and the breathing surfaces, and it is tucked in at both ends of the alimentary tract as a lining of the foregut and the hindgut. In the regions between the segmental and

appendageal joints, the cuticle is thickened into a hard, exoskeletal cover. Hardness results not so much from chitin itself as from secreted impregnating materials such as horny scleroproteins and, in aquatic forms, also calcium salts. Around a segment this hard cover occurs fundamentally in the form of four plates, a dorsal *tergum,* a ventral *sternum,* and two *pleura,* that is, one pleuron on each side (see Fig. 15.34). These and the plates of adjacent segments are articulated by interior, segmentally arranged muscles.

Internally, the alimentary tract consists of foregut, midgut, and hindgut (Fig. 15.35). The first and last portions are lined with chitin, as noted, and they are derived from ectoderm; only the midgut is endodermal. Digestive glands, in many cases large and conspicuous, connect with the stomach of the midgut. The hindgut terminates at the anus, usually located ventrally in the telson. Breathing is accomplished in most arthropods by gills, gill books, lung books, or tracheal systems, all chitin-lined and metamerically arranged outgrowths or ingrowths on the body segments or

15 · 35 *The basic internal structure of arthropods, as exemplified by a lobster, A, and a grasshopper, B.*

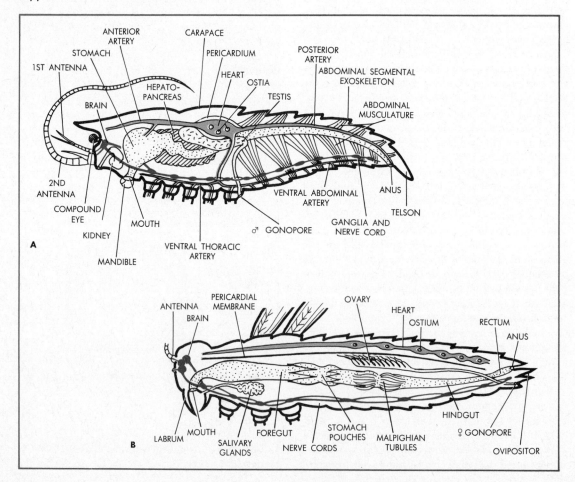

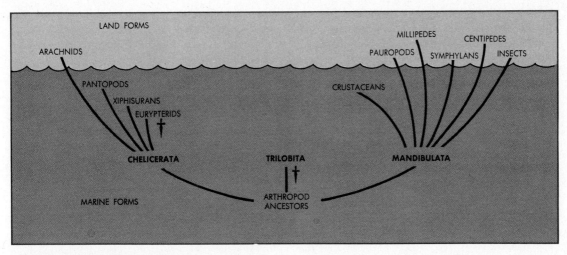

15 · 36 *Presumable evolutionary interrelations of the principal arthropod groups. Primarily aquatic groups are indicated below the water surface, primarily terrestrial groups, above.*

the appendages. Gills are feathery extensions from the leg bases. Gill books and lung books are chambers containing breathing plates resembling the pages of a book, the ones operating in water, the others in air. And tracheal systems are interconnecting air ducts leading from the body surface to all interior body parts.

Segmental coelom sacs arise in the embryo but these later disappear, leaving an unlined body cavity functioning as a blood sinus. The circulation is thus open; a dorsal tubular heart is the principal vessel, though others are often present. Excretion takes place principally through two kinds of organs, one kind opening at the bases of given body appendages, the other attached to and opening into the hindgut. Organs of the first type are variously called *coxal glands, renal glands, green glands,* and other names; they are characteristic primarily of aquatic arthropods, for example, horseshoe crabs and Crustacea. Organs of the second type are known as *Malpighian tubules;* they are characteristic of terrestrial arthropods, for example, arachnids and insects.

The nervous system is basically of the ladder type, as in polychaetes. In many cases, however, segmental ganglia formed in the embryo become concentrated into one or a few larger adult ganglia. Arthropods typically also possess endocrine systems. These consist of neurosecretory cells in the brain and of a variety of glands in the thorax and at the bases or in the stalks of the compound eyes. Hormone secretions play a major role in the control of molting and in reproduction and development, and also in regulating the activities of pigment-containing epidermal cells, which adjust the body coloration according to external backgrounds.

Evolution within the phylum appears to have proceeded along three separate major lines (Fig. 15.36). One gave rise to the aquatic trilobites, subphylum Trilobita, extinct for at least 200 million years and probably representing the most ancient group. The second line now constitutes the subphylum Chelicerata, and the third, the subphylum Mandibulata. Each of these subphyla was primitively aquatic but then gave rise to terrestrial subgroups. Thus, the chelicerates now include the aquatic horseshoe crabs and sea spiders and terrestrial arachnids such as scorpions and spiders; and the mandibulates include the aquatic crustaceans and the terrestrial centipedes, millipedes, and insects.

SUBPHYLUM CHELICERATA

Adult body usually comprising cephalothorax, generally unsegmented, and abdomen, either segmented or not; cephalothorax typically with six pairs of appendages; first pair *chelicerae,* second pair *pedipalps,* last four pairs, *walking legs;* jaws or antennae never present; abdominal appendages not primarily locomotor or absent.

Class Xiphosurida (horseshoe crabs): marine; cephalothorax with carapace and hinged to fused abdomen; telson a spine; compound eyes present; development via larvae. *Limulus*
Class Pantopoda (sea spiders): head and thorax with long, thin legs; abdomen vestigial; mouth on proboscis; compound eyes absent; egg-carrying legs on head of both sexes; development via larvae or direct. *Nymphon*

Class Arachnida (scorpions, spiders, mites, ticks): terrestrial, some secondarily aquatic; usually carnivorous, predatory; cephalothorax typically unsegmented, abdomen segmented or unsegmented; compound eyes absent; breathing by lung books, tracheae, or both; development largely direct.

The characteristics of the subphylum as a whole are illustrated well if we consider the organization of a horseshoe crab, a scorpion, and a spider.

Representing the nearest existing relatives of trilobites, the four surviving species of horseshoe crabs are "living fossils" found along sandy shores, where they lead a burrowing, semisedentary existence. The cephalothorax of *Limulus* consists of eight embryonic segments (see Table 12). These later fuse and develop a conspicuous, horseshoe-shaped carapace dorsally, which bears two small anterior ocelli and two lateral compound eyes (Fig. 15.37). Ventrally, the first segment is embryonic only and does not develop appendages. The remaining seven cephalothoracic segments each possess a pair of appendages. The first pair of *pedipalps* behind them is indistinguishable from the next three pairs of *walking legs*. All these are pincer-equipped (*chelate*) in females and young males, but they terminate in claws in adult males. All legs and the chelicerae are equipped with prominent *gnathobases*, that is, basal joints bearing horny, toothlike projections. Legs are positioned in such a way that the gnathobases surround the mouth. Horseshoe crabs feed on clamworms, soft-shelled clams, and other small animals. Such food is crushed and minced by the gnathobases when the legs are moved, and the food pulp, including sand and pieces of shells, is then pushed into the mouth by the chelicerae. These animals are the only chelicerates eating solid food; all others subsist on liquid food, a practice conditioned by the absence of jaws. The eighth cephalothoracic segment bears a seventh pair of appendages, the *chilaria*, small projections without known function. (See Color Plate XXV, 40.)

The cephalothorax as a whole is hinged to the abdomen, composed of a broad anterior region of fused segments and, hinged to them posteriorly, a telson spine. Apart from the telson, the abdomen is formed from six embryonic segments. Each of these develops a pair of appendages. The first pair is fused along the mid-line and forms a transverse plate, the *operculum*, which covers and protects all posterior appendages. On the back face of the operculum are the reproductive openings. The next five pairs of appendages are broad, flat *gill books*, on the back face of which are numerous gill plates. By flapping their gill books horseshoe crabs may not only breathe but also swim to some extent.

Internally, the alimentary tract contains a chitin-lined gizzard and a large, highly lobulated digestive

TABLE 12   SEGMENTS AND APPENDAGES IN CHELICERATE ARTHROPODS

		HORSESHOE CRAB	SCORPION	SPIDER
1		embryo only	embryo only	embryo only
2		chelicerae (chelate)	chelicerae (small)	chelicerae (fangs)
3		pedipalps (chelate)	pedipalps (large)	pedipalps (tactile)
4	cephalothorax	walking legs (chelate)	walking legs (clawed)	walking legs (clawed)
5		walking legs (chelate)	walking legs (clawed)	walking legs (clawed)
6		walking legs (chelate)	walking legs (clawed)	walking legs (clawed)
7		walking legs (chelate)	walking legs (clawed)	walking legs (clawed)
8		chilaria	embryo only	embryo only
9		operculum, gonopores	operculum, gonopores	embryo only
10		gill books	pectines	lung books/tracheae
11	abdomen	gill books	lung books	lung books/tracheae
12		gill books	lung books	spinnerets
13		gill books	lung books	spinnerets
14		gill books	lung books	14–18 embryo only
		telson	15–20 "tail" without appendages	
			telson	

gland occupying much of the space under the carapace. The anus opens at the base of the telson. Excretion occurs via a pair of coxal glands opening at the bases of the last pair of legs. Females lay large, yolky eggs in sand burrows and males fertilize the spawn externally. The larvae resemble trilobites and also the adult horseshoe crabs, though a telson is absent. Maturation lasts up to 10 or 11 years, and several larval molts occur during this time. Adults do not molt.

A scorpion has a segmental structure similar to that of a horseshoe crab (Fig. 15.38 and Table 12). The cephalothorax is formed from eight embryonic segments and is covered dorsally by a carapace. On the carapace are a pair of median ocelli and from two to five lateral ocelli on each side. Some scorpions are without eyes, however. Ventrally, the second segment bears short pincered chelicerae; the third carries the large pedipalps, also chelate; and on the next four segments are the walking legs, each terminating in a pair of claws. The pedipalps and the first two pairs of legs have gnathobases with a chewing function, as in *Limulus*. Scorpions feed mostly on insects and spiders, which are crushed by the gnathobases. The juices are then sucked into the mouth, located between the second and third segments. The eighth segment, like the first, is embryonic only (and corresponds to the chilarial segment of *Limulus*).

The abdomen consists of 12 segments and a telson. On the first is a small operculum containing the reproductive openings, and the second bears a pair of

15 · 37   The horseshoe crab Limulus. *The segmental appendages in ventral view.*

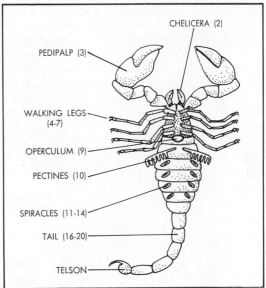

15 · 38   Scorpions. *Photo: a living specimen in lateral view. Diagram: external segmental structure, ventral view.*

pectines, fringed, comblike flaps. These structures are tactile; they brush over the ground when a scorpion walks and they represent important touch receptors in these nocturnal animals. On each of the next four abdominal segments is a pair of ventrolateral *spiracles*, slits leading into chambers containing the *lung books*. Both the pectines and the lung books are undoubtedly homologous to the gill books of horseshoe crabs. The seventh abdominal segment is without appendages. This is true also for the remaining five segments, which are narrowed into a "tail." The telson contains a poison gland with a sharp, terminal sting. Scorpions carry their tail arched up

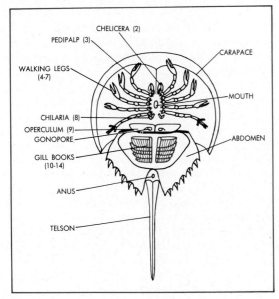

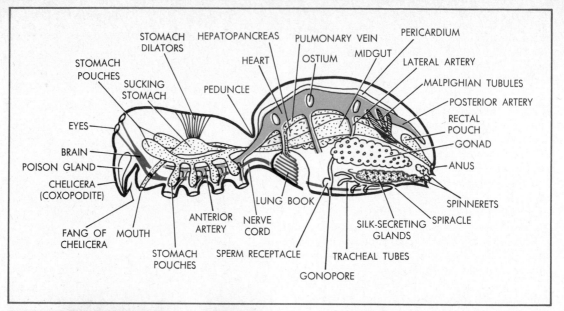

STOMACH DILATORS — HEPATOPANCREAS — PULMONARY VEIN — PERICARDIUM
STOMACH POUCHES — HEART — OSTIUM — MIDGUT — LATERAL ARTERY
SUCKING STOMACH — PEDUNCLE — MALPIGHIAN TUBULES
EYES — POSTERIOR ARTERY
BRAIN — RECTAL POUCH
POISON GLAND — GONAD
CHELICERA (COXOPODITE) — ANUS
FANG OF CHELICERA — MOUTH — ANTERIOR ARTERY — NERVE CORD — LUNG BOOK — SPINNERETS — SPIRACLE
STOMACH POUCHES — SPERM RECEPTACLE — SILK-SECRETING GLANDS
GONOPORE — TRACHEAL TUBES

15 · 39 Spiders. *Diagram: sagittal section showing interior structure. The peduncle refers to the "waist" connecting the cephalothorax with the abdomen. Photo: front view of head of a wolf spider. Note large and small eyes, and the chelicerae with fangs.*

and forward, and they use the poison sting to paralyze and kill prey that has been grasped with the pedipalps.

Scorpions possess a long midgut connecting with several pairs of digestive glands. To the beginning of the hindgut are joined several groups of excretory Malpighian tubules. A large, well-developed heart lies between segments 7 and 13. Each segmental section of the heart bears a pair of lateral openings, or *ostia*, as well as a pair of ventrolateral arteries. Anterior and posterior arteries are present as well. Fertilization is internal and occurs after elaborate courtship dances. Internal development of the eggs follows, and miniature adults are born.

Although a spider is quite dissimilar in appearance

to a scorpion, the basic segmental structure of the two is nevertheless almost identical, at least in the embryos. In a spider embryo are formed 18 antero-posterior coelomic sacs, each corresponding to an embryonic segment. The first 8 give rise to the adult cephalothorax, the last 10 to the abdomen (Fig. 15.39 and Table 12). In the cephalothorax, the first

15 · 40 Trends in crustacean evolution: *progressive reduction of trunk segments and enlargement of head and antennae. A and B, subclass Branchiopoda. A, the brine shrimp Artemia; numerous segments and like appendages, legs locomotor, no carapace. B, the water flea Daphnia; antennae locomotor, carapace encloses trunk, legs fewer but still alike. C, subclass Ostracoda, genus Cypris; antennae locomotor, body enclosed in carapace, thorax and abdomen highly reduced, legs few and not alike. D and E, subclass Copepoda, genus Cyclops; antennae locomotor, head carapace encloses some of trunk, free trunk segments and legs reduced. F and G, subclass Cirripedia, the rock barnacle Balanus; sessile, carapace forms shell plates (as named), segments reduced, legs ingestive. The parasitic and structurally highly simplified Sacculina (Fig. 9.16) is also a cirriped.*

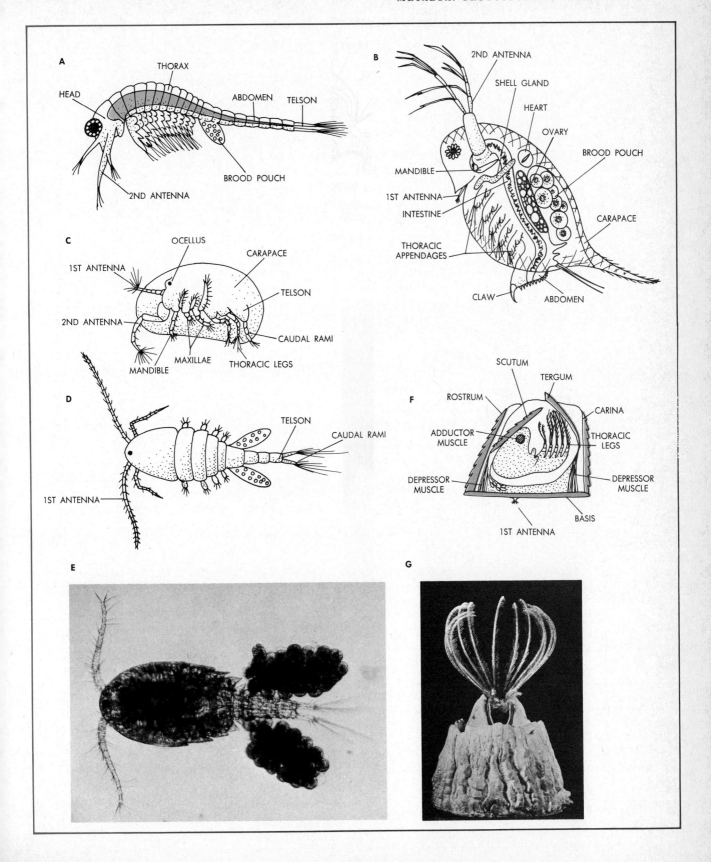

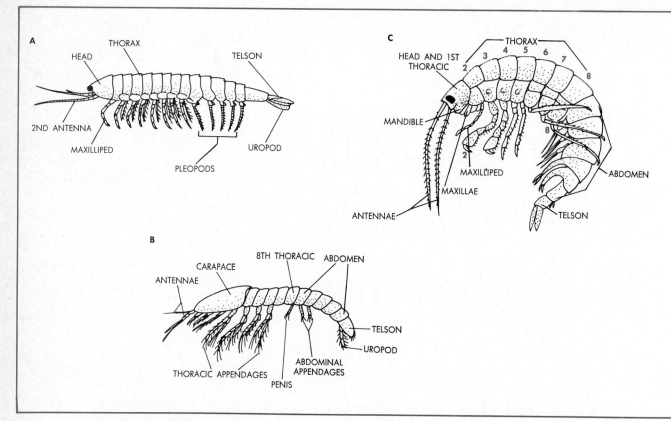

15 · 41 Trends in crustacean evolution: *retention of all segments and appendages, but increasing diversification of them and increase in the size of the carapace. All types illustrated belong to the subclass Malacostraca. A, superorder* Syncarida, *the primitive genus* Anaspides; *note absence of carapace, appendages generally alike* (*pleopod is a general term for any abdominal appendage*). B, *superorder* Pancarida, *genus* Thermosbaena; *carapace present, appendage*

15 · 42 Crustacean larvae. *A through E, series of larvae hatched at successively later developmental stages* (*segmental stage attained is indi-* *cated below each figure*). *Thus, a just-hatched brine shrimp nauplius still must develop a great deal to attain adult form, but a just-hatched*

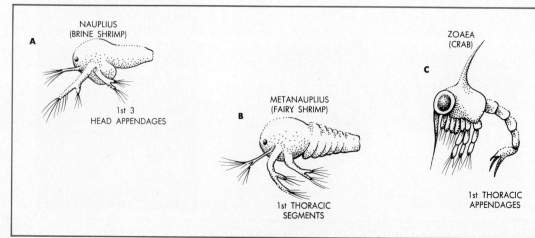

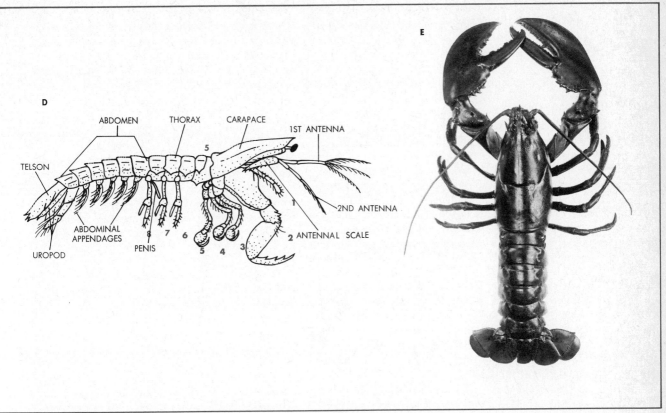

diversification in evidence. C, superorder Pera-
carida, the sandhopper Gammarus; appendage
diversification extensive, carapace small. D,
superorder Hoplocarida, the mantis shrimp
Squilla; appendage diversification very extensive,

carapace larger than in C. E, superorder Eucarida,
order Decapoda, the lobster Homarus; both ap-
pendage diversification and carapace in most
highly developed condition.

mysis of a lobster already resembles the adult
considerably. If hatching occurs very late, as in

some shrimps and prawns, a larval phase is
absent altogether.

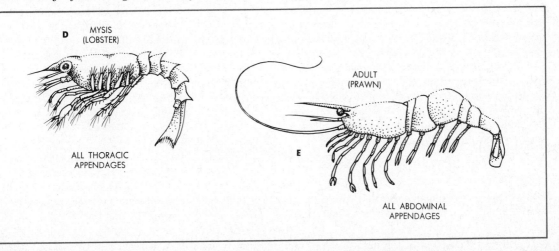

embryonic segment remains without appendages, the second and third form chelicerae and pedipalps, respectively, the next four develop legs, and the eighth is again without appendages. In the abdomen, the first segment disappears; the second and third each develop a pair of lung-book chambers, a pair of tracheal bundles, or both; and the fourth and fifth form the silk-spinning *spinnerets*. All remaining embryonic abdominal segments disappear in later development. In the adult the segments of both the cephalothorax and the abdomen are fused, and these two body parts are joined by a narrow *peduncle*, the characteristic "waist" of a spider. Up to eight eyes are borne on the cephalothorax.

The chelicerae are poison-gland-containing fangs, with poison ducts opening at the tips. The pedipalps are tactile, and in males they contain a specialized receptacle for the transfer of sperms during copulation. The gnathobases of the pedipalps are the principal chewing devices of spiders. Food consists chiefly of insects. Prey is killed with the poison fangs, is chewed and torn with the gnathobases, and is predigested for an hour or more by proteinases secreted from salivary glands opening into the mouth. The food juices are then sucked up, suction being produced by the stomach.

The *spinnerets* are modified abdominal appendages providing outlets for the *silk glands* in the abdomen. Spider silk is a scleroprotein that hardens on contact with air. All spiders produce silk, but not all construct webs. Silk is used in numerous other ways. For example, the animals spin egg cocoons, sperm cases, molting sheets, attachment disks, burrow linings, trapdoors, with hinges, binding threads for prey, drag lines, and also gossamer for "ballooning," that is, riding air currents at the end of a free-floating thread.

Internally, the midgut connects with a large, dorsal digestive gland and also pouches into a pair of sacs which pass forward and send branches into the legs. Malpighian tubules open into the hindgut. The heart has three pairs of ostia and it gives off an anterior and posterior artery as well as three pairs of lateral vessels. In the nervous system, all ventral ganglia are concentrated anteriorly. Fertilization occurs internally, the pedipalp of the male serving as sperm-transferring organ. Highly elaborate courtship dances usually precede copulation. In some species the females kill and eat the males after sperm transfer. Batches of fertilized eggs are usually laid into spun cocoons and development is direct.

SUBPHYLUM MANDIBULATA

Body comprising cephalothorax and abdomen; or head, thorax, and abdomen; or head and trunk; cephalothorax or head unsegmented externally; thorax, abdomen, or trunk segmented; head segments typically with one or two pairs of *antennae*, one pair of *mandibles*, two pairs of *maxillae;* thoracic appendages two or more pairs; with or without abdominal appendages.

Class Crustacea

Marine and freshwater, some terrestrial; head and thorax or cephalothorax, often with carapace; thorax and abdomen usually segmented; with telson; two pairs of antennae; compound eyes typically present; breathing via gills; excretion through antennal or maxillary glands; typically with *nauplius* or other free larval stages.

Crustacean evolution appears to have produced two principal lines of descent. In one, the primitive members still retain many of the presumably ancestral characteristics, particularly the presence of numerous like segments, with like appendages serving in locomotion, feeding, and breathing. Primitive types of this sort are represented by the fairy shrimps and brine shrimps (Fig. 15.40, page 379). Later groups in this line of descent exemplify three general kinds of changes: (1) shortening of the trunk and reduction of the number of segments and of trunk appendages, paralleled by an enlargement of the head appendages, which then assume the main feeding and locomotor functions; (2) development of a carapace covering progressively more of the body; and (3) adoption of parasitic or sessile ways of life. Water fleas (*Daphnia*) and copepods illustrate the first two of these changes, and barnacles illustrate the third.

The second major crustacean series again exhibits three kinds of general deviations from the presumed ancestral organization: (1) retention of all trunk segments and appendages, including abdominal ones, but increasing diversification of these appendages in different body regions; (2) development of a progressively larger carapace which eventually fuses the entire thorax to the head; and (3) substitution of filter feeding by predatory and scavenging means of nutrition in the advanced groups. These characteristics are displayed clearly in the most familiar of all crustaceans, namely, the order Decapoda, which includes shrimps, prawns, lobsters, and crabs (Fig. 15.41, page 380).

Crustacea typically develop via a succession of larval stages, each separated from the next by a molt. In the course of this larval series, the number of fully developed segments increases progressively. Thus, the characteristic first larval stage is the nauplius, in which only the first few head segments and their appendages are elaborated. The later larval forms are called, successively, *metanauplius, protozoaea, zoaea,* and *mysis,* each identified by a larger number of fully developed segments (Fig. 15.42, page 380). A mysis larva lacks only the last few abdominal segments, and these develop during the change to the next and last stage, namely, the adult condition. Many crustacea pass through the whole series of larval forms, but in many others given stages may be part of the embryonic period or may be reduced or omitted altogether.

The adult organization of crustaceans is typified in large measure by the structure of a lobster (Fig. 15.43 and Table 13). The head and thorax are covered dorsally by a carapace, an extension of the dorsal exoskeletal plate on the third head segment. The head itself consists of six fused segments, five of them with paired appendages. In addition, the head also contains a median ocellus (reduced in lobsters) and compound eyes (stalked in lobsters). The first antennae are short and contain at their bases balancing organs. At the bases of the second antennae are the openings of the *antennal glands,* the excretory organs of lobsters. The mandibles on the third segment are the chewing jaws, and they lead into the mouth. This opening is guarded by an upper lip, or *labrum,* and an underlip, or *metastoma,* flaplike extensions of the body wall and not segmental appendages. Two pairs of maxillae on the head pass bits of food toward the mouth.

In the eight segments of the thorax, the first three carry maxillipeds, which aid in macerating food and in passing it to the mouth. At the bases of the second and third maxillipeds are attached feathery gills. The remaining five segments bear walking legs. The first legs are large and terminate in crushing and cutting pincers. At the bases of the third pair of legs are the female reproductive openings, and at the bases of the fifth pair, the male openings. Associated with each leg is also a gill, attached not to the leg base itself but to the side of the body. The dorsal carapace extends down on each side over the gills and the leg bases.

In the abdomen, the appendages of the first segment are modified in males into copulatory or sperm-transferring organs. In female lobsters these appendages are greatly reduced but in many other crustacea they are fashioned into brood pouches or into structures to which batches of developing eggs remain attached. Lobsters possess egg-holding appendages, the *swimmerets,* on the second to fifth abdominal segments. In other crustacea, the posterior abdominal appendages, if present at all, serve chiefly in locomotor or breathing functions. The last abdominal appendages are flat, platelike *uropods,* which together with the telson form a tail fan.

Internally, crustacea exhibit typical arthropod structure (see Fig. 15.35). In a lobster the stomach has two compartments. An anterior *gastric mill* equipped with chitinous teeth and other hard outgrowths grinds coarse food. And a posterior filter compartment sorts food: coarse particles are returned into the gastric mill; fine particles pass into the intestine; and liquefied food is taken up into the capacious *hepatopancreas* ("liver") of the midgut, where the bulk of digestion and absorption occur. The nervous system has a ladder-type organization. In primitive crustacea the heart is elongated, with a pair of ostia in each segmental portion. In advanced groups the heart is shortened and possesses fewer ostia. For example there are three pairs of ostia in lobster hearts.

Crustacea possess a well-developed endocrine system. Important components are a so-called *X-organ,* located in each eyestalk near the eye, and a *sinus gland,* also located in each eyestalk, near its base. This gland appears to be primarily a storage site for hormones produced in the X-organ. Another endocrine component is the *Y-organ,* situated in the antennal or maxillary segments of the head. Hormones of the X-organ can be shown in part to regulate the activities of the epidermal pigment cells, in part to control the secretions of the Y-organ. Hormones produced by the latter promote the growth of the reproductive system and they also inhibit or accelerate molting. Crustacea molt throughout life, but progressively less often as they age.

Class Chilopoda (centipedes)

Carnivorous, predatory; head with one pair of antennae, one pair of mandibles, two pairs of maxillae; trunk with 1 pair of poison-claw-containing prehensors and 15 or more pairs of walking legs; eyes compound or simple or absent; tracheae branched; reproductive openings at posterior end of trunk.

Class Diplopoda (millipedes)

Herbivorous, scavenging; head with one pair each of antennae, mandibles, and maxillae; first four trunk segments single, rest double and fused; with ocelli; tracheae unbranched; reproductive openings on third trunk segments.

The head of a centipede is structured like that of an insect (Fig. 15.44 and Table 13). The first trunk segment is equipped with fanglike *prehensors,* which contain poison glands and ducts opening at the tips.

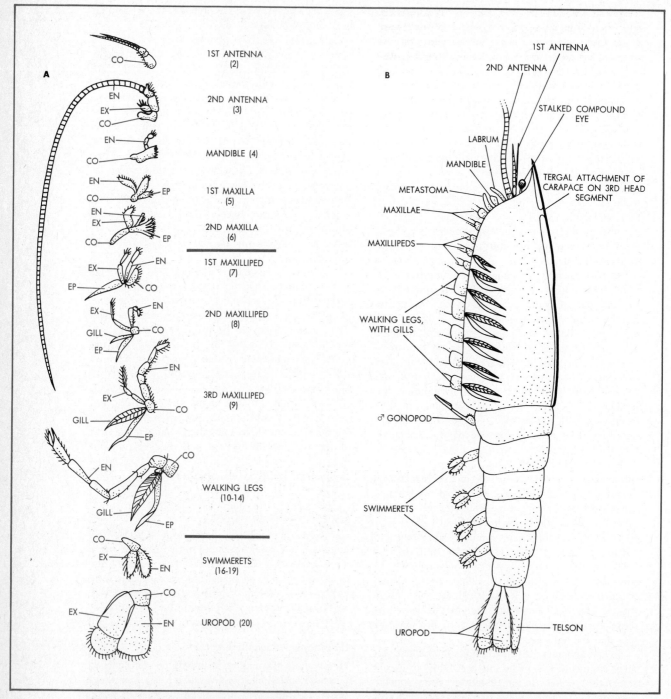

15 · 43 *Segmental structure of a lobster.* A, *segmental appendages of left side. co, coxopodite; ex, exopodite; en, endopodite; ep, epipodite. Segmental numbers counted from anterior end and indicated in parentheses. Note that some appendages are without exopodites. Gills are part of the* epipodites. *The first abdominal segment (no. 15) bears a copulatory appendage in males (gonopod). B, diagram of position of appendages in whole animal. The labrum and metastoma, which guard the mouth, and the eyes are extensions of the body wall, not metameric appendages.*

PLATE XXI

34. Top view of Obelia medusa.
*Note central manubrium, sex organs
along radial canals, marginal tentacles,
and absence of velum in this genus.*

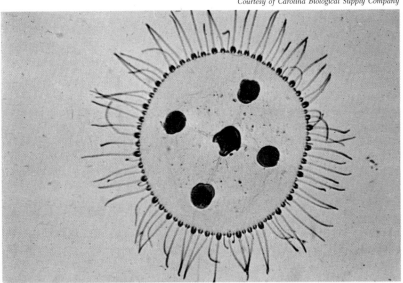

35. Jellyfish
*of the common genus Aurelia,
stranded on the seashore. Note the
four gonads (pink).*

D

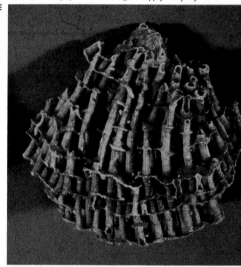

D, E, F, courtesy of Carolina Biological Supply Company

E

F

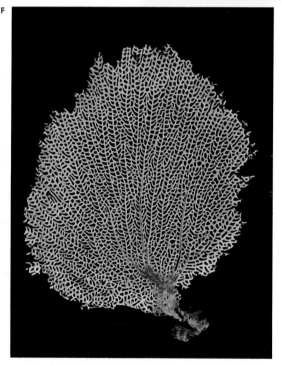

36. Anthozoa.
A, color varieties of the
sea anemone Metridium.
B, two anemones of
the genus Actinia. C, portion of the
sea fan Eunicella, with expanded polyps.
D, portion of the stony coral
Astrangia, with expanded polyps.
E, skeleton of the organ-pipe coral Tubipora.
F, skeleton of the sea fan Gorgonia.

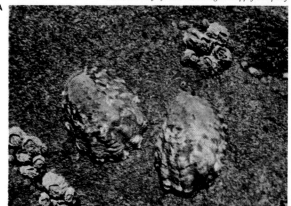

PLATE XXIV

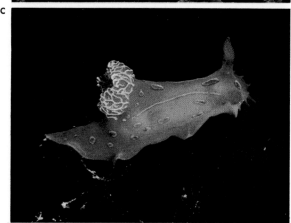

37. Snails.
A, limpets (Acmaea); *note uncoiled
shell. B, a nudibranch (Dirona),
with conspicuous cerata. C, the nudibranch
Polycera, a sea slug; note the breathing
rosette dorsoposteriorly.
D, the edible, air-breathing land
snail Helix pomatia.*

The remainder of the trunk consists of leg-bearing segments, different numbers of them in different types of centipedes. Each such segment contains a pair of *spiracles*, openings leading into branching bundles of tracheal breathing tubes. The nervous system is of the primitive ladder-type pattern, and the heart extends throughout the trunk and contains in each segmental portion a pair of ostia and lateral arteries. Excretion occurs through Malpighian tubules. Fertilization takes place by copulation. Centipedes molt throughout life. The animals typically are rapid run-

TABLE 13 SEGMENTS AND APPENDAGES IN MANDIBULATE ARTHROPODS

	LOBSTER	CENTIPEDE	INSECT
1			
2	antennae	antennae	antennae
3	antennae		
4	mandibles	mandibles	mandibles
5	maxillae	maxillae	maxillae
6	maxillae	labium (maxillae)	labium (maxillae)
7	maxillipeds	prehensors	legs
8	maxillipeds	legs	legs, wings, (spiracles)
9	maxillipeds	legs	legs, wings, (spiracles)
10	chelate legs	legs	(spiracles)
11	legs	legs	(spiracles)
12	legs, (♀ gonopore)	legs	(spiracles)
13	legs	legs	(spiracles)
14	legs, (♂ gonopore)	legs	(spiracles)
15	reproductive	legs	(spiracles)
16	swimmerets	legs	(spiracles)
17	swimmerets	legs	(spiracles), ♀ ovipositor, ♂ copulatory organ
18	swimmerets	legs	
19	swimmerets	legs	(anus)
20	uropods	legs	(anal cerci)
21	telson	legs	
22		legs	
		legs	
		legs (gonopores)	
		telson	

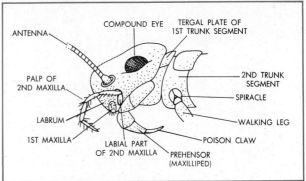

15·44 Centipedes. *Photo: whole specimen, from life. Diagram: head structure. Mouth and mandibles are hidden behind the labrum and the maxillae. Note that the prehensors on the first trunk segment are homologous to crustacean maxillipeds.*

ners, in correlation with their predatory mode of existence. They shun exposure, however, and during the day they tend to hide under stones and leaves and in crevices and crannies. At night they emerge in search of food, which consists of earthworms, insects, and snails.

In millipedes (Fig. 15.45) the head bears but a single pair of maxillae. In the first four trunk segments, the second, third, and fourth each bears a single pair of legs, and the reproductive ducts open on the third. The subsequent trunk segments of millipedes are fused in pairs. Each such double segment arises from two pairs of coelomic sacs and possesses two pairs of ostia in the heart, two pairs of spiracles, and two pairs of legs. The number of such double segments varies considerably in different groups. Spiracles lead into bundles of unbranched tracheae.

Courtesy of Carolina Biological Supply Company.

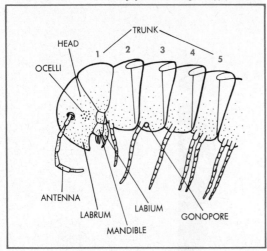

15 · 45 Millipedes. *Photo: whole specimen. Note that there are two pairs of legs in most trunk segments. Diagram: the anterior region. Numbers refer to trunk segments. Note dorsally overlapping plates of segmental exoskeleton.*

Fertilization is internal, as in centipedes. Millipedes are poor runners despite their large number of legs; the herbivorous life of the animals does not require rapid locomotion. The animals are retiring in habit, and when they are exposed, they may roll up into a ball.

Class Insecta (Hexapoda)

Terrestrial, some secondarily freshwater, exceptional cases marine; head six segments, typically with antennae, mandibles, maxillae, labium; thorax three segments, typically with three pairs of legs, two pairs of wings, two pairs of spiracles; abdomen typically eleven segments, without locomotor appendages, with eight pairs of spiracles; compound eyes and ocelli present.

Subclass Apterygota (Ametabola): primitively wingless; without metamorphosis.
Subclass Pterygota (Metabola): with wings, with metamorphosis.

> Superorder Exopterygota (Hemimetabola): wing growth external on larval body; metamorphosis gradual; compound eyes already present in larvae.
> Superorder Endopterygota (Holometabola): wing growth internal in larval body; metamorphosis abrupt; larval stages are caterpillars and pupae; compound eyes not yet present in larvae.

Insect evolution has produced three levels of specialization. The most primitive level is represented by the wingless Apterygota (Fig. 15.46), in which the hatched young are miniature adults and in which therefore larvae and metamorphosis are essentially absent. Springtails and bristletails (silverfish) are among the representatives of this smallest living group.

A second level of specialization is displayed by the winged Exopterygota (Fig. 15.47). In these insects the hatched young are larvae, or *nymphs* (*naiads* if they are aquatic). They are wingless initially, but they metamorphose gradually into winged adults via a series of molting steps. In the process, wing buds on the outside of the body grow progressively larger. The members of this huge group include, for example, grasshoppers, termites, lice, dragonflies, mayflies, bugs, locusts, aphids, and very many others.

15 · 46 Apterygote (*primitively flightless*) *insects. Top, a silverfish (order Thysanura). Bottom, a springtail (order Collembola).*

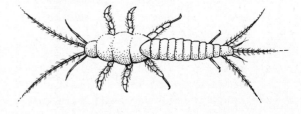

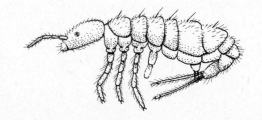

The third and most specialized level is represented by the Endopterygota (Fig. 15.48). Here the larvae are caterpillars or caterpillarlike. They undergo a series of molts and the last of these transforms the caterpillar into a *pupa*. During the pupal phase a drastic metamorphosis takes place, in the course of which wings and other adult structures arise from internal buds called *imaginal disks*. The adult then extricates itself from the pupal envelopes. To this largest group belong, for example, moths, butterflies, flies, mosquitos, fleas, beetles, bees, ants, wasps, and numerous others.

The head of an insect consists of six fused segments of which four bear appendages (Fig. 15.49 and Table 13). The mandibles and first maxillae lie lateral

15 · 47 Exopterygote insects. A, cockroach (order Orthoptera). B, mayfly (order Ephemoptera). C, human body louse (order Anopleura). D, 17-year locust (order Homoptera). See also Color Plate XXVI, 42.

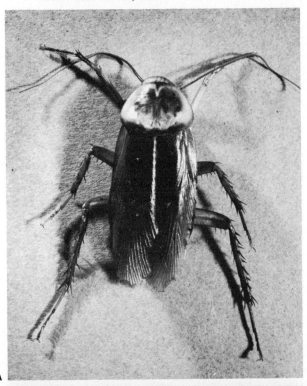

A

C

B

D

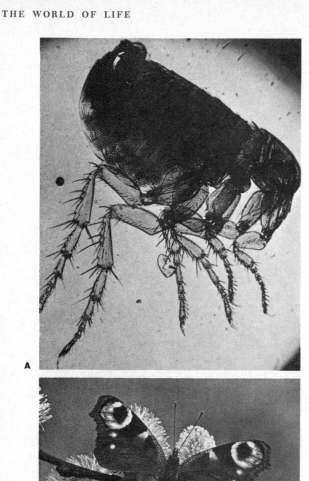

A

D

B

E

C

15 · 48 Endopterygote insects. *A, flea (order Siphonaptera). B, peacock butterfly (order Lepidoptera); C, larvae and one pupa of mosquito, suspended from water surface (order Diptera). D, hercules beetle (order Coleoptera). E, wood wasp, with ovipositor functioning as wood borer (order Hymenoptera).*

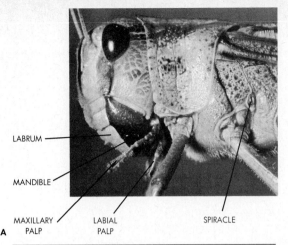

LABRUM

MANDIBLE

MAXILLARY PALP

LABIAL PALP

SPIRACLE

A

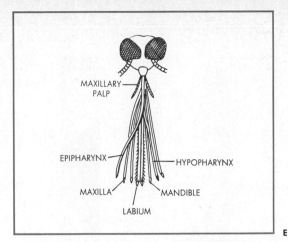

MAXILLARY PALP

EPIPHARYNX

HYPOPHARYNX

MAXILLA

MANDIBLE

LABIUM

E

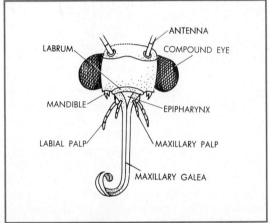

ANTENNA

LABRUM

COMPOUND EYE

MANDIBLE

EPIPHARYNX

LABIAL PALP

MAXILLARY PALP

MAXILLARY GALEA

B

F

C   **D**

F, H, courtesy of Carolina Biological Supply Company.

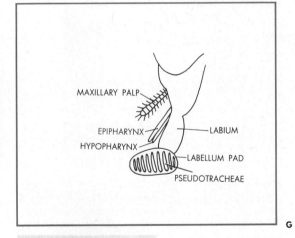

MAXILLARY PALP

EPIPHARYNX

HYPOPHARYNX

LABIUM

LABELLUM PAD

PSEUDOTRACHEAE

G

15 · 49 *Insect head structure and mouth parts. A, side view of head and thorax of locust, exemplifying biting and chewing mouth parts. B, front view of butterfly head, showing sucking proboscis (galea) formed from maxillary components. C and D, rolled-up and extended position of butterfly proboscis. E and F, front views of the head of a female mosquito. The epipharynx is an extension of the labrum, the hypopharynx, an extension of the floor of the mouth; together they form a food (blood)-conducting channel. G and H, side and front views of the proboscis apparatus of a housefly.*

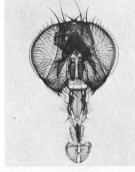

H

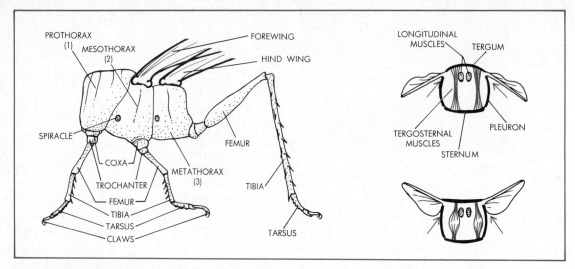

15 · 50   The insect thorax. *Left, thorax of grass-hopper. The coxa of a leg is homologous to the coxopodite, the trochanter to the basipodite, and all other joints to the endipodite. See also Fig. 2.13 for photo of insect leg. Right, the indirect, flight-producing wing musculature. A wing is an extended fold of body wall. Arrows point to the fulcrums of wings, at the dorsal edges of the pleura. At top, tergosternal muscles are relaxed, longitudinal muscles contracted, wings moved down. At bottom, the converse, with wings moved up.*

to the mouth, and an upper lip, the *labrum*, protects the mouth anteriorly. The second maxillae are fused and form an underlip, the *labium*. Primitively, labrum, mandibles, maxillae, and labium form *biting-and-chewing* mouth parts. Most Exopterygota possess oral structures of this type.

In more advanced forms, these basic oral appendages are modified into *sucking, licking,* or into *piercing-and-sucking* structures. In a butterfly, for example, the maxillae are drawn out into an elongated proboscis, each maxilla forming a complete sucking tube. The two tubes are interlocked, can be extended deep into the nectar-containing region of a flower, and can be rolled up toward the head when not in use. Flies, mosquitos, bees, and many other Endopterygota likewise possess variously modified mouth parts.

The head joins the thorax via a narrow neck. Of the three thoracic segments, each carries a pair of legs and the second and third each typically also bears a pair of wings. A wing is a flattened fold of the body wall, extending out from between the dorsal and lateral exoskeletal plate (Fig. 15.50). Air-filled tubular spaces within the wing form the supporting veins. Muscles attaching directly to a wing are used primarily to move the appendage into a flying or a rest position. An indirect musculature between the dorsal and ventral skeletal plates brings about the flying motions themselves. Contraction of these muscles flattens the normally arched dorsal plate and moves the wing up; relaxation permits the elastic dorsal plate to recoil to its arched position and this brings the wing down. Either pair of wings may be modified. For example, the hind wings are reduced to knobbed stumps, or *halteres,* in flies and mosquitos (and the vibrations of the halteres during flight produce the buzzing sounds made by these insects). The forewings are hardened into protective covers in grasshoppers, earwigs, and beetles. In fleas and many members of other groups, both pairs of wings are secondarily absent.

The abdomen (Fig. 15.51) typically consists of 11 segments, though the number is often reduced secondarily. In the first seven segments, appendages begin to form in the embryo but they never mature (except in some of the Apterygota) and are absent in the adult. The appendages of the eighth and ninth segments in the females of most insects become *ovipositors,* accessory egg-laying structures, but are formed into stings, saws, and piercers in bees and related groups. The appendages of the ninth segment in males form copulatory organs. The anus is on the tenth segment in most cases. The eleventh, if present, is often extended as a pair of variously shaped posterior projections, the *anal cerci* (for example, the "forceps" of earwigs).

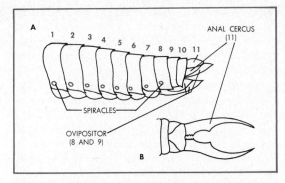

15 · 51   The insect abdomen. *A, side view of abdomen as in grasshopper; numbers refer to segments. B, dorsal view of hind end of earwig (order Dermaptera), showing anal cerci elongated into horny forceps.*

The last two thoracic and the first eight abdominal segments typically bear a pair of *spiracles* each, equipped with muscle-operated valves. These air pores lead into a highly developed tracheal system, which includes interconnecting longitudinal tubes, air sacs, and branching tracheae. Contraction of muscles attached to the dorsal and ventral skeletal plates of the segments brings about exhalation, and relaxation of these muscles leads to recoil of the skeletal plates and thus to inhalation. Such breathing motions

15 · 52   Development of insect appendages. *A, ventral views of two stages in embryonic development, showing gradual anteroposterior formation of segments and segmental appendages. Note movement of mouth backward. B, growth of a wing as an imaginal disk in an interior epidermal pocket, as in endopterygotes. The colored layer is the epidermis.*

of the abdomen can be observed readily in a quiescent fly.

The nervous system of insects is of the ladder type, various numbers of ventral ganglia often being concentrated into single units, as in other arthropods. The circulatory system consists of an elongated heart, typically with 13 but often fewer pairs of ostia (see Fig. 15.35). The heart lies dorsal to a usually well-developed pericardial membrane. Excretion occurs through Malpighian tubules opening into the hindgut. Reproductive organs are paired, and their ducts lead to a single opening located ventrally between the ninth and tenth abdominal segments in males, on the eighth, ninth, or tenth in females. With very few exceptions, fertilization takes place by copulation and the fertilized eggs are laid (with the assistance of the ovipositors).

In the embryos, appendage buds arise in anteroposterior succession on the ventral side (Fig. 15.52). In Apterygota and Exopterygota, such buds develop into adult appendages. Thus, when apterygotes hatch, they are essentially miniature adults; and when exopterygotes hatch, they resemble adults greatly though the wings are still lacking. The wings then grow in the larval nymphs as exterior folds on the second and third thoracic segments. In Endopterygota, however, the embryos hatch in a less fully developed condition, and the caterpillar larvae therefore retain an embryonic character. In the wormlike, annelidlike caterpillars, pockets arise in the body wall in which the imaginal disks begin to develop. These disks will give rise to the adult appendages, for example, mouth parts, legs, and wings. The larva thus possesses mouth parts (for example) developed originally in the embryo, whereas the adult possesses a new set of mouth parts developed later from imaginal disks. In some groups it

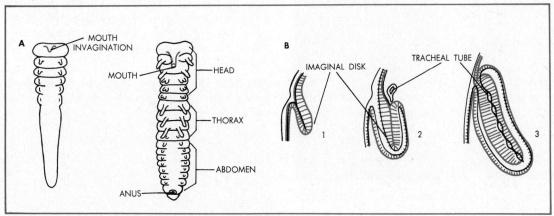

15 · 53   Insect development. Stages in the development of the silkworm moth Bombyx mori. *A, caterpillar; B, spinning of pupation cocoon.*

happens that the caterpillar is equipped with biting-chewing parts but that the adult comes to possess piercing-sucking parts. Transformation of caterpillar to adult occurs in the pupa. At this stage the pockets containing the imaginal disks open out and the developing appendages become exteriorized. The wings, for example, then make their first external appearance. (Fig. 15.53 and Color Plate XXVI, 41.)

The nymphal molts in exopterygotes and the larval and pupal molts in endopterygotes are under precise hormonal control. Three types of glands have been shown to participate in these metamorphoses: certain specialized *neurosecretory cells* (NS) in the brain ganglia; a pair of *corpora allata* (CA) located in the mandibular segment dorsal to the pharynx; and a pair of *prothoracic glands* (PT) in the first thoracic segment. The NS cells rhythmically secrete a hormone which stimulates the PT glands, and the latter then secrete a hormone in their turn which acts on the body tissues and induces molting (Fig. 15.54). The nature of the molt is governed by whether or not hormones are secreted by the CA glands. If CA hormones are being produced, then the next molt will transform a larva into a later larva. But if CA hormones are not secreted, then PT hormones acting alone will transform the larva into an adult in the case of exopterygotes. In endopterygotes, a first molt induced by PT hormones alone will change the larva into a pupa, and a second such molt will establish the adult.

15 · 54   Hormonal controls of insect development. Neurosecretory cells from the brain (NS) stimulate production of prothoracic gland hormone (PT) which, in conjunction with corpora allata hormones (CA), determine larval molting (step 1). After CA ceases to become available (step 2), the next PT-induced molt produces the adult in exopterygotes, the pupa in endopterygotes. The pupa often passes through a dormant phase, the diapause, and the following PT-induced molt then yields the adult.

REVIEW QUESTIONS

1. Give taxonomic definitions of coelomates, protostomial coelomates, lophophorates, and schizocoelomates. Which phyla are included in each of these groups? What is a lophophore? How does a lophophorate animal feed?

2. Describe the general structure of a phoronid. Describe the subdivisions of the coelom. What is the organization of the (a) nervous system, (b) circulatory system, (c) excretory system? What is the metasome pouch?

3. Describe the structure of an ectoproct. How do ectoprocts differ from entoprocts and why must these two groups be classified as separate phyla? What kinds of polymorphs occur among ectoprocts? How do these animals develop? What is a statoblast?

4. Review the structure of a brachiopod. How does the symmetry here differ from that of a clam? What is the organization of the nervous, circulatory, alimentary, and excretory systems? Outline the characteristics of actinotrochs, trochophores, and veligers.

5. Give taxonomic definitions of the phylum of mollusks and of each of the molluscan classes. Describe the structural traits of the hypothetical molluscan ancestor and show in what ways living mollusks still exhibit the ancestral body design to greater or lesser degree.

6. Review the development and adult structure of a representative of each of the molluscan classes. What are torsion and detorsion? What is a glochidium? A radula? A ctenidium? Which mollusks develop via (a) trochophores, (b) veligers, (c) neither?

7. What is the presumable evolutionary relation of the molluscan classes and orders to one another? How are mollusks as a whole presumably related to (a) lophophorates, (b) segmented protostomial coelomates? Make a diagram indicating these various interrelations and review the evidence on which you base them.

8. Define (a) Sipunculida and (b) Echiuroida taxonomically and describe the structure of these animals. Where do sipunculids live and how do they feed? Move? In what respects is echiuroid structure different from that of (a) a sipunculid, (b) an annelid?

9. Give taxonomic definitions of annelids and of each of the annelid classes. Describe the development of a segmented body organization from a trochophore larva. Then describe the segmental structure of an adult polychaete. What is the organization of a parapodium? What are the basic adaptive advantages of metamerism?

10. Describe the nervous, circulatory, and excretory systems of *Nereis*. How is breathing accomplished? Where do the gonads form and how does fertilization occur? What is a heteronereis? In what respects do (a) archiannelids, (b) oligochaetes differ from polychaetes?

11. Describe the external and internal structure of an earthworm and contrast the body design with that of *Nereis*. What are typhlosole, crop, and lime glands and what are their functions? Describe the structure of the reproductive systems of an earthworm and show how mating and fertilization occur. Contrast the structure of a leech with that of an earthworm.

12. Define Oncopoda and each subphylum taxonomically. Describe the organization of *Peripatus* and list features that are (a) annelidlike, (b) arthropodlike, (c) unique to onychophorans. Describe the structure of tardigrades.

13. Characterize the phylum Arthropoda taxonomically and name the subphyla and classes. How are these subgroups presumably interrelated historically? How have the chitinous exoskeleton and the metameric body design probably promoted the broad diversification of the phylum?

14. Describe the basic exterior structure of the arthropod body and the general organization of the 10 organ systems. Review the structure of arthropod eyes. Review the segmental structure of the chelicerate cephalothorax and the structure and function of the appendages of that body division. Describe the structure of a horseshoe crab, a scorpion, and a spider.

15. Distinguish between the chelicerate and mandibulate subphyla. Describe the segmental structure of the crustacean head, thorax, and abdomen. Name and state the functions of all appendages of a lobster. Where is the sinus gland located and what is its function?

16. Describe the internal anatomy of a lobster. In the process review the organization of every organ system. Review the nature of the larval stages of crustacea. What evolutionary trends are in evidence among crustacea?

17. Give taxonomic definitions of centipedes and millipedes. Describe the segmental head structure and the trunk structure of these animals and contrast the external anatomy of a centipede and a millipede. What features are similar to those of insects?

18. Give taxonomic definitions of the class of insects and of the subclasses and superorders. Name representatives of each such group. Describe the segmental structure of an insect and contrast it with that of a crustacean. Review the internal anatomy of an insect and in the process describe the organization of every organ system.

19. Review the structure of insect mouth parts. What is the structure of an insect wing and how is flight motion produced? Show how (*a*) wings, (*b*) legs are modified in different insect groups. How do insects breathe?

20. Describe the early development of an insect and show how later development differs according to the subclass or superorder. Describe the hormonal controls of insect molting and development. Compare the species abundances of all phyla among protostomial coelomates.

COLLATERAL READINGS

Abbott, R. T.: "American Sea Shells," Van Nostrand, Princeton, N.J., 1954. A nice account for both the amateur and professional student of mollusks.

Berrill, N. J.: "Growth, Development, and Pattern," Freeman, San Francisco, 1961. Chapters 12 and 13 in particular contain interesting discussions of segmental growth and development in annelids.

Buchsbaum, R.: "Animals without Backbones," University of Chicago, Chicago, 1948. All invertebrate groups are examined in elementary fashion, including those discussed in this chapter; well illustrated.

Carpenter, F. M.: The Geological History and Evolution of Insects, *Am. Scientist*, vol. 41, 1953. Valuable for basic background on this subject.

Chu, H. F.: "How to Know the Immature Insects," William C. Brown, Dubuque, Iowa, 1949. A useful handbook, particularly in conjunction with the book by Jacques listed below.

Comstock, J. H., and W. J. Gertsch: "The Spider Book," 2d ed., Doubleday, Garden City, N.Y., 1940. Must reading for those interested in spiders.

Gertsch, W. J.: "American Spiders," Van Nostrand, Princeton, N.J., 1949. Consult in conjunction with preceding entry.

Green, J.: "A Biology of Crustacea," Quadrangle Books, Chicago, 1961. Well worth consulting for more detailed background information.

Hocking, B.: Insect Flight, *Sci. American*, Dec., 1958. The subject is discussed from a functional standpoint.

Hyman, L.: The Invertebrates," vol. 5, McGraw-Hill, New York, 1959. This volume contains detailed accounts of the lophophorate phyla and the sipunculids.

Jacques, H. E.: "How to Know the Insects," William C. Brown, Dubuque, Iowa, 1947. Valuable in identifying and characterizing different types of insects.

Johnson, C. G.: The Aerial Migration of Insects, *Sci. American*, Dec., 1963.

Marcus, E.: Tardigrada, in "McGraw-Hill Encyclopedia of Science and Technology," vol. 13, 1960. A short but very thorough account.

Metcalf, C. L., W. P. Flint, and R. L. Metcalf: "Destructive and Useful Insects," 4th ed., McGraw-Hill, New York, 1962. The ecologic and economic biology of insects is examined thoroughly in this book.

Morton, J. E.: "Mollusks," Hutchinson, London, 1958. Strongly recommended for further reading on this phylum.

Murphy, R. C.: The Oceanic Life of the Antarctic, *Sci. American*, Sept., 1962. The article pays particular attention to krill, a fundamentally important shrimplike crustacean.

Savory, T. H.: Daddy Longlegs, *Sci. American*, Oct., 1962. An interesting account of a familiar arachnid related distantly to spiders.

Snodgrass, R. E.: "A Textbook of Arthropod Anatomy," Cornell, Ithaca, N.Y., 1952. One of the standard texts, strongly recommended.

————: Arthropoda, in "McGraw-Hill Encyclopedia of Science and Technology," vol. 1, 1960. A short but thorough synopsis of the biology of the phylum.

Van der Kloot, W. G.: Brains and Cocoons, *Sci. American*, Apr., 1956. Neurosurgery on insect pupae reveals some relations between the nervous system and behavior.

Waterman, T. H.: A Light Polarization Analyzer in the Compound Eye of Limulus, *Science*, vol. 111, 1950. Research shows that horseshoe crabs can orient themselves by polarized light from the sun.

————: Flight Instruments in Insects, *Amer. Scientist*, vol. 38, 1950. The orientation mechanisms of flying insects are examined.

Wigglesworth, V. B.: Metamorphosis and differentiation, *Sci. American*, Feb., 1959. A noted student of insect development discusses the mechanisms of metamorphosis in these animals.

Williams, C. M.: The Metamorphosis of Insects, *Sci. American*, Apr., 1950. An interesting account of some of the original experiments that have led to our present understanding of the subject.

————: Insect Breathing, *Sci. American*, Feb., 1953. The structural and functional aspects of the tracheal system are discussed.

Zahl, P. A.: Mystery of the Monarch Butterfly, *Nat. Geographic*, Apr., 1963. A well-illustrated description of the development of this insect.

CHAPTER 16
METAZOA: DEUTERO-STOMIAL COELOMATES

The enterocoelomate animals are deuterostomial; the first opening of the embryo becomes the adult anus, and the second opening formed later at the opposite end becomes the mouth (see Fig. 14.7). Enterocoelomates are also identified by coeloms that arise enterocoelically, that is, by outgrowth and separation of mesoderm pouches from the endoderm. Moreover, if larvae are present they are never trochophores but are of special types unique to the different groups. Five phyla are included, the *Chaetognatha*, the *Pogonophora*, the *Hemichordata*, the *Echinodermata*, and the *Chordata*. Enterocoelomate evolution, like that of schizocoelomates, analogously gave rise to unsegmented types first. These are represented today by the first four phyla listed above and by the most primitive group of the fifth. The remaining groups of the fifth phylum, notably the vertebrates, comprise segmented animals (see Fig. 14.13).

The chaetognaths do not appear to be related very closely to the other enterocoelomates; they probably exemplify an independent, early branch of enterocoelomate evolution. The remaining phyla, that is, pogonophorans, hemichordates, and echinoderms, and indeed also the chordates, probably do represent a broadly interrelated assemblage. Hemichordates may be closest to an ancestral enterocoelomate line, and the others may have arisen from it

as independent branch lines. However, precise interrelations of enterocoelomate groups can be determined even far less definitely than those of schizocoelomates.

PHYLUM CHAETOGNATHA (ARROWWORMS)

Marine, mainly planktonic; head with grasping spines and hood; trunk with lateral and tail fins; coelom subdivided into three compartments; without circulatory, breathing, or excretory systems; development without larvae; 50 species. *Sagitta*

Chaetognaths are small, torpedo-shaped animals, so abundant in places that they often are among the principal constituents of zooplankton (Fig. 16.1).

The body of an arrowworm is marked into head, trunk, and tail, and the internal coelomic cavity is subdivided analogously by partitions. A transverse head-trunk septum lies just behind the head, and a vertical longitudinal septum divides the trunk cavity into two lateral compartments. Secondarily, another transverse septum partitions the trunk cavity into an anterior main compartment and a posterior tail compartment. The body wall consists of an epidermis; covered with a nonchitinous cuticle externally and a basement membrane internally, and of a layer of longitudinal body-wall muscles. A peritoneum is absent. The septa in the body cavity are extensions of the basement membrane, and the latter is also extended exteriorly into *fin rays*, that is, supporting strands in the cuticular fins. One or two pairs of trunk fins and a posterior rounded tail fin are present. All are positioned horizontally and they are unmuscled; they are not used in locomotion but probably serve primarily as stabilizers and buoyancy-promoting devices.

The head bears one or two pairs of rows of tiny, anterior teeth, a pair of dorsolateral eyes, and a row of prominent, chitinous *grasping spines* on each side of a ventral mouth. The teeth and the spines are moved by a powerful head musculature, and the spines are the principal food-catching structures; they can be closed in toward the mouth, forming a tiny cage in which food animals may become trapped. Head muscles also operate a *hood*, a fold grown out from the body wall at the head-trunk juncture (and containing part of the coelom). This hood can be

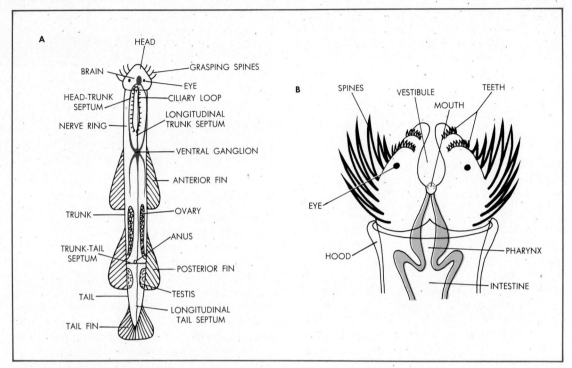

16 · 1 Chaetognath structure. *A, general anatomy. B, anterior end from ventral side, hood retracted.*

extended forward to cover almost the whole head, spines included; it probably streamlines the head when the animal darts about rapidly.

The nervous system comprises a dorsal brain ganglion, a ventral trunk ganglion, a connective cord on each side between these, and posterior cords emanating from the trunk ganglion. In the alimentary system, the esophagus is expanded posteriorly into a bulbous enlargement, and the intestine extends into a pair of anteriorly pointing digestive pouches. The anus opens ventrally, just before the trunk-tail septum.

All arrowworms are hermaphrodites. Paired testes are situated just behind the trunk-tail septum, paired ovaries just in front of it. Eggs develop externally, and after hatching the animals resemble miniature adults. They gradually become mature adults without special larval stages.

PHYLUM POGONOPHORA (BEARD WORMS)

Marine, tube-dwelling, abyssal; with anterior tentacles; alimentary system entirely absent; circulatory system closed; without breathing system; coelom divided into *protocoel*, *mesocoel*, and *metacoel*; 25 species. *Polybranchia*

This interesting group was first discovered in 1933 in material dredged up from deep sea bottoms. The animals can be quite long but they are exceedingly thin, with a diameter of not more than 1 mm (Fig. 16.2). They live in close-fitting secreted tubes, which probably stick vertically in the ooze of the ocean floor. Such tubes are composed of polysaccharide-containing *tunicin*, the same celluloselike material that also forms the cover of the chordate tunicates. Beard worms are without mouth, anus, digestive tract, or any other trace of an alimentary system—the only free-living animals so characterized.

The body of a beard worm is marked by transverse internal septa into an anterior *protosome*, a middle *mesosome*, and a posterior *metasome*. The coelomic cavities corresponding to these divisions are the *protocoel*, the *mesocoel*, and the *metacoel*, respectively. As we shall see, such divisions are generally characteristic also of all other deuterostome phyla. This internal division of beard worms is not clearly marked externally, but the protosome bears the tentacles, the mesosome forms a short, slightly thickened collarlike section, and the metasome represents the entire remainder of the body. Beard worms are believed to feed by arranging their tentacles into a tube, and ciliary tracts on the tentacles are assumed to draw food-bearing currents into the tube. Trapped inside, food organisms would be digested extracellularly, and the resulting nutrients would be absorbed directly into tentacular blood vessels. We may note, however, that actual feeding has so far remained unobserved.

The pogonophorans are definitely enterocoelomates and their embryology and adult coelomic structure relate them clearly to the other enterocoelomates, hemichordates in particular.

PHYLUM HEMICHORDATA

Marine, wormlike, colonial in secreted housings or solitary in sand burrows; body marked prominently into protosome, mesosome, metasome, and coelom divided into protocoel, mesocoel, metacoel; mostly with gill slits; development typically via larvae; 100 species.

> *Class Pterobranchia:* colonial, individuals microscopic; with or without gill slits; alimentary tract U-shaped; with tentacles on mesosome. *Cephalodiscus*
> *Class Enteropneusta* (acorn worms): solitary; with many gill slits; alimentary tract straight; without tentacles; often with *tornaria* larvae. *Balanoglossus*

These animals share one important trait with the

16 · 2 Pogonophora, *outline of external features.*

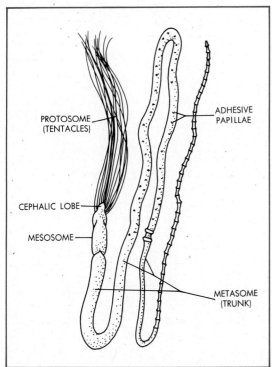

PROTOSOME (TENTACLES)

ADHESIVE PAPILLAE

CEPHALIC LOBE

MESOSOME

METASOME (TRUNK)

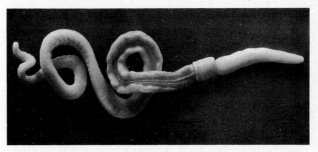

16 · 3 Acorn worm, *model, dorsal view. Note proboscis at left, conspicuous collar, and row of paired gill slits along anterior portion of trunk. The lateral edge of this region of the trunk is folded up on each side, forming the genital ridges.*

chordates, namely, gill slits in the pharynx. Of the two hemichordate classes, the pterobranchs are probably the more primitive group; but the enteropneusts are the more familiar and their larvae may be of great theoretical significance.

Enteropneusts live singly in sand burrows along shallow water shores (Fig. 16.3). The body of an acorn worm consists of a short or long *proboscis* (protosome), a short *collar* (mesosome), and a long *trunk* (metasome). The proboscis is a muscular burrowing organ. The mouth lies ventrally at the base of the proboscis, under a forward flange of the collar. Anteriorly on each side of the trunk are a series of gill slits, usually U-shaped. The body wall here may be extended into prominent folds that curve up and cover the gill slits partially. The reproductive organs lie within these folds, which are therefore called *genital ridges*. At the end of the trunk is the anus.

Much of the coelom of these animals is filled with connective tissue and muscle, formed directly from the peritoneum in the embryo and thus accounting for the lack of this membrane in most adults. The nervous system is a primitive intraepidermal plexus, thickened into a ventral and dorsal cord in the trunk (Fig. 16.4). At the collar-trunk juncture the ventral cord joins the dorsal cord, and the latter then continues forward as the *collar cord*. This section represents the neural center of the animal. In many cases it is hollow and one or two *neuropores* provide communication between this neural cavity and the exterior of the body.

The proboscis contains a small protocoel which communicates with the outside via a dorsal *proboscis pore*. The mesocoel in the collar is similarly reduced, and it opens posteriorly into the first gill chamber (see below). Both the proboscis and collar coeloms thus have access to sea water and are probably filled

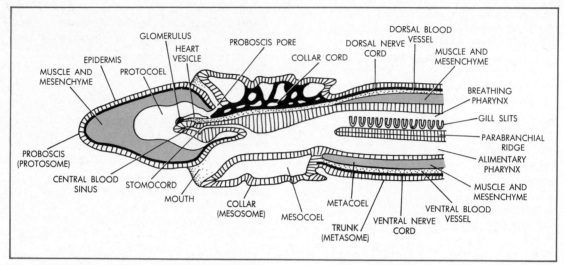

16 · 4 Hemichordate structure, *sagittal section of anterior region. The parabranchial ridge is a fold of endoderm separating the pharynx into an upper breathing and a lower alimentary chamber.*

with it. By contrast, the metacoel of the trunk is closed. The alimentary tract leads from the mouth into a mouth cavity extended anteriorly into a pouch, the *stomocord.* In the anterior portion of the trunk the alimentary tract contains a long pharynx, perforated dorsally by the paired gill slits. Basically the slits are food strainers; water passes through them to the outside, while food and sand are retained and fall to the ventral gutter of the pharynx (Fig. 16.5). Secondarily such slits also serve in breathing, a specialized function developed most clearly in chordates. Gill slits open into deep, communicating pockets invaginated from the body wall, the *branchial sacs,* or gill chambers. These in turn open to the outside via *gill pores.* The collar coelom on each side of the body communicates with the most anterior branchial sac on that side. Behind the pharynx the alimentary tract continues as an esophagus and an intestine.

In the circulatory system, blood flows forward in a dorsal longitudinal vessel, backward in a ventral one (Fig. 16.6). Anteriorly, just above the stomocord at the proboscis base, the dorsal vessel widens into a noncontractile "heart." Above the latter in turn is a contractile *heart vesicle,* a muscular coelom sac which presses rhythmically against the heart and maintains blood circulation through it. On each side of the heart is a *glomerulus,* an accumulation of mesodermal tissue believed to have an excretory function. Blood is forced to pass from the heart

through the glomeruli and is presumably filtered there. In the pharyngeal region the ventral trunk vessel sends branches into the gill-slit region, and another set of branch vessels leaves that region and enters the dorsal trunk vessel. Oxygenated blood thus passes anteriorly.

The sex organs open into the branchial sacs.

16 · 5 Hemichordate structure. *Frontal section through anterior gill region shows relations between mesocoel, branchial sacs, pharynx, and gill pores.*

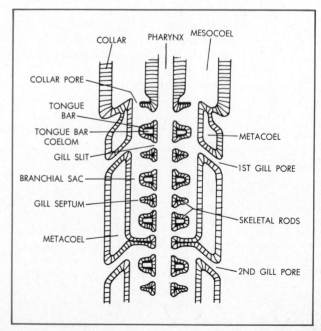

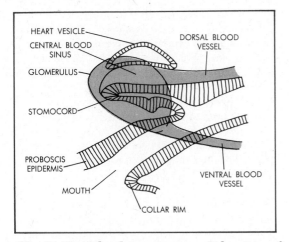

16 · 6 Hemichordate structure. *Side view of the proboscis base, showing circulatory and excretory structures. One glomerulus lies to the right and another to the left of the stomocord. Blood-filled portions are colored.*

Fertilization takes place externally in sea water. The larva of *Balanoglossus* is a *tornaria,* equipped with a conspicuous ciliary band winding sinuously over the larval surface (Fig. 16.7). The tornaria is remarkably like the larva of starfishes. This similarity constitutes a main argument for regarding hemichordates and echinoderms as being closely related. Indeed, it is widely believed that both phyla originated from a hypothetical *dipleurula* ancestor, a form postulated to have resembled the tornaria and the starfish type of larva (see also below and Fig. 16.7). Tornariae metamorphose gradually into adult worms.

The members of the class Pterobranchia are basically similar to the enteropneusts, but they differ in a number of conspicuous ways (Fig. 16.8). Thus, they are individually of microscopic dimensions and they are colonial. All zooids of a colony arise by budding from a single starting individual, as in ectoprocts, and a whole colony shares a common secreted housing. The latter may have tubular, branching, globular, or other forms. Each zooid consists of a plump metasome with a long slender stalk at the posterior end, a mesosome collar which bears a set of tentacles anterodorsally, and a shieldlike protosome which tilts down over the mouth area like a lid. Internally, only a single pair of gill passages is present and the circulatory system is distinctly open, blood vessels being entirely absent. At the posterior end of the metasome stalk is a budding zone where numerous new individuals may be formed.

Inasmuch as hemichordates as a whole suggest both echinodermlike traits in some of their larvae

and chordatelike traits in their pharynx, quite aside from exhibiting embryological similarities to both these phyla, they presumably represent an evolutionary link between echinoderms and chordates. Hence it is possible that hemichordates, echinoderms, and pogonophora all may have arisen from a more or

16 · 7 Hemichordate development. *Diagram: the structure of the hypothetical dipleurula ancestor of deuterostomes. This dipleurula resembles certain of the actual embryonic and larval stages of hemichordates and echinoderms. Photo: tornaria larva, from life. Note ciliary bands and parts of alimentary tract. Compare with Figs. 16.15 and 16.17.*

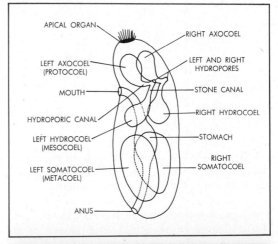

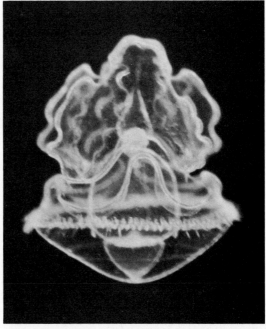

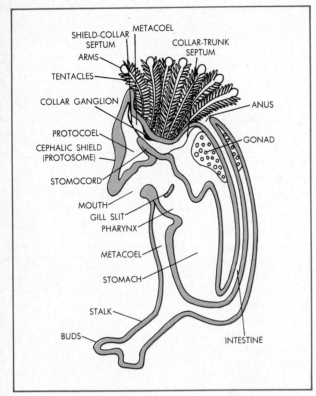

SHIELD-COLLAR SEPTUM
METACOEL
COLLAR-TRUNK SEPTUM
ARMS
TENTACLES
COLLAR GANGLION
ANUS
PROTOCOEL
CEPHALIC SHIELD (PROTOSOME)
GONAD
STOMOCORD
MOUTH
GILL SLIT
PHARYNX
METACOEL
STOMACH
STALK
BUDS
INTESTINE

16 · 8   Pterobranchs. *Sagittal section through a zooid of the pterobranch* Cephalodiscus.

less common enterocoelomate ancestry. The chordate group then may have branched off later from the line leading to hemichordates (see Fig. 14.13).

PHYLUM ECHINODERMATA
(SPINY-SKINNED ANIMALS)

Exclusively marine; larvae bilateral, with protocoel, mesocoel, and metacoel in early stages; adults pentaradial; with calcareous endoskeleton and coelomic water-vascular system; 6,000 species.

Class Crinoidea (sea lilies, feather stars): body cup-shaped, free or attached; endoskeleton limited to aboral side, oral side membranous; arms branched, with open ambulacral grooves; tube feet food-catching; development via *doliolaria* larvae or direct. *Antedon*
Class Holothuroidea (sea cucumbers): secondarily bilateral; mouth region with tentacles; ambulacral grooves closed; endoskeleton reduced to ossicles; oral-aboral axis horizontal; development via *auricularia* larvae or direct. *Cucumaria, Holothuria, Thyone*

Class Asteroidea (sea stars, starfishes): star-shaped; ambulacral grooves open; tube feet locomotor and projecting between endoskeletal plates; development via *bipinnaria* larvae or direct. *Asterias, Solaster, Heliaster*
Class Ophiuroidea (brittle stars, serpent stars, basket stars): star-shaped, with long, highly flexible arms; ambulacral grooves closed, tube feet reduced; madreporite on oral side; without intestine or anus; development via *ophiopluteus* larvae or direct. *Ophiura, Ophiothrix, Gorgonocephalus*
Class Echinoidea (sea urchins, sand dollars): spherical to disk-shaped, without arms; ambulacral grooves closed; endoskeleton fused, nonflexible, with pores for tube feet and with movable spines; development via *echinopluteus* larvae or direct. *Arbacia, Echinus, Echinarachnius*

Echinoderms generally develop via bilateral free-swimming larvae which later metamorphose into sessile or sluggish adults. The latter are organized pentaradially around a comparatively short oral-aboral axis. In crinoids, the oral side is directed upward and both mouth and anus are present on that side. In sea cucumbers the oral-aboral axis is horizontal, the mouth marking one end of the axis and the anus the other. In all other groups the oral side is directed downward, with the mouth in the center (Fig. 16.9). Two fundamental features characterize all echinoderms: an *endoskeleton* produced in the dermis and consisting of separate or fused calcareous plates overlain by epidermis; and, most particularly, a *water-vascular system* consisting of a series of coelomic tubes filled with sea water. The exterior parts of this system are numerous hollow, muscular tube feet, or *podia*, which starfishes, for example, use as little legs.

How could such a unique water-vascular system have evolved? It is quite clear that the original function of the system could not have been locomotor, for ancient fossil echinoderms were, and many of the primitive living crinoids still are, sessile attached types. Crinoids possess highly branched arms, and the tube feet present on the oral side of the arms serve entirely in feeding; they trap small organisms which are then passed along an arm toward the mouth, in a ciliated *ambulacral groove*. Primitively, therefore, the tube feet are food-catching tentacles, and the system of arms as a whole represents a tentacular apparatus. Further, we may be reasonably sure that echinoderms evolved from bilateral, free-swimming ancestors whose descendants later adopted

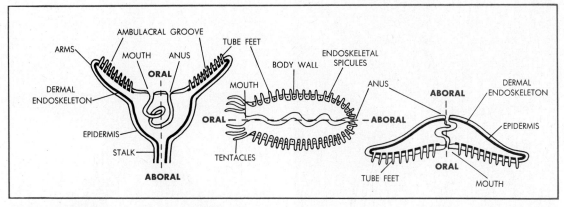

16 · 9 Echinoderm body plans. *Left, the crinoid pattern, with vertical oral-aboral axis, mouth and tube feet pointing up. Center, the holothuroid pattern, with horizontal axis. Right, the asteroid-ophiuroid-echinoid pattern, with vertical axis and mouth, and tube feet pointing down.*

a sessile way of life. Indeed, as already pointed out earlier, a hypothetical bilateral ancestor, the *dipleurula,* is assumed to have been a common evolutionary starting point of hemichordates as well as of echinoderms (see Fig. 16.7); and it is true that the embryos and early larvae of both groups are remarkably alike. Most particularly, echinoderm larvae develop protocoel, mesocoel, and metacoel cavities just as hemichordates do, and they are bilateral.

Thus, we may surmise that ancestral bilateral echinoderms later evolved into attached sessile types with arms serving as feeding tentacles. However, the tentacles then became clothed with endoskeletal plates, a circumstance that aided in protection but must have severely limited the mobility and thus the food-trapping capacity of the arms. This restriction could be circumvented subsequently by the formation of small mobile branch tentacles on the arms, that is, tube feet, as well as food passages to the mouth in the form of ambulacral grooves. We may therefore interpret the water-vascular system as a modified tentacular system, evolved in primitive echinoderms in specific correlation with sessilism and endoskeleton-induced body rigidity.

Once a tube-foot system had evolved, it could be adapted secondarily to functions other than feeding, most particularly, to locomotion. Thus, the later echinoderm groups relinquished the stalked, attached mode of life and became motile, with the oral side directed downward. Tube feet, and in some cases also endoskeletal spines and the arms themselves,

could function in propulsion. The animals thus could move to food actively, use the mouth directly, and no longer needed to depend on what the arms could strain out of the water. The ambulacral grooves then largely ceased to be of importance, and they are actually closed over by folds of the body wall in all living echinoderms except the crinoids and asteroids (Fig. 16.10).

The basic traits of echinoderms as a whole are exemplified well in the asteroids, animals which combine some of the primitive as well as some of the advanced traits of the phylum. The body of a common starfish consists of a central *disk* and, typically, five

16 · 10 Echinoderm arms. *Diagrams of cross sections illustrating open ambulacral groove as in starfish and crinoids* (left) *and closed ambulacral groove as in other living echinoderms* (right). *The epineural canal is the result of groove closure, the latter brought about by body-wall folds which grow over and fuse around the open groove.*

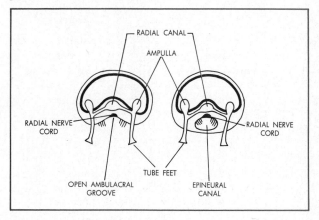

A

B

B, courtesy of Carolina Biological Supply Company.

16 · 11 Starfish structure, external features. A, the oral side. The mouth is at the center of the disk, and a tube-foot–lined ambulacral groove passes along the oral side of each of the five arms. B, the aboral side of Asterias. An anus lies at the exact center of the disk but is too small to be visible. The buttonlike madreporite is apparent excentrically on the disk, between the uppermost and the upper right arm.

arms (Fig. 16.11). In the center of the disk on the underside, or oral surface, is the mouth. Leading to the mouth along the oral side of each arm is an *ambulacral groove*, bordered on each side by a row of hollow, muscular tube feet, or *podia*, the terminal parts of the water-vascular system. On the upper, or aboral, side, a tiny anal opening lies in the center of the disk, and near the angle between two of the arms is a reddish *madreporite*, a sieve plate representing

16 · 12 An arm of starfish in cross section.

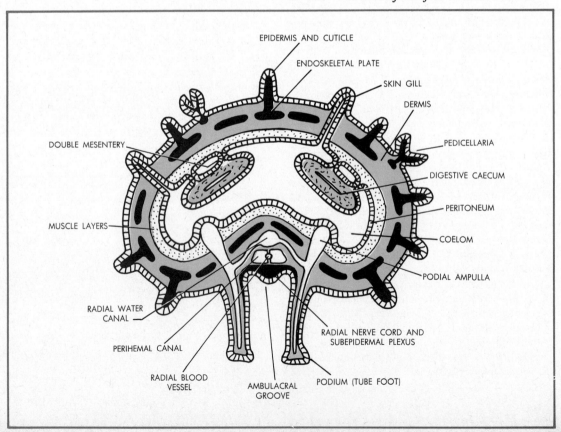

EPIDERMIS AND CUTICLE

ENDOSKELETAL PLATE

SKIN GILL

DERMIS

PEDICELLARIA

DIGESTIVE CAECUM

PERITONEUM

COELOM

PODIAL AMPULLA

RADIAL NERVE CORD AND SUBEPIDERMAL PLEXUS

PODIUM (TUBE FOOT)

AMBULACRAL GROOVE

RADIAL BLOOD VESSEL

PERIHEMAL CANAL

RADIAL WATER CANAL

MUSCLE LAYERS

DOUBLE MESENTERY

the entrance to the water-vascular system. The body wall contains a cuticle, an epidermis, and a well-developed underlying dermis. The latter consists of connective tissue which secretes the endoskeleton. In a starfish, such a skeleton is made up of separate knobby calcareous plates held together by the dermal connective tissue and by muscles (Fig. 16.12). In places the dermis and the overlying epidermis are folded out into microscopic *pedicellariae,* muscle-operated pincers which protect the epidermal surface of a starfish from small animals. Underneath the dermis lie muscle layers, and a peritoneum lines the body wall internally. Studding the exterior surface are numerous microscopic fingerlike projections, the *skin gills.* Made up of all layers of the body wall, peritoneum included, the gills are hollow; their internal spaces are extensions of the coelom which project between adjacent skeletal plates. The pedicellariae protect the skin gills particularly.

Sea water communicates with the water-vascular system via the madreporite, which leads into a small bulbous cavity, the *madreporic ampulla* (Fig. 16.13). From there a calcified *stone canal* conducts water into a circular channel ringing the esophagus of the animal. Along this *ring canal* are usually present one or more sacs, the *polian vesicles,* which are probably water reservoirs (not present in the common starfish *Asterias*), and five pairs of *Tiedemann's bodies,* whose specific function is unknown. From the ring canal also emanate five *radial canals,* one each into arm. There each radial canal gives off short lateral branches, and each of the latter bifurcates at its end into a saclike *podial ampulla,* located inside the arm, and a tube foot protruding from the oral surface of the arm. Stiffened by water pressed into them from

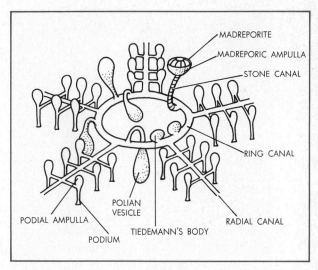

16 · 13 The water-vascular system *of a starfish. Polian vesicles are absent in the common starfish* Asterias.

the ampullae, tube feet can be used as tiny walking legs. A podium also serves as a suction disk when its end is placed against a solid surface and the inner parts of the end plate are then lifted away. By such means the tube feet of a starfish may exert enough steady pull on the shells of a clam to tire the clam and force its shells open.

The mouth leads through a short esophagus into a spacious stomach (Fig. 16.14), which may be everted through the mouth into the soft tissues of a clam.

16 · 14 Section *through the disk and one arm of a starfish.*

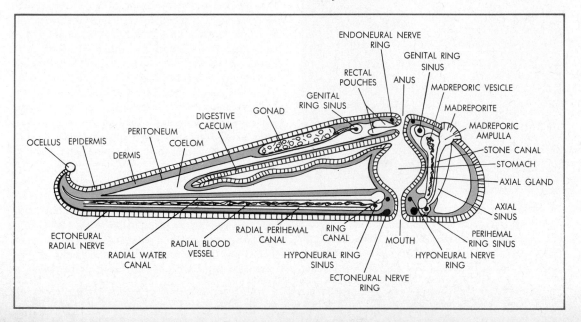

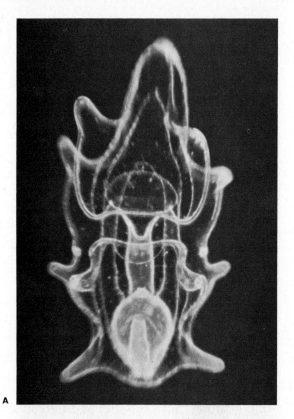

16 · 15 Asteroid larvae. A, bipinnaria, from life. Note ciliary bands and alimentary tract. B, brachiolaria, from life. At top, note the three fringe-ended arms at which attachment will occur. At bottom the definitive star is developing.

Small food particles and fluid foods pass into a short intestine, and from there into five pairs of large digestive glands, the *pyloric caeca*, one pair occupying most of the free space within each arm. Near the anus the intestine connects with two *rectal pouches* which probably have an excretory function. As in echinoderms generally, the nervous system consists of three subsystems, but only one of these is well developed. This subsystem contains a *nerve ring* under the body wall on the oral side, near the ring canal of the water-vascular system. From this nerve ring emanate five *radial nerves*, one into each arm. These nerves run along the bottom of the ambulacral grooves, just underneath the epidermis, and they are part of a subepidermal nerve net. At the tip of each arm a radial nerve terminates at an ocellus.

The circulatory system consists of a series of blood channels that are without walls but lie within coelomic ducts. The center of the system may be considered to be the *axial gland*, a meshwork of contractile channels lying next to the stone canal. Pulsations of this gland presumably maintain a circulation of blood. All the blood-carrying coelomic channels lie in the spacious coelomic body cavity, which contains numerous amoeboid cells. The latter are partly excretory; they may absorb excretory waste and carry it to the exterior via the skin gills.

Starfishes possess five pairs of sex organs, one pair per arm, lying laterally near the arm bases. Each opens via a short duct near the base of the arm. A few asteroids mate by copulation, some brood their offspring in chambers on the oral side of the disk, but most spawn, fertilization and development occurring externally. Development passes through a bilateral, distinctly dipleurulalike stage, namely, the early *bipinnaria* larva (Fig. 16.15). In it arise three pairs of coelomic sacs, the protocoels, mesocoels, and metacoels. The left protocoel and mesocoel will later give rise to the water-vascular system, the right protocoel will form the upper part of the axial gland, and the left and right metacoels will develop into the adult coelom and the coelomic blood channels. The right mesocoel degenerates. In the course of its free-swimming life the bipinnaria acquires conspicuous epidermal arms and is then known as a *brachiolaria* larva. The latter eventually undergoes a very complex metamorphosis into a young adult star.

Crinoids

This class comprises the stalked, sessile sea lilies, and the unstalked, motile feather stars (Plate XXVII, 43). The latter can creep and swim gracefully by means of their arms. In all crinoids the endoskeleton has the form of a cup, the oral side being protected by a

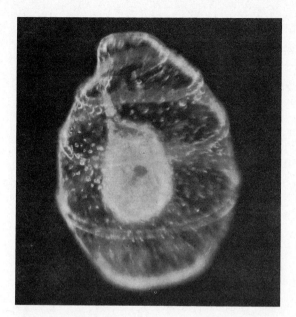

They are extensions of the body wall and contain canals of the water-vascular system branched off from the five radial canals underneath the actual or reduced tube feet. Between each radial canal and the body surface lies an ectoderm-lined *epineural canal*, the remnant of the ambulacral groove which in these animals has ceased to be functionally significant and has closed over by growth of the body wall (see Fig. 16.10). At the base of the tentacles on the dorsal side many sea cucumbers possess a *hydropore*, the equivalent of a madreporite. In many cases, however, the stone canal terminates directly

16 · 16 Doliolaria larva, from life. Note ciliary hoops and alimentary tract.

16 · 17 Holothuroids. A, the sea cucumber Cucumaria. *B, an auricularia larva, from life. Compare with bipinnaria, Fig. 16.15.*

A, courtesy of Carolina Biological Supply Company.

leathery body wall without calcareous plates. The branched arms emanate from the rim of the cup, and the ambulacral grooves pass from the oral side of the arms across the oral part of the body wall toward the mouth. The internal structure of crinoids corresponds substantially to that of asteroids. However, the water-vascular system is without connection to the exterior. Instead, the ring canal extends into numerous stone canals which terminate within the coelom and which communicate directly with that cavity. Also, the intestine is long and coiled and pyloric caecae are not present. Crinoids develop via a *doliolaria*, a bilateral barrel-shaped larval form equipped with four or five separate transverse bands of cilia (Fig. 16.16).

Holothuroids

The horizontal position of the oral-aboral axis in sea cucumbers introduces a secondary bilateral symmetry, often reinforced by the elaboration of a distinct ventral *sole* on which the animals lie (Fig. 16.17). Tube feet may be in orderly rows or distributed randomly or reduced altogether to warty papillae. The endoskeleton is also reduced, microscopic *ossicles* being scattered throughout the body wall.

The principal food-gathering organs are the retractile, highly branched *tentacles* around the mouth.

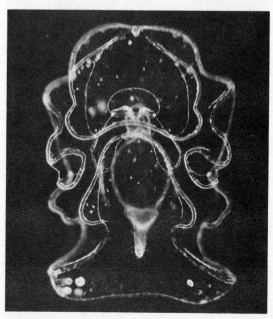

A

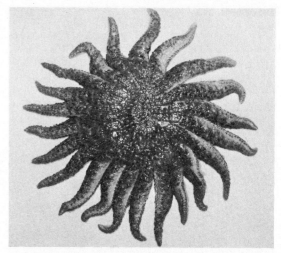

B

16 · 18   Asteroids. A, Leptasterias, *from under-side, with embryos in brood pouch. B, a many-armed starfish.*

in the coelom, as in crinoids, and a hydropore is then absent in the adult.

Around the pharynx lies a *calcareous ring*, which provides attachment for the retractor muscles of the tentacles. The alimentary tract is long and looped and near the anus are a pair of large, extensively

branched outgrowths from the cloaca. These *respiratory trees* serve in breathing and in excretion. Most holothurians spawn, and the fertilized eggs then develop externally via *auricularia* larvae. They resemble bipinnarias in most respects (see Fig. 16.17).

Asteroids

Little needs to be added to the account on starfishes above. Most asteroids are characterized by arms numbering five or multiples of five. In some, however, there are six, seven, or eight arms, as in sun

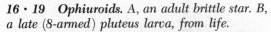

16 · 19   Ophiuroids. A, *an adult brittle star. B, a late (8-armed) pluteus larva, from life.*

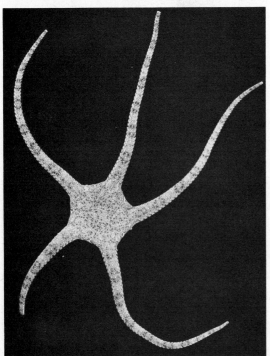

A

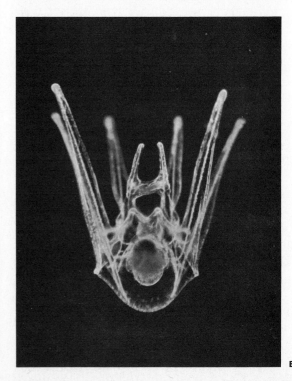

B

stars such as *Solaster;* numerous arms, up to 20 or more, identify sun stars such as *Heliaster* (Fig. 16.18).

Ophiuroids

Brittle stars may be regarded as highly specialized variants of starfishes. Ophiuroid arms are marked off sharply from the central disk, and they are long and highly mobile in sinuous fashion (Fig. 16.19). Inasmuch as the arms serve very adequately in locomotion, tube feet are reduced to warty knobs and podial ampullae are lacking internally. The ambulacral grooves are closed over as in holothurians, and the madreporite lies on the oral side of the disk.

Ophiuroids also differ from asteroids in the absence of pedicellariae and skin gills. Breathing is accomplished instead by five pairs of *bursae,* specialized pouches located on the oral side of the disk near the bases of the arms. Further, brittle stars are without intestine or anus, the stomach ending as a blind sac. The mouth is armed with five muscle-operated calcareous teeth. Ophiuroids are primarily carnivorous, but they usually will eat any kind of food found along the sea bottom. The larvae are conical *plutei,* which develop up to four pairs of ciliated, buoyancy-increasing arms. Such larvae are remarkably similar to those of echinoids.

Echinoids

Sea urchins are readily identified by their globular shapes and their protective and movable spines (Fig. 16.20). Often up to a foot long, the spines are outgrowths from the endoskeletal plates and they are covered over their whole surface with epidermis. The skeletal plates are fused together into a rigid shell, with rows of pores through which the tube feet protrude. There are five pairs of such rows.

The ambulacral grooves are closed in. Five pairs of skin gills are present along the rim of the small, leathery oral disk; on other parts of the surface the tube feet play a substantial role in breathing. Pedicellariae, which represent modified spines, occur abundantly on the body surface. In many sea urchins the anus lies in the center of the aboral side, but in others this opening has become shifted to an excentric position.

In many respects the internal structure of sea urchins is like that of holothurians, particularly in the region of the pharynx. Thus, corresponding to the calcareous ring of sea cucumbers, sea urchins possess an exceptionally well developed chewing organ, the *lantern of Aristotle.* It consists of 40 separate calcareous ossicles, including five sharp-pointed teeth converging toward the center of the mouth. Interiorly

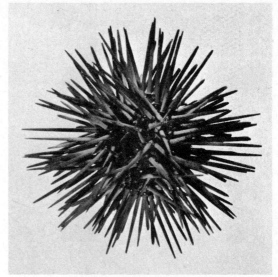

A

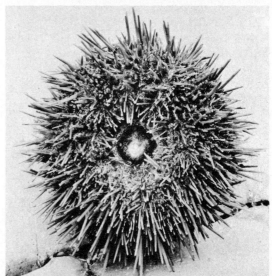

B

C

A, courtesy of Carolina Biological Supply Company.

16 · 20 Echinoids. A, *the sea urchin* Arbacia. B, *the urchin* Strongylocentrotus, *from oral side. Note mouth with teeth.* C, *aboral and oral views of sand dollars.*

these teeth lie in and grow continuously from five *dental sacs,* pouched out from the pharynx. Muscles move the teeth and all other hard parts of the lantern apparatus. Sea urchins are omnivorous and scavenging, mostly along rocky or stony sea bottoms.

Sand dollars (for example, *Echinarachnius*) are highly flattened in an oral-aboral direction, and their movable locomotor spines are generally quite short. The podial rows occur in an oral and an aboral set, those on the aboral side usually being arranged like the outline of flower petals. None of the tube feet is locomotor here, breathing being the main function. The anus lies at a point along the edge of the disk.

Most echinoids spawn and the eggs develop externally. The larvae are *plutei,* hardly distinguishable from those of ophiuroids.

PHYLUM CHORDATA

Notochord, pharyngeal gill slits, and dorsal hollow nerve cord present in preadult stages or throughout life; development via tailed larvae (*tadpoles*) or direct; 50,000 species. *Urochordata,* tunicates; *Cephalochordata,* amphioxus; *Vertebrata,* vertebrates

Because this phylum includes man and the animals most directly important to man, it is unquestionably the most interesting from almost any standpoint. The phylum also has a special evolutionary significance, for it comprises what is by far the most progressive group of animals. Other phyla may include more species and may be more diversified; but only among chordates do we encounter, within one and the same phylum, types as primitively organized as tunicates and types as complexly organized as men.

16 · 21 *The probable evolutionary and taxonomic interrelations* among chordates.

The specific ancestors of chordates are unknown, but a distant and probably indirect affinity to hemichordates, pterobranchs particularly, is suggested by chordate structure. Thus, both hemichordates and chordates exhibit a basically similar pattern of embryonic development, and both groups possess a pharynx with gill slits used primitively in ciliary plankton feeding. A dorsal hollow nerve cord also qualifies as a common trait. Two additional major chordate features, namely, notochord and metameric segmentation, evolved as original inventions directly within the phylum.

Chordates are classified into three subphyla: the headless and unsegmented *urochordates,* or *tunicates;* the headless and segmented *cephalochordates,* or *amphioxus;* and the head-possessing and segmented *vertebrates,* or *craniates.* Tunicates generally and ascidian tunicates specifically are undoubtedly the primitive members of the phylum. Ancestral stocks of ascidians appear to have given rise to all present tunicates, independently to the amphioxus group, and, again independently, to the vertebrates (Fig. 16.21).

Subphylum urochordata (tunicates)

Marine, sessile or free-swimming, often colonial through budding; with secreted external envelope (*tunic*); unsegmented; coelom not clearly elaborated; pharynx with endostyle and gill slits, used for breathing and ciliary filter feeding; circulatory system open; hermaphroditic.

Class Ascidiacea (sea squirts): larvae if present free-swimming tadpoles, nonfeeding, with notochord and dorsal nerve cord in tail; adults without tail, sessile, colonial through budding or solitary; gill slits numerous; alimentary

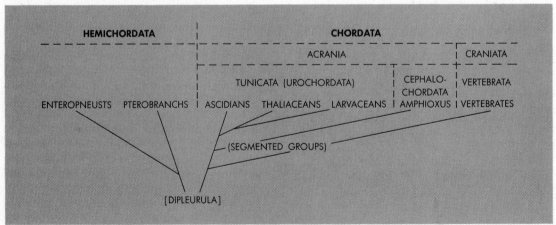

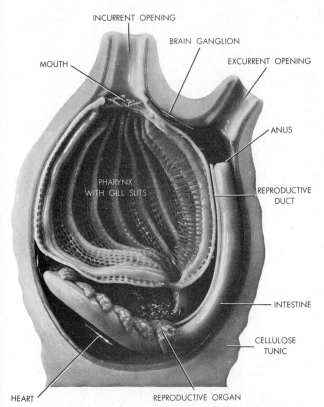

INCURRENT OPENING

BRAIN GANGLION

MOUTH

EXCURRENT OPENING

ANUS

PHARYNX
WITH GILL SLITS

REPRODUCTIVE
DUCT

INTESTINE

CELLULOSE
TUNIC

HEART

REPRODUCTIVE ORGAN

16 · 22   Cutaway model of an adult ascidian. Food-bearing water is drawn into the pharynx through the incurrent siphon. Food passes into the U-shaped alimentary tract, and water emerges through the gill slits and via atrium and excurrent siphon to the outside.

tract U-shaped. *Ascidia, Ciona, Botryllus*

Class Thaliacea (chain tunicates): larvae if present free-swimming, with notochord and dorsal nerve cord in tail; adults without tail but free-swimming, locomotion by "jet" propulsion; gill slits few to numerous; polymorphic, with colonial stages budded in chains. *Pyrosoma, Doliolum, Salpa*

Class Larvacea (appendicularians): tail with notochord and nerve cord permanent throughout life; adults larvalike, free-swimming; tunic formed into complex housing used with tail in feeding; one pair of gill slits. *Appendicularia, Oikopleura, Fritillaria*

Most of the approximately 2,000 species in the tunicate subphylum belong to the sessile ascidians. These animals live in sand, mud, or attached to rocks, and many of them form flat, budding colonies.

An individual sea squirt is covered externally by a tunic, or *test,* composed of tunicin, largely cellulose (Fig. 16.22). On the upper, nonattached side the animal has two openings, an incurrent *branchial siphon,* through which water and food enter toward the mouth, and an excurrent *atrial siphon,* through which water, elimination products, and reproductive cells leave from a large cavity, the *atrium.*

The mouth leads into a large pharynx, or *branchial basket.* This chamber is perforated by rows of numerous gill slits. Blood vessels traverse the pharyngeal wall between the slits. Each such slit is elongated and just wide enough to accommodate the cilia set around its rim. Cilia also line the interior surface of the pharynx. Along the ventral gutter of the chamber is a band of specialized tissue called the *endostyle* (Fig. 16.23). In it, a median strip of cells bears long flagella and strips adjacent along each side are ciliated and glandular. The endostyle secretes mucus continuously, and the flagella and all the pharyngeal cilia distribute this mucus over the inner surface of the branchial basket. The cilia, particularly those around the gill slits, also draw in a continuous food-bearing water current through the branchial siphon and the mouth. Food particles become entangled in the mucus and water passes through the gill slits into the atrium, oxygenating blood in the process. From the atrium, water is expelled in a forceful excurrent stream through the atrial siphon. Concurrently, food in mucus collects along the dorsal wall of the branchial basket and is propelled by ciliary action into the esophagus, continuous posteriorly with the pharynx. The esophagus leads into a stomach at the bottom of the alimentary U, and an intestine terminates at the anus, which opens into the atrial cavity.

The nervous system consists of a single neural ganglion located anteriorly between the two siphons. The open circulatory system includes a tubular heart as well as blood vessels passing into the pharynx and the stomach region. The heart is of interest in that it exhibits a reversing beat; it pumps blood in one direction for a short period, then reverses its action and pumps in the opposite direction. A pericardial space surrounding the heart is the only cavity qualifying as a coelom. Many sea squirts possess an *epicardium* close to or around the heart (see Fig. 16.23). This structure arises as a pair of outfoldings from the posterior part of the pharynx. In many cases these folds enlarge and envelop all the organs in the posterior part of the body, like peritoneum and mesentery. In other cases the folds fuse into one and condense into a *renal organ* lying alongside the heart. This organ stores solid excretory wastes, which simply continue to accumulate in the renal organ throughout the life of the animal.

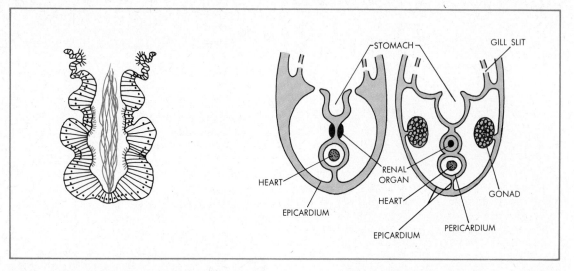

16 · 23 Ascidian structure. *Left, cross section through the endostyle, showing the glandular and ciliated cells on each side, as well as the flagellated cells (color) in the ventral gutter. Right, two stages in the development of the ventral body region near the posterior end of the pharynx, showing the formation of the heart, the epicardium, and the renal organ. The heart is a tube in the pericardial coelom. The epicardia are a pair of folds evaginated from the posterior end of the pharynx which eventually envelop all ventral and posterior organs. The renal organ, formed from the epicardia, accumulates a solid excretory concretion in its interior.*

16 · 24 Colonial Ascidians. *Left, section through a rosette colony of* Botryllus, *showing common atrial siphon. Center, exterior view of* Botryllus. *Right, diagram of stolonic colony of* Perophora.

Buds arise in various specific ways in different ascidians. In all cases, however, budding involves a pinching off from the parent animal of a small epidermal sphere in which are included pieces of some interior tissue. In different ascidians such buds can form almost anywhere on the epidermis, and the bud interior can derive from almost any relatively unspecialized adult tissue. In some instances, for example, in *Botryllus*, buds arise in the body wall of the atrial region, mesenchyme from the body wall supplying the internal cells of the bud. In other instances buds form more posteriorly and the epicardium then usually contributes the interior bud cells. If many buds originate more or less simultaneously in a compact group, they may form a colony surrounded by a common tunic and even a common atrial siphon, as in the rosette colonies of *Botryllus* (Fig. 16.24). A single bud may also elongate into a stalk, or *stolon*, along which more or less separate zooids may develop at intervals. The capacity of budding is believed to be primitive among ascidians; solitary forms such as

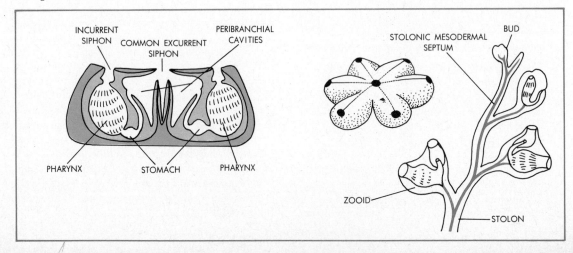

Ciona are considered to have lost the budding potential.

Sea squirts are hermaphroditic. Male and female reproductive organs lie in the loop of the alimentary tract or in the atrial body wall, and their ducts open into the atrium. Most ascidians spawn and the eggs develop externally. A tadpole larva then arises which has little resemblance to the adult (Fig. 16.25). The most conspicuous difference is the presence of a tail, in which a single longitudinal row of cells forms a skeletal supporting rod, the *notochord*. On each side of this rod, bands of mesoderm cells will become a tail musculature. Dorsal to the notochord lies a hollow nerve cord, which extends into the anterior part of the larva and widens at the forward end into a brain vesicle. Inside this vesicle, an ocellus develops as an inward projection from the roof of the brain wall and a balancing organ forms on the floor. Just behind the level of the brain, the dorsolateral ectoderm on each side of the larva folds in and produces a pair of atrial pouches; the two openings to the outside will later fuse and form the single atrial siphon of the adult. The endoderm in the meantime has differentiated into the parts of the alimentary tract. An endostyle arises in the pharynx, and the first three pairs of gill slits break through and establish communication between the pharyngeal cavity and the atrial chambers. Additional gill slits form later, by subdivision of the first ones.

Anteriorly the tadpole possesses *adhesive papillae* by which it will eventually become attached. Everywhere else the surface of the larva is enveloped in the rudiments of the tunic, which covers the mouth and so makes this opening nonfunctional. The tadpole swims about for only a short period—from minutes to a few hours at most. Then it settles, becomes attached, and undergoes a fairly drastic metamorphosis. This transformation involves degeneration of the tail, including notochord, nerve cord, and the tail muscles. Parts of the brain vesicle persist as the neural ganglion of the adult. Also, a rapid proliferation of the body wall between the attachment area and the mouth shifts the mouth toward the free end of the animal and produces the U shape of the adult alimentary tract. The tunic is resorbed in the region over the mouth and a feeding adult thus becomes established.

It is generally believed today that the sessile

16 · 25 The ascidian tadpole and metamorphosis. *A, sagittal section through a tadpole. B, early metamorphosis; tail, notochord, and most of nerve cord resorbed, neuropore becoming opening from neural gland duct into pharynx. C, late metamorphosis; rotation of internal organs completed and siphons functional.*

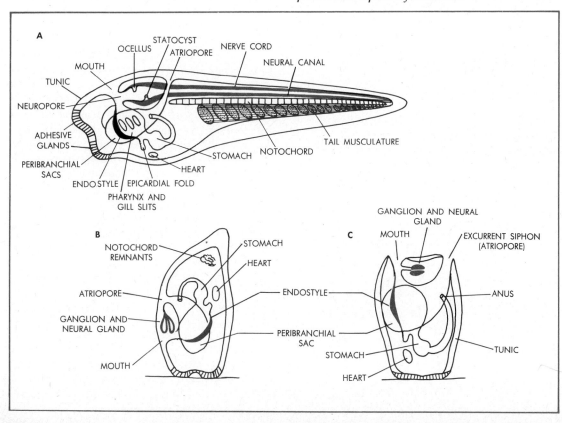

A

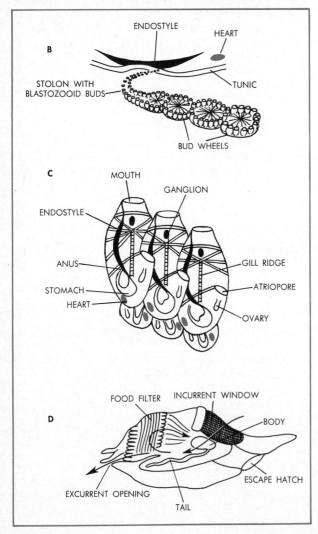

B
ENDOSTYLE
HEART
STOLON WITH
BLASTOZOOID BUDS
TUNIC
BUD WHEELS

C
MOUTH
GANGLION
ENDOSTYLE
ANUS
GILL RIDGE
STOMACH
ATRIOPORE
HEART
OVARY

D
FOOD FILTER
INCURRENT WINDOW
BODY
ESCAPE HATCH
EXCURRENT OPENING
TAIL

ascidian adults are basically primitive types, and that they probably represent direct descendants of possibly hemichordatelike, filter-feeding, chordate ancestors. The tadpole larva is envisaged as constituting an original evolutionary invention of this early chordate stock. As more efficient dispersal agents than buds, tadpoles would have been adaptively highly advantageous to the sessile adults. Moreover, a tailed, well-muscled tadpole could become adapted readily to a prolonged free-swimming existence; and if the larva also developed sex organs precociously, a new type of adult could actually be evolved. It is believed that from such a free-swimming larval starting point have arisen not only all the other tunicates, namely, Thaliacea and Larvacea, but all other chordates as well.

Thaliacea are permanently free-swimming tunicates in which the body is organized around a straight rather than a U-shaped alimentary system (Fig. 16.26). Thus, the branchial siphon is at one end of the generally barrel-shaped animal and the atrial siphon is at the other. Water forced through this system as in ascidians jet-propels the thaliacean in the opposite direction. The animals develop via tadpoles, and tailless adults then often become colonial. In many cases, chains of adults arise by budding from a stolon growing out from the endostyle: the endostyle of one zooid forms a stolon giving rise to a next zooid, the endostyle of that zooid then forms a stolon producing a third zooid, and so on. In most cases, also, the life cycle of thaliaceans includes one or more polymorphic variants.

Larvacea are tunicates in which the larval tail persists permanently. Indeed it becomes several times longer than the rest of the animal and functions as the main locomotor and feeding organ. The whole animal is enveloped by a complexly constructed house fashioned from the tunic, and the tail is tucked under the body of the animal along the floor of this house. Undulations of the tail draw food-bearing water through the house and also propel the animal.

16 · 26 *A, photo of the thaliacean* Doliolum, *in plankton, from life. Note muscle hoops, gill slits, siphons. B, ventral region of parent salp (oozoid) showing endostylar stolon carrying chains and wheel arrays of sexual blastozooids. Terminal bud wheels of this type form in Cyclosalpa, straight chains in Salpa. C, detail of stolonic chain showing a few paired blastozooids. Eggs from such blastozooids give rise to new adult gonozooids. D, side view of the larvacean* Oikopleura. *Note complex house, comparatively small body, and long tail of interior animal.*

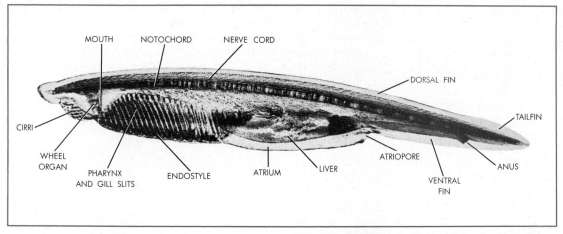

MOUTH NOTOCHORD NERVE CORD

DORSAL FIN

TAILFIN

CIRRI

WHEEL
ORGAN

PHARYNX
AND GILL SLITS ENDOSTYLE ATRIUM LIVER ATRIOPORE

ANUS

VENTRAL
FIN

16 · 27 Amphioxus. *Some of the gross anatomical features.*

Subphylum Cephalochordata
(amphioxus, lancelets)

Marine, in sand; notochord and dorsal nerve cord throughout life; head or brain absent; coelom well developed, metamerically segmented; filter-feeding, with atrium, numerous pharyngeal gill slits, and endostyle; circulation open, without heart; with asymmetrical larvae. *Branchiostoma, Asymmetron*

The whole subphylum consists of about 30 species included in the two genera above. Amphioxus is slender, laterally compressed, and pointed at both ends (Fig. 16.27). It lies in sand of shallow coastal waters, only its anterior end sticking out of its burrow.

Externally, a median dorsal fin extends over most of the length of the animal, a median ventral fin occurs in roughly the posterior third, and a tail fin connects the dorsal and ventral fins around the hind end. The dorsal and ventral fins are strengthened internally by boxlike *fin rays* composed of connective tissue. At the junction between the ventral fin and the tail fin lies the anus. Anteriorly the ventral fin terminates at the *atriopore*, the exit from the atrium. The alimentary system begins at an *oral hood*, an epidermal fold fringed with fingerlike *cirri*. These form a coarse screen when the animal is feeding. On the inner surface of the oral hood are projections with complex bands of cilia, the whole forming a *wheel organ*. It produces a spiraling ingoing water current. The cavity of the oral hood extends posteriorly to a transverse membrane, the *velum*, in the center of which is the mouth.

Behind the mouth, the long pharynx contains 60 to more than 100 pairs of lateral, sloping gill slits. As in ascidians, cilia are present around the gill slits and on the inner pharyngeal lining. An endostyle again forms the ventral pharyngeal gutter and an analogous

strip of ciliated tissue lies along the roof of the pharynx. The whole branchial basket operates as in ascidians. Gill slits open into the atrium, a ventral cavity in these animals. Behind the pharynx, a straight intestine receives enzymatic secretions from a digestive gland, or "liver," a hollow elongated sac extending forward from its ventral intestinal attachment along the right side of the pharynx.

The notochord passes through the entire length of the body. Directly over it lies the hollow nerve cord. Anteriorly the cord tapers to a point and contains a brain vesicle only slightly larger than the neural canal. A pigment spot and an olfactory pit are the only sensory structures present. The absence of a distinct brain is probably not primitive but a secondarily simplified condition correlated with the predominantly sedentary life of the animal. On each side the nerve cord gives off paired segmental nerves, some of them innervating the lateral V-shaped segmental muscles.

The circulation is open (Fig. 16.28). A contractile ventral aorta below the pharynx pumps blood forward and then up through *aortic arches* between the gill slits. Blood collects above the pharynx in a pair of dorsal aortae. These two vessels join behind the pharynx into a single systemic aorta which gives off branches to the tissues. From an intestinal network of spaces, blood drains as in vertebrates into a hepatic portal vein passing into the liver. A hepatic vein from there and other veins from blood spaces in various body parts conduct blood to a *sinus venosus*, a chamber which continues anteriorly as the ventral aorta. The blood is colorless and without cells.

The coelom arises from segmental coelomic sacs in the embryo. In the pharyngeal region the coelom is small and consists only of a pair of flattened sacs dorsal to the pharynx. Posteriorly the coelom is rep-

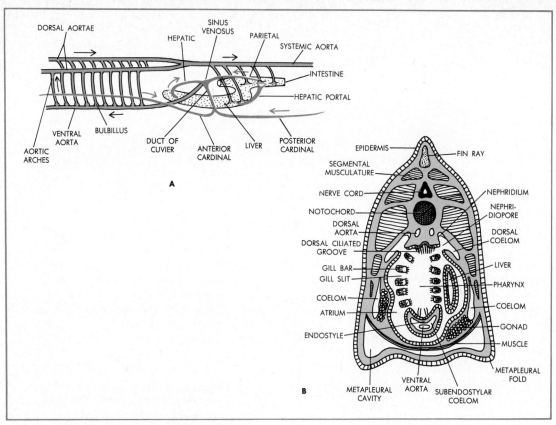

16 · 28 Amphioxus structure. A, the basic plan of the circulatory system of amphioxus. Veins in dark color, arteries in lighter tint. Direction of venous blood flow indicated by colored arrows, that of arterial blood flow, by black arrows. A bulbillus is a contractile vesicle. The sinus venosus is formed by the confluence of the main veins of the body and the exit of the ventral aorta; it corresponds in position to (and forms part of) the heart of vertebrates. B, cross section through the pharyngeal region.

resented by the space surrounding the alimentary tract. The excretory systems consist of nephridia, of a type similar in some respects to flame-bulb systems and encountered otherwise only in trochophore larvae and certain polychaete annelids. Most biologists consider this very puzzling occurrence of such nephridia in amphioxus to represent a very remarkable instance of parallel evolution. In amphioxus one such organ is located near the dorsal end of each gill slit. The nephridia abut against blood vessels in the coelom lining, and the collecting tubule of each nephridium opens into the atrium.

Reproductive organs are paired in *Branchiostoma*, unpaired and present on the right side only in *Asymmetron*. They form an anteroposterior succession of saclike organs in the lateral wall of the atrium. Sex cells escape through ruptures into the atrium and out via the atriopore. In an early larva the mouth is located on the left side. Gill slits begin to form in pairs, but all of these lie on the right side of the body. Later the larva does become symmetrical and a fairly gradual metamorphosis follows.

Although amphioxus is evidently quite specialized in many respects, the animal does display numerous vertebrate features in very primitive form, and thus it may suggest in a rather distant way what ancient vertebrates might have been like. Most probably, amphioxus exemplifies a transitional stage in the evolution of ancestral ascidian stocks into the first vertebrate stocks. In some of the ancestral ascidians, segmentation may have developed originally in the tail musculature and its nerve supply, an advantageous step which would have increased the locomotor power and the fine control of the tail. Such added efficiency would have been particularly important if the early chordate shifted its habitat from the open sea to shallow shore waters, especially around river mouths, where influx of minerals promotes rich plankton growth. Waves, surf, undertow, and also the currents of discharging river water would have made efficient locomotor control exceedingly important. Segmentation thus may have evolved in adaptation to such conditions.

Through segmented and finely controlled tails, furthermore, the basic means would have become available for an *ascent* into the rivers. However, actual entry into rivers would have required at least two additional evolutionary changes, and these the ancestors of amphioxus apparently did not perfect. Instead, they appear merely to have adopted a sedentary existence in shallow coastal regions, and modern amphioxus still exhibits this mode of life. By contrast, related ancestral types certainly did succeed in evolving the necessary evolutionary adjustments, and they became the first vertebrates. The required adjustments were strongly muscled larvae that could surmount the force of river currents as soon as they hatched; and excretory systems that could cope with the continuous osmotic inflow of water into the body, unavoidable in a freshwater environment. The first requirement was met by the evolution of a large, very yolky egg, which could develop without additional food to an advanced, fully segmented stage even before hatching; and the second was met by the development of a new type of kidney, specialized originally for the elimination of osmotic water.

SUBPHYLUM VERTEBRATA (VERTEBRATES)

Segmented, with head, trunk, and tail; cranium (skull) enclosing brain; dermal bone typically present; embryo with notochord; adult with notochord and/or vertebral column of cartilage or replacement bone; typically with two pairs of trunk appendages; with pharyngeal gills or lungs; coelom well developed; circulation closed, heart with two, three, or four chambers; excretion pronephric, mesonephric, or metanephric; endocrine system elaborate; development various. *Agnatha*, jawless fishes; *Placodermi*, extinct armored jawed fishes; *Chondrichthyes*, cartilage fishes; *Osteichthyes*, bony fishes; *Amphibia*, amphibians; *Reptilia*, reptiles; *Aves*, birds; *Mammalia*, mammals.

The overriding orienting factor in vertebrate evolution was the fresh water. As just noted above, ancestral vertebrates probably invaded the rivers as segmented, tailed derivatives of ascidian stocks. Their larvae were well developed at hatching and possessed strongly muscled tails, and their adults were pharyngeal filter feeders like their marine forebears. Also, they possessed kidneys capable of forming a copious watery urine (Fig. 16.29). Such a kidney (still encountered today in the larvae of fishes) was a segmentally developed *pronephros*. In each of the anterior body segments was present a *nephron*, consisting of a

double-layered cup (*nephric capsule*) and a ball of blood capillaries (*glomerulus*) projecting into the capsule. Water filtered from glomerular blood into the capsule, and a duct from there joined other such ducts in the neighboring segments and led to the exterior near the anus. In later vertebrates, many more nephron units developed in the segments of the middle and hind regions of the body, and the anterior original nephrons actually degenerated. Such a kidney is a *mesonephros;* it is characteristic today of the adults of all fishes and amphibia.

16 · 29 The primitive vertebrate kidney. A, a basic vertebrate nephron unit. B, diagram of a pronephric kidney. C, diagram of a mesonephric kidney (general labeling as in B). Note the nephrostomal openings into the pericardial (coelomic) cavity in B, absence of such openings in C. An actual pronephros or mesonephros contains many more nephron units than sketched here.

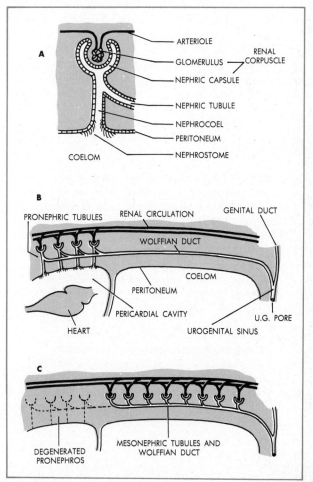

An early fundamental consequence of such an excretory pattern was that whereas the kidneys could eliminate water well, they were not as yet adapted to eliminate salt. Retention of minerals was undoubtedly counteracted by export via the gills, as still happens today in aquatic vertebrates. Yet it is possible that, in early stages of vertebrate evolution, minerals may have tended to accumulate internally. Many of them apparently were disposed of by deposition in the skin, and dermal bone in the form of heavy plates then probably evolved as a basic vertebrate trait. Indeed, the earliest known fossil vertebrates were jawless fishes which were armored in bone, and most other vertebrates still possess dermal bone in their skulls. Calcium deposits later also came to form replacement bone in the rest of the skeleton, where cartilage was present primitively as a strengthening material around the notochord.

This conversion of an original mineral liability into an adaptive asset may have been facilitated by the concurrent evolution of an endocrine system that could control mineral metabolism. The glands of the system would necessarily have had to be sensitive to salt levels coming into the body via food and leaving the body via excretion. It is therefore probably not a coincidence that, although other organs contribute as well, mineral-regulating functions in vertebrates are carried out to a large extent by the thyroid and parathyroid glands, evolved from the endostyle in the floor of the chordate pharynx,

and by portions of the adrenal glands situated along the kidney (see Chap. 22).

Like their ancestors, the most primitive vertebrates of record still are pharyngeal filter feeders: the larvae and adults of Agnatha are jawless, and in the larvae the ciliation of the pharynx sucks in water with small food particles through a round, open mouth. Such a pattern holds in principle even for the living ectoparasitic adult lampreys, whose food consists of body fluids and tiny tissue fragments rasped off the host. A considerable evolutionary gap then separates the agnaths from all other vertebrates. In the latter, the principal food-collecting organ is no longer the pharynx but the mouth itself, which has become equipped with jaws and true teeth. The nature of the food has changed concurrently, to bulk nutrients, and the ancestral method of filter feeding has largely ceased. This change has left the branchial basket primarily as a breathing organ; and since therefore tiny particles no longer needed to be strained out of water, the number of gill slits could become reduced. Indeed, such a reduction has proceeded in parallel with jaw development, for the skeletal supports in the most anterior gills came to be remodeled into jaw supports (a condition persisting even in mammals and man; Fig. 16.30).

But even though fewer gill slits now remained, these could become more efficient oxygenators; for the circulation had become closed, extensive capillary nets were developed, and an originally two-chambered heart moved blood more rapidly than in any of the chordate ancestors. Such increased circulatory efficiency actually constituted a necessary corollary to the active, food-hunting mode of existence, and also to the still-persisting requirement of excreting osmotic water rapidly. A further corollary to the development of a food-hunting way of life was a new burst of neural evolution, resulting in the elaborate brains and sense organs of vertebrates.

The freshwater environment continued to orient also the later stages of vertebrate evolution. Pharyngeal air sacs appear to have been a primitive, original trait of bony fishes, in adaptation to occasional periods of drought. Such sacs then evolved into swim

16 · 30 *Evolution of the pharyngeal region in vertebrates. A, original filter-feeding condition, with six pairs of gill slits and aortic gill arches, external nares, and air sac with duct. B, the number of gill slits and aortic arches is reduced, the air sac functions as a lung, and the nostrils communicate with the pharynx. Also (not shown), the first pair of skeletal gill supports has become the jaw skeleton. C, gill slits absent in adult, aortic arches reduced still further, heart three-chambered.*

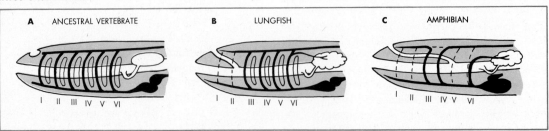

A ANCESTRAL VERTEBRATE   B LUNGFISH   C AMPHIBIAN

I   II   III IV V VI   I   II   III IV V VI   I   II   III IV V   VI

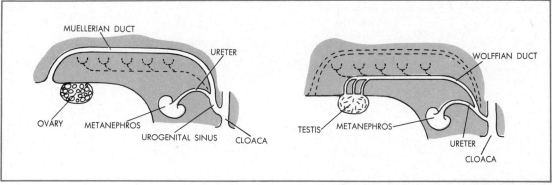

16 · 31 The metanephros. In reptiles, birds, and mammals this kidney arises as an outgrowth from the posterior region of the Wolffian (meso-nephric) duct. In females (left) the anterior parts of this duct and the mesonephros degenerate, and the Muellerian duct (oviduct) serves as a separate reproductive channel. In males (right) the Wolffian duct ceases to be excretory but be-comes a sperm duct from the testes. Note that most mammals are without a cloaca, the excre-tory and reproductive ducts opening to the out-side separately, not through the hindgut (see also Fig. 16.48).

bladders in some of these fishes, into lungs in others (see Fig. 16.30). Other adaptations to at first tem-porary and later permanent terrestrial life developed as well: fleshy fins, elongated subsequently into legs; yolky eggs and aquatic tadpoles, followed by even yolkier land eggs with shells and direct development; three and then four chambers in the heart, per-mitting efficient separation of arterial and venous blood and thus providing enough oxygen for the increased energy requirements on land; a distinct energy-saving neck, with a swivel joint for the head; controls for maintenance of constant body tempera-ture, including insulating surface layers of fat, feathers, and fur; improved breathing and circulatory machinery in mammals, including a diaphragm and highly specialized blood corpuscles; and a new mam-malian reproductive mechanism, in which laid shelled eggs became substituted by internal development, birth of young, and milk for the newborn.

Furthermore, terrestrial living by reptiles, birds, and mammals came to depend on a new, land-adapted kidney, in which the earlier water-secreting function became reversed to a water-saving function. This kidney, called *metanephros*, developed as an out-growth from the most posterior region of the earlier mesonephros (Fig. 16.31). In this bean-shaped meta-nephros, the principal new feature in each of the nephrons is a highly elongated and coiled tubule specialized particularly to reabsorb water from urine flowing through it, and thus to retain as much water as possible within the body (see Fig. 24.13). Reptiles, birds, and mammals still develop a mesonephros dur-ing the embryonic phase, but in later stages the meta-nephros arises. Consequently, whereas the aquatic vertebrates excrete a dilute, watery urine, the ter-restrial vertebrates can adapt to the scarce water supply on land by excreting a highly concentrated, salty urine.

With at least 25,000 species, the bony fishes rep-

resent the largest class, roughly half of all verte-brates. Birds constitute the next largest, with about 10,000 species. Next in order are reptiles (6,000 species), mammals (5,000 species), amphibia (3,000 species), cartilage fishes (600 species), and jawless fishes (50 species).

Class Agnatha (jawless fishes)

With notochord throughout life; internal skeleton cartilaginous, dermal bony armor absent in living forms; sucking mouth; without true (dermal) teeth; typically with single nostril; pineal eye present; paired fins absent; heart two-chambered; excretion pronephric in larva, metanephric in adult; sex organ single, without duct. *Sea lampreys, brook lampreys, hagfishes.*

The jawless fishes, or *cyclostomes*, of today possess an eellike body bearing low median dorsal and caudal fins (Fig. 16.32). The round mouth lies in the center of a shallow funnel studded with horny epidermal teeth. A tongue, similarly equipped with horny teeth, can be protruded through the mouth. In lampreys a single dorsal nostril leads into a closed nasal sac, but in hagfishes the nasal passage opens into the posterior part of the mouth cavity (*internal*

16 · 32 The lamprey Petromyzon. Note gill slits, fins.

Courtesy of Carolina Biological Supply Company.

nares). Just behind the nostril lies a functional *pineal eye*, connecting with the brain by a nerve like the lateral eyes.

Internally, the persisting notochord is stiffened by incompletely developed segmental cartilage supports, and cartilage also forms the brain case and additionally surrounds the heart (Fig. 16.33). The gill chamber is an elongated sac pouched out from the pharynx and lying ventral to the esophagus. In lampreys the seven pairs of gill slits open directly to the exterior, but in hagfishes water from the gills exits via a single pair of gill pores. A stomach is absent, the esophagus continuing directly into the intestine. The circulation is patterned according to the characteristic vertebrate plan, already foreshadowed in amphioxus. A single atrium and a single ventricle compose the heart, as in all fishes. The blood too is typically vertebrate, with hemoglobin-containing red corpuscles and leucocytes. The coelom is well developed, and a single sex organ discharges into it. Reproductive cells reach the outside via a genital

pore along the course of the excretory duct, which opens just behind the anus.

All lampreys spawn in rivers. An egg develops into an eyeless *ammocoete* larva, which possesses an endostyle and filter-feeds in upstream river bottoms in the ancestral manner (Fig. 16.34). Metamorphosis does not occur for three to seven years, and then the young adults migrate downstream. Sea lampreys head into the open sea, where they lead a parasitic mature life. These animals are blood-sucking ectoparasites which attach to fish by their mouths and rasp through the skin of the hosts. While attached, the animals pump water both in and out of the gills directly, the mouth not being free for breathing. Brook lampreys are permanently freshwater forms. The adults here are not parasitic. Indeed they do not feed at all, but spawn within a few days and die. Hagfishes are marine. All are hermaphroditic and develop directly, without larval stages.

Class Chondrichthyes (cartilage fishes)

Mostly marine; notochord reduced but persisting in adult; scales are denticles; nostrils paired, internal nares absent; without air sac; fertilization

16 · 33 Lamprey structure. A sagittal section of the anterior region is shown.

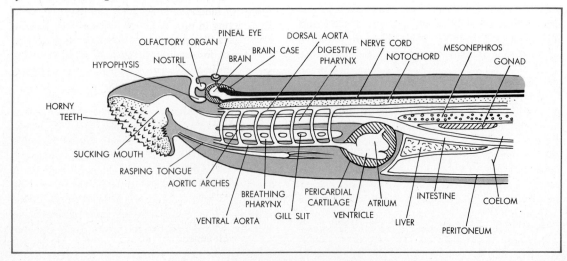

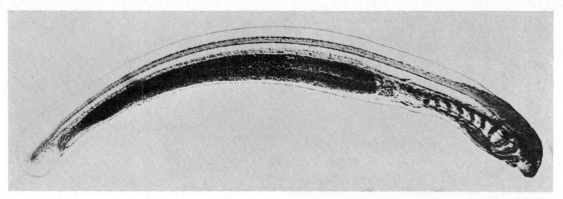

16 · 34 Ammocoete larva, *cleared specimen. Note gill slits, nerve cord and brain, and position of notochord just underneath nerve cord.*

internal, development direct. *Dogfishes, sharks, rays and skates, electric "eels," devilfishes, manta and sting rays, chimeras.*

In a shark, the skin is studded with tiny dermal scales which contain enamel on the outside and dentine on the inside. The scale is extended into a pointed spine, and the whole *denticle* resembles and is homologous to a mammalian tooth (Fig. 16.35). The notochord, though present, no longer forms a continuous rod. It persists only between adjacent vertebrae, which are cartilaginous but well developed. Anteriorly the skull is a cartilaginous box, with lateral capsules for the eyes and ears. The jaws are attached to the skull by ligaments, and the evolution of jaws from the most anterior gill supports (in the extinct placoderms) has resulted in sharks in a reduction of the first gill slit to a small opening, the *spiracle.* Behind the spiracle are five well-developed gill slits. In addition to median fins, paired fins are present and are jointed to pectoral and pelvic girdles.

The mouth is rimmed by several rows of pointed teeth, homologous to the surface denticles. The alimentary tract includes a stomach and, opening into the intestine, a large liver and a separate pancreas. In the intestine is present a conspicuous *spiral valve,* a tissue fold which increases the absorptive surface. Cartilage fishes possess a cloaca, that is, the reproductive and excretory ducts open into the terminal part of the hindgut. A salt-secreting *rectal gland* is also attached to the cloaca. In many sharks the female reproductive ducts are enlarged into uteri. The males typically possess a pair of copulatory organs, the *fin claspers,* between the pelvic fins.

Most sharks are fiercely carnivorous, but the largest, namely, whale and basking sharks, are plankton feeders. Basking sharks are the largest of all fishes, attaining lengths of over 50 ft. Many rays and skates exhibit interesting offensive and protective adaptations, among them snouts extended into "saws"

in the sawfishes, poison spines at the end of the tail in sting rays, and electric organs lateral to the eyes in the torpedo rays.

Class Osteichthyes (bony fishes)

Typically with scales, of ganoid, cycloid, or ctenoid type; spiracles only in primitive types; with opercula; nostrils paired, with or without internal nares; lung or swim bladder present, the latter with or without duct.

> Subclass Sarcopterygii (flesh-finned fishes): paired fins with internal bony skeleton and fleshy exterior; notochord persisting; two dorsal fins; often with internal nares; air sac functions as lung. *Lobe-finned fishes* (coelacanths); *lungfishes.*
> Subclass Actinopterygii (ray-finned fishes): paired fins with soft or hard fin rays; single dorsal fin; without internal nares; air sac usually functions as swim bladder; notochord persisting in primitive types, replaced by bone in most. *Chondrostei* (for example, sturgeons); *Holostei* (for example, garpikes); *Teleostei* (modern bony fishes).

The scales of bony fishes are of three types (Fig. 16.36). In the primitive groups they are most often *ganoid,* that is, diamond-shaped and covered externally with a layer of hard, glossy enamel. In more advanced fishes the scales are *cycloid* if their free posterior parts are smooth, *ctenoid* if the free parts are rough-textured or spiny. The median fins, that is, dorsals, anals, and caudals, are supported by elongated bony fin rays. The support of the paired fins differs sharply in the two great subclasses of bony fishes. In the flesh-finned Sarcopterygii, the pectorals and

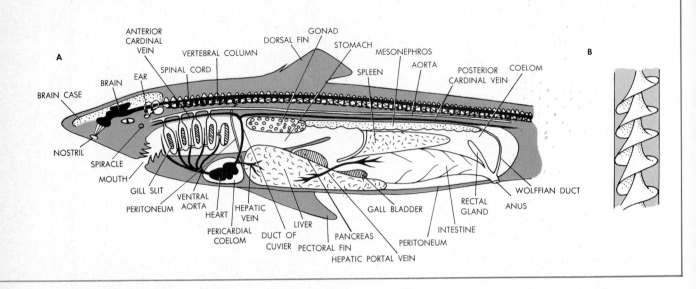

16 · 35   The structure of sharks. *A, sagittal section of a dogfish. In a female a uterus (Muellerian duct) would be present in addition to the Wolffian duct. The dorsal aorta gives off arteries (not shown) to stomach, intestine, liver, kidney, and the other internal organs. B, diagram of the spiral valve in the intestine. C, close-up view of shark skin, showing toothlike denticles.*

pelvics contain internal bony skeletons, the parts corresponding substantially to the limb bones of terrestrial vertebrates. In the ray-finned Actinopterygii, by contrast, the paired fins are supported like the median fins by bony rays.

The skull is composed of some 60 bones, a number which has become reduced in later vertebrate classes (for example, to about 20 in mammals). In primitive bony fishes the notochord often still persists into the adult stage, but in most groups it is replaced partly or (more usually) wholly by bony vertebrae preformed in cartilage. The nostrils of bony fishes are paired, and they lead either into closed nasal sacs or into the mouth cavity via internal nares. In the pharynx, gills usually number four and never more than five pairs. They are covered externally by an *operculum*, a bony plate hinged on a skeletal gill arch behind the jaws. Each gill is a double plate composed of fine *gill filaments*, epithelial and highly vascularized (Fig. 16.37). A skeletal gill arch supports the gill tissue. The inner edges of the gills are often expanded into *gill rakers*, which prevent food from passing through the gill slits. An air sac pouches out from the pharynx. The sac serves as a lung primitively and as a swim bladder in more advanced forms. Swim bladders in some cases still do and in others do not connect with the pharynx via a duct.

Both the flesh-finned and the ray-finned bony fishes were primitively freshwater forms, and both presumably used their air sacs originally as lungs. The flesh-finned groups then continued and perfected the air-breathing habit, but the ray-finned types soon came to use the air sac purely as a swim bladder.

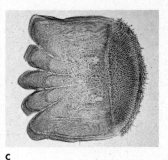

A   B   C

Photos, courtesy of Carolina Biological Supply Company.

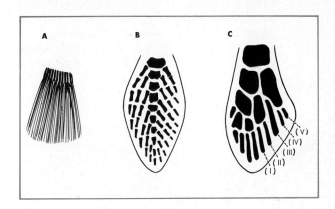

16 · 36 Scales and fins of bony fishes. Photos: A, ganoid scale; B, cycloid scale; C, ctenoid scale. In the latter, the smooth portion is overlapped by the scale before it and the spiny part is exposed. Diagrams: A, fin of ray-finned bony fish; bony rays support the fin. B, bony elements in fin of lungfish. C, fin of lobe-finned fish, indicating the basic ancestral bony elements of all vertebrate walking limbs.

Flesh-finned fishes also used their skeleton-supported pectorals and pelvics as primitive walking organs. One group among them, the lobe-finned fishes (see Fig. 32.21), probably gave rise to the amphibia. In the course of this transition the fin skeleton elongated into the typical tetrapod leg. Amphibia and all later vertebrates also inherited the internal nares from these ancestors, as well as an upper jaw fused directly with the skull.

The whole subclass Sarcopterygii today consists of only four surviving genera. By contrast, the subclass of ray fins now constitutes the most abundant group of vertebrates. The two primitive superorders, Chondrostei and Holostei, are alike in that their scales are generally ganoid and the notochord tends to persist. Both these superorders are represented today by only about 40 surviving species. All are either freshwater forms or, like some of the sturgeons, they live in the sea but return to rivers for spawning.

All remaining bony fishes are members of the large and highly diversified superorder Teleostei, in which the skeleton is fully ossified. Two broad general

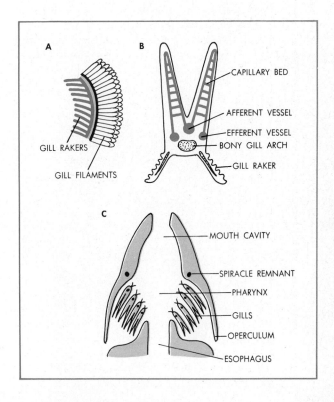

16 · 37 The gills of bony fishes. Left, diagram of a left gill in side view, showing double row of gill filaments pointing away from pharynx and gill rakers pointing into pharynx. B, horizontal section through a gill filament; the afferent vessel is the part of the aortic arch coming from the ventral aorta, the efferent vessels, the parts leading to the dorsal aorta. C, horizontal section through fish head, showing position of the four pairs of gills.

patterns of teleost structure may be distinguished (Fig. 16.38). In one, the *clupeiform* pattern (named after the order including trout, salmon, and herring), fin rays are soft, scales are cycloid, the swim bladder has a persisting duct, and the pelvic fins are in a primitive abdominal, that is, posterior, position. In the other, *perciform* pattern (named after the order containing perch, tuna, and bass) fin rays are hard and spiny, scales are ctenoid, the swim bladder is without duct, and the pectoral fins have moved far forward, either into a thoracic position or even as far anteriorly as the head region. Thus, the pelvic fins lie in front of the pectorals. These two patterns are not always sharply distinct, and many teleost groups exhibit mixed and intergrading characteristics.

Class Amphibia

Freshwater and terrestrial; paired appendages are legs; skin without scales (most living species); with internal nares; upper jaws fused to skull; heart three-chambered; breathing via gills, lungs, skin, and mouth cavity; 10 pairs of cranial nerves; fertilization mostly external, development mostly via tadpole larvae.

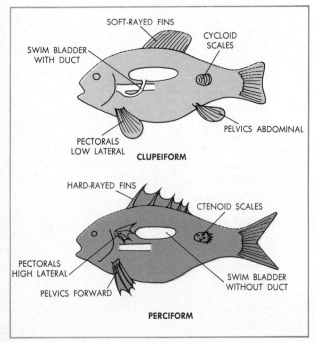

16 · 38   Teleost traits. *The principal characteristics of the clupeiform pattern (as in herring, goldfishes, or guppies) and the perciform pattern (as in perches, basses, or tunas). Many teleosts possess a mixture of clupeiform and perciform traits.*

Subclass Gymnophiona (Apoda) (cecilians): wormlike; up to 200 vertebrae; without limbs or girdles; skull topped with bone; skin smooth, often with embedded dermal scales; eyeless; tail short.
Subclass Urodela (Caudata) (salamanders, newts); body with head, trunk, tail; aquatic larvae resemble adults; larvae and some adults with teeth on upper and lower jaws; eyelids typically present in terrestrial adults, absent in aquatic adults.
Subclass Anura (Salientia) (toads, frogs): tailless, without neck; hind limbs usually long, feet webbed; 10 vertebrae; with eyelids; adults mostly terrestrial.

The most notable traits of amphibians are those which adapt the animals to an at least partly terrestrial life; and most of these traits trace their origin to the ancestral lobe-finned fishes. For example, the paired appendages have elongated to distinct walking legs, each with five (or fewer) toes. Though primitive amphibia still live entirely in water, the majority of these possess lungs serving actively in air breathing. Gills occur in the larvae and in exceptional cases also in some of the adults (where lungs may or may not be present in addition). Correlated with the air-breathing habit, the internal nares inherited from the lobe fins provide an important adaptation, for they make breathing possible while the mouth remains closed. As in ancestral lobe fins, moreover, the upper jaw is fused to the skull. The skin has become thin and scaleless, providing a breathing organ auxiliary to gills, lungs, and the lining of the mouth. At the same time the skin has become highly glandular and mucus-secreting, a necessary protection against desiccation. Also adaptive in air breathing is the three-chambered heart, capable to some extent of preventing the mixing of oxygenated blood returning from the lungs and venous blood returning from the body: arterial blood enters one atrium, venous blood the other. The two bloods then mix in the single ventricle, to be sure, but not so much as they do in a two-chambered heart.

Thus, from a lobe-finned starting point, the amphibian descendant has become able to walk and to breathe air on a permanent basis, even though these activities are still carried out in an aquatic environment in some instances. Actually, even the most land-adapted amphibian requires a moist environment, and reproductive and developmental processes still retain ancestral fishlike characteristics altogether. Eggs must typically be laid into water, and fertilization and development take place externally, as in bony fishes. Development includes aquatic tadpole larvae and these are thoroughly fishlike, regardless of whether or not the adults are also aquatic.

Of the three living subclasses, the cecilians probably represent a very primitive amphibian stock, though the animals today are secondarily highly specialized. These mostly tropical amphibians are blind, limbless soil burrowers, leading a life somewhat like earthworms. The Urodela include a wide range of types, from fully aquatic ones to those in which terrestrial habits are developed to various degrees (Fig. 16.39). But whereas urodeles are on the whole more aquatic than terrestrial, the reverse holds for the Anura, toads and frogs. Most anurans have eyelids, an adaptation to their life in an aerial environment. Also, they are often highly specialized as jumpers, with hind legs far longer and stronger than the forelegs. Correlated with this locomotor specialization the tail is absent and the head is joined directly to the trunk, without neck. Indeed, the whole body has become squat and foreshortened, and the number of vertebrae is reduced to 10. The tongue can be hurled out of the mouth at an insect, posterior end first. Toads are toothless; frogs possess teeth on the upper jaw and the roof of the mouth. None of the anurans possess gills as adults and all possess lungs.

Class Reptilia

Epidermis with cornified scales; limbs five-toed, clawed; breathing by lungs; heart four-chambered, ventricular separation usually incomplete; one pair of aortic arches; 12 pairs of cranial nerves; excretion metanephric; fertilization internal; eggs with shells; development direct.

>   Order Chelonia (turtles, tortoises, terrapins): body encased in bony shell and epidermal cover; teeth absent in living types.
>   Order Rhynchocephalia (tuataras): pineal eye functional.
>   Order Squamata (lizards, snakes): skull bones reduced; with or without pectoral girdle, limbs; halves of lower jaw articulated or united by ligament.
>   Order Crocodilia (alligators, crocodiles, caimans, gavials): heavy-bodied, semiaquatic; epidermal scales with dermal reinforcements; webbed feet; teeth in sockets.

As the first fully terrestrial vertebrates, reptiles exhibit many characteristics encountered also in the later mammals and birds. The reptilian skin is dry and protected from desiccation typically by epidermal scales, homologous to fur and feathers. Limbs are

16 · 39 Amphibia. A, the Mexican axolotl Amblystoma mexicanum. *This is a neotenous species, permanently retaining larval traits such as external gills and a larval tail. B, egg-carrying male of the midwife toad* Alytes obstetricans.

perfected as walking legs, and they raise the body off the ground more than the amphibian limbs. Reptiles are strictly air breathers, with a breathing system constructed like that of mammals and birds; that is, tracheal and bronchial tubes pipe air to the lungs (see Chap. 24). The heart is four-chambered, completely so in crocodiles, nearly so in the other orders; it keeps arterial separated from venous blood, essentially as in mammals and birds (see Chap. 23). The adult excretory system is metanephric, as in mammals and birds, and is capable of producing a highly hypertonic, water-conserving urine.

The single most essential adaptation to land life is the shelled egg, about which a great deal will be said in Chap. 28. All reptiles lay eggs on land, whether or not they are adapted secondarily to an aquatic existence. Fertilization is always internal, as in mammals and birds; a penis in males may be absent (tuatara), single (turtles, crocodiles), or double (lizards, snakes). These organs are located in or near the cloaca and are protruded during copulation.

With their unique protective body covering, turtles are among the most readily recognizable animals. The shell consists of a dorsal *carapace* and a ventral *plastron*. The carapace is a dome of bone, formed from fused vertebrae and from broadened and fused ribs. Analogously, the bony plate of the plastron is constructed from flattened and fused parts of the pectoral and pelvic girdles and the sternum. The pectoral girdle is actually wholly inside the shell of the rib cage. (Fig. 16.40). The bony parts of the shell are overlain by skin, which may be soft but tough or hardened into epidermal horn.

Some 95 per cent of all living reptile species embrace the lizards and snakes. Snakes may be characterized as limbless lizards, though they differ from lizards in many specialized respects. In snakes, the left and right halves of the lower jaws are not fused together but are joined by ligaments, and the upper and lower jaws are often similarly joined by ligaments only. Consequently, the mouth can be distended greatly and a snake may ingest an animal several times wider than its own diameter.

Snakes are without external ear openings but they "hear" vibrations transmitted from the ground via the

16 · 40 The turtle skeleton. *The ventral part (plastron) is cut away and hinged back, showing the limb girdles underneath the dorsal part (carapace) formed by the rib cage.*

Courtesy of Carolina Biological Supply Company.

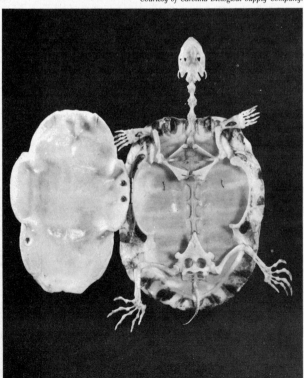

skeleton. Eyes are lidless and covered by a transparent membrane. Vertebrae may number up to 400. Limb girdles and limbs are generally absent as well, though vestigial remains of pelvic girdles persist in pythons and related types. The tuatara of New Zealand is the sole surviving species of the order Rhynchocephalia. The animal is generally lizardlike and its most distinctive trait is the presence of a functional pineal eye, as in lampreys (Fig. 16.41).

Crocodilia ·are the closest living relatives of dinosaurs on the one hand and of birds on the other. These reptiles possess a four-chambered heart with fully separated ventricles and a palate extended far back, separating the nasal passages from the mouth cavity right to the pharynx (Fig. 16.42). These traits are specific adaptations to a·secondarily aquatic existence; they improve breathing efficiency, especially when the mouth is submerged or full with food or both. Other adaptations to aquatic life include closable nostrils; recessed eardrums that can be covered by a flap of skin under water; webbed feet; and a powerful, laterally flattened tail serving in swimming as well as in offense and defense. Crocodiles and gavials have narrow jaws, and the fourth pair of teeth on the lower jaw remains exposed when the mouth is closed. Alligator and caiman jaws are broader and rounded anteriorly, and none of the teeth are exposed after mouth closure.

Class Aves

Skin with feathers; forelimbs wings, with three fused fingers in hand; hind limbs legs, each with four or fewer toes; living types with horny beak, teeth absent; heart four-chambered, single aortic arch on right; lungs with extended air pouches; body temperature constant.

> Superorder Palaeognathae (walking birds, or "ratites"): flightless; sternum typically without keel. *Ostrich, emu, kiwi, cassowari, rhea*
> Superorder Neognathae (flying birds): generally capable of flight; sternum typically with keel.

Because flying requires a structural design that cannot deviate too greatly from fixed aerodynamic specifications, birds are more like one another than the members of most other animal groups. Birds require considerable quantities of food to provide the energy, the high operating temperature, and the high metabolic level generally essential for efficient flight. Feathers are the important heat regulators and also the means of flight. Different sets of feather serve these two different functions. All types of feathers are horny outgrowths from the epidermis

A

B

C

16 · 41   Reptilia. *A, Sphenodon, the lizardlike tuatara, sole surviving member of the reptilian order Rhynchocephalia. B, the lizard Chamaeleon, catching grasshopper with tongue. C, the skeleton of a snake. Note the numerous vertebrae and the absence of limb girdles, limbs, and sternum.*

16 · 42   Characteristics of Crocodilia. *A, some of the adaptations in head structure to a semi-aquatic existence. Note the bones composing the palate. B, identifying differences in head structure among Crocodilia.*

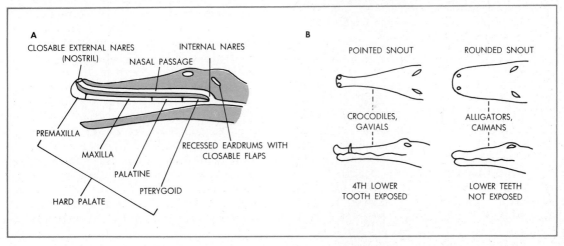

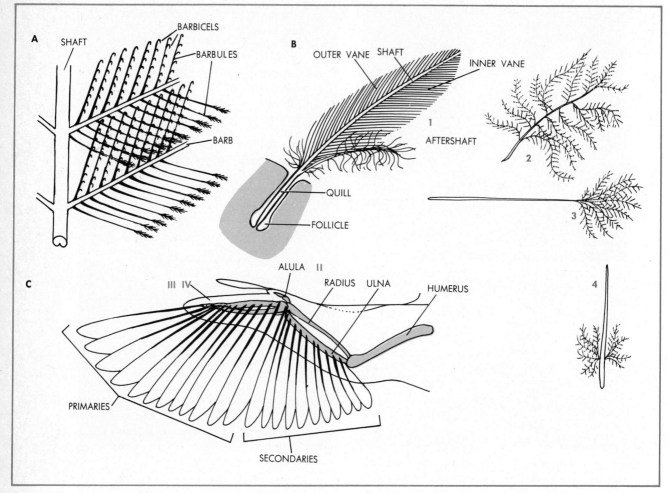

16 · 43   Feathers. *A, diagram of part of a contour feather showing interlocking of the barbicels of adjacent barbules. (After Mascha.) B, 1, whole view of contour feather, with aftershaft and pattern of insertion in skin; 2, down feather; 3, filoplume; 4, bristle. C, arm skeleton with position of flight feathers superimposed. Roman numerals refer to digits of hand.*

(Fig. 16.43). Flight feathers are located on the wings and usually also on the tail. Muscles in the arm maintain an overlap between adjacent feathers when the wing moves down; and during the upstroke the feathers are canted like Venetian blinds, letting air pass through with but little drag. Heat-regulating body feathers are shorter and form a light mat which efficiently retains a layer of insulating dead air between the skin and the environment. The same smooth muscles in the skin that produce "gooseflesh"

in man may erect these down feathers of birds and permit cooling of the body.

The skeleton of birds is thoroughly flight-adapted. Bones are light and delicate, with a minimum of spongy bone in the interior and correspondingly larger free spaces. Skull bones are fused, and the whole head is rounded and streamlined. Jaw bones are extended into a toothless bill or beak and are covered with a layer of epidermal horn. Eardrums are recessed deeply, and the bony canal leading to them is usually without external lobes or other projections that might disrupt smooth air flow over the head. The neck vertebrae provide extreme head mobility, but these vertebrae lock to one another firmly during flight. Flying birds possess a large sternum with a prominent keel, the latter serving as the attachment surface for the powerful flight muscles. Of these, the *pectoralis major* connects to the underside of the forearm and pulls the wing down.

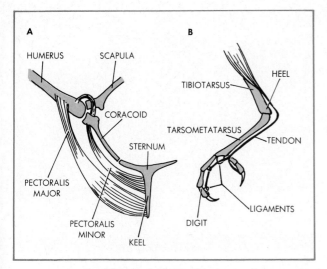

16 · 44 Flying and perching. *A, the arrangement of the flight muscles in relation to bones of shoulder girdle and arm. The pectoralis minor pulls the arm up, the pectoralis major pulls it down. B, the tendon system in the foot does not stretch. When the leg is straight, as in walking, the tendon permits the toes to move readily. But when the leg and the toes are bent, as in perching, the tendon becomes taut as a result of the flexed heel and holds the toes tightly curled around the perching branch.*

The *pectoralis minor* loops to the upper surface of the forearm, through a canal in the arm socket (Fig. 16.44).

The pelvic girdle is fused to the sacral vertebrae and, except in ostriches, the pubic bones are not joined mid-ventrally but leave a wide open passage (for the large eggs). In perching birds, systems of tendons permit the toes to curl tightly over a tree branch. Body weight alone ensures maintenance of a tight hold, and the energy expenditure and mental concentration required for perching are minimal. A remarkable breathing system provides the large quantities of oxygen needed in flying. Lungs are actually rather small, but from them are pouched out several large air sacs which occupy much of the space between the internal organs. Some of the sacs extend forward into the neck, where they may play an added role in distending the neck during courtship and other activities (Fig. 16.45).

The reproductive pattern too is adjusted to the condition of flying. External genitalia are absent (except in the flightless ostriches, in which the males possess a penis). This lack, perhaps another adaptation toward maintenance of smooth body contours, necessitates strong cooperation during mating, for the cloaca of the male must be apposed precisely against that of the female. Such cooperation in turn requires behavioral adaptations in the form of more or less elaborate courtship activities. The latter in their own turn are correlated with the evolution of colorful display plumage and color vision. Thus, color vision in birds may be correlated at least in part with the absence of a penis in males.

The very earliest birds flew and had feathers; the flightless ratites living today are descendants of flying ancestors. The flying birds are among the best known and most familiar of all animals, and the domesticated groups among them are of considerable economic importance. The flying types also include the song birds, which typically build elaborate nests and in which song and brilliant mating plumage are usually characteristic of the males only.

Class Mammalia

Skin with hair; teeth in sockets; seven neck vertebrae; ears with three middle-ear bones; limbs typically five-toed; heart four-chambered, single aortic arch on left; red corpuscles nonnucleated; coelom divided by muscular diaphragm; brain comparatively elaborate; external genitalia present; body temperature constant; fertilization internal; young nourished by milk from mammary glands.

Subclass Prototheria (egg-laying mammals): adults with horny bill; testes in abdomen; nipples absent, numerous ducts of mammary glands open individually; without uterus or

16 · 45 Internal structure of birds. *The diagram shows the position of the lungs, air sacs, and coelomic spaces.*

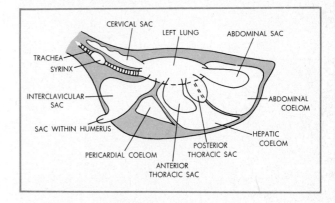

16 · 46 Egg-laying mammals. A, duck-billed platypus. B, echidna, or spiny anteater.

vagina; eggs with pliable shells. *Duck-billed platypus; spiny anteaters* (Fig. 16.46).

Subclass Metatheria (pouched marsupial mammals): nipples in ventral abdominal pouch, or *marsupium;* immature young complete development in pouch, attached to nipples; uterus and vagina double, vaginae opening separately; penis often forked terminally. *Opossums, kangaroos,* all other marsupials (Fig. 16.47).

Subclass Eutheria (placental mammals): in male, duct from bladder and sperm ducts join

16 · 47 Marsupial, or pouched, mammals. A, *opossum, the only marsupial surviving in North America.* B, *Tasmanian devil.*

into single duct through penis opening at urogenital orifice; in females, urethra and vagina open at separate urinary and reproductive orifices; uterus double or single, vagina always single; young develop in uterus throughout, attached and nourished via placenta, born in mature condition (Fig. 16.48).

The vast majority of living mammals are placental types, and these represent four parallel evolutionary series (Fig. 16.49). One includes insectivores (shrews, moles), bats, anteaters and armadillos, and particularly primates (lemurs, tarsiers, monkeys, apes, and men). A second series comprises rabbits and all rodents. The third is exemplified by whales, dolphins, and porpoises. And the fourth includes all carnivores such as dogs and cats, as well as elephants and all hoofed, or *ungulate,* mammals: horses, pigs, cattle, and

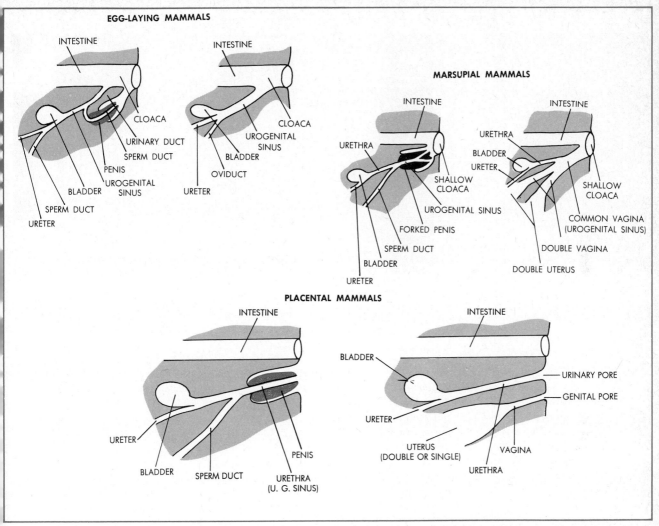

16 · 48 The urogenital ducts of mammals.
Ducts in males are at left of each pair; ducts in females, at right. Top left, the pattern in egg-laying mammals. Top right, the pattern in pouched, marsupial mammals. Bottom, the pattern in placental mammals. In mammalian evolution, the ducts of the alimentary, excretory, and reproductive systems all start in more or less joined condition (as in the two right-hand sections of the top drawings), and then progressively acquire their own separate openings, a condition realized fully only in placental mammals (as at bottom right).

sheep. In each of these four series independently, rather similar adaptive trends have become elaborated in the course of evolution.

First, body size has tended to increase, an advantageous change helpful both in searching for food and in avoiding becoming food. Second, the number of teeth has tended to decrease; and, instead of all teeth remaining alike as in the reptilian ancestors, the fewer teeth have become differentially specialized, in parallel with a specialization of the types of food eaten. Third, the legs have tended to become longer and stronger, the body and often also the heels being lifted off the ground more and more. The result has been an evident improvement in locomotor efficiency and, indeed, a significant diversification in the types of locomotion in correlation with the alimentary specializations. Fourth, in conjunction with newly developed modes of locomotion, a spreading into diverse habitat zones has occurred. And

lastly, partly as a result of the increase in body size, partly in conjunction with the improved motility, the size of the brain has increased; in the course of evolutionary time, more powerful intellects have simply been acquired by mammals of all kinds.

That these adaptive trends are actually in evidence

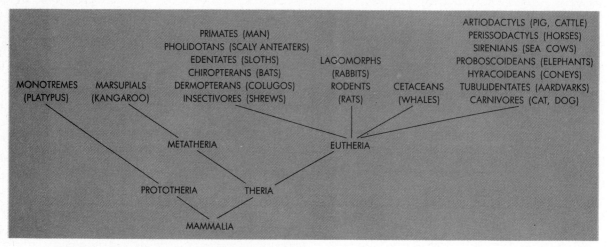

16 · 49   The orders of mammals, arranged according to their main evolutionary groupings. Read from bottom up. A representative type is indicated for each order. The four eutherian series represent the placental mammals.

can be demonstrated readily. Thus, in the first series mentioned above, the evolutionary progression from insectivore to primate and man has 'indeed been accompanied by size increase; by brain increase; by a locomotor change from four-footed to two-footed methods and to flying; and by a habitat diversification from an original arboreal to later terrestrial, aerial, and subterranean environments (see also Chap. 32). And with regard to teeth, a mole, for example, possesses 44, whereas a man possesses 32. In the rabbit-rodent series, adaptive change in brain size has not been particularly spectacular, though on a rodent level a rat is an exceedingly brainy animal. The other adaptive trends are more clearly evident. Fossils show that these groups have indeed become larger-bodied; rabbits exhibit a very obvious locomotor specialization, that is, long hind legs adapted to leaping; and dental specialization involves a well-known modification of the incisors, namely, "rabbit teeth." All these changes are correlated with a vast habitat diversification; rodents comprise nearly half the number of all mammalian species, and we already know that each species represents a distinct ecological niche (see Chap. 8). In the whale series, analogous trends are manifest. No group has increased in body size more dramatically or has altered its habitat and its locomotion more drastically. Tooth reduction has become maximal, that is, vertical baleen plates replace teeth altogether in the whalebone whales.

Also, the intelligence of the whale group is well known, porpoises particularly being noted for their mental prowess.

Finally, in the carnivore-ungulate series, most of the groups have exploited the possibilities of a running life on the plains. Leg and foot structures thus show major adaptive modifications. In several subseries within the group, the heel has become lifted off the ground, the foot has become elongated, and the animal has come to walk on its toes, as in cats or gazelles, for example. Concurrently, toes have become increasingly hoofed, and the number of toes has become reduced. For example, carnivores are five-toed and still nonungulate; elephants have small naillike hoofs on each toe; and a fully ungulate condition with varyingly reduced toe numbers is in evidence in the horse group and the deer-cattle group. Major changes have also occurred in differential tooth specializations, in line with the different eating habits and the diversified ecological niches. For example, in carnivores all teeth are pointed and adapted for tearing, and the canines form particularly long fangs. By contrast, the herbivorous ungulates have incisors adapted for cutting, molars adapted for grinding, and canines are often absent altogether. Body size has increased independently in the several subseries of the group; for example, bears, horses, elephants, and cattle all have evolved from far smaller ancestors. And intelligence likewise has reached higher levels several times; bears, cats, dogs, horses, and elephants all are well known as "smart" animals.

Such fairly parallel results offer perhaps the best proof that the same adaptive forces operate universally for all organisms; and that, if the environmental opportunities are similar, organisms very similar in many respects may result several times independently. Furthermore, it should be clear that the primary adaptive forces that have shaped mammalian nature ultimately reduce to just two, namely, feeding and locomotion. These are the very same that have also shaped the nature of all other organisms since the first primeval cell types appeared in the ocean.

REVIEW QUESTIONS

1. Give taxonomic definitions of deuterostomial coelomates as a whole and of each of the phyla. Discuss the possible evolutionary interrelations of the phyla and the evidence from which such possibilities are deduced. What is the dipleurula hypothesis?

2. Describe the structure of a chaetognath. Show how the coelom is subdivided and in what respects these divisions (a) correspond, (b) do not correspond, to coelomic subdivisions of other deuterostomes. Where do arrowworms live and how and on what do they feed?

3. Describe the structure of a pogonophoran. How does a beard worm feed and where does such an animal live? Review the exterior and interior structure of an acorn worm. What structural features do such worms have in common with chordates?

4. What is the possible evolutionary significance of a tornaria? Contrast the structure of an enteropneust with that of a pterobranch. Define the echinoderm phylum and the living classes. What evolutionary and adaptive factors have probably led to the development of echinoderms and their water-vascular systems?

5. Describe the symmetries of various echinoderm body plans. Define podium, ambulacral groove, epineural canal. Describe the structure of a skeletal element and of the whole skeleton of echinoderms. What variant skeletal organizations are encountered in different classes?

6. Describe the external and internal structure of a starfish and review the organization of every organ system. What is the function of the water-vascular system and how are such functions performed? How and on what does a starfish feed?

7. What are the protocoel, mesocoel, and metacoel? What body parts correspond to these in (a) beard worms, (b) hemichordates, (c) echinoderms? Name the various echinoderm larvae and contrast their structure. Describe the adult characteristics of representatives of each of the echinoderm classes.

8. Give taxonomic definitions of the phylum Chordata and the acraniate subphyla. Analogously define the tunicate classes. Review the presumable evolutionary interrelations of these various groups. Describe the structure of an adult ascidian and review the organization of every organ system. Describe the feeding process of a sea squirt. What are the endostyle and epicardial folds?

9. Show how the ascidian tadpole develops from the embryo, how mesoderm arises, and how the adult ascidian structure emerges during larval development and metamorphosis. What is the probable evolutionary significance of the ascidian tadpole? What are the salps? Larvacea?

10. Describe the structure of amphioxus and outline the organization of every organ system. What ecological factors might have played a role in the evolution of cephalochordate segmentation? What factors probably contributed to keeping cephalochordates in a marine environment whereas vertebrates could become freshwater forms?

11. Give taxonomic definitions of the subphylum Vertebrata and of each of the classes. Show how most of the basic vertebrate traits are direct adaptations to a life in fresh water.

12. Describe the external and internal structure of a lamprey. In what ways are lampreys adapted to an ectoparasitic existence? What are ammocoetes? Which cyclostomes (a) live permanently, (b) spawn, in fresh water?

13. What changes in vertebrate anatomy were correlated with the change from ancestral filter feeding to bulk feeding by mouth? Give taxonomic definitions of the subclasses of bony fishes. Which group was probably ancestral to amphibia?

14. What different scale types occur among bony fishes? Describe the gill structure of a bony fish. Distinguish between clupeiform and perciform fishes. Review the structure and taxonomic definition of a shark.

15. Review the taxonomy and the biological characteristics of amphibia, reptiles, birds, and mammals. Describe the structure of feathers and show how birds are adapted to flying. List the evolutionary groups of (a) mammals, (b) placental mammals, and describe the evolutionary trends characteristic of each of the latter.

COLLATERAL READINGS

Applegate, V. C., and J. W. Moffett: The Sea Lamprey, *Sci. American*, Apr., 1955. The biology and economic harmfulness of this parasitic vertebrate is examined.

Berrill, N. J.: "The Origin of the Vertebrates," Oxford, Fair Lawn, N.J., 1955. A masterful documentation of the probable evolution of vertebrates from ascidian ancestors.

————: Growth, Development, and Pattern," Freeman, San Francisco, 1961. Chapters 13 and 14 contain analyses of growth processes in tunicates, including those taking place during budding.

Buchsbaum, R.: "Animals without Backbones," University of Chicago, Chicago, 1948. This well-illustrated volume contains a brief account of echinoderms.

Ditmars, R. L.: "Reptiles of the World," Macmillan, New York, 1926.

————: "The Reptiles of North America," Doubleday, Garden City, NY., 1936. Key classics on reptiles.

Frieden, L.: The Chemistry of Amphibian Metamorphosis, *Sci. American*, Nov., 1963. The article describes the controlling role of hormones in the metamorphic process.

Gilbert, P. W.: The Behavior of Sharks, *Sci. American*, July, 1962. The senses of sharks and their role in feeding behavior are examined.

Griffin, D. R.: The Navigation of Bats, *Sci. American*, Aug., 1950. A description of the "sonar" mechanism by which bats fly and steer even in the dark.

Hyman, L.: "Comparative Vertebrate Anatomy," 2d ed., University of Chicago, Chicago, 1942. A detailed, book-length manual on the structure of various vertebrates.

————: "The Invertebrates," vols. 4 and 5, McGraw-Hill, New York, 1955, 1959. These volumes contain advanced accounts of all deuterostomes except the chordates.

Morgan, T. H.: The Development of Balanoglossus, *J. Morphol.*, vol. 9, 1894. The now classical paper which established the close similarity of tornaria and bipinnaria larvae and thus suggested the evolutionary relation between the hemichordates (and chordates) and the echinoderms.

Noble, G. K.: "The Biology of the Amphibia," McGraw-Hill, New York, 1931. A key classic on amphibians.

Pope, C. H.: "Snakes Alive and How they Live," Viking, New York, 1939. The best-known and most authoritative book on snakes.

Romer, A. S.: "Man and the Vertebrates," University of Chicago, Chicago, 1941. An introductory, well-illustrated account of vertebrate biology, with special emphasis on man.

————: "The Vertebrate Body," Saunders, Philadelphia, 1950. More advanced than the preceding; highly recommended nevertheless.

Wallace, G. J.: "An Introduction to Ornithology," Macmillan, New York, 1955. One of a vast number of books on birds.

Warden, C. J.: Animal Intelligence, *Sci. American*, June, 1951. Psychological tests measure the comparative intelligence of various vertebrates.

Young, J. Z.: "The Life of Vertebrates," 2d ed., Oxford, Fair Lawn, N.J., 1962. A large and highly recommended volume on the biology and evolutionary history of vertebrates.

UNIT TWO
THE OPERATIONS
OF LIFE
PART FIVE
METABOLISM
PART SIX
SELF-PERPETUATION: STEADY STATES
PART SEVEN
SELF-PERPETUATION: REPRODUCTION
PART EIGHT
SELF-PERPETUATION: ADAPTATION

Up to this point, our primary concern has been the "what" of living matter: What are the characteristics of the living world as a whole and its subordinate parts? What are the small-scale and large-scale forms of the living material, and what kinds of organisms and groupings of organisms exist on earth? From here on, we shall continue to heed the what, but our primary concern will be the "how": How is the living world maintained? How are the structures developed and how are the functions carried out? In other words, our preoccupation will be less with the *organizational* and more with the *operational* nature of living material.

We already know that the operations of living matter are circumscribed by two words: metabolism and self-perpetuation. Metabolism includes all processes that *maintain* the living organization, the chief subprocesses here being nutrition, respiration, and synthesis. Self-perpetuation includes processes that *control* the living organization and thus ensure its continuance in time. Short-range control is exercised by preservation of internal *steady states*, and long-range control, by *reproduction* as well as by *adaptation* (the latter comprising the phenomena of *sex*, *heredity*, and *evolution*). The four parts of this unit deal with these various operational characteristics of living matter.

PART FIVE
METABOLISM
CHAPTER 17
NUTRITION: RAW MATERIALS AND TRANSPORT
CHAPTER 18
RESPIRATION: CELLULAR ENERGETICS
CHAPTER 19
SYNTHESIS AND PHOTOSYNTHESIS
CHAPTER 20
PROTEIN, NUCLEIC ACID, AND PHYSICAL METABOLISM

We recall that metabolism may be described broadly as a set of events through which an otherwise inert, dead system may remain active and living. Specifically, the nutritional phase of metabolism supplies raw materials from the exterior and distributes them in the interior. The respiratory phase consumes some of these raw materials and provides energy in usable form. And the remainder of the raw materials as well as portions of the energy then make possible chemical activities such as synthesis of new living matter and physical activities such as movement.

CHAPTER 17
NUTRITION:
RAW
MATERIALS
AND
TRANSPORT

The mere transfer of raw materials from the external environment into the body of an organism is by no means all of nutrition; the nutritional function is not completed until every individual *cell* of an organism has obtained all the raw materials it requires, that is, all substances it cannot produce on its own. Thus, nutrition usually includes not only mere "intake" by an organism but also internal *transport* and *distribution* of raw materials to all cells of the body. In many cases, moreover, nutrition additionally includes preliminary processing of *obtainable* supplies into *usable* ones. To be usable in cells, supplies must almost invariably be in the form of individual molecules or ions, and indeed they must be molecules or ions of particular kinds. Therefore, to the extent that raw materials as obtained are not already in specific molecular or ionic forms, they must be changed appropriately before they can serve as usable nutrients.

Usable substances may also be called *metabolites*, that is, compounds playing a role in metabolism. Metabolites are either inorganic or organic chemicals, and we may note that the term *food* is customarily restricted to the organic ones; inorganic

metabolites are referred to simply as nutrients, a collective designation embracing foods as well.

FORMS OF NUTRITION

Organisms do not differ with respect to the procurement of *inorganic* metabolites; all organisms obtain them in finished, prefabricated form from the physical environment. However, organisms do differ with respect to the procurement of foods. Some organisms manufacture foods from their inorganic supplies and thus are able to subsist in an exclusively inorganic environment. We already know such organisms to be *autotrophs*. Other organisms are unable to create foods out of inorganic nutrients and must therefore obtain from the environment certain minimum amounts and kinds of prefabricated foods. We recognize such organisms as *heterotrophs*.

Autotrophs actually require not only external sources of inorganic materials but also external sources of *energy*, for the conversion of inorganic materials into foods is an endergonic process. In some cases, external energy for food manufacture is obtained from *light*, and such organisms are the *photosynthesizers*. In other cases, inorganic chemicals serve not only as raw materials for food manufacture but also as external energy sources, and such organisms are the *chemosynthesizers*. Analogous subgroups of light-using and chemical-using types may be distinguished among heterotrophs.

We may therefore characterize nutrition from the standpoint of food sources, that is, its autotrophic or heterotrophic nature, and we may also characterize it from the standpoint of external energy sources, that is, its photosynthetic or chemosynthetic nature. If we characterize it from both standpoints simultaneously, we may identify four nutritional categories among organisms:

1. *photolithotrophs,* which use inorganic raw materials and light energy to manufacture foods on their own.

2. *chemolithotrophs,* which use inorganic raw materials and chemical energy obtained from some of these raw materials to manufacture foods on their own.

3. *photoorganotrophs,* which convert preexisting

organic raw materials into usable foods with the aid of light energy.

4. *chemoorganotrophs,* which use preexisting organic raw materials directly as foods.

The first two categories include all the autotrophs; the last two, all the heterotrophs. The first and third categories include all the photosynthetic organisms; the second and fourth, all the chemosynthetic organisms (Table 14).

AUTOTROPHS

Chemically the simplest foods are carbohydrates and these are composed of the elements carbon, hydrogen, and oxygen. It is clear therefore that every autotroph requires an inorganic source of each of these elements. In addition, an external energy source is required to combine the three elements into organic substances.

Autotrophs of all kinds use environmental carbon dioxide as their inorganic source of carbon and oxygen:

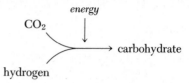

In virtually all cases the carbohydrate formed is a sugar or a derivative, and from this basic food all the other constituents of the organism are then produced.

Autotrophs differ according to the energy and hydrogen sources they use.

Photolithotrophs

As Table 14 indicates, this large group includes all Metaphyta, most algae, blue-green algae, and most pigmented bacteria. In all these photosynthetic autotrophs, the external energy source is *light,* and

TABLE 14   THE CLASSIFICATION OF ORGANISMS ON THE BASIS OF ENERGY SOURCES AND METHODS OF FOOD PROCUREMENT.

	FOOD		
	manufactured from inorganic source	*absorbed from prefabricated organic source*	
from light source ↑ PRIMARY ENERGY ↓ *from chemical source*	**PHOTOLITHOTROPHS** *purple sulfur bacteria* *green sulfur bacteria* *blue-green algae* *algae (except colorless)* *metaphytes*	**PHOTOORGANOTROPHS** *purple nonsulfur bacteria*	**PHOTO-SYNTHETIC TYPES**
	CHEMOLITHOTROPHS *sulfur bacteria* *iron bacteria* *hydrogen bacteria* *nitrifying bacteria*	**CHEMOORGANOTROPHS** *saprophytic bacteria (including decay, some N-fixing, some denitrifying types)* *symbiotic bacteria (including some N-fixing types)* *fungi* *slime molds* *protozoa* *colorless algae* *metazoa*	**CHEMO-SYNTHETIC TYPES**
	AUTOTROPHIC TYPES	**HETEROTROPHIC TYPES**	

one or more varieties of *chlorophyll* are present to trap the energy of light.

The hydrogen source of all photolithotrophs (except for one group of bacteria) is environmental *water*. Light energy is used to split the water and free hydrogen is made available in this manner. Thus, for the vast majority of photosynthesizers, the pattern of food production has the general form:

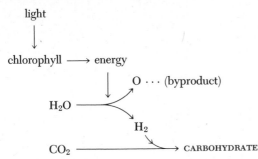

Free oxygen is a byproduct here. This is by far the most important form of photosynthesis, and we shall examine the details of it in Chap. 19.

In an exceptional group of light-using bacteria, the hydrogen source is not water and oxygen is never a byproduct of photosynthesis. Two families of bacteria belong to this group, the *purple sulfur bacteria* and the *green sulfur bacteria*, both members of the order Pseudomonadales. The first family possesses a variety of chlorophyll known as *bacterio-chlorophyll*. It is green, but its color is masked by red and yellow carotenoids present as well. Green sulfur bacteria possess a unique chlorophyll different from bacteriochlorophyll. Also, its green color is not masked by the additional yellow carotenoids. Both types of bacteria live in sulfur springs and other sulfurous regions, where hydrogen sulfide (H_2S) is normally available. This compound serves as the hydrogen source. For the photolithotrophic bacteria, therefore, the special pattern of photosynthesis becomes:

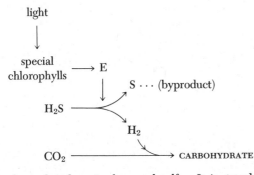

The byproduct here is elemental sulfur. It is stored inside the cells in the purple sulfur bacteria and is excreted from the cells in the green sulfur bacteria.

Chemolithotrophs

This group consists entirely of bacteria. The organisms cannot use light, and their external energy source in food manufacture is a variety of inorganic raw materials absorbed from the environment. In most cases, these raw materials are combined exergonically with oxygen in the cells, resulting in energy and a variety of inorganic byproducts. Water and carbon dioxide are the inorganic metabolites in subsequent food manufacture. The general pattern is

$$\text{inorganic metabolites} \xrightarrow{+O} \text{inorganic byproducts}$$

Among the best-known chemolithotrophs are the *sulfur bacteria*, the *iron bacteria*, the *hydrogen bacteria*, and the *nitrifying bacteria*. All are members of the order Pseudomonadales. Sulfur bacteria absorb either hydrogen sulfide (H_2S) or molecular sulfur (S_2) from the environment and combine these metabolites with oxygen. The resulting energy is used toward food manufacture as outlined above, and the byproducts are either S_2 if the original nutrient is H_2S or sulfate ions if the original nutrient is S_2 (Fig. 17.1). If the byproduct is sulfur, granules of this element are deposited inside or outside the cell; and if the byproduct is sulfate, these ions either become part of the mineral content of the cell or are excreted. Note that some of the sulfur bacteria (notably species of *Thiobacillus*) also play an important role in the global nitrogen cycle, by virtue of their *denitrifying* activities; that is, these sulfur bacteria convert nitrate ions into atmospheric nitrogen (see Chap. 10).

Iron bacteria are stalked organisms living in fresh and salt waters containing iron compounds in solution. The bacteria absorb these compounds and combine oxygen with them, reactions resulting in insoluble byproducts and energy. Hydrogen bacteria utilize molecular hydrogen as nutrient. By combining such molecules with oxygen, energy is again gained and water forms as a byproduct (see Fig. 17.1). As noted in Chap. 10, nitrifying bacteria are of two types, one using ammonia and excreting nitrite ions, the other using nitrite ions and excreting nitrate ions. Both types combine their specific nutrient with oxygen and in each case energy is gained (see Fig.

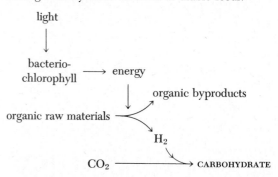

17 · 1 Energy sources in chemolithotrophic bacteria. *The two steps in the oxidation of* H_2S *and* NH_3 *are each carried out by different bacterial types.*

17.1). For the bacteria themselves, the important product here is energy, which makes food manufacture possible. For all other living organisms, the important products are the excreted byproducts, which make the global nitrogen cycle possible.

HETEROTROPHS

Organisms in this group can acquire inorganic metabolites such as H_2O and CO_2 from the environment but cannot convert them into foods. Heterotrophs must therefore obtain prefabricated organic raw materials from the environment. It follows that the survival of heterotrophs is strictly contingent on the preexistence of autotrophs, for these must be the ultimate sources of the needed organic metabolites. Frequently a heterotroph obtains organic materials from another heterotroph, according to a particular food chain (see Chap. 9); but the last heterotroph in such series always depends on autotrophs for its organic supplies.

Photoorganotrophs

The identifying feature of these very interesting nutritional types is that their external energy source is light; the organisms are photosynthesizers, yet they require organic raw materials nevertheless. To this group belong mainly the *purple nonsulfur bacteria* (or simply "purple bacteria"), another family of the Pseudomonadales. Like the purple sulfur bacteria, the purple nonsulfur bacteria possess bacteriochlorophyll as well as red and yellow carotenoids, which mask the color of the green pigment.

Purple bacteria absorb organic materials from the environment but these metabolites are not or cannot be used directly as foods. Instead, the metabolites serve as sources of hydrogen. Extracted hydrogen is then combined with carbon dioxide, and the resulting carbohydrates do serve as usable foods:

$$\text{light} \downarrow$$

$$\text{bacterio-chlorophyll} \longrightarrow \text{energy}$$

$$\text{organic raw materials} \longrightarrow \nearrow \text{organic byproducts}$$

$$H_2$$

$$CO_2 \longrightarrow \text{CARBOHYDRATE}$$

Purple bacteria may manufacture foods in this manner only if light is present and oxygen is *absent*. In some species, absorbed organic raw materials may be used as foods *directly* if light is absent and oxygen is present. The organisms then are essentially chemoorganotrophs, that is, like all other heterotrophs.

Chemoorganotrophs

The vast majority of heterotrophs belongs to this nutritional category, in which organic raw materials represent prefabricated, directly usable foods. Chemoorganotrophs can only *use* foods, not produce them.

The three kinds of organisms are included in this group are the holotrophs, the saprotrophs, and the various kinds of symbionts. Holotrophs are free-living bulk feeders characterized nutritionally by *alimentation* processes. Some of these organisms are protists which ingest food via gullets or pseudopodia and then carry out digestion in intracellular vacuoles. Most are Metazoa in which digestion takes place intracellularly or more commonly extracellularly within alimentary systems.

Saprotrophs comprise the slime molds, most colorless algae, and, above all, very many bacteria and fungi. They all subsist on anything and everything nonliving that contains organic components. These organisms decompose such organic matter chemically and absorb nutrient molecules from the resulting juices. Saprotrophs thereby bring about *decay*, and we may note again that decay occurs *only* if and when saprotrophs are at work. As a result of their decay-causing nutritional activities, saprotrophs are vital links in global nutrient cycles. The final decomposition products of decaying organic matter are H_2O, CO_2, and N_2, and these materials return to the environment from which living matter obtained them originally. All the decay-causing organisms participating in the water, oxygen, and carbon cycles belong to the saprotrophic chemoorganotrophs. And of the various types of organisms participating in the nitrogen cycle, three are likewise saprotrophic: the decay-causing bacteria and fungi, some of the denitrifying bacteria, and some of the nitrogen-fixing bacteria.

Symbionts include commensalistic, mutualistic, and parasitic types (see Chap. 9). Some organisms within each of these subgroups actually are bulk-feeding holotrophs or belong to other nutritional categories. But most of them, parasites particularly, must absorb nutrients in prefabricated molecular form directly from their hosts. Specific food requirements vary greatly. For example, one bacterial parasite may have to obtain a given vitamin or amino acid in prefabricated form, but another may be able to manufacture such a nutrient from other organic starting materials. Biochemical differences of this sort are exceedingly numerous, and they are one reason why a symbiont cannot pick hosts at random. Survival is possible only in hosts in which all required types of nutrients are available.

As noted in earlier chapters, a single individual of some species, particularly among Protista, may be capable of using several alternative methods of nutrition. Such an organism correspondingly belongs to at least two of the above four basic nutritional categories at the same time. But most organisms are limited to just one of the four methods, and the vast majority actually are photolithotrophs and chemoorganotrophs.

PROCESSES

Possibly the most important single component of all nutritional processes is *absorption*. It plays a role in all forms of nutrition, contributes to most processes of nutrient intake and internal transport, and constitutes the chief means of cellular nutrition. Absorption may be defined as the transfer of compounds from the environment through a cell surface into the interior of a cell. "Environment" here means both biological and physical surroundings; when a cell obtains nutrients from adjacent cells or from sap or blood flowing by, that is absorption too.

If we disregard cellular intake by phagocytosis and pinocytosis, which are essentially variants of amoeboid engulfment, then absorption includes at least three kinds of processes: water is absorbed in part by *osmosis;* inorganic and organic materials dissolved in water are absorbed in part by *diffusion;* and water and all dissolved materials are absorbed additionally and most particularly by energy-consuming *chemical work* done by a cell, or *active transport* (see Chap. 4). Virtually any cell chosen at random may serve to illustrate these events, for the basic mechanism of absorption is the same regardless of the cell type or the nature of the organism.

Whenever the concentration of dissolved materials is greater within a cell than in its surroundings, the cell will absorb water osmotically. A good example is the uptake of soil water by the root-hair cells of vascular plants (Fig. 17.2). Normally a root-hair cell contains a higher concentration of dissolved particles than soil water, and osmotic pressure therefore moves soil water into the root hair. However, osmotic force cannot be the only agency responsible for water absorption. If the soil is made to contain a higher concentration of dissolved particles than the root-hair cells (for example, by "salting" the soil), then the plant should *lose* water to the soil. Yet under such conditions the roots still take up water, though less than before.

Clearly, osmotic pressure normally contributes some absorptive force, but another agency contributes as well. This other agency depends on the *living* condition of the root cell, and it is best described as *active absorptive work* done by the cell. That work is required is known, for water absorption consumes energy and is contingent on continued cellular respiration. When the respiratory machinery of the cells is stopped with poison, then biological water absorption is likewise stopped, though purely physical osmotic absorption still continues. Thus, in ways that actually are understood only poorly as yet, a living root cell actively moves water into itself through the cell surface (see Fig. 17.2).

An exactly similar combination of physical osmotic forces and living biological forces appears to govern water absorption not only in root-hair cells but in all other cells as well, for example, when any plant or animal cell absorbs water from another, or from body fluids such as sap or blood, or when a single-celled aquatic organism absorbs water from its external environment.

Minerals and foods dissolved in water may be absorbed into a cell by *diffusion*, but only if the concentration of dissolved particles outside the cell is greater than inside. However, this is actually the case rather rarely, the opposite being far more

440

METABOLISM

usual. Consider again a root-hair cell of vascular plants. As just noted above, the concentration of particles within the cell normally is far greater than the concentration of soil minerals outside. Therefore, if mineral absorption were merely a matter of physical diffusion, the root-hair cell would lose ions to the soil. This does not happen. On the contrary, ions migrate from the soil *into* the root, *against* the prevailing diffusion gradient. Moreover, some ions are absorbed readily; others are not (see Fig. 17.2).

In other words, selective, active, energy-consuming absorptive work is again done by the living root cell. Poisoned cells cannot carry out such absorption. And in a living cell, as noted, much of the energy needed for absorption is actually expended in counteracting and overcoming the outwardly directed force of diffusion. The pattern here described for root-hair cells again applies equally to *any* cells that absorb materials dissolved in water. Moreover, the pattern holds not only for mineral absorption but also for food absorption.

Indeed, in the case of at least one food something of the detailed chemistry of "living" absorption is known. Specifically, it is now fairly well established that cells do not take up glucose as such (except to the extent that purely physical diffusion may occur). Suppose that glucose is about to be absorbed by a saprotrophic bacterium, or by a nongreen parenchyma cell in a green vascular plant, or by an intestinal mucosa cell in an animal, or by any other heterotrophic cell. If the glucose molecule is to be transferred through the cell surface, it usually must be *phosphorylated*, or combined chemically with organic phosphate ($-O-PO_3H_2$; see Chap. 4 and Fig. 17.3). The result is phosphorylated glucose, or glucose-6-phosphate; that is, the phosphate group becomes attached at carbon 6 of glucose and there replaces a hydroxyl ($-O-H$) group. The phosphorylation reaction requires energy, which is obtained from a molecule of ATP. The latter is both the phosphate donor and the energy donor; as the terminal third phosphate group of ATP is split off and added to glucose, the high-energy bond of this third phosphate breaks and makes its energy available for the reaction. The reaction also requires a specific enzyme, *hexokinase* (and note that the name "kinase" always refers to enzymes catalyzing reactions in which ATP participates). In vertebrates, moreover, glucose uptake into cells is additionally facilitated by the pancreatic hormone *insulin*. We may understand, therefore, why insulin deficiency as in diabetes leads to impairment of cell function: without the hormone,

17 · 2 Osmosis and diffusion in roots. Left, osmosis. Particle concentrations are greater in root cells than in soil; hence more water moves into root cells from soil than in the reverse direction. Center, the effect of "salting" the soil. Even if the particle concentration in soil is made greater than in the root, water still moves into the root (black arrows), *against the osmotic gradient* (colored arrows). *This indicates that osmosis is not the only agency in water absorption; active absorption by living root cells is also important. Right, diffusion. Because root cells contain a higher concentration of mineral ions than soil, ions should be expected to diffuse out of roots* (colored arrows). *Yet ions actually migrate from soil into roots* (black arrows), *against the diffusion gradient. This indicates that active absorption, rather than diffusion, is responsible for ion absorption by living root cells.*

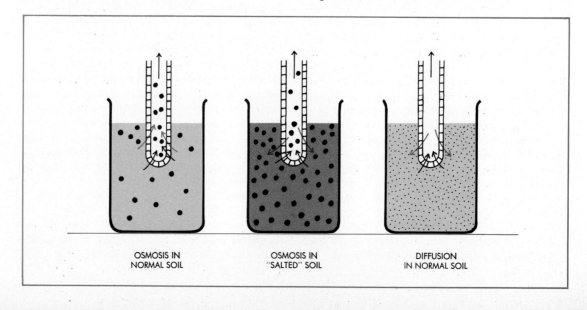

OSMOSIS IN NORMAL SOIL   OSMOSIS IN "SALTED" SOIL   DIFFUSION IN NORMAL SOIL

glucose cannot be well absorbed into cells; and while the cells then starve, the sugar accumulates uselessly in blood and is eventually excreted in urine.

The phosphorylation reaction is believed to occur at, or in, the cell surface, and the carbohydrate then present within a cell therefore is glucose-6-phosphate. Various cell-surface reactions may also take place in the absorption of noncarbohydrate foods, but in most of these instances the details are still obscure. Once a metabolite of any kind has been absorbed into a cell, intracellular distribution is then achieved mainly by diffusion and cyclosis. Through these processes, every part of a cell comes to have access to all nutrients the cell may have acquired only at specific points of its surface.

In unicellular and in simple tissue-level multicellular organisms, absorption generally constitutes the entire nutritional process or at least forms a major part of it. Thus, saprotrophic and many symbiotic heterotrophs obtain *all* nutrients by cell-surface absorption, and holotrophic heterotrophs as well as autotrophic unicells acquire most or all of their inorganic supplies through direct absorption. Absorptive intake also plays a critical role in all complexly constructed multicellular organisms, in which nutrient procurement occurs only at limited, specialized regions and in which body-wide nutrient distribution is then accomplished by internal transport. Nutrient procurement in such cases is achieved by roots and leaves in plants, by an alimentary system in animals; and internal transport includes *short-distance conduction* in all cases and *long-distance conduction* in most cases (Fig. 17.4).

Short-distance transport means nutrient transfer from one cell to immediately adjacent cells. Such cell-to-cell transfers are achieved by *secretion* of metabolites from one cell and *absorption* by the next. Secretion is more or less the exact reverse of absorption, the same forces working in opposite directions. Thus, water moves out of a cell partly by osmosis, partly by energy-consuming active transport; and dissolved materials leave partly by diffusion and again partly by active transport. The selective, "living" action of cell membranes is particularly evident here, for a given metabolite absorbed by a cell may not necessarily be also secreted. In very many cases, *more* of a particular nutrient is allowed into a cell than is allowed out, or vice versa. By this means, cell-to-cell transfers of given metabolites may become unidirectional. Also, one and the same cell group may act differently with different metabolites, or indeed with the same metabolite at different times. It is largely impossible to predict beforehand how given cells will transport given metabolites, and only experiment can determine this in each case.

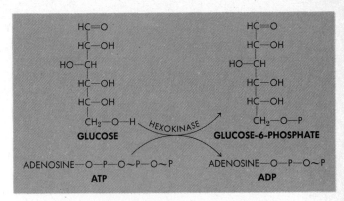

*17 · 3 **The phosphorylation reaction.** Glucose reacts with ATP in the presence of the enzyme hexokinase, resulting in phosphorylated glucose and ADP. Note that ATP serves both as energy and phosphate donor. The —O—H at position 6 of glucose is replaced by —O~P of ATP, the high-energy bond becoming a low-energy bond in the process. (P stands for —PO_3H_2 here and in subsequent illustrations.)*

*17 · 4 **The nutritional pattern in multicellular organisms.** After nutrients are obtained in localized regions and by various methods, short-distance transport serves as a feeder mechanism carrying the nutrients to the long-distance rapid-transit channels (dark colored area: xylem and phloem in plants, blood and lymph vessels in animals). From these conduits, nutrients are delivered to cells again by short-distance cell-to-cell transfer (arrows).*

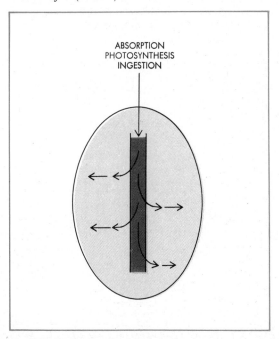

In addition to short-distance conduction, comparatively rapid long-distance conduction may be carried out by the *vascular* tissues: xylem and phloem in plants, blood and lymph vessels in animals. Where the internal structure of an organism is elaborate, the presence of "rapid-transit" long-distance conductors clearly is an important adaptive advantage. In tracheophytes, the longitudinal extension of the body may be relatively enormous (up to 400 ft in sequoias and eucalyptus trees, counting only stem and crown), and long-distance conduction occurs only along the vertical axis. In animals, body size is often a less critical factor than organizational complexity, and here long-distance conduction via a circulatory system is extensively multidirectional.

But note that, in all cases, rapid-transit long-distance transport must operate in conjunction with short-distance conduction. In a tracheophyte, cell-to-cell transfers must serve as the "feeder" mechanism carrying nutrients from root or leaf cells to the rapid-transit channels. In animals, analogously, nutrients procured in an alimentary system must then be brought by short-distance transfers from the alimentary cavity through the gut wall to the circulatory channels. Furthermore, at the terminals of the rapid-transit lines in both plants and animals, nutrients must be delivered to the receiver cells by local short-distance conduction. We may conclude, therefore, that *cellular* nutrition is basically absorptive even in multicellular organisms. Elaborate organ systems functioning in procurement and transport serve

merely as auxiliary devices in the principal nutritional process, namely, nutrient absorption by individual cells.

How do procurement and transport actually occur in complex multicellular organisms?

PLANTS:
ABSORPTION AND CONDUCTION

Uptake of inorganic metabolites in tracheophytes includes procurement and exchange of atmospheric gases and absorption of water and dissolved mineral ions. Internal transport includes distribution of these inorganic materials from the points of entry to all body parts, as well as distribution of photosynthesized foods from the points of manufacture to all other body parts.

All divisions of the plant body participate in these functions. Leaves and green stems procure gases and manufacture foods: roots absorb water as well as minerals and atmospheric gases dissolved in the water; and stems conduct nutrients of all kinds from leaves to roots and vice versa. Xylem and phloem serve as the long-distance vertical conductors and to some extent also as short-distance lateral conductors. The chief lateral conductors are the cortical parenchyma tissues in roots and stems and the mesophyll tissues in leaves.

ROOTS, LEAVES, AND XYLEM TRANSPORT

Metabolites obtained by the root system are absorbed largely in the root-hair cells of the root epidermis, for these cells provide most of the available absorbing surface. After being absorbed by processes described in the preceding section, the inorganic supplies are transported by lateral cell-to-cell transfers to the xylem at the root core. Containing linear series of vertical tracheids and vessels reaching uninterruptedly from root tip to leaf tip, xylem provides the channels for upward conduction.

When a root-hair cell absorbs water and dissolved minerals and gases, the most immediate effect is that the excess water tends to dilute the substance of the cell. Should we not also expect that cell to swell? We should indeed, but this does not happen to any appreciable extent, for most of the absorbed water and the dissolved materials are removed almost as soon as they enter the cell. The fluid is secreted from the root-hair cell and is absorbed by the cortex cells immediately adjacent to the root epidermis. As a result, water which first has been in the soil and then in the epidermis is now in the outermost layer of the root cortex. *These* cells then tend to swell, and their interior tends to become more dilute.

17 · 5   Absorption paths within a root. Water and dissolved minerals are absorbed by successively deeper layers of cells. In this manner, supplies eventually reach the xylem.

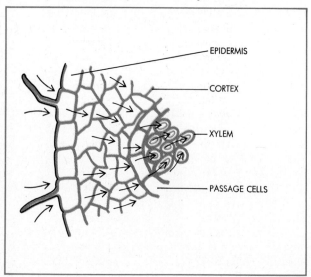

EPIDERMIS

CORTEX

XYLEM

PASSAGE CELLS

However, excessive swelling is prevented by the cell walls and water is therefore transferred again, into the next inner layer of cortex cells (Fig. 17.5).

In this manner, water and dissolved materials in it are drawn progressively from cell layer to cell layer, toward the core of the root. Some of these nutritional supplies are retained by the cells along the route, but the bulk soon reaches the root endodermis. This tissue, which often includes specialized unsuberized *passage cells,* provides a path into the stele of the root. Water and dissolved materials are moved through the endodermis, through the layers of the pericycle, and from there they are pushed into xylem vessels.

"Pushed" is the right word. The water stream from soil to xylem vessel is continuous and uninterrupted, and it is not a stream that trickles lazily by its own weight. Rather, the combined osmotic pressure and the combined absorptive force of all root cells are behind the water and thereby generate *root pressure.* It is this pressure which drives water forcefully into the xylem tubes at the root core and so drives sap upward through the xylem vessels (Fig. 17.6).

In a healthy plant xylem tubes are never empty of water. Even before a xylem vessel becomes functional, cellular water already fills the interior of the vessel elements. Later, when the cell substance of these elements disintegrates, the water remains. As the plant grows in length, each new vessel element joined to the top of an existing vessel adds a corresponding cylinder of water to the column below. Water thus *grows* up as the plant grows up. No matter how high the plant, therefore, continuous uninterrupted water columns range from every root-hair membrane, through root cortex, pericycle, and xylem vessels, to every leaf mesophyll membrane. Upward "transportation" consequently consists of adding water at the bottom of such columns and withdrawing an equivalent amount from the top, minus the fraction that living tissues incorporate into their substance. As we have seen, absorption by the root adds water at the bottom and generates root pressure. This is one force, and often the main one, which pushes the water columns up. It alone suffices to drive water right to the top of a tree in early spring, before leaves have matured.

Accompanying and reinforcing this lift from below, a second force generates pull from above. This force is *transpiration,* or evaporation of water from leaves (see Fig. 17.6). As water vaporizes from a mesophyll cell, the cell tends to develop a water deficit and so the concentration of cellular particles tends to increase. The resulting increase in osmotic pressure therefore moves water in from neighboring cells. *These* cells now tend to develop a water deficit.

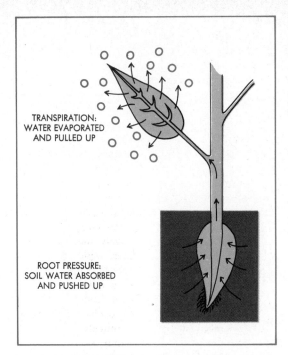

17 · 6 Xylem tubes *contain continuous columns of water. Root pressure adds more water at the bottom, and transpiration removes water at the top through evaporation. Hence a water column in xylem moves upward.*

Osmotic pull is propagated back in this manner, along cell paths leading to xylem terminals. As in roots, osmotic pull is accompanied here by active cellular absorption. The combined osmotic and absorptive action of leaf cells then pulls water up through the xylem, in quantities commensurate with the amount evaporated. The effectiveness of this pull from above is quite familiar. An isolated leaf or a flower with a stub of stem and a few leaves survives for a considerable time when put into a glass of water; as water transpires from exposed plant tissues, fluid is pulled up from below.

It should be clear that a mechanism of transport such as this, consisting of push by root pressure and pull by transpiration, depends on uninterrupted continuity of the water columns. The circumstance that the transport fluid is water rather than another medium greatly facilitates the maintenance of column continuity, for water possesses a high degree of *cohesion.* Being strongly polar, water molecules generate van der Waals forces which produce considerable mutual attraction (see Chap. 4). A column of water therefore "hangs together" with appreciable tenacity.

The mechanism of water conduction is the same where transport is not through xylem vessels but through tracheids. The pit membranes of tracheids are permeable to water and dissolved mineral ions

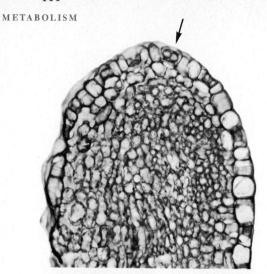

17 · 7 Section through a hydathode. Note column of cells forming a water-conducting channel. Arrow points to permanently open stoma of hydathode.

17 · 8 Grafting experiments show that tobacco leaves, when grafted onto tomato roots (left), will not contain nicotine. This indicates that nicotine is formed in the roots but not in the leaves of tobacco plants. If tomato leaves are grafted onto tobacco roots (right) the leaves will eventually contain nicotine. This experiment shows that nicotine is manufactured only in the tobacco roots and is transported upward by the phloem.

and gases, and present no barrier to continuous flow. Indeed, the bordered pits along the side walls of tracheids permit a measure of *lateral conduction* as well as equilibration of flow pressure among adjacent columns of water.

We may make note here of the phenomenon of *guttation,* the occasional exudation of water droplets from the surfaces of leaves. So-called *hydathodes* are responsible for guttation. Some hydathodes are merely cell paths offering little resistance to water coming from xylem. In these cases, water is forced out by root pressure through modified stomata incapable of closing. But in other cases hydathodes are distinct glands that actively discharge water from the interior of a leaf to the surface. Guttation is a means of eliminating water when the roots absorb more than the leaves can transpire, for example, under conditions of high environmental humidity (Fig. 17.7).

The key point in xylem transport is that the power source lies in living roots and leaves. The nonliving xylem channels as such are passive, in the same way that a pipeline between two pumping stations is passive. Conduction through phloem is different in this respect. In this system the power source appears to be spread out all along the transportation route.

LEAVES, STEMS, AND PHLOEM TRANSPORT

Atmospheric gases in plants play a role both in photosynthesis and in respiration. Oxygen is a byproduct of photosynthesis and a required gas in respiration, and CO_2 and water are raw materials in photosynthesis

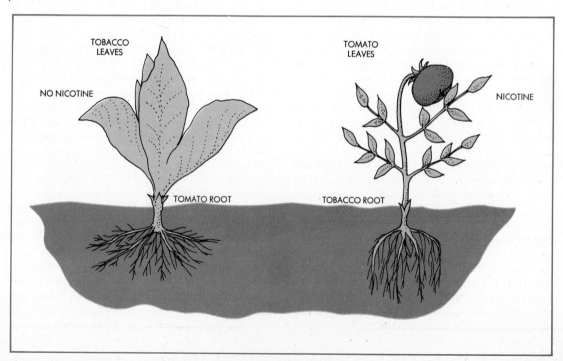

as well as byproducts in respiration. Tracheophytes are so constructed that most living cells are in direct or nearly direct contact with the external environment; and gas exchange may take place in correspondingly direct fashion.

Most of the atmospheric oxygen, carbon dioxide, and water vapor used by a plant enter via the stomata in the leaves. The internal air spaces connecting with the stomata then permit distribution to the leaf mesophyll, and there the gases diffuse through the cell surfaces and dissolve in cellular water. Some fraction of the gases may also be carried into the phloem channels along with water, and stem and root tissues may be supplied in this fashion. Gases also enter the plant through the roots, dissolved in soil water. Root cells may retain some of these supplies and the remainder reaches xylem vessels. Stem and leaf tissues may therefore obtain gases over that path. If the stem is green, stomata on its surface provide a third entry point for air. And if the stem is woody, lenticels and any crack in the bark will do similarly. Finally, inasmuch as green tissues produce oxygen during photosynthesis and all tissues produce CO_2 during respiration, plants also possess their own internal sources of aerial gases. Conversely, whenever any of these gases accumulate as net excess, they may diffuse straight into the environment from cells exposed directly to soil or air. Deeper-lying cells may release gases into the xylem or phloem, and the stomata may then pass them into the atmosphere.

In effect, exchange of gases in plants can be accomplished without specialized breathing systems; gas diffusion to and from individual cells and a certain amount of transport by xylem and phloem suffice. Since much of the deeper substance of a vascular plant is nonliving supporting and conducting material in any case, the gas requirement in such regions is zero.

Food transport is more specialized activity, and the sieve tubes of phloem are the specific food-conducting channels: photosynthesized carbohydrates and their derivatives migrate from leaves and green stems downward; and stored foods or their derivatives travel from roots and stem upward. Some upward conduction of organic substances also occurs in xylem vessels. For example, small amounts of sugar are generally present in this channel. All along the sieve tubes of phloem, lateral conduction of organic supplies may take place by cell-to-cell transfer.

Unlike the xylem channels, sieve tubes evidently are two-way paths. Downward conduction in sieve tubes has long been known to occur: many roots store carbohydrates, photosynthesized only in leaf or stem. The occurrence of upward conduction has come

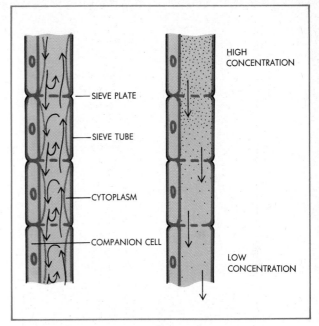

17 · 9 Conduction in phloem units. *Left: materials in the sieve tubes are kept circulating by cyclotic streaming. Differentials in concentration determine whether or not a given substance will pass through sieve plates of one phloem unit to another. Right: if a given nutrient is highly concentrated at one end of a phloem channel and less highly concentrated at the other, as shown, then a diffusion gradient will point from the high to the low concentration. The nutrient thus will be translocated in that direction.*

to light through grafting experiments. For example, a stem of a tobacco plant grafted to a root of a tomato plant develops normal tobacco leaves, but these are entirely free of nicotine. Conversely, a tomato stem transplanted to a tobacco root produces tomato leaves, but these are full of nicotine. The first graft indicates that only the roots of a tobacco plant synthesize nicotine; the second graft, that the drug is transported upward. And since xylem channels are virtually free of nicotine, upward conduction must occur largely in phloem (Fig. 17.8).

The driving forces in phloem are probably generated by the individual sieve-tube cells, and the forces appear to be cyclosis and diffusion, the same that bring about internal transport in *any* cell. In a sieve tube, the vertical direction of conduction may be imposed by the anatomic arrangement. Thus, absorption of food into sieve-tube cytoplasm and secretion out of it may well be accomplished most easily at the top and bottom perforations, where the barriers may be minimal (Fig. 17.9).

The two-way aspect of phloem conduction be-

445

comes intelligible on this basis. Mesophyll cells in the leaf photosynthesize and thereby acquire relatively high carbohydrate concentrations. Terminal sieve-tube cells in the vicinity do not photosynthesize, hence their carbohydrate content will be lower. Consequently, diffusion will tend to equalize the concentrations, and the terminal sieve-tube cells will absorb some of the mesophyll-produced carbohydrate. As a result, their own carbohydrate content will increase relative to that of lower sieve-tube cells next in line along the conduction path. These lower sieve-tube cells will then absorb from units above them, and in this fashion nutrient conduction will continue downward (see Fig. 17.9). Cells along the way may retain greater or lesser amounts of the carbohydrate; but the bulk will be carried into the roots step by step from one section of sieve tube to the next, under the influence of the diffusion gradient pointing from the leaves toward the roots. Conversely, organic materials may be carried upward if the concentrations of such materials are high in the roots and lower above. This is the case, for example, in winter and early spring, when leaves are absent and photosynthesis does not take place. Foods stored in the roots during the preceding summer then travel upward into the food-requiring regions of the stem and the crown.

Like so many other cell membranes, the cellular membranes of phloem exhibit selective activity. If a horizontal disk is cut from a stem and if this disk is allowed to grow back into its original space in an inverted position, then the stem will be intact but a section of it will have reversed polarity. Such an arrangement need not interfere with xylem conduction, but phloem conduction may be impaired. Substances like glucose may still travel downward through the inverted section of stems. Yet growth hormones manufactured only in apical shoot meristems (see Chap. 22) generally may not. Sieve-tube membranes evidently let some substances through in one direction only.

Phloem conduction, up or down, is slow compared with xylem conduction. In phloem, also, we do not find a distinct flowing sap as in xylem vessels. The transportation medium, sieve-tube cytoplasm, flows and shifts within its cellulose confines only but does not itself flow up or down bodily. Nutrient molecules alone are handed from one unit to the next. Such conduction in phloem is therefore often spoken of as *translocation*.

Note that absorption of inorganic supplies and all transport by phloem and xylem not only contribute to but also depend on photosynthesis; for it is this most vital nutritional activity that produces the very building materials and the energy for the construction of the whole green plant, including roots, leaves, transport tissues, and all other structures it may possess. Being a creative, synthesizing activity, the process of food manufacture will be discussed later in the specific context of synthesis (Chap. 19).

ANIMALS:
ALIMENTATION AND CIRCULATION

We already know that, in most animals, procurement of nutrients of all types is achieved by ingestion via a mouth, by digestion in stomach and intestine, and by egestion of unusable remains via an anus. Usable supplies resulting from digestion are then absorbed through the wall of the alimentary tract into the circulatory system, where nutrient transport to all cells of the body may occur indirectly via a *liver*, as in vertebrates, or directly from intestine to other tissues where a liver is absent. In many cases, also, procurement of gases does not occur adequately through the alimentary system or the body surface and a specialized breathing system is present for this function (see Chap. 24).

INGESTION

A plant cell may survive if it is given water and minerals and if it is supplied with or is allowed to photosynthesize organic carbon. From these three categories of chemicals a plant cell is able to construct all the other components of its substance. But if an animal cell is given only these three types of nutrients, it soon dies; for it requires four additional types of materials which, unlike the plant cell, it cannot manufacture on its own.

First, water, minerals, and photosynthesized organic carbon do not provide usable organic nitrogen required for the construction of, for example, proteins and nucleic acids. The simplest form of organic nitrogen is the amino group, $-NH_2$, and plants are able to make $-NH_2$ out of mineral nitrates (see Chap. 19). But even though nitrates are available to them, animals cannot convert these ions into $-NH_2$. Their cells therefore must be supplied with prefabricated $-NH_2$ or other forms of usable organic nitrogen. Other animals or ultimately plants must be the source of supply.

Second, plants can convert organic starting materials into all the vitamins they require. Animals cannot do likewise. Most animals do manufacture at least some of the vitamins, although in many cases only in inadequate quantities. Specific abilities here vary with the species, but no species is so self-sufficient in this regard as a green plant. Missing vitamins consequently must be supplied in prefabricated form and plants are again the ultimate source of supply.

Third, unlike plants, animals are unable to convert organic starting materials into all two dozen or so kinds of amino acids needed for protein synthesis. Depending on the species, eight or ten kinds, so-called "essential" amino acids, must be supplied in prefabricated form, and plants are the ultimate suppliers here as well.

Lastly, again unlike plants, many animals are unable to convert organic starting materials into all necessary kinds of fatty acids. Accordingly, various "essential" fatty acids must be obtained ready-made from plants.

The minimum nutrient supplies to an animal cell must therefore include at least seven types of materials: *water, minerals, organic carbon, organic nitrogen, vitamins, essential amino acids,* and *essential fatty acids.* Evidently, animals cannot survive without plants, which provide five of these seven items (Fig. 17.10).

This reduced manufacturing ability of animal cells undoubtedly is a result of mutation and evolution. In all probability, the ancestors of animals—as of plants—were able to synthesize all needed cellular compounds on their own. In the course of time, random mutations must have led to the loss of various synthesizing abilities in different organisms. If the affected organism was photosynthetic, it must have become extinct for it could not have obtained the missing ingredients in any other way; and all plants surviving today still must synthesize all needed ingredients on their own. But if the affected organism was an animal it could survive readily, for, as a heterotroph, it could obtain any missing compound from plants or another animal by way of food. That mutations may indeed destroy cellular capacities for synthesizing certain compounds can be demonstrated experimentally.

If an animal could obtain all the nutrients it requires in the form of pure, immediately usable ions and molecules, it would not need an alimentary system. It could then simply acquire such nutrients from the environment by direct absorption through its cell surfaces. This is actually the nutritional pattern in many saprotrophic and symbiotic heterotrophs. But, apart from water and minerals dissolved in water, directly usable nutrients in ionic and molecular form are largely unavailable to free-living animals. What a holotroph requires is plant or animal matter in *bulk,* living or dead. And it is the principal function of an alimentary system to separate bulk nutrients into individual ions and molecules directly usable by cells. The first step here is ingestion.

Most animals eat whenever food is available;

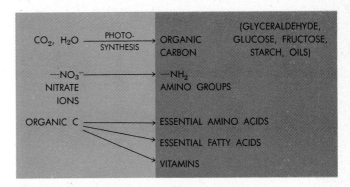

17 · 10 Five classes of compounds *that green plants can synthesize and that the cells of most animals cannot synthesize. Animals must depend on green plants for these products.*

hunger is virtually permanent. In a few animals, however, man most particularly, food intake usually tends to be more limited, both in quantity and kind. What prompts us to eat *what* we eat? What makes us decide *how much* to eat? As yet, neither question can be answered fully. The first focuses attention on the nature and control of *appetite* and is much more difficult to answer than the second, which raises the problem of the nature and control of *hunger.*

The brain unquestionably plays an important role in appetite control, just as, in mammals, this organ is now known to control the *amount* of food eaten. According to an early popular hypothesis, the stomach was believed to regulate the quantities of food consumed. Muscular contractions of an empty stomach were thought to give rise to sensations of hunger, and a hungry animal was assumed to eat until its stomach was filled. Such filling then was believed to stop the hunger pangs, hence also food intake. But this hypothesis turned out to be untenable long ago, for even after surgical removal of the entire stomach hunger sensations nevertheless continue to come and go as before. Moreover, a "stomach hypothesis" of hunger control does not account for chronic overeating or undereating.

A better explanation has emerged from experiments which have revealed the existence of special eating-control centers in the mammalian brain. In a brain region known as the *hypothalamus* (see Chap. 25), two such centers have been identified. One is a *hunger center.* When it is stimulated, it sends out nerve impulses to various parts of the body prompting the animal to eat. The other is a *satiety center,* which, when stimulated, prompts the animal to refuse food. In test rats, tiny electrodes have been used to stimulate one or the other of these centers continuously. The result has been that the treated animals either overeat and become extremely obese or undereat and starve despite a plentiful food supply. Evidently, the amount of food a mammal normally eats is determined by the commands that the hunger and satiety centers send to the body.

How do these centers decide whether to send a command "eat" or a command "do not eat"? Experiments have shown that *blood glucose* is the critical agent stimulating one or the other of the eating control centers. As will become apparent below, glucose circulating in the blood is a very sensitive indicator of the hour-by-hour nutritional state of the body. Shortly after a meal, the glucose concentration in blood tends to rise. Long after a meal, blood-glucose levels tend to fall. If blood reaching the brain contains a high glucose level, the satiety center probably becomes selectively sensitive to this level and issues the command "do not eat." Conversely, low glucose levels probably stimulate the hunger center selectively, resulting in the command "eat" (Fig. 17.11).

Thus, any condition that directly or indirectly influences glucose delivery to the brain, or affects the operation of the brain centers as such, is bound to affect food intake. Dozens of such conditions may actually do so. Proper glucose delivery depends, for example, on normal digestive processes, normal liver function, normal blood circulation, and normal hormone balances. As we shall see, all these factors affect glucose metabolism profoundly. If, through disturbances in any of these functions, the brain receives consistently false information about the actual glucose supplies in the body, then consistent overeating or undereating may result.

Moreover, the brain centers are themselves subject to faulty operation. And they are influenced by a large variety of psychological factors, by reflexes, and by habits of long standing. They are also influenced by inherited genetic constitution, which, in the final analysis, governs the detailed operation of the body in all its aspects. Clearly, if the brain centers receive correct information but interpret it incorrectly, or interpret correctly but send out faulty commands, then abnormal food intake may again be the result. We note that whether or not to eat, a seemingly simple decision, actually is determined by a multitude of interdependent, interacting internal processes. It is therefore not surprising that, as is well known, practically *any* disturbance of *any* body function has an effect on food intake.

Granting that appropriate kinds and amounts of food are being ingested, how is such food digested?

17 · 11   Control of food intake. *Desire or lack of desire for food is governed by the satiety (S) and hunger (H) centers of the brain, which in turn respond differentially to the glucose concentration in blood.*

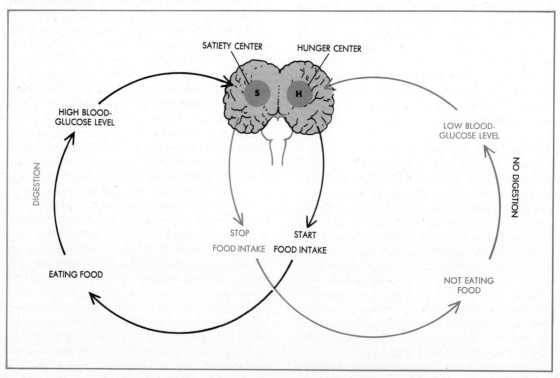

DIGESTION

Patterns

Digestion in different parts of an alimentary tract is achieved by either *mechanical* means or *chemical* means or both. Mechanical digestion, carried out mainly by teeth, tongue, the muscular grinding action of a stomach, or by other specialized structures, achieves a progressive physical subdivision of ingested materials into fine particles suspended in water. Chemical digestion then reduces these particles to molecular dimensions. In the process, usable ions and molecules become separated out and more complex molecules are broken up into smaller, usable ones. In this chemical dissolution of bulk foods, *digestive enzymes* secreted by *digestive glands* play important roles.

Digestion produces a food solution in which three groups of substances may be found. First, it includes nutrients which animal cells require but cannot manufacture on their own. These comprise water, minerals, and the five categories of plant-derived substances listed above. Second, it includes nutrients that *can* be manufactured by animal cells but, since eaten food generally supplies them, need not be manufactured. For example, animal cells may manufacture various carbohydrates and fats from organic precursors, but they may not need to do so if carbohydrates and fats are included in eaten food. And third, the food solution usually contains indigestible or otherwise unusable materials. Plant cellulose, for example, is a common indigestible component of bulk foods. Substances in this last category are eliminated by egestion.

No matter where they occur or what foods are involved, all instances of chemical digestion are *enzymatic hydrolyses*. In other words, they are reactions of dissolution or decomposition in which *water* is the active dissolving agent. A generalized digestive reaction may be written

$$\text{food} + H_2O \xrightarrow{enzyme} \text{food components}$$

In most animals digestive enzymes are *extracellular* enzymes; they are produced within cells but they are secreted and function outside cells. This puts them into a special category, for virtually all other enzymes in organisms are intracellular and function within cells. Moreover, digestive enzymes are relatively unusual also in that many of them may act on entire categories of chemicals. For example, digestive *lipase* promotes the decomposition of fat into fatty acids and glycerin:

$$\text{fat} + H_2O \xrightarrow{lipase} \text{fatty acids} + \text{glycerin}$$

Here the lipase may be effective with any kind of

fat, regardless of what specific types of fatty acids a fat is composed of. Analogously, certain protein- and carbohydrate-digesting enzymes decompose many *different* kinds of proteins and carbohydrates, respectively. By contrast, most other intracellular enzymes are highly specific and each is effective only in reactions involving one particular type of molecule (see Chap. 5).

The reason for this broader effectiveness of some digestive enzymes is that many different food molecules contain groups of atoms bonded in the same way. In a fat, for example, any fatty acid present is always bonded to glycerin via an ester link

$$-C-O-C-;$$
$$\overset{\|}{O}$$

(see Chap. 6), and the enzyme lipase catalyzes this type of link specifically. Lipase may therefore promote the digestion of any substance in which such an ester link is present, namely, *any* fat. In a protein, similarly, various amino acids are joined together by peptide bonds, and digestive proteinases act specifically on such bonds. Because the bonds occur in all types of proteins, proteinases may aid in the decomposition of all of these. In general, we may say that digestive enzymes, like all others, act specifically on particular chemical bonds; and because certain kinds of bonds are common within broad categories of food molecules, digestive enzymes are broadly effective. Note again, however, that digestive decomposition is accomplished not by an enzyme itself but by water; as elsewhere, enzymes merely increase reaction rates. And like all enzymes, also, digestive ones likewise operate best at particular temperatures and pH. Appropriately acid, alkaline, or neutral conditions are actually maintained in the digestive juices and the alimentary organs in which enzymes are present.

Note further that animals with specialized feeding habits are correspondingly specialized in the kinds of digestive enzymes they manufacture. For example, blood feeders among worms and insects secrete digestive proteinases in comparative large amounts but may manufacture only small quantities of carbohydrases. Clothes moths, which eat nothing but the protein keratin in sheep hair (wool), likewise produce digestive proteinases almost exclusively. By contrast, flour beetles and boll weevils secrete an abundance of carbohydrases. Analogous digestive specializations are encountered among silk- or glue-eating insects, among wood-digesting types such as the molluscan shipworms, certain beetles, and the flagellates living symbiotically in the gut of termites. Also, numerous parasitic animals are fairly narrowly specialized in their digestive capacities. In general, the broadest assortment of digestive enzymes is usually found in

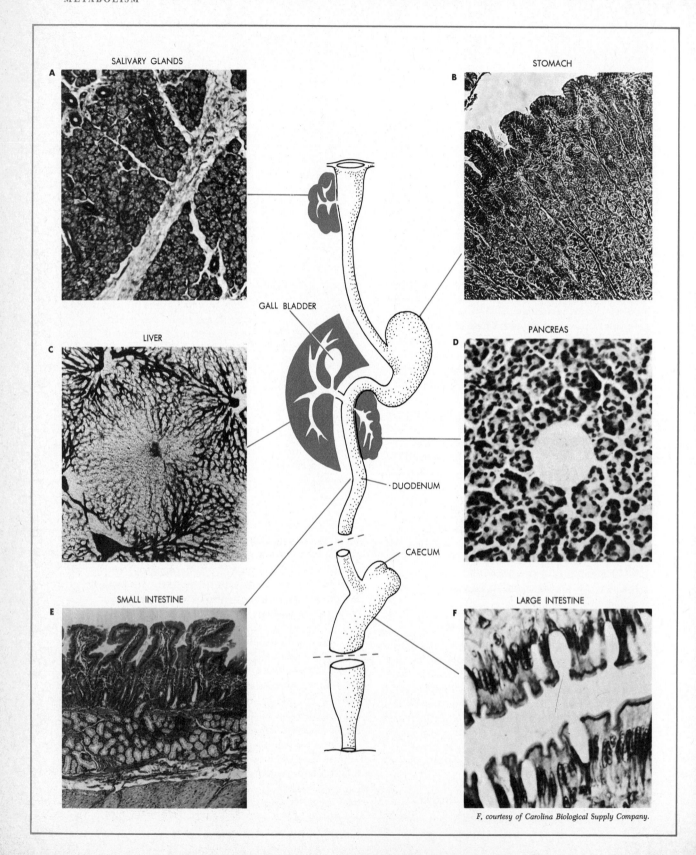

SALIVARY GLANDS

A

STOMACH

B

LIVER

C

PANCREAS

D

GALL BLADDER

DUODENUM

CAECUM

SMALL INTESTINE

E

LARGE INTESTINE

F

F, courtesy of Carolina Biological Supply Company.

◄ **17 · 12   The mammalian alimentary tract** (diagram) *and photomicrographic sections through the principal organs. In the diagram of the liver, note the gall bladder and the common bile duct passing from both liver and gall bladder into the duodenum. Other representations of liver tissues are shown in Figs. 7.32 and 17.19. Photo insets: A, section through a salivary gland. Note the connective tissue stroma (light areas in photo) traversing the gland and binding groups of gland cells together. Note also the several small salivary ducts (dark rings). B, section through a portion of stomach wall. Note folded mucosa near top of photo. C, section through liver, showing parts of a few lobules injected to reveal the blood channels (sinusoids; dark). Blood brought by the hepatic portal vein to a lobule passes to the hepatic vein in the center of the lobule (see also Fig. 7.32). D, section through pancreas. The large round space is a branch of the pancreatic duct. E, section through the wall of the duodenum. The cavity of the gut is toward the top. Underneath the folded inner surface tissues note the glandular layer. Its secretion is discharged into the gut cavity and contributes to the composition of intestinal juice. F, section through a mucosal fold of the large intestine. Note the many so-called goblet cells, mucus-secreting cells in the mucosal lining.*

omnivores, that is, free-living animals that may survive on virtually any kind of food. In this category are, for example, some mammals, man included. In the following we shall concentrate on the digestive pattern in man as an illustrative example.

Oral Digestion

In the mouth, tongue and teeth initiate mechanical digestion, and *saliva* mixed into the food mass initiates chemical digestion.

Saliva is manufactured in paired salivary glands located along the floor and roof of the hind portion of the mouth cavity and connecting with the mouth by ducts (Fig. 17.12). Salivary secretion is started reflexly. Food in contact with the tongue and the lining of the mouth stimulates nerve endings which transmit nerve impulses to the brain, and the latter in turn sends impulses to the salivary glands. These glands respond by secreting saliva. As is well known, smell, sight, or mere thought of food may start the flow of saliva. Such secretion is brought about by *conditioned reflexes* (see Chap. 25); pleasant past experiences with food here have the same effect as actual food in the mouth.

Saliva contains water, a variety of inorganic ions, mucus proteins, and two digestive enzymes, *salivary amylase* and *salivary maltase* (Fig. 17.13). The whole mixture is chemically neutral or very slightly alkaline or acid. The two enzymes promote the preliminary digestion of eaten carbohydrates. If starch or glycogen or other polysaccharides are eaten, salivary amylase accelerates their conversion into disaccharides such as maltose or monosaccharides such as glucose. In its turn, maltose eaten as such or produced by oral digestion of polysaccharides then may become converted to glucose with the aid of salivary maltase. These salivary enzymes evidently attack the 1,4-α and 1,6-α links in carbohydrates.

Since food does not remain in the mouth very long and since brief periods of chewing do not always bring saliva into intimate contact with every part of a bite of food, oral carbohydrate digestion usually occurs only to a superficial degree. But saliva

17 · 13   Composition of the principal digestive juices. *Note that saliva has a pH around neutrality, that gastric juice is highly acid, and that the other juices listed are alkaline. All these juices also contain water, various inorganic ions, and mucus proteins.*

SALIVA	GASTRIC JUICE	INTESTINAL JUICE	BILE	PANCREATIC JUICE
AMYLASE	HCl (H⁺ + Cl⁻)	ENTEROKINASE	BILE SALTS	TRYPSINOGEN
MALTASE	PEPSIN	SECRETINS	BILE PIGMENTS	CHYMOTRYPSINOGEN
	RENNIN	AMINO-PEPTIDASE		CARBOXY-PEPTIDASE
	LIPASE	DI-PEPTIDASE		AMYLASE
		DISACCHARASES		LIPASE
		AMYLASE		
		LIPASE		

mixed into the masticated food is carried along into the stomach, and it is there that most of the digestive action of saliva takes place.

From the mouth food passes through the *pharynx*, where the food channel crosses the air channel leading from the nasal passages to the windpipe (Fig. 17.14). When food actually crosses the air channel during swallowing, the upper end of the windpipe (larynx) is raised muscularly and pressed against a flap of tissue, the *epiglottis*. The opening into the air channel is thereby closed off and food is forced to pass from the pharynx into the *esophagus* leading to the stomach. A bite of food is moved through the esophagus by *peristalsis*, a wavelike progression of muscular contraction in the wall of the esophagus that pushes a ball of food along. The direction of esophageal peristalsis may be reversed on some occasions, for example, in vomiting.

Gastric Digestion

The stomach completes mechanical and continues chemical digestion. *Gastric juice* plays a role in both. Sight, smell, and thought of food, which initiate salivary secretion by conditioned reflex, may at the same time initiate gastric secretion. Moreover, actual

17 · 14 *The nasal passages and the upper parts of the human breathing system*. *Note that in the pharynx the air path (from nasopharynx to glottis) crosses the food path (from mouth cavity to esophagus).*

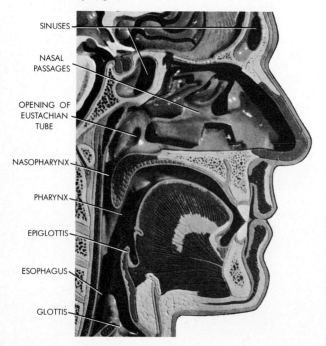

SINUSES

NASAL PASSAGES

OPENING OF EUSTACHIAN TUBE

NASOPHARYNX

PHARYNX

EPIGLOTTIS

ESOPHAGUS

GLOTTIS

food in mouth or esophagus reflexly stimulates the stomach. As a result of these nervous effects, gastric juice is already flowing to some extent even before food has arrived. A more copious flow is produced once food comes into direct contact with the stomach lining (see Fig. 17.12). This mechanical stimulation also initiates the production of *gastrin*, a hormone. Stomach cells in contact with food release gastrin, and the hormone is picked up by blood vessels and distributed throughout the body. When some of the hormone returns to the stomach and reaches the specialized cells capable of manufacturing gastric juice, these cells are activated. Gastric secretions thus may be started and maintained by nervous, mechanical, and chemical stimuli.

Gastric juice is a mixture of water, mineral ions, mucus proteins, *hydrochloric acid* in the form of H^+ and Cl^-, and three enzymes, *pepsin, rennin,* and *lipase* (see Fig. 17.13). By virtue of the presence of HCl, the whole is very strongly acid—pH 2, approximately. Different sets of cells in the stomach lining secrete the acid and the enzymes.

Hydrochloric acid macerates and breaks up food in the same way that any strong acid decomposes substances on which it is spilled. Tough fibrous material in plant and animal food is loosened, the cement between cells is eroded, and the food mass literally falls apart. Hydrochloric acid does not act similarly on the stomach wall itself because the acid is normally produced in appreciable quantity only when food is actually present or is on the way. Moreover, the mucus proteins of gastric juice coat the stomach lining and protect it, and HCl is also soon diluted by water in food. But despite these protections, hydrochloric acid (and gastric enzymes) may sometimes be secreted in excessive quantity, for example, by continued nervous stimulation of the stomach under chronic emotional stress, when food may not always be present. Portions of the stomach wall may then be eroded and a gastric ulcer may result.

In parallel with acid maceration, the food mass is thoroughly churned and ground by the powerful muscular action of the stomach wall. This action contributes greatly to reducing solid food to fairly small particles suspended in fluid. All further breakdown is chemical.

The enzyme *pepsin* is secreted in the form of *pepsinogen,* an enzymatically inactive molecule. In the presence of hydrogen ions from HCl, pepsinogen is converted to active pepsin. The conversion is thought to be an unmasking process in which pepsinogen splits into active pepsin and a smaller molecular fragment:

$$\text{pepsinogen} \xrightarrow{H^+} \text{pepsin} + \text{fragment}$$

Once some pepsin has so formed, it may itself convert more pepsinogen into pepsin:

$$\text{pepsinogen} \xrightarrow{\textit{pepsin}} \text{pepsin} + \text{fragment}$$

Pepsin formation here is *autocatalytic;* that is, the enzyme promotes formation of more of itself. Secretion of inactive pepsinogen and conversion to active pepsin in the stomach protect the stomach wall; if active pepsin were secreted as such, this strong enzyme might digest the very cells which produce it rather than food.

In the acid medium of the stomach cavity, active pepsin catalyzes the breakdown of proteins into free amino acids. But during the relatively short time of stomach digestion, pepsin usually cannot act long enough to reduce all proteins in food to amino acids. Many protein molecules are broken up only partially into variously long polypeptide chains. A good many proteins usually escape peptic digestion altogether, for pepsin may not reach all the food particles present.

Rennin is an enzyme unique to mammals. It acts specifically on *caseinogen,* the protein of milk. Secreted as inactive *prorennin* and converted to the active state by hydrogen ions, rennin splits caseinogen into two smaller proteins, *casein* and *whey.* In the presence of calcium ions (for example, from milk) casein then coagulates, or *curdles,* and this protein curd subsequently may be digested by pepsin. The entire sequence is

$$\text{prorennin} \xrightarrow{H^+} \text{rennin}$$
$$\downarrow$$
$$\text{caseinogen} \longrightarrow \text{casein} + \text{whey}$$
$$\downarrow Ca^{++}$$
$$\text{curd} \longrightarrow \text{peptic digestion}$$

The presence of a special enzyme aiding the digestion of milk is a useful mammalian adaptation. Milk is the first and for some time the only food of a young mammal. But milk is a liquid and its proteins are present in dissolved form. Therefore, milk would pass through the stomach as quickly as water and pepsin could not act on it for any length of time. The rennin mechanism coagulates milk, however, and the now-solidified, curdled milk proteins do stay in the stomach long enough to permit appreciable peptic digestion.

Lipase in the stomach digests fats into fatty acids and glycerol. Much of the gastric lipase is not actually produced in the stomach but is regurgitated from the intestine. Gastric fat digestion is particularly superficial. Thorough breakdown of fats requires bile and an alkaline environment, neither of which exists in the stomach. Moreover, fats do not mix with water, and lipase, present in water, therefore does not readily reach the interior of large drops of fat. Consequently, gastric lipase acts largely on fats already divided up into fine colloidal droplets, for example, the fat in milk or in cheese or in mayonnaise.

Since gastric juice does not contain carbohydrases, the only carbohydrate digestion in the stomach is that brought about by saliva carried down from the mouth. Even this stops fairly soon, for in the highly acid medium of the stomach the salivary enzymes do not remain active long. By the time food is ready to leave the stomach, it is a semifluid macerated mass containing some digestion products: a certain amount of glucose, fatty acids, glycerin, and polypeptides. But most carbohydrates, most fats, and a considerable portion of the proteins in food have so far not been digested. Complete gastric digestion of an average meal may take 3 to 4 hr.

Intestinal Digestion

The uppermost foot or so of the small intestine is the *duodenum* (see Fig. 17.12). In this section adjoining the stomach, the most important digestive fluids are mixed with food as it enters. These fluids are *intestinal juice, bile,* and *pancreatic juice.* As they and food are slowly propelled by peristalsis through the length of the small intestine, chemical digestion is carried to completion.

Intestinal juice is secreted by specialized glands in and just under the lining of the duodenum (see Fig. 17.12). Secretion is started by contact of food with this lining. Under the influence of HCl carried over from the stomach, the duodenal wall also manufactures *secretins,* a group of hormones. Picked up by blood, these hormones are distributed through the body. Two organs respond to them specifically, the *liver* and the *pancreas.* Stimulated by secretins, liver cells secrete bile. Excess bile produced at other times may have been stored in the gall bladder, an organ which may contract and expel some of its store. Ducts from both liver and gall bladder join into a *common bile duct* and bile passes through it into the duodenum (see Fig. 17.12). Also under the stimulus of secretins, pancreatic juice flows through a *pancreatic duct* into the duodenum, entering near the opening of the bile duct.

Thus, the appearance of food in the duodenum triggers directly through contact the secretion of intestinal juice, and indirectly through secretins the arrival of bile and of pancreatic juice within a short time. All three fluids are alkaline and, mixed with food, they soon abolish the acidity of the gastric product. All three fluids contain water, inorganic ions, and mucus proteins. In addition, they contribute a number of other agents, as indicated in Fig. 17.13.

Protein digestion is accomplished with the aid of *trypsinogen, chymotrypsinogen,* and the three *peptidases* listed in Fig. 17.13. Trypsinogen and chymotrypsinogen are inactive enzymes. Their secretion in inactive form protects pancreas and the pancreatic duct from being digested. Conversion to the active enzymes takes place in the duodenum. When trypsinogen and chymotrypsinogen arrive in the duodenum, intestinal juice is already flowing and *enterokinase* is therefore available. This substance is an enzyme but not a digestive one. It acts on a few trypsinogen molecules and transforms them into active trypsin. Enterokinase thus initiates the formation of trypsin. In turn, trypsin now acts autocatalytically and activates all remaining trypsinogen, producing more trypsin, and acts also on chymotrypsinogen, producing active chymotrypsin:

$$\text{trypsinogen} \xrightarrow{+\,enterokinase} \text{trypsin}$$

$$\text{trypsinogen} \xrightarrow{+\,trypsin} \text{trypsin}$$

$$\text{chymotrypsinogen} \xrightarrow{+\,trypsin} \text{chymotrypsin}$$

Active trypsin and chymotrypsin digest whole protein molecules to polypeptides, like pepsin in the stomach. Accordingly, whole proteins that have escaped gastric digestion are now broken up in the intestine.

At this stage, the *amino-peptidase* from the intestinal juice and the *carboxy-peptidase* from the pancreas enter the digestive reactions. These enzymes

accelerate the further decomposition of any polypeptides present in the gut. The result of such peptidase activity is the appearance of *dipeptides,* molecules consisting of only two joined amino acids. Finally, the *dipeptidase* from intestinal juice reduces all the dipeptides to individual amino acid molecules (Fig. 17.15).

Pancreatic and *intestinal amylase* have essentially the same digestive effect as salivary amylase. Since food remains longer in the gut and is more finely divided than in the mouth, polysaccharide digestion here is more thorough. Disaccharides form, and these, as well as disaccharides eaten as such or produced by salivary digestion, are converted to monosaccharides by the *disaccharases* of intestinal juice. Thus, intestinal *maltase* splits malt sugar into two glucose molecules: *sucrase* (or *invertase*) splits cane sugar (sucrose) into glucose and fructose; and *lactase* splits milk sugar (lactose) into glucose and galactose. Added to whatever glucose has formed by salivary digestion, these and other monosaccharide sugars are the usable nutrients obtained from complex carbohydrates (see Fig. 17.15).

Note that quite a number of complex carbohydrates cannot be digested at all. For example, cellulose passes through the alimentary tract unchanged since this molecule contains 1,4-β linkages not subject to attack by the amylases (see Chap. 6). Note also that, unlike the proteinases, the amylases are not secreted in inactive form but are immediately active as produced. Protection of the secreting glands and ducts is evidently not required, probably because animal tissue generally does not contain more than 1 per cent carbohydrate. Moreover, most of this carbohydrate is accumulated in the interior of cells, where it is beyond the reach of the extracellular amylase-containing juices flowing by along the cell surfaces.

Fat digestion is accomplished efficiently only in the presence of bile salts. As pointed out in Chap. 4, these produce an emulsion of colloidal fat droplets in water and so they increase the available fat-water surface tremendously. Even so, only about one-half of all ingested fat is digested chemically. The remainder stays in the form of finely divided whole fat.

Fat that is digested chemically is split by *intestinal* and *pancreatic lipase* into fatty acids and glycerol. These two types of molecules, produced in part also in the stomach, plus the undigested colloidal whole fat, represent the usable nutrients obtained from eaten fat (see Fig. 17.15). Bile salts may combine with fatty acids into complexes utilized more readily than fatty acids alone.

Bile pigments do not appear to have any digestive function. They are metabolic wastes produced in the

17 · 15 *The pattern of enzymatic digestion of the main classes of foods is summarized in this diagram.*

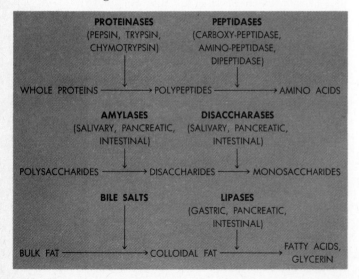

liver as byproducts of the destruction of red blood corpuscles (see Chap. 24), and they are egested along with the unusable food remains (to which the pigments give their characteristic color). Some quantities of bile pigments do not go through the gut but are picked up from the liver and gall bladder by the blood and are transported to the kidneys. Excreted from there, the pigments are responsible for the characteristic color of urine. When the gall bladder or the bile ducts are blocked by gallstones, bile dams up and cannot reach the intestine. Fat digestion is then impaired. Under such conditions, moreover, bile pigments are absorbed in excessive amounts by the blood and, carried in part into the skin, produce jaundice. In birds, bile pigments may be excreted by being incorporated into the shells of eggs. For example, the blue color of robins' eggs is due to chemically modified bile pigments.

EGESTION

As more and more usable nutrients are liberated by intestinal digestion, food becomes increasingly fluid. The resulting solution is kept continuously agitated by peristaltic contractions of the intestinal wall, a process which mixes and remixes food with the digestive juices and thereby permits hydrolytic decomposition of virtually all potential food substances present. Moreover, agitation of the food solution brings usable nutrients into extensive contact with different regions of the intestinal lining tissue, the mucosa, a necessary condition for thorough absorption of food. We may note here that the mucosa is highly folded and is formed into millions of near-microscopic *villi*, finger-like protrusions producing a velvety, carpet-like texture (see Fig. 17.17*B*). By virtue of the folds and the villi, the surface area of the mucosa is exceedingly large. And the villi move continuously from side to side, stirring the food solution and circulating it thoroughly about the mucosal lining.

During the 4- to 8-hr stay of food in the small intestine, this organ absorbs most of the minerals and the usable organic nutrients—monosaccharides, amino acids, fatty acids, glycerol, colloidal whole fat, and vitamins (see below). The small intestine removes relatively little water from the food solution. On the contrary, by pouring digestive juices into the gut cavity it actually adds water to food. Water is absorbed primarily in the large intestine, or *colon*. The first portion of this section of the alimentray tract is the *caecum*, a blind pouch which in man and a number of other mammals carries a terminal fingerlike extension, the *appendix* (Figs. 17.12 and 17.16). In many herbivorous mammals (for example, rodents), the caecum is extremely large. It serves as a temporary food-

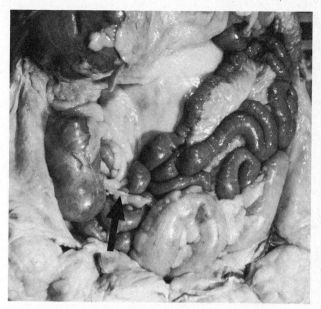

17 · 16 *Abdominal dissection, man. Portions of the large intestine are shown on the left of the photo and toward the top. The rounded termination of the large intestine, near left bottom, is the caecum, a blind pouch. Attached to it is the appendix* (arrow).

storage pouch and provides additional time for digestion, an advantage in a plant-eating animal. At the far end, the large intestine joins the *rectum*, a short tube opening to the outside through the *anus*.

The large intestine has a dual function. First, it is an *absorbing* and *excreting* organ. During the 10- to 12-hour stay of materials in the colon, the bulk of the water and the remaining inorganic nutrients are absorbed. At the same time, many metabolic wastes and inorganic substances present in the body to excess are excreted into the colon cavity (see Fig. 17.12). By differentially absorbing from and adding to the materials in the gut cavity, the large intestine thus aids in maintaining a properly balanced internal composition of the body. That the colon actually does regulate the internal water balance, for example, is indicated by the familiar upset conditions of diarrhea and constipation.

Second, in the large intestine the indigestible and unabsorbable materials undergo decay. This action is brought about by dense, permanent populations of saprotrophic bacteria that live in the gut as symbionts. The microorganisms obtain food from many of the materials the host cannot digest or absorb, and as a result of such bacterial activity, the substances in the colon undergo rapid decay. Frequently the bacteria release byproducts of their own metabolism, and some

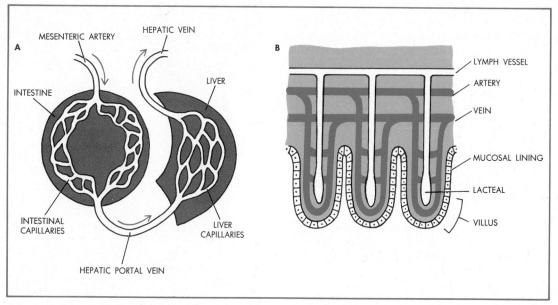

17 · 17 Circulatory paths in the intestine. A, the hepatic portal circulation. Blood reaches the intestine via a branch of the aorta, the mesenteric artery. Intestinal capillaries join and form a hepatic portal vein, which enters the liver. Blood leaves the liver via a hepatic vein and carries nutrients to all parts of the body. B, diagram of the blood and lymph circulation through the villi of the vertebrate intestine. Colloidal whole fat enters the blind-ended lymphatic lacteals, passes from there into the lymph circulation of the body, and so bypasses the liver. All other organic nutrients from the intestine are absorbed directly into the blood circulation of the villi and are transported from there to the liver.

of these may be nutrients usable by the host. Vitamins are among them. Mammals actually obtain an appreciable fraction of their vitamin supply from the intestinal bacteria.

After passing the large intestine, what is left of the original eaten food is largely *roughage*: tough fibers, gristle, pieces of cellulose, and unmacerated plant tissue, all suspended in more or less reduced quantities of water. Mixed with this are bile pigments, colon excretions, bacteria and bacterial products, and whatever else may have been added or left over in the passage of food through the gut. These *feces* are in a more or less advanced state of decay and they are ultimately egested as semisolid masses.

ABSORPTION AND DISTRIBUTION

Absorption achieves a transfer of usable nutrients into the circulating blood and lymph. A few substances, alcohol, for example, can be absorbed through the stomach wall, but most foods are absorbed through the intestine. Here nutrients must first be transferred from the gut cavity into the mucosal lining cells of the intestine, and from there food must then be released into the deeper tissues of the gut wall, where blood and lymph vessels are situated.

Absorption of nutrients into the mucosa is brought about by osmosis of water, diffusion of materials dissolved in water, and selective absorptive work by mucosal cells. The selective action of the mucosa is illustrated well by the different rates with which foodstuffs are absorbed. For example, the hexoses glucose, galactose, and fructose all have the same molecular size and atomic composition, namely, $C_6H_{12}O_6$; yet of these three sugars galactose is absorbed most rapidly, fructose least rapidly. Moreover, sugar molecules containing only 3, 4, or 5 carbon atoms, though smaller than the 6-carbon molecules, are generally absorbed much more slowly, if at all. Mucosal cells evidently "recognize" and select among the substances present in digested food.

Uptake of glucose at the surface of mucosal cells, as elsewhere, is accompanied by *phosphorylation* (see Fig. 17.3). When sugar is subsequently secreted from mucosal cells into the deeper tissues of the gut wall, *dephosphorylation* occurs and free sugar is reformed. Water, minerals, amino acids, and vitamins diffuse through the mucosa unchanged. Similarly, colloidal fat droplets, still undigested chemically, as well as fatty acids and glycerin, are passed as such through the mucosa and reappear on the other side. Here some of the fatty acids and glycerin may recombine immediately into whole fats, thereby increasing the amount of colloidal fat transported away from the gut.

In each villus of the intestinal wall are present capillaries of the blood circulation (Fig. 17.17). Blood is pumped to the intestine through a few large mesenteric arteries, which then branch out in the gut wall into extensive networks of microscopic capillary vessels. These capillaries pick up most of the nutrients absorbed through the intestinal mucosa, namely, water, minerals, vitamins, monosaccharides, amino acids, and fatty acids and glycerol. In this short-distance transfer into the blood, nutrient compounds must pass from the intestinal tissues through the walls of the blood capillaries. Such walls are exceedingly thin, consisting of a single layer of greatly flattened cells. To a great extent, nutrient transfer through these cells is achieved by diffusion, but active absorption by the capillary walls undoubtedly plays a role as well. Within blood, the nutrients are carried as dissolved ions and molecules.

Food-laden blood now leaves the intestine. The capillaries in the gut collect into larger vessels, these join and rejoin, and a single very large channel eventually emerges from the whole intestine, the *hepatic portal vein.* This vessel leads directly into the *liver.* Whatever nutrients are not or cannot be transported to the liver in this fashion are collected by the *lymph* system. Among such nutrients are mainly the colloidal droplets of whole fat, which are enormously larger than molecules; but the lymph also receives water, minerals, and variable quantities of other substances which may have escaped transport by blood.

The lymph system (Fig. 17.18) returns to blood any fluid lost from the blood circulation. As blood flows in its closed network of vessels, a certain amount of fluid normally passes through the thin walls of the capillaries. Consisting principally of water, mineral ions, and molecular organic nutrients, this escaped fluid is lymph. It is responsible for the moist condition of all body tissues, and it is through lymph that blood ultimately provides the cells of the body with water and all other necessary supplies. Lymph thus lost from the blood circulation is ultimately channeled back into the circulation via the lymph system. Microscopic lymph capillaries originate in all parts of the body, intestine included, and they pick up any free fluid in the tissues. Lymph capillaries then join into progressively larger, progressively

fewer ducts until a single large channel is formed. This channel empties into a vein in the left shoulder region and so returns to the blood circulation all the lymph lost originally.

The lymph capillaries originating in the intestine are called *lacteals.* One lacteal is situated in each villus (see Fig. 17.17). Also present in a villus is intestinal lymph, fluid that has become mixed with the nutrients absorbed by the intestinal mucosa. Most of these nutrients enter the blood stream, as noted, but all others, including chiefly the colloidal whole fats, remain in lymph and then pass into the lacteal. After a heavy meal, the lacteals may become milky white from the large quantities of emulsified fat suspended in them. From the lacteals, nutrients are transported through the larger lymph vessels of the body and eventually into the blood. The whole fats are then carried by blood into the principal fat-storing regions of the body, and such fats therefore bypass the liver. But any other nutrients eventually do circulate via the blood into the liver, where they join those already carried in over the more direct route of the hepatic portal vein.

In the liver, the hepatic portal vein breaks up into a very extensive network of unlined blood channels (*sinusoids;* see Fig. 17.12). Every liver cell thus comes into direct contact with incoming blood. The

17 · 18   The lymph circulation of the body, diagrammatic. Fluid (lymph) escapes from the blood capillaries into the tissues of the body (colored arrow) and returns via lymph vessels into the blood circulation.

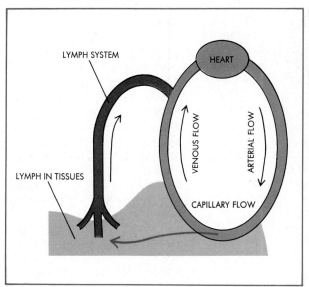

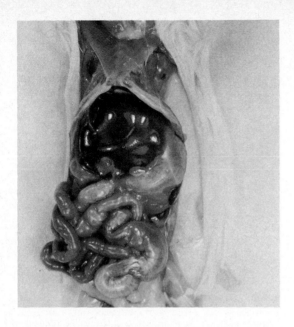

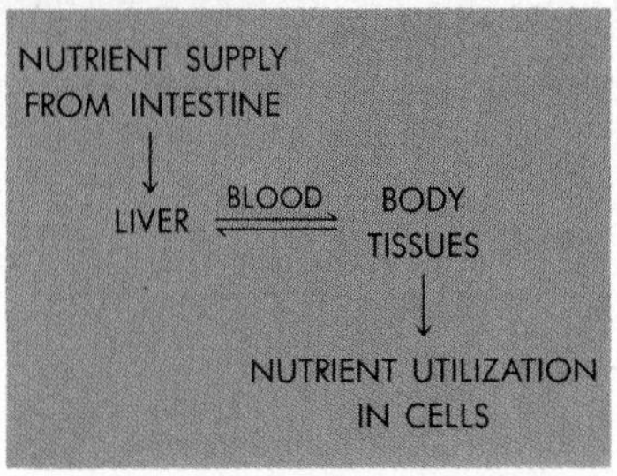

NUTRIENT SUPPLY
FROM INTESTINE

LIVER ⇌ BLOOD ⇌ BODY TISSUES

NUTRIENT UTILIZATION
IN CELLS

17 · 19   The liver. *Photo: abdominal dissection of a mouse showing the position and gross external appearance of the liver (large dark organ). For histological and internal structure of the liver see Figs. 7.32 and 17.12. Diagram: generalized summary of the food-distributing role of the liver.*

cells absorb blood-borne nutrients, process them, and return the finished products to the blood in the sinusoids. These drain into capillaries, which join and form larger vessels, and such vessels ultimately empty into a single large *hepatic vein*. Blood in this vein carries all liver-processed foods away from the liver into the general body circulation. In this manner, nutrient supplies reach all parts of the body (see Fig. 17.17).

Representing the largest gland of the vertebrate body, the liver (Fig. 17.19) has been estimated to carry out some 200 separate functions. Many of these are not concerned directly with nutrient transport, but the many that are make the liver the principal receiving station, processing plant, warehouse, distributing organ, and traffic control center, all rolled into one. Liver cells regulate not only what kinds but also what quantities of nutrients are sent out into body tissues. The cells carry out numerous chemical transformations of incoming materials and serve as storage depots for some of them. Through such quartermastering activities, the liver plays a major role in the maintenance of optimal working conditions throughout the body.

The adaptive advantage of an organ such as the liver is evident. No matter when or at what regular or irregular intervals a vertebrate eats, the liver collects most of the food as it is absorbed from the gut and then releases it into the body at a pace adapted to the particular requirements of the moment. Therefore, whereas the metabolism of other animals reaches peaks just after food has been eaten, the metabolism of vertebrates may remain at a continuously steady level.

We may regard the liver as one side of a vast balance. The other side is the remainder of the body, and blood serves as carrier, signal mechanism, and general connecting link between the two sides (see Fig. 17.19). Nutrients coming or not coming from the gut into the liver may shift the balance one way; nutrients used up or not used up by the body tissues may shift it the opposite way. As Chap. 19 will make clear in specific detail, these balancing processes operate through chemical equilibria. They normally adjust in such a manner that the original balance is maintained or, if upset, reattained.

Thus, among the nutrients delivered to individual animal cells are glucose; all different kinds of amino acids; fats, fatty acids, and glycerol; water and mineral ions; vitamins; and also various special organic compounds. Being thus supplied through the digestive and absorptive agency of the intestine, the regulative agency of the liver, and the transportive agency of blood, the animal cell like the plant cell may now see to the main business of metabolism: *liberation of energy* on the one hand and *construction of new living matter* on the other.

REVIEW QUESTIONS

1. Define nutrition. What are the major nutritional processes of organisms? Define autotroph, heterotroph, photolithotroph, photoorganotroph, chemolithotroph, chemoorganotroph. Which groups of organisms belong to each of these categories?

2. Review the general patterns of food procurement in the various groups of (a) autotrophs, (b) heterotrophs. Review the different nutritional patterns of (a) purple sulfur bacteria, purple nonsulfur bacteria, green sulfur bacteria, and nongreen sulfur bacteria, (b) nitrifying bacteria, denitrifying bacteria, and nitrogen-fixing bacteria.

3. Where and through what processes do different groups of organisms obtain (a) water, (b) other mineral substances, (c) molecular foods, (d) atmospheric gases? What is phosphorylation and what role does it play in nutrition? What processes bring about short-distance transport of nutrients (a) within individual cells, (b) from cell to cell?

4. Describe the mechanism of xylem conduction. What kinds of nutrients are transported in xylem and in which direction? What is (a) root pressure, (b) transpiration? How are these forces generated. What roles do they play in xylem conduction? What is the importance of cohesion of water in xylem conduction?

5. What forces bring about phloem conduction? What kinds of nutrients are carried in phloem and in which direction? Describe in detail the processes which would bring about the upward translocation of a given nutrient.

6. If a cut length of stem bearing some leaves were put upside down into a glass of nutrient-rich water, how would (a) xylem conduction and (b) phloem conduction be affected? How has it been proved that phloem may transport in both directions? Can all phloem-transported substances migrate in either direction?

7. Review the general nutritional pattern of animals and contrast the nutrient requirements of plants and animals. For which materials are animals dependent on plants and why? What is the basic function of an alimentary system?

8. Review what is known about appetite and hunger control. What role does the brain play in such control? Discuss the chemical aspects of digestion generally. What roles do enzymes play in digestion and how are digestive enzymes distinct from others?

9. Review the events of oral digestion. What is the composition of saliva and how is salivary secretion initiated? What mechanical and chemical digestive processes occur in the mouth? Through what processes is food transferred into the stomach?

10. What is the composition of gastric juice and by what processes is secretion of this fluid controlled? Review the mechanical and chemical events of gastric digestion. What are the specific functions of HCl, pepsin, and rennin? What are the results of gastric digestion?

11. Which digestive fluids are added to food in the duodenum and what is the composition of these fluids? Where are the fluids manufactured and what processes stimulate their secretion? What is enterokinase and what is its function?

12. Review the specific course of protein, carbohydrate, and fat digestion in the intestine. What enzymes are involved in each case? What are the results of these digestive processes? What are intestinal villi and what are their functions? How and in what form are different categories of food absorbed into the intestinal wall?

13. What are the functions of the large intestine? What is the role of the intestinal bacteria? Do these symbionts live mutualistically, commensalistically, or parasitically? If pure glucose were eaten, where would it be digested? Why are eaten vitamins or orally administered medicines not digested in the alimentary tract?

14. Describe the blood circulation through the intestine. Which food materials are carried away from the intestine by blood? Describe the pattern of the lymph circulation in the body as a whole. What is the arrangement of the lymph vessels in the intestine?

15. By what pathways do foods reach the liver? What is the pathway and destination of colloidal fat? By what pathways do processed foods leave the liver? What is the broad, general function of the liver and what is the adaptive advantage of this organ?

COLLATERAL READINGS

Beaumont, W.: "Experiments and Observations on the Gastric Juice and the Physiology of Digestion," Harvard, Cambridge, Mass., 1929. A reprint of the original (1833) book by the father of modern functional studies on the stomach. Highly recommended.

Biddulph, S., and O. Biddulph: The Circulatory System of Plants, *Sci. American,* Feb., 1959. The article describes experiments with radioactive tracers on xylem and phloem transport.

Carlson, A. J., and V. Johnson: "The Machinery of the Body," 4th ed., University of Chicago, Chicago, 1953. A very useful book for further data on the functioning of the digestive and other systems of mammals.

Clayton, R. K., and M. Delbruck: Purple Bacteria, *Sci. American*, Nov., 1951. An interesting account of these photoorganotrophs.

Crafts, A. S.: "Translocation in Plants," Holt, New York, 1961. A small book containing detailed descriptions of all circulatory functions in plants.

Galston, A. W.: "The Life of the Green Plant," 2d ed., Prentice-Hall, Englewood Cliffs, N.J., 1964. This paperback contains a section on plant nutrition, including xylem and phloem functions.

Greulach, V. A.: The Rise of Water in Plants, *Sci. American*, Oct., 1952. A good discussion of the forces playing a role in the ascent of sap.

Griffin D. R.: "Animal Structure and Function," Holt, New York, 1962. A short chapter on the mammalian digestive tract is included in this paperback.

Hambidge, G.: "Hunger Signs in Crops," American Society of Agronomy, Madison, Wis., 1941. A useful account of the role of mineral nutrients in plant nutrition.

Holter, H.: How Things Get into Cells, *Sci. American*, Sept., 1961. A good general discussion of processes and forces of cellular nutrition.

Mayer, J.: Appetite and Obesity, *Sci. American*, Nov., 1956. A noted nutritionist discusses the control mechanisms of food intake in man.

Postgate, J.: The Sulphur Bacteria, *New Biol.*, vol. 17, 1954. A case study of chemolithotrophs.

Prosser, C. L., and F. A. Brown, Jr.: "Comparative Animal Physiology," 2d ed., Saunders, Philadelphia, 1961. Chapters 4 and 5 of this text contain detailed discussions of alimentary functions in various animal types.

Salisbury, F. B.: Translocation, in "Plant Biology Today," Wadsworth, Belmont, Calif., 1963. A strongly recommended chapter on the movement of nutrients and other metabolites in plants.

———— and R. V. Parke: "Vascular Plants: Form and Function," Wadsworth, Belmont, Calif., 1964. This paperback includes a shorter account of translocation similar to the preceding entry.

Solomon, A. K.: Pores in the Cell Membrane, *Sci. American*, Dec., 1960. The mechanical aspects of cellular absorption are reviewed.

————: Pumps in the Living Cell, *Sci. American*, Aug., 1962. A discussion of active transport, specifically for sodium ions.

Steward, F. C.: "Plants at Work," Addison-Wesley, Reading, Mass., 1964. In this paperback a short chapter on mineral nutrition of plants is included. Recommended.

CHAPTER 18
RESPIRATION: CELLULAR ENERGETICS

Respiration may be defined as a conversion of the chemical energy of organic molecules into metabolically usable energy within living cells.

The last part of this definition, "within living cells," means largely *mitochondria*. The main phases of respiration take place in these specialized cytoplasmic organelles. Concerning the first part of the definition, we may note that the chemical energy of organic molecules ultimately represents *stored solar energy*. It is the sun which, through photosynthesis, makes possible the construction of primary organic molecules. All other organic substances are derived secondarily from these. And if then the carbon bonds of organic molecules are broken under appropriate conditions, the energy becomes available for metabolic work.

A similar process is very familiar from the nonliving world: burning. Fuels burned in a furnace are principally wood, coal, oil, or "gas," that is, organic materials containing stored solar energy. Energy is obtained from them by breaking bonds, and the principle involved is precisely the same as in respiration. Indeed, respiration may properly be regarded as a form of combustion or, more specifically, as a series of exergonic decomposition reactions. These reactions constitute the crucially important "motor" that drives *all* living processes.

THE PATTERN

NUTRIENTS AND OXIDATION

If respiration is equivalent to combustion, why does it not produce the high temperatures of a fire? For

two reasons. First, a fire is *uncontrolled* combustion, in the sense that all the bonds within a fuel molecule may be broken simultaneously. A maximum amount of energy may then be released all at once. Such sudden, explosive release generates the high temperature of a fire. Respiration, on the contrary, is *controlled* combustion; energy is obtained from one bond at a time. If a fuel is respired completely, the total energy yield is the same as if it were burned in a furnace, but in respiration the energy is removed bit by bit, bond by bond. Temperatures therefore stay low. Enzymes exercise the necessary control. Respiration is a series of enzymatic reactions, and biological combustion cannot take place any faster than the controlling enzymes will permit. Second, the energy produced in a fire is dissipated largely as heat and to some extent as light. But in respiration only some of the available energy escapes as heat and practically none as light. The remainder, constituting a substantial fraction of the total available energy, is "packaged" directly into new *chemical* energy. Fuel energy creates *new* chemical bonds, and it is in this form that metabolic energy is used in cells. Since chemical bonds are not "hot," temperatures stay low during respiration.

What kinds of substances are the actual fuels in cells? The answer is, any organic compound that contains bond energies—in effect *any* organic constituent of cells: carbohydrates, fats, proteins, nucleotides, their various derivatives, vitamins, other special compounds, and indeed all the innumerable substances that together make up a cell. Like a fire, respiration is no respecter of materials. Anything that can be decomposed will be decomposed, and in cells this is the very substance of cells itself. Respiration does not distinguish between the expendable and the nonexpendable. For example, an amino acid which is an important structural member of the framework of a cell or is part of an enzyme may be respired away just as readily as an amino acid which has just been obtained by a cell as an external food.

However, if a fire is fed much of one fuel but little of another, more of the first is likely to be burned. Indeed, under normal conditions a cell receives a steady enough supply of external foods to make *them* the primary fuels rather than the structural parts of a cell. Also, some kinds of materials decompose more readily than others, and some are more accessible to the decomposing apparatus than others. On this basis, foods, carbohydrates and fats in particular, are again favored as fuels, and the finished components of a cell tend to be spared. Yet the sparing is relative only. The formed parts of a cell *are* decomposed gradually, including even those which make up the decomposing apparatus itself.

But if a cell itself decomposes, how can it remain intact and functioning? Only by continuous construction of new living components, offsetting the continuous destruction through respiration. Note that these two processes go on side by side, at all times: destructive energy metabolism and constructive synthesis metabolism. One is in balance with the other, and foods serve both as fuel for the one and as building materials for the other. We say that the components of a cell are continuously "turned over," existing parts being replaced continuously by new

ones. The living substance, we note, can never be quite the same from instant to instant.

The decomposition reactions of respiration are a series of successive energy-yielding, exergonic processes characterized by an overall $-\Delta F$; the end-products are more stable than the starting materials. It is this thermodynamic circumstance which ultimately "drives" all respiratory events.

Inasmuch as the energy yielded by respiration stems principally from the chemical bonds formed by carbon atoms, we may profitably examine the comparative stabilities of various carbon bonds. The least stable, hence most energy-rich, carbon combinations generally are the *hydrocarbon* groups, that is, atomic groupings containing only carbon and hydrogen. These occur in organic molecules in forms such as CH_4, $-CH_3$, $-CH_2-$, $=CH-$. The most stable carbon combination on the contrary is CO_2, $O=C=O$, an *anhydride* (that is, a hydrogen-free grouping). In general, therefore, we may predict that usable respiratory energy will result from conversions of hydrocarbons to anhydrides, that is, from the replacement of H atoms by O atoms bonded to carbon.

Such conversions, and particularly the removal of hydrogen from carbon, or *dehydrogenations*, involve electron shifts. As will become specifically apparent below, removal of a hydrogen atom also means removal of the electron that the hydrogen atom had contributed for sharing with carbon. In effect, therefore, dehydrogenations represent instances of the general category of chemical processes we have called *oxidation-reduction* reactions, or *redox* reac-

18 · 1 Redox reactions. *The general pattern of an oxidation-reduction (redox) process is illustrated here by a dehydrogenation. In the oxidizing half-reaction, AH_2 is the hydrogen donor, and energy is expended in the separation of H_2 from A. In the subsequent reducing half-reaction, B is the hydrogen acceptor, and energy is gained as B combines with H_2. This energy gain is greater than the earlier energy expenditure, hence BH_2 is stabler than AH_2 (and the ΔF will be negative, as per Fig. 5.4). The net overall redox reaction below is $AH_2 + B \longrightarrow A + BH_2$.*

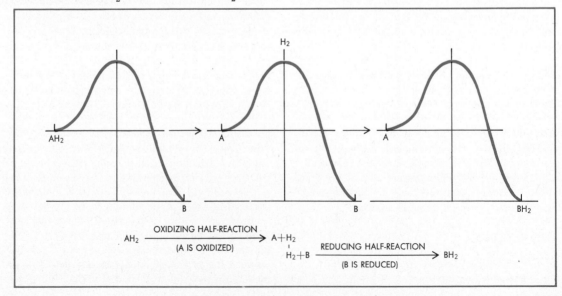

tions, in Chap. 3. Every such reaction may be considered to consist of two half-reactions, one being an oxidation, the other a reduction (Fig. 18.1). In the case of dehydrogenations, for example, removal of H from a *hydrogen donor* compound represents the oxidizing half-reaction. The reducing half-reaction follows when the removed hydrogen is attached to another compound, a *hydrogen acceptor*. Dehydrogenation is oxidation, hydrogenation is reduction; the one can occur only if the other occurs as well. The energy relations are such that, at the end of both half-reactions, the endproducts are more stable than the starting materials, and the overall reaction has a $-\Delta F$. For example, in the overall reaction

$$CH_4 + 2\,O_2 \longrightarrow CO_2 + 2\,H_2O \qquad -\Delta F$$

the carbon of methane is oxidized to CO_2, but at the same time oxygen is also reduced to H_2O. Methane is the hydrogen donor, oxygen the hydrogen acceptor. To symbolize the two half-reactions separately, we may write:

$$CH_4 + O_2 \longrightarrow CO_2 + 2\,H_2 \qquad +\Delta F,$$
oxidation of carbon, half-reaction

$$2\,H_2 + O_2 \longrightarrow 2\,H_2O \qquad -\Delta F,$$
reduction of oxygen, half-reaction

$$\overline{CH_4 + 2\,O_2 \longrightarrow CO_2 + 2\,H_2O \qquad -\Delta F,\ \text{net,}}$$
overall reaction

The oxidizing half-reaction *requires* a certain amount of energy, but the reducing half-reaction *yields* a greater amount. Hence the net ΔF of the overall reaction is negative; and CO_2 and water are more stable than methane and oxygen.

We may therefore speak of different *oxidation states*, or *oxidation levels*, of given carbon groupings (see Chap. 3). Thus, the carbon in methane has a lower oxidation state (but a higher reduction state) than that in CO_2; in CH_4, the state is -4, in CO_2, it is $+4$. For convenience, we may refer to the whole reaction simply as an "oxidation." This is actually common practice in respiration reactions, which are often termed "biological oxidations." However, we must keep in mind that, notwithstanding the incomplete name, every oxidation implies and is accompanied by a reduction. Indeed, it is the reducing half, not the oxidizing half, of any "oxidation" that is the actual source of the energy yield.

In respiration, the transformation of hydrocarbon to anhydride does not occur in a single oxidation-reduction process, as just shown for methane. Instead, respiration takes place through a *series* of consecutive redox reactions, each resulting in a successively higher oxidation level. One H atom at a time is removed from a carbon atom, and one O atom

at a time is added. At each step, therefore, the relative H:O ratio decreases. For example, if methane were to be oxidized in steps, the first step would be removal of one H atom from the carbon of methane and the addition of one O atom:

methane   methyl alcohol
 (−4)   (−2)

Note here that H need not be taken away altogether but need only be separated from its direct bonding to carbon. Oxygen achieves such a separation, and the resulting methyl alcohol is stabler than the original methane. Also, note that the oxidation state of carbon has changed from -4 to -2. As shown in the first equation of Fig. 18.2, the actual chemical process by which an O atom is interposed between C and H includes an oxidizing half-reaction in which H_2O is added and H_2 is removed. Subsequent combination of the removed H_2 with an appropriate hydrogen acceptor (oxygen in Fig. 18.2) then completes the overall reaction.

The next higher oxidation state of the carbon of methyl alcohol is attained if two H atoms are removed from the molecule entirely. The result, shown in Fig. 18.2, is *formaldehyde*. Carbon here has an oxidation level of zero, and we note that the H:O ratio now is even smaller; it was 4:0 in methane and 4:1 in methyl alcohol, and it is 2:1 in formaldehyde. A still higher oxidation level may be attained if an additional O atom is bonded to the carbon of formaldehyde. This again takes the form of simultaneous addition of H_2O and removal of H_2 (Fig. 18.2, third equation). The endproduct, HCOOH, is *formic acid*. In it, carbon has an oxidation state of $+2$, and the H:O ratio now is 1:1. A final removal of the two H atoms remaining in formic acid leads to the highest attainable oxidation state of carbon ($+4$), that is, the acid anhydride carbon dioxide (Fig. 18.2, fourth equation). The sum of all four oxidative half-reactions from methane to carbon dioxide is shown in Fig. 18.2, and this figure also indicates the overall result if oxygen is supplied as the hydrogen acceptor for all four reducing half-reactions.

We end up with the same final equation and the same net energy yield as in a single-step oxidation of methane, but here the oxidation has been a four-step process. Such stepwise oxidation occurs generally in the respiration of all foods. Indeed, although methane itself is not a food, the oxidation steps for actual foods are nevertheless the same as those outlined for methane: *the carbon groupings of food molecules are transformed successively from hydrocarbon to alcohol to aldehyde to acid to anhydride* (Fig. 18.3). Moreover, the oxidation states of carbon change successively from -4 to -2 to 0 to $+2$ to $+4$.

18 · 2 The stepwise oxidation of methane. *Only the four oxidizing half-reactions are shown separately; at each step an H_2 emerges and combines with oxygen, a process representing the reducing half-reaction of that step. The sum of all oxidizing and reducing half-reactions is indicated at the bottom, as is also the overall reaction. This overall reaction is identical with the one-step oxidation of methane discussed in the text. Note that more energy is gained during the reduction than is expended during the oxidation, hence the net ΔF is negative; in other words, CO_2 is more stable than CH_4.*

METHANE $\quad CH_4$

$\downarrow +H_2O$

$$\left[\begin{array}{c} H \\ H-C-H\cdot H-O-H \\ H \end{array}\right]$$ 1 FIRST OXIDATIVE HALF-REACTION

$\downarrow -H_2 \ldots [\text{to O}]$

METHYL ALCOHOL $\quad H-\overset{H}{\underset{H}{C}}-O-H$

2 SECOND OXIDATIVE HALF-REACTION

$\downarrow -H_2 \ldots [\text{to O}]$

FORMALDEHYDE $\quad H-\overset{}{\underset{H}{C}}=O$

$\downarrow +H_2O$

$$\left[\begin{array}{c} H-C=O \\ H \\ \cdot \\ H-O-H \end{array}\right]$$ 3 THIRD OXIDATIVE HALF-REACTION

$\downarrow -H_2 \ldots [\text{to O}]$

FORMIC ACID $\quad H-\overset{}{\underset{O-H}{C}}=O$

$\downarrow -H_2 \ldots [\text{to O}]$

CARBON DIOXIDE $\quad \overset{}{\underset{O}{C}}=O$

4 FOURTH OXIDATIVE HALF-REACTION

$CH_4 + 2 H_2O \longrightarrow CO_2 + 4 H_2$ (SUM OF OXIDATIONS, $+\Delta F$)

$4 H_2 + 2 O_2 \longrightarrow 4 H_2O$ (SUM OF REDUCTIONS, $-\Delta F$)

$CH_4 + 2 O_2 \longrightarrow CO_2 + 2 H_2O$ OVERALL REACTION, NET $-\Delta F$

We may ask at this point why biological oxidations proceed stepwise at all, and why food molecules should not be completely oxidized to CO_2 in single steps. The answer is that a single-step oxidation would release the entire energy yield as a single large "packet." Most of this energy would then be wasted as heat. As we shall see shortly, cells are not equipped to make metabolic (that is, chemical) use of single energy quantities which exceed certain magnitudes. Indeed, too intense an evolution of heat would kill a cell. Stepwise oxidations, on the other hand, make energy available in smaller, successive packets, and each of these can become metabolically useful. Moreover, heat wastage is thereby reduced and heat death is avoided.

Given food molecules possess carbon groupings at various different oxidation levels. For example, one of the carbons of a fatty acid is at the acid level $(+2)$, the others are at the hydrocarbon level (-4); a sugar such as glucose contains one carbon at the aldehyde level (0), five others at the alcohol level $(-2;$ Fig. 18.4). Oxidations of individual carbon groups here will proceed stepwise from any given starting level until the anhydride $(+4)$ stage is attained. Correspondingly, the energy yields will differ according to how many oxidation steps may still occur for each carbon group.

How is oxidation actually accomplished in foods?

HYDROGEN TRANSFER

If fuel dehydrogenation is to take place—and note from Fig. 18.3 that each oxidation step from hydrocarbon to CO_2 actually does require the removal of a hydrogen pair—then two conditions must be fulfilled. First, a specific enzyme must catalyze the reaction. Such enzymes are known as *dehydrogenases.* Each particular food compound requires its own specific dehydrogenase for each specific oxidation step. Second, since hydrogen removal as such represents only an oxidizing half-reaction, the process cannot proceed unless a reducing half-reaction takes place as well. In other words, an appropriate hydrogen acceptor must be present. The ultimate hydrogen acceptor in cells is oxygen. This is why most organisms must supply the gas to all cells as a respiratory raw material. Water then becomes one of the final endproducts of respiration (Fig. 18.5).

However, cellular fuels do not release hydrogen to oxygen directly. Instead, H from fuel is first passed along a whole succession of intermediate hydrogen carriers, and only the last of these finally yields hydrogen to oxygen. The advantage of such serial transfers is that more usable energy may be obtained than if H and O were allowed to combine directly.

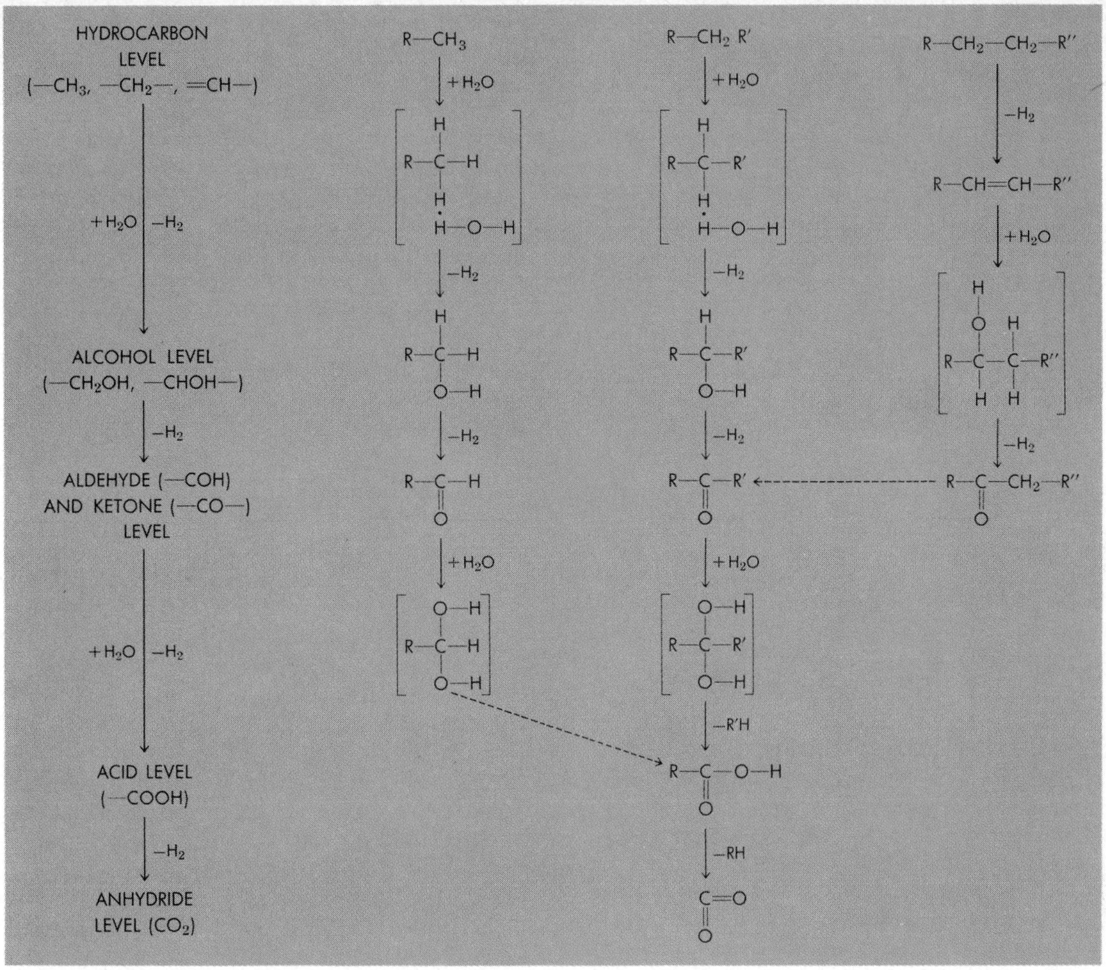

18 · 3

HYDROCARBON LEVEL $(-CH_3, -CH_2-, =CH-)$

$+H_2O \quad -H_2$

ALCOHOL LEVEL $(-CH_2OH, -CHOH-)$

$-H_2$

ALDEHYDE $(-COH)$ **AND KETONE** $(-CO-)$ **LEVEL**

$+H_2O \quad -H_2$

ACID LEVEL $(-COOH)$

$-H_2$

ANHYDRIDE LEVEL (CO_2)

18 · 3   Steps in the oxidation of carbon groupings. *Column at far left indicates the general oxidative sequence from hydrocarbon to acid anhydride. The next column illustrates the changes taking place in the oxidation of a terminal hydrocarbon, namely, a methyl group (—R here representing the rest of the molecule). The column at right center outlines the corresponding steps for a nonterminal hydrocarbon group, and so does the column on the far right, in which two adjacent hydrocarbon groups are nonterminal. These two oxidative sequences at right differ only in detail down to the ketone level and become identical thereafter. As in the stepwise oxidation of methane (Fig. 18.2), all sequences involve four reaction steps, two characterized by hydration and all four by dehydrogenation.*

We already know that, as a reducing half-reaction, a combination of hydrogen and oxygen is an energy-yielding process ($-\Delta F$, above). That this is so can also be demonstrated readily in the test tube; when mixed in the right proportions, hydrogen and oxygen

18 · 4   Oxidation levels *of different carbon groups are illustrated by the structures of fatty acid (top), glucose (middle), and fructose (bottom). The amount of further oxidation still possible for each group depends on its particular oxidation level in the intact molecule.*

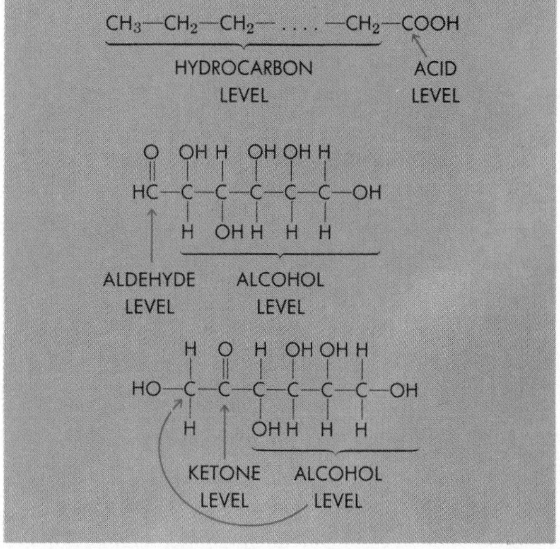

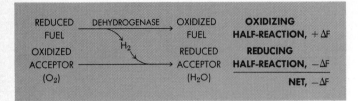

18 · 5 *The pattern of hydrogen transfer and the energy yield in respiration.*

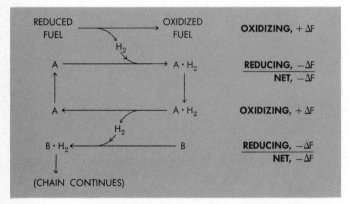

18 · 6 *Hydrogen transfer. If A and B represent the first two carriers in a hydrogen transfer chain, then the successive transfers of H_2 from food to A to B may be symbolized as above. Each step of transfer is thermodynamically possible because it is characterized by a negative net ΔF.*

18 · 7 *Coenzymes in respiratory hydrogen transfer from foods, leading to the ultimate production of water. In this series, Q stands for a carrier which is still known only poorly; it is sometimes referred to as "coenzyme Q" and it probably belongs to the chemical category of quinone compounds. A more detailed illustration of the steps in hydrogen transfer is given in Fig. 18.10.*

combine explosively. We should not conclude, however, that a similarly direct combination in cells would lead to explosion of cells; the quantities of gases involved there at any moment would probably be far too small to cause damage. The important conclusion is, rather, that in a direct combination of the two gases any energy released would appear as a single large packet, which would dissipate almost entirely as heat. Thus, H transfer to oxygen undoubtedly takes place in stepwise fashion for exactly the same reasons that fuel oxidation to CO_2 occurs in small steps; smaller, more numerous energy packets become available for metabolic use.

Indeed, like fuel oxidation to CO_2, each step in a serial hydrogen transfer is itself a complete redox process. The general nature of such serial redox reactions is indicated in Fig. 18.6. Note that, just as $A \cdot H_2$ in this figure is more stable than reduced fuel, so $B \cdot H_2$ is more stable than $A \cdot H_2$. Note also that the intermediate H carriers are alternately reduced and oxidized; they operate cyclically, first accepting H_2, then passing it on, then accepting new H_2, and so on.

The actual intermediate H carriers are some of the coenzymes already encountered in Chap. 6. The sequence in which such coenzymes actually transfer hydrogen is shown in Fig. 18.7. In this sequence, Q is an incompletely known coenzyme, and the cytochromes consist of a family of at least four slightly different variants that operate in succession. They are named, in order, cytochromes c_1, c, a, and a_3.

Note that, after H removal from food, *either* NAD or NADP may accept hydrogen. This is not a free choice, however, but depends on the nature of specific oxidation steps in specific foods. In certain particular cases, H transfers to NAD, in others to NADP. In the mitochondria of a cell, where most respiratory oxidations take place, it is usually NAD which serves as H carrier after food.

Some of the coenzymes, notably FAD, carry hydrogen in the form of whole atoms. NAD and the cytochromes, however, in part carry *electrons* rather than H atoms. In such cases H atoms dissociate, into H^+ and e^-. The resulting electron combines with the coenzyme, and the H ion remains free in the reaction medium. Subsequently the coenzyme either may transfer the electrons to another coenzyme or may release the electron back to H^+, in which case a reconstituted whole H atom moves on to the next carrier. In the specific case of NAD, this coenzyme normally exists in the form of NAD^+; the molecule lacks one electron and is therefore electropositive (Fig. 18.8). When it accepts a hydrogen pair from fuel, one H atom dissociates and the resulting electron

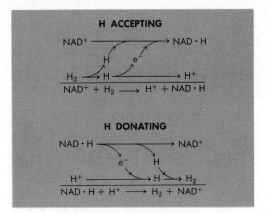

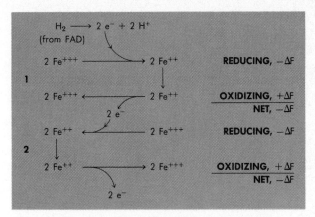

18 · 8 The role of NAD. *Of each* H_2 *yielded by food, one whole* H *atom and an electron from the other* H *atom join with* NAD^+, *resulting in neutral* $NAD \cdot H$. *An* H^+ *ion remains in the medium. In* H *release, these reactions are reversed. Note that NADP functions analogously.*

18 · 9 The pattern of H *transfer between the iron components of two successive cytochromes (1 and 2). Each time a (negative) electron is gained, the positive charge on iron decreases; and each time an electron is lost, the positive charge increases. Note particularly that, like transport of whole* H *atoms, electron transport is likewise a redox process; electron gain is a reduction, electron loss, an oxidation. Thus, electron transport is characterized thermodynamically by a negative net* ΔF.

neutralizes NAD^+ to NAD; the second H atom remains whole and attaches to NAD. Thus, $NAD \cdot H$ represents the reduced state and a H^+ remains available in the reaction medium. This H^+ is used in the later reoxidation of the coenzyme, when H_2 is released again.

In the case of the cytochromes, both H atoms of a pair dissociate, and each resulting electron is carried by one coenzyme molecule:

$$H_2 \longrightarrow 2\,H^+ \longrightarrow 2\,H^+$$
$$2\,e^-$$
$$2 \text{ cyt.} \longrightarrow 2 \text{ cyt. } e^-$$

The active H-carrying component of a cytochrome molecule is the iron in the center of its tetrapyrrol ring. This iron normally exists in the form of Fe^{+++} (ferric ion). When it accepts an electron, therefore, it becomes Fe^{++} (ferrous ion); its electropositivity is reduced by one charge unit:

$$Fe^{+++} + e^- \longrightarrow Fe^{++}$$

The pattern of hydrogen transport between two successive cytochromes is illustrated in Fig. 18.9. Note here especially that, like H transfer itself, electron transfers likewise are redox reactions. As already pointed out in Chap. 3, electron *loss* is oxidation, electron *gain*, reduction. Thus, the dissociation $H \longrightarrow H^+ + e^-$ involves electron loss by H, and H is therefore oxidized. And we may note again that H transfers are redox processes because H atoms contain electrons; every H removal or addition implies, and includes, removal or addition of an electron.

The energy changes in redox reactions ultimately always result from actual or "hidden" electron transfers, and it is this which is the key to any oxidation or reduction. The cytochromes evidently undergo redox changes in the most basic form, whereas in foods and in coenzymes like FAD the essential redox agent, the electron, remains hidden within H atoms.

The last cytochrome in the series, a_3, also known as *cytochrome oxidase*, releases electrons back to H^+, which has remained in the reaction medium. Whole H atoms then combine with oxygen, forming water. The entire sequence of H transport is summarized in Fig. 18.10.

AEROBIC AND ANAEROBIC TRANSFER

Because H transport as above requires atmospheric oxygen as the ultimate hydrogen acceptor, this pattern of transfer is said to define an *aerobic* (with air) form of respiration. It is the standard, universal form in the vast majority of organisms.

Several observations may be made concerning this aerobic pattern of H transport. First, as everywhere else in metabolism, each of the transport reactions must be catalyzed by a specific enzyme. We may note also that vitamins C, E, and K are known

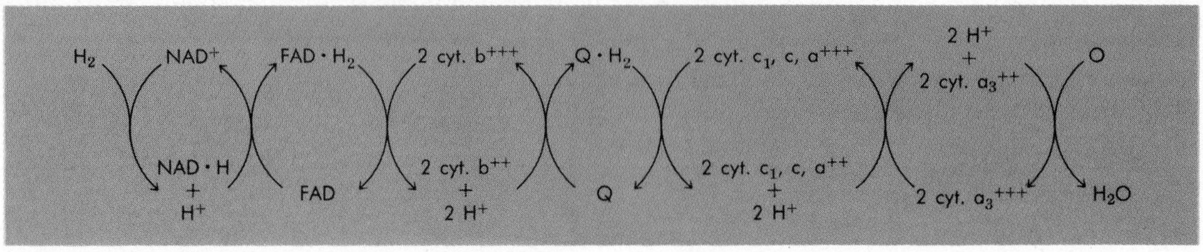

18 · 10 Summary of hydrogen transfer. *The carrier Q is probably interposed within the cytochrome transfer sequence, as indicated. Cytochromes c_1, c, and a actually function individually and in succession, though they are shown above to operate as a group as a space-saving convenience. Cytochrome a_3 is cytochrome oxidase. All cytochromes transport electrons, not whole H atoms. NAD transports partly electrons, partly H atoms, and FAD, Q, and O transport whole H atoms only.*

to be required in the reactions, although the precise role of these compounds is still obscure.

Second, it is clear that relatively small quantities of the hydrogen carriers suffice to transport comparatively large quantities of hydrogen; each carrier molecule functions cyclically and may be used repeatedly.

Third, if any one of the reactions is stopped, the whole transport system becomes inoperative, and the energy it normally supplies cannot be obtained. Reaction blocks may occur in a number of ways. For example, *inhibitor* substances of various kinds may interfere specifically with given transport reactions. Thus, potassium cyanide specifically inhibits the cytochrome system, and this is why cyanide is such a violent poison. Another form of reaction block is produced if one of the carriers is in deficient supply. For example, inasmuch as riboflavin (vitamin B_2) is a structural part of the FAD molecule, a consistently riboflavin-deficient diet would soon impair the reactions in which FAD participates.

Any such reaction barrier introduced into the transport sequence will act like a roadblock and will lead to an accumulation of hydrogen back of the barrier. For example, if the cytochrome system is blocked, $FAD \cdot H_2$ cannot get rid of its hydrogen. All available FAD will then soon hold H_2 to capacity, and none will be free to accept more H_2 from NAD. Therefore, NAD cannot get rid of its own hydrogen, and free NAD will no longer become available to accept more hydrogen from fresh fuel. Respiration will be effectively stopped.

To be sure, cyanide poisoning and vitamin B deficiencies are not particularly common hazards in the life of an organism, and most organisms would probably survive quite well even without special protective adaptations against such contingencies. But there is one hazard affecting H transport which all organisms do have to cope with quite frequently: unavailability of enough atmospheric oxygen. Lack of oxygen is a reaction barrier of the same sort as cyanide poisoning or vitamin deficiencies. The consequence is a damming up of hydrogen all the way back to NAD, with the further consequence that respiration as a whole becomes blocked.

Whenever oxygen supplies are inadequate or whenever hydrogen transport to oxygen is otherwise blocked, organisms may respire in a way which does not require oxygen. This is *anaerobic respiration*, or *fermentation*, probably a more ancient form of energy production than the aerobic kind (see Chap. 11). Under conditions of oxygen deficiency, this anaerobic type of respiration may become a substitute or a subsidiary source of energy.

The principle of anaerobic hydrogen transport is relatively simple: with the path from NAD to FAD and oxygen blocked, another path, from NAD to another hydrogen acceptor, must be used. Such an alternative path is provided by *pyruvic acid*, CH_3—$COCOOH$, one of the compounds normally formed in the course of carbohydrate oxidation (see below). If oxygen is amply available, pyruvic acid is merely one of the intermediate steps in the decomposition of carbohydrates. In other words, it is a fuel which, in the presence of oxygen, may be oxidized further to CO_2. But pyruvic acid has the property of reacting readily with hydrogen. And if NAD cannot use its normal hydrogen outlet to FAD, pyruvic acid is used instead. The acid then ceases to be a fuel and becomes a hydrogen carrier.

When pyruvic acid reacts with hydrogen, the result in plants and most microorganisms is the formation of alcohol and CO_2, and in animals and certain bacteria, the formation of lactic acid:

$$NAD \cdot H + H^+ \longrightarrow NAD^+$$

$$CH_3COCOOH \xrightarrow{\quad H_2 \quad} \begin{cases} CH_3CH_2OH + CO_2 \text{ (in plant} \\ \textit{alcohol} \\ CH_3CHOHCOOH \text{ (in animal} \\ \textit{lactic acid} \end{cases}$$

pyruvic acid

Different enzymes in plants and animals account for these different results. Through beer, wine, and other alcoholic beverages man has known longer about the results of fermentation (carried out largely by yeast) than about the chemical details of this process.

The reaction above in effect completes anaerobic respiration. Alcohol or lactic acid accumulates in a cell and eventually diffuses into the cellular suroundings. The energy gained through fermentation suffices to maintain the life of organisms such as yeasts, many bacteria, and other so-called obligate or facultative *anaerobes,* that is, organisms which must or may survive in the absence of oxygen. However, the vast majority of organisms belongs to the category of *aerobes,* organisms which must have oxygen and for which fermentation energy by itself is insufficient. If in such organisms oxygen is absent, the energy normally obtained through H transfer to oxygen cannot be realized. Moreover, anaerobic fuel oxidation has stopped at the pyruvic acid stage, and the potential energy still contained in this acid therefore remains untapped and locked in alcohol or lactic acid. As we shall see below, fermentation actually yields only about 5 per cent of the energy obtainable by aerobic respiration. This is too little to maintain the life of plants or animals; as is well known, complete absence of oxygen leads to death within minutes. (Plants and animals generally cannot store oxygen. At any given moment only enough of the gas is in the body to suffice for immediate needs.)

But even though fermentation alone cannot sustain life, it may *supplement* the aerobic energy gains. Whenever energy demands are high, as during intensive muscular activity in animals, for example, then the oxygen supply to the cells may become insufficient despite faster breathing. Under such conditions of *oxygen debt,* fermentation may proceed in parallel with aerobic respiration and provide a little extra energy. Lactic acid then accumulates, particularly in the muscles. This increase in concentration appears to be associated specifically with fatigue. Eventually, fatigue becomes so great that the animal must cease its intensive activity. During an ensuing rest period, faster breathing at first continues. The oxygen debt is thereby being repaid, and the extra oxygen permits the complete oxidation of the accumulated lactic acid. However, note that mammalian muscles do not use lactic acid as fuel directly. Instead, the acid diffuses from muscles into the blood, is carried by blood into the liver, and here the acid is converted to glucose. This sugar then passes back via the blood to the muscles, where it is transformed to glycogen. Finally, under aerobic conditions, muscles may oxidize glycogen to pyruvic acid and, ultimately, to CO_2. Thus, the potential energy still present in lactic acid need not be lost permanently to a fermenting cell. With the gradual disappearance of

lactic acid, fatigue decreases and the breathing rate slows back to normal (Fig. 18.11).

Up to this point, we have found that respiration consists of stepwise fuel oxidation accomplished through dehydrogenation, and of hydrogen transport either to pyruvic acid or, more usually, to oxygen. The latter process as well as fuel oxidation itself constitute the sources of the respiratory energy yields. However, we have so far considered energy yields only in general terms. How are such yields made useful, and how *much* of the yield can actually become useful?

ENERGY TRANSFER

As noted, biological oxidations take place without appreciable increases in cellular temperatures because much of the energy yield does not appear primarily as heat. Instead, the metabolically important fraction of the yield is harvested in the form of high-energy phosphate bonds within ATP. If we symbolize organic phosphate groups simply as —O—P, we may write:

$$\text{—O—P} \xrightarrow{\text{respiratory energy}} \text{—O}\sim\text{P} \quad \text{adenosine—O—P—O}\sim\text{P}$$
$$ADP$$
$$\text{adenosine—O—P—O}\sim\text{P—O}\sim\text{P}$$
$$ATP$$

18 · 11 Anaerobic respiration. *If the path of H_2 to oxygen is blocked, pyruvic acid cannot be respired to CO_2 (dashed lines). Fermentation, or anaerobic respiration, then may take place. In this process, pyruvic acid accepts H_2 and becomes lactic acid. If produced in muscle, lactic acid passes via blood to the liver, becomes glucose there, and eventually returns via blood to muscle where it becomes glycogen. After the block to oxygen is no longer present, such glycogen may be respired completely to CO_2 (via pyruvic acid, which then is not required as a hydrogen acceptor).*

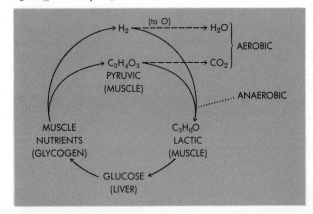

18 · 12   High-energy bonds. *The general pattern of their creation by phosphorylation and oxidation and of the transfer of such bonds to ADP.*

This scheme clearly implies, that, before $-O \sim P$ groups can be transferred to ADP to form ATP, such groups must first be created. They are indeed created in respiration. Two general events take place. First, in a preparatory process, a fuel molecule is *phosphorylated*, that is, a phosphate group, $-O-P$, is attached to it. Secondly, the phosphorylated fuel is oxidized, that is, dehydrogenation occurs. We already know that this process yields energy, but inasmuch as a $-O-P$ group is now present on the fuel molecule, the energy is not released as heat. Instead, the energy becomes redistributed within the fuel molecule and becomes incorporated directly into the phosphate bond, without being "released" at all. The bond restricts resonance (see Chap. 4) and can therefore hold extra energy. The phosphate $-O-P$ thus becomes a high-energy phosphate, $-O \sim P$, and the latter is then transferred to ADP (Fig. 18.12).

As pointed out above, there are two general respiratory sources of energy, hence of $-O \sim P$ and ATP: fuel oxidation itself, and hydrogen transfer from fuel to oxygen. The second source is quantitatively probably the more important, but the precise mechanism of ATP formation here is still incompletely known. In H transfer from NAD to FAD, for example, ATP is believed to arise by processes outlined in Fig. 18.13. In this figure, X and Y are unknown compounds. In a first reaction, NAD·H is thought to become oxidized by FAD, resulting in a high-energy bond between NAD^+ and compound X. The $\sim$X fraction is then believed to be transferred successively to compound Y and to phosphate (reactions 2 and 3). The latter finally reacts with ADP, yielding ATP (reaction 4). Analogous events are thought to take place in the oxidation of any given H carrier by the next carrier in the series. It can be shown that H transfer through the complete carrier series from NAD to oxygen yields a net of three ATP molecules for every H_2 transferred. As we shall see, this yield is the prime source of respiratory energy in most cases.

Much better understood is the process of ATP

formation during oxidation of a food. Consider an actual aldehyde to acid oxidation, for example:

$$-\overset{|}{\underset{H}{C}}=O \longrightarrow -C\overset{\nearrow}{\underset{\searrow}{=}}\overset{O}{\underset{O-H}{}}$$

aldehyde   *acid*

Under biological conditions as just noted, the first event is a preliminary phosphorylation of the aldehyde. The phosphate donor here can be inorganic phosphoric acid, $H-O-P$:

$$-\overset{|}{\underset{H}{C}}=O \xrightarrow{+H-O-P} \left[-\overset{|}{\underset{H \cdot H-O-P}{C}}=O \right] \quad (1)$$

The next step (which takes place almost simultaneously) is oxidation by hydrogen removal; the energy yield of this process appears as a high-energy bond:

$$\left[-\overset{|}{\underset{H \cdot H-O-P}{C}}=O \right] \xrightarrow{\quad\quad} -C\overset{=O}{\underset{O \sim P}{}} \quad (2)$$

The resulting hydrogen may be accepted by NAD^+, for example. The final step is transfer of the high-energy phosphate to ADP, in exchange for a $-O-H$ group.

$$-C\overset{=O}{\underset{O \sim P}{}} \qquad -C\overset{=O}{\underset{O-H}{}}$$

$$ADP \qquad\qquad ATP \qquad (3)$$

The original aldehyde thus has become transformed into an acid, $-COOH$, and ADP has become ATP. As we shall see shortly, this particular series of reactions occurs normally at one point in carbohydrate respiration. But we may note that the pattern is analogous in principle for any other direct oxidation of a food.

In the example above, the phosphate donor for the preparatory phosphorylation has been phosphoric acid. This is relatively unusual, and in most cases the phosphate donor actually is ATP. We have already found earlier, for example, that glucose uptake into a cell is accompanied by phosphorylation and that ATP is the phosphorylating agent. In this and all analogous instances, the terminal high-energy phosphate of ATP is split off (and ATP thus

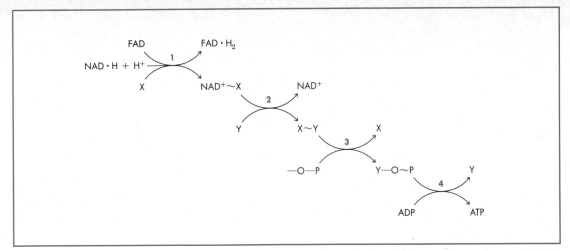

18 · 13   *ATP generation during H transfer.* H
*carriers such as NAD are believed to interact
with hypothetical compounds X and Y and with
phosphates in a four-step sequence as shown,
resulting in high-energy phosphate bonds* (color)
incorporated in ATP.

becomes ADP), but an ordinary low-energy phosphate is added onto the fuel molecule:

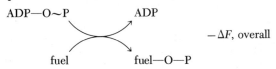

ADP—O~P   ADP

                                                      −ΔF, overall

fuel   fuel—O—P

In other words, ATP supplies not only phosphate, but also more than enough energy to produce a phosphorylated compound. Any energy excess here dissipates unavoidably as heat. Many phosphorylations can be achieved only by ATP, even though not all the energy supplied by ATP is being used. Note, furthermore, that ATP is the primary endproduct of respiration but that respiration cannot proceed unless ATP is available for preliminary phosphorylations; some of the endproduct is needed at the starting point, and prior respiration thus becomes a necessary condition for further respiration.

How much ATP can actually be formed in respiration? The quantity varies with the nature of the fuel, that is, the number of possible oxidation steps. Moreover, it is important to realize that every single oxidation step does not necessarily yield a large enough amount of energy sufficient for the formation of ATP. It can be shown that the conversion of ADP to ATP requires on the average 7,000 cal per gram-molecular weight (mole) of ADP. In other

words, 7,000 cal represent a kind of minimum energy packet in metabolism, and any oxidation which yields less than that will not result in ATP formation. Many oxidations actually yield more. In fuel oxidations, for example, energy yields range from about 5,000 to about 11,000 cal, with an average of about 8,000 cal, per mole of fuel oxidized. Most of such oxidations may result in ATP formation (and any energy excess dissipates as heat). On the other hand, some of the oxidation steps in hydrogen transport to oxygen produce less than the minimum energy amounts required for ATP formation, hence only three ATP arise per H_2 transferred, even though the total number of oxidation steps during the transfer is greater than three (Fig. 18.14).

18 · 14   *Two sources of ATP are fuel oxidation
and H transport to oxygen. The latter yields
high-energy phosphates in three places of the
carrier sequence, as indicated. This second energy
source thus yields 3 ATP for every H_2 transferred.*

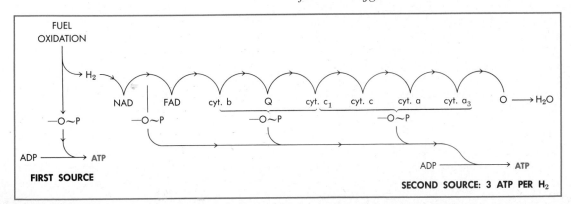

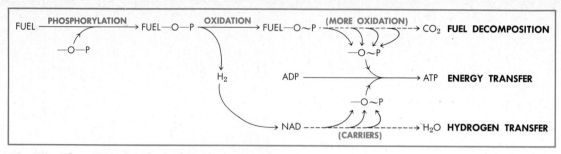

18 · 15 *The common three-phase pattern of respiration: breakdown of fuel, hydrogen transfer from fuel, and energy transfer from fuel.*

Figure 18.15 may be regarded as a comprehensive summary of the general pattern of respiration. The process always includes three principal phases: (1) *fuel decomposition,* which takes the form of phosphorylation and oxidation and results in the end-product CO_2; (2) *hydrogen transfer* from fuel to oxygen (or to pyruvic acid), which results in the end-product H_2O (or alcohol or lactic acid); (3) *energy transfer* from fuel to ADP, which results in the end-product ATP. The first two phases are the sources

of usable energy. The second and third phases are the same for all kinds of fuels, and respiratory events differ principally according to the different specific fuels used as raw material. We now proceed to examine some of these actual reaction pathways by which given fuels are oxidized.

THE PROCESS

In the course of being oxidized progressively, the carbon groupings of a fuel molecule eventually become CO_2 and this gas escapes into the environment. Thus, fuel molecules containing given numbers of carbon atoms at the start lose their carbons one at a time, until sooner or later the entire molecule will have been converted into C_1 fragments, or CO_2. If we follow this decomposition sequence backward, the next to last stage in fuel breakdown should be a 2-carbon C_2 fragment. This is the case; every fuel molecule sooner or later appears as a 2-carbon fragment, which in fact is always the same regardless of what the starting fuel may have been. In a last step, the C_2 fragment is then decomposed into two C_1 fragments, CO_2. The common C_2 stage for all fuels in respiration is a derivative of acetic acid called *acetyl,* $CH_3C\!=\!O$. It does not exist as such by itself but is attached to a carrier coenzyme, namely, the sulfur-containing coenzyme A, or CoA (see Chap. 6). The resulting complex is acetyl CoA, which may be symbolized as $CH_3CO\!\sim\!S\!-\!CoA$. Note that this complex contains a high-energy $-C\!\sim\!S-$ bond. As pointed out in Chap. 4, such bonds restrict resonance like high-energy phosphate bonds. The acetyl portion of acetyl CoA subsequently yields 2 CO_2.

The manner in which the acetyl CoA stage is reached differs for different types of fuels. For example, many carbohydrates are first broken up into 3-carbon compounds. Complex carbohydrates often are built up from 3-carbon units, and their carbon numbers then are whole multiples of 3. This holds, for example, for glucose and all other 6-carbon sugars, for 12-carbon disaccharides, and for polysaccharides such as starch and glycogen. As we shall see, when any of these are used as respiratory fuels, the original

18 · 16 *Main pathways in aerobic combustion of fuels. Pyruvic acid, acetyl* CoA, *and carbon dioxide form a main sequence which other pathways join, like branches of a tree.*

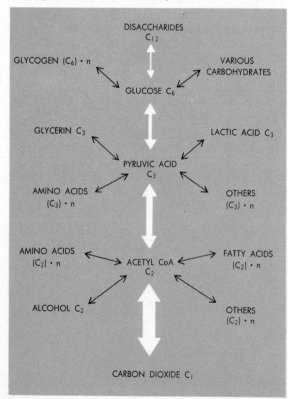

3-carbon units reappear in the course of breakdown. Many other organic substances, glycerin, for example, are 3-carbon molecules to begin with. All such C_3 compounds are eventually converted to *pyruvic acid* ($C_3H_4O_3$). This acid is the common representative of the 3-carbon stage in respiration. Pyruvic acid subsequently loses one carbon in the form of CO_2 and becomes acetyl CoA.

Fatty acids and related molecules consist of long, even-numbered carbon chains. These do not break up into 3-carbon units but become 2-carbon units directly. Other fuels are 2-carbon molecules to begin with, and all such C_2 compounds eventually appear as acetyl CoA. Amino acids break down partly to pyruvic acid (which subsequently becomes acetyl CoA), partly to acetyl CoA directly. This holds also for many other organic substances which may happen to be used as fuel.

Thus, the overall pattern of aerobic fuel combustion may be likened to a tree with branches or to a river with tributaries (Fig. 18.16). A broad main channel is represented by the sequence pyruvic acid $\longrightarrow$ acetyl CoA $\longrightarrow$ carbon dioxide. Numerous side channels lead into the sequence, some funneling into the 3-carbon pyruvic acid step, others into the 2-carbon acetyl CoA step. The side channels themselves may be long or short, and each may have smaller side channels of its own. In the end, the flow from the entire system drains out as 1-carbon CO_2.

Because the respiratory degradation of acetyl CoA to CO_2 occurs according to a single common reaction pathway regardless of what the original food may have been, it is best to discuss this pathway first.

FORMATION OF CO_2: THE CITRIC ACID CYCLE

The breakdown of the C_2 acetyl fragment takes the form of a *cycle* of reactions. The C_2 fragment first becomes attached to a C_4 molecule normally present in the mitochondria of a cell, yielding a C_6 molecule. The latter then loses one CO_2 and becomes a C_5 molecule; and in its turn the C_5 molecule subsequently loses another CO_2, resulting in a C_4 molecule. This last rearranges into the same C_4 compound which started the cycle. The net result is the conversion of acetyl into 2 CO_2 and the production of 12 ATP. The whole sequence is known as the *citric acid cycle*, after one of the participating (C_6) compounds, or as the *Krebs cycle*, after its discoverer. It occurs exclusively in the mitochondria of cells. A simple version of the cycle is given in Fig. 18.17, a more detailed one in Fig. 18.18.

It will be seen from Fig. 18.18 that the cycle consists of nine consecutive steps. In a first step, acetyl

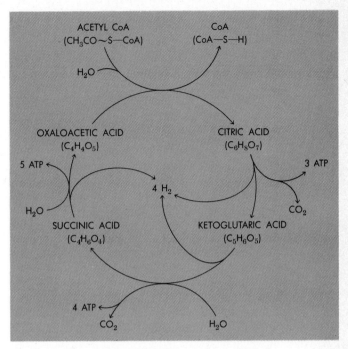

18 · 17 The citric acid cycle, *greatly simplified. For greater detail see Fig. 18.18.*

CoA reacts with the C_4 compound *oxaloacetic acid*, yielding free CoA and *citric acid*. The —C~S— bond of acetyl CoA provides the energy for joining acetyl to oxaloacetic acid. Citric acid next reorganizes by two steps into *isocitric acid*. The net effect of this reorganization is a shift of the alcohol group at position 4 in citric acid to position 5 in isocitric acid. An oxidation now occurs at this position, yielding the ketone-containing *oxalosuccinic acid*. NAD is the hydrogen acceptor, and note that the oxidation has *not* affected either of the carbons contributed by the acetyl group at the start of the cycle.

Oxalosuccinic acid is subsequently simplified by removal of CO_2, or *decarboxylation*, at position 3, yielding α-*ketoglutaric acid*. This C_5 compound now undergoes an *oxidative* decarboxylation; that is, H_2 is removed along with CO_2. The process takes the form of a series of subreactions, as outlined in Fig. 18.19. We may note here, for later reference, that α-ketoglutaric acid (like oxaloacetic acid above) is one of several kinds of α-*keto acids;* as in fatty acids, the α position is the carbon next to the acid group, and this α carbon is a ketone. Other α-keto acids similarly are of the type R—COCOOH, where R— may be one of a large variety of different groupings. All α-keto acids readily lose CO_2 from the acid group. This process requires the participation of a specific enzyme, *carboxylase*, as well as a specific coenzyme,

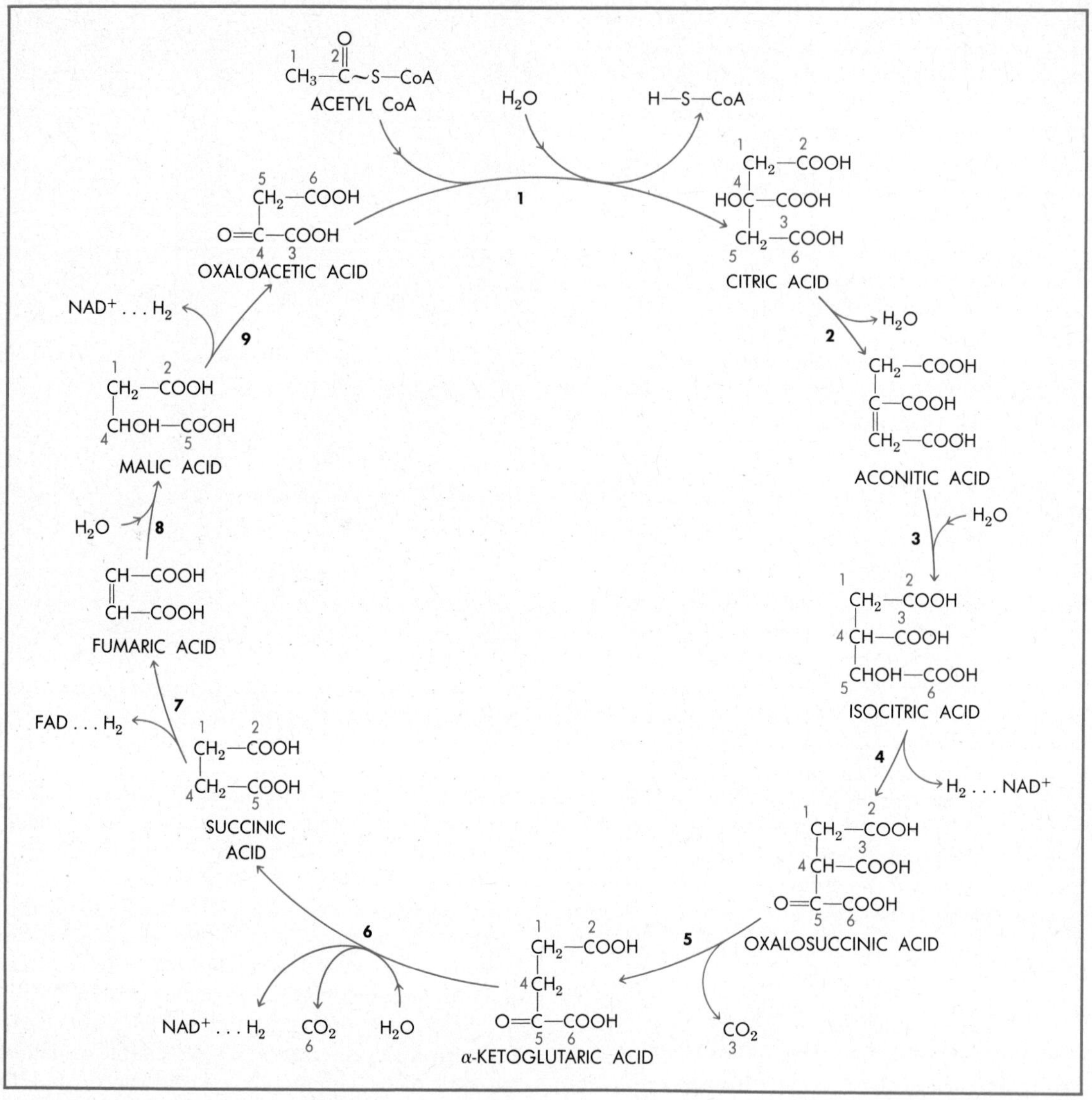

O
‖
CH_3—C~S—CoA
ACETYL CoA

H_2O H—S—CoA

CH_2—COOH
HOC—COOH
CH_2—COOH
CITRIC ACID

CH_2—COOH
$O=C$—COOH
OXALOACETIC ACID

$NAD^+ \ldots H_2$

9

CH_2—COOH
CHOH—COOH
MALIC ACID

1

2   H_2O

CH_2—COOH
C—COOH
CH_2—COOH
ACONITIC ACID

H_2O 8

CH—COOH
‖
CH—COOH
FUMARIC ACID

3   H_2O

CH_2—COOH
CH—COOH
CHOH—COOH
ISOCITRIC ACID

FAD $\ldots H_2$ 7

CH_2—COOH
CH_2—COOH
SUCCINIC
ACID

4        $H_2 \ldots NAD^+$

CH_2—COOH
CH—COOH
$O=C$—COOH
OXALOSUCCINIC ACID

6

5

$NAD^+ \ldots H_2$ CO_2 H_2O

CH_2—COOH
CH_2
$O=C$—COOH
α-KETOGLUTARIC ACID

CO_2

18 · 18 The citric acid cycle. *Small colored numbers next to carbon atoms identify positions during a first turn of the cycle. Thus during step 9, carbons 1, 2, and 4 of malic acid become carbons 1, 2, and 4 of second-turn oxaloacetic acid and citric acid; carbon 5 of malic acid becomes 3 of the second-turn citric acid; and the two carbons of the second-turn acetyl CoA assume positions 5 and 6 of the second-turn citric acid. The enzymes required at each step of the cycle are as follows: 1, condensing enzyme; 2, 3, aconitase; 4, isocitric dehydrogenase; 5, oxalosuccinic decarboxylase; 6, see Fig. 18.19; 7, succinic dehydrogenase; 8, fumarase; 9, malic dehydrogenase.*

cocarboxylase. The latter is a derivative of *thiamine,* or vitamin B_1. Thiamine reacts in cells with ATP to yield *thiamine pyrophosphate,* or cocarboxylase:

thiamine + ATP $\longrightarrow$
$\qquad$ thiamine—O ~ P—O ~ P + AMP

The coenzyme functions as a temporary CO_2 carrier after carboxylase catalyzes the extraction of CO_2 from —COOH (Fig. 18.19, reaction 1). Removal of CO_2 converts α-ketoglutaric acid into an aldehyde, which then joins with CoA and becomes dehydrogenated. The hydrogen acceptor in this oxidation is *lipoic acid,* a derivative of an 8-carbon fatty acid containing a disulfide bond. When this acid accepts hydrogen and becomes reduced, the —S—S— bond splits and forms

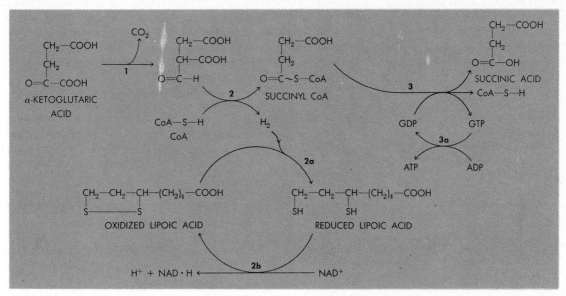

two —SH groups (Fig. 18.19, reaction 2a). Reduced lipoic acid subsequently yields H_2 to NAD^+, resulting in reoxidized lipoic acid (Fig. 18.19, reaction 2b). The original dehydrogenation has also produced succinyl CoA, which contains a —C~S— bond (Fig. 18.19, reaction 2). The energy of this bond is transferred next into GTP (guanosine triphosphate) and ultimately into ATP. The net result of the whole sequence is the transformation of α-ketoglutaric acid to *succinic acid*, a C_4 compound.

The next main steps of the citric acid cycle consist of a reorganization of succinic acid in three consecutive reactions (see Fig. 18.18). First, dehydrogenation produces an unsaturated double bond, FAD here being the hydrogen acceptor. Next, the resulting *fumaric acid* is hydrated to *malic acid*, which carries an alcoholic group at a subterminal carbon (position 4). Finally, this alcoholic group is dehydrogenated, NAD now being the H acceptor. This process results in the regeneration of *oxaloacetic acid*.

What is the overall tally? We may note, first, that the carbon atoms fed into the cycle as acetyl are not transformed immediately to CO_2. After a first turn of the cycle, these carbon atoms appear in the following turn at positions 5 and 6 of citric acid. Thus, an acetyl group fed into the cycle in any given turn appears as CO_2 byproduct only in later turns. Second, we may note that the $2 CO_2$ eventually formed in any one cycle turn derive from carbons 3 and 6 of citric acid; hence as one turn follows another, different carbon atoms become shifted successively into given positions within citric acid. Third, carbon 5 of citric acid is oxidized twice (steps 4 and 6), carbon 4 is oxidized once (step 9).

18 · 19   Transformation of α-ketoglutaric acid to succinic acid. The first step is a decarboxylation, requiring the participation of carboxylase, cocarboxylase, and Mg^{++}. The second step is a dehydrogenation, lipoic acid and NAD here being successive hydrogen acceptors. The third step represents an energy transfer via GTP and ADP.

Carbon 5 is thus brought from an alcohol via a ketone to an acid level, and carbon 4, from an alcohol to a ketone level. Fourth, the cycle uses up four molecules of water (steps 1, 3, 6, and 8), but yields $1 H_2O$ at step 2. Fifth, of the four hydrogen pairs removed in the cycle (steps 4, 6, 7, and 9), three pairs pass from NAD to oxygen, one pair from FAD to oxygen. These transfers yield $4 H_2O$ as well as 11 ATP; and one additional ATP arises from the conversion of succinyl CoA to succinic acid. The whole cycle may therefore be summarized as follows:

$$CH_3COSCoA + 3 H_2O \longrightarrow$$
acetyl CoA

$$2 CO_2 + 4 H_2 + CoASH$$
$$\searrow \text{ to oxygen: } 4 H_2O, 12 ATP$$

The cycle runs exceedingly rapidly; an acetyl fraction may be degraded in a fraction of a second. Such speed is probably made possible by the highly organized condition of the mitochondrial apparatus. Enzymes, H carriers, and all other required reaction ingredients appear to be lined up in functionally proper sequence along the inner membrane of a mitochondrion, and indeed these reaction ingredients are probably building blocks in the very structure

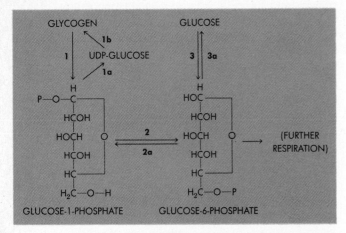

18 · 20 *Reversible conversions of glycogen and glucose to glucose-6-phosphate. Numbers refer to the enzymes and energy sources required for each reaction as follows: 1, glycogen phosphorylase; 1a, uridine triphosphate (UTP); 1b, transferase; 2, glucophosphokinase; 2a, glucophosphomutase; 3, ATP, hexokinase; 3a, phosphatase. Note that, in these particular instances, the forward reactions (1, 2, 3,) are catalyzed by enzymes differing from those of the reverse reactions (1a, b, 2a, 3a). Note also that each glycogen molecule produces many molecules of glucose-1-phosphate.*

of this membrane. Thus, a fuel may be respired as if it were on a rapidly moving belt in an assembly line, the product of one operation being passed along to the adjacent station in the line where the next operation takes place. Mitochondrial structure evidently reduces the element of chance in respiratory reactions; appropriate reactants need not "wait" until they happen to collide by random thermal movement. High reaction rates and great efficiency are the result.

As pointed out earlier, acetyl is not generally an original fuel itself but usually appears as an intermediate in the respiratory degradation of various original foods. By what respiratory pathways do such foods funnel into the citric acid cycle?

CARBOHYDRATE RESPIRATION

Carbohydrates are converted to acetyl in two successive reaction sequences. The first, often referred to as *glycolysis*, results in pyruvic acid, the common 3-carbon stage regardless of what the original carbohydrate may have been. In the second sequence pyruvic acid is then transformed to acetyl and the latter feeds into the citric acid cycle.

Glycolysis

The starting point of glycolysis may be considered to be glucose-6-phosphate. Free glucose becomes glucose-6-phosphate with the phosphorylating aid of

18 · 21 *Glycolysis. In the nine steps of this sequence, the first four include rearrangements and a preliminary phosphorylation. Steps 5 and 6 constitute a first oxidation and energy transfer; that is, carbon 1 of glyceraldehyde-3-phosphate is simultaneously phosphorylated and oxidized. That carbon thereby changes from an aldehyde*

level to an acid level (in 3-phosphoglyceric acid). In this product of reaction 6, carbon 2 is at an alcohol level; in the remaining reactions this carbon is phosphorylated and then oxidized to the ketone level (in pyruvic acid). Thus, of the original glucose, carbon positions 2, 3, 4, and 5 are each oxidized once during glycolsis. The

ATP, as noted earlier (see Fig. 17.3). Glycogen or starch, main fuels in many animal and plant cell types, respectively, is phosphorylated by inorganic phosphates. Such polysaccharides thereby break up into numerous molecules of glucose-1-phosphate, and the latter are then converted enzymatically to glucose-6-phosphate (Fig. 18.20).

The subsequent glycolytic fate of glucose-6-phosphate is charted in Fig. 18.21. Note here that glucose-6-phosphate is first transformed into fructose-6-phosphate, a stage also reached directly from free fructose. Phosphorylation (by ATP) of fructose-6-phosphate at the 1 position then results in fructose-1,6-diphosphate. The latter subsequently splits between carbons 3 and 4, yielding two slightly different C_3 molecules. These two become rearranged into two identical molecules, glyceraldehyde phosphate (or phosphoglyceraldehyde, or PGAL). Up to this point, all steps have been in the nature of preparatory reactions. Although the alcoholic carbons at positions 3 and 4 of the original glucose are now aldehyde carbons at position 1 of PGAL, ATP-forming oxidations have not yet taken place.

The next series of steps does produce ATP. PGAL is first phosphorylated at position 1, the phosphate donor being inorganic phosphoric acid (step 5 in Fig. 18.21). Simultaneously, dehydrogenation occurs in the presence of NAD^+, and a high-energy bond is thereby created at position 1 (1,3-diphosphoglyceric acid). The high-energy phosphate is then transferred to ADP, resulting in ATP. Events here clearly correspond to those in the example used earlier, in the section on energy transfer. The compound so formed is 3-phosphoglyceric acid (PGA), and we note that the aldehyde carbon of PGAL has been oxidized to the acid carbon of PGA.

In a following sequence, the alcoholic carbon at position 2 of PGA becomes oxidized. As a preliminary to this, the phosphate group at position 3 of PGA is shifted enzymatically to position 2, resulting in 2-phosphoglyceric acid. Next (step 8, Fig. 18.21), *oxidative dehydration* takes place: H is removed from position 2 and —OH is removed simultaneously from position 3. In other words, a hydrogen pair is extracted along with an O atom, and since oxygen is a perfect carrier for hydrogen, NAD^+ is here not required. The result is water and phosphoenolpyruvic acid, which contains a high-energy phosphate at position 2. When the latter is then transferred to ADP, the endproducts are ATP and pyruvic acid. This acid contains a ketone group at position 2; the alcohol carbon of PGA has been oxidized to a ketone carbon in pyruvic acid. We already know from Fig. 18.3 that ketones have essentially the same oxidation level as aldehydes, that is, one level higher than alcohols.

The formation of pyruvic acid terminates glycolysis; a quantitative summary of the whole sequence is given in Fig. 18.22. If free glucose is considered to be the original raw material, we note that four phosphorylations have occurred, two by H—O—P and two by ATP. Each of the four added phosphates

following listing indicates the enzymes for each step: 1, phosphohexose isomerase, catalyzes rearrangement; 2, phosphofructokinase, adds —O—P in 1 position; 3, aldolase, splits chain between carbons 3 and 4; 4, phosphotriose isomerase, makes top compound same as one at bottom; 5, glyceraldehyde dehydrogenase, removes H_2 after *phosphoric acid addition; 6, phosphoglyceric kinase, transfers —O~P to ADP; 7, phosphoglyceromutase, switches phosphate from 3 to 2 position; 8, enolase, catalyzes dehydration with —O~P formation; 9, pyruvic kinase, transfers —O~P to ADP.*

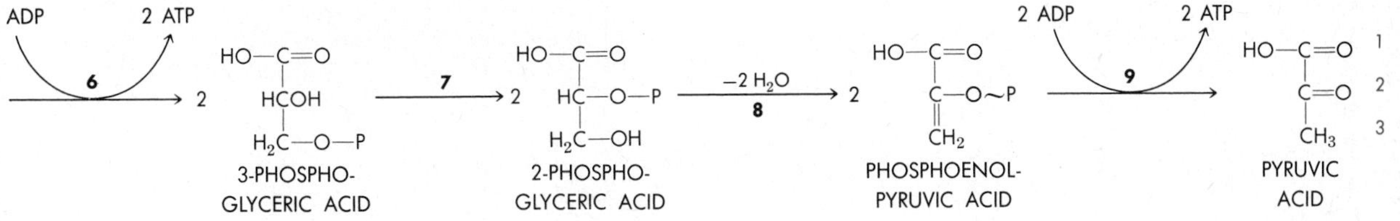

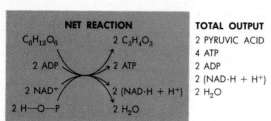

TOTAL INPUT	NET REACTION	TOTAL OUTPUT
GLUCOSE	$C_6H_{12}O_6$ → 2 $C_3H_4O_3$	2 PYRUVIC ACID
2 ATP		4 ATP
4 ADP	2 ADP → 2 ATP	2 ADP
2 NAD⁺		2 (NAD·H + H⁺)
2 PHOSPHORIC ACID	2 NAD⁺ → 2 (NAD·H + H⁺)	2 H_2O
	2 H—O—P → 2 H_2O	

18 · 22 Summary of glycolysis. *It is assumed here that glucose is the original starting fuel, that is, one ATP must be expended and one ADP gained to convert glucose to glucose-6-phosphate. From that stage on, all inputs and outputs can be verified from Fig. 18.21. The summary net reaction is indicated in the center panel above.*

eventually becomes a high-energy phosphate; and of the four ATP then formed, two "pay back" for the two expended at the start of the sequence, while two represent the net gain. The fate of the atoms in glucose may be described by the equation

$$C_6H_{12}O_6 \longrightarrow 2 C_3H_4O_3 + 2 H_2$$

Thus the net loss of atoms from glucose amounts to 2 H_2, and these are held by NAD.

If respiration occurs under anaerobic conditions, pyruvic acid must now serve as the final hydrogen acceptor. Carbohydrate oxidation in this case stops with the formation of alcohol plus CO_2 or lactic acid, and the two ATP gained represent the net energy yield of the entire process.

But if conditions are aerobic, two desirable consequences supervene. First, the 2 H_2 held by NAD may be passed on to oxygen. As noted earlier, this transfer yields three additional ATP molecules per H_2, or 6 ATP total. Second, since pyruvic acid need not serve as a hydrogen carrier, it may be oxidized

further and much more of its energy may be harvested as ATP.

Pyruvic acid ——→ acetyl CoA

The transformation of pyruvic acid to acetyl CoA is an oxidative decarboxylation quite analogous to the one discussed earlier, in the conversion of α-ketoglutaric acid to succinyl CoA in the citric acid cycle. Pyruvic acid is an α-keto acid with an α carbon at position 2, and the conversion to acetyl CoA is formally equivalent to the conversion of α-ketoglutaric acid to succinyl CoA. Indeed, carboxylase, cocarboxylase, Mg⁺⁺, and lipoic acid are again required, at analogous reaction steps.

In a first reaction (Fig. 18.23), pyruvic acid loses CO_2 from the —COOH group at position 1. Note that this group is originally alcoholic in glucose, then becomes aldehydic in PGAL, next becomes acidic in PGA, and is still acidic in pyruvic acid (see Fig. 18.21). Now the carbon atom of this group is removed as the anhydride CO_2, that is, this carbon

18 · 23 Conversion of pyruvic acid to acetyl CoA. *The numbered steps identify the following reactions: 1, decarboxylation (with carboxlase, cocarboxlase, Mg⁺⁺); 2, oxidizing half-reaction; 2a, reducing half-reaction; 2b, H transfer to NAD. In this series the ketone (α) carbon of pyruvic acid first becomes an aldehyde, which is then oxidized and a high-energy —C~S— bond is formed. Lipoic acid accepts the hydrogen released and then passes it on to NAD; hence lipoic acid does not appear in the net reaction summary at the upper right. Note that reactions 2a and 2b are equivalent to the correspondingly numbered reactions in Fig. 18.19, and acetyl CoA is formally equivalent to succinyl CoA in that figure.*

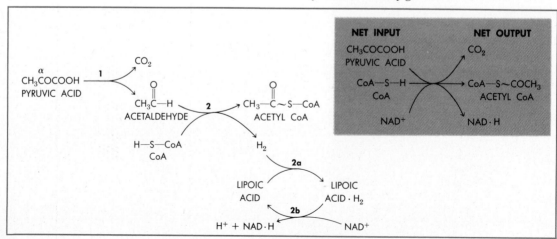

atom becomes oxidized to its highest level. The result of decarboxylation of pyruvic acid is an aldehyde, namely, *acetaldehyde*, CH_3COH. This compound next joins with CoA and becomes dehydrogenated to acetyl CoA, the hydrogen acceptor being lipoic acid (Fig. 18.23, reaction 2b). The hydrogen then becomes transferred from lipoic acid to NAD^+ and from there eventually to oxygen. Three ATP molecules are thereby gained (or 6 ATP if the *two* pyruvic acid molecules formed from glucose are converted to acetyl CoA). The fate of the atoms in pyruvic acid is given by the statement

$$CH_3COCOOH + CoA—S—H \longrightarrow$$
$$CH_3CO \sim S — CoA + CO_2 + H_2$$

Acetyl CoA is subsequently respired via the citric acid cycle, and we already know that, per one acetyl fraction and one cycle turn, 12 ATP are gained. We may therefore assess the total energy yield if carbohydrates are respired completely to CO_2. If we assume that the starting fuel is free glucose and that it is respired aerobically, then this molecule can be shown to yield 38 ATP, as outlined in Fig. 18.24. Such a net total contrasts sharply with an anaerobic yield of only 2 ATP, or about 5 per cent of the aerobic yield. If we further assume that the energy gain per 1 mole of ATP formed represents, on the average, 7,000 cal, then 38 moles of ATP amount to an energy gain of 266,000 cal. One mole of free glucose can be shown to contain a potential total of 686,000 cal. Thus, carbohydrate respiration has an average efficiency of 266/686, or about 40 per cent. In other words, some 40 per cent of the potential fuel energy is actually harvested as ATP, and the remaining 60 per cent escapes as heat. We may note that this escaping energy represents the principal internal heat source of organisms, and that, though it does not become trapped chemically, it may nevertheless be exceedingly useful simply as heat (for example, in counteracting low environmental temperatures). We may also note that a "burning" efficiency of 40 per cent is comparable to that of the very best fuel-using engines man can construct.

Hexose Monophosphate Shunt

Where glycogen is used as a primary carbohydrate fuel, as in muscle, the respiratory pathway leads to CO_2 almost entirely via glycolysis and the citric acid cycle. In many other tissues, however (for example, brain, liver), the primary carbohydrate fuel may be—and in brain must be—glucose, not glycogen. In plants, similarly, glucose as such is often a primary fuel. In such cases an important alternative respiratory path exists which involves neither glycolysis nor the Krebs cycle, nor indeed even the mitochondria. Known as the *hexose shunt*, this oxidation process occurs in the free cellular cytoplasm. In such cells it may account for anywhere from 10 to 90 per cent of all carbohydrate respiration, with an average at about 30 per cent.

The pattern of this cyclical pathway is illustrated in Fig. 18.25. As shown, the starting fuel is glucose-6-phosphate. Six molecules of it first are dehydrogenated twice in succession and decarboxylated once. The hydrogen acceptors in these reactions are NADP molecules. Six CO_2 form as byproduct and six molecules of ribulose-phosphate then remain. The latter undergo a complex series of rearrangements in which C_4, C_5, and C_7 sugars are intermediates at certain points. The ultimate result is the appearance of five molecules of glucose-6-phosphate, one less than present at the start. Thus the net effect of the cycle is the conversion of one out of six glucose molecules to $6 CO_2$.

The chemical tally evidently is the same as that in glucose respiration via glycolysis and citric acid cycle. But the energy tally differs somewhat, as 12

18 · 24 Summary of glucose respiration. The last equation represents the net input and output.

$C_6H_{12}O_6$ $\longrightarrow$ 2 $CH_3COCOOH$ + 2 H_2		GLYCOLYSIS, 8 ATP
GLUCOSE PYRUVIC ACID		
2 $CH_3COCOOH$ + 2 CoA—SH $\longrightarrow$ 2 $CH_3COSCoA$ + 2 H_2 + 2 CO_2		ACETYL CoA, 6 ATP
PYRUVIC ACID CoA ACETYL CoA		
2 $CH_3COSCoA$ + 6 H_2O $\longrightarrow$ 2 CoA—SH + 8 H_2 + 4 CO_2		CITRIC CYCLE, 2 TURNS 24 ATP
$C_6H_{12}O_6$ + 6 H_2O $\longrightarrow$ 6 CO_2 + 12 H_2		38 ATP
6 O_2 $\longrightarrow$ 12 H_2O		
$C_6H_{12}O_6$ + 6 O_2 $\longrightarrow$ 6 CO_2 + 6 H_2O + 38 ATP, net		

pairs of hydrogen atoms are eventually transferred to oxygen, yielding 36 ATP. Of these, 1 ATP must "pay back" for the ATP used up in converting one molecule of free glucose to glucose-6-phosphate. Thus the net yield is 35 ATP, which compares favorably with the 38 ATP obtainable via glycolysis. We may note here that NADP accepts hydrogen in the free cytoplasm, whereas H transfer to oxygen takes place within the mitochondria via NAD. A "transhydrogenation" reaction serves as a bridge between the free cytoplasm

18 · 25   The hexose shunt. *The formulas for the principal participants in reactions 1 and 2 are shown in the figure; formulas of the other components will be found in earlier parts of this and the previous chapter. Phosphates are indicated by the letter P; PGAL represents glyceraldehyde phosphate; the sources of H_2 and CO_2 in reactions 1 and 2 are indicated by atoms printed in color. Reaction 1 is oxidative in that it changes carbon position 1 from an aldehyde to an acid; reaction 2 is oxidative in that it converts carbon position 3 of phosphogluconic acid to the ketone of ribulose. Reactions 3 to 8 collectively regenerate glucose-6-phosphate, the total carbon numbers here remaining the same: six C_5 compounds (ribulose-P) become five C_6 compounds (glucose-P). The summary at the bottom shows that, net, one glucose-P molecule is converted into CO_2 and water.*

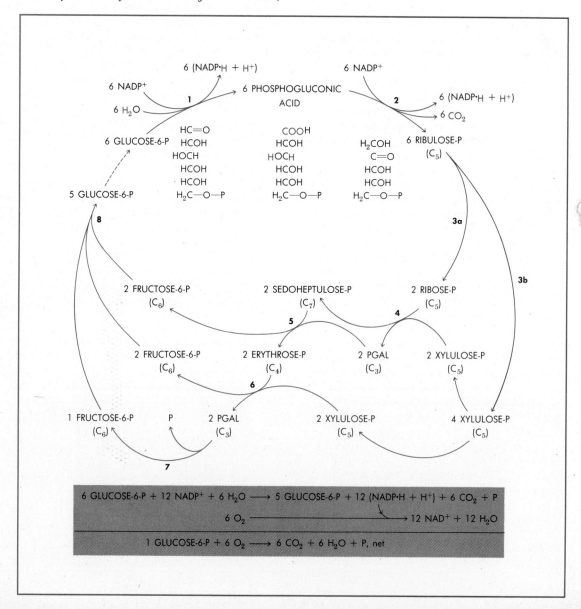

6 GLUCOSE-6-P + 12 NADP$^+$ + 6 H_2O $\longrightarrow$ 5 GLUCOSE-6-P + 12 (NADP·H + H$^+$) + 6 CO_2 + P

6 O_2 $\longrightarrow$ 12 NAD$^+$ + 12 H_2O

1 GLUCOSE-6-P + 6 O_2 $\longrightarrow$ 6 CO_2 + 6 H_2O + P, net

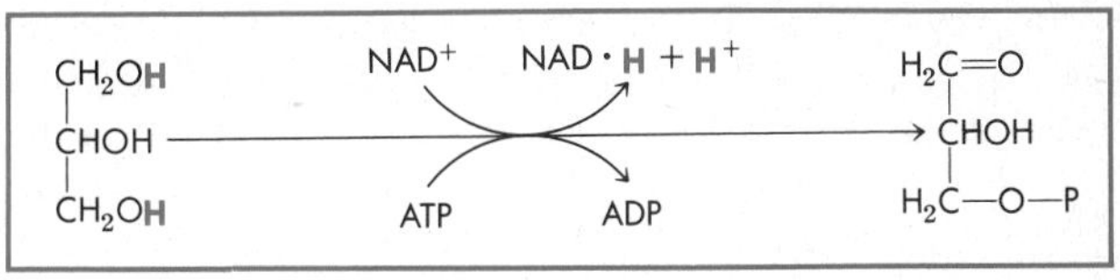

18 · 26 *Conversion of glycerol* (left) *to phosphoglyceraldehyde* (*PGAL*, right).

and the mitochondria; NADP·[H$_2$] reacts with NAD across the mitochondrial boundary, resulting in NADP and NAD·[H$_2$]. The latter then transfers hydrogen to oxygen within the mitochondria.

Apart from representing an alternative process of glucose oxidation, the hexose shunt is significant also because it generates reduced NADP, required in fat synthesis as will become apparent presently, and because it generates sugars other than hexoses. We already know, for example, that the C$_5$ sugars in particular are important components of nucleotides.

LIPID RESPIRATION

A first step in the degradation of fats is *digestion*, that is, enzymatic hydrolysis into glycerol and fatty acids, with lipase as the specific enzyme. Glycerol may then be phosphorylated by ATP and oxidized to phosphoglyceraldehyde, PGAL (Fig. 18.26). Note that this process requires 1 ATP for the phosphorylation but yields 3 ATP in H$_2$ transfer from NAD to oxygen. PGAL may subsequently take part in the usual sequence of carbohydrate respiration via glycolysis and the citric acid cycle, a process which yields 17 ATP for every one molecule of PGAL. Complete aerobic respiration of one molecule of glycerol thus produces a total net gain of 19 ATP.

The respiratory decomposition of fatty acids is known as *β-oxidation;* the second, or *β*, carbon of the acid undergoes oxidative changes. The result is the splitting off of successive 2-carbon fragments from a fatty acid chain until only a last 2-carbon fragment remains.

Figure 18.27 outlines the five reactions included in *β-oxidation*. In the first, *activation*, a fatty acid molecule is linked terminally with CoA. ATP here provides the necessary energy by being split between its first and second phosphate groups, yielding AMP

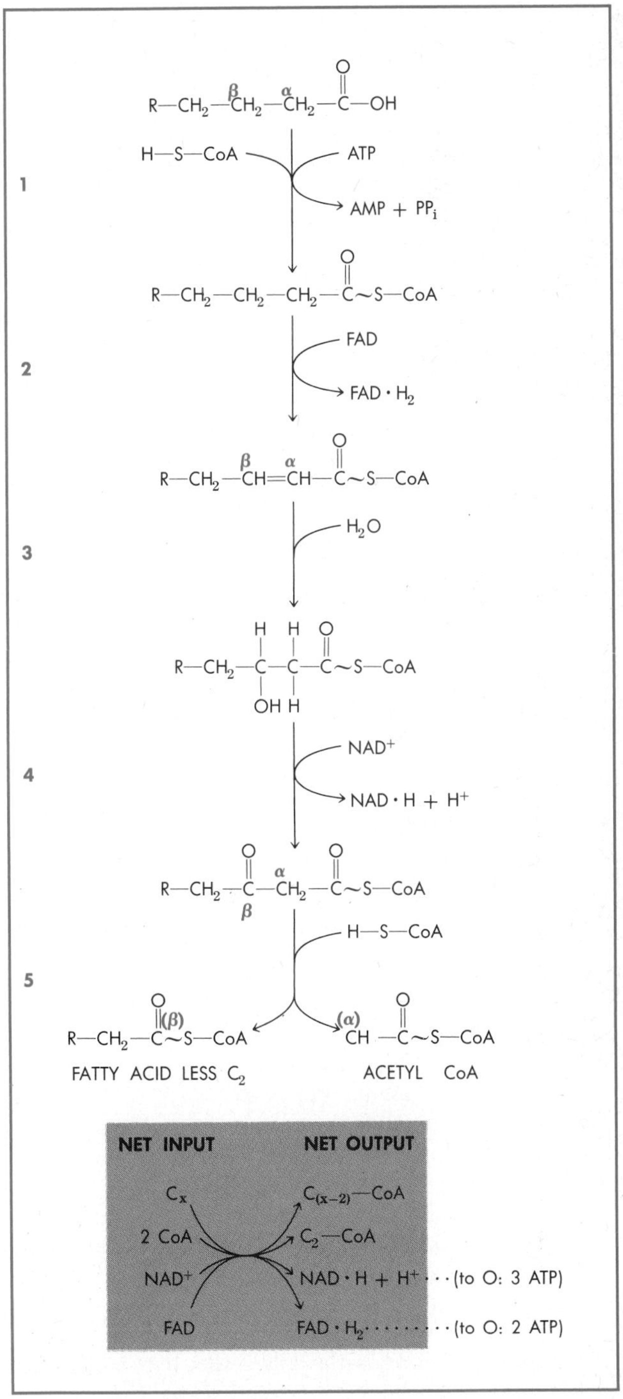

18 · 27 *β-oxidation of fatty acids. In step 1, a fatty acid is activated by combination with* CoA. *Step 2 is dehydrogenation,* FAD *here being the* H *acceptor. Step 3 is a hydration, and step 4 represents the β-oxidation proper: the alcoholic carbon becomes a ketone. In step 5 the 2-carbon fragment acetyl is split off, resulting in acetyl* CoA *and a fatty acid shorter by two carbons than the original one. The summary shows that 5 ATP are gained through H transport to oxygen.* C *here stands for a fatty acid with x numbers of* C *atoms.*

and a separate inorganic double phosphate (usually abbreviated as PP_i). The activated fatty acid next undergoes a first *dehydrogenation,* one H being removed from each of the α and β carbons. An unsaturated double bond, —CH=CH—, is thus created. We know from Fig. 18.3 that such unsaturated hydrocarbons represent a higher oxidation level than the saturated ones. The specific hydrogen carrier in this reaction is FAD. NAD is bypassed completely in this particular H transfer to oxygen.

The next reaction is a *hydration,* which resolves the unsaturated double bond and produces an alcoholic group on the β carbon. This group is subsequently oxidized to a ketone, NAD being the hydrogen acceptor (Fig. 18.27, reaction 4). This is the *β-oxidation* from which the entire sequence derives its name. The resulting compound lastly reacts with another molecule of CoA, yielding two fragments. One is acetyl CoA; the other is an activated fatty acid which is shorter by two carbons than the activation complex formed in reaction 1, at the start of the whole sequence. The shorter complex may now be β-oxidized in its own turn, and consecutive acetyl CoA molecules thus may be cut off.

What is the energy gain? From the summary of β-oxidation in Fig. 18.27, we find that transfer of H_2 from FAD to oxygen yields 2 ATP (not 3, since the NAD step is bypassed), and analogous transfer from NAD yields 3 ATP. Thus there is a gain of 5 ATP per one molecule of acetyl CoA formed. If, for example, we assume an actual starting fuel to be stearic acid, a C_{18} fatty acid very common in animal fats, then β-oxidation of this acid may occur successively eight times, yielding acetyl CoA each time and leaving a ninth acetyl CoA as a remainder. At 5 ATP per β-oxidation, the yield is therefore $5 \times 8 = 40$ ATP, minus 1 ATP expended for the original activation of the free stearic acid starting molecule. Therefore, one C_{18} fatty acid yields a net of 39 ATP and 9 acetyl CoA. The latter generate 9×12, or 108 ATP in the citric acid cycle, so that the total energy gained from the complete respiration of stearic acid is 147 ATP.

By way of comparison, we know that one glucose molecule yields 38 ATP. Since stearic acid is a C_{18} compound whereas glucose is a C_6 compound, the fatty acid should yield three times as much ATP. However, three glucose molecules yield only 114 ATP, which means that an 18-carbon-long fatty acid actually produces *more* than three times as much—almost four times as much—ATP than a 6-carbon-long carbohydrate. Fatty acids evidently are a richer source of usable energy than equivalent quantities of carbohydrates. The reason for this is that the carbons in a fatty acid still are largely at the hydrocarbon

level, whereas those in a carbohydrate are already at the alcohol or aldehyde level of oxidation from the outset.

The figures above suggest a reason why fats are the preferred animal storage foods and why animal metabolism is highly fat-oriented generally: a given quantity of energy stored in the form of fat *weighs* less than if it were stored in the form of carbohydrate or protein. Fat storage therefore makes for less bulk, adaptively important in a motile organism. Yet even smaller quantities of fat still concentrate enough energy in them to provide sufficient power for motion. In this connection it is interesting to note that clams, for example, which move very little, do store their foods largely as carbohydrates, like rooted plants, whereas plant seeds designed for dispersal through air store foods largely as lipids, like motile animals. Note, moreover, that every food surplus in the diet of animals leads to the deposition of additional storage fat; and although extra weight of any kind is not advantageous, lesser extra weight in the form of fat is preferable to greater extra weight in the form of carbohydrates.

Apart from the greater energy content of fats, the efficiency of fat respiration nevertheless is roughly equivalent to that of carbohydrates. If we consider tristearin, for example, a common animal fat, it can be shown by burning it nonbiologically that its energy potential is about 8 million cal per mole. Tristearin consists of three C_{18} fatty acids (stearic acid) and one C_3 carbohydrate (glycerol), hence its complete biological oxidation will yield $3 \times 147 + 1 \times 19$, or 460 ATP. At 7,000 cal per mole of ATP formed, the actual energy yield thus will be about 3.2 million cal. The efficiency therefore is 3.2/8, or about 40 per cent. Fats evidently give rise to the same proportions of ATP and heat as carbohydrates.

AMINO ACID RESPIRATION

If a cell obtains adequate supplies of carbohydrate and lipid fuels, proteins tend to be spared from decomposition. Yet to some extent even proteins are broken up by enzymatic hydrolysis, and their constituent amino acids then may become respiratory raw materials. Amino acids may also be respired before they even become cellular proteins, as soon as they enter a cell as individual food molecules.

Amino acids enter oxidative pathways after their amino groups, —NH_2, have been removed. Such *deaminations* may take place in two ways. In one, *oxidative deamination,* an ammonia molecule, NH_3, is extracted from an amino acid. The reaction is catalyzed by an *oxidase,* an enzyme specific for the deamination of a particular type of amino acid:

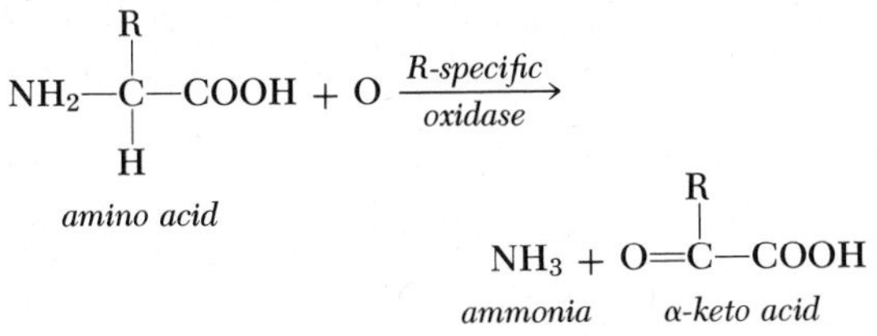

$$NH_2-\underset{\underset{H}{|}}{\overset{\overset{R}{|}}{C}}-COOH + O \xrightarrow[\text{oxidase}]{\text{R-specific}}$$

$$NH_3 + O=\underset{}{\overset{\overset{R}{|}}{C}}-COOH$$

ammonia   α-keto acid

amino acid

In vertebrates this process takes place particularly in liver cells, where any amino acid excess supplied via eaten food is deaminated. In other animals and in plants the reaction may occur in a large variety of cell types (including animal excretory cells particularly). The resulting free ammonia is a toxic substance because of a potentially very high pH after reaction with water, and is ultimately excreted by the organism. Excretion occurs either in the form of ammonia as such (as in most aquatic types), or, after NH_3 has undergone various chemical transformations, in the form of *uric acid* (for example, insects, birds) or *urea* (for example, mammals, some reptiles, amphibia). We shall pursue this topic further in the next chapter.

The other product of deamination is an α-keto acid which, depending on the nature of the R— group, is respired either like a carbohydrate or like a lipid. For example, if alanine is the original amino acid, then deamination yields pyruvic acid:

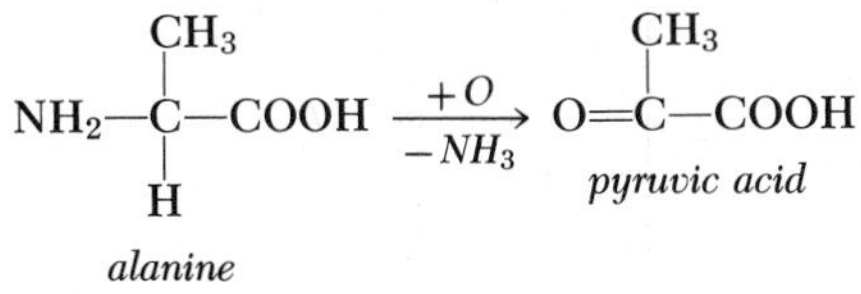

$$NH_2-\underset{\underset{H}{|}}{\overset{\overset{CH_3}{|}}{C}}-COOH \xrightarrow[-NH_3]{+O} O=\underset{}{\overset{\overset{CH_3}{|}}{C}}-COOH$$

pyruvic acid

alanine

This and analogous types of amino acids are said to be *glucogenic*, that is, the α-keto acids resulting from deamination have chemical affinity to carbohydrates and are respired as such. However, if the original amino acid is *leucine*, for example, then deamination produces an α-keto acid which resembles a fatty acid rather closely:

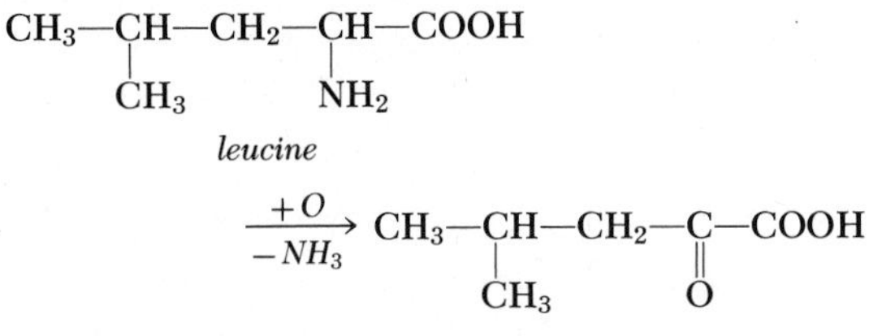

$$CH_3-\underset{\underset{CH_3}{|}}{CH}-CH_2-\underset{\underset{NH_2}{|}}{CH}-COOH$$

leucine

$$\xrightarrow[-NH_3]{+O} CH_3-\underset{\underset{CH_3}{|}}{CH}-CH_2-\underset{\overset{||}{O}}{C}-COOH$$

Such amino acids are said to be *ketogenic;* after deamination they have affinity to lipids. Their respiration actually yields acetyl CoA molecules directly. A few amino acids are both glucogenic and ketogenic at the same time, their deamination products oxidizing to 3-carbon as well as to 2-carbon fragments.

From the generalized deamination reaction above, we may note that for each amino acid there exists a structurally corresponding α-keto acid. Conversely, if a given α-keto acid adds an amino group, a corresponding amino acid will be formed. These considerations lead us to the second method by which amino acids may lose their —NH_2 groups and enter respiratory pathways. On theoretical grounds, removal of an amino group could occur if a suitable amino acceptor were available; and in practice, α-keto acids actually represent excellently suited acceptors. Thus the —NH_2 group of an amino acid A may be transferred to a keto acid B, resulting in keto acid A and amino acid B:

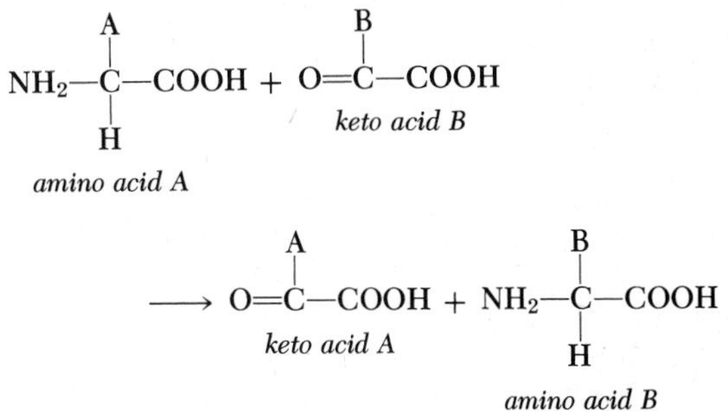

$$NH_2-\underset{\underset{H}{|}}{\overset{\overset{A}{|}}{C}}-COOH + O=\underset{}{\overset{\overset{B}{|}}{C}}-COOH$$

keto acid B

amino acid A

$$\longrightarrow O=\underset{}{\overset{\overset{A}{|}}{C}}-COOH + NH_2-\underset{\underset{H}{|}}{\overset{\overset{B}{|}}{C}}-COOH$$

keto acid A

amino acid B

This equation symbolizes a so-called *transamination* reaction. Its occurrence depends on the participation of a specific *transaminase,* and of a coenzyme which serves as temporary —NH_2 carrier and transferrer. This coenzyme is a derivative of *pyridoxine,* or vitamin B_6.

Unlike oxidative deaminations, transaminations occur in all types of cells. The reactions are significant for two reasons. First, they permit almost any given amino acid to be transformed into almost any other; the only requirement is availability of the appropriate α-keto acid. Transaminations actually are of considerable importance in the synthesis of different amino acids and proteins. Second, the transamination of certain particular amino acids yields corresponding α-keto acids which happen to be normal participants in glycolysis and in the citric acid cycle. More specifically, if alanine transaminates with some other α-keto acid, alanine becomes pyruvic acid, the α-keto acid corresponding to alanine. Analogously, if glutamic acid participates in a transamination, this amino acid becomes α-ketoglutaric acid. And if aspartic acid is transaminated, the corresponding α-keto acid formed is oxaloacetic acid (Fig. 18.28). These reactions, particularly the glutamic-ketoglutaric transformation, provide important direct pathways for the respiration of amino acids and of nitrogenous compounds generally.

The ATP yields of protein and amino acid res-

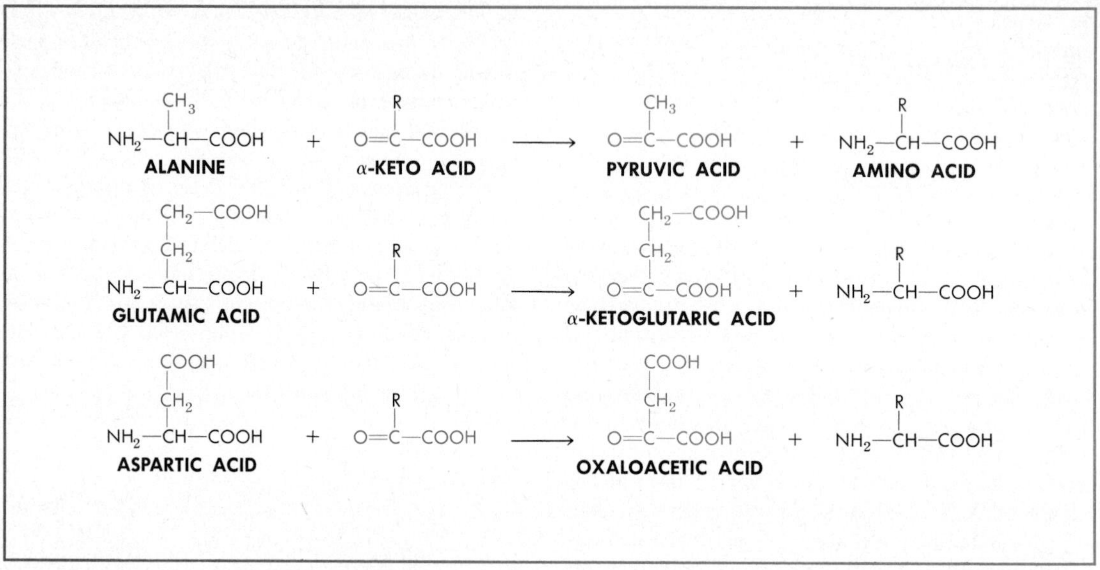

18 · 28 *Three transamination reactions important in amino acid respiration. The α-keto acids resulting from transamination happen to be participants in glycolysis and the citric acid cycle, hence through the reactions above amino acids may enter the same final respiratory pathways as carbohydrates and fatty acids. Various transaminases catalyze the reactions above.*

piration vary considerably, particularly depending on whether the respiratory pathways follow glucogenic or ketogenic routes. The efficiency of protein respiration is roughly equivalent to that of carbohydrates or fats, that is, about 40 per cent. On a gram basis, proteins contain about as much potential energy as carbohydrates (that is, about 4,000 cal per gram of either protein or carbohydrate, as compared with about 9,000 cal per gram of fat). We may note also that, far more so than carbohydrate or fat respiration, that of proteins is accompanied by many other energy-requiring and therefore heat-producing reactions. As we have seen, for example, transaminations, deaminations, and urea or uric acid synthesis occur in parallel with amino acid respiration, and many of these processes consume ATP and release heat to the environment. It has been shown that for every energy total of 100 cal supplied by protein, heat to the extent of some 30 cal is generated via other, accompanying reactions (as compared with a heat generation of only about 5 cal for every 100 cal supplied by fat or carbohydrate). Thus, the net usefulness of protein as an energy source is only about 70 per cent of its potential value, and this is probably why carbohydrates and fats are the principal energy sources in organisms. The large heat generation accompanying protein degradation is known as the *specific dynamic action* of protein.

A comprehensive summary of all major respiratory pathways is given in Fig. 18.29. As noted, these various metabolic events take place exceedingly rapidly within cells. In vertebrates, moreover, respiratory rates are greatly influenced by the thyroid hormone thyroxin. This hormone accelerates respiration in proportion to its concentration. How this effect is achieved and what particular reactions are influenced are still more or less completely unknown. Most organisms are not vertebrates, however, and their respiration is not under thyroxin control. Nevertheless, respiratory breakdowns still occur extremely rapidly. Very efficient enzyme action is probably one condition making great speed possible. Another undoubtedly is the close, ordered proximity of all required ingredients in the submicroscopic recesses of the mitochondria. Just as a well-arranged industrial assembly line turns out products at a great rate, so do the even better-arranged mitochondria.

THE ENERGY REQUIREMENT

How much energy must be expended by a cell to maintain life? The answer here varies, according to the varying intensities of cellular activity. But while a cell lives, its activities are never zero. Accordingly, if life is to continue, at least a basic minimum quantity of energy is required under all conditions. And *every* such energy requirement must be met by respiration; demand must be balanced by supply.

To measure the energy demand of an organism under specified conditions of activity, could one not simply determine the energy content of all the food obtained by the organism during a stated period? No, because all this food is normally not used toward energy production. An indeterminable fraction may be stored; another fraction may be used in synthesis rather than in respiration; and some food may also be eliminated unused. Moreover, an organism very often acquires more food or less food than actually needed. The amount of energy potentially supplied by food thus is not a reliable measure of actual energy requirements.

A much better measure is *oxygen consumption.*

Atmospheric oxygen is not stored; it is used specifically in respiration only; and it is taken into an organism in amounts geared precisely to actual requirements. Moreover, one can easily determine how much fuel may be burned with the aid of a given quantity of oxygen. For example, 1 liter of oxygen will support complete oxidation of 1.25 g (gram) of glucose.

18 · 29 Generalized summary of the major metabolic pathways in respiration. Note that most of the reactions are theoretically reversible. Actual reversal would require a supply of external energy to counteract the normal negative ΔF's of these reactions.

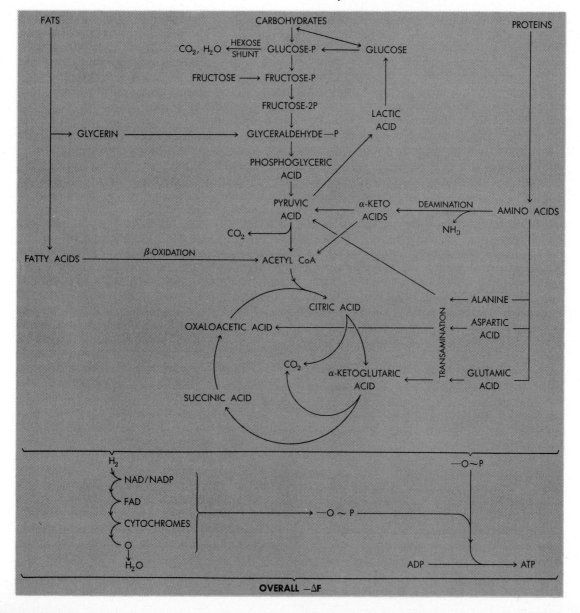

Therefore, to determine the energy requirement of an organism it is necessary to specify, first, the activity of the organism and environmental conditions such as temperature, humidity, and other physical factors; second, the period of time during which the energy requirement is to be measured; and third, the amount of oxygen consumed during this period.

If one measures not only oxygen consumption but at the same time also carbon dioxide output, then it is possible to determine what kinds of foods an organism burns to meet its energy requirement. The ratio of CO_2 released to O_2 consumed, known as the *respiratory quotient* (RQ), is quite characteristic for each of the main food classes. For example, when glucose is respired aerobically, the quantitative relation between the two respiratory gases is given by the statement:

input	*output*
$C_6H_{12}O_6$	$6\ H_2O$
$6\ O_2$	$6\ CO_2$

In other words, for every six molecules of oxygen consumed, six molecules of CO_2 are obtained. The respiratory quotient therefore is $CO_2/O_2 = 1.0$. Such an RQ is characteristic for carbohydrates generally. Accordingly, whenever measurement shows that RQ = 1.0, this value indicates that the organism respires carbohydrates.

Different RQ's are obtained for other food materials. For example, complete respiration of the fat tristearin is described by

input	*output*
$2\ C_{57}H_{110}O_6$	$110\ H_2O$
$163\ O_2$	$114\ CO_2$

Here RQ = 114/163 = 0.7, which is characteristic for fats generally. Thus, when a measured RQ is about 0.7, the organism undoubtedly respires fats. In analogous manner, it can be shown that an RQ of about 0.8 characterizes the combustion of proteins; and if a mixture of carbohydrates, fats, and proteins is used as fuel, the RQ will usually fall somewhere between 0.8 and 0.9.

Most actual measurements of energy requirements have been made on man, but the same procedures apply in principle to any organism. The conditions chosen are often those of *basal* metabolism, that is, when body activity is reduced to a minimum. The test subject is at complete physical and mental rest, as during quiet sleep, and the digestive system is empty. Oxygen consumption and CO_2 output are then measured over a given period of time. Under such conditions, the energy expended by the test subject represents the *basal metabolic rate*, BMR for

short. It indicates the energy necessary just to remain alive during complete rest or sleep: the energy required to maintain minimum breathing and heartbeat, minimum activity of brain, liver, kidneys, and all other vital organs, and minimum respiration and other chemical activities in all cells.

Tests have shown that under basal conditions a human adult consumes on an average about 14 liters of oxygen per hour. Since 1 liter burns 1.25 g of glucose and since 1 g of glucose yields about 4,000 cal, the energy expenditure will be $13 \times 1.25 \times 4,000$, or 70,000 cal. In other words, some 18 g, or less than 1 oz, of glucose will supply just enough energy to keep an adult alive during 1 hour of sleep.

BMR values vary widely. A growing individual expends more energy per pound of tissue than a nongrowing adult. A male metabolizes slightly more intensely than a female. If the temperature of the environment is low, more energy is expended toward maintenance of body temperature. A small individual possesses a large surface area in proportion to its volume, and it uses more energy to offset the greater heat loss through surface radiation and evaporation. Because of such variables, actual BMR determinations are quite complicated in practice and require control and measurement of numerous factors.

BMR varies not only with age, sex, weight, size, season, and climate but also with state of health. During disease, BMR values may become abnormally low or high, and this may sometimes be a clue to the nature of the disease. An abnormal BMR usually indicates that the utilization of foods is somehow defective. This is the case in diabetes, for example, where insulin production is inadequate and glucose utilization is impaired. Or respiration within cells could be impaired as a result of vitamin or thyroid deficiencies.

TABLE 15 CALORIC REQUIREMENTS DURING VARIOUS ACTIVITIES, PERFORMED CONTINUOUSLY FOR 1 hr[*]

basal activity (sleep)	*70*
sitting at rest	*100*
walking (leisurely)	*200*
moderately active work (carpentry)	*250*
walking down stairs	*350*
sawing wood	*450*
swimming	*500*
very fast running	*600*
walking up stairs	*1,100*

[*] *Caloric values are given here in dietary, or large, calories (Cal); 1 Cal = 1,000 cal (small calories).*

Conditions are not basal when the body is active. Energy requirements then are greater in proportion to the intensity or the amount of activity. Thinking, speaking, sitting, eating, walking, chopping wood, or merely keeping one's eyes open, all raise the energy requirement beyond BMR levels. Table 15 lists the requirements of various kinds of activities. It will be noted that profound thinking (sedentary work) comes cheap in terms of energy. However, this does not mean that brainwork is valued low in the scheme of nature. On the contrary, animals have become so adapted that cerebration, like heartbeat and other essential processes, is guaranteed even if only a minimum of energy is available. It can be shown that a moderately active human adult requires about 3 million cal every 24 hr (or 3,000 Cal, that is, dietary "large" calories). Thus, about $\frac{3}{4}$ lb of fat (333 g) would satisfy such an energy requirement. However, it should be clear that such an intake would not represent an adequate diet. Additional food is needed for cellular synthesis, and this, as well as respiration itself, requires a wide *variety* of foods. The caloric value of a diet is only one aspect of adequate nutrition.

The energy expended continuously by an organism sustains both the chemical and the physical activities of its cells. The following two chapters will show what these activities are and how the energy of ATP supports them.

REVIEW QUESTIONS

1. Describe the uptake of glucose and oxygen by cells. Compare and contrast a fire with respiration. What do they have in common? What is different? Which materials are fuels in respiration?

2. What are redox reactions? Half-reactions? What energy relations exist during redox reactions? Show how progressive changes of oxidation level may occur during the transformation of hydrocarbons to anhydrides.

3. What is dehydrogenation? Where does it occur, and what role does it play in respiration? Under what conditions does it take place? How is hydrogen transferred to oxygen?

4. Describe the sequence of carriers and the specific role of each during aerobic hydrogen transport. What role does electron transport play?

5. Distinguish between aerobic and anaerobic respiration. Under what conditions does either take place? How and where may aerobic respiration become blocked? How is alcohol or lactic acid formed? How and under what conditions is lactic acid respired? What is an oxygen debt and how is it paid?

6. Describe the role of adenosine phosphates in respiration. What is a high-energy bond? How and where are such bonds created in fuels? During H transfer? How much energy is required for ATP formation?

7. Describe the general sequence of events in the citric acid cycle. Which steps are oxidative, and what changes in oxidation level take place? What is the total input and output of the cycle? How much ATP is gained and through what steps?

8. Review the sequence of events in glycolysis. Which steps are oxidative, and what changes in oxidation level take place? How much energy is obtained? Which classes of nutrients pass through a pyruvic acid stage in respiration?

9. Review the conversion of pyruvic acid into acetyl CoA. What are the functions of carboxylase, cocarboxylase, lipoic acid, and coenzyme A? How much energy is gained and where? What classes of nutrients pass through an acetyl CoA stage in respiration?

10. Review the sequence of events in the hexose monophosphate shunt. What respiratory role does this process play, and where does it occur? How does the energy gain compare with that of glycolysis?

11. Describe the process of β-oxidation. Which steps are oxidative? How much energy is gained, and where?

12. Distinguish between oxidative deamination and transamination. What are glucogenic and ketogenic amino acids? Show how amino acids are respired.

13. How efficient is respiration? How much potential energy does each of the main classes of nutrients contain? What is a respiratory quotient and how is it determined? What does it indicate? What is basal metabolism? How is it determined and what does it indicate?

14. Review and summarize the overall fate of one molecule of glucose during complete respiratory combustion. What is the total net input and what is the total net output? What happens to the individual atoms of glucose? What is the total ATP gain, and how much is gained during each of the main steps of breakdown?

15. Where in cells does respiration occur? What factors probably contribute to the speed of respiration? Inasmuch as respiratory reactions are reversible, how does it happen that energy continues to be produced?

COLLATERAL READINGS

Baker, J., and G. Allen: "Matter, Energy, and Life." Addison-Wesley, Reading, Mass., 1965. A paperback containing good introductions to the chemical aspects of nutrition, respiration, and metabolism in general.

Giese, A. C.: Energy Release and Utilization, in "This Is Life," Holt, New York, 1962. A good, concise review of respiratory processes.

Green, D. E.: Enzymes in Teams, *Sci. American,* Sept., 1949. The integrated action of respiratory enzymes is discussed.

————: The Metabolism of Fats, *Sci. American,* Jan., 1954. An article on the respiration of fats specifically.

————: Biological Oxidation, *Sci. American,* July, 1958. An account of the process as a whole.

Jensen, W. A.: "The Plant Cells," Wadsworth, Belmont, Calif., 1964. This paperback contains a chapter reviewing the course of respiration in plants.

Lehninger, A. L.: Energy Transformation in the Cell, *Sci. American,* May, 1960. The article includes a specific discussion of respiratory enzymes from both the structural and functional standpoint.

————: How Cells Transform Energy, *Sci. American,* Sept., 1961. The photosynthetic role of chloroplasts and the respiratory role of mitochondria are correlated.

Loewy, A. G., and P. Siekevitz: "Cell Structure and Function," Holt, New York, 1963. A paperback containing good accounts of all general aspects of respiratory chemistry.

McElroy, W. D.: "Cellular Physiology and Biochemistry," Prentice-Hall, Englewood Cliffs, N.J., 1961. Like the preceding reference, a paperback that includes a general review of respiration.

Siekevitz, P.: Powerhouse of the Cell, *Sci. American,* July, 1957. The structure and function of mitochondria are discussed.

Steward, F. C.: "Plants at Work," Addison-Wesley, Reading, Mass., 1964. A good, detailed discussion of respiration is included in this paperback.

Stumpf, P. K.: ATP, *Sci. American,* Apr., 1953. An article on the cellular roles of this energy carrier.

White, A., P. Handler, and E. L. Smith: "Principles of Biochemistry," 3d ed., McGraw-Hill, New York, 1964. Very complete, detailed accounts of all aspects of respiration may be found in this large text.

CHAPTER 19
SYNTHESIS
AND
PHOTO-
SYNTHESIS

Once a cell has available nutritional raw materials and ATP, it may carry out other metabolic activities essential to its maintenance. Among the most crucial of such activities are processes of *synthesis*. Of these in turn, *photosynthesis* is unquestionably the most fundamental; all other syntheses in cells, plant or animal, continue where photosynthesis ends. Appropriately, therefore, this process occupies our first attention below. Other syntheses are examined in the remainder of this chapter and also in part of the next.

PHOTOSYNTHESIS

The importance of the set of reactions in which CO_2 and H_2 are transformed into carbohydrates cannot be overestimated. Carbohydrates produced through photosynthesis are the primary substances from which virtually the whole organic fraction of the living world is constructed and on which therefore virtually all organisms also depend for their food. The only organisms not dependent on photosynthesis are the chemolithotrophic bacteria (see Chap. 17), which together amount to probably less than 0.0001 per cent of all the living matter on earth.

The global impact of photosynthesis is underscored by statistical data. Every year, some 200 billion tons of carbon go through the photosynthetic process. This makes it the most massive chemical event and the second most massive event of all kinds on earth. Only the global evaporation-precipitation cycle of water involves more material. Carbon dioxide is used up in photosynthesis in enormous amounts. If the gas were not replenished through plant and animal respiration and other combustion processes, then the CO_2 content of the entire atmosphere would be exhausted in a few months and that of the ocean in about 300 years. Oxygen is released through photosynthesis so voluminously that all the O_2 of the present atmosphere could be generated in about 2,000 years, an incredibly short time from a geologic standpoint. Finally, the solar energy harvested annually through photosynthesis in the form of carbohydrates amounts to fully one-fourth of the total energy now available to man from all sources.

This quantitative and qualitative importance of photosynthesis has been appreciated for only a very short time. Research on the nature of the process began in the seventeenth century, when work by Van Helmont implied that plant growth could not be a result of any soil eating by roots, as Aristotle had believed. Van Helmont planted a willow twig in a measured amount of soil and, after caring for this plant for some years, found that the weight of the soil had decreased by only a few ounces. But the twig had become a young tree weighing many pounds (Fig. 19.1). Van Helmont's work therefore suggested that water added to soil, not soil itself, must serve as nourishment in plant growth.

Around the middle of the eighteenth century, Priestley discovered that an animal and a plant sealed together in a glass chamber could survive, although the animal or the plant alone could not survive (see Fig. 19.1). He concluded that the plant changed "fixed air" exhaled by the animal into "good air"; or as we would say today, plants take up CO_2 exhaled by the animal and the animal takes up O_2 released by the plant. Later, Ingenhousz showed that the Priestley effect hinged on the presence of light and of living green tissue. Work during the nineteenth century demonstrated that CO_2 and water absorbed by a green plant yielded O_2 and an *organic* endproduct. This endproduct was subsequently identified as a carbohydrate. Thus, not until almost the beginning of the present century could the overall photosynthetic equation be written:

$$CO_2 + H_2O \xrightarrow[chlorophyll]{light} \text{carbohydrate} + O_2$$

We know today that this equation does not describe the actual photosynthetic reaction. Contrary to what the equation suggests, carbohydrates are *not* formed simply by mixing carbon dioxide and water;

19 · 1 Early experiments on photosynthesis. *A, Van Helmont's experiment showed that added water, not soil eating by roots, accounted for plant growth. B, Priestley's experiment showed that a plant and an animal, when sealed in separate chambers, could not survive, but that they could survive if they were sealed in a chamber together.*

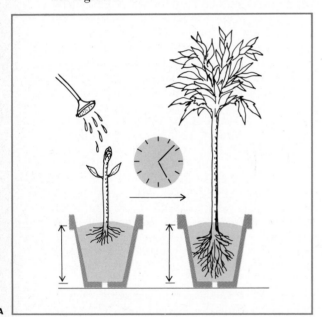

A

B

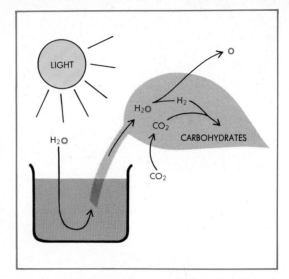

19 · 2 Oxygen in photosynthesis. *If a plant is given water in which the oxygen is isotopic, then the oxygen released during photosynthesis will be isotopic. This indicates that the oxygen source for the photosynthetic manufacture of carbohydrates is* not *water.*

the product of such mixing would merely be carbonic acid. The above is, in fact, little more than a general statement of *input* and *output*. It indicates what kinds of materials go into photosynthesis and what kinds come out, but it does not, for example, give information about the specific events which convert the input into the output. Moreover, it indicates neither the role of chlorophyll and of light nor the amount or kind of light required. And it does not specify the requirement of living cells with intact chloroplasts and grana.

What is now actually known about these details?

THE PATTERN

Photosynthesis may be regarded as a series of chemical events in which the elements carbon, hydrogen, and oxygen are joined in such a way that the result is a carbohydrate. The process as a whole is endergonic and has a positive ΔF. It will therefore continue only so long as adequate amounts of energy are funneled into it. We know the source of the necessary energy to be light and the sources of the elements C, H, and O to be CO_2 and H_2O.

In view of these raw material requirements, the carbon source in photosynthesis evidently must by CO_2 and the hydrogen source must be H_2O. But what serves as oxygen source? Is it CO_2 or H_2O or both or either? This question has been answered by experiments, including some in which plants were supplied with either H_2O or CO_2 containing labeled, isotopic oxygen, O^{18}. Since the labeled oxygen can be identified by its physical properties (see Chap. 3), its fate can be followed through the photosynthetic reactions. These and other analytic procedures have shown clearly that the oxygen of CO_2 always becomes incorporated into the carbohydrate endproduct of photosynthesis, whereas the oxygen of H_2O always appears as an escaping byproduct in the form of gaseous molecular oxygen, O_2 (Fig. 19.2).

Thus, CO_2 is *both* the carbon and the oxygen source in photosynthesis, and H_2O serves as hydrogen source only. This finding leads to the important inference that, at some point in the course of photosynthesis, water must become separated into H and O, and that photosynthesis therefore must occur according to the following two-step pattern:

step 1 $2 H_2O \longrightarrow [2 H_2] + O_2 \cdots$ (byproduct)

step 2 $CO_2 + [2 H_2] \longrightarrow$

$[CH_2O] + H_2O \cdots$ (byproduct)
carbohydrate unit

In step 1, two molecules of H_2O are needed for every O_2 generated from it, hence in step 2, CO_2 is a hydrogen acceptor which must interact with $2 H_2$; water must then be among the endproducts. In other words, water is a raw material in step 1, and half the original amount of water again reappears as a byproduct in step 2.

That a first step as above actually does occur has been documented through a now classical type of experiment, known as the *Hill reaction* (Fig. 19.3). Leaves are dried and powdered, and the chloroplasts in this powder are isolated and cleaned. The pure chloroplast preparation is then suspended in water to which are added certain iron salts to serve as hydrogen acceptors. The whole is now illuminated. The result: as soon and as long as the light is on, the chloroplasts actively release oxygen. If an oxygen acceptor such as hemoglobin is added to the medium, the released oxygen will combine with it and form oxyhemoglobin. The amounts of the latter, hence amounts of oxygen released by the chloroplasts, can be measured.

Such an experiment evidently simulates the first photosynthetic step above. The release of oxygen in the presence of light and chlorophyll must mean that water, the only significant oxygen source present, is separated into hydrogen and oxygen, and that light energy and chlorophyll must be associated specifically with this separation process. The iron salts in the experiment then serve as hydrogen acceptors in lieu of CO_2 as in step 2, above, and oxygen either escapes or can be trapped in the form of oxyhemoglobin. The

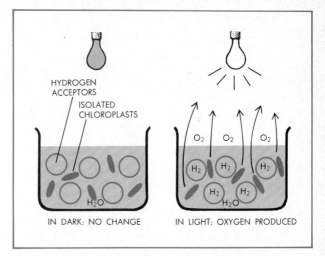

HYDROGEN
ACCEPTORS
ISOLATED
CHLOROPLASTS

IN DARK: NO CHANGE   IN LIGHT: OXYGEN PRODUCED

19 · 3 Light and chlorophyll. Chloroplasts and hydrogen acceptors are suspended in water. In the dark, no change occurs (left). If the light is turned on, oxygen bubbles form (right). This indicates that water is split into H_2 and O in the chloroplasts, with the aid of light energy. Oxygen escapes (or may be captured by acceptors such as a hemoglobin), and hydrogen is picked up by the hydrogen acceptors.

important conclusion from this type of experiment is, first, that water does indeed become separated into H and O, and second, that the specific function of light and of chlorophyll is to promote just this chemical separation of water.

We may therefore generalize that photosynthesis actually does consist of two consecutive main phases (Fig. 19.4). The first, or Hill reaction, may also be termed *photolysis*, that is, the separation of water in the presence of light and chlorophyll. This light-dependent phase is oxidative, inasmuch as water is being dehydrogenated. The second phase may be termed CO_2 *fixation*, that is, the combining of the

19 · 4 Photolysis and CO_2 fixation, the two phases of photosynthesis. Both phases take place within the grana of chloroplasts.

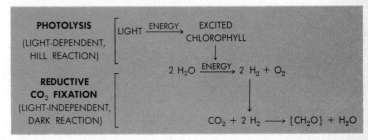

| PHOTOLYSIS (LIGHT-DEPENDENT, HILL REACTION) | LIGHT $\xrightarrow{\text{ENERGY}}$ EXCITED CHLOROPHYLL |
| REDUCTIVE CO_2 FIXATION (LIGHT-INDEPENDENT, DARK REACTION) | $2 H_2O \xrightarrow{\text{ENERGY}} 2 H_2 + O_2$ $CO_2 + 2 H_2 \longrightarrow [CH_2O] + H_2O$ |

hydrogen produced by photolysis with the carbon and oxygen of CO_2. The process is light-independent and therefore constitutes the so-called *dark reaction* of photosynthesis. Inasmuch as it achieves an addition of hydrogen to CO_2 and so yields the carbohydrate endproduct, this dark reaction may be categorized specifically as *reductive* CO_2 fixation. What events take place in each phase?

PHOTOLYSIS

Chlorophyll, Light, and Electrons

A chlorophyll molecule contains a tetrapyrrol skeleton formed into a ring, with an atom of magnesium in the center of the ring (see Fig. 6.16). Such a ring represents the "head" of the chlorophyll molecule.

19 · 5 *The internal structure of a granum.* In a chloroplast a granum consists mainly of alternate layers of protein (dark-colored bands) *and fatty substances* (colored blocks). *The layered arrangement is also apparent in Fig. 7.7.*

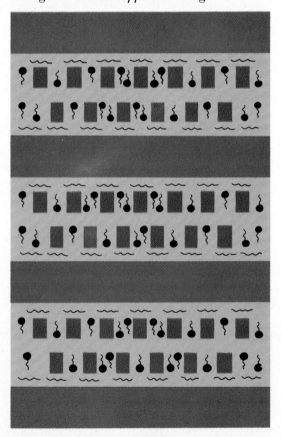

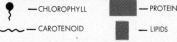

Attached to it at one point is a "tail," a long chain of linked carbons. The chemical variants of chlorophyll found in different moneran and protistan groups differ from the chlorophylls of the Metaphyta mainly in the kinds and arrangements of other atoms joined to the basic head-tail skeleton. The chlorophylls are concentrated within grana, the structural and functional units of chloroplasts (see Chap. 7). Between the protein layers of a granum are present not only the chlorophyll molecules, but also lipids, DNA, carotenoid and xanthophyll pigments, as well as enzymes, hydrogen carriers, and all other ingredients of the photosynthetic process (Fig. 19.5). The fairly orderly arrangement of the molecules in the diagram may depict actual conditions; the pigment molecules are believed to be positioned with a regularity approaching that of a crystal.

In the chloroplasts of different plant groups the various chlorophylls, carotenoids, and xanthophylls are present in different proportions, a circumstance accounting for the various external colors of plants and also the various lighter and deeper shades of green in a landscape. In flowering plants and in many others, the production and maintenance of chlorophyll within chloroplasts ordinarily require exposure to light. A young shoot, for example, does not turn green until it is well above the soil surface. In a plant grown in a dark chamber, chlorophyll soon breaks down and the plant loses its green color. In the continued absence of light new chlorophyll is then not synthesized. In certain green tissues, however, chlorophyll may disintegrate even in the presence of light as a normal process of development. For example, immature fruits are green, and as they ripen the color of chlorophyll in many cases gives way to the brilliant shades of the carotenoid and other pigments.

Some evidence exists that the manufacture of chlorophyll within cells may be assisted by the carotenoids normally present in chloroplasts. Carotenoids are essentially long chains of carbon atoms (see Fig. 6.14), and parts of such chains may form the "tails" of the chlorophyll molecules.

A green cell may possess from 1 up to about 80 chloroplasts. In a mature tree, all the chloroplasts together may provide a surface area for light absorption totaling some 150 square miles. The DNA within chloroplasts probably plays a role in the multiplication of these organelles in pace with cell division. Thus the chloroplast population grows as the cell number of green tissues increases.

What happens when light strikes a chlorophyll molecule? Inasmuch as the compound appears green to us, we may infer that the "green" wavelengths of light are reflected from it or transmitted through it (and so produce subjective color sensation when these wavelengths reach our eyes). Further, it follows that all *but* the green wavelengths must be absorbed into the chlorophyll molecule, that is, some of the energy of these nongreen waves must become part of the molecule. The actual known result of such absorption of red and blue-violet light energy is that the chlorophyll molecule becomes *excited*, a process in which one of the orbital electrons in an atom of chlorophyll is raised to a higher quantum level (see Chap. 3). Two specific events are possible and both probably occur in different cases. One is *photoexcitation*, in which an orbital electron makes a single quantum jump to the next higher orbit. The other is *photoionization*, in which an electron jumps right out of the atom altogether, leaving an ionized, positively charged chlorophyll molecule behind.

Chlorophyll is evidently so constructed that light energy can produce such electron jumps. As in the atoms of any other substance, the energy of at least one photon is required to raise the orbit of an electron by one level. And the important consideration in both photoexcitation and photoionization is that, as already discussed in Chap. 3, an electron displaced to a higher quantum level incorporates more energy than it did before. This is the fundamental energy-supplying process in photosynthesis as a whole; as we shall see, all subsequent events merely contribute to a conversion of this greater, light-induced electron energy into usable, chemical form. The photons in red light have just sufficient energy to excite or ionize chlorophyll. Blue-violet light is more energetic, but it can be shown that it excites or ionizes chlorophyll to no greater extent than red light does. When blue-violet light is absorbed, some of this energy affects chlorophyll and the remainder merely dissipates as heat.

Many materials other than chlorophyll are known to be excited or ionized readily by light. This phenomenon is the basis of the action of photoelectric cells, for example, of wide use in industry. But only excitation of chlorophyll specifically appears to be able to support the process of photosynthesis; another substance will not do. Indeed, if chlorophyll itself is to be useful in photosynthesis, it must be present in very specific states and forms. For example, there is good evidence that the orderly, neatly layered arrangement of chlorophyll molecules in the grana may be of extreme importance. Efficient functioning of such molecules appears to be uniquely associated with their crystallike array in intact grana. If their internal arrangement is destroyed, the grana no longer mediate photolysis. Similarly, if chlorophyll is extracted from grana, the pigment is no longer effective as a photolytic agent.

Furthermore, chlorophyll *a* appears to be the specific pigment required for photolytic reactions. Other pigments are known to contribute to photolysis, but only indirectly. For example, carotenoids absorb blue light (and therefore appear red-orange-yellow to the eye). The energy of this absorbed blue light may be transferred successively to other carotenoid molecules, then to chlorophyll *b*, and may eventually contribute to the excitation of chlorophyll *a*. Similarly, *r*-phycoerythrin of red algae absorbs blue light, and this energy may be transferred to chlorophyll *d* and from there to chlorophyll *a*. In all such serial transfers, chlorophyll *a* is always the last receiver of energy. Moreover, regardless of which other pigments absorb light, *only* excitation of chlorophyll *a* can promote photolysis directly; photosynthesis may occur in the absence of other pigments or other chlorophylls, but it cannot occur in the absence of chlorophyll *a*. As outlined in Chaps. 11 and 12, blue-green algae possess chlorophyll *a* only and protistan algae possess one of various chlorophylls in addition to chlorophyll *a*. This particular variant appears to be the universal key to photolysis. It might be argued here that photosynthetic bacteria do not contain chlorophyll *a*, but bacteriochlorophyll or various unique kinds of chlorophyll. Note, however, that these autotrophs also do not photolyze; as shown in Chap. 17, their hydrogen source is never water but substances such as H_2S, and they also do not liberate oxygen.

The presence of accessory pigments probably accounts for an observed *enhancement* phenomenon: if a given light quantity X is supplied to chloroplasts containing both chlorophylls *a* and *b*, then the amount of photosynthesis carried out is greater than if the same light quantity X is supplied when only chlorophyll *a* is present alone. In the latter case, chlorophyll *a* probably becomes light-saturated by less than the quantity X, and the excess light energy then available would be unusable and would dissipate. But if chlorophyll *b* or other accessory pigments are present as well, these may absorb the energy of the excess light. They may presumably "store" it temporarily by transferring it back and forth among one another, and may eventually pass it on to chlorophyll *a* after that compound has ceased to be light-saturated. It is conceivable, therefore, that the various accessory pigments may have become a standard evolutionary feature in photosynthetic organisms because the presence of such pigments may make possible a more complete utilization of available light.

In the accessory pigments may also lie the answer to an "energy sink" problem in photosynthesis. One photon suffices for the production of one high-energy electron, as noted above, and, as will become apparent presently, one such electron suffices for the liberation of 1 H atom from water. However, a theoretical minimum of 4 H atoms (or 2 H_2) is required for later combination with one CO_2 molecule (see equations in Fig. 19.4). A unit reaction of photosynthesis therefore requires the energy of at least 4 photons. But since a chlorophyll molecule can absorb only 1 photon at a time, a means of accumulating energy up to 4-photon packets must exist in the grana. It is possible that the accessory pigments aid in such accumulation. We may also note here that, in a granum, some 400 or so adjacent chlorophyll *a* molecules appear to act as a functional working unit. One photon appears to light-saturate such a unit, and the energy of the photon is probably passed back and forth within the unit via electron excitation of different molecules until the energy is used in later reactions. Possibly, one very particular chlorophyll *a* molecule within such a unit may be an

19 · 6 *Absorption of light by chlorophyll results in an electron jump from the ground state to a higher, photoexcited level. Return to the ground state then yields electron energy which somehow achieves a separation of water into free [H] and [OH] groups (not ions; step 1). These groups then yield the products in step 2. Water and molecular oxygen are byproducts, and hydrogen and electrons participate in further photosynthetic reactions.*

"active center" from which energy is ultimately funneled out into the subsequent photolytic processes.

Water, Electrons, and ATP

At least two alternative pathways appear to be available for the utilization of electron energy.

One is probably brought into play primarily after photoexcitation of chlorophyll. In this case an electron diplaced to a higher orbit by light returns almost immediately to its ground state and releases its excess energy in the process. Sometimes such emitted energy appears in the form of heat, sometimes even in the form of light. Reradiation of originally absorbed light energy represents fluorescence (see Chap. 3), and chlorophyll is actually known to fluoresce to a minor extent. However, energy so emitted merely dissipates into space without doing useful work. Yet in a good many instances, evidently, the electron energy does not dissipate but instead is captured in some way within the grana and is utilized in achieving a chemical separation of water (Fig. 19.6).

The actual mechanism of such direct utilization of electron energy is still unclear. However, it does appear to be clear that the process really occurs and that the immediate results of the separation of water are not ions but free groups of H and OH, as shown in step 1 of Fig. 19.6. Subsequently, as outlined by step 2, the hydrogen atoms do ionize into H^+ and e^-, and we shall presently follow the fate of these products. Analogously, the OH radicals formed appear to be short-lived and rearrange to yield water and molecular oxygen. The latter is the photosynthetic byproduct which escapes as a gas and accumulates in the atmosphere.

The second alternative for utilization of electron energy is an indirect one, and it is understood in somewhat greater detail. It probably comes into play primarily after photoionization, that is complete removal of a high-energy electron from chlorophyll. In a small percentage of cases such electrons may again be recaptured by the same molecules which released them, thus contributing to fluorescence. In most instances, however, the electrons appear to be captured by organic electron acceptors present in the grana, more specifically, by either *vitamin K* or by *FMN* (flavin mononucleotide; see Chap. 6):

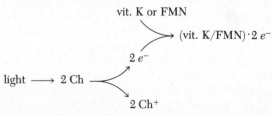

Either acceptor can carry two electrons per molecule. The resulting vitamin $K \cdot 2e^-$ or $FMN \cdot 2e^-$ complexes subsequently participate in a series of redox reactions in which the electrons are transferred over a succession of other acceptors. In this stepwise process, the energy of the electrons is reduced progressively and is harvested in part as ATP. Creation of ATP in this fashion, known as *photophosphorylation*, rather resembles ATP formation during electron transfer in aerobic respiration. In the latter case high-energy electrons are likewise passed via redox reactions over a succession of acceptors, eventually to oxygen, and the electron energy is stepped down gradually and is harvested as ATP. Indeed, as will become apparent presently, the respiratory and the photosynthetic acceptors are partly identical and the thermodynamics of both processes are similar as well: the acceptor-electron combination at the end of the transfer sequence is more stable than that at the beginning, and the transfer sequence taken as a whole has a negative ΔF. An energy differential therefore exists between the beginning and end states, and it is part of this differential that can become useful as ATP.

In photolysis, the pathway of electron transfer from vitamin $K \cdot 2e^-$ or $FMN \cdot 2e^-$ may occur over at least three different alternative routes. Two of these lead to photophosphorylation only, and the third results in photophosphorylation as well as in food manufacture.

In the first of the transfer patterns, the electron acceptors functioning after vitamin K or FMN are the components of the cytochrome system, already encountered in the discussion of respiratory electron transfers. As in respiration, the transfers in photolysis yield energy and result in ATP formation:

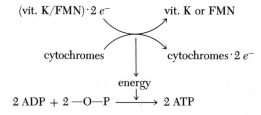

The precise mechanism by which electron energy becomes converted into high-energy bonds within ATP is as obscure here as it is in respiration. Compounds X and Y or equivalents of these are probably involved again (see Fig. 18.13).

In a next step the cytochromes interact with a third electron acceptor, which now is the same ionized chlorophyll that initiated the whole sequence by losing electrons to begin with. The transfer again yields energy and results in creation of more ATP:

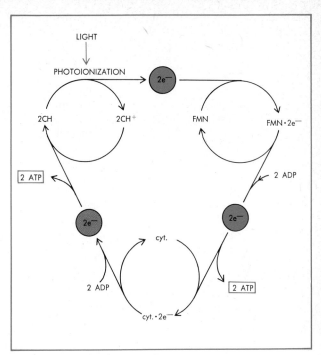

19 · 7   Cyclic electron transfer. *The same electrons that escape chlorophyll through photoionization again return to chlorophyll and, in two steps, transfer their energy into ATP. Actual formation of ATP probably follows the steps outlined in Fig. 18.13. Four ATP's are gained for every two electrons carried through the cycle. The cycle as a whole requires more energy than it yields, and can therefore continue only so long as light is available for photoionization.*

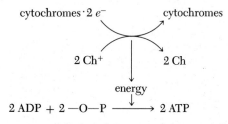

By so regaining the electron it lost originally, a chlorophyll molecule ceases to be ionized and becomes electrically neutral, ready to be photoionized once more (Fig. 19.7).

The net result of the whole sequence is that electrons have traveled in a complete cycle, from chlorophyll back to chlorophyll. But in this so-called *cyclic electron transfer* the electrons at the start have been brought to a high energy level by light, and at the end they are at a low energy level. The energy difference is incorporated into four molecules of ATP for every two electrons carried through one

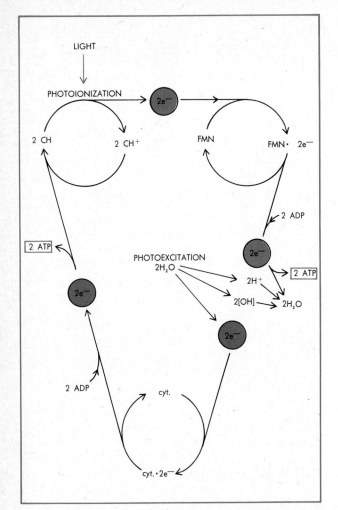

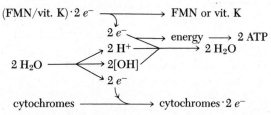

19 · 8 Noncyclic electron transfer. *Photoexcitation as in Fig. 19.6 separates water into the components shown. Electrons escaping from chlorophyll then contribute to re-formation of water, and electrons formed from water by photoexcitation eventually return to chlorophyll. In each cycle, four ATP's are again gained for every two electrons.*

cycle turn. Note that the original photoionization of chlorophyll by light is characterized by a positive ΔF and that the photophosphorylation cycle has a negative ΔF. However, the energy input in the form of light is greater than the energy yield in the form of ATP, hence the cycle as a whole still has a net positive ΔF; it will run only as long as light energy continues to be funneled into it.

In a second, alternative pattern of transfer, the initial event is again a photoionization of chlorophyll and the capture of the resulting high-energy electrons by FMN or vitamin K. A next event is that *water*

functions as a sort of electron acceptor. As noted above, water may become separated by energy from photoexcitation into three types of components, namely, H^+, e^-, and OH. Electrons so derived from water may be considered to possess intermediate amounts of energy. These electrons normally do not remain free but are trapped immediately by acceptors, which here happen to be the cytochromes. If now, virtually at the same instant that water is separated and its electron is trapped by cytochrome, another electron is supplied to the remaining H^+ and OH, then a whole water molecule can be reconstituted. Such another electron may actually be supplied by FMN or vitamin K. Thus, high-energy electrons carried by FMN or vitamin K may come to *substitute* for electrons in water, and in this process of substituting the electron energy is reduced and ATP may be formed:

$$(FMN/vit.~K) \cdot 2\,e^- \longrightarrow FMN~or~vit.~K$$

Subsequently, the electrons carried by the cytochromes may be transferred to ionized chlorophyll as in the earlier pattern, and in this process more ATP may be created.

The whole reaction sequence is outlined in Fig. 19.8. Note that in this essentially *noncyclic transfer* pattern the electrons regained by chlorophyll are not the same that had been lost originally. Instead, an electron exchange has occurred with the aid of water, which here functions simultaneously as an acceptor and a donor of electrons. Also, note that three energy levels of electrons may be distinguished, namely, a high level as in $FMN \cdot 2e^-$, an intermediate level as in water, and a low level as at the end of the cycle in chlorophyll. The total ATP gain is the same as in the earlier cyclic pattern, that is, 4 ATP for every 2 electrons transferred.

The two transfer patterns just described represent effective means of converting the physical energy of light into the chemically usable energy of ATP. However, neither pattern furthers photolysis as such, namely the procurement of hydrogen in a form suitable for later CO_2 fixation and food manufacture. A third transfer pattern does contribute to photolysis. This pattern may be regarded as a composite of the results of photoionization and photoexcitation. A first step here again yields FMN or vitamin K joined to high-energy electrons. In a second step, water becomes separated as above into H^+, e^-, and OH. Also as above, OH reorganizes into H_2O and O_2, and the electrons of water are trapped by cytochromes. These electrons then are regained by ionized chlorophyll and contribute their energy to ATP formation. One product of water separation is now still unaccounted for, namely, H^+. These ions analogously do not remain free, but they interact with the electrons carried by FMN or vitamin K and so become whole H atoms. The latter are then immediately trapped by a hydrogen acceptor. The specific acceptor in this case is $NADP^+$, the coenzyme related to NAD^+ and already encountered earlier as one of the H acceptors in respiration (for example, in the hexose shunt pathway). In photosynthesis, $NADP^+$ plays a quite similar hydrogen-carrying role. The result of hydrogen addition is reduced NADP, or $(NADP \cdot H + H^+)$, according to the sequence outlined in Fig. 19.9.

Formation of reduced NADP completes photolysis, for this product is the immediate hydrogen source in the subsequent manufacture of carbohydrates. Note also that the electrons incorporated in reduced NADP derive directly from photoionized chlorophyll and that the incorporation is achieved *without loss of electron energy*. It is this circumstance which is of crucial metabolic importance and makes the hydrogen in reduced NADP essentially different from hydrogen in, for example, water or another similar H source; the electrons in such other sources are only at intermediate energy levels at best, whereas those in $NADP \cdot H$ are still at a high level. These are therefore far more active and reactive, and indeed they are capable of entering a CO_2-fixing process. In this reactivity of $NADP \cdot H$ actually lies the fundamental significance of photosynthesis as a whole; for if any hydrogen from any random source were capable of combining with CO_2, many means of food production other than photosynthesis could be available to living matter, and photosynthesis would probably not have evolved at all. Combination of CO_2 with H does require high-energy hydrogen, and such hydrogen is present in $NADP \cdot H$ by virtue of an undiminished energy flow from light via energized electrons in chlorophyll. As a result, the sequence described in Fig. 19.9 is distinctly noncyclic; electrons lost from chlorophyll end up in $NADP \cdot H$, and electrons regained by chlorophyll come from water. Moreover, ATP forms only in the cytochrome-chlorophyll segment.

The grand scheme of the thermodynamics of life thus becomes discernible (Fig. 19.10). Inasmuch as $NADP \cdot H$ later contributes to carbohydrate manufacture, the organic constituents of virtually all living matter derived from such carbohydrates incorporate energy that originated in light. And when such organic materials are subsequently respired, the energy becomes harvested as ATP. Moreover, the electrons that carry and then lose this energy during respiration ultimately become part of the respiratory byproduct water, and thus they return to the place from where they had come originally during photosynthesis. There exists therefore a continuous cyclical stream of electrons, from water into chlorophyll, then into $NADP \cdot H$ and the organic components of

19 · 9 Noncyclic electron transfer. *This pattern differs from the one in Fig. 19.8. in that high-energy electrons from chlorophyll become incorporated into $NADP \cdot H$, the important H carrier in subsequent food manufacture. Chlorophyll regains low-energy electrons from water. Only 2 ATP's per cycle are gained here; $NADP \cdot H$ contains the remaining usable energy.*

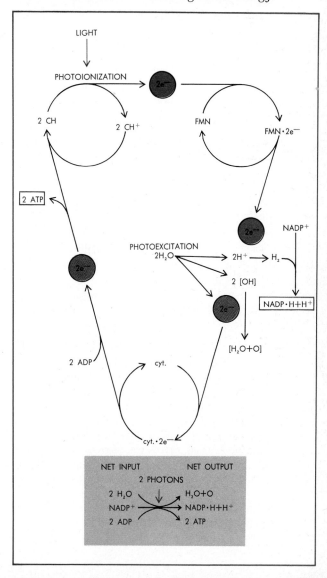

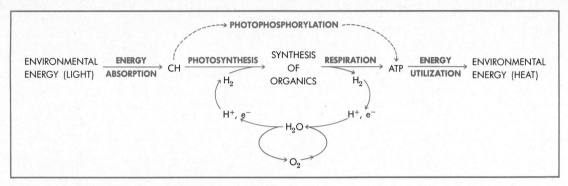

19 · 10 Scheme of the thermodynamics of life. *In a step-down process of energy from light to heat, the energy difference is incorporated into living matter via electron transfers in photosynthesis and is utilized via electron transfers in respiration. Hydrogen derived from water serves as the major electron carrier, and oxygen as the principal hydrogen carrier.*

living matter, then into the hydrogen extracted from these components during respiration, and ultimately to oxygen and so back to water. At the same time, this electron stream is the vehicle for an energy stream which starts in light, enters chlorophyll and becomes part of the makeup of living matter, and in the end appears as respiratory ATP. In this form the energy is partly utilized to maintain living matter, is partly dissipated immediately, and is ultimately dissipated altogether. Thus, living matter represents a temporary construction built with the aid of an energy beam starting in the sun, riding part of the way on electrons cycling from water back to water, and ending up as environmental heat.

CO₂ FIXATION

Just as the use of isotopes has aided the study of photolysis, so also has this technique helped to elucidate the mechanism of CO_2 fixation. Photosynthesizing plants can be given artificially prepared $C°O_2$, in which the carbon atom is C^{14}, an isotope two mass units heavier than ordinary carbon (C^{12}). At successive periods during photosynthesis, plants using such $C°O_2$ as raw material can be killed and their cells analyzed for substances containing the isotope C^{14}. Since the plants must manufacture such substances from the $C°O_2$ given initially, the procedure can reveal not only the identity of the photosynthetic endproduct but also the sequence of reactions leading to its formation.

This sequence is now known in fairly complete

detail. CO_2 fixation turns out to be a cycle of reactions, just as the formal reverse of it, CO_2 release during respiration, is a cycle (namely, the citric acid cycle). The CO_2 fixing process, known also as the *Calvin cycle*, consumes the raw materials CO_2, NADP·H, and ATP, and it yields as endproducts carbohydrates, oxidized NADP, and ADP. In the course of it, the compounds representing the "endless belt" of the cycle are continually regenerated.

The cycle consists of 10 major steps, outlined in Fig. 19.11. The first three of these are the fundamental ones that yield the carbohydrate endproduct and the remaining seven regenerate the starting compound. This substance is *ribulose diphosphate*, RDP, a ketopentose phosphorylated at positions 1 and 5. It can be shown that the cycle must run completely through three consecutive turns before a single molecule of carbohydrate endproduct is obtained. To condense the presentation of these reactions we may add the three turns together as in Fig. 19.11; and instead of starting with one molecule of RDP and running the cycle three times, we may start with three molecules of RDP and run the cycle just once. Keep in mind, however, that a description of events in such terms is an artificial *summation* and does not correspond to the reaction sequence as it is actually believed to take place.

If, then, three molecules of RDP are assumed to be the starting point, the first step of the cycle begins with a carboxylation in which the three molecules of RDP combine with three molecules of CO_2, the first of the raw materials. Through this reaction, the C_5 chain of each RDP becomes lengthened into a C_6 chain, the addition of the extra carbon occurring between positions 2 and 3 of RDP. The C_6 molecules so formed are unstable, however; they each react immediately with a molecule of water and split into two equal C_3 fragments. The latter are 3-*phosphoglyceric acid*, or *PGA*, already familiar as an intermediate compound in glycolysis (see Fig. 18.21). Thus, with 3 RDP as starting ingredients, addition of 3 CO_2 and 3 H_2O in step 1 will yield 6 PGA molecules.

In the second step these 6 PGA become phosphorylated at position 1 by 6 ATP, yielding ADP and *diphosphoglyceric acid*. And in the third step this acid interacts with NADP·H from photolysis, the second principal raw material. The result is the formation of six molecules of *phosphoglyceraldehyde*, PGAL, as well as six molecules each of NADP and phosphate.

Several points are noteworthy in these initial steps. First, they represent the critical reduction

19 · 11   The Calvin cycle. *The reaction at bottom indicates how, in step 1, addition of CO_2 and H_2O lengthens the 5-carbon chain of RDP to a 6-carbon chain, by addition of an extra carbon between positions 2 and 3. The 6-carbon chain then reorganizes into two identical 3-carbon PGA molecules. The enzymes participating in the numbered steps of the cycle are: 1, carboxylation enzyme; 2, phosphoglyceric kinase; 3, PGAL dehydrogenase; 4, triose isomerase, aldolase; 5, phosphatase; 6, transketolase; 7, transaldolase; 8, transketolase; 9, epimerase; 10, phosphoribulokinase.*

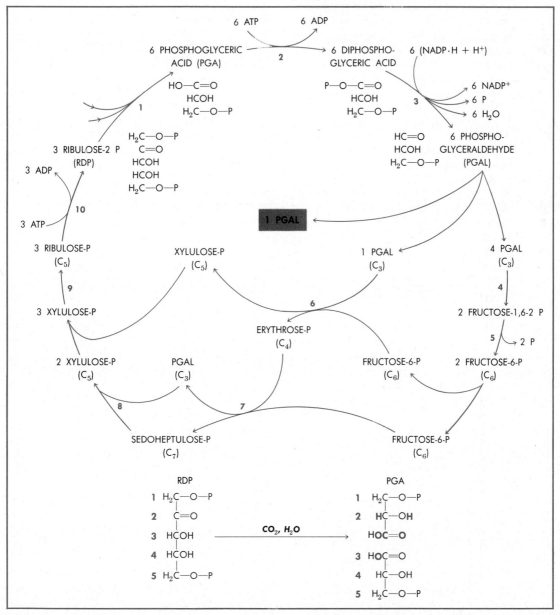

process of the whole cycle, for through them an *acid,* namely, PGA, is reduced to an *aldehyde,* namely, PGAL. This reduction is virtually the exact reverse of a principal oxidation step in glycolysis, the one in which PGAL is oxidized to PGA (see Fig. 18.21, reactions 5 and 6). In that oxidation ATP is gained and NAD·H is a byproduct, and in the present reduction ATP must be expended and NADP·H is a raw material. The latter is normally supplied by photolysis, as noted, but recall that NADP·H is also generated in the hexose shunt pathway, an alternative to glycolysis (see Fig. 18.25). Therefore, carbohydrate degradation via the hexose shunt may likewise keep the Calvin cycle going. We may conclude generally that this cycle may run in the dark and is fundamentally not dependent on light, for it can be maintained by already preformed and preexisting NADP·H regardless of the immediate source of this raw material.

Second, steps 1 to 3 above require 2 ATP for every CO_2 participating in the cycle, or 1 ATP for every NADP·H. The photolysis summary in Fig. 19.9 shows that, for every NADP·H produced by photolysis, 2 ATP are produced by photophosphorylation as well. Clearly, photolysis generates not only the hydrogen required in the Calvin cycle but also more than the necessary amount of ATP.

Third, of the six PGAL molecules formed, *one* represents the principal carbohydrate endproduct of photosynthesis as a whole. Solar energy, grana, chlorophyll, photolysis, CO_2 fixation—all cooperate to yield this final result. A billion years of cellular evolution was needed to make that one molecule of PGAL, and on its foundation rests the whole living world. We shall discuss the fate and function of this molecule in the next section.

The five remaining PGAL now undergo a series of transformations in which 3 RDP, the starting compounds of the cycle, are regenerated (Fig. 19.11, steps 4 to 10). The overall pattern here is that $5 C_3$ molecules, as in PGAL, are converted into $3 C_5$ molecules, as in RDP. Inasmuch as 5 PGAL supply five phosphate groups whereas 3 RDP contain six such groups, a net addition of one phosphate is required. This addition occurs through steps 5 and 10. In step 5 two phosphates become byproducts, but in step 10 three phosphates enter the cycle as raw materials, via ATP. Utilization of this ATP in step 10 also represents an expenditure of additional photolysis-derived energy. Note generally that the whole reaction pattern of steps 4 to 9 is virtually the reverse of much of the hexose shunt pathway (see Fig. 18.25). The Calvin cycle includes intermediates such as phosphorylated erythrose, xylulose, and sedoheptulose, and the hexose shunt includes these same intermedi-

ates but in reversed sequence. This mirror-image correspondence is a result of the nearly exactly reversed functions of the two reaction sequences. The function of this portion of the Calvin cycle is to convert 3-carbon and 6-carbon carbohydrates (PGAL and fructose) into 5-carbon carbohydrates (ribulose), and the function of the pertinent portion of the hexose shunt is a transformation of 5-carbon into 6-carbon carbohydrates. The cell evidently employs the same chemical road but uses it in opposite directions in the two cases.

An input-output summary of the Calvin cycle is given in Fig. 19.12. To supply the 6 NADP·H required for three turns of the cycle, photolysis must occur to an extent indicated by equation 2 in Fig. 19.12. And if we now combine the inputs and outputs for both photolysis and the Calvin cycle, we find that, for the formation of one molecule of the PGAL endproduct, the net overall input and output is as in equation 3 of Fig. 19.12. Note that 3 ATP molecules from photolysis are still unused. Note also that the three *inorganic* carbons supplied via separate CO_2 molecules are now "fixed," that is, joined together as *organic* carbon in the single molecule PGAL.

THE ENDPRODUCT

The principal endproduct of photosynthesis, PGAL, is a *food.* A plant nourished artificially with prefabricated PGAL may survive without photosynthesis and without any other organic supplies.

As PGAL forms in the grana, it does not accumulate to any great extent, for it soon undergoes one of three main fates: it may be used directly as a *nutrient* in the cell which produced it; it may be "packaged" for *export* to other cells; or it may be packaged for *storage.*

As a nutrient, PGAL is usable immediately in respiration. It may happen, therefore, that some of the PGAL just manufactured is respired at once, via pyruvic acid and the citric acid cycle. PGAL is also usable directly as a building material, and it may contribute to the synthesis of any of the innumerable structural components of plant cells. For example, PGAL just produced could be used to build anew, or to repair, some of the chemical machinery required for PGAL production itself: chlorophyll, or NADP, or RDP, or any one of the enzymes taking part in CO_2 fixation. Some of the pathways in such syntheses will be outlined in the following sections of this chapter.

But a green cell generally manufactures much more PGAL than it requires for its own maintenance. The bulk of the photosynthetic product then becomes

1

$$3 \text{ RDP} \qquad 3 \text{ RDP}$$
$$3 \text{ CO}_2 \qquad 1 \text{ PGAL}$$
$$3 \text{ H}_2\text{O} \qquad 6 \text{ H}_2\text{O}$$
$$9 \text{ ATP} \qquad 9 \text{ ADP} + 8 \text{ P}$$
$$6 \text{ (NADP·H, H}^+\text{)} \qquad 6 \text{ NADP}^+$$

$$3 \text{ CO}_2 + 9 \text{ ATP} + 6 \text{ (NADP·H, H}^+\text{)} \longrightarrow 1 \text{ PGAL} + 3 \text{ H}_2\text{O} + 9 \text{ ADP} + 8 \text{ P} + 6 \text{ NADP}^+$$

2

$$12 \text{ H}_2\text{O} \quad \overset{12}{\underset{\text{photons}}{}} \quad 6 \text{ H}_2\text{O} + 3 \text{ O}_2$$
$$6 \text{ NADP}^+ \qquad 6 \text{ (NADP·H, H}^+\text{)}$$
$$12 \text{ (ADP, P)} \qquad 12 \text{ ATP}$$

$$6 \text{ NADP}^+ + 6 \text{ H}_2\text{O} + 12 \text{ (ADP, P)} \longrightarrow 6 \text{ [H}_2\text{]} + 3 \text{ O}_2 + 12 \text{ ATP} + 6 \text{ (NADP·H, H}^+\text{)}$$

3

$$3 \text{ H}_2\text{O} + 3 \text{ CO}_2 + 3 \text{ ADP} + 4 \text{ P} \longrightarrow 1 \text{ PGAL} + 3 \text{ O}_2 + 3 \text{ ATP}$$

available for export to the nonphotosynthesizing cells of the plant. However, PGAL is not exported as such; it is probably too reactive a material. In transit from leaf to root, for example, it would react with other substances long before it could reach its destination. A less reactive, packaged form of PGAL clearly would be more advantageous. The green cell actually does package PGAL, by converting it into sugars such as glucose, fructose, and sucrose.

In the conversion to hexose, two PGAL molecules are joined to form one monosaccharide molecule. The reaction pathway here greatly resembles the reverse of the glycolytic respiratory sequence from glucose-6-phosphate to PGAL. The key steps are given in Fig. 19.13. Note that, when free fructose or glucose is formed, two phosphate groups appear as byproduct. Thus, if we combine the summary equation for the photosynthetic production of 2 PGAL with that of glucose production from 2 PGAL, we obtain a net input-output statement for glucose manufacture via photosynthesis as indicated in Fig. 19.13. Evidently, glucose synthesis following photosynthesis still leaves unchanged the photosynthetic net gain of ATP.

When carbohydrates are transported in a plant from cell to cell or from tissue to tissue, the vehicles are primarily sugars such as glucose or fructose or disaccharide combinations such as sucrose. These sugars are less reactive than PGAL, hence they are not so likely to be altered chemically during transit. Since conversion to sugars (particularly sucrose) and

19 · 12 Chemical summaries in photosynthesis. 1, the total input and output of the Calvin cycle and (color) the net input-output equation. Note that one phosphate (P) is incorporated into PGAL, hence the output shows only 8 free P groups. 2, total and (color) net inputs and outputs of photolysis, required to create the 6 NADP·H for the Calvin cycle (as in reaction 1). 3, net input and output of photosynthesis as a whole, obtained by adding the net inputs and outputs of reactions 1 and 2; this equation summarizes the formation of one PGAL molecule, the net endproduct.

export to other cells is the fate of most of the photosynthesized carbohydrate, sugar is often, though not quite correctly, regarded as the primary endproduct of photosynthesis.

Clearly, the green cells of a plant must in daytime manufacture enough PGAL for themselves, and must export enough sugar to all other cells, to suffice for a 24-hour period. Actually green cells normally produce so much PGAL that some of it may be stored. Storage occurs largely in roots and stem, but small amounts are generally stored in leaves as well. Like carbohydrate transport, carbohydrate storage does not involve PGAL as such. In any storage problem, two considerations are paramount. First, the stored material should take up as little space as possible, and second, it should be "out of circulation," or relatively unavailable for participation in persist-

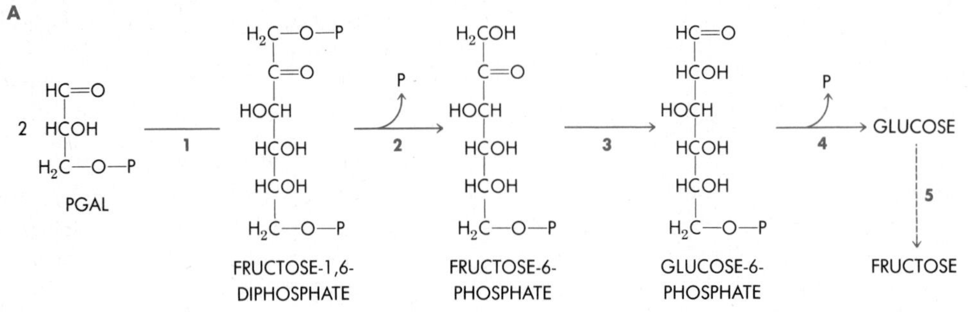

B

$$6\ H_2O + 6\ CO_2 + 6\ ADP + 8\ P \longrightarrow 2\ PGAL + 6\ O_2 + 6\ ATP \quad \text{(CALVIN CYCLE, 6 TURNS)}$$

$$2\ PGAL \longrightarrow C_6H_{12}O_6 + 2\ P \quad \text{(GLUCOSE FORMATION)}$$

$$\left.\begin{array}{l} 6\ H_2O,\ 6\ CO_2 \longrightarrow C_6H_{12}O_6,\ 6\ O_2 \\ 6\ ADP,\ 6\ P \longrightarrow 6\ ATP \end{array}\right\}\ \text{NET}$$

19 · 13 *Glucose formation.* *A, the steps in glucose production from photosynthetic PGAL. The sequence is the reverse of glycolytic reactions (compare with Fig. 18.21). Free fructose may also form by this pathway. The enzymes required at the numbered steps are: 1, aldolase; 2, phosphatase; 3, phosphohexose isomerase; 4, phosphatase; 5, NAD⁺, NADP·H (two-step process). B, to produce 2 PGAL for glucose formation, the Calvin cycle must run six times, with an input and output as shown (twice the amounts in reaction 3, Fig. 19.12). The overall net input and output for the photosynthetic production of one glucose molecule is then as shown at bottom.*

ing activities. Since PGAL reacts readily with cellular components in its vicinity, it would not remain out of circulation for long. Even glucose, though less reactive, would enter metabolic processes fairly rapidly. Moreover, both these carbohydrates take up considerable molecular space.

Plants actually condense PGAL molecules into more compact, sufficiently unreactive packets. Some plants store transported fructose or sucrose directly. Many kinds of fruits, and sugar beets and sugar cane, owe their sweetness to stored fructose and sucrose. Numerous other plants accumulate carbohydrates in the form of disaccharides such as maltose or, most particularly, polysaccharides such as amylose and amylopectin, that is, starches. Still other plants manufacture storage fats instead of or in addition to carbohydrate reserves (for example, olive oil, castor oil, peanut oil, cocoanut oil). We shall examine the reaction pathways of some of these syntheses in the following sections. However, we may note here that such storage syntheses take place both in green and in nongreen cells, the latter using sugars imported from green cells as starting materials. We may also note that virtually all storage molecules are physically more compact than the separate starting units from which they are constructed. For example, carbohydrate storage molecules generally are smaller by as many water molecules as there are additional C_6 units in the stored product. Thus, maltose consists of two C_6 units and contains one water molecule less than two separate glucose molecules. Analogously, an amylose composed of, say, 500 C_6 units contains 499 water molecules less than 500 separate glucose molecules. It is this physical condensation that makes storage syntheses of adaptive value.

Photosynthesis is a very efficient process. It has been estimated that, of all the light energy absorbed by chloroplasts, some 50 to 60 per cent is recovered as energy built into carbohydrates. However, in terms of light energy absorbed by plants in a given surface area of the earth, photosynthesis is markedly less efficient. For example, the energy absorbed by a field of wheat represents only about 2 per cent of the total light energy delivered by the sun; chloroplasts are spread rather thinly over the whole field. Yet this 2 per cent of sunlight, produced by thermonuclear reactions 93 million miles away, constitutes the whole power source which through photosynthesis keeps living organisms alive.

INTERMEDIARY SYNTHESIS

The metabolic link between photosynthesis and finished living matter is a large variety of reactions which we may refer to collectively as *intermediary syntheses*. If we here also include processes associated intimately with syntheses but that are not necessarily synthetic themselves, we may use the more general term *intermediary metabolism* to distinguish all such activities from respiratory, nutritional, or other aspects of metabolism.

The overall role of intermediary synthesis is the manufacture of all those constituents that a cell does not obtain directly as prefabricated nutrients or secretions from other cells. Such missing constituents include most of the critically necessary compounds for cellular survival: nucleic acids, structural and enzymatic proteins, polysaccharides, fats, and numerous other groups of complex organic substances. In most cases, such synthesis reactions are endergonic and have a net $+ \Delta F$. They require molecular raw materials obtained by nutrition (including photosynthesis) and ATP obtained by respiration (or also by photophosphorylation). A cyclical interrelation is therefore in evidence. On the one hand, breakdown of organic compounds leads to a net buildup of ATP through respiration. On the other, breakdown of ATP leads to a net buildup of organic compounds through chemical synthesis (Fig. 19.14).

Synthesis and breakdown of cellular components occur simultaneously, all the time. As already noted in the last chapter, breakdown may affect any cellular constituent regardless of composition or age. A protein just synthesized through long reaction sequences and at great expense of energy is as likely to be destroyed as a glucose molecule already present for days. A certain *percentage* of all cellular constituents is decomposed every second. Which constituents actually make up this percentage is largely a matter of chance. Such randomness applies also to synthesis. Regardless of the source of materials, a certain percentage of available molecular components is synthesized every second into finished cell substances. If synthesis and breakdown are exactly balanced, the net characteristics of a cell may remain unchanged. But continuous turnover of energy and materials occurs nevertheless, and every brick in the building is sooner or later replaced by a new one. Thus, the house always remains "fresh."

However, synthesis and breakdown cannot sustain each other in a self-contained, self-sufficient cycle, even when the two processes are exactly balanced; for energy dissipates irretrievably in the utilization of ATP and through heat losses in chemical reactions generally, and materials dissipate through elimination, evaporation, and friction. Just to maintain a steady state, therefore, a cell must be supplied continuously with energy and raw materials. Very often, moreover, the rate of supply must exceed the rate required for mere maintenance, for net synthesis may exceed net breakdown. This is the case, for example, in growth, in repair after injury, and in cells which manufacture secretion products.

In the following we shall examine the ways in which carbohydrates, lipids, and amino acids participate in synthesis and in intermediary metabolism generally. Protein and nucleic acid metabolism will be dealt with in the next chapter.

CARBOHYDRATE METABOLISM

The most basic and sole original process of carbohydrate synthesis is photosynthesis; *only* autotrophic cells can fix CO_2 reductively and create original PGAL from inorganic sources. Once such PGAL is available, however, *all* cells, including nongreen plant cells and the cells of animals, may fix additional CO_2 to existing carbohydrates. Through carboxylations of this sort, given carbon chains may become lengthened. For example, phosphoenolpyruvic acid, a C_3 intermediate in glycolysis, may fix CO_2 and transform into oxaloacetic acid, a C_4 intermediate in the citric acid cycle. Analogously, pyruvic acid (C_3) may by carboxylation convert into malic acid (C_4). Such fixation reactions are not reductive but oxidative, and they require the participation of the B vitamin *biotin* as a CO_2-carrying coenzyme

19 · 14 *The metabolic balance of cellular energy and materials. All synthetic and other creative processes of metabolism are sometimes collectively referred to as "anabolism," and all respiratory and other destructive processes, as "catabolism."*

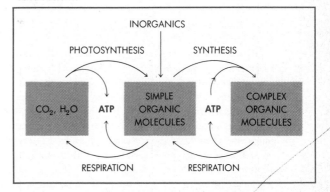

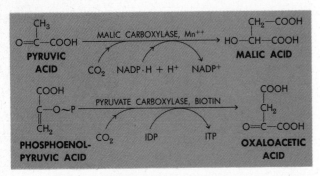

19 · 15 Oxidative CO_2 fixation. *The first reaction is reversible, the second apparently is not. The first reaction provides a bypass of most of the citric acid cycle, or, in the reverse direction, a bypass of oxaloacetic acid and acetyl CoA. Analogously, the second reaction bypasses the acetyl CoA step of the citric acid cycle. The vitamin biotin is a required participant and IDP is the —O~P acceptor. IDP is inosine-diphosphate, inosine being a combination of hypoxanthine and ribose. Hypoxanthine in turn is a purine, related to adenine. Thus, the IDP-ITP system functions like the ADP-ATP system. Other oxidative CO_2-fixing reactions are known, and through them given carbon chains may be lengthened in all organisms by one carbon atom at a time.*

(Fig. 19.15). Note that, in their net effects, carboxylations are the opposite of decarboxylations, that is, removal of CO_2 from existing carbohydrates. Recall here also that carbohydrates other than those of the C_3 type are generated in the hexose shunt pathway and, in green cells, via the Calvin cycle itself. Quantitatively, however, most non-C_3 carbohydrates probably arise by polymerization of C_3 units into the common C_3 multiples: monosaccharides, disaccharides, oligosaccharides, and polysaccharides.

In plants as well as animals, the principal monosaccharide and one of the most fundamental raw materials generally is glucose. The compound can be formed within plant or animal cells from C_3 units such as PGAL, through reactions already outlined above (see Fig. 19.13). Alternatively, a cell may obtain glucose as a prefabricated nutrient, in plants by transport in phloem from regions that store or manufacture carbohydrates, in animals by transport in blood from the gut or the liver. Within any cell, glucose may then enter either respiratory reactions such as glycolysis or synthesis reactions yielding more complex carbohydrates. Some of these synthesis pathways are outlined in Fig. 19.16. This important figure illustrates, for example, the mechanisms of

the storage syntheses proceeding from glucose. Thus, glucose entering a cell is first phosphorylated by ATP. The resulting glucose-6-phosphate then becomes rearranged into glucose-1-phosphate (step 2), and the latter interacts with UTP, or uridine triphosphate (step 3). This nucleotide derivative is functionally equivalent to ATP; Fig. 19.16 indicates its structure and the nature of its reactions with glucose-1-phosphate. The result of the reaction is UDP-glucose and a joined double-phosphate byproduct (PP_i, in which one phosphate group is derived from UTP, the other from glucose-1-phosphate).

UDP-glucose is the principal immediate precursor in numerous glucose-requiring syntheses. For example, monosaccharides such as galactose or glucose derivatives such as glucuronic acid are formed by enzymatic rearrangements of the glucose portion of UDP-glucose. Sucrose is produced in plant cells when UDP-glucose reacts with fructose. Also, polymerization of many UDP-glucose units yields amylose, cellulose, and other polysaccharides in plant cells, or glycogen in animal cells. In such storage syntheses, polymerization of UDP-glucose usually gives rise first to linear polysaccharides exhibiting 1,4 linkages. Certain "branching enzymes" (*transglycosidases*) may then split some of these 1,4 links and rejoin the resulting fragments by means of 1,6 linkages. In this way are formed branching polysaccharides such as amylopectin or glycogen.

We may note here that starches within plant cells and glycogen within animal cells are normally the most abundant carbohydrates and therefore the most frequent participants in any phase of carbohydrate utilization. Starch and glycogen actually are the usual starting carbohydrates in respiration as well as in synthesis. Whenever these polysaccharides are drawn on for use they are converted first to glucose-1-phosphate, and then to UDP-glucose for most syntheses or to glucose-6-phosphate for respiration (see Fig. 19.16). Glucose-6-phosphate may also be dephosphorylated (by the enzyme *phosphatase*) and become exported from a cell as free glucose. In most organisms a chemical balance is probably maintained between polysaccharides within cells and free glucose outside them. Such balances are actually known to be very precise in vertebrates, mammals most particularly, animals in which the liver performs an important carbohydrate-regulating function.

Glucose and other monosaccharides coming from the vertebrate intestine to the liver are partly synthesized there into storage glycogen, partly released into the general blood circulation as glucose. Other tissues draw on this blood glucose and utilize some of it directly, but synthesize most of it into tissue

PLATE XXV

38. *Clam worm at the breeding stage; the egg-filled heteronereis portion is the reddish part of the worm.*

38, 39, courtesy of Carolina Biological Supply Company

39. *Photo of whole Peripatus.*

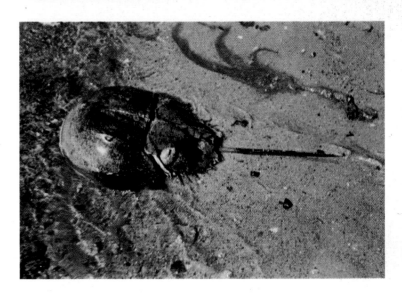

40. *Horseshoe crab.*

PLATE XXVI

42. Molting in a cicada
(*exopterygote, order Homoptera*).
*A, larva with skin beginning to split
along dorsal midline.
B, adult emerging from larval skin.
C, adult and discarded
larval skeleton.*

41. Metamorphosis of silkworm.
*A, cocoon and pupa within.
B, emergence of adult, wings
still uninflated.
C, some minutes later,
wings attaining mature size.*

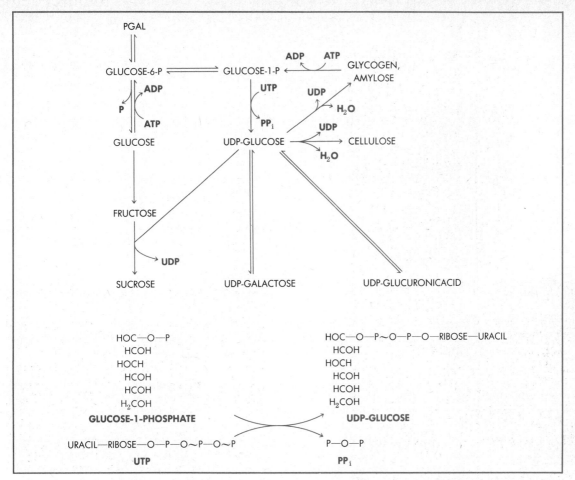

glycogen and then utilize these reserves. All tissues store and use at least some glycogen in this manner, and muscle and skin contain and use very considerable amounts. We may therefore consider the liver to represent one side of a body-wide carbohydrate scale, the other side being represented by all other tissues, and the interconnecting link, by blood glucose (Fig. 19.17).

The particular state of this balance is affected from hour to hour by the relative rates of supply of carbohydrates from the gut and utilization of carbohydrates in the tissues. Thus, whenever the rate of carbohydrate supply from the gut exceeds the rate of utilization in the tissues, then a net excess of carbohydrates will accumulate in the form of higher blood-glucose concentrations. Such an excess of blood sugar will be converted by the liver into stored liver glycogen. This occurs, for example, after a meal is digested, when large quantities of carbohydrates usually arrive in the liver from the gut. Conversely, if intestinal supply does not keep up with tissue utilization, then blood-glucose concentrations will tend to fall. The liver then makes up the deficit by releasing some of its stored glycogen as blood glucose. This happens, for example, during periods of fasting

19 · 16 *Synthetic pathways involving uridine-diphosphate-glucose (UDP-glucose). The formation of this compound from glucose-1-phosphate is symbolized by the reaction at the bottom; it requires the enzyme pyrophosphate uridyl transferase. Glucose-1-phosphate may itself interconvert reversibly to glucose-6-phosphate, the latter forming from free glucose or from PGAL, as already discussed earlier. UDP-glucose may then give rise to sucrose or other UDP-hexoses, or may condense to branched polysaccharides such as glycogen or amylose or to straight-chain polysaccharides such as cellulose (see Fig. 6.7).*

19 · 17 *The carbohydrate balance of the body is summarized schematically in this diagram.*

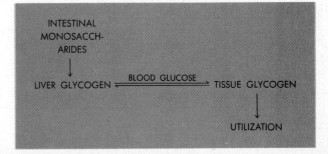

INTESTINAL MONOSACCH-ARIDES
↓
LIVER GLYCOGEN ⇌ BLOOD GLUCOSE → TISSUE GLYCOGEN
↓
UTILIZATION

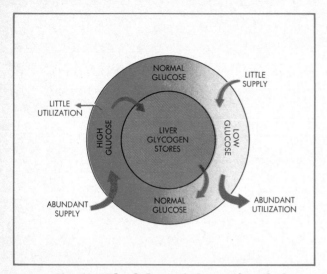

NORMAL
GLUCOSE

LITTLE
SUPPLY

LITTLE
UTILIZATION

HIGH GLUCOSE

LOW GLUCOSE

LIVER
GLYCOGEN
STORES

ABUNDANT
SUPPLY

NORMAL
GLUCOSE

ABUNDANT
UTILIZATION

19 · 18   *Blood-glucose balance. If much glucose is supplied to blood from food and little is used, then the blood-glucose concentration will tend to be high* (left). *Under such conditions the liver withdraws glucose and stores it as glycogen, so establishing a normal glucose level* (top). *But if much glucose is used up and little is supplied, then the blood-glucose concentration will tend to be low* (right). *The liver then adds glucose to blood from its glycogen stores, and so reestablishes the normal glucose level* (bottom). *Through these actions, the liver maintains a* constant *blood-glucose concentration.*

or sleep and also during strenuous body activity, when muscles and other tissues use up glycogen at a faster than normal rate (Fig. 19.18).

In effect, the liver actually maintains a *constant* blood-glucose concentration, irrespective of rates of supply and utilization. Small-scale fluctuations of blood sugar levels may and do occur, but they are normally rebalanced quite rapidly. The term "constancy" here therefore implies maintenance of steady conditions within set limits. In this nonmathematical, biological sense, the blood-glucose concentration is known to be one of the most precisely regulated constancies in the vertebrate body. And we may note explicitly that the frequent interconversions of glucose to glycogen and vice versa follow the reaction pathways outlined in Fig. 19.16. Thus, glucose becomes glycogen via glucose-6-phosphate and UDP-glucose, and glycogen becomes glucose via glucose-1-phosphate and glucose-6-phosphate.

In ways which are poorly understood as yet, glucose-glycogen interconversions in vertebrates are affected materially by hormones. As already pointed out in Chap. 17, the hormone insulin, secreted from specialized pancreatic cells, promotes the conversion of glucose into glycogen. In a diabetic vertebrate insulin production is inadequate, and glucose then becomes unusable. The liver and all other tissues consequently cannot manufacture glycogen. Glucose accumulates in the blood, yet the tissues become starved of carbohydrates and fats and proteins must make up for the lack of cellular carbohydrates. Much of the unusable blood sugar is excreted in urine, but the blood-glucose level remains abnormally high nevertheless. Conversely, if too much insulin is produced, glucose will be converted to liver and tissue glycogen to such an extent that the blood-glucose level drops drastically. The brain is particularly dependent on glucose, and when the glucose supply in blood becomes abnormally low, "insulin shock" and eventual death may ensue.

Effects opposite to those of insulin are exerted by the hormones *glucagon* and *adrenalin*, which promote the conversion of glycogen into glucose. Glucagon too is manufactured in the pancreas, in cells distinct from those that secrete insulin. Adrenalin is produced in the adrenal medulla, the core tissues of the adrenal gland. This hormone is secreted particularly during intense emotional or physical stress. Adrenalin then causes a large-scale conversion of liver glycogen into blood glucose, appropriately at a time when the body tissues require a great deal of fuel. As will become apparent in Chap. 22, several other hormones directly or indirectly affect carbohydrate balances as well.

What happens if the liver and all body tissues hold glycogen to capacity, all current carbohydrate needs are satisfied, yet still more sugar is being supplied by the gut? Internal carbohydrate saturation may actually be reached rather rapidly, since even at peak storage the carbohydrate content of a vertebrate does not exceed 1 per cent of the total weight. If sugars supplied by food exceed the internal capacity, then a small fraction of the excess may escape into urine. This occurs, for example, right after a heavy meal. But the bulk of any carbohydrate excess goes to the liver and some of it from there to other tissues, where it is *converted into fats*. We shall see presently by what pathways such transformations are accomplished. Lipid production explains why even a nonfatty diet may produce increased layers of body fat, particularly if over a long period of time more food is eaten than the body requires. Conversely, if an animal subsists on reduced food intake or undergoes outright starvation, then the internal glycogen stores soon will be greatly diminished. Yet up to a point the blood-glucose level and the carbohydrate supply to the tissues may still remain normal. For under such conditions the liver draws on the fat of the body and converts as much of it as required into glycogen and into glucose.

One major role of the vertebrate liver thus emerges. The organ ensures that all cells of the body receive a carbohydrate supply adequate to their changing requirements, regardless of when or how often food is eaten. Plants and animals other than vertebrates either do not possess a liver at all or do not possess one of this type, and in such organisms carbohydrate balances are far less regulated. By and large, the body tissues here will or will not obtain carbohydrates according to whether or not these compounds become available directly through photosynthesis or alimentation.

LIPID METABOLISM

In both plants and animals, the basic lipid reserves are fatty acids and glycerol circulating in the body fluids or whole fats stored in given body regions. For example, plants frequently store fats (oils) in fruits and seeds, where these concentrated energy reserves are particularly advantageous during the early phases of plant growth. Analogously, animals usually produce lipid-rich eggs, and the adults often also possess fat bodies or equivalent specialized regions for lipid storage. In vertebrates, we already know from Chap. 17 that digested fats are absorbed in the gut as fatty acids and glycerol and that these compounds are transported via blood to the liver. Colloidal droplets of whole, undigested fat are absorbed into the lymph system and, bypassing the liver, are then carried via lymph and blood into the *fat depots* of the body, the regions where fats are stored in bulk: under the skin, around the heart and the kidneys, and particularly along the mesenteries enveloping the intestine.

The liver too is an important fat depot. It not only receives fatty acids and glycerol but, as just noted above, also manufactures fats from excess carbohydrates. The total fat content of the liver is in balance with that of the other fat depots of the body. If liver fat increases too much, the excess is sent via the blood to the other depots. Conversely, the other depots make up any deficiency in liver fat. In these redistributions, fat is transported largely in the form of fatty acid and glycerol. The nonstoring tissues of the body are supplied either by the liver or by the other fat depots. Consequently, the overall fat balance in a vertebrate is maintained by a three-cornered equilibrium, as shown in Fig. 19.19.

A vertebrate could survive if it were fed a carbohydrate-free diet which contained a compensating amount of fat. The liver could then transform fat into the required carbohydrates. What would happen in the converse situation, when an animal is on a fat-free diet but eats a proportionately larger amount of carbohydrates? Such an animal could probably not survive. To be sure, liver and depot fat would be kept at normal levels, through fat manufacture from carbohydrates. The fat requirements of tissue cells would be satisfied similarly. Yet health would be impaired nevertheless, for certain fatty acids (for example, *linoleic acid*) cannot be manufactured by many animals. Such essential fatty acids must be supplied in eaten food in fully prefabricated form (see Chap. 17).

In the utilization of fats within cells, plant or animal, we already know that the glycerol portions enter the pathways of carbohydrate metabolism via conversion to PGAL, and that the fatty acid portions may be respired by repeated β-oxidations (see Chap. 18). Alternatively, fatty acids may become lengthened by 2-carbon units at a time, a process constituting fatty acid synthesis. The reactions here are almost the exact reverse of β-oxidation, the principal difference being the last step. Thus, reaction 4 in Fig. 18.27 becomes the first step of synthesis, except that now the H donor is reduced $NADP \cdot H$, whereas in respiratory β-oxidation the H acceptor is oxidized NAD^+. Note that the principal source of $NADP \cdot H$ for fatty acid synthesis is often the hexose shunt pathway. And note also that C_2 fragments in the form of acetyl CoA are the fundamental building blocks in the manufacture of fatty acids and indeed of most other lipids and related compounds as well. Odd-numbered fatty acids may be formed in various ways, for example, from certain amino acids (see below) or by decarboxylation of succinyl CoA, a C_4 intermediate of the citric acid cycle (Fig. 19.20).

19 · 19 The lipid balance of the body, summarized schematically.

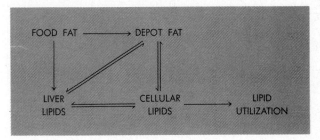

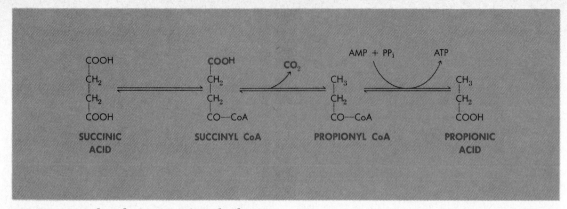

19 · 20 Decarboxylation reactions *leading to conversion of an even-numbered to an odd-numbered fatty acid. The sequence is reversible, and in that case represents an oxidative CO_2 fixation. The conversion of succinyl CoA to succinic acid (or the reverse) occurs by steps outlined in Fig. 18.19.*

Carbohydrates are convertible quite readily to fatty acids, the process following the pathway:

$$\text{carbohydrate} \\ \Updownarrow \\ \text{pyruvic acid} \xrightarrow{\;CO_2\;} \text{acetyl CoA} \\ \Updownarrow \\ \text{fatty acid}$$

The reverse conversion of fatty acid to carbohydrate is achieved less readily, for under normal thermodynamic conditions the step from pyruvic acid to acetyl CoA proceeds preferentially to the right. Thus the reverse sequence will occur only if large amounts of energy are supplied to it. Alternative reverse conversions are also available, however. For example, one involves degradation of fatty acids to acetyl CoA, entrance of the latter into the citric acid cycle, consequent formation of oxaloacetic acid, decarboxylation of this α-keto acid to phosphoenolpyruvic acid, and transformation of this intermediate of glycolysis to carbohydrates by the reverse glycolytic sequence (Fig. 19.21). Note here that, since just as much oxaloacetic acid must preexist to run the citric acid cycle as can be gained from this cycle, transformation of fatty acids in this way cannot lead to a net gain of carbohydrates. Another possible conversion pathway exists in plants and microorganisms (but not generally in animals). Fatty acid–derived acetyl CoA can be condensed enzymatically directly into succinic acid, and the latter may then be converted to carbohydrates via oxaloacetic acid as above (see Fig. 19.21).

Just as significant as transformation of fatty acids into carbohydrates is the synthesis of fatty acids into whole fats. The principal steps are outlined in Fig. 19.22. One of the starting compounds is seen to be *glycerophosphate*, which may arise by phosphorylation of glycerol or, for example, from already phosphorylated C_3 compounds such as PGAL or PGA. Glycerophosphate then combines with two CoA-joined fatty acid units, and the resulting *phosphatidic acid* next is dephosphorylated to a *diglyceride*. This compound is the basic precursor of both fats (triglycerides) and phospholipids (for example, lecithin). Fat formation only requires addition of a third CoA-

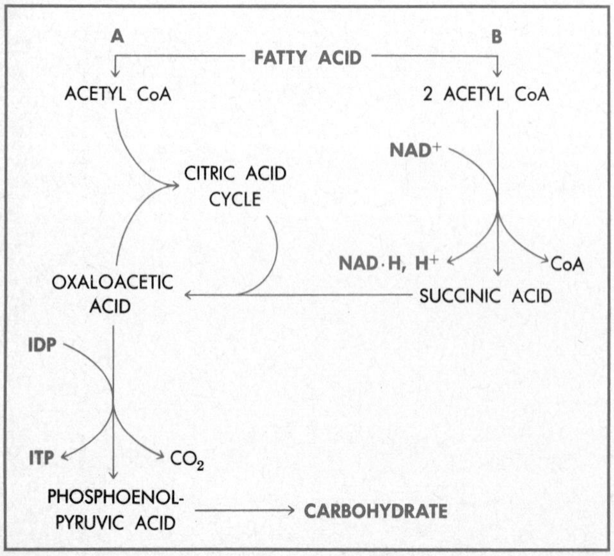

19 · 21 Conversion of fatty acids to carbohydrate. *Sequence A (left column) characteristically occurs in animals, sequence B (right column and lower part of left) in plants and microorganisms. The A sequence is self-limiting, since oxaloacetic acid cannot maintain the citric acid cycle and convert to carbohydrate at the same time. The B sequence is a condensation process, two 2-carbon acetyl fragments being joined into one 4-carbon succinic acid. In both sequences, IDP/ITP are inosine phosphates, another set of nucleotide derivatives functioning like ADP/ATP.*

joined fatty acid unit. Phospholipid production takes place by combination of diglycerides with choline derivatives, as shown in the figure. Phospholipids other than lecithin arise in similar fashion. (Note that in such syntheses, CDP-choline plays a role rather analogous to that of UDP-glucose in polysaccharide manufacture.) Virtually all cells, plant or animal, are capable of transforming fatty acids into whole fats. By contrast, phospholipids are produced primarily in given specialized tissues.

Two other groups of processes in which fatty acids play a role may be mentioned here. First, as generators of acetyl CoA, fatty acids are major precursors of the *sterol* compounds, among which are several vitamins and hormones (see Fig. 6.15). Acetyl CoA is the basic building material in the biosynthesis of all sterols. Second, fatty acids may transform reversibly to amino acids and other nitrogenous compounds, a subject discussed next.

AMINO ACID METABOLISM

Amino acid synthesis in cells ordinarily takes place by transamination, a reaction already referred to in Chap. 18. Thus, any amino acid may be formed if a —NH_2 donor interacts with an appropriate keto acid derived from lipids or carbohydrates:

$$\underset{\text{amino donor}}{NH_2\!-\!X} + \underset{\text{keto acid}}{O\!=\!\overset{\overset{\displaystyle R}{|}}{C}\!-\!COOH} \xrightarrow{\text{transaminase}}$$

$$\underset{\text{amino acid}}{NH_2\!-\!\overset{\overset{\displaystyle R}{|}}{\underset{\underset{\displaystyle H}{|}}{C}}\!-\!COOH} + O\!=\!X$$

Other available amino acids often serve as —NH_2 donors. Clearly, however, transamination only redistributes already existing amino groups but does not create such groups. As noted in Chap. 17, the original source of —NH_2 is mineral nitrate (ionic $NO_3{}^-$), which can be converted by microorganisms and plants into amino groups. Animals are unable to carry out such conversions, and their source of usable organic nitrogen thus must be other animals or, ultimately, plants. Indeed, recall also that animals depend on plants for their supply of "essential" amino acids, or more specifically, those R— portions of amino acids that animal cells cannot synthesize on their own.

Supplied with amino groups and manufactured keto acids, plant cells usually synthesize just the quantity of amino acids they require for protein synthesis and other construction processes. The rate of supply therefore tends to be equal to the rate of utilization, and little if any excess or deficiency of amino acids is likely to exist. Animal cells are different in this respect, for their supply of amino acids, particularly "essential" ones, depends on the food intake of the whole animal, a factor not under direct

19 · 22 Biosynthesis of fat. *Precursors are glycerol or also PGA or PGAL. Step 1 is a phosphorylation (with the aid of the enzyme* glycerokinase)*, and in step 2 two activated fatty acid molecules join to yield phosphatidic acid. This acid is dephosphorylated (with the aid of the enzyme* phosphatase, *step 3), and when another activated fatty acid molecule is then joined, a fat, or triglyceride, results (step 4a). Diglyceride is also the parent compound in the synthesis of phospholipids such as lecithin; choline derivatives here enter the reactions as indicated (step 4b).*

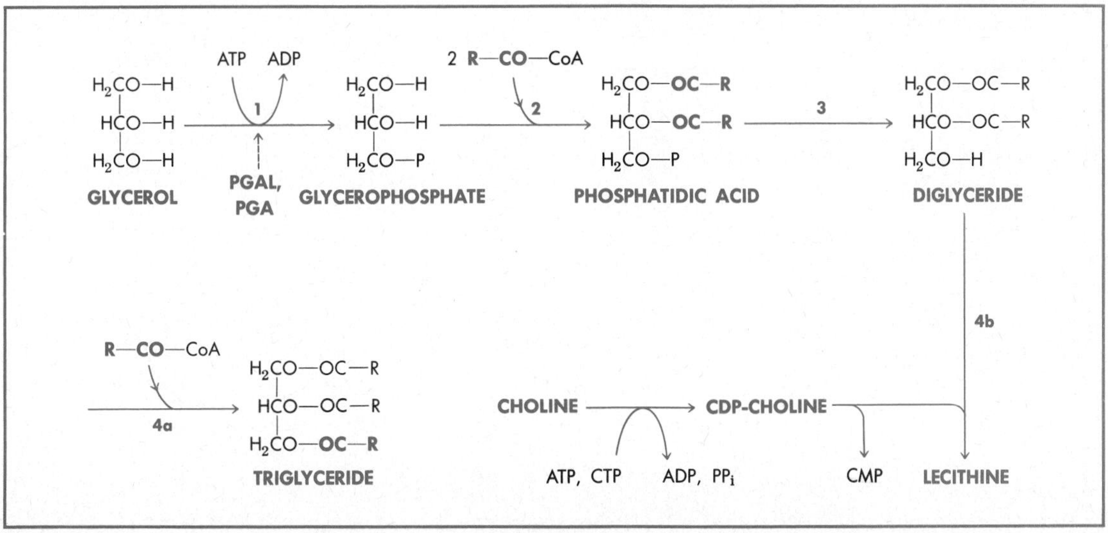

control of any individual cell. Thus, if the rate of supply from the gut falls below or exceeds the rate of utilization in the tissues, then an amino acid deficit or excess will develop. In a deficiency, transamination or hydrolytic breakdown of cellular proteins may alleviate the shortage temporarily, but the cell and indeed the whole animal must ultimately suffer disease or death if the essential amino acids remain unavailable. Evidently, animals must consume daily doses of essential amino acids or derivatives of them.

However, an amino acid excess is actually the more usual situation. Amino acid requirements are greatest in young, growing animals, in pregnant females, and in animals in which extensive tissue repair is under way, as after disease. In all such cases, protein synthesis and growth proceed at a very high rate and large quantities of amino acids are utilized in the cells. But even then, more amino acids are usually eaten than are required. In healthy adults, where processes of growth and structural replacement occur at a much reduced rate, amino acid requirements are reduced correspondingly.

Unlike carbohydrates or fats, excess amino acids are not stored. Some tissues may accumulate more protein than they require, and such proteins in a sense may be considered to represent amino acid reserves. But specialized storage of amino acids comparable to storage of carbohydrates or fats does not occur. Unused excess quantities of amino acids are then degraded, in vertebrates primarily in the liver

19 · 23 *Metabolic pathways of nitrogen compounds. Urea production via the ornithine cycle in the vertebrate liver is outlined at left. Atoms in color indicate the fate of the NH_3 and CO_2 raw materials. The net input and output of the cycle is seen to be given by the equation $2 NH_3 + CO_2 \longrightarrow NH_2CONH_2 + H_2O$. The pathways at right show that NH_3 may also arise from the stepwise degradation of purines such as adenine or guanine, processes yielding the series of excretion products indicated, including uric acid and urea. Uric acid is a major excretory endproduct in, for example, insects, birds, and some reptiles; allantoin, in turtles and some mammals; allantoic acid, in some bony fishes. NH_3 as such is excreted in most invertebrate groups, and urea, in most vertebrate groups not named above. Animals generally excrete mixtures of various endproducts, but one or the other substance tends to predominate. The enzymes for the lettered steps are: a, adenase; b, oxidase; c, guanase; d, oxidase; e, uricase; f, allantoinase; g, allantoicase; h, urease.*

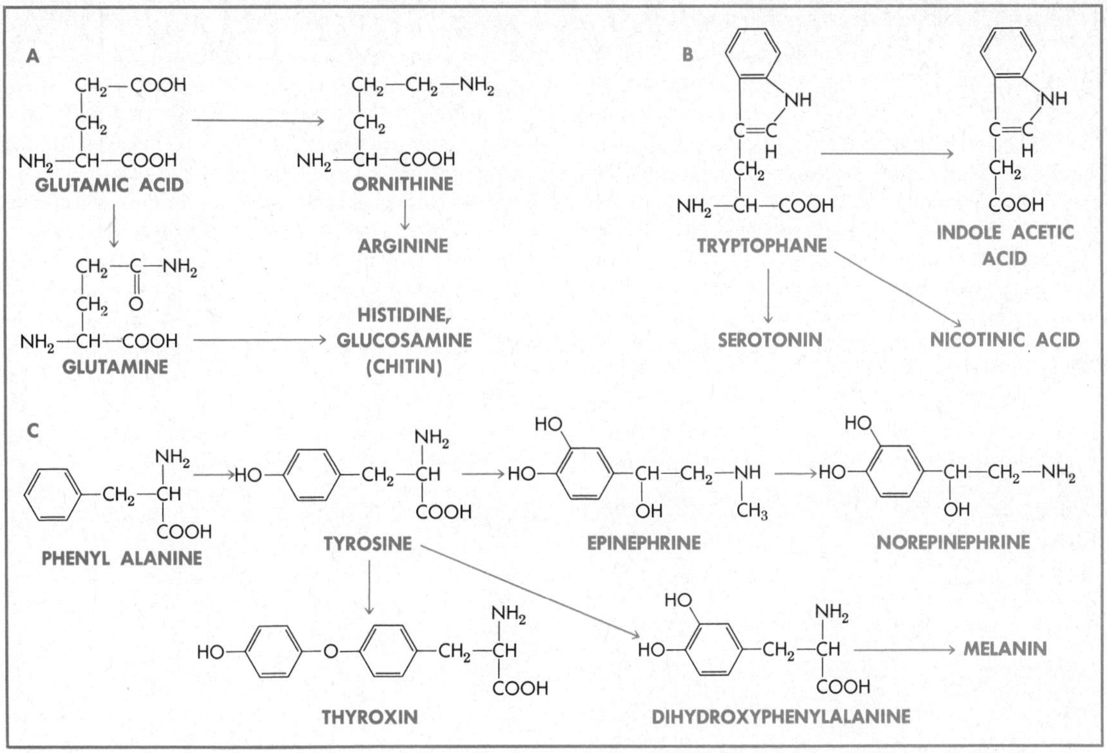

19 · 24 Synthetic pathways *involving the amino acid precursors glutamic acid (A), tryptophane (B), and phenyl alanine (C). The arrows do not necessarily imply single reaction steps. Among the synthesized products shown are some hormones (indole acetic acid, thyroxine, serotonin, and the epinephrines, or adrenalines), pigments (melanin), and other amino acids (ornithine, arginine, glutamine, tyrosine). Many other products are formed in cells from these three precursors.*

and in other animals probably directly in most cells. As already shown in Chap. 18, this degradation takes the form of oxidative deamination. The keto acids thereby produced then enter the metabolic pathways of carbohydrates or lipids, according to whether the acids are glucogenic or ketogenic. And, depending on the kind of animal, the resulting ammonia is either excreted as such or is converted into urea or uric acid and excreted in this form.

Urea synthesis as in liver cells occurs largely via an *ornithine cycle,* a reaction sequence in which the amino acids ornithine, citrulline, and arginine form an "endless belt" (Fig. 19.23). For every urea molecule generated, one ATP, one CO_2, and two NH_3 molecules feed into the cycle. As indicated in the figure, urea may also arise in another, indirect way, after NH_3 (or $—NH_2$) is used in cells as a building material in the synthesis of purine nitrogen bases such as adenine and guanine. Whenever purines are later degraded, they undergo a sequence of enzymatic transformations in which both uric acid and urea appear. Some organisms possess all the enzymes for the complete transformation sequence, but in other organisms different particular enzymes are lacking. Thus, purine degradation will proceed to different degrees of completion in different organisms. In insects, birds, and also in many plants, uric acid is the chief excretion product. This compound is usually eliminated in more or less solid urine, but in some cases it

is deposited within or on the organism in crystalline form (for example, the powdery material on the wings of many butterflies and moths). In some mammals (man included), a small amount of uric acid likewise appears in urine normally or forms larger internal deposits abnormally, as in gout. But in other cases most purines are degraded further, to urea or even to NH_3 and CO_2.

Amino acids not deaminated in the liver of vertebrates are supplied to all cells via blood. In all other organisms analogously, individual cells of the body retain intact amino acids procured either by alimentation or by direct intracellular synthesis. Such compounds then serve as raw materials in a large and diverse array of synthetic processes. For example, as outlined in Fig. 19.24, glutamic acid is the source for the formation of *ornithine* and *arginine* and also of *glutamine*, a cell constituent functioning frequently as —NH_2 donor and participating specifically in *chitin* synthesis. The amino acid tryptophane is the precursor for the B vitamin *nicotinic acid* (derivatives of which are NAD and NADP); for *serotonin,* a hormone of the nervous system (see Chap. 25); and for *indole acetic acid,* one of the chief growth hormones of plants (see Chap. 22). Phenylalanine gives rise to tyrosine, another amino acid, and the latter in turn is the starting compound in the synthesis

of the hormones *thyroxin* and *adrenalin* as well as the important animal pigment *melanin.* Numerous other cell constituents are produced from individual amino acids, but we shall not have occasion to deal with most of these.

On the contrary, one group of amino acid derivatives is of crucial significance in all cells, and their synthesis will occupy our attention greatly in the next chapter. This group comprises the proteins.

REVIEW QUESTIONS

1. What physical processes are implied in the statement "Chlorophyll is green"? What is the visible spectrum and how is chlorophyll affected by visible light? What is the general chemical structure of chlorophyll? What are plastids and what kinds are there? What is the internal architecture of chloroplasts?

2. Review the sources of the carbon, the hydrogen, and the oxygen atoms that compose photosynthesized carbohydrates. What experiments have demonstrated the derivation of the oxygen in such carbohydrates?

3. What are the functions of light and chlorophyll in photosynthesis? What experiments have demonstrated these functions? What are the events of photolysis? Distinguish between photoexcitation and photoionization. Show how water becomes separated into several components. What is photophosphorylation?

4. Review the events in cyclic and noncyclic electron transfers, and show how such transfers contribute to (*a*) ATP formation, (*b*) food manufacture. Distinguish between the various energy levels of electrons, and show how water is both a donor and acceptor of electrons. What carrier compounds participate in electron transfers?

5. What is fluorescence? What are the light-trapping functions of carotenoids and of chlorophyll *a* and *b*? How is photolytically produced hydrogen transferred into CO_2-fixing reactions? What are the net input and the net output of photolysis?

6. Review the general pattern of reductive CO_2 fixation. What are the major steps? What roles do phosphorylated carbohydrates play? What role does energy play in CO_2 fixation? In what sense are the first two steps the key reactions? Describe these steps. What are the net input and output of CO_2 fixation as a whole? Of photosynthesis as a whole?

7. What is the principal net endproduct of photosynthesis? Review the possible fates of this endproduct. What are the main transportation and storage forms of carbohydrates in plants and how is the photosynthetic endproduct converted into these?

8. Review general and specific patterns of carbohydrate synthesis. How can carbon chains be lengthened in cells? Shortened? What is the pathway of glycogen synthesis? What is the role of UDP-glucose and what compounds may be formed from it?

9. What happens to carbohydrates reaching the vertebrate liver? What happens if carbohydrate supplies are exceedingly excessive?

10. By what processes is the constancy of the blood-glucose concentration maintained? Discuss several specific situations in which the blood-glucose level tends to change and show how such tendencies are counteracted by the liver.

11. How is a C_{18} fatty acid synthesized from acetyl CoA? How is a fat synthesized? Where in a cell do such syntheses take place? Describe the interplay between liver, fat depots, and body tissues in animal fat metabolism. Can an animal survive if fats are substituted for carbohydrates in its diet? Can an animal similarly survive in the converse situation?

12. How does a cell synthesize amino acids? What precursors are required? Describe the chemistry of transamination and oxidative deamination. When and where does the latter occur and what are the results of this process? In which form do various organisms eliminate nitrogenous wastes? Review the ornithine cycle.

13. Show how the following interconversions may occur: (*a*) carbohydrate to fat; (*b*) fat to carbohydrate; (*c*) carbohydrate to amino acid or vice versa; (*d*) fat to amino acid or vice versa.

14. Suppose that an animal were not given any food for a considerable length of time. What specific progressive changes would then occur in the body-wide balances of carbohydrates, fats, and amino acids? Could an animal survive if its foods consisted of (*a*) only carbohydrates, (*b*) only fats, (*c*) only proteins, (*d*) carbohydrates and fats only, (*e*) carbohydrates and amino acids only, (*f*) fats and amino acids only?

15. Describe the basic balance between synthesis and breakdown in cells and explain the meaning of metabolic turnover. Name some compounds synthesized in cells from amino acids and describe the general pathway of such syntheses. How is chlorophyll synthesized?

COLLATERAL READINGS

Arnon, D. I.: The Role of Light in Photosynthesis, *Sci. American,* Nov., 1960. The conversion of light energy into chemical energy is discussed.

Aronoff, S.: Chlorophyll, *Botan. Rev.,* vol. 16, 1950. An account of the structure of the photosynthetic unit in chloroplasts, with special attention to the role of chlorophyll.

Bassham, J. A., and M. Calvin: The Path of Carbon in Photosynthesis, in "Handbook of Plant Physiology," vol. 5, part 1, Springer, Berlin, 1960. A detailed review of reductive CO_2 fixation.

————: The Path of Carbon in Photosynthesis, *Sci. American,* June, 1962. A more general account of the Calvin cycle.

Bogorad, L.: Photosynthesis, in "Plant Biology Today," Wadsworth, Belmont, Calif., 1963. A very thorough, general discussion of the subject; recommended.

Calvin, M.: The Photosynthetic Cycle, University of California Research Laboratories, vol. 2924, 1955. A description of the Calvin cycle by its discoverer.

Gabriel, M. L., and S. Fogel: "Great Experiments in Biology," Prentice-Hall, Englewood Cliffs, N.J., 1955. This paperback includes reprints of several classical early articles on the nature of photosynthesis; highly recommended for historical review.

Galston, A. W.: "The Life of the Green Plant," 2d ed., Prentice-Hall, Englewood Cliffs, N.J., 1964. A good review of photosynthesis is included in this paperback.

Green, D. E.: The Synthesis of Fat, *Sci. American,* Feb., 1960. The title of this article describes its contents adequately.

Jensen, W. A.: "The Plant Cell," Wadsworth, Belmont, Calif., 1964. A short section on chloroplasts and photosynthesis is included in this paperback.

Kamen, M. D.: "Primary Processes in Photosynthesis," Academic Press, 1963. In this treatise, the biological, chemical, and physical aspects of photosynthesis are integrated.

Loewy, A. G., and P. Siekevitz: "Cell Structure and Function," Prentice-Hall Englewood Cliffs, N.J., 1963. The brief section on metabolic pathways in this paperback is pertinent to the topics of this chapter.

Meyer, B. S., D. B. Anderson, and R. H. Böhning: "Introduction to Plant Physiology," Van Nostrand, Princeton, N.J., 1960. This book may be consulted for further background on the details of synthesis and photosynthesis in plants.

Rabinowitch, E. I., and Govindjee: The Role of Chlorophyll in Photosynthesis, *Sci. American,* July, 1965. A very up-to-date account on the redox process by which H atoms of water are incorporated into organic materials.

Steward, F. C.: "Plants at Work," Addison-Wesley, Reading, Mass., 1964. This paperback contains a short chapter on the chemistry of photosynthesis.

White, A., P. Handler, and E. L. Smith: "Principles of Biochemistry," 3d ed., McGraw-Hill, New York, 1964. All topics of carbohydrate, lipid, and amino acid metabolism are discussed in detail in this text; a short section on photosynthesis is also included.

CHAPTER 20 PROTEIN, NUCLEIC ACID, AND PHYSICAL METAB-OLISM

Apart from photosynthesis in certain cells, protein and nucleic acid syntheses are the most important manufacturing processes in all cells. Proteins form the enzymes required for each of the hundreds of metabolic and self-perpetuative events in a cell, and proteins are the principal architectural constituents of a cell. Thus, the whole structural and functional nature of a cell is determined and maintained by its proteins. Synthesis of these compounds depends on and is associated intimately with the synthesis of the nucleic acids DNA and RNA, the first of which forms the genes of a cell. Accordingly, protein and nucleic acid production are examined together in the first part of this chapter, which rounds out the present analysis of the *chemical* aspects of cellular metabolism.

Cells use nutrients and ATP not only in chemical activities, however, but in *physical* ones as well. Among the most common physical expressions of metabolism are the generation of heat, in some cases also the generation of light and of electricity, and above all, the production of movement of cells and cell parts. These topics are discussed in the last part.

THE GENETIC CODE: DNA, RNA, AND PROTEIN SYNTHESIS

THE PATTERN

The biosynthesis of proteins is bound to differ in at least one fundamental respect from the manufacture of most other cellular compounds: a cell cannot make use of just any newly made proteins but requires very *specific* proteins. These must be largely different in structure from proteins formed in other types of cells or in other organisms; for only if newly formed proteins are exactly like those present earlier can a cell maintain its own special characteristics. Such a specificity problem does not arise with most other kinds of compounds. A cellulose molecule, for example, being composed of identical glucose units, will be almost automatically like any other cellulose molecule containing the same number of glucose units. But a protein molecule may be composed of 20 or more different kinds of amino acid units, and random linking together here would make one polypeptide chain quite different from every other. Clearly, protein synthesis requires *specificity control;* a "blueprint" must be available, to provide instructions regarding the precise sequence in which given numbers and types of amino acids are to be polymerized into polypeptides. Ultimately, such specificity control is exercised by the *genes* of a cell, the genetic DNA of the chromosomes. The *primary function of genes is to control specificities in protein synthesis.*

That genes are in fact DNA and not some other constituents has been established through two classical lines of evidence, both obtained through work on bacteria. It is possible to extract DNA from a strain of bacteria and to place the extract into a medium in which another strain of bacteria is present. These organisms then absorb some of the foreign DNA and, as a result, acquire some of the genetic traits of the original DNA donors. However, if similar experiments are performed with protein or other extracts of the donor bacteria, genetic changes do not occur in the recipient organisms. Evidently, the *bacterial transformation* is brought about specifically by DNA, and DNA therefore must be the substance of genes (Fig. 20.1).

Substantially the same conclusion is warranted by

the phenomenon of *transduction*. In it, genetic material from one bacterium is transferred to another bacterium through the agency of *bacteriophages*, viruses which parasitize bacteria (see Chap. 9). Such a virus infects a bacterium and reproduces within the bacterial cell at the expense of the host. The host then dies and the offspring viruses are released, free to infect more bacteria. It happens on occasion that bits of the genetic material of a host bacterium become incorporated into newly forming offspring viruses. When the latter subsequently infect new bacterial hosts, they carry the genetic material of the old hosts into the new. In this way the new hosts acquire additional genetic agents and may develop changed or new traits as a result (Fig. 20.2). The important point here is that the genetic material so transferred by viruses is DNA. Incidentally, recall from Chap. 9 that, whenever a virus infects a cell, only the virus DNA enters the cell and takes over control of the metabolism of the host cell; the protein portion of the virus remains outside the host cell. Clearly, virus genes are equivalent to virus DNA.

There is little question, therefore, that gene func-

20 · 1 Bacterial transformation. *The cell substance of a rough-coated bacterial type is extracted, and separate DNA and non-DNA fractions are prepared. If a smooth-coated bacterial type is allowed to absorb the DNA fraction, it will change into a rough-coated type. But it will remain smooth-coated if it absorbs only the non-DNA fraction. Experiments of this sort show that the nucleic acids are of genetic importance.*

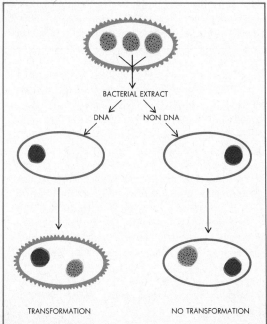

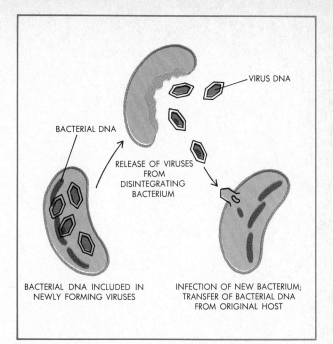

20 · 2 The principle of transduction. *Newly forming bacteriophage viruses may incorporate into their own structure pieces of the genetic material (DNA) of the host bacterium (left). When such viruses infect new bacterial hosts (center and right), these hosts acquire additional bacterial genes.*

tion must be interpreted on the basis of DNA structure. As already noted briefly in Chap. 6, the particular sequence of the nitrogen-base pairs in genetic DNA represents a chemical code, which specifies a particular sequence of amino acid polymerization. The different genes in a cell carry different codes, and a cell can manufacture proteins only as these codes dictate. In so far as the genes themselves remain stable, therefore, any new sets of proteins synthesized in a cell will match the preexisting sets precisely.

The "blueprints" are housed in the chromosomes within the nucleus, but the "factories" where proteins are actually put together are the ribosomes, in the cytoplasm. Evidently, some kind of instruction-transmitting device must exist. It does exist, in the form of RNA. The chromosomes are known to manufacture RNA, and in the course of this manufacturing process the chemical code of DNA becomes transferred exactly, or *transcribed*, into the structure of RNA. Chromosomal RNA thus becomes just as specific as the genetic DNA. The specific RNA molecules then leave the chromosomes and diffuse into the cytoplasm (possibly after temporary storage in the nucleoli), and they eventually reach the ribosomes. Here amino acids are joined together into proteins in accordance with the genetic code supplied by the RNA molecules (Fig. 20.3).

We may therefore regard genes essentially as passive information carriers. All that they do, or allow to be done to them, is to have their specific code information copied by RNA molecules, which then serve as information carriers in their turn. Genes consequently may be likened to important original "texts" carefully stored and preserved in the "library" of the nucleus. There they are available as permanent, authoritative "master documents" from which expendable duplicate copies may be prepared. RNA passing into the cytoplasm actually is expendable and comparatively short-lived. Very soon after it has exercised its function as code carrier, it is destroyed and respired away; new RNA from the nucleus must then become available in the cytoplasm if repeated protein synthesis is to occur. The genes on the contrary persist and are protected from respiratory destruction by the nuclear boundary. Clearly, presence of a distinct cell nucleus with a distinct boundary membrane may be an important evolutionary adaptation, an advantageous device which might further the preservation of gene stability. We may also appreciate the advantage of having the permanent message center and the manufacturing center at different locations within a cell. If both were at the same location in the nucleus, the manufacturing center probably would be too distant and isolated from the energy sources and the raw material supplies; and if both were at the same location in the cytoplasm, the message center would be subject to rapid respiratory destruction.

20 · 3 *The pattern of protein synthesis. The genetic code in the chromosomal DNA of a cell is transcribed into RNA, and from there the code is further transcribed into specific amino acid sequences in proteins manufactured in the ribosomes of the cytoplasm.*

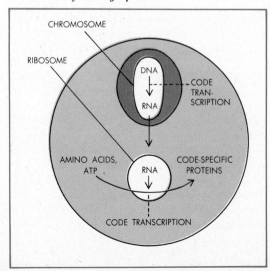

Inasmuch as the RNA manufactured in the chromosomes carries chemical messages to the ribosomes, it is called *messenger* RNA, or *m*RNA. Two additional types exist in a cell. One is *ribosomal* RNA, or *r*RNA; it is a normal structural component of the ribosomes. Conceivably, *r*RNA may play a role in ensuring the proper attachment of *m*RNA to the ribosomes. It is known that *m*RNA, a chainlike polymer of nucleotides and thus shaped like a filament, must preserve its extended filamentous form if it is to function properly. *m*RNA is believed to become draped over the surface of one or more ribosomes, like a thread becoming draped over one or more spherical objects; and it is possible that *r*RNA in the ribosomes supplies a matching surface which may force or otherwise direct the proper linear deposition of *m*RNA (Fig. 20.4).

The third type of RNA is *transfer* RNA, or *t*RNA. It functions as *amino acid carrier*. A cell possesses 20 or more different kinds of *t*RNA, just as many as there are different kinds of amino acids. When a particular kind of amino acid enters a cell as food and is to be used in protein synthesis, a specific corresponding kind of *t*RNA becomes attached to the amino acid and carries it to the ribosomes. Here the *t*RNA "delivers" its amino acid at a particular place along the *m*RNA filament already present, and other *t*RNA carriers similarly deliver their amino acids at other specific places along the *m*RNA. Large numbers of amino acids so become lined up along *m*RNA in a particular sequence. Through a mechanism to be described presently, the specific nature of this sequence has been determined by the code within the *m*RNA. The "correctly" stationed amino acids then become joined to one another by enzymatic formation of peptide bonds, and a polypeptide chain with a gene-determined specificity so results (see Fig. 20.4).

CODE TRANSCRIPTION: DNA ⟶ *m*RNA

We already know that, in line with the Watson-Crick model of DNA structure, DNA is a spiraled double chain of polynucleotides (see Figs. 6.27 and 6.28). In it, the genetic code is based on a four-letter alphabet of nitrogen-base pairs, namely, $A \cdot T$, $T \cdot A$, $G \cdot C$, $C \cdot G$, and the code consists of a specific succession of such pairs. If the code of a given segment of a DNA chain is to be transcribed, a first requirement appears to be an unspiraling of this segment and an at least temporary "unzipping" of the double chain into two separate single chains. The exact mechanisms through which these events might occur are still uncertain. For purposes of illustration, let us assume that a double DNA chain

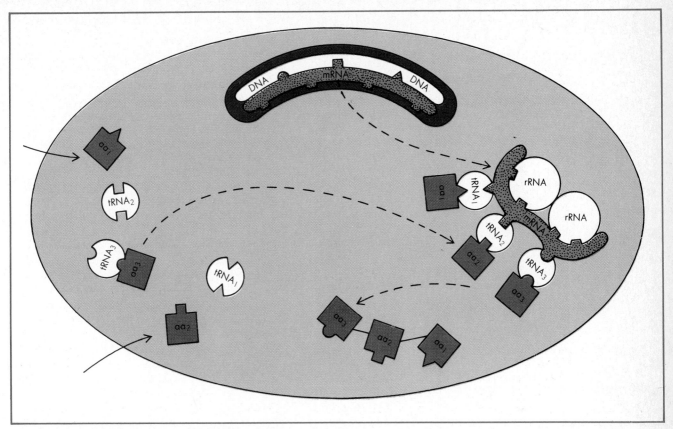

20 · 4 The pattern of protein synthesis. *Specific (messenger) mRNA manufactured in chromosomes becomes attached to ribosomes, and the (ribosomal) rRNA of the latter probably aids in the attachment. Amino acids (aa) entering a cell as food become joined to specific (transfer) tRNA molecules, and the tRNA-aa complexes then attach at specific, code-determined sites along mRNA. The amino acids subsequently link together through peptide bonding. The completed, code-specific polypeptide chains ultimately become free.*

20 · 5 Code transcription *from DNA to mRNA. A, T, G, C, U, purine and pyrimidine bases; R, ribose, P, phosphate. In a first step, the DNA double chain unzips. It is assumed that the N-base sequence of the lower single chain (color) is to be transcribed. In the second step, the nucleotide-diphosphate raw materials ADP, GDP, CDP, and UDP become hydrogen-bonded to appropriate N-bases along the DNA chain. Formation of a linked ribose-phosphate chain, as in the third step, then yields finished mRNA, with an N-base sequence specifically determined by that of DNA.*

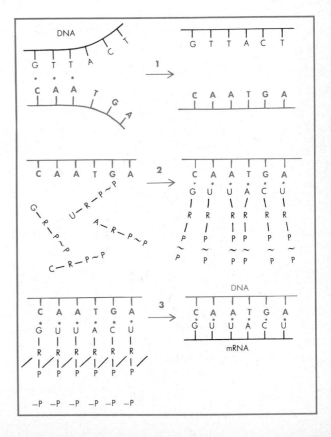

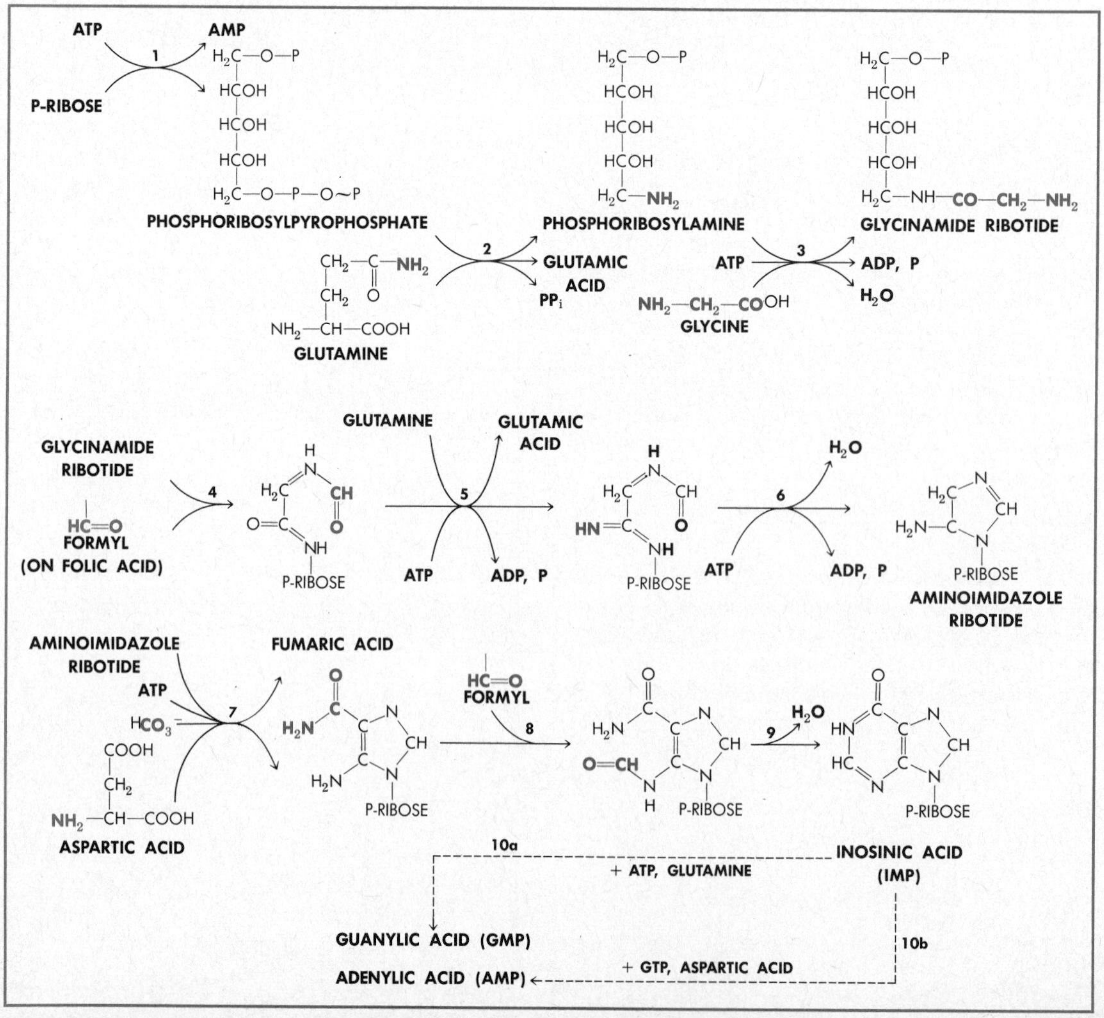

20 · 6 Cellular purine synthesis. *At any step, atoms or atomic groups added to the preceding compounds are shown in color. For the first three steps, a basic nitrogen-carbon chain attached to phosphoribose is built up. Note that glutamine serves as an amino donor here, as also in many other instances where a* —NH₂ *group is required in synthesis metabolism. In step 4, a 1-carbon fragment is added in the form of formyl, a group carried on the B vitamin folic acid. This vitamin is a very common carrier and donor of 1-carbon pieces. In step 5 glutamine donates another amino group, and step 6 produces the closed 5-membered ring of the eventual purine. Steps 7 through 9 build a 6-membered ring onto the 5-membered one. As shown, aspartic acid and another formyl fragment are the sources of the needed atomic groups. The result is the purine nucleotide IMP, the parent compound in the synthesis of other nucleotides such as GMP and AMP (see Chap. 6 for the full structure of these nucleotides).*

containing six nitrogen-base pairs does unzip into two single chains (Fig. 20.5, part 1). Let us also assume that the nitrogen-base sequence *CAATGA* of one of the single chains is to be transcribed into RNA just being synthesized.

The manufacture of RNA requires adequate supplies of raw materials. We know that RNA contains four types of ribonucleotides, namely, adenine-ribose-phosphate (adenylic acid, AMP), guanine-ribose-phosphate (guanylic acid, GMP), cytosine-ribose-phosphate (cytidylic acid, CMP), and uracil-ribose-phosphate (uridylic acid, UMP, which substitutes for TMP of DNA). Clearly, before RNA can be synthesized, the four constituent nucleotides themselves must first be manufactured. The first two nucleotides listed above are purine derivatives, and the pattern of their synthesis is outlined in Fig. 20.6. The main building materials are seen to be ribose, ATP, the amino acids glycine and aspartic acid, and glutamine, derived from the amino acid glutamic acid. All these are formed into a fundamental purine-containing nucleotide, *inosinic acid* (inosine monophosphate, IMP). This compound may then be converted either into the adenine-containing adenosine phosphates (AMP, ADP, ATP) or into the guanine-containing guanosine phosphates (GMP, GDP, GTP). The main pathways in the synthesis of the pyrimidine-containing nucleotides are illustrated in Fig. 20.7. Here the starting materials are CO_2, NH_3, aspartic acid, and ATP. These compounds are built into a fundamental pyrimidine, *orotic acid*, from which are then derived all three of the pyrimidine-containing nucleotides: uracil-containing uridine phosphates (UMP, UDP, UTP), cytosine-containing cytidine phosphates (CMP, CDP, CTP), and thymine-containing thymidine phosphates (TMP, TDP, TTP). The last are used in DNA synthesis only (see below). Evidently, nucleotide synthesis creates the funda-

20 · 7 Cellular pyrimidine synthesis. *The enzyme required specifically in step 2 is aspartic transcarbamylase. In this reaction, the colored atoms in carbamyl-P and aspartic acid emerge as phosphoric acid (H—O—P), and the NH_2—CO— part of carbamyl-P becomes linked to aspartic acid (where the colored line is drawn in ureidosuccinic acid). In step 3, ring closure occurs by removal of H_2O (atoms in color). Also, a dehydrogenase in conjunction with NAD^+ catalyzes H_2 removal from the —CH_2—CH— group of ureidosuccinic acid. The resulting orotic acid is the key compound in the synthesis of pyrimidine nucleotides. The ribose-phosphate parts of a nucleotide are contributed by the* compound phosphoribosyl-pyrophosphate, and through steps 4 and 5 the uracil derivative UMP is formed (the source of the byproduct CO_2 here being the —COOH group of orotic acid). Through reactions outlined in steps 6 through 9, other uracil and also cytosine and thymine derivatives may be manufactured (that is, all the principal pyrimidine nucleotides in cells). Note that TMP manufacture requires the vitamin biotin, an agent essential in the transfer of a methyl (—CH_3) group from a donor molecule to the TMP-producing reaction. See Chap. 6 for the structure of nucleotides not depicted fully below.*

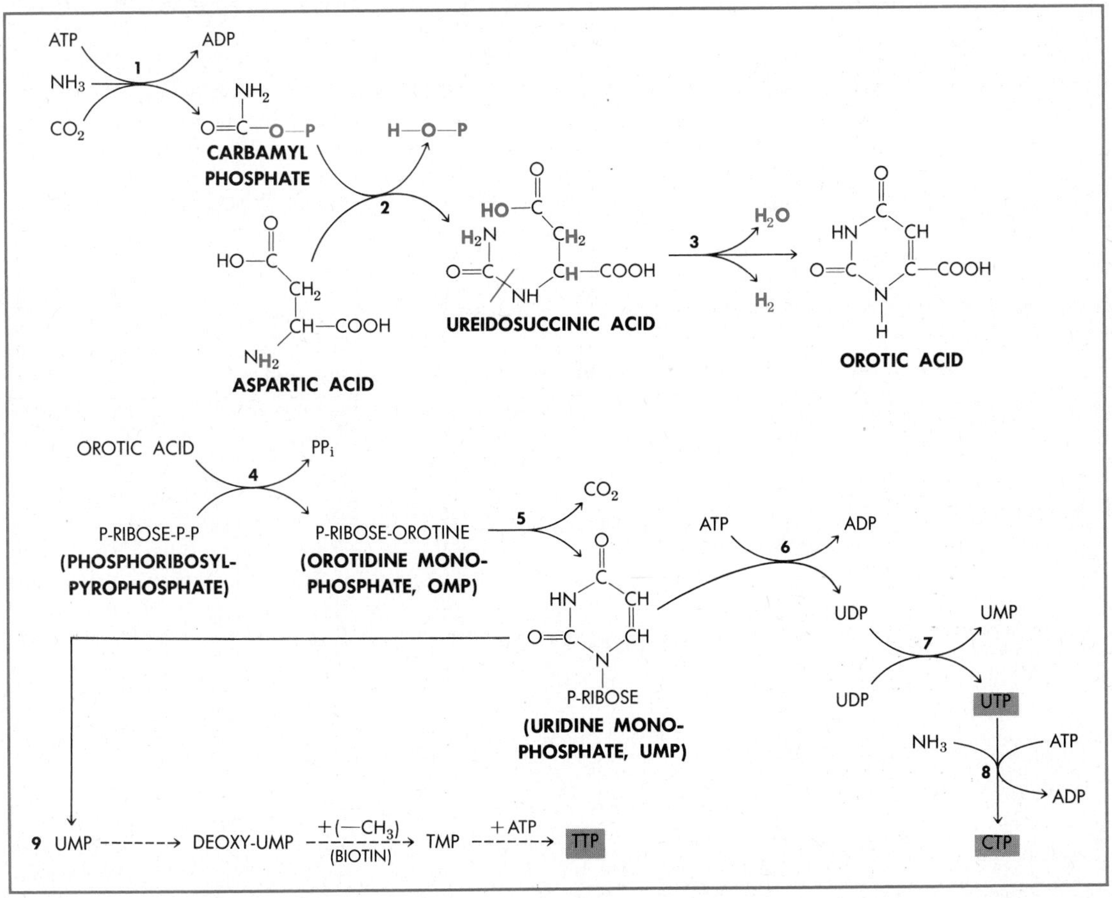

mental energy carriers of cells as well as the ingredients required for nucleic acid manufacture.

It has been found that the actual cellular raw materials for RNA synthesis are the diphosphate derivatives of the four nucleotides: ADP, GDP, CDP, and UDP. Each of the latter carries a high-energy bond between the first and second phosphate groups. In our sample DNA sequence to be transcribed (Fig. 20.5, part 1) the first nitrogen base is noted to be C, cytosine. We know that such a base may, by hydrogen bonding, join specifically to the nitrogen base G, guanine, and form a $C \cdot G$ pair. If therefore the available raw materials in a chromosome include GDP (G—R—P in Fig. 20.5, part 2) this molecule may become bonded to the C of DNA. Quite analogously, the A's of DNA may each bond to a UDP raw material, the T may bond to an ADP, and the G may bond to a CDP (Fig. 20.5, part 2). In other words, the DNA sequence serves as a *template*, or mold, along which specific molecules of raw material may become attached in a specific sequence. To form a complete RNA thereafter, it is necessary only to link the aligned raw materials together into a polynucleotide chain. In cells this is accomplished with the aid of the high-energy bonds already built into

TABLE 16 PROBABLE TRIPLET CODES FOR AMINO ACIDS IN *m*RNA (*A*, ADENINE; *U*, URACIL; *G*, GUANINE; *C*, CYTOSINE)

AMINO ACID	CODE TRIPLET
alanine	CCG, CGU
arginine	CCG
asparagine	CAU, AAU, AAC
aspartic acid	GAU, CAA
cysteine	GUU
glutamic acid	GAU, GAA
glutamine	AAC, AGG
glycine	GGU
histidine	CAU, CAC
isoleucine	AUU
leucine	AUU, GUU, CUU
lysine	AAU, AAA
methionine	GAU
phenylalanine	UUU
proline	CCU, CCC
serine	CUU, CCU
threonine	AAC, ACC
tryptophane	GGU
tyrosine	AUU
valine	GUU

the raw materials and with the aid of an enzyme, *RNA polymerase:*

$$(\text{N-base—ribose—O—P—O}\sim\text{P})_x \xrightarrow{\text{RNA polymerase}}$$

$$(\text{—O—P})_x + (\text{N-base—ribose—O—P})_x$$

In this equation, x refers to the number of ribonucleotide units linked together. In our example sequence, therefore, the result will be as in Fig. 20.5, part 3.

The finished RNA chain represents *m*RNA, which separates from the DNA template and eventually reaches a ribosome. Note that the specific DNA code is imprinted in *m*RNA in the form of *corresponding* nitrogen bases, in somewhat the same way that a photographic negative shows light objects as dark areas or that a plaster cast shows elevated objects as depressions. Such "inverted," negative codes in *m*RNA represent the actual working blueprints for protein synthesis.

CODE TRANSCRIPTION: *m*RNA ⟶ PROTEIN

How does the code in *m*RNA specify a given amino acid sequence—just what does the genetic code actually say?

We know the code must somehow "spell out" in chemical terms an identification of 20-plus different amino acids and that it must do so with a four-letter alphabet. Assuming that nature is as terse as it can be, how are 20 or more different identifying "words" constructed out of four letters, such that each word contains as few letters as possible? If the code consisted of one-letter words, a four-letter alphabet *A-B-C-D* would allow only four different identifications: *A, B, C, D*. If the code were made up of two-letter words, there would be 4^2, or 16 different letter combinations: *AA, AB, AC, AD, BB, BA, BC,* etc. Yet 16 combinations are still too few to specify 20+ words. However, if the code contained three-letter words, there could be 4^3, or 64 different letter combinations, more than enough to spell out 20+ words.

On the basis of such reasoning, it has been hypothesized and later actually confirmed that the genetic code "names" each amino acid by a sequence of three "letters," that is, three adjacent nitrogen bases in DNA and *m*RNA. In such a *triplet code,* 20+ triplets would be "meaningful" and spell out amino acid identities; the remainder of the 64 possible triplets would be "meaningless."

Which N-base triplets identify which amino acids? The answer has been obtained through ingenious experiments. It has been possible to extract RNA polymerase from bacteria and to add to this enzyme,

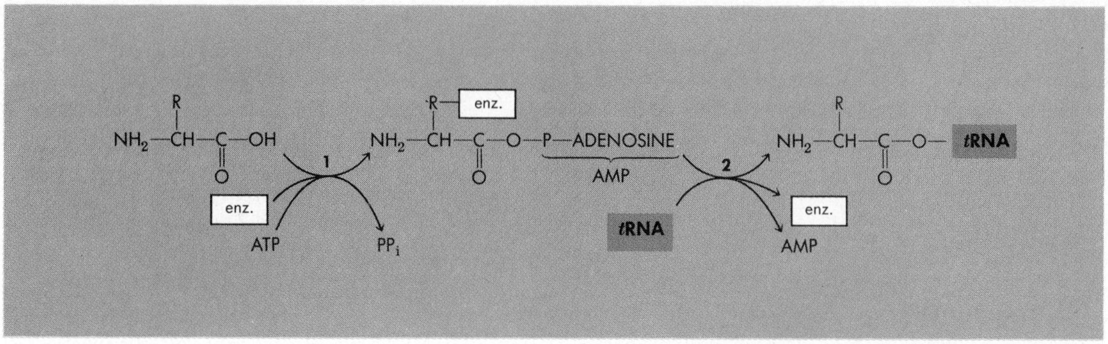

20 · 8 Amino acid activation. In reaction 1, the energy of ATP serves to link a specific enzyme and AMP to amino acid. In reaction 2, a tRNA specific for that amino acid and that enzyme replaces the AMP, and the enzyme disengages as well. The amino-acid-tRNA complex then migrates to mRNA.

in the test tube, known mixtures of ADP, GDP, CDP, and UDP. From such reaction systems could be obtained artificial RNA molecules which contained known sequences of N-bases. To the RNA could then be added a mixture of known amino acids, and artificial polypeptides could so be synthesized in the test tube. Analysis of such polypeptides shows which amino acids they contain and in what sequence, and this information could be correlated directly with the N-base sequence in the RNA. In the first experiment of this kind, for example, only UDP was used as raw material for artificial RNA synthesis. The resulting RNA molecules then were "poly U," that is, they consisted entirely of a sequence of uracil-containing ribonucleotides. After mixed amino acids were added, it was found that the polypeptide formed in the test tube consisted entirely of the amino acid *phenylalanine*. From this it could be concluded that the triplet code for phenyl alanine must be *UUU*.

Later work along related lines has led to the identification of the code triplets for all 20+ amino acids (Table 16). It should be noted here that, although the N-bases for each meaningful triplet are now known, the exact sequence of the three bases within each triplet is still not clear in all cases. For example, we know that the code triplet for the amino acid aspartic acid contains *G, A,* and *U,* but we do not yet know whether the triplet reads *GAU* or *AGU* or *GUA* or some other sequence of these three bases. Thus, although the code triplets for aspartic acid, glutamic acid, and methionine all contain *A, G,* and *U,* the three triplets undoubtedly differ in their internal base sequences. Moreover, it has been found that certain amino acids are coded by more than a single triplet. Leucine, for example, is coded as *AUU, GUU,* and *CUU.* Because of such multiple codings, the genetic code is said to be somewhat *degenerate*. There are therefore more than 20+ meaningful triplets in actuality, and fewer meaningless ones than might be assumed theoretically. A limited degree of degeneracy is of considerable adaptive

advantage, for change of one code letter—by mutation, for example—still may preserve the meaning of the whole triplet. Thus, if *AUU* were to mutate to *GUU,* the specification of leucine could remain intact nevertheless.

In our sample *m*RNA above (Fig. 20.5), the six-base sequence *GUUACU* thus consists of two consecutive triplets, which could represent the code for the amino acid combination valine-histidine. How does such an *m*RNA code in the ribosomes control the formation of a valine-histidine portion in a polypeptide? To answer this, we must turn our attention to *t*RNA.

The joining of amino acids with their specific *t*RNA carriers in the free cytoplasm is referred to as *amino acid activation*. This process requires the participation of ATP as energy donor and of an enzyme, specific for each given amino acid, which links the amino acid with its specific *t*RNA carrier (Fig. 20.8). Each *t*RNA is a comparatively short ribonucleotide polymer in which both ends of the molecule play a critical role. At one end, which serves as "carrier" end, all *t*RNA types appear to possess the same N-base triplet, namely, *ACC,* and it is at this end that *t*RNA is joined to its amino acid (Fig. 20.9). Thus the carrier end of *t*RNA appears to be nonspecific, and all amino acids become linked in the same way. However, the other end of *t*RNA is specific for a given amino acid. At this "recognition" end is present an N-base triplet which spells out a positive (that is, DNA-like) code for a particular amino acid. In the case of valine, for example, the *t*RNA specific for valine would carry the terminal recognition triplet *CAA,* the inverse of *GUU;* and

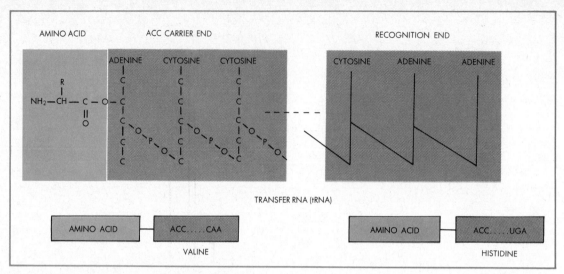

AMINO ACID   ACC CARRIER END   RECOGNITION END

TRANSFER RNA (tRNA)

AMINO ACID	ACC.....CAA

VALINE

AMINO ACID	ACC.....UGA

HISTIDINE

20 · 9 *The structure of transfer RNA. At the ACC carrier end, the amino acid is linked to carbon 2 of ribose. The phosphate joins adjacent nucleotides between carbon 3 of one ribose and carbon 5 of the next, as shown. Behind the ACC carrier triplet, tRNA possesses a series of other nucleotides. The terminal triplet forms a recognition end, which is CAA in the case of valine, UGA in the case of histidine (bottom row). It is this recognition end which specifically attaches to an appropriate N-base along mRNA on the ribosomes.*

20 · 10 *Reactions of tRNA. Top, link-up between mRNA and recognition ends of amino acid–carrying tRNA. Bottom, reaction pattern in link-up between two adjacent tRNA-carried amino acids, resulting in peptide bonding (and formation of polypeptide chains).*

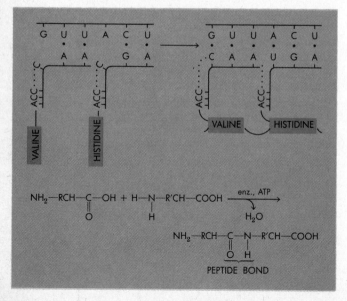

in the case of histidine, analogously, the recognition triplet would be *UGA*, the inverse of *ACU* (see Fig. 20.9). It is the specific enzyme in the activation reaction which "recognizes" and promotes interaction of a given amino acid and its corresponding *t*RNA; the enzyme thus must ensure that a particular acid becomes linked to the "correct" type of *t*RNA.

When a *t*RNA carrier then arrives at a ribosome, the positive recognition triplet of *t*RNA will be able to become hydrogen-bonded only to a corresponding negative code triplet along *m*RNA. Thus, as in our example, a valine-carrying *t*RNA with the recognition triplet *CAA* will be able to bond to a *GUU* triplet along *m*RNA; and a *t*RNA with the triplet *UGA* may bond to an *ACU* triplet of *m*RNA. In this way, amino acids become stationed along *m*RNA in a code-determined sequence (Fig. 20.10). The final link-up of amino acids into polypeptides may then be accomplished by formation of peptide bonds between adjacent amino acids. This process requires ATP and specific enzymes, among them various *peptidases* and *proteinases*. The reactions may take the form of dehydrations (see Fig. 20.10). The finished polypeptide disengages from its RNA connections, and the *t*RNA and *m*RNA molecules on the ribosomes soon decompose. The polypeptide formed represents the primary structural element of a protein molecule built according to gene-determined instructions.

Figure 20.4 may now be consulted again for a summary representation of the whole pattern of protein synthesis. In full accordance with this scheme, and with the use of extracts of *m*RNA, *t*RNA, and ribosomes from bacterial cells, it has actually been possible to synthesize in the test tube several artificial protein enzymes which are otherwise manufactured only in living cells. But note that, although we can now explain the formation of a specific primary structure of a protein, we have as yet little precise knowledge of how specific secondary, tertiary, or quaternary structures are determined. If two proteins differed, for example, in tertiary structure but not in primary structure, then the same *mRNA* should provide the code for both. Conceivably, the higher structural specificities of proteins may be governed by the various specific proteinases which promote amino acid polymerization, and perhaps by other reaction participants as well.

Newly formed proteins become part of the structural and functional makeup of a cell. Thus, by virtue of their particular specificities, some proteins might become incorporated into various fibrils, membranes, mitochondria, chromosomes, ribosomes, or indeed any other cellular organelle. Other proteins, again by virtue of their particular specificities, might come to function as specific enzymes and thus determine what kinds of reactions can take place in a cell. It has been estimated that there are on the order of 2,000 to 10,000 genes per chromosome, and it is known that there may be up to several dozen different chromosomes in a cell. Each of the many genes present controls the manufacture of a different kind of protein, and the totality of the proteins formed then maintains the nature of the cell.

One major aspect of nucleic acid synthesis now remains to be examined: if genetic DNA governs the specific synthesis of RNA and of proteins, how is DNA itself synthesized in specific fashion?

CODE TRANSCRIPTION: DNA ⟶ DNA

The DNA of genes controls its own synthesis; each existing gene controls the manufacture of new genes exactly like it. DNA is therefore said to be self-duplicating.

New formation of DNA has many features in common with code transcription from DNA to *mRNA*. Thus, as outlined in Fig. 20.11, the DNA double chain first unwinds and unzips into two single chains. Each single chain then links to itself, via hydrogen

20 · 11 DNA *duplication*. *A, G, C, T, nitrogen bases; D, deoxyribose; P, phosphate. If a double DNA chain (1) is to be duplicated, it separates (2) into two single chains (3). The single chain shown in (3) may be followed through the reaction sequence. Nucleotide-diphosphate raw materials (4) then become attached to each free nitrogen base (5 bottom), and the deoxyribose and phosphate parts of adjacent nucleotides become joined (5, top). The role of DNA polymerase in this process is described by the equation below the figures. Two DNA double chains thus result (6), identical to each other as well as to the original "mother" chain. Note that, in each newly formed double chain, one single chain preexisted and served as the code-specific template in the manufacture of the new single chain. In certain respects this code transcription from DNA to DNA resembles that of transcription from DNA to mRNA (compare with Fig. 20.5).*

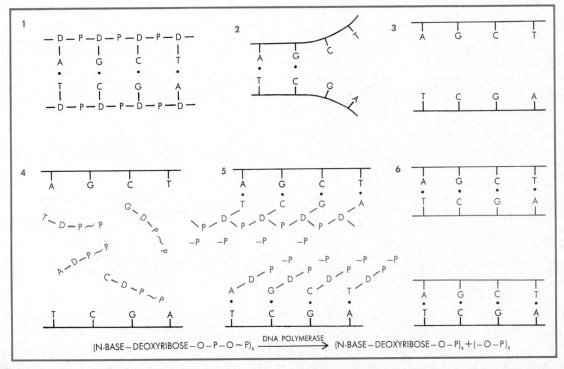

bonds, appropriate nucleotide raw materials. The latter in this case are the deoxyribose derivatives ADP, GDP, CDP, and TDP. After such raw materials have become attached to appropriate places along single DNA chains, an enzyme, *DNA polymerase*, links the raw materials together into a new DNA chain. The action of this enzyme is quite comparable to that of RNA polymerase. Note here that DNA synthesis is equivalent to DNA *reproduction*: one DNA double chain gives rise to two identical DNA

20 · 12   Tracer experiments show that newly produced DNA contains both preexisting and newly manufactured nucleotide chains. A cell about to divide is provided with radio-labeled raw materials for DNA synthesis (top). During division each chromosome duplicates, and both offspring chromosomes are then found to contain radio-labeled DNA (white). The diagram shows that, in each of these offspring chromosomes, only one of the two nucleotide chains is radio-labeled. This one has been newly manufactured; the other has preexisted. That such an interpretation is valid is proved if the offspring chromosomes are allowed to divide again (bottom). For when one of the radio-labeled chains now duplicates, it synthesizes a new, unlabeled chain as its partner. Hence in the DNA so formed, one chain (radio-labeled) has again preexisted; the other chain (unlabeled) has been newly formed. When an originally unlabeled chain duplicates, neither of the two resulting chains carries a label.

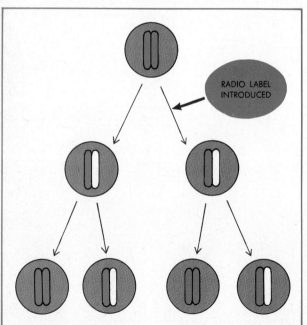

double chains. In each "daughter" DNA, one of the two single chains has preexisted in the "parent" DNA, the other single chain has been newly manufactured. In this manner, the genetic code is transmitted faithfully from one DNA "generation" to the next.

That old DNA actually becomes part of new DNA can be demonstrated experimentally. A cell about to divide can be supplied with radio-labeled raw materials needed in the manufacture of DNA. After cell division, the chromosomes of both offspring cells then contain radio-labeled DNA. This suggests that each newly manufactured DNA double chain contains one radio-labeled, newly produced nucleotide chain and one unlabeled, preexisting nucleotide chain. If now such an offspring cell is allowed to divide again (without further additions of radio-labeled raw materials), then only one of the resulting cells contains labeled chromosomes; the other contains unlabeled chromosomes. Such a result can be obtained only if DNA actually duplicates as described above (Fig. 20.12).

Reproduction of DNA characteristically takes place after more or less extended periods of cell growth. The genes of a cell normally transcribe their codes into newly forming *m*RNA, and abundant protein synthesis then occurs as a consequence. The structural proteins so formed increase cell size directly; the enzymatic proteins make possible the synthesis of other compounds, and these enlarge cell size in their turn. After a cell has grown in this manner for a given length of time, some—so far unknown—stimulus brings about a change in chromosome activity: the manufacture of *m*RNA stops for the time being and DNA produces new DNA instead. One set of genes thus becomes two sets, and one chromosome set correspondingly becomes two sets. Chromosome reproduction then appears to be the trigger—again in an unknown manner—for cell division.

Genetic DNA is among the most stable of all organic compounds. Indeed, unless a code carrier were relatively stable, it would cease to be useful as a repository of important information. In addition to the inherent chemical stability of genes, several safeguards exist which ensure that the specific genetic messages in DNA are not lost or altered. One such device is the nucleus itself. We may actually regard the evolutionary "invention" of distinct nuclei by the early Protista as adaptations useful primarily in shielding genes from destructive metabolism of the cytoplasm. Another safeguard is *redundancy;* when one wishes to ensure that a message is not lost or altered, he makes it redundant, that is, repeats it several times. Indeed, the genetic messages are stored

RADIO LABEL INTRODUCED

in more than one place. Each cell of most organisms ordinarily contains two complete sets of genes, one set having been inherited originally from the egg-producing parent and the other from the sperm-producing parent. Moreover, each cell type is usually represented by many like cells. Even if some cells die, therefore, the DNA of the remaining cells still possess the specific information characteristic of that cell type.

Yet despite inherent stability, protected existence, and redundancy, structural change is bound to occur; DNA is no more exempt from the modifying impact of the environment than any other component of the earth. As we shall see later, a variety of physical and chemical agents may affect and alter gene structure and therefore gene specificity. Such new specificities will be stable and will be passed on into all subsequent DNA duplicates. Protein synthesis will be affected accordingly, and, as a result, cell traits will become changed. *Mutations* of this sort may probably arise also during the process of DNA duplication, for, like any other process, gene duplication is probably not error-free. If an occasional error occurs during the formation of new DNA chains, then an imperfect copy will in effect be a mutated copy (Fig. 20.13).

Inasmuch as the genetic code is somewhat degenerate, a mutation at one nitrogen-base position in a code triplet may in some cases be without further effect. But in most cases a mutational change of this type probably would affect code transcription, and a given protein synthesized by the cell would henceforth exhibit altered characteristics. A stable change in cellular characteristics would then follow as well (see also Chap. 30), and unless such changes are lethal immediately they will be preserved in the DNA code and transmitted to offspring cells. If mutations occur in reproductive cells, a whole organism formed from such a cell may thus come to exhibit altered traits. Such alterations are the basis of evolution.

It becomes eminently clear, therefore, that the crucial significance of genes is not simply that they are inherited; by governing the synthesis of new genes and of specific proteins, genes play so strategic a role that they ultimately control the whole nature and the very life of every cell in every organism (Fig. 20.14).

First, since proteins make up more of the formed organic framework of cells than any other constituents, genes determine the basic *architecture* of every cell. Moreover, every normal architectural change during the life cycle of a cell, and every architectural difference among the cells of one or of different organisms, is ultimately gene-determined.

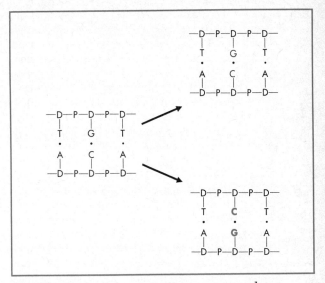

20 · 13 *Errors may sometimes occur when DNA molecules reproduce; for example, the inverted position of the C · G pair at lower right (color). Imperfect copies so formed would be stable mutated copies, and mutations would be transmitted to later molecular generations.*

20 · 14 *The controlling role of genes in metabolism and steady-state maintenance. The principal action of genes is control of their own duplication and control of protein synthesis, via RNA. Through this, genes exert secondary and tertiary effects, as shown.*

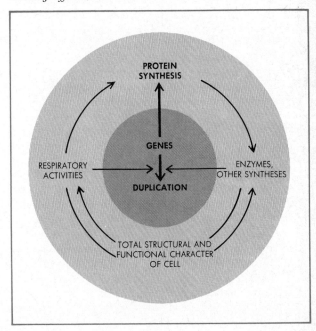

Second, by controlling the nature of proteins and thus of enzymes, genes determine what kinds of *metabolic processes* are possible in a cell; for every metabolic process requires at least one enzyme. Nutritional reactions, respiratory reactions, motion-producing reactions, synthesis reactions of all kinds—all are enzyme-dependent, hence gene-dependent. Third, by so governing the whole metabolic character of a cell, genes are the ultimate maintainers of *steady states*. For genes control not only themselves by governing gene duplication but also all other control agents within cells (see Chap. 21). Fourth, by governing synthesis in general and production of new genes in particular, genes direct growth, development, and the *reproduction* of cells. By being exchanged among cells and pooled within cells, as we shall see, genes become the basis of *sex*. By duplicating and being transmitted to offspring cells, genes become the basis of *heredity*. And through the final property of mutability, genes become the key to *evolution*.

In summary, therefore, we find that DNA serves in just one primary role: it allows its specificities to be copied. Three indirect secondary roles emerge from this: DNA controls protein specificities; DNA controls the specificities of new DNA; and, to the extent that DNA stability is imperfect, DNA may change its specificities. Through these three secondary activities, DNA indirectly has tertiary effects which govern every aspect of living. For by controlling all metabolism and all self-perpetuation, DNA governs cell structure, cell function, and cell development. And by controlling cells, DNA governs the life of all organisms, hence the survival of the whole living world. Genes started life, genes still continue it, and, by their failure or absence, genes ultimately end it (Fig. 20.15).

It may be pointed out in this context that recent experiments with DNA and RNA have already contributed much toward an eventual test-tube synthesis of living matter. It is now possible, for example, to create by laboratory synthesis a test-tube system in which known nucleotide precursors give rise to nucleic acid chains carrying specific information, in which such chains together with added ATP promote transformation of amino acids into specific proteins, and in which these proteins function enzymatically and catalyze specific chemical reactions. To be sure, such a system is still far from being alive; but inasmuch as it metabolizes in precisely the same way as a living system, the test-tube system represents a major element of a living unit. Recall, furthermore, that starting materials like amino acids and sugars can be produced artifically from simple materials such as ammonia, methane, and water (see

Chap. 11). Thus there does not appear to be any theoretical obstacle to the experimental production of a lifelike metabolizing system from the simplest inorganic precursors. And perhaps within a decade or two, artificial metabolizing systems may even have been perfected to such an extent that their nucleic acids might self-duplicate and so initiate self-perpetuation of the whole system. Living units created in this way probably would have roughly viruslike characteristics. Experimental creation of complete living cells, however, is undoubtedly still very far in the future. In any event, it is worth noting generally that research is now being widely pursued which, usually as an incidental byproduct, provides important data for a possible future laboratory synthesis of life.

In the foregoing and in the last chapter we have examined the synthesis patterns of all major classes of organic cell constituents—carbohydrates, lipids, amino acids, proteins, nucleic acids, and the principal derivatives of these. We have therefore completed the discussion of all fundamental *chemical* activities in cellular metabolism. To complete the discussion of metabolism as a whole, we proceed now to a consideration of the *physical* activities occurring in parallel with the chemical ones.

PHYSICAL ROLES OF METABOLISM

Probably the most important and most widespread physical functions of cells comprise *mechanical* activities. Of these, the most readily discernible are those which produce movement, in the form of either locomotion of whole organisms or internal motion of parts of organisms. We shall deal first with one major type of movement, namely, the contraction of specialized animal muscle cells.

MUSCULAR MOVEMENT

The characteristic activity of muscle cells ranks among the most important activities carried out by animal cells generally, for few animal functions exist that do not include muscular contraction. Moreover, muscles are quantitatively the most abundant tissue of an animal, particularly a vertebrate. A proportionately large amount of all available energy must be expended to keep muscles contracting. Even during "inactive" periods like sleep, for example, the muscular system maintains not only posture and shape but also vital functions such as breathing, heartbeat, and blood pressure. Mainly because of muscular movement, the energy requirements of animals are far greater pound for pound than of any other kind of organism.

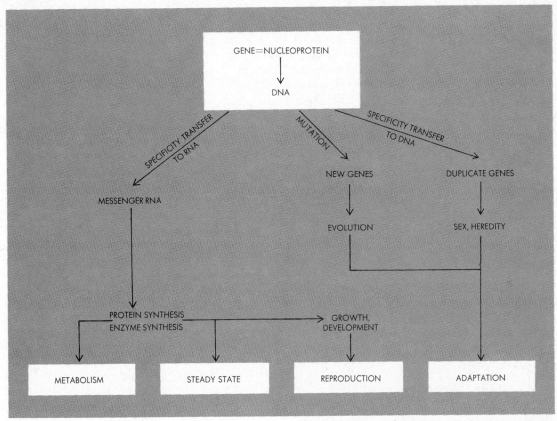

20 · 15 *The pattern of gene action is summarized in this diagram. Through their fundamental action of transferring their specificities, genes control cellular metabolism and all phases of cellular self-perpetuation.*

The Contractile Units

The functional units of all kinds of muscles are long, thin, intracellular filaments called *myofibrils*. Each muscle cell or muscle fiber contains many such myofibrils aligned in parallel and extending in the same direction as the long axis of the whole cell or fiber (Fig. 20.16 and see also Color Plate II, 6). In striated muscles, the myofibrils exhibit alternate dark and light crossbands (*A bands* and *I bands,* respectively) visible under the microscope. The A and I bands in turn display finer cross-markings within themselves. When such a muscle contracts, only the I bands become shorter. The total contraction is the sum of all the individual contractions of the I bands.

The electron microscope shows that each myofibril is actually a bundle of many long, ultrathin, parallel filaments. These are composed principally of five kinds of materials: water, inorganic ions, ATP, and two proteins called *actin* and *myosin.* Together, these form the basic contraction apparatus.

That this is so has been demonstrated dramatically by experiment. With appropriate procedures, actin and myosin can be extracted from muscle, and it can be shown that neither actin nor myosin alone

is able to contract. But by mixing actin and myosin together, artificial fibers of *actomyosin* can be made. To these fibers may be added water, inorganic ions, and ATP. When this is done, it is found that as soon as ATP reaches an actomyosin fiber, the latter contracts violently. Such contracting fibers may lift up to 1,000 times their own weight, just as a living muscle may do. And it is also found that, in a contracted fiber, ATP is no longer present but low-energy phosphates are present instead.

Experiments of this sort provide clues as to how contraction might be brought about in a living muscle. The process is far from being fully understood, but some of the main events are known. Muscle activity is at least a two-step cycle involving alternate *contraction* and *extension*. Energy is used up at some point or points in such a cycle. One view is that the energy makes possible the contraction of a muscle, like compressing a spring. Subsequent extension then is thought to be essentially an automatic recoil, like releasing a compressed spring. According to an alternative view, energy must be expended to extend a muscle, as in stretching a rubber band. Contraction would then be automatic, like releasing an extended rubber band. A good deal of evidence appears to favor this second hypothesis, but the first cannot be ruled out; indeed there are indications that muscle may require energy for both contraction and extension. Muscle is shorter and thicker when contracted, longer and thinner when extended.

20 · 16 The structure of skeletal muscle. *Whole muscle fibers are shown in A. Note the cross striations, the faintly visible internal longitudinal myofibrils, and the nuclei, which appear as dark patches. B, electron micrograph of portions of two horizontal myofibrils (in the tail muscles of a frog tadpole), separated by a layer of cytoplasmic material (endoplasmic reticulum). Note that each myofibril in turn consists of bundles of still finer filaments. The predominantly dark A bands and predominantly light I bands are labeled. (See also Color Plate II, 6.)*

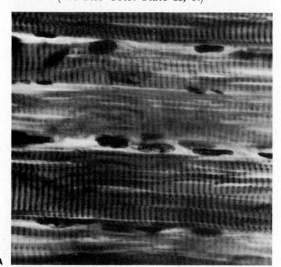

A

The Energy Cycle

The energy donor in muscle activity is ATP, which, together with actin and myosin, forms an actomyosin-ATP complex. The ATP here appears to be not only the energy donor but also a necessary structural part of the contraction apparatus; ATP makes actomyosin supple and elastic and able to contract at all. When ATP disappears or separates from actomyosin—for example, in extreme fatigue or during rigor mortis after death—muscle becomes rigid and stiff.

During a contraction-extension cycle, the ATP of actomyosin-ATP yields up its energy. To prepare a muscle for a new contraction-extension cycle, new energy must be supplied from the outside. Respiration is the ultimate source of this energy, but it is not the immediate source. Fast though oxidation of muscle glycogen is, it is far too slow to supply the ATP required by an active muscle. A glycogen molecule in muscle may decompose within a second, but in that second the wing muscle of an insect may contract up to 100 times and use up energy far faster than could be supplied directly by fuel oxidation.

Unlike most other cells, muscles are able to store large amounts of energy. Cells other than muscles usually may store energy only in the form of ATP. The amounts of ADP available for conversion to ATP are limited, and in such cells energy utilization can occur only as rapidly as ATP can be formed and re-formed by respiration. But some cells, most notably muscles, are alternately highly active or virtually in-

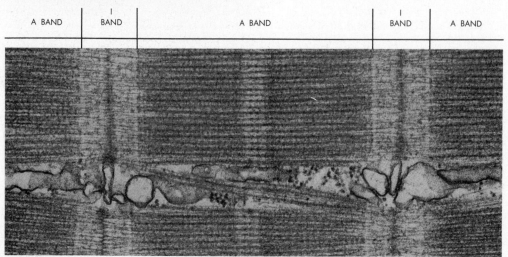

| A BAND | I BAND | A BAND | I BAND | A BAND |

B

active. During periods of intense activity, therefore, more ATP may be required in a muscle than respiration is able to create. Conversely, during rest, fuel oxidation in muscles may produce more —O ~ P than the entire ADP/ATP system can hold. Muscles and a few other animal tissues are able to cope with such excess supplies or demands. They possess a device which can store high-energy phosphate bonds beyond the storage capacity of ATP.

This device operates through one of several compounds. One of them is *creatine*, a nitrogen-containing organic substance found in the muscles of most vertebrates and some invertebrates. Another is *arginine*, an amino acid which, apart from its other functions, plays the same role in the muscles of many invertebrates as creatine plays in other animals. We may describe this role as follows:

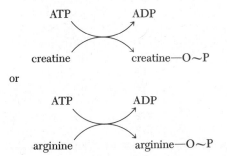

In other words, creatine or arginine may accept —O ~ P from ATP and so become creatine-phosphate and arginine-phosphate, respectively. These last two compounds as well as others functioning in like manner are referred to collectively as *phosphagens*. Conversely, a phosphagen may donate —O ~ P to ADP and so revert to compounds such as creatine or arginine.

The adaptive value of these reactions in muscle is clear. If, during rest, fuels supply more —O ~ P than can be harvested as ATP, then the reactions above proceed to the right; ATP unloads —O ~ P into phosphagen and becomes ADP. This ADP is now free to collect more —O ~ P from fuel. Phosphagen stores accumulate in this manner in far greater quantities than ATP could accumulate. When a muscle subsequently becomes active, the energy of the ATP in actomyosin-ATP is used up, as noted earlier. If then the muscle is to be reenergized, new actomyosin-ATP must be formed. The immediate energy sources for such "recharging" of muscles are the phosphagens. They transfer their —O ~ P and later they are themselves reenergized by respiration. Thus, respiratory ATP slowly and continuously replenishes the phosphagen stores, and these ample stores rapidly and repeatedly re-create actomyosin-

ATP while a muscle is active. Figure 20.17 summarizes these energy relations.

Muscular activity clearly can continue only as long as the energy stores of phosphagen last. If these stores become exhausted, actomyosin-ATP cannot be regenerated and muscle becomes fatigued. As noted in Chap. 18, fatigue is associated with comparative oxygen lack, fermentation, and lactic acid accumulation. Muscle *can* contract in the complete absence of oxygen so long as fermentation alone can maintain the phosphagen stores and so long as lactic acid concentrations are not excessive. Indeed, muscle normally probably respires anaerobically as well as aerobically, and any lactic acid formed can be carried off by blood as fast as it appears. Lactic acid tends to accumulate only during intense activity, and increasing fatigue then brings the activity to a halt sooner or later. Thereafter, aerobic combustion of muscle glycogen continues at a rapid pace, and depleted phosphagen stores are replenished. At the same time, lactic acid slowly diffuses into the blood, becomes liver glycogen, and returns to muscle and other tissues as blood glucose (see Fig. 18.11).

The Action Cycle

What is the mechanism of muscle contraction and extension? It is generally believed that, in an actomyosin-ATP complex, the actin and myosin components are arranged as parallel fibrils which may be joined side by side, perhaps by temporary chemical cross-linkages. The myosin fibrils are thought to extend lengthwise through the A bands, contributing to the dark appearance of these bands. The actin

20 · 17 Energy relations in muscle activity.
Respiration supplies energy for muscles via the phosphagen stores.

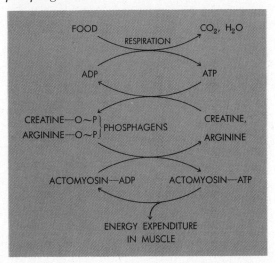

fibrils may extend through an I band and overlap partly at each end with the ends of myosin fibrils. Contraction and extension of such units is thought to be brought about by a sliding of actin fibrils past stationary myosin fibrils (Fig. 20.18).

At least three groups of data must be taken into account in any hypothesis designed to explain how such sliding movements would be initiated and controlled. First, it is known that the specific trigger for the contraction of a muscle is a nerve impulse. Second, it is known that inorganic ions, notably Mg^{++} and Ca^{++}, are associated with or attached to the actomyosin-ATP complex. By virtue of such positive charges, the complex may possess an electric potential over its surface; and one of the known effects of nerve impulses is to bring about a reduction of electric potentials (see Chap. 25). Third, it is known that muscles, like several other tissues, contain ATPases, that is, enzymes which promote the conversion of ATP into ADP. The specific ATPase of muscle either is identical with myosin itself or is so closely linked with myosin that available techniques are unable to separate the two. Evidently, the actomyosin-ATP complex possesses not only built-in potential energy in the form of ATP but also the

20 · 18 *The presumed sliding action of actin during muscle activity. Myosin, colored bars; actin, black lines. Top, contracted state; bottom, extended state. The A band and the portions of the adjacent I bands of a muscle fiber shown here are intended to represent a working unit repeated horizontally many times in a whole fiber. (See also Fig. 20.16.)*

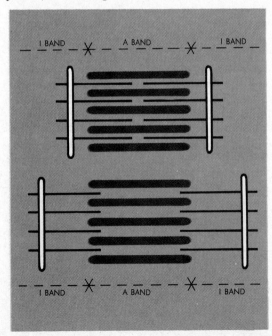

necessary built-in enzyme which may make this energy available. The action of the enzyme is believed to remain inhibited in some unknown way prior to arrival of a nerve impulse; directly or indirectly, the impulse appears to be the necessary stimulus for ATPase activation.

The following events might then take place during muscle action (Fig. 20.19). Initially, the actin and myosin components of actomyosin-ATP would be stretched apart, and the muscle would be extended. Such a condition might be maintained by the electric charges; since like charges repel one another, any contraction of the actomyosin-ATP complex would be prevented by electric repulsion of the actin and myosin. However, when a nerve impulse arrives, it may reduce the electric potentials and thus might remove the obstacle to contraction. The nerve impulse would also activate the ATPase, ATP would be split, and the potential energy of actomyosin-ATP would become actual. As noted, it is still not quite clear whether this energy brings about the actual contraction of the actomyosin complex or a reextension after the complex has contracted. In either event, the energy might promote the formation of new cross-linkages between actin and myosin. After the energy is spent, new potential energy is supplied by phosphagen. Muscle extension and recovery must also be accompanied by an inhibition of ATPase activity, by rebuilding of electric potentials, and by a sliding apart of the actin and myosin components.

Whatever the actual details of the fundamental action cycle in muscle may prove to be, cycles of this sort clearly take place fast enough to propel a cheetah, for example, at speeds of 50 mph; and they are powerful enough to permit many animals to lift objects weighing more than the animals themselves.

OTHER PHYSICAL ACTIVITIES

Nonmuscular Movement

All cellular motion, muscular or otherwise, appears to be ATP-dependent. However, it is largely unknown how the chemical energy of ATP is translated into the mechanical energy of motion. In the case of flagella and cilia, the locomotor apparatus is at least identifiable. Some evidence suggests that the beat of a flagellum or cilium might be produced by alternate contraction and relaxation of some of the 11 filaments present in these organelles (see Chap. 7). If so, a machinery somewhat like that in muscles may conceivably be involved. In the case of amoeboid motion, distinct cell structures specialized to produce movement do not appear to exist. The machinery for locomotion here undoubtedly resides diffusely in all or most parts of the cell cytoplasm. Our understanding of these locomotor processes is at present quite limited. We know, however, that if energy is unavailable to a cell, propulsion cannot occur.

Not all motion is locomotion, and some of these nonlocomotor movements within cells occur universally. For example, all cells move metabolites through their boundaries, both in absorption and secretion. We have already spoken of the requirement of respiratory energy in some of these processes, for example, in the active transport of water and minerals and in phosphorylation during glucose uptake. All cells move compounds also within their substance, partly through diffusion, partly through cyclosis. The role of ATP is less clear here, but that it plays some role, even if very indirectly, seems almost certain. For example, localized heat production by ATP may create convection currents which might contribute to cyclotic streaming of cytoplasm. Moreover, cyclosis stops if respiration stops. Among other intracellular movements are the precise migrations of chromosomes during cell division (see Chap. 26). The mechanism of these motions is again unknown. Some preliminary evidence suggests that contractile protein filaments energized by ATP might play a role here just as in flagellar and muscular motion.

In addition to such intracellular movements, groups of cells and indeed whole tissues and organs undergo numerous types of motions associated with growth, development, and the maintenance of steady states. We shall discuss some of these movements in later contexts and note here only that all of them are undoubtedly ATP-dependent too; if the ATP supply of an organism is stopped, the various movements also stop.

Heat Production

One source of internal heat has already been referred to earlier; if the high-energy phosphate of ATP is used in low-energy phosphorylations, then any excess energy of $-O \sim P$ becomes heat. Another, and most important, heat source is food which, as we have seen, yields about 40 per cent of its energy as ATP but about 60 per cent directly as heat. Still another internal heat source is ATP-energized movement; friction of moving parts generates heat. Moreover, ATP is not used with 100 per cent efficiency in the production of movement. Conversion of the chemical energy of ATP into the mechanical energy of motion is accompanied by a loss of energy, and this energy dissipates into the substance of a cell in the form of heat. Added to whatever heat is supplied by the external environment, food- and ATP-derived heat maintains the temperature of an

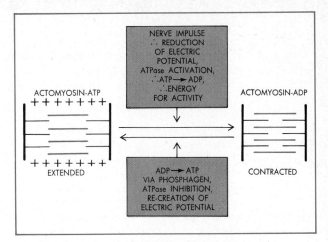

20 · 19 A unit cycle of muscle activity. *The probable events are summarized here. Events correlated with contraction are listed in the box above the reversible arrows; events correlated with extension, in the box below the arrows.*

organism and offsets heat lost to the environment by evaporation and radiation; creates tiny convection currents within cells and thus assists in diffusion and cyclosis; and, above all, provides adequate operating temperatures for enzymes and all other functional parts of cells.

As pointed out in Chap. 16, heat production in birds and mammals is balanced dynamically against heat loss and a constant body temperature is thereby maintained. These animals are said to be warm-blooded, or *homoiothermic*. In all other organisms proper internal operating temperatures are maintained ultimately by the external environment, and the internal temperature of such organisms by and large matches that of the external. Animal organisms of this type are said to be *poikilothermic* (the term cold-blooded often used is rather inappropriate, since the blood may be either hot or cold, depending on external temperatures, and since many of these animals do not even possess blood). If the environment is either too cold or too hot, poikilothermic forms cannot survive. Within these extremes, however, ATP and food combustion create internal heat, which to some extent counteracts low environmental temperatures; just as the cooling effect of evaporation may reduce internal heat, and this to some extent counteracts high environmental temperatures.

Bioluminescence

"Living" light is emitted by almost all major groups of organisms. Monera, Protista, and virtually all metazoan phyla include marine or terrestrial rep-

531

resentatives which are bioluminescent. Evidently, the capacity to produce light has evolved independently several times. Yet the essentials of the light-generating mechanism appear to be alike in all cases.

This mechanism consists of at least six components: water, inorganic ions, oxygen, ATP, and two groups of substances called, respectively, *luciferin* and *luciferase*. These last differ in composition in different species. Luciferin and the enzyme protein luciferase are the principal light-generating elements. They can be extracted from light-producing cells, and they are nonluminous on their own. If ATP is added to luciferin, a luciferin-ATP complex is formed. If, in the presence of ions and oxygen, a solution of luciferase is now added, the mixture emits light. At the same time, oxygen is used up and ATP becomes ADP. If after the light disappears more oxygen and more ATP are added, light is generated again. Light production evidently is an oxygen-requiring, ATP-dependent process (Fig. 20.20).

Bioluminescent organisms may stay lit up for appreciable periods or may produce brief flashes (see Fig. 11.14). In bioluminescent animals, light emission depends on nervous stimulation of specialized cells in light-producing organs (see Fig. 10.23). The light emitted by different organisms may be of any wavelength in the visible spectrum; that is, to the human eye it may be red, yellow, green, or blue. Little or no nonvisible radiation is generated. The actual wavelength of the emission is probably determined by the particular chemical makeup of luciferin. In some cases, two or more kinds of luciferin may occur in a single organism, and such an organism then may light up in several colors. In all cases, the available

energy is spent very efficiently, for little heat is lost during light production. Hence the frequent designation of living light as "cold" light. Also, the unit intensity of the light is remarkably great. It compares favorably with that of modern fluorescent lamps.

Bioelectricity

Bioelectricity is a byproduct of all cellular processes in which ions play a part. In other words, electricity is as common throughout the living world as table salt. However, certain eels and rays are highly specialized in their capacity to produce electricity. These fish possess *electric organs,* composed mainly of modified muscles. The component cells are disk-shaped and noncontractile, and they are piled into stacks. Assemblies of this sort have an appearance and a function reminiscent of storage batteries connected in series.

The details of operation here are understood less well than those of light production. However, it is known that the generation of electricity depends on ATP and a substance called *acetylcholine.* This chemical will be encountered again later, for it functions widely as a key agent in the transmission of nerve impulses. It also functions in the generation of bioelectricity. This event is apparently accompanied by a splitting of acetylcholine into separate acetyl and choline fractions. The two are then recombined into acetylcholine with energy from ATP (Fig. 20.21).

As in light production, the efficiency of energy utilization is remarkably great. So also is the intensity of the electricity generated. An electric eel

20 · 20 *The pattern of light production in bioluminescent organisms.*

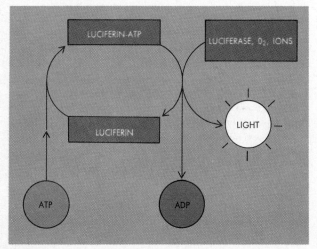

20 · 21 *The pattern of bioelectricity production.*

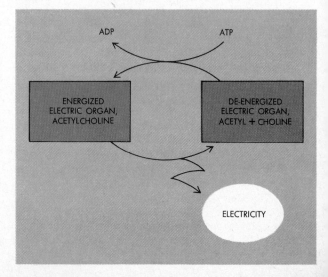

may deliver a shock of up to 400 volts, enough to kill another fish or to jolt a man severely or to light up a row of electric bulbs wired to a tank into which such an eel is put. Nervous stimulation of the electric organ triggers the production of electricity.

It is still unknown just how the chemical energy of ATP is actually converted into light energy or electric energy. But that ATP is the key is clearly established, and this versatile compound emerges as the source of all forms of living physical energy, usual or unusual (Fig. 20.22). Indeed we already know ATP to be even more versatile, for it is also the source of all living chemical energy.

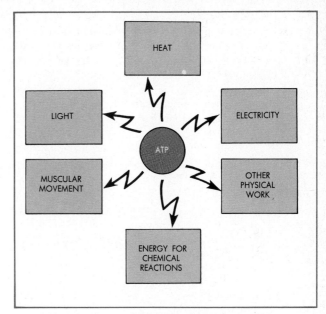

20 · 22 Summary of the functions of ATP.

SUMMARY

Our examination of metabolism is now substantially completed. Broadly speaking, the total metabolic effort of a cell may be considered to serve two general functions. One is *interior maintenance*, or activities promoting primarily the survival of the cell in which the activities take place. Among physical activities here are, for example, heat generation and all internal motions, and the chemical activities consist of procurement and utilization of all substances required for survival. Collectively, all such processes of interior maintenance serve in counteracting normal decomposition and wear and tear, in replacing cellular parts after injury, and in making possible cellular growth, development, and reproduction.

The other general function may be described as *exterior maintenance*, or processes contributing primarily to the survival of other cells or of the organism as a whole. Thus, motion or heat produced in a given cell may have far less significance for survival of the generating cell itself than for survival of the entire organism. The contraction of muscle cells offers a good example. On a chemical level, every cell exports compounds that it produces but that often constitute waste in its own metabolism—CO_2 or H_2O, for example. Yet what is waste for one cell may well be an essential metabolite in another. Indeed, many cells not only export excretions but also synthesize *secretions* specifically required by other cells or the organism as a whole. Any specialized secreting cell or cell group may be termed a *gland*, and we already know from many earlier chapters that the products of glands can have a very wide variety of roles. Thus, secretions may be *nutritive* (for example, glucose secreted by photosynthesizing cells); *digestive* (for example, enzymes produced by glands in the leaves of carnivorous plants, or enzymes poured into the gut from duct-possessing *exocrine* glands); *regulative* (for example, hormones secreted by given plant cells or by duct-

less *endocrine* glands in animals); *supportive* (for example, secretion of cellulose in plants, bone substance in animals); *reproductive* (for example, secretions from various organs of reproductive systems, as well as scents secreted by plants and animals); or variously *protective* (for example, secretion of oils and waxes from animal skin glands, secretion of bud-protecting gums from glandular hairs on sprouting leaves, secretion of irritants and poisons, including antibiotics formed by microorganisms). Indeed there is hardly any function in any organism in which cellular secretions of some sort do not play a role.

We note that a cell obtains its required ingredients in three general ways. Some components, like water, mineral ions, and in animal cells also organic materials such as vitamins and certain amino acids, must come in already synthesized final form from the external environment. Some others, like hormones, must come as fully synthesized secretions from other cells within the organism. And all other cellular materials must be synthesized from basic food compounds within the cell itself. This total multitude of chemicals, built up at the expense of ATP, then maintains and perpetuates the body of a cell. But it must not be imagined that newly synthesized compounds just happen to arrange themselves into new living substance. If the proteins, fats, and other components were merely mixed together in water, the result would be a complex but lifeless soup. As has long been appreciated, *omnis cellula e cellula*—all cells arise from preexisting cells; all life arises from preexisting life. New cellular constituents become living matter only if older living matter provides the framework. The house may be added to and its parts may be replaced or modified, but an altogether new house cannot be built. That apparently occurred only once during the history of the earth, when living matter arose originally.

This consideration leads us to the topic of the entire remainder of this book: by what means can metabolism continue in time as an ordered, sensibly functioning series of events rather than as a mere jumble of random activities? The answer is *self-perpetuation;* processes that control, integrate, and coordinate metabolic events and thereby convert the merely active system into a living one.

REVIEW QUESTIONS

1. Review the chemical structure of DNA and state the general way in which DNA is vital as the component of genes. Review the structure of RNA and distinguish between *m*RNA, *r*RNA, and *t*RNA. Where in a cell do each of these occur and how do they operate?

2. Describe the mechanism of amino acid activation. What is the genetic code, what are code triplets, and on the basis of what reasoning has a triplet code been postulated for amino acid specification? What is a degenerate code?

3. How may amino acids lined up along *m*RNA become joined into polypeptides? Review the entire pattern of genetically controlled protein synthesis. Show how such synthesis is the key to all metabolism and self-perpetuation of a cell.

4. Describe the pathways of purine and pyrimidine synthesis. How does DNA synthesis take place? What is the role of RNA polymerase and of DNA polymerase? What are mutations and what are their characteristics? What type of change would constitute a mutation?

5. How is the stability of genes safeguarded? What is the importance of gene stability? What is the effect of alterations in gene structure? In what way is genetic information redundant?

6. Review the pattern of gene function as a whole. Which function may be regarded as primary? Which indirect secondary functions derive from this and which tertiary functions result in turn from the secondary ones?

7. Describe the internal fine structure of a muscle. What and where is actomyosin? What are the roles of ATP in muscle? In what specific ways is the ATP supply maintained? Describe the energetic aspects of a unit cycle of muscle activity.

8. Describe the nervous, chemical, mechanical, and electrical events which, according to current hypotheses, may conceivably occur during a unit cycle of muscle activity.

9. What different kinds of movements occur in organisms and their cells? What is known about the role of energy in these movements?

10. In what ways does an organism obtain and produce heat? What are the functions of heat in metabolism?

11. How do organisms produce bioluminescence? Which groups of organisms are bioluminescent? How do the properties of living light compare with those of nonliving light? How and by what organisms is bioelectricity produced?

12. Describe the basic balance of synthesis and breakdown in living organisms. Review and summarize the broad components of metabolism as a whole, and review also the general relation between metabolism and self-perpetuation.

COLLATERAL READINGS

Allfrey, V. G., and A. E. Mirsky: How Cells Make Molecules, *Sci. American,* Sept., 1961. The role of DNA in protein synthesis is discussed.

Barry, J. M.: "Genes and the Chemical Control of Living Cells," Prentice-Hall, Englewood Cliffs, N.J., 1964. A recommended paperback, covering all aspects of DNA structure and function and the subject of protein synthesis.

Beadle, G. W.: The Structure of the Genetic Material and the Concept of the Gene, in "This Is Life," Holt, 1962. A recommended review of DNA function; contains a discussion of the coding problem.

Beerman, W., and U. Clever: Chromosome Puffs, *Sci. American,* Apr., 1964. Regional enlargements in giant insect chromosomes probably represent the places where code transcription from DNA to *m*RNA actually occurs.

Crick, F. H. C.: The Structure of the Hereditary Material, *Sci. American,* Oct., 1954. The first nontechnical account of the investigations that have led to our present understanding of the Watson-Crick structure of DNA; written by one of the discoverers of that structure.

————: Nucleic Acids, *Sci. American*, Sept., 1957. A discussion of the structure of these compounds.

————: The Genetic Code, *Sci. American*, Oct., 1962. An early review of the triplet code; see also the later article by Nirenberg cited below.

Fraenkel-Conrat, H.: The Genetic Code of a Virus, *Sci. American*, Oct., 1964. The article shows how the hereditary material of tobacco mosaic viruses directs host cells to manufacture the specific proteins of the viruses.

Gamov, G.: Information Transfer in the Living Cell, *Sci. American*, Oct., 1955. The arithmetic from which the nature of the genetic code has been predicted is discussed in this article.

Hayashi, T. : How Cells Move, *Sci. American*, Sept., 1961. The molecular basis of flagellary, amoeboid, and muscular motion is discussed.

Hotchkiss, R. D., and E. Weiss: Transformed Bacteria, *Sci. American*, Nov., 1956 A description of some of the classical experiments which established the DNA nature of the genetic material.

Hurwitz, J., and J. J. Furth: Messenger RNA, *Sci. American*, Feb., 1962. A good discussion of the role of this type of RNA. See also the article by Rich, below.

Huxley, H. E.: The Contraction of Muscle, *Sci. American*, Sept., 1958. A good review of present knowledge of the fine structure and function of muscle cells.

Ingram, V. M.: How Do Genes Act?, *Sci. American*, Jan., 1958. A disease of man resulting from a mutation of a single amino acid in hemoglobin is analyzed.

Kornberg, A.: Biologic Synthesis of Deoxyribonucleic Acid, *Science*, vol. 131, p. 1503, 1960. The test-tube self-duplication of DNA is described in this Nobel prize lecture.

Loewy, A. G., and P. Siekevitz: "Cell Structure and Function," Holt, New York, 1963. This paperback includes a review of DNA function and protein synthesis.

McElroy, W. D., and H. H. Seliger: Biological Luminescence, *Sci. American*, Dec., 1962. A comprehensive review of bioluminescence in various organisms and of the chemistry of the process.

Nirenberg, M. W.: The Genetic Code II, *Sci. American*, Mar., 1963. Experiments that have uncovered the nature of the triplet code are described by one of the leading investigators in the field; a sequel to Crick's article cited above.

Rich, A.: Polyribosomes, *Sci. American*, Dec., 1963. An analysis of the role of ribosomes in protein synthesis.

Stahl, F. W.: "The Mechanics of Inheritance," Prentice-Hall, Englewood Cliffs, N.J., 1964. This paperback includes an up-to-date, very detailed and thorough account of the structure and function of nucleic acids and of protein synthesis. Recommended.

Taylor, J. H.: The Duplication of Chromosomes, *Sci. American*, June, 1958. A description of the experiments with radio-labeled chromosomes referred to in this chapter.

Watson, J. D.: "The Molecular Biology of the Gene." Benjamin, New York, 1965. An exceedingly worthwhile paperback containing a lucid, very complete account of the relation of genes to proteins and cell duplication.

Zinder, N. D.: Transduction in Bacteria, *Sci. American*, Nov., 1958. An interesting account of the phenomenon, which incidentally proves the DNA nature of genes.

PART SIX
SELF-PERPETUATION: STEADY STATES
CHAPTER 21
CONTROL SYSTEMS AND CELLS
CHAPTER 22
HORMONES AND BEHAVIOR
CHAPTER 23
BODY FLUIDS AND CIRCULATION
CHAPTER 24
BREATHING AND EXCRETION
CHAPTER 25
NERVE, BRAIN, AND SENSE ORGAN

We recall that self-perpetuation comprises three groups of processes: first, those which maintain the *steady state* of living units and adjust and coordinate their internal operations; second, processes of *reproduction*, which extend the operations of living units in space and in time; and third, processes of *adaptation*, which mold and fit the long-term characteristics of living units to the characteristics of specific environments. Through self-perpetuation, living matter in the global aggregate becomes potentially indestructible.

Adaptation depends on reproduction, and reproduction depends on steady-state control. All three components of self-perpetuation operate on all levels of the living hierarchy, and *cellular* self-perpetuation is prerequisite for the persistence of all higher levels. Maintenance of steady states within cells therefore becomes the foundation of self-perpetuation as a whole.

Accordingly, this part begins with an examination of the nature of control functions generally and of cellular controls specifically. The steady-state controls of higher organizational levels are considered thereafter. Included in this discussion are behavior-influencing hormonal activities in plants and animals, as well as the purely animal control functions performed by the circulatory, breathing, excretory, and nervous systems.

CHAPTER 21 CONTROL SYSTEMS AND CELLS

The general function of all control activities in an organism is to maintain *optimal* operating conditions despite frequent and often rapid changes in the internal and external environment of that organism. The net result of control is steady state, and the net result of steady state is maintenance of life for the longest possible time.

Different types of control devices in living matter produce steady states in different characteristic ways, yet all such devices operate according to the same fundamental principles. This common *pattern of control* is the subject of the first part of the chapter. The two subsequent parts deal with the specific control operations on the cellular level, particularly those performed by *genes, enzymes,* and growth factors such as *vitamins*.

THE PATTERN OF CONTROL

To define "control" we must define stress. Any external or internal condition which tends to upset the normal, smooth operations of a system may be regarded as a stress. In a living organism, *external* stresses are often produced by the environment: by enemies, injurious agents, lack of food, change of temperature, and innumerable other physical, chemical, and biological conditions. *Internal* stresses arise continuously as a result of the very processes of life; fuels are used up, concentrations change, parts age and wear out, waste products accumulate, and

so on. Insofar as any external or internal change affects living matter, it also becomes a more or less significant stress. Actually, the living system is under stress all the time.

The problem of maintaining a steady state, therefore, is to counteract or to relieve stress. The requirements here are, first, ability to *recognize* stress when and where it exists, and second, ability to *react* to such stress in self-preserving fashion. What is needed, in other words, is ability to recognize a *stimulus* and ability to carry out an appropriate *response* to that stimulus. So long as a system recognizes stimuli and reacts to them with fitting responses, it exercises *control*. And it may then remain intact and functioning despite stresses which would otherwise upset its internal coordination.

In a system composed of many parts acting cooperatively, as in living matter, steady state will be preserved if the parts continue to act in harmony despite stress. If a stimulus should change the action of one part, then, in response, the action of all other parts should change accordingly and the total action of the system should still remain integrated and coordinated. To achieve such internal coordination, a first fundamental requirement is continuous and rapid flow of *information* among the parts of the system. Each part must be kept informed of what other parts are doing, and if a stimulus affects one part, other parts must receive notice of it. Moreover, if the system is capable of responding to a stimulus in more than one way, a second fundamental requirement is ability to make *selections*. A simple system designed to give always the same response is not required to select. But where several response possibilities exist, ability to decide among them clearly is crucial, for choice of inappropriate responses leads to unsteady, not steady, states (Fig. 21.1).

Thus, "control" ultimately becomes a matter of information and selection. These terms imply messages or signals of some sort, message carriers, senders, receivers, transmission pathways, relays, switches, channel selectors—in short, all the components of a communications system. Indeed, in one form or another communications systems are found wherever steady states are maintained. In living matter we find them within cells and between cells, within

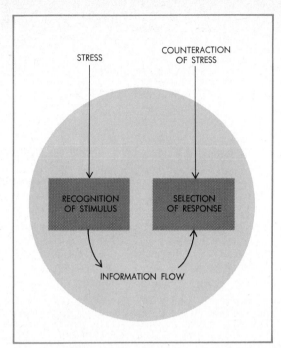

21 · 1 *Steady state: the general pattern of maintenance and control.*

organisms and between organisms, on all levels of organization. Such systems are control systems.

All living control systems operate on a common pattern. An initial stimulus irritates, or *excites*, a receiving device, called a *receptor*. Excitation of this receptor causes the emission of a signal, which is transmitted over a *sensory pathway* to an interpreting and response-selecting device. The latter may be referred to generally as the *modulator*. This component sends out an appropriately chosen command signal over an appropriately chosen *motor pathway*. The signal leads to an *effector*, a device which executes the commands. This is the response which counteracts the original stimulus (Fig. 21.2).

We may illustrate the operation of such a system by means of a mechanical model. Suppose that the water level of a flow tank, as in Fig. 21.3, is to be maintained in steady state: despite possible variations of inflow or outflow (for example, if an obstruction

develops in one of the pipes, or if someone resets the speed of inflow or outflow), the water level is to stay at a predetermined height. Such a system is an *open system*, since materials are continuously entering and leaving; and the problem is to maintain a *dynamic equilibrium*. In these respects the model corresponds closely to living entities, which also are open systems maintained in dynamic balance.

To establish a dynamic equilibrium in our model, we must install an automatic control device. Without help from external agencies, such a mechanism ought to be able to "sense" any change in water flow, and by means of valves it should so readjust the inflow and the outflow that the water level in the tank remains relatively constant. We have equipped our tank with automatic controls in Fig. 21.4. An air-filled float R functions as receptor. Inasmuch as it moves up or down with the water, it senses changes of water level. Any up or down motion of R is communicated via a rod sp, the sensory pathway, to the modulator M. Here the sensory message—up or down motion of sp—is interpreted and appropriate commands for response are sent out. Imagine M to be a simple electrical trigger mechanism. It might be so built that any upward motion of sp trips a switch which makes an electric current of certain strength and duration flow through the wires mp. Similarly, any downward motion of sp would reverse the switch position and another electrical impulse, of different strength and duration, would be produced. Indeed, possible switch positions might be more numerous and each might cause the flow of a current of unique characteristics. These electrical impulses are the command signals, transmitted over the motor pathways mp to the two effectors E. The effectors are engines which operate the valves at the inflow and the outflow. They are so built that each different command signal received makes them move the valves into different positions.

Imagine now that for some external reason the inflow decreases. The outflow is still as before, hence the water level will begin to drop. But at once the modulator M will be informed of this change via R and sp. Appropriate electric signals will now go to the effectors and the inflow valve will open more,

21 · 2 *Control components in living matter.*

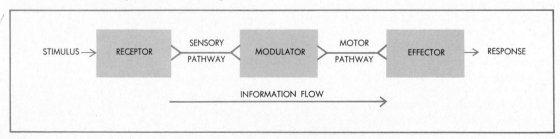

the outflow valve close more. As a result, before the water level can drop very far, the net inflow will increase and the water will rise back to normal. This new change of level will again be communicated to the modulator; new signals will go out to the effectors; and the valves will be returned to their original position. If at this point the inflow is still reduced, the control device will go into action once more, precisely as above. Clearly, by readjusting as often as necessary, the device is capable of maintaining a steady state despite changes in the "environment."

This model illustrates a number of features common to control systems, living ones included. First, internal *operating energy* is needed to make the system work. In the model, energy is required for the transmission of electric signals and for the motors which move the valves. Signal transmission itself can be accomplished on little energy. Indeed, the sensitivity of the whole device can be made desirably great if the float and the rod *sp* are built very light and easily movable, and if the modulator sends signals on a minimum of energy. On the other hand, the effectors will be the more useful the more powerful they are, that is, the faster and the more forcefully they can respond even against the push

21 · 3 Open and closed systems. *An open system is characterized by continuous flow; if it attains a balanced condition, the equilibrium is dynamic. Nothing enters or leaves the closed system, and if an equilibrium is attained it is static.*

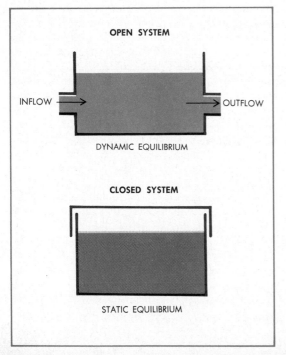

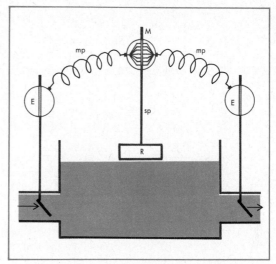

21 · 4 Model of a device maintaining a steady state. R, receptor; M, modulator; E, effector; sp, sensory pathway; mp, motor pathway. If the system is adjusted as described in the text, then any change of inflow or outflow will bring about signals through R ⟶ sp ⟶ M ⟶ mp ⟶ E. Valve positions will then be adjusted so that the valves will counteract the change of inflow or outflow and reestablish an original water level in the tank.

of the flowing water. The effectors therefore should have available an ample supply of energy—certainly more than they receive from the modulator in the form of signal energy. Consequently, an *amplifier* should be built into the effector to increase the power of the incoming signal energy to a level sufficient to move the valves. Controls within organisms are designed on just this principle. The receptors, modulators, and connecting pathways are highly sensitive and operate on a minimum of energy supplied by ATP. And the effectors work on amplifier energy supplied by comparatively large amounts of ATP.

A second common feature of control devices is that response to a stimulus is not a sudden, single event, but a stepwise, repeated one. In our model, a small initial change in valve position will produce a small initial change in water level. The receptor immediately signals to the modulator that a certain adjustment has been carried out. Accordingly, the modulator then cues the effectors to continue, to stop, or to reverse operations. The resulting effector action is essentially a new stimulus, which is again communicated back via the receptor to the modulator. Continuous information thus passes from sensory to motor component and from motor back to sensory component. Many such cyclical passages of information, each contributing a small effector action, are usually required before a total response to a stimulus can be achieved. Indeed, the control device is not at rest even then. For in the absence of environmental stimuli, the receptor in effect signals "no change" to the modulator, the modulator sends "no adjustment required" to the effector, and the effector then informs the receptor of "no operation."

In such unceasing cyclical passages of information, we note that a response is "fed back" into the sensory end of the regulating device as a new stimulus, informing of the degree of counteraction already accomplished. The new stimulus in turn, fed into the modulator, informs of the degree of counteraction yet to be carried out. *Feedback* is to the motor-sensory segment of the cycle what modulation is to the sensory-motor segment (Fig. 21.5). Both feedback and modulation control the direction, the amount, and the duration of adjustment. In living matter, as elsewhere, control activity becomes *effective* control only if appropriate feedbacks are operative. Without feedback the modulator would never become aware of what the effector has been doing and it would never be able to send out "correct" new commands.

Feedbacks and continuous cycles of information account for a third common property of control systems: they function essentially by *trial and error*, by "hunting" for the correct equilibrium condition. Refer again to our model. Suppose that the inflow

changes so as to cause an initial drop in water level. Depending on the sensitivity of the apparatus, a given number of seconds may elapse before the valves are brought into corrective positions. By that time, the water level may be down 1 in., say. Now the water begins to rise, but again there will be a time lag of some seconds before the effectors receive the new command to return the valves to normal. By that time the water may already have risen somewhat *above* the correct level. Fresh signals to reverse valve positions a bit will now be forthcoming, and by the time that action is executed, the water may again be down *below* the appropriate level.

Most controls *overshoot* in this fashion, and they undergo hunting oscillations to either side of the equilibrium state. Clearly, it will be important that such oscillations either become smaller and smaller till they subside or else continue at constant amplitude. Poorly adjusted controls often produce ever-increasing hunting oscillations, in which case "steady" state of course will not be maintained.

The seemingly erratic motion of a unicellular flagellate protist is a good example of the trial-and-error nature of control operations. If such an organism moves from a region of darkness to one of light, for example, it does not normally follow a straight, beeline course. Instead, it moves forward and a little to the left, then it "tacks" and moves right, then perhaps it changes course upward, or downward, and so on. In other words, the internal controls of the cell make it "hunt" for regions of ever-increasing brightness in trial-and-error fashion. In the process the cell often overshoots the "correct" path. Each such overshoot leads to a more or less rapid feedback via the eyespot, which signals the internal controls that light intensity is decreasing, not increasing as it should. Reversal of direction or change to a new direction is then initiated. Another good example of overshoots is the zigzagging locomotion of a drunk walking toward a stated object. Under the influence of alcohol, nervous control over locomotion becomes loose and imprecise and increased hunting oscillations occur. Normally, such oscillations are so small and subside so rapidly that straight-line locomotion is possible.

A fourth common property of control systems is that they have inherent limits of efficiency. If they are overloaded, that is, if they must work too fast or too hard, they may become "neurotic." They may make *errors* in sensing stimuli or in interpreting signals or in selecting and executing responses. Extreme overloading may cause internal structural breakdowns, which may make the device inoperative altogether. In living organisms, functional or struc-

21 · 5 *A control cycle and the role of feedback in such a cycle.*

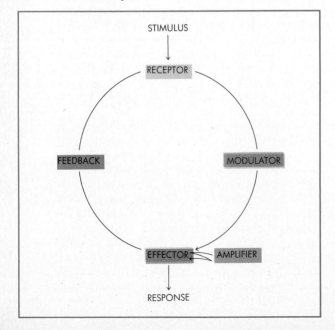

tural failures of control systems result in *disease.* Disease itself is a stress stimulus to other, still intact regulating devices and repair or circumvention of the diseased condition may ensue.

The regulating devices of living matter form a hierarchy paralleling that of the organizational levels. Thus, molecules and organelles represent the control systems of cells, whole cells are the control components of tissues, tissues in turn constitute the control apparatus of organs, and so forth. Within cells, for example, many organelles serve as receptors. Pigmented granules absorb light and form excellent photoreceptors (for example, eyespots, chloroplasts). Long filaments are sensitive to displacement, to pressure, to touch, and they may therefore serve as receptors of mechanical stimuli (for example, sensory hairs, fibrils). Other organelles may be sensitive to particular classes of chemicals and may function as chemoreceptors (for example, mitochondria, storage granules).

Organelles also function as modulators. Of these, the cell nucleus with its chromosomes and genes is the most complex. Analogously complex cellular modulators also include, for example, the ribosomes, the kinetosomes, the chloroplasts, and other bodies. Cellular effectors are equally varied. Many contribute to the numerous physical and chemical responses necessary in the internal maintenance of a cell. Others link a cell to its external environment. Thus, some bring about cell movement (for example, kinetosomes, flagella), and some absorb or secrete various substances through the cell surface (for example, Golgi bodies).

Note that virtually every control component present in a cell contributes to *multiple* regulating functions. It may serve as receptor in one instance, as modulator in another, as effector in yet a third. For example, the cell surface is a receptor when it "recognizes" a glucose molecule, but it is an effector when it allows that molecule to pass through. The cell nucleus has been referred to above as a modulator, which indeed it often is. But it may also serve as a receptor—it receives many stimuli from the cytoplasm; or it may be an effector—it executes many responses. Similarly, kinetosomes, chloroplasts, and most other organelles may each function variously as receptors, modulators, or effectors. Functional labels evidently are not fixed, and how one designates a structure participating in several control processes depends largely on which of these processes one wishes to emphasize.

Note also that the cellular level is the lowest on which we encounter modulators capable of distinguishing between various sensory messages and of *selecting* among various response possibilities.

For example, the cell surface is *selectively* permeable. Functioning as a modulator, it may interpret the chemical nature of different kinds of molecules in contact with it and it may "decide" how fast and to what extent each such molecule is to be passed through. Similar selectivity is displayed by other complex control components within a cell (and also by all supracellular control systems). This crucial capacity of making decisions may be a result of the presence, within any one organelle, of many and different *molecular* control systems, each capable of a single response. It is therefore likely that the number of decisions a complex modulator may make is correlated with the number of different molecular unit systems of which it is composed.

The control activities within a cell may collectively constitute important elements of control on the tissue level. Thus, if a cell as a whole functions as receptor, its response may represent a sensory signal on the tissue level. Or the cell may function as modulator, which makes its response a motor signal on the tissue level. Or the cell may function as effector, and its response then becomes a feedback signal on the tissue level. In such control operations, the response of one cell may be propagated to adjacent cells by direct contact or may be transmitted more widely by the internal transport systems—xylem and phloem in plants, blood circulation in animals. If one cell stimulates others in the manner of a chain reaction, a whole tissue or organ or organism may eventually be drawn into a larger response. Steady-state regulation of this kind is still essentially cellular. Although more than one cell is involved, receptors, modulators, and effectors beyond those present in the individual cell do not exist.

This form of functional control constitutes the highest pattern found among plants and among animals such as sponges. Steady state of such organisms is achieved by cell- and tissue-level controls and no tissues are specialized primarily or exclusively for control functions only; given cells or tissues carry out many functions and, to a greater or lesser degree, control is generally one of them. In this respect most animals are different. They possess organs and organ systems specialized more or less exclusively for control functions—nervous systems, for example. In nervous control, sense organs on and within the body are receptors. A brain or brain ganglia are the chief modulators; muscles and glands are effectors; and nerves serve as sensory and motor connecting paths. Transmission of information through such a sequence of specialized neural structures constitutes a *reflex,* the basis of nervous steady-state control (Fig. 21.6).

Where present, endocrine systems analogously exercise important control through their hormones,

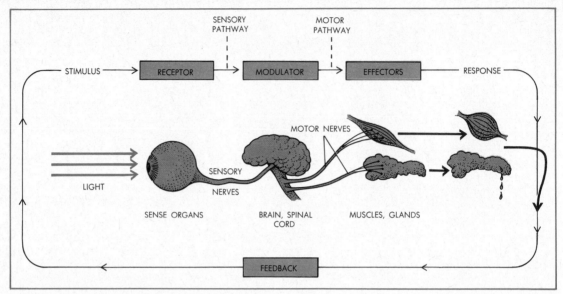

21 · 6   Steady-state control and reflex activity.
The components of any kind of steady-state-maintaining device are indicated along the top row and those of a nervous reflex, immediately underneath. A stimulus (such as light) will produce a response such as muscle contraction and/or glandular secretion. The response itself then becomes a feedback, that is, a new stimulus, through which the modulator is informed whether or not the response produced an adequate reaction to the original stimulus. The feedback stimulus now may, or may not, initiate a new reflex.

but note that *every* other organ system actually contributes to control as well, even though it also carries out other functions. For example, the vertebrate liver is not only a digestive gland but also a major regulator in nutrient distribution (see Chap. 19). The circulatory system is not only a series of transport channels but also an important contributor to body defense, to internal chemical regulation, and to other control functions—analogously for excretory and breathing systems, and indeed for most organs and systems of the animal body. In effect, every part of living matter is controlled *by* all other parts and at the same time contributes *to* the control of all other parts. "Controlling" thus becomes a major component of "living," and without control, life becomes nonlife. Conversely, nonlife became life when the first control mechanism came into existence. That was the nucleic acid molecule, the gene. All evolution ever since may be looked upon as a progressive development of more varied and more efficient con-

trol mechanisms. These were capable of counteracting more environmental stresses and so they permitted the extension of life in any given environment for longer periods.

How do genes and other cellular constituents actually exercise control within a cell?

CELLULAR CONTROLS: GENES AND ENZYMES

Regardless of how a cell is stressed, the stress stimulus usually affects one or more *metabolic* processes. For example, changes in nutrient supplies, waste accumulation, injury, pH change, temperature change, sol-gel transformations, or indeed any other physical or chemical stimuli are likely to influence a cell either by *accelerating* or by *decelerating* particular metabolic reactions. Also, regardless of how a cell responds, the response is ultimately produced by metabolic processes. For whatever the effector action of a cell may be, acceleration or deceleration of respiration or of chemical activities such as synthesis or of physical activities such as movement is likely to be involved.

Steady-state maintenance in a cell therefore becomes largely a matter of controlling cellular metabolism. The duration, speed, and amount of every reaction must be suitably geared to the duration, speed, and amount of every other reaction. To maintain such coordination, every accelerated reaction must eventually be decelerated back to normal and every decelerated reaction must be accelerated back to normal.

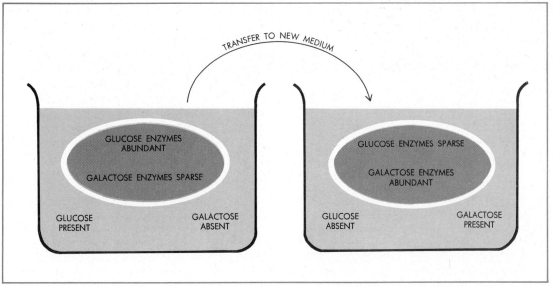

21 · 7   Adaptive enzymes. *The colored ovals within the containers represent bacteria. As the available external nutrients vary in abundance, so the internal enzymes capable of acting on these nutrients come to vary in abundance too.*

DNA AND OPERONS

Since the rates of all metabolic reactions depend critically on specific enzymes, and since the availability of enzymes depends on their being synthesized under gene control, it follows that genes will be the ultimate cellular controllers. Indeed, we may say that cells ultimately maintain steady states *by controlling and adjusting the rates of protein synthesis.* Control and adjustment of cellular reactions then follow, via presence or absence of particular enzymes. But if the rate of protein synthesis in each cell is adjustable, it is clear that such adjustments must be brought about by alterable gene action; the functioning of genes must somehow be capable of being turned "on" and "off."

An answer to the question of how genes may be turned on or off has been suggested by the chemical phenomena of *repression* and *induction*. It has long been known that, in certain metabolic reaction sequences within cells, the endproduct of the sequence often tends to inhibit some earlier point of the sequence. For example, in a sequential transformation of compound A into compound Z, the endproduct Z, once formed in given amounts, might inhibit some reaction such as $B \longrightarrow C$:

$$A \xrightarrow{enz.\ 1} B \xrightarrow{enz.\ 2} C \xrightarrow{enz.\ 3} \cdots \xrightarrow{enz.\ x} Z$$

Such "endproduct inhibitions," or repressions (symbolized by the transverse double bar above), prevent more endproduct from being formed. The evidence indicates that repressions are brought about by interference with the enzymes which catalyze given re-

action steps. To cite a specific example, it has been shown in the synthesis of pyrimidine-containing nucleotides that the endproducts CMP and UMP repress the reaction step in which carbamyl phosphate becomes linked to aspartic acid (reaction 2, Fig. 20.7); and the repression appears to be a specific result of an inhibition of the enzyme aspartic transcarbamylase.

Conversely, for some sequential reactions in cells it has been found that addition of excess amounts of reactants leads to a rapid formation of excess amounts of specific enzymes. Thus, in a sequential transformation of A into Z, an excess of A may lead to an increase in the amount of enzyme which converts A into B, hence to a more rapid formation of Z:

$$A \xrightarrow{enz.\ 1} B \xrightarrow{enz.\ 2} C \xrightarrow{enz.\ 3} \cdots \xrightarrow{enz.\ x} Z$$

A classic instance of such "adaptive enzyme formation," or induction, is the effect of the C_6 sugar derivative *galactoside*, which, when added to a cell in excess amounts, brings about the appearance of large quantities of corresponding enzyme *galactosidase* (Fig. 21.7).

Inasmuch as enzymes are proteins, both repressions and inductions must somehow relate to the mechanism of protein synthesis or, more specifically,

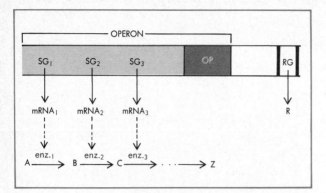

21 · 8   The postulated structure of an operon.
SG, structural gene; OP, operator gene; RG, regulator gene (all three of these types located in a chromosome); R, protein product formed by RG and influencing OP in ways to be shown in next two illustrations. A to Z represents a reaction sequence in which a succession of specifically required enzymes (enz) is manufactured under the control of SG and mRNA.

to the *rate control* of protein synthesis. A recent hypothesis, based on considerable evidence, shows how repressions and inductions might actually operate through a switch mechanism that turns gene activity on and off.

This so-called *operon hypothesis* (Fig. 21.8) postulates the existence of two types of genes, *regulator genes* (RG) and *structural genes* (SG). Regulator genes are thought to control the manufacture of protein products R, which function specifically by affecting the activity of structural genes. The latter are genes which control protein synthesis generally; that is, they transcribe their codes via mRNA and ribosomes into cellular proteins. Such proteins then function in part as enzymes and promote metabolic reactions, for example, sequential transformation of A into Z. All the structural genes controlling the successive steps of a given reaction sequence are thought to be located close to one another on a chromosome. Such a chromosome region is also postulated to contain an *operator gene* (Op), which must be active if the nearby structural genes are to be active. The whole region, including operator and associated structural genes, is said to form an *operon;* it represents the section of a chromosome that controls all the reaction steps in the transformation of a raw material A into an endproduct Z.

In a repression (Fig. 21.9), the product R of the regulator gene is assumed not to affect the operator gene Op, and the latter is then active. This permits the structural genes to be active as well, resulting

ultimately in the formation of endproduct Z. However, Z is now believed to combine with R, and the complex RZ then "covers," or attaches to, the operator Op, thereby inhibiting it. The structural genes therefore would become inactive also, specific transcription would cease, and the reaction sequence A to Z would soon be halted. Endproduct Z then would no longer be formed. The repression would last as long as Z is present above critical amounts, after which Op would again become uncovered and formation of Z could recur temporarily.

In an induction (Fig. 21.10), the product R of the regulator gene would be an inhibitor of Op, and endproduct Z thus could not be manufactured. But if raw material A were introduced into the cell, A would combine with R, and the complex RA would abolish the inhibition of Op. The structural genes could then become active, and A could be transformed into Z. After all of A is used up, Op would again become inhibited, and the enzymes (enz. 1, enz. 2) would no longer be synthesized. We note that induction is equivalent to removal of a repression, that is, it is a *derepression.*

Clearly, an operon control mechanism saves a cell considerable amounts of energy and materials; enzyme proteins are synthesized only when they are actually needed, that is, when given raw materials are actually available and when given endproducts are not already present in excessive quantities. Quite as importantly, an operon mechanism permits a cell

21 · 9   Operon functioning: repression. *R by itself does not affect OP, but if R combines with reaction endproduct Z, then the complex RZ inhibits the operator gene OP (transverse double bar denotes inhibition). As a result, OP also prevents the SG's from functioning, enzymes will not be produced, and the reaction sequence A to Z will cease. Thus, the endproduct Z eventually represses the continuation of its own manufacture.*

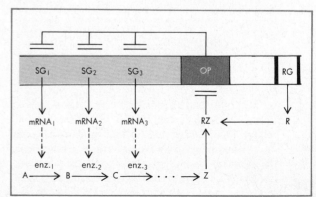

to be responsive to its environment: compounds entering a cell as food can be the specific stimuli for their own utilization, via enzyme induction; and compounds accumulating as finished products can be the specific stimuli halting their own manufacture, via enzyme repression. As a result, a cell may control its metabolic activities in accordance with the conditions of the moment, and the cell thus may exercise steady-state control.

ENZYMES AND COFACTORS

The enzymes synthesized in a cell may be considered to represent modulators in the simplest and most basic kinds of control systems, namely, metabolic reactions. In such molecular systems, the starting compounds qualify as receptors, the endproducts as effectors, and the water medium in which a reaction takes place as the sensory and motor pathways. For example, in the reversible sequence

$$\text{glucose} \xrightleftharpoons{\textit{enzymes}} \text{polysaccharide}$$

the totality of glucose molecules in a cell, or *glucose pool*, may function as receptor. If additional glucose arrives in the cell as food, this will be a stimulus "sensed" by the glucose pool as an increase in concentration. By mass action the reaction to the right will then outbalance that to the left and more polysaccharide will be formed. The polysaccharide pool here is the effector and increase of polysaccharide concentration is the response. For as polysaccharide accumulates at the expense of glucose, the glucose pool decreases back to normal and the original stimulus is thereby removed. The extra polysaccharide in turn may represent a new stimulus in the cell, initiating other reactions and new responses.

But note that the designations "receptor" and "effector" are not fixed. If a cell were to acquire additional polysaccharide rather than glucose, than the *polysaccharide pool* would be the receptor and the glucose pool the effector. Note further that, in either case, the function of the modulator is performed by the *enzymes*. Mass action notwithstanding, it takes a specific enzyme to "interpret" a specific stimulus and to direct the specific response. Because it is specific for a particular reaction, an enzyme cannot interpret various different stimuli but only one. And it cannot select among several possible responses, but must promote the same response every time.

In addition to DNA- and RNA-dependent enzymes, calls also make use of variety of *growth factors* which function as secondary modulators in metabolic control systems. A growth factor is any controlling agent a cell requires but cannot manufacture on its own.

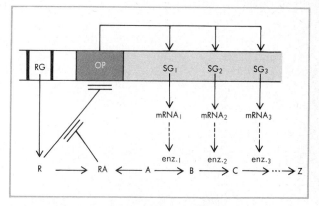

21 · 10 Operon functioning: induction. R inhibits OP, hence the SG's do not operate and Z is not formed. But if starting material A is introduced into the system, R combines with A and the complex RA inhibits the inhibition exerted by R on OP; in effect, RA permits OP to function again. The SG's then will function too, enzymes will be formed, and A can be converted to Z. Thus, A removes a repression, or it derepresses OP, hence it promotes its own conversion to Z.

Included in this category are chiefly *mineral* ions, *vitamins,* and *hormones,* and they have been termed "growth" factors because they often reveal their action most obviously through specific effects on growth. In this sense genes and enzymes qualify as growth factors too, but these are produced directly in the cell in which they act. Once a growth factor is obtained by a cell it is then used as a *cofactor* in particular reactions, either directly in the form in which it had been obtained or after it has undergone certain chemical transformations. Thus, as has already become amply clear in preceding chapters, many reactions require the presence of, for example, Mg^{++}. Analogously, vitamins serve as precursors of critical coenzymes, and various hormones participate in given metabolic processes as well. Indeed, most reaction sequences analyzed closely have been found to depend on a whole battery of cofactors in addition to enzymes, including mineral ions, vitamin-derived coenzymes, and often also hormones (Fig. 21.11).

All these agents are functionally similar, that is, they are essentially enzyme*like* in action. They are specifically necessary for specific reactions and they aid in accelerating such reactions; small quantities of them suffice; and they do not become part of the endproduct but are recoverable intact and unchanged after the reaction. In short, they all function more or less like catalysts. And in the language of

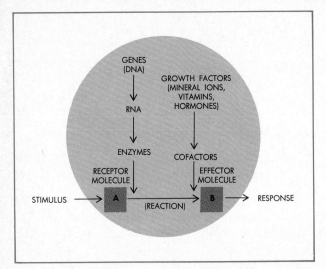

21·11 The molecular modulators within cells, and the pattern of their control over steady-state-maintaining metabolic reactions. Through RNA, enzymes, and control over synthesis reactions, genes also control the nature of the growth factors and cofactors present in a cell.

21·12 Alternative pathway switching. Assume that A_1, A_2, A_3 and B_1, B_2, B_3 are two reaction pathways requiring the enzymes a', a" and b', b" respectively. Assume also that A_2 has the property of inhibiting b', and B_2, of inhibiting a'. If then the A sequence is operative, it will inhibit the B sequence; and if the B sequence is operative, it will inhibit the A sequence. Also, if presence of A induces the enzymes a' and a" through an operon mechanism, then the B sequence will be automatically inhibited through the effect of A_2 on b'. By such means, two or more separate metabolic pathways may exert significant control over one another and thus over the kinds and amounts of materials synthesized in a cell.

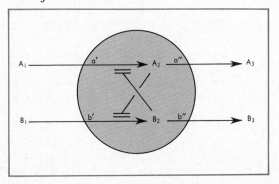

control systems, they function as information relays, or as modulators. They share with enzymes the property of being differentially sensitive to single sensory messages only and of promoting the same reaction responses every time, without freedom of choice. Like enzymes, moreover, they are ultimately gene-dependent; genes exercise control over all other cellular controllers and so serve as the final regulators of steady state. Hormones and coenzymes are synthesized directly under gene control, and the genes of a cell also determine indirectly what mineral ions a cell will be capable of acquiring through its surface membranes. In the case of minerals and coenzymes, we already know how acceleration of reactions is probably brought about; the cofactors appear to facilitate the action of the enzymes (see induced fit hypothesis, Chap. 5). The specific effects of hormones are understood far less well as yet, but in any event we may conclude generally that they too somehow speed up the reactions in which they participate.

Metabolic control requires not only acceleration, however, but also deceleration of reactions. Ultimately, reactions are slowed down by genes, through reduction of the rates of enzyme synthesis. Secondarily, deceleration may also occur in at least four other ways. One is a result of the inherent *reversibility* of most metabolic reactions; a reaction in one direction can be inhibited by accelerating the opposite reaction. This principle actually holds not only on the molecular level but also in steady-state control on any other level. Brakes and accelerators are present together and hold one another in mutual check. The net reaction they allow to occur is a restrained compromise between excitation and inhibition. Any change in the concentrations of the reactants or in the quantities of the modulators will change the balance between excitation and inhibition. And the reaction will then speed up in one direction, hence slow down in the other.

It happens in certain cases that an acceleration of one reaction inhibits not only the opposite reaction but also some quite different reaction as well. Such *alternative pathway* effects are produced when one or more compounds in one reaction sequence inhibit the enzymes participating in another sequence (Fig. 21.12). Specific examples are provided by certain instances of adaptive enzyme formation, already referred to above. Thus, in the presence of large amounts of glucose, for example, adaptive enzyme formation in a cell may lead to an increased synthesis of the enzymes necessary to metabolize glucose. It is found at the same time, however, that enzymes for other sugars—galactose, for example—are manufactured in very reduced amounts only, and such sugars are therefore metabolized very little or not at all. But if then galactose is supplied in large amounts and the glucose supply is stopped, galactose-metabolizing enzymes soon increase in quantity whereas glucose-metabolizing enzymes soon decrease. Evidently, glucose metabolism inhibits enzyme formation for galactose metabolism and vice versa, as diagrammed generally in Fig. 21.12. Such switch-on, switch-off alternatives probably are important not only in cellular steady-state control but also in cell development; for when an embryonic cell specializes in one of several possible adult directions, an ultimately gene-controlled switching to one particular metabolic pathway may well be involved (see also Chap. 29).

Reactions may also become decelerated by *competition among modulators* for reactants. For example, we know that glucose can become either polysaccharide or pyruvic acid. Either step requires specific modulators (M_1, M_2):

$$\text{pyruvic acid} \xleftarrow{M_1} \text{glucose} \xrightarrow{M_2} \text{polysaccharide}$$

M_1 and M_2 in this case compete for available glucose. If M_1 has a competitive advantage—for example, by combining more easily with glucose or by being present in larger amount—then polysaccharide synthesis will be decelerated and pyruvic acid formation will be speeded up. Here again the modulators hold one another in check and the net reactions are quickly adjusted when any part of the balance shifts.

Lastly, reactions can be decelerated by *competition among reactants* for modulators, the converse of the above. This may occur when given cellular reactions are so alike that the same modulator may promote them. For example, the same lipase could transform different fatty acids (along with glycerin) into either fat A or fat B:

| fatty acids A | fatty acids B |
| +glycerin | +glycerin |

$\longleftarrow$ — *lipase* ———→

| fat A | fat B |

The reactants of the A side here compete with those on the B side for the required enzyme. Accordingly, whenever concentrations or other conditions favor one reaction, the other will be inhibited. We may therefore appreciate how competition for a limited quantity of modulator in a cell may crowd out one reaction at the expense of another.

Note that chemical competition as above is often the cause as well as the cure of disease. For example, disease may be caused by a poison, which competes either with a normal modulator or a normal reactant and so crowds out an essential reaction. Cure may then be effected by reversing the abnormal competition, that is, by supplying normal modulators or normal reactants in sufficient quantities to crowd out the disease reaction (see also Fig. 5.11).

Control of cellular metabolism may now be envisaged as follows (consult Fig. 21.13). In a given sequence of reactions, each separate reaction is influenced by several modulators of various types—genes and enzymes always, vitamin-derived coenzymes very often, and inorganic ions and hormones in many cases. Some of these modulators promote a given reaction in one direction (M_1, M_2, M_3), others promote it in the opposite direction (M_4, M_5). Some modulators compete for reactants (M_4, M_6) and such modulators act *antagonistically*. Similarly, some reactants compete for modulators, for example, B and B' compete for M_7. Other modulators are mutually reinforcing in their activity (M_4, M_5) and these are said to act *synergistically*.

Depending on the specific balances between all modulators and all reactants at any moment, the whole sequence or parts of it will proceed one way or the other for certain lengths of time, in certain amounts, and at certain rates. The overall result of such multiple excitations and inhibitions is a steady state, a dynamic equilibrium. When a stimulus then affects any part of the sequence, the balance between the excitations and inhibitions will shift auto-

21 · 13 *The pattern of control of molecular metabolism. A, B, C, . . . , X, Y, Z symbolize molecular reactants, and* M_1, M_2, *etc., symbolize molecular modulators. Some of these modulators act synergistically and reinforce each other in their action. Others act antagonistically. Also, just as modulators may compete for reactants, so reactants may compete for modulators. Each step of a reaction sequence is controlled by a battery of modulators, and the net reaction is a resultant of the various modulator effects.*

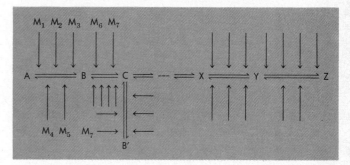

matically; and so, like ripples in a pond traveling away from a center of disturbance, the reaction sequence will undergo "hunting oscillations" until a steady state is reattained.

CELLULAR CONTROLS:
VITAMINS AND COENZYMES

All organisms require mineral substances as growth factors, and all also require vitamins. With respect to minerals, note that these materials serve in two general capacities: in part they are nutrients used as structural components of cells and in part they are growth factors used in reaction control. In some cases the same mineral contributes to both functions. For example, magnesium is both a structural component (as in chlorophyll) and a controlling agent (as a cofactor). With respect to vitamins, these substances actually are growth factors primarily in animals only, for in all autotrophs and some heterotrophs vitamins are synthesized right within the organism, in most cases directly within the cells in which they act. In such organisms vitamins therefore belong to the same self-manufactured group of control agents as genes and enzymes.

Even animals usually synthesize at least some vitamins, but generally not enough or not all necessary kinds. Insects, for example, may synthesize all except the B vitamins. A few rodents, apes, and man cannot manufacture their own vitamin C, but other animals can. Man happens to be a particularly poor vitamin synthesizer, being unable to produce sufficient quantities of any except the D vitamins. We have already noted in Chap. 17 that such differences in synthesizing ability between different species probably result from loss mutations; and once the capacity of synthesizing a particular vitamin has been lost, that vitamin then becomes a required growth factor for that species.

More than 30 compounds are known to possess the properties of vitamins. They are needed in very small amounts and their prolonged absence from a cell impairs metabolic processes and produces unsteady or diseased states. In this connection, careful distinction should be made between the *biological* and the *clinical* effects of a deficiency. *All* cells of an organism require *all* vitamins; if a vitamin deficiency exists, some metabolic process in all cells will be impaired. This is a biological effect. For example, we already know that the B vitamin thiamine is a precursor of the coenzyme cocarboxylase, required in all cells in the citric acid cycle and in the conversion of pyruvic acid to acetyl CoA. If thiamine is in deficient supply, respiratory reactions in all

cells will be affected. Superimposed on such biological effects are clinical ones. That is, the cells of given tissues or organs may be more sensitive to a deficiency than other cells and such body parts will then exhibit symptoms of disease sooner or more pronouncedly than other body parts. For example, thiamine deficiency in man has long been known to lead to the clinical disease *beriberi*, characterized in severe cases by nervous and muscular paralysis. By themselves, clinical data alone would imply that thiamine is required specifically by nerve and muscle tissues. Actually, however, clinical results represent only the large-scale secondary consequences of the deeper biological effects of deficiency which influence all cells. Thus, clinical results can be a beginning of vitamin studies, but they must not be mistaken for the end.

When they were first investigated, vitamins were given letter designations. Later, virtually every vitamin so labeled was found to consist of not one but several, often related substances. Letters with subscripts then came into use. Today, the tendency is to refer to a new vitamin by its chemical name only. Many vitamins therefore do not have a letter designation, and some have both letter and chemical labels (Table 17). Some vitamins are fat-soluble, others are water-soluble. The first group includes vitamins A, D, E, and K; the latter, vitamins B and C.

Vitamin A Group

The several closely related substances so designated are derivatives of the *carotene* pigments synthesized by plants. As noted in Chap. 19, carotenes are present in the chloroplasts and chromoplasts of plant cells. Carotenes may therefore be found in leaves, and particularly rich sources are red–orange–yellow plant parts such as carrots, tomatoes, squash, sweet potatoes. Egg yolk, butter, and cream are among animal products rich in carotene. Spinach contains more carotene than an equal weight of egg yolk. In yellow foods, depth of color is an index of comparative carotene content.

Carotene becomes vitamin A by enzymatic hydrolysis; one molecule of carotene splits into two molecules of vitamin A in the presence of water (see also Fig. 6.14):

$$C_{40}H_{56} + 2\,H_2O \longrightarrow 2\,C_{20}H_{30}O$$

carotene   *vitamin A*

The vitamin is stored in the vertebrate liver to a considerable extent. Fish livers and their oils are particularly rich sources of the finished vitamin

TABLE 17   THE PRINCIPAL VITAMINS AND THEIR FUNCTIONS

NAME	FOOD SOURCES	CHIEF CELLULAR FUNCTIONS	EFFECTS OF DEFICIENCY
vitamin A	*leaves, yellow foods, liver*	*chemistry of vision; membrane integrity*	*night blindness; infectious diseases; bone, nerve abnormalities*
thiamine (B₁)		*cocarboxylase precursor*	*beriberi*
riboflavin (B₂)		*FMN and FAD precursor*	*hair loss; growth failure*
nicotinic acid		*NAD and NADP precursor*	*pellagra*
pantothenic acid	*grain products, yeast, beans, nuts, liver, eggs, meat*	*coenzyme A precursor*	
biotin (H)		CO_2*-carrying coenzyme precursor*	*anemia; growth failure; hemorrhages; bone disorders; nerve, skin disorders; infectious diseases*
choline		*—CH₃-carrying coenzyme precursor*	
pyridoxine (B₆)		*—NH₂-carrying coenzyme precursor*	
folic acid vitamin B₁₂		*nucleic acid metabolism*	
vitamin C	*citrus fruits, tomatoes, cabbage*	*aerobic H transfer; synthesis of cell cement*	*scurvy*
vitamin D	*liver, fish oils*	*Ca and P regulation*	*rickets*
vitamin E	*most foods*	*aerobic H transfer*	*sterility; eye abnormalities; nerve, muscle disorders*
vitamin K			*failure of blood clotting*

(hence the nutritive value of, for example, cod-liver oil). Fish obtain carotene through food chains originating with algae.

One specific cellular function of vitamin A is known; the compound plays an essential part in the chemistry of vision (see Chap. 25). Unavailability of the vitamin leads to night blindness. The following are among its other, less clearly understood functions: it controls proper growth of bones, of tooth enamel, and of nerve tissue; and it prevents drying and cracking of exposed, normally moist membranes, such as the membranes in the eyes, the breathing system, the alimentary tract, and the urogenital tract. Probably through this action, it reduces the incidence of infectious diseases. Indeed, vitamin A is sometimes called the "anti-infection vitamin," but such a designation might apply equally well to many another vitamin.

Vitamin B Group

Included among these water-soluble vitamins are *thiamine* (B₁), *riboflavin* (B₂), *nicotonic acid* ("niacin"), *pyridoxine* (B₆), *biotin* (H), *vitamin B₁₂*, *pantothenic acid*, *folic acid*, and *choline*. These substances are not particularly related in chemical structure or in biological function. They are grouped together largely because they tend to occur together in plant and animal foods. Most of the vitamins have been identified chemically and many can be synthesized in the laboratory. The B vitamins are present in natural foods of all types, particularly rich sources being whole-grain products, yeast, peas, beans, and nuts among plant foods, and liver, egg yolks, and meat among animal foods. Intestinal bacteria synthesize many of the B vitamins.

As earlier chapters have shown, the compounds are well known as precursors of cellular coenzymes. Thus, thiamine gives rise to cocarboxylase; riboflavin to FMN and FAD; nicotinic acid to NAD and NADP; pantothenic acid to coenzyme A (see Fig. 6.26 for the structures of most of these vitamins). Pyridoxine is a precursor of a coenzyme serving as $-NH_2$ carrier in transaminations (see Chap. 18), and biotin becomes a CO_2-carrying coenzyme in oxidative CO_2-fixing reactions (see Fig. 19.15). Analogously, a choline-derived coenzyme carries methyl groups ($-CH_3$) in chemical transformations, and folic acid and vitamin B_{12} are known to participate in nucleotide metabolism specifically.

A more or less well-defined clinical disease is associated with lack of each of the B vitamins. Mild thiamine deficiency, for example, produces fatigue, weakness, and lassitude. More severe thiamine starvation over a period of weeks may result in beriberi, as noted. Riboflavin deficiency leads to loss of hair, growth failure, and eye disorders (Fig. 21.14); niacin deficiency, to *pellagra*, a disease of the skin and the nervous system; vitamin B_{12} and folic acid deficiencies, to anemia; choline deficiency, to bone deformities (in chickens) and internal hemorrhages; and

21 · 14 Some effects of riboflavin deficiency. *Top, riboflavin-deficient rat. Pronounced loss of hair, sickly appearance. Weight 63 g. Bottom, same rat as above, 6 weeks later, after riboflavin-rich diet. Recovery complete. Weight 169 g.*

pyridoxine and pantothenic acid deficiencies, to growth failure, anemia, lowered resistance to infections, and nerve and skin disorders. In all these cases, administration of the appropriate vitamin usually relieves the disease.

Vitamin C

This compound is *ascorbic acid*, chemically related to monosaccharide sugars (see Fig. 6.9). It is widely synthesized in plants, particularly rich sources being citrus fruit, cabbage, and tomatoes. Most animals—but not man—manufacture it, as noted above. Ascorbic acid is one of the least stable vitamins. Cooking destroys it, and in fresh and canned foods much of this water-soluble vitamin diffuses out into the food juices.

That vitamin C participates in aerobic hydrogen transfer is known, but it is not yet known which specific reaction the vitamin affects. Like other vitamins participating in respiratory reactions, ascorbic acid is generally found in the mitochondria of cells. Vitamin C additionally controls a phase of synthesis metabolism, and its absence here leads to the best-known deficiency symptoms. The vitamin apparently regulates the manufacture of the cement which binds cells together. When this function is impaired, *scurvy* results. Blood vessels become abnormally permeable and hemorrhages may occur in any part of the body. Connective tissues no longer bind efficiently, and teeth, for example, loosen from their sockets. In more advanced stages, bones may weaken, muscles degenerate, and death ultimately supervenes. Mild deficiencies of vitamin C may not lead to an outright scorbutic condition, but they may nevertheless impair energy metabolism sufficiently to produce lassitude and to cause fleeting, rheumatismlike pains in limb joints.

Vitamin D Group

Some ten related sterol compounds are included in this group (see Fig. 6.15). Two of these, D_2 and D_3, are particularly potent. In man, precursors of the D vitamins are present in skin. Such precursors are converted into active vitamins by irradiation with ultraviolet light, hence the designation of the D vitamins as "sunshine vitamins." The active vitamins are stored in the liver along with vitamin A in the lipid reserves. Good external sources of D vitamins are fish-liver oils, dairy foods, and, in general, foods rich also in vitamin A.

The specific mode of action of these growth factors is obscure, but their area of action is fairly well established. They regulate reactions involving calcium and phosphorus, particularly in the complex processes of bone formation and bone maintenance. In the cells of the gut, these vitamins probably balance calcium and phosphorus absorption against excretion of these elements into the gut cavity. The vitamins thus maintain an optimum supply of Ca and P within the body, and they subsequently regulate the deposition of these raw materials as bone and tooth substance.

Deficiency of the D vitamins leads to *rickets*. Among the clinical symptoms of this disease are softening and bending of bones, beading of ribs, erosion of teeth, and elimination of calcium and phosphorus in large quantities. Conversely, continued overdoses of vitamin D may produce abnormal thickening of bones and some calcification of soft tissues.

The D vitamins so far appear to be uniquely animal growth factors; their functions, if any, in plants are unknown as yet.

Vitamin E Group

Several very closely related compounds are in this category. The vitamins are relatively unstable, but they are so widely distributed in the fatty fraction of both plant and animal foods that a deficiency is not likely to arise on any normal diet. The chemical nature of vitamin E is known; the compound consists of two fused carbon rings to which is attached a fatty-acid–like chain of hydrocarbon groups.

These substances are often called "antisterility vitamins"; deficiency can be shown to lead to permanent infertility in male rats and to death of embryos or to premature births in pregnant female rats. Experiments have indicated that vitamin E is required during human pregnancy at a particular stage of embryonic development, namely, at a time when eyes are formed. Vitamin E–deficient embryos often exhibit a characteristic abnormality in eye development. Among other clinical results of vitamin E deficiency are injury to the nervous system and muscular atrophy.

The fundamental biological function of the E vitamins within cells has already been briefly noted; they participate in hydrogen-transfer reactions during aerobic respiration (see Chap. 18).

Vitamin K Group

A few related compounds of known structure are so classified. They occur widely in food and are synthesized by intestinal bacteria.

Clinically, the vitamins are known best for their role in blood clotting; deficiency leads to failure of the clotting mechanism (see Chap. 23). For this reason vitamin K is often administered before surgery, particularly surgery on bile ducts blocked by gallstones. Since vitamin K is dissolved in the fatty portions of food, bile is required for its proper absorption from the gut cavity. Therefore, if the bile duct is blocked, an individual is likely to be vitamin K–deficient and his blood-clotting mechanism will be impaired as a result. Ingestion of the vitamin (along with bile salts) before an operation may forestall severe surgical hemorrhage.

The cellular function of vitamin K corresponds to that of vitamin E. Thus, vitamin K participates in electron- and hydrogen-transfer reactions, and we have dealt with it in this connection in the account on photosynthesis, for example (see Chap. 19). Vitamin K is also somewhat similar structurally to vitamin E.

REVIEW QUESTIONS

1. What general kinds of processes take place in the execution of control activities? What general function do such controls serve in the maintenance of life? What is the role of information flow in the maintenance of steady states?

2. What are the structural components of every control system in living matter? What specific role does each component play in the maintenance of dynamic equilibria? Review the functional properties of control systems. How is the energy requirement distributed among control components?

3. What is feedback, and what is its significance in control activities? What is the significance of trial and error in control activities? What happens when control systems are overloaded? Interpret the temperature-regulating action of a home thermostat in terms of a control system and indicate the specific roles of feedback and of trial and error.

4. In what sense does a molecular reaction constitute a control system? What kinds of substances may serve as molecular modulators? What functional characteristics do these have in common? What is the relation of genes to control systems?

5. For each microscopic body usually present in cells, describe a cellular activity in which that body functions as (*a*) receptor, (*b*) modulator, (*c*) effector, and (*d*) sensory or motor pathway.

6. Review the general pattern of steady-state control on supracellular levels. How do plants and animals differ in this respect? Which parts of an organism do not participate in control activities?

7. Review the pattern of processes by which genes control (*a*) cellular metabolism, (*b*) other cellular controllers, including other genes, and (*c*) all aspects of self-perpetuation. What are growth factors? Cofactors?

8. What are chemical repression, inductions, derepression, operator genes, regulator genes, structural genes? Review the operon hypothesis and show what role it plays in accounting for control of cellular operations. How might it account for developmental changes in a cell?

9. Review the chemical nature and the cellular functions of all vitamins, as far as known. How do autotrophs and heterotrophs differ in their vitamin requirements? How, and why, do different heterotrophs differ in their vitamin requirements?

10. Distinguish between clinical and biological effects of vitamin deficiencies. Which vitamins are fat-soluble and which are water-soluble? Review the food sources and the chemical nature of the principal vitamins. What are the clinical effects of deficiencies of these vitamins?

COLLATERAL READINGS

Barth, L. J.: "Development," Addison-Wesley, Reading, Mass., 1964. Chapter 10 of this paperback contains a brief review of the operon hypothesis and its relevance to development.

Benzinger, T. H.: The Human Thermostat, *Sci. American,* Jan., 1961. Temperature regulation in man is discussed as a case study of control systems operations.

Brown, G. S., and D. P. Campbell: Control Systems, *Sci. American,* Sept., 1952. A general discussion of the operation of such systems.

Changeux, J.: The Control of Biochemical Reactions, *Sci. American,* Apr., 1965. A description of cellular feedback controls governing enzyme synthesis on the one hand and enzyme activity on the other. Very pertinent to the topics of this chapter.

Gabriel, M. L., and S. Fogel: "Great Experiments in Biology," Prentice-Hall, Englewood Cliffs, N.J., 1955. Included in this paperback is a section on vitamins in which some of the original classical studies on these growth factors are reprinted. Recommended.

Jacob, F., and J. Monod: Genetic Regulatory Mechanisms in the Synthesis of Proteins, *J. Molec. Biol.,* vol. 3, 1961. The evidence for regulator genes is discussed by the originators of the operon hypothesis.

Nagel, E.: Self-regulation, *Sci. American,* Sept., 1952. A good account of this component of control operations.

Penrose, L. S.: Self-reproducing Machines, *Sci. American,* July, 1959. An examination of how mechanical control systems may become self-reproducing and similar in this respect to living systems.

Tustin, A.: Feedback, *Sci. American,* Sept., 1952. A good account of this component of control operations.

White, A., P. Handler, and E. L. Smith: "Principles of Biochemistry," 3d ed., McGraw-Hill, New York, 1964. Chapters 55 and 56 of this text contain detailed accounts of the biology and chemistry of vitamins.

PLATE XXVII

43. Adult feather stars
(Antedon).

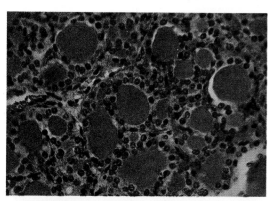

44. Section through a thyroid gland.
In this photomicrograph,
spaces filled with red-colored
material are the regions where
thyroxin accumulates before being
transported away by blood.

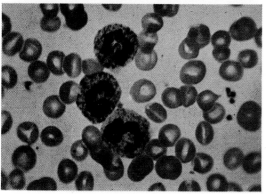

45. Smear of human blood.
Most of the round bodies are red corpuscles;
note absence of nuclei.
Three nucleated white cells are
in center of photo, and a few blood
platelets are near right edge.

PLATE XXVIII

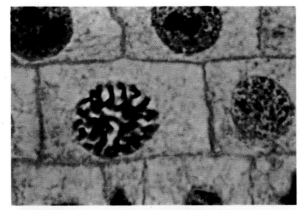

46. Prophase in plant mitosis.
*Distinct chromosomes are clearly
visible, and the nuclear membrane has
just dissolved. A spindle is not yet
sharply marked.*

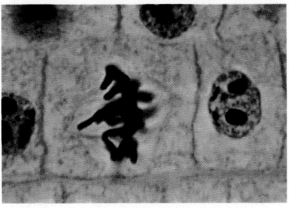

47. Metaphase
*in plant mitosis. Note the spindle
and the metaphase plate, at right angles
to the spindle axis.*

48. Anaphase
in plant mitosis.

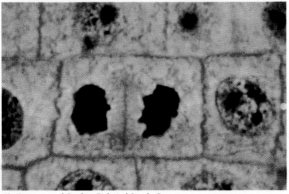

49. Telophase
*in plant mitosis. Two daughter nuclei
are in process of formation.
Note also the faint indications of
a division plate, just beginning to form
midway between the daughter nuclei
and at right angles to the former
spindle axis.*

46–49, courtesy of Carolina Biological Supply Company

CHAPTER 22
HORMONES
AND
BEHAVIOR

As a general class of growth factors, hormones differ from vitamins and mineral ions in several respects. First, although hormones are not produced within the cells in which they exert specific effects, they are nevertheless synthesized somewhere else *within* the organism and, unlike other growth factors, need not be obtained from the external environment. Second, hormones do not appear to function as cellular cofactors directly, and just how they actually do influence rates of metabolic reactions is not well known as yet; very recent evidence indicates that in some way they probably affect the activity of genes, that is, perhaps the transcription of the genetic code during protein synthesis. Third, although the primary activity of hormones is cellular and metabolic, their effects most often extend well beyond the cellular level; far more so than other growth factors, hormones usually play critical controlling roles on supracellular and organismic levels, and they thereby contribute importantly to the overt *behavior* of a whole organism. Lastly, the categories of substances known to have hormonal effects differ chemically to a great extent in different groups of organisms and also within single groups.

As in the case of mineral ions and vitamins, however, the normal control functions of a hormone are usually investigated by deliberately making an organism deficient in that hormone or by supplying an excess of it. In either case abnormal *unsteady* states are induced, and these often give clues about the normal regulating activity of the hormone. Some of the principal data obtained in this fashion on

plant and animal hormones are outlined in the following sections.

PLANT HORMONES

AUXINS, GIBBERELLINS, KININS

The three groups of substances here named constitute the principal hormones of plants. Other types of hormones apparently exist (see below), but the three types listed are best known and have been studied most. In some cases, certain vitamins function as hormones in plants. For example, root tissues usually do not produce enough thiamine on their own, but they obtain additional supplies of this vitamin from stem and leaf tissues. In this instance thiamine is a hormone.

Auxins were the first to be identified definitely as hormones. The effects of auxins had already been observed in the nineteenth century by the eminent biologist Charles Darwin. He noted that, as young grass seedlings elongated, they curved toward the light source. Using lightproof caps, Darwin was able to show that the light-sensitive region was the apical tip of a seedling, not the region farther back which underwent the actual bending (Fig. 22.1).

Later work by other investigators on grass and also oat seedlings showed that a material diffusible substance must be moving from the apical tip of a seedling to the elongating cells farther back. It was found that if the tip of a seedling was cut off and then returned, but with a layer of gelatin between the cut surfaces, then the bending toward light still occurred. This result indicated that the diffusible substance was water-soluble and could move through the aqueous gelatin. By contrast, a lipid-containing layer or a nonporous barrier of mica would not let the substance through. In other experiments the tip of a seedling was cut off in the dark and was then replaced along one side of the cut surface of the seedling stump. Under such dark conditions, the seedling still curved as it grew. Moreover, the direction of bending was always toward the side opposite to that of the attached tip. Thus, curving growth was apparently caused by an uneven distribution of the growth-promoting substance; the side of the seedling receiving more of the substance grew faster

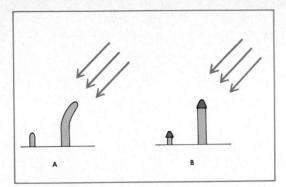

22 · 1 *Darwin's experiments with grass seedlings. If the tip of a seedling is capped (B), bending toward a light source will not occur (colored arrows).*

than the opposite side, resulting in bending. If the seedling tip was cut off and not replaced at all, the seedling ceased to elongate altogether. All these data suggested strongly that the growth-promoting substance functioned rather like a hormone (Fig. 22.2).

Isolation of the hormone was first achieved in 1928. Many seedling tips were placed on an agar block, and this block could be shown to collect the hormone diffusing out of the tips. For if the tips were removed and the block was placed on the stump of a decapitated seedling, the hormone in the agar actively promoted the elongation and bending of the seedling (Fig. 22.3). The chemical nature of this hormone, named auxin, was later identified. It is *indole acetic acid*, *IAA* for short ($C_{10}H_9O_2N$), a derivative of the amino acid tryptophane.

Also called *heteroauxin*, IAA is but one of a group of similarly acting substances. Two others, for example, are naphthalene acetic acid ($C_{12}H_{10}O_2$) and 2,4-dichlorophenoxyacetic acid, or 2,4-D for short ($C_8H_6O_3Cl_2$). Still other auxins exist and many can

be synthesized in the laboratory. Indeed, it is often possible to predict whether a given new compound will be an auxin in plants. For the characteristic effect of an auxin, namely, its ability to promote bending of a seedling, appears to be correlated with the presence of particular atomic groupings in an auxin molecule. Such a molecule is likely to possess an unsaturated carbon ring, an acid side chain, and a certain spatial arrangement of the ring and the side chain (Fig. 22.4). Notwithstanding such usually common structural features, auxins differ in their biological potency and also in their specificity.

IAA is known to occur in many Monera, Protista, and Metaphyta. Chemical derivatives of it, without hormonal effects, are also found in Metazoa. In a plant IAA is manufactured in various body parts. Actively growing and developing regions generally produce the largest amounts. For example, particularly auxin-rich regions are meristems of all kinds (including shoot tips, root tips, and cambia), and also young leaves, developing flower parts, fruits, and plant tumors during their active growth phases. How does IAA actually affect a plant cell? Available data indicate that auxins promote the *elongation* of individual cells by influencing cell-wall metabolism. Auxin activity appears to have the basic effect of inducing a cell to synthesize more primary wall material and to deposit this material at the two ends of a cell.

Thus, the apical tip of a shoot (or a root) normally produces IAA which then diffuses to cells farther back where it brings about cell elongation. If the cross-sectional distribution of IAA is roughly even, the shoot will elongate straight up. The growth-promoting effect of auxin is known to be reduced in some way by light, hence an illuminated shoot does not grow so fast as if it were kept in darkness. Under normal field conditions, therefore, plant growth is a compromise between, on the one hand, stimulation by light via photosynthesis and food pro-

22 · 2 *Experiments with oat coleoptiles.*

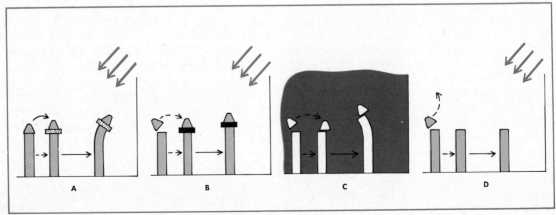

duction and on the other, inhibition by light via reduced auxin effects. If a shoot is illuminated predominantly from one side, auxin will be less effective on that side than on the other. The shoot will then curve toward the light source as it elongates. As will become apparent below, these primary effects of IAA and of auxins generally have numerous secondary consequences that influence the steady-state maintenance of the whole plant.

Apart from auxins, the best-known hormones of plants are the gibberellins. The clue to their existence has been the so-called "foolish seedling" disease in rice, in which a fungus of the genus *Gibberella* infects a young rice plant. The latter then grows extremely tall, projecting well above neighboring plants in a field. Extracts of the fungus can similarly increase the size of rice plants, and from such extracts pure gibberellins have been isolated. Gibberellins are now known to occur not only in fungi but also in vascular plants, where they are normal constituents qualifying as hormones. Four different but closely related compounds are included in the group, *gibberellic acid* being the most potent.

The visible effects of gibberellins appear to be primarily on stem length. In young stems particularly, the hormones increase the length of all the internodes without affecting the number of nodes. The results can be striking. For example, by applying gibberellic acid to dwarf peas, such plants can be made to grow to the size of normal peas. Similarly, dwarf varieties of corn will grow to normal height if a little gibberellic acid is placed on the leaves. Many biennial plants can be induced to complete their whole life cycle in a single year by treatment with gibberellins. And if gibberellic acid is applied to cabbage, normally a low head with closely packed leaves, then the plant can be induced to become tall and vinelike (Fig. 22.5).

Such results appear to be produced by increases in the rates of cell division. Just how gibberellins actually accelerate cell divisions is not clearly understood as yet. Unlike auxins, gibberellins do not cause bending of a seedling, and they affect the whole

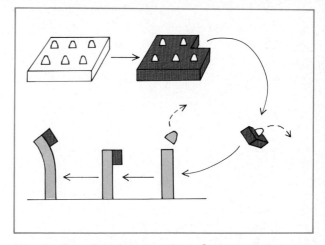

22 · 3   Experiments on auxin isolation.

stem, not only the region behind the apical tip. Also, gibberellins do not exert control over buds, roots, and leaves in the same manner as auxins (see below). The discovery of gibberellins has shown clearly that cellular steady-state control in plants is far more complex than had been thought when only minerals and auxins were known to play regulatory roles. And the complexity increases even more as additional categories of hormones are being discovered. A case in point are the *kinins*, which, like gibberellins, promote cell division. Kinins are degradation products of purines. They may be normally present in plants as hormones, but to date their action has been studied mainly by application of manmade kinin preparations.

Through their control of cellular activities, growth factors of all kinds modulate the behavioral reactions of a whole plant. Explicit behavior may be regarded as the response to the various stimuli which affect a plant. Such responses manifest themselves principally in two ways, namely, in the form of *movement* and in the form of *development*.

22 · 4   The chemical structure of auxins. Colored portions emphasize the similar atomic groupings often present in auxins.

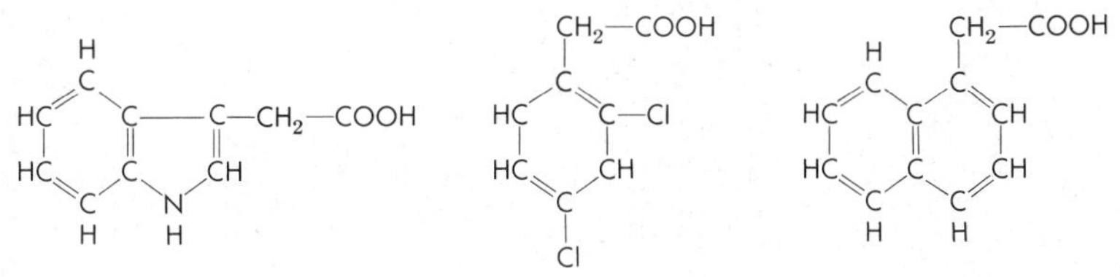

INDOLEACETIC ACID (IAA)

2,4-DICHLOROPHENOXYACETIC ACID (2,4-D)

α-NAPHTHALENEACETIC ACID (NAA)

22 · 5 The effects of gibberellins. *Left, untreated cabbage, and right, cabbage after gibberellin treatment. Note enormous elongation of internodes.*

22 · 6 Growth movements *of plants in response to internal stimuli.*

RESPONSES OF MOVEMENT

These behavioral responses involve greater or lesser portions of a fixed plant and they are of two types: *growth movements* and *turgor movements*.

Growth Movements

Growth movements are elicited by both *internal* and *external* stimuli. Internal stimuli of so far unspecifiable nature (and probably accompanied to some extent by external stimuli as well) are known to result in three kinds of growth responses. All occur too slowly to be observable directly, but time-lapse movies reveal them clearly (Fig. 22.6).

One of these responses is *nutational* movement. This is a back-and-forth rocking or nodding motion of the apical shoot tips of certain species, caused by alternately changing growth rates on opposite sides of the apical tip. A second type of response includes *spiral* motions of various sorts. These are characterized by rotational growth of an elongating shoot around its long axis. One form of spiral motion is *twining*, in which rotational growth of the shoot tip produces a spirally curving stem. External stimuli, gravity in particular, may be partly responsible for twining growth. External stimuli such as temperature and light are probably also partly involved in a third type of response, so-called *nastic* movements. These occur in leaves, petals, and other flattened parts of plants when one surface of such an organ grows faster than the other. Nastic motions thus may result either in an opening and folding out of a body part, as in the opening of maturing buds, or in a closing and folding in.

Growth movements brought about wholly by external stimuli are called *tropisms*. The stimuli producing such tropic responses are clearly identifiable, and in many cases the specific role of growth factors is also known. Several kinds of tropisms are

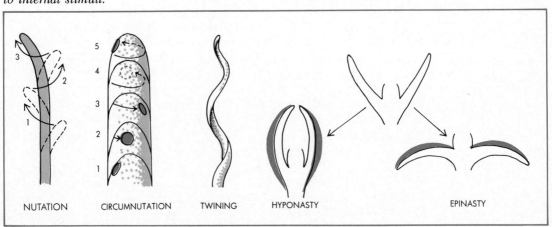

NUTATION   CIRCUMNUTATION   TWINING   HYPONASTY   EPINASTY

22 · 7 Tropic movements. Left, the effect of gravity: geotropic response. Right, the effect of light: phototropic response. The plant is illuminated from the left.

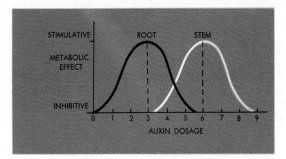

22 · 8 Auxin effects at different concentrations on root and stem.

distinguished on the basis of the various growth-inducing stimuli: light-induced *phototropism*, gravity-induced *geotropism*, contact-induced *thigmotropism*, chemical-induced *chemotropism*, and others (Fig. 22.7). A given tropic response may be either *positive* or *negative*, that is, a plant or plant part may grow toward or away from the stimulus. For example, leaves and stems are positively phototropic and negatively geotropic; they grow toward light and away from the gravitational center of the earth. Roots, on the contrary, are positively geotropic and negatively phototropic. Pollen tubes are positively chemotropic, growing toward chemical agents produced within a flower ovary. And the shoot tips and tendrils of climbing plants are positively thigmotropic, growing along objects on which they can become attached. Most tropic responses are adaptively advantageous in fairly obvious and often very important ways.

Of all responses of plants, phototropism and geotropism are among the best understood. These movements, and possibly other tropisms as well, are under the control of auxins. As already noted, unilateral

illumination of a growing stem reduces the auxin effect on the side facing the light source. Cells on the opposite side therefore elongate more extensively, and the stem then curves toward the light. The net result is the observed positive phototropism of stems. How can the negative phototropism of roots be explained?

It has been found that the optimum IAA concentration for elongation of root cells is about 100,000 times less than the optimum for elongation of stem cells. In other words, an IAA concentration that stimulates stem growth *inhibits* root growth. Conversely, an IAA concentration that stimulates root growth is so low that it inhibits stem growth, or at any rate does not promote it (Fig. 22.8). Therefore, if a stem-root system (in water rather than soil) is illuminated from one side, the stem tip will curve toward the light. But any auxin diffusing into the root on the side away from the light will be sufficiently concentrated to inhibit root elongation on that side. As a result, the side facing the light will grow faster and the root tip will curve away from the light stimulus; hence the negative phototropism of roots (Fig. 22.9).

22 · 9 Interaction of light and auxin in the control of stem and root growth.

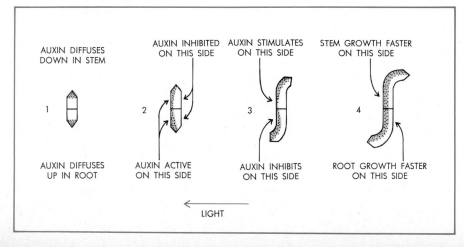

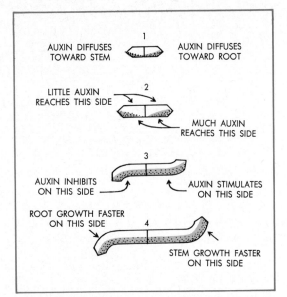

22 · 10 *Interaction of gravity and auxin in the control of stem and root growth.*

The negative geotropism of stems and the positive geotropism of roots can be explained by migration of auxin under the influence of gravity. It is well known that if a plant is placed horizontally, the stem tip grows upward, the root tip downward. These responses take place even in the dark; they are gravity-dependent, not light-dependent. It can be shown that, in a horizontal plant, as much as two-thirds of all the auxin in a shoot tip is present on the lower side of this tip. As auxin moves back to

22 · 11 *Leaf epidermis, showing a pair of guard cells. Upper figures, surface view; lower figures, cross-sectional view; left figures, stoma open; right figures, stoma closed.*

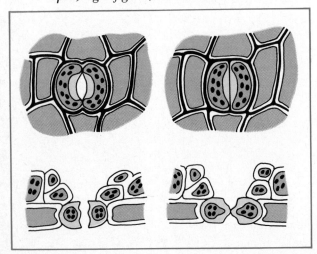

cells capable of elongating, most of the hormone therefore reaches cells located on the lower side of the stem. These cells consequently elongate more than cells on the upper side and the stem tip curves upward as a result. When auxin then reaches root cells, the concentration of the hormone is still highest on the lower side, which means that the cells on that side will be inhibited most. Root cells on the upper side therefore elongate to a comparatively greater extent. The root tip consequently curves downward, in the direction of the center of the earth (Fig. 22.10).

Changes in hormone distribution and differential effects of given hormone concentrations on different plant parts probably play a role in other tropisms as well. In most of these cases, however, it is still not quite clear how the external stimulus actually elicits particular hormone activities.

Turgor Movements

These responses of plant parts are initiated largely by external stimuli. The movements result from changes in the turgor (water pressure) of given cells or cell groups. Unlike growth movements, which are slow and produce more or less permanent results, turgor movements are rapid, often exceedingly so, and they are transient and repeatable. In some cases at least, auxins again appear to be the chief controlling agents. The most widespread turgor movements are the opening and closing of the epidermal *guard cells* in leaves and stems. Other turgor movements include *contact movements* of leaves in sensitive and carnivorous plants and *sleep movements* of leaves in certain plants.

A pair of green, crescent-shaped guard cells possesses walls which are thickest and stiffest on the inner sides, where they form the stomatal pore (Fig. 22.11). This construction permits a stoma to open or close when turgor increases or decreases within the guard cells. Turgor increases when additional water enters the cells. As they then become more turgid they swell, and their thin outer side walls curve out farther under the increased water pressure. The result is that the inner thicker portions of the walls are moved apart and so the stoma opens. Conversely, guard cells become less turgid when water leaves them. Their elastic walls then revert to their original position and the stoma closes.

The turgor of guard cells can become increased through two interconnected processes (Fig. 22.12). Since guard cells are photosynthetic they may produce carbohydrates. The concentration of the particles present in the cells then increases, and water will be drawn osmotically into the guard cells from surrounding epidermal cells and turgor increases. Under illumination, therefore, and if other conditions are optimal, stomata will open and will permit photosynthesis to occur in the leaf mesophyll; CO_2 may enter the air spaces of the leaf and O_2 may depart. Conversely, in darkness the stomata will close.

The second process leading to an increase in guard-cell turgor is initiated when the stomata are closed and when photosynthesis does not occur. At night, for example, respiratory CO_2 accumulates in the guard cells. The gas is present in chemical combination with water, in the form of carbonic acid or, more precisely, in the form of bicarbonate and hydrogen ions:

$$H_2O + CO_2 \rightleftharpoons H_2CO_3 \rightleftharpoons H^+ + HCO_3^-$$

When guard-cell photosynthesis resumes the following morning, CO_2 will be used up in food production and this changes the direction of the reaction above to the left. As H^+ ions thus disappear, the pH will rise and the interior of the guard cells will become more alkaline. But alkaline conditions are known to promote the enzymatic conversion of storage starch into glucose. Therefore, since one starch molecule yields many glucose molecules, this increase in the concentration of particles leads to an osmotic intake of additional water, hence to increase in turgor and an opening of the stoma. Leaf pores so reopen with the reappearance of the morning sun, permitting photosynthesis to occur again in the mesophyll (see Fig. 22.12).

Could not permanently open leaf pores without guard cells serve just as well? Gases would then enter or leave freely and photosynthesis would or would not occur inside the leaf depending on illumination. But lighting is not the only factor controlling the turgor movements of guard cells. Humidity, temperature, and possibly other environmental conditions appear to play a role as well, and it is in connection with such factors that guard cells display perhaps their most important adaptive function. For example, on a very dry, hot summer day the stomata may be almost fully closed, despite the ample illumination. The rate of photosynthesis in a leaf is then reduced, inasmuch as not enough CO_2 can enter. But the evaporation of internal water, a problem of more immediate concern, is held down at the same time. Besides, if leaf pores were permanently open, they would permit unnecessary evaporation of water during the night.

A second category of turgor movements is elicited by contact stimuli. Probably the most dramatic instance of such *contact movements* is encountered in the legume *Mimosa*, the "sensitive plant." It has

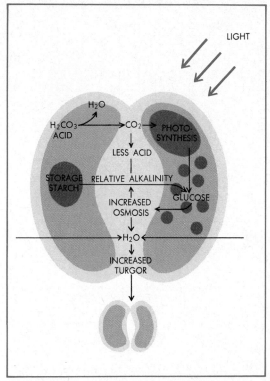

22 · 12 *The control of guard-cell movements.*

long been known that the leaves of this plant are exceedingly sensitive to touch and also to sudden increases in temperature; the leaves drop down from an erect position almost instantaneously after being stimulated, as if they possessed nervous reflexes. But the mechanism is again movement of water into and out of cells.

At the base of each leaf petiole of *Mimosa* (and of several other legumes) is a so-called *pulvinus,* a swelling containing large cells with many spaces between them (Fig. 22.13). When a *Mimosa* leaf is erect, all the cells of the pulvinus are turgid; it is the mechanical rigidity maintained by this turgor which keeps the leaf erect. But any touch or heat stimulus applied to some part of the leaf quickly leads to the transmission of a signal through the leaf to the pulvinus. A diffusible chemical agent is known to bring about this transmission; some evidence indicates that it may be an auxin. The signal affects the cells on the lower side of the pulvinus in such a way that they lose water rapidly. This water moves into the surrounding intercellular spaces and into other, neighboring cells. As a result of the suddenly reduced turgor in the lower portion of the pulvinus, the leaf as whole drops down. The time elapsed between external stimulus and leaf response

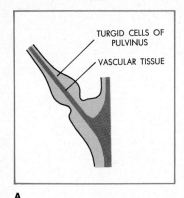

TURGID CELLS OF
PULVINUS

VASCULAR TISSUE

A

B

C

22 · 13 *The sensitive plant Mimosa. A, length-wise section of a pulvinus. B and C, photos of* Mimosa, *before and after stimulation of leaflets and leaves.*

is less than $\frac{1}{10}$ sec. However, it takes about 10 min for the recovery of the turgid condition.

Reversible turgor movements may also play a role in the insect-trapping action of the leaves of carnivorous plants such as Venus's-flytrap. The trapping mechanism in this plant is triggered off by touch-sensitive hairs on the inner leaf surfaces. Subsequent events are not yet fully understood. Some still un-identified diffusible chemical agent again appears to transmit the excitation from the stimulated receptor hairs to the effector cells (Fig. 22.14).

Variously different contact movements are known in several other plants. In some, for example, the stamens of flowers snap to altered positions when an

insect touches them and pollen is thereby powdered over the insects. In other flowers, the stigma of a pistil forms two joined lobes which snap together when pollen grains touch them, so trapping the pollen. Turgor changes and signal transmission by diffusible chemical agents appear to be involved in all such cases. Beyond this, details of the action mechanisms are still unknown.

Changes in light intensity are the specific stimuli for so-called *sleep movements* in many plants, legumes in particular. In such turgor-produced motions, the leaves assume one position during the day and an-other during the night. The day position is usually horizontal, the night position usually vertical, either upright or hanging. Here again the mechanism of action is not understood as yet, nor is the possible functional significance of these particular movements.

RESPONSES OF DEVELOPMENT

Numerous developmental responses of plants have been shown to be under auxin control and to be initiated normally by internal stimuli. Some of these

22 · 14 *Venus flytrap. A, whole plant with traps in various states of closure. B and C, a fly enters a trap and is caught.*

A

A, courtesy of Carolina Biological Supply Company.

B

C

responses can also be produced by artificial stimulation through the use of externally applied auxin preparations. Many other important developmental responses are elicited normally and naturally by the external environment. Various physical, chemical, and biological agents are the effective stimuli.

The Effects of Auxins

Normal internal stimuli lead to an auxin effect which promotes *bud development.* As shown in Chap. 13, lateral stem buds form in the axils of leaves. Buds near the stem tip usually remain dormant, but those farther back along the stem may break dormancy and develop into branch stems. It can be shown that this evident dominance of the main apical tip is due to auxin. IAA produced by the dominant tip moves back toward the axillary buds. However, the optimum IAA concentration for bud growth is only about 1/1,000 of the optimum concentration for cell elongation. Therefore, as high IAA concentrations reach them, buds near the tip are inhibited from breaking dormancy. The apical dominance extends backward for considerable distances until auxin becomes sufficiently dilute to stimulate rather than inhibit bud development. Clearly, these differential sensitivities account for the usual tapering growth pattern of the branch system of a plant (Fig. 22.15). One question remains to be answered: why is the development of the dominant bud not inhibited by the very high auxin concentration within the bud itself?

Auxins exert developmental control over *meristems* such as cambia. It has been suggested that, in woody plants, auxins produced in the spring by actively growing shoots diffuse to the cambia, where they may activate the cambial tissues and stimulate them to form that season's wood and bark. The effects of auxin on meristem development are evident also in the formation of *callus* tissue. If the stem of a bean plant is cut off and the cut surface is covered with a paste containing large amounts of IAA, then this external stimulus will lead to the development of a callus, a tumorous mass of cells which includes meristematic regions. Such a callus may be cut off and kept growing indefinitely in tissue culture, provided IAA is continually added to the medium.

Calluslike tissues are formed also in plant tumors known as *crown galls,* encountered in sunflowers, marigolds, tomatoes, beans, and other plants (Fig. 22.16). Production of a crown gall is initiated by an external biological stimulus, namely, by parasitic bacteria of a particular kind. These organisms infect plant tissues and the latter respond by excessive growth and crown-gall formation. Bacteria-free

22 · 15 *The effect of auxin on bud development. The assumption here is that auxin (dark color) released from a terminal bud is concentrated enough to inhibit the development of the first three branch buds behind the terminal bud. Branch buds farther back receive less than an inhibitory concentration of auxin and thus may break dormancy.*

22 · 16 *Crown gall on the stem of a sunflower. Callus overgrowths of this type are formed also when high concentrations of IAA are applied on cut surfaces of, for example, bean plants.*

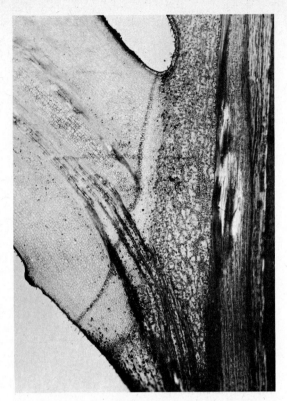

22 · 17 *Section through junction of leaf and stem, showing abscission layer (dark transverse cell layer) across leaf base. If auxin concentrations are higher on the leaf side, abscission will not occur; in the converse situation the abscission cells die and the leaf drops off.*

portions of such a tumor may be isolated and grown in tissue culture. Mature crown-gall tissues manufacture large amounts of auxin on their own. These hormones then maintain the meristematic characteristics and the continuing growth of the tissues without any further external bacterial or hormonal stimulation. In their independent, autonomous growth, crown galls evidently resemble the malignant tumors of animals. In the latter, however, auxin is never responsible for maintenance of autonomous growth.

Another important developmental function of auxins is their control of leaf fall and fruit drop. Leaves and fruits separate from a plant at an *abscission layer*, a region of special cells formed where a leaf petiole or a fruit stalk joins the stem (Fig. 22.17). In such a layer, the cement between adjacent cells dissolves, cell-wall permeability is lost, and the weakened cells finally die. Abscission of the leaf or the fruit is the consequence. It has been shown that such separations are governed by the relative auxin concentrations on the two sides of the abscission area. So long as IAA concentrations in a leaf or a fruit are higher than in the stem, abscission normally does not occur. This is the case while leaf

or fruit growth is under way, that is, while these organs actively produce auxins of their own. But when auxin manufacture ceases, at full maturity, for example, or when cold autumn weather slows growth rates, then IAA concentrations in a leaf or a fruit decrease relative to the concentrations in the stem. Abscission is then likely to take place.

Fruit growers make practical use of these relationships. In spring they may spray auxins on the stems, a procedure which raises the hormone concentrations of the stems relative to those of flowers or young fruits. The result will be many premature abscissions and a consequent thinning of the fruits on a tree. The fewer remaining fruits may then become larger and better, since more food will be available to them. Later in the year auxin spray may be applied to the fruits, a procedure that will delay abscission and permit longer tree-ripening of the fruits.

Auxins play an important role in controlling the development of adventitious roots. As is well known, if a terminal piece of stem with an apical bud and some leaves is cut away from a plant and is put into soil or water, then adventitious roots will form from the base of the stem piece. Such *cuttings* are a means of propagating mature plants, and this method of making new individuals is used widely in horticulture. In early attempts to explain root formation in cuttings, it was postulated that some substance moved from the apical regions of the shoot to the vascular regions of the stem base, where it stimulated development of root tissues. Such a substance was later actually found to exist and it was demonstrated to be IAA. Weak solutions of IAA are now frequently used to promote root formation in stem cuttings (Fig. 22.18).

Auxins not only aid in making new plants but also in killing old ones. When auxins are applied externally to certain plants at much higher concentrations than those which normally promote growth, then the hormones interfere drastically with the metabolism and development of the plants. Dicotyledonous weeds are particularly sensitive to very high auxin levels, and plant death is a frequent consequence. Just how auxins exert this lethal effect is not clearly understood, but the effect itself has become extremely important in weed control: monocotyledonous crop plants such as corn and grain-formers are hardly affected by auxin concentrations lethal to dicotyledonous weeds.

Evidently, auxins perform vital controlling functions in a multiplicity of developmental processes. A basic stimulation or inhibition of cell elongation appears to account for many of these functions, even though others cannot be explained in this way alone.

The Effects of Light

In view of the absolute nutritional dependence of green plants on light, it is not surprising that this form of energy should have become one of the most profound external stimuli in the life of plants. Some responses to light have been outlined above. Certain of these, such as the auxin-mediated phototropic responses, are clearly adaptive in plant nutrition; they bring the photosynthetic organs into optimum positions relative to the light source. Similarly adaptive in plant metabolism are the response of guard cells to light and the light-dependence of chlorophyll synthesis and chlorophyll maintenance in flowering plants. However, many other responses to light are more directly of developmental, not of metabolic, significance. A different set of developmental responses is produced by each of the three main attributes of light, namely, *intensity, quality,* and *duration.*

Some responses to varying light intensities are auxin-mediated, and they result from the reduced effectiveness of auxin in bright light. For example, plants grown in darkness or in dim light develop taller stems with longer internodes and larger, more succulent leaves than plants grown in bright light. Even within the same plant, outer leaves that receive the full light of the sun remain smaller than inner, more shaded leaves. Where leaf size is of commercial importance, as in tobacco, for example, plants are often shielded by light screens or nets. Such reduction of intensity of illumination may promote development of larger leaves.

Extended maintenance of plants in darkness or

22 · 18 The effect of auxin on root development. *After auxin application, the cut stems on left develop roots as on right.*

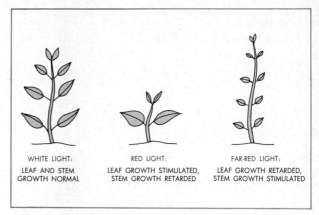

WHITE LIGHT: LEAF AND STEM GROWTH NORMAL

RED LIGHT: LEAF GROWTH STIMULATED, STEM GROWTH RETARDED

FAR-RED LIGHT: LEAF GROWTH RETARDED, STEM GROWTH STIMULATED

22 · 19 The effects of red and far-red light on leaf and stem growth.

in exceedingly dim light usually leads to the pathological condition known as *etiolation:* stems are excessively long and without sufficient supporting fiber tissue, and leaves are whitish, without adequate amounts of chlorophyll. If light intensity does not increase, death ultimately follows. Conversely, long exposure to excessively bright light stunts plant development abnormally and may also lead to death.

Within an adequate range of light intensities, different species of plants develop best at different intensity levels. Some plants, for example, tomatoes and grasses, require bright, direct light for optimum development. In such plants the synthesis of living matter increases in roughly direct proportion with increasing light intensities (up to a maximum corresponding to somewhat less than the full light of the summer sun). On the contrary, plants such as violets and ferns develop optimally in dim, diffuse light and are stunted by the direct sun. Still other plants, for example, roses, do well both in bright and in diffuse light, although growth and flowering may be retarded or may cease if the light intensity is too low.

At any given light intensity, the different wavelengths of light exert considerable effect on plant development. For example, it has been shown that brief exposure to red light often retards stem elongation in plants such as oats, peas, beans, or barley. However, these retardations can subsequently be reversed and stem growth can be stimulated by exposing the plants to light close to the limit of visibility, in the far-red region of the spectrum. In leaves, red–far-red treatment produces opposite effects; far-red light retards leaf development, red light reverses the retardation (Fig. 22.19). Such red–far-red effects on stem and leaf development may be induced repeatedly within the same plant. The nature

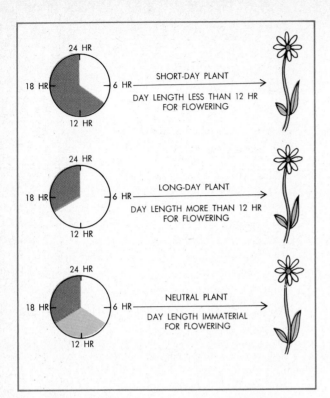

of the stimulus receptors and the functional significance of these responses to different light qualities are not yet known.

Developmental responses of plants to varying light durations are described by the term *photoperiodism*. Flower development is particularly affected by different day lengths, or *photoperiods*. On the basis of the photoperiod required for flowering, plants may be divided into three groups (Fig. 22.20). In so-called *short-day plants*, flowers develop only if the plants are illuminated for less than 12 hr daily. Violets, asters, cockleburs, strawberries, chrysanthemums, and rice are among many plants in this category. In *long-day plants*, flowers develop only if the

22 · 21 Experiments on photoperiodism. *Left, experiments showing that leaves are the stimulus receptors in photoperiodic responses. Right, experiments showing that red light produces the most pronounced photoperiodic responses.*

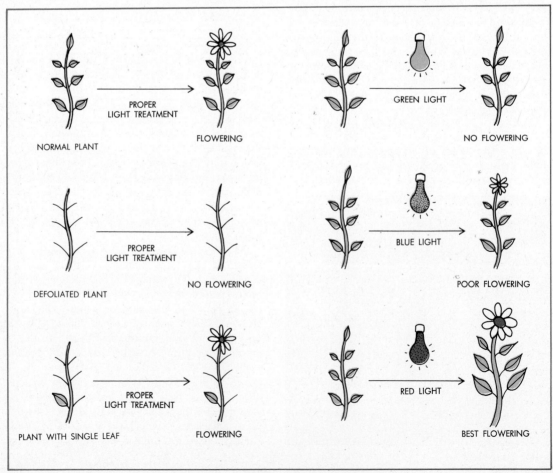

daily photoperiod is more than 12 hr. This group includes, for example, wheat, clover, beets, and lettuce. A third group of plants is not limited in its illumination requirements, and such *indeterminate plants* produce flowers regardless of the length of the daily photoperiods. Tomatoes, cucumbers, cotton, sunflowers, and dandelions are representative members of this group.

Short-day plants fail to flower or their flowering is greatly retarded if they are exposed to long photoperiods only. Conversely, long-day plants flower late or not at all if they are grown under short photoperiods. Often only a brief exposure to appropriate day lengths is needed to induce flowering. For example, if the short-day cocklebur plant is grown under long photoperiods, it will not flower. But if it is exposed to only one single short day and one long night, it will flower even if the long photoperiods are continued thereafter. Different species exhibit different requirements in this respect.

Some of the factors involved in eliciting photoperiodic responses are known. First, it has been shown that the receptor organs specifically sensitive to light durations are the leaves. Defoliated plants cannot be induced to flower even with proper light treatment. The light sensitivity of leaves differs at different stages of development. Very young leaves are generally insensitive, but as they age they become progressively more sensitive until, in many species, sensitivity is again lost at very old stages. Even a portion of a sensitive leaf may be an adequate receptor.

Second, it can be demonstrated that the red portion of the spectrum is more effective as a flower-inducing stimulus than the blue portion. The middle green portion is generally ineffective. Also, the amount of flowering can be shown to vary in direct proportion to the total amount of light energy received by the leaves. For example, if two plants are illuminated for the same period but one receives light of greater intensity, then that plant is likely to flower faster or more extensively (Fig. 22.21).

Third, it has been found for short-day plants that the length of the *night* is just as important as the length of the day. If the dark periods are of less than a certain critical length, then flowering will not occur even if the light periods are of appropriate length. Moreover, if an appropriately long dark period is interrupted by even a single brief flash of light, then flowering will again be suppressed. The suppression is most pronounced if the light interruption takes place at or near the middle of the dark period. Evidently, short-day plants may justifiably also be called "long-night plants" (Fig. 22.22).

Fourth, aerial CO_2 is required to induce flower-

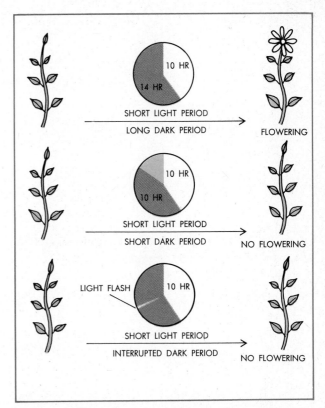

22 · 22 Experiments on photoperiodism. *The importance of right length and of the continuity of the dark period in short-day plants is illustrated.*

ing. The role of the gas here is apparently not nutritional, for even a plant with ample food supplies cannot be induced to flower if CO_2 is not present. It has been suggested that CO_2 may be necessary in leaves as a raw material in the synthesis of a special compound required for flower induction. Such a compound *A* may be produced from CO_2 during the light period. During the ensuing dark period, *A* may be converted into another necessary compound *B*. Therefore, if the dark period is too short or is made too short by a light interruption, there may not be enough time available for the production of sufficient amounts of *B*. Flowering will then not occur. Moreover, the more light energy the leaves receive the more *A* can be formed, hence also the more *B*.

Lastly, compounds *A* and *B* probably cannot be the only substances required for flower induction. *A* and *B* are produced in the leaves, but flowers are formed near the shoot tips. It becomes necessary, therefore, to postulate the existence of a hormone *C*. This hormone must be manufactured in the leaves from

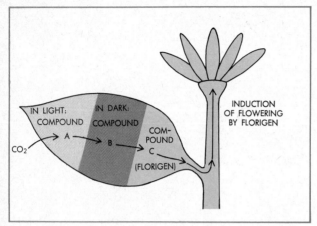

22 · 23 *Hypothetical sequence of events leading to a photoperiodic response.*

22 · 24 *A flowering stimulus resulting from appropriate light treatment may pass from one plant to a grafted partner. Both graft partners are short-day plants. One (top left) has received proper short-day treatment; the other (top right) has received improper long-day treatment.*

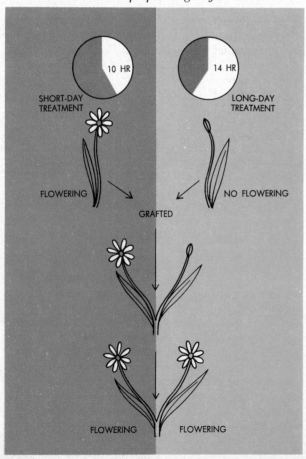

compound B and must then migrate to a shoot tip where it initiates flowering (Fig. 22.23). The actual existence of such a flowering hormone, or *florigen*, can be demonstrated experimentally. In short-day cocklebur plants, for example, one individual may be grown under short photoperiods, which leads to flowering. Another individual may be kept under long photoperiods, which suppresses flowering. If then the two plants are grafted together and if their earlier photoperiods are maintained, it is found that the previously nonflowering plant now begins to flower too. Evidently, a diffusible florigen has moved from one plant into the other and has induced the latter to flower. Indeed, if a wet filter paper is interposed in the graft area between the two plants, the florigen still penetrates through this barrier (Fig. 22.24).

All attempts to isolate florigens (or the postulated compounds A and B) have so far been without success. But the flower-inducing mechanism suggested by the experiments does account for the difference between short-day and long-day plants. In short-day plants, long days would make the nights too short for adequate conversion of compound A into B. Florigen would then be formed in insufficient quantity and flowering could not occur. In long-day plants, short days would not provide adequate illumination for the formation of enough A, again leading to insufficient amounts of florigen and a suppression of flowering. Indeterminate plants would be able to form enough A, B, and florigen under any naturally occurring photoperiods. Evidently, the photoperiodic differences among plants appear to be quantitative rather than qualitative.

As might be expected, the global distribution of plants reflects their photoperiodic nature. Thus, the days in tropical and subtropical regions are fairly uniformly short (rarely more than 12 or 13 hr), and the plants in these regions are largely short-day species. The temperate zone supports both short-day and long-day plants. The former flower mainly during the short-day seasons of spring and autumn, the latter during the long-day season of summer. In higher latitudes beyond the temperate zone, most plants are long-day species adapted to the long days and short nights which characterize most of the growing season. Indeterminate plants are distributed widely over all climatic zones.

Knowledge of photoperiodic responses has been turned to horticultural advantage. By artificially lengthening or shortening day lengths under controlled conditions, given commercially important plants can be induced to flower at virtually any season of the year or may be inhibited from developing flowers.

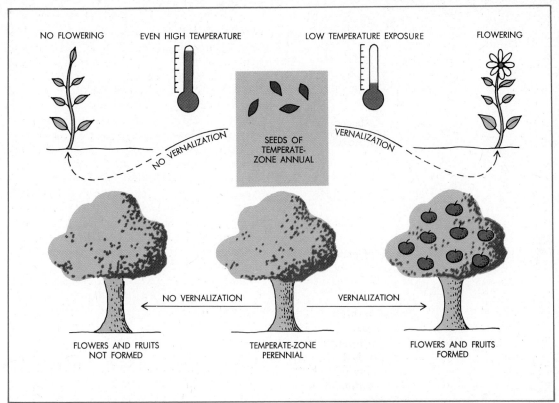

NO VERNALIZATION

VERNALIZATION

SEEDS OF
TEMPERATE-
ZONE ANNUAL

FLOWERS AND FRUITS
NOT FORMED   TEMPERATE-ZONE
PERENNIAL   FLOWERS AND FRUITS
FORMED

NO VERNALIZATION   VERNALIZATION

The Effect of Temperature

Among physical stimuli other than light, temperature is probably the most important. Different plants are adapted to live within different temperature ranges, a range of 70 to 90°F being optimal for most species of the temperate zone. Tropical plants are generally adjusted to higher temperature levels. They may thrive even at 100°F, but they are injured or killed if the temperature drops much below 60°F. By contrast, north-temperate and subarctic plants readily withstand temperatures below 0°F. As noted in Chap. 13, many plants have evolved special adaptations which permit them to cope with extremes in their usual temperature range.

The basic effects of temperature are metabolic; within limits, the rate of chemical processes increases in a direct proportion with increasing temperature (see Chap. 5). But temperature also elicits other, developmental responses, and these probably are not due merely to quantitative changes in metabolic rates. The most striking developmental results of temperature treatment, or *vernalization*, again are flowering responses, like those produced by given photoperiods.

Whether or not flowering will occur in mature annual plants can be shown to depend on the temperatures to which the germinating seeds of these plants were exposed. Different species here exhibit

22 · 25 Vernalization. *Read from middle to either side. Top, vernalization at the seed stage. Bottom, vernalization at the adult stage.*

different temperature requirements. For example, seeds of temperate-zone annuals like winter wheat must be exposed to low temperatures if flowering is to occur later in the mature plants. Such seeds are normally sown in the fall, and the ensuing winter provides the required low temperature. If the seeds are not vernalized in this manner, flowers will not be formed later. By contrast, seeds of tropical annuals such as rice must be vernalized at high temperatures (80°F or more) if later flowering is to take place (Fig. 22.25).

The receptor of the temperature stimulus in a seed is the embryo. The suggestion has been made that vernalization may permit manufacture of a special hormonal substance which persists as the plant matures and which eventually induces flowering. The name *vernalin* has been proposed for this hormone, but attempts to extract it have so far not been successful. In any event, experiments show that a plant must be vernalized first before it will respond to photoperiodic stimuli. Conceivably, vernalin produced early in development may be a prerequisite for the later manufacture of florigen.

In nature, annual plants are normally vernalized in the seed stage, as just described. Biennial and

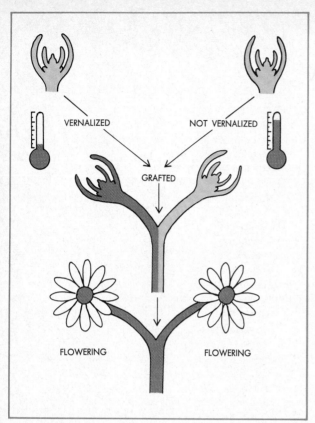

VERNALIZED   NOT VERNALIZED

GRAFTED

FLOWERING   FLOWERING

22 · 26 A flowering stimulus resulting from appropriate vernalization may pass from one plant to a grafted unvernalized partner.

perennial plants usually become vernalized at a later stage, during vegetative growth. Biennials such as celery, beets, and henbane grow vegetatively during a first season and the ensuing winter effects the vernalization. Flowering then occurs during the following season. The cycle may be speeded up by early vernalization in the laboratory. For example, if a young first-year henbane plant is cold-treated early during the year, it may be induced to flower during the same year. Perennials such as apples or peaches are normally vernalized in the mature vegetative condition by each successive winter. It follows that if apple or peach trees or temperate-zone perennials in general are grown in tropical or otherwise uniformly warm climates, then they will continue to develop vegetatively but will not flower. Conversely, if tropical perennials are grown at very high latitudes, then they too will not become vernalized and will not flower.

Whenever vernalization occurs in mature plants, the receptors of the temperature stimulus are the apical buds. That this is so can be demonstrated by grafting experiments. For example, a vernalized apical bud of one plant may induce flower formation in a nonvernalized apical bud of another plant

if the two are grafted together. The transmitted signal is apparently quite unspecific, for flower induction occurs even when the graft partners are of different species (Fig. 22.26).

Data such as the foregoing warrant the conclusion that the importance of flowering in the life of plants is fully matched by the complexity of its control. We already know that the process is governed by temperature, by light, and by hormones; and many other partly suspected and partly unsuspected stimuli undoubtedly play additional roles. All the external stimuli affect a plant simultaneously, and, eliciting varied internal responses, the ultimate outcome is the development or nondevelopment of a flower. In all probability, the adaptive value of such a multiplicity of control factors is that they save energy and materials; a flower is normally formed only under the best possible environmental conditions, when the reproductive effort is most likely to succeed.

The Effects of Other Stimuli

In addition to light and temperature, *mechanical* stimuli are among other physical factors that often affect plant development. For example, the pressure of rocks around roots makes root shape conform to the available space. Wind pressure from a constant angle makes stems and branches lean away from the wind. Contact with various inert objects makes plants twine around them or attach to them. In their own turn, plants resist pressure and generate growth pressure themselves, as when growing roots split rocks and crack pavement.

Numerous *chemical* stimuli in soil, water, and air also influence plant development. Some of them are more or less beneficial and, like the auxins applied by man, may act in the manner of growth stimulants. Others are variously toxic and poisonous, and they stunt growth or retard development and flowering. Soil decomposition products of given plants often tend to be toxic to later individuals of the same species. This may result in a gradual decline of vigor in successive generations. Crop rotation is beneficial partly for this reason. In heavily industrialized regions, noxious fumes in air and chemical wastes in water also have variously toxic effects on plants. The rapid disappearance of vegetation from such areas is probably due as much to these harmful chemical stimuli as to restrictions of space.

Reference to the main *biological* stimuli has already been made in the earlier account on symbiosis (see Chap. 9). As noted in that context, mutualism, commensalism, and parasitism may affect plant growth and development in a beneficial, a neutral, or a harmful manner. One of the frequent developmental responses of plants to biological agents is overgrowth of given tissues, as in the case of bacteria-induced root nodules and crown galls.

Thus, by virtue of the built-in hierarchy of its control systems, a plant is eminently able to become "aware" of the multitude of stimuli continuously impinging on it and to respond to most of them in adequately self-preserving fashion. As a result, the whole plant and all its parts may be maintained in steady state. And as a further result, the plant may attain an actual life span which approaches that potentially inherent in it.

ANIMAL HORMONES

It is fairly certain that all animals possess chemical agents which, after being produced in one body part, have specific regulatory or coordinating effects in other body parts. Such substances are usually manufactured in cells not specialized exclusively for regulatory functions, and they may be generally referred to as *humoral* agents. For example, CO_2 qualifies as a simple humoral agent in mammals; among other effects, it exerts a controlling role over breathing (see Chap. 24).

In certain instances, humoral agents are produced in cells specialized particularly for such manufacturing functions. Agents of this sort are *hormones*, and the cells producing them are *endocrine* cells. For example, nerve cells are endocrine inasmuch as they secrete hormones at their ends (see Chap. 25). Indeed, in animals in which specialized endocrine cells have been found, such cells in numerous instances are *neurosecretory cells:* modified or unmodified nerve cells that secrete a variety of hormones having a variety of functions outside the nervous system. In other instances, endocrine cells are not part of the nervous system but are often components within elaborate endocrine organs. Several of such organs within an animal, together with any neurosecretory cells present, then form an endocrine system. As already pointed out earlier, endocrine glands discharge their secretions not into ducts but directly into the body fluids.

Hormones vary greatly in chemical composition. Some are proteins, a few are amino acids, others are sterols, and the rest are various other simple or complex kinds of compounds. A few can be synthesized in the laboratory, a few have known chemical structure, and the remainder are known only through the effects of hormone deficiency (for example, undersecretion, excision of the secreting cells) and of hormone excess (for example, oversecretion, injection of hormone).

To date, the presence of endocrine cells has been demonstrated more or less definitely only in animals such as nemertine worms, certain segmented worms, mollusks, most arthropods, and chordates, including tunicates and all vertebrates. Cells of the neurosecretory type occur in all these groups, but nonnervous endocrine cells are conspicuous only in arthropods and vertebrates. Also, only in these two are there distinct endocrine organ systems. The known functions of the endocrine secretions differ greatly among the groups named. In some worms the hormones play a role in growth and (regenerative) development; in mollusks such as squids and octopuses, neurosecretory hormones appear to control mainly the expansion and contraction of pigment-containing cells in the integument. By such means, the animal may change its coloration in conformity with environmental backgrounds or in response to external stimuli of various kinds (for example, color changes in an "excited" octopus). The specific functions of the arthropod hormones have already been discussed in Chap. 15. Note that, apart from influencing body tissues generally, the endocrines of crustaceans and insects also affect one another: a hormone synthesized by one gland exerts a specific excitatory or inhibitory effect on another gland. It is this which makes the endocrine glands an integrated system, even though they are structurally unconnected.

Such functional interdependences are particularly pronounced in vertebrate endocrine systems, by far the most complex of all animals. In vertebrates, the number of different endocrine glands is much greater than elsewhere (Fig. 22.27), and hardly any body

22 · 27 *The principal endocrine organs of vertebrates.*

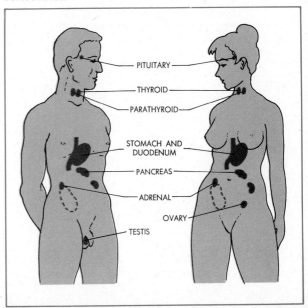

TABLE 18   THE PRINCIPAL VERTEBRATE ENDOCRINE GLANDS AND THEIR HORMONES

GLAND	HORMONES	CHIEF FUNCTIONS	EFFECTS OF DEFICIENCY OR EXCESS
pituitary, anterior lobe	TTH (thyrotropic)	stimulates thyroid	
	ACTH (adrenocorticotropic)	stimulates adrenal cortex	
	FSH (follicle-stimulating)	stimulates ovary (follicle)	
	LH (luteinizing)	stimulates testes in male, corpus luteum in female	
	prolactin (lactogenic)	stimulates milk secretion, parental behavior	
	growth	promotes cell metabolism	dwarfism; gigantism
pituitary, midlobe	intermedin	controls adjustable skin-pigment cells (for example, frogs)	
pituitary, posterior	at least five distinct fractions	controls water metabolism, blood pressure, kidney function, smooth-muscle action	increased or reduced water excretion
thyroid	thyroxine	stimulates respiration; inhibits TTH secretion	goiter; cretinism; myxedema
parathyroid	parathormone	controls Ca metabolism	nerve, muscle abnormalities; bone thickening or weakening
adrenal cortex	cortisone, other steroid hormones	controls metabolism of water, minerals, carbohydrates; controls kidney function; inhibits ACTH secretion; duplicates sex-hormone functions	Addison's disease
adrenal medulla	adrenaline	alarm reaction, for example, raises blood pressure, heart rate	inability to cope with stress
pancreas	insulin	glucose $\longrightarrow$ glycogen conversion	diabetes
	glucagon	glycogen $\longrightarrow$ glucose conversion	
testis	testosterone, other androgens	promote cell respiration, blood circulation; maintain primary and secondary sex characteristics, sex urge; inhibit FSH secretions	atrophy of reproductive system; decline of secondary sex characteristics
ovary: follicle	estradiol, other estrogens		
ovary: corpus luteum	progesterone	promotes secretions of oviduct, uterus growth in pregnancy; inhibits LH secretions	abortion during pregnancy

function occurs that is not influenced at least in part by hormones (Table 18). Endocrine control usually operates in conjunction with nervous control, and in many instances the nervous system supplies information about the external environment while the endocrine system regulates the internal response to this information.

We may note also that, in vertebrates, *all* cells of the body probably require all hormones, just as all cells require all vitamins. Accordingly, terms such as "sex hormone," for example, are somewhat misleading. To be sure, sex hormones are manufactured in sex organs and the hormones contribute to the proper functioning of these organs. As we now know, however, sex hormones also contribute to the functioning of virtually every other organ in the vertebrate body. It happens that the effect of deficiency or excess of a given hormone may reveal itself first or most obviously in a particular body part. For convenience we may then *name* the hormone according to this body part, but we cannot conclude that the hormone functions only there.

Apart from their other controlling roles in cells, some vertebrate hormones perform an additional special function: they control the manufacture and secretion of one another. For example, many endocrine glands cannot secrete their hormones unless they are stimulated to do so by other hormones, secreted in other endocrine glands. As a group, such glands in effect function like a board of directors, in which the members hold one another in close mutual check. The output of each gland is controlled wholly or partially by the output of one or more other glands. As a result, the overall output by all glands is carefully balanced.

Of particular importance in this respect are some of the hormones of the pituitary gland.

PITUITARY HORMONES

Situated approximately in the center of the head, the pituitary gland is made up of three parts: the *anterior lobe,* the *intermediate lobe,* and the *posterior lobe* (Fig. 22.28). Each of these is a complete, functionally distinct endocrine gland secreting its own hormones. A short stalk of tissue from the posterior lobe attaches the whole gland to the underside of the brain.

The *anterior lobe* exercises control over several other endocrine glands; the lobe secretes a set of *tropic hormones* required specifically if other endocrine organs are to be active. For example, the rate of manufacture of thyroid hormone depends on the supply of *thyrotropic hormone* (TTH) from the pitui-

tary. Analogously, production of sex hormones in the gonads (testes and ovaries) is controlled by *gonadotropic hormones* (GTH). A third type of tropic hormone is *adrenocorticotropic hormone* (ACTH), which controls the hormone output of the outer cortex layers of the adrenal glands.

In exercising such tropic effects, the anterior lobe does not act autonomously but is itself governed by the very glands it stimulates. For example, as more and more TTH is secreted by the anterior lobe, more and more thyroid hormone will be released by the thyroid gland. But once the concentration of thyroid hormone has reached a certain level in the blood, that hormone has an *inhibitive* effect on the anterior lobe. It stops or reduces further secretion of TTH. But by this very action, further production of thyroid hormone is reduced or stopped and the concentration of thyroid hormone consequently does not rise further. Conversely, if the blood concentration of thyroid hormone is low, the anterior lobe will be inhibited rather weakly and correspondingly much TTH will be secreted. The thyroid gland will therefore be stimulated strongly and more thyroid hormone will be produced. We note that the two glands and their two hormones form an automatic, organ-level control system with built-in feedback.

22 · 28 *Longitudinal section through a pituitary gland. The left side of the photo points in the direction of the face. Note the anterior lobe in the left part of the gland and the intermediate and posterior lobes in the right part. The posterior lobe continues dorsally as a stalk which joins the whole gland to the brain. The structure of the posterior lobe, i.e., a sac pouched out from the brain floor, is well visible here.*

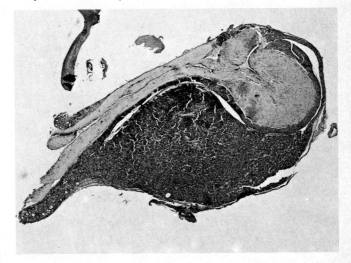

Sex hormones and adrenocortical hormones control their own secretion rates analogously (Fig. 22.29).

In addition to producing the tropic hormones, the anterior lobe also synthesizes hormones functioning primarily as metabolic regulators (see Fig. 22.29). In this category is *prolactin,* a hormone responsible for maternal or paternal behavior in vertebrates generally (for example, broodiness and care of young in females, nest-building and protective attitudes in males). In mammals the hormone regulates milk production specifically and is here called the *lactogenic hormone.* Injection of the hormone stimulates mammary secretions, and hormone deficiency reduces them. Note, however, that removal of milk by suckling young is at least as essential for continued lactation as is presence of the hormone. Either hormone deficiency or milk accumulation alone may lead to cessation of milk flow.

Another anterior-lobe secretion is a *growth hormone.* In the young, this hormone maintains growth rates of cells generally. *Gigantism* and *dwarfism* are the results of hormone excess and deficiency, respec-

tively. Most circus giants and dwarfs are of this "pituitary" type; that is, their growth has been accelerated or retarded abnormally during early youth, sometimes as a result of pituitary tumors. When the growth hormone reaches excessive concentrations in the adult, tissues still capable of growing are stimulated to do so. Characteristic overgrowths are then produced, particularly in parts of the skeleton. A result is the coarse-featured condition known as *acromegaly.*

The anterior lobe exerts very definite effects on carbohydrate, protein, and fat metabolism in cells. Some of these effects are direct, produced by specific pituitary hormones such as the growth hormone. Others are indirect, produced via tropic stimulation of other endocrines (see below).

All the hormones of the anterior lobe are proteins. Most vertebrates manufacture very similar hormone proteins, and those of one species are effective when injected into another. Cattle, sheep, and pigs are the sources of most commercial hormone preparations, those of the anterior lobe included.

The intermediate lobe of the pituitary gland secretes *intermedin,* a hormone functioning most conspicuously in vertebrates possessing adjustable skin pigmentation. In a frog, for example, the hormone produces an expansion of pigment cells and a consequent lightening of the skin color. Intermediate-lobe extracts from any mammal exert the same effect when injected into a frog. Mammals evidently possess intermedin, but, in the absence of adjustable pigment cells, the hormone is probably without function. This example illustrates that a control agent can be inherited from early ancestors even though the target of control is not inherited.

22 · 29 Actions of the pituitary gland. *Left, summary of the secretions of the anterior lobe of the pituitary. Arrows tipped with transverse double bar symbolize known inhibitory feedbacks by which the secretion rate of pituitary tropic hormones is adjusted. Right, illustration of the specific stimulative effect of thyrotropic hormone on the thyroid gland and the inhibitive effect of thyroid hormone on the pituitary. Through such control cycles, the output of tropic pituitary hormones is automatically self-adjusting.*

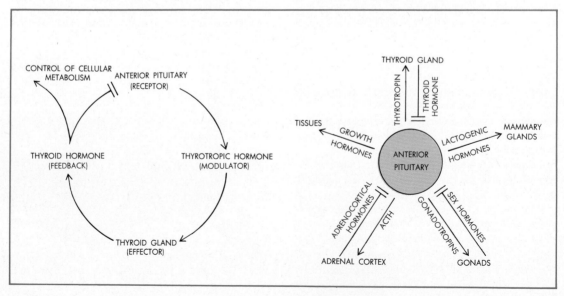

The posterior lobe secretes several distinct hormones. Some regulate the excretion of water, a function performed in conjunction with adrenal hormones (see below). Other posterior-lobe secretions stimulate the contraction of smooth muscles, particularly those in the blood vessels and in the uterus. Through these effects on blood vessels and on water balance, the posterior lobe influences blood pressure decisively. The effect on the smooth muscles of the uterus may play a particular role during the process of childbirth, when strong labor contractions expel the offspring from the womb.

THYROID HORMONES

The thyroid gland lies along the trachea, just underneath the larynx. Secreting cells form single-layered hollow spheres held together by connective tissue (Color Plate XXVII, 44). The space within the spheres is a storage depot for thyroid secretion.

This secretion is *thyroglobulin,* composed of a globulin protein which probably serves as a carrier, and of *thyroxin,* the functionally active hormone. Thyroxin ($C_{15}H_{11}O_4I_4N$; see Fig. 6.17) is one of the naturally occurring amino acids. Its potency as a hormone is in some way associated with its four iodine atoms. If two of them are removed or substituted by other atoms, potency is sharply reduced. If all four iodine atoms are removed, potency disappears altogether.

The clinical effects of thyroxin presumably are secondary consequences of the basic function of the hormone as an accelerator of respiratory rates. If a thyroxin deficiency develops during early youth, *cretinism* may be the result. In this disease, growth is stunted even though the pituitary growth hormone may be secreted normally; mental development is retarded severely; sexual development is delayed or does not take place at all; and body weight increases, since little food is burned in cells but much is stored as fat. In the adult, thyroxin deficiency leads to *myxedema.* This condition is characterized by reduction of mental and bodily vigor, loss of sex drive, loss of hair, and abnormal thickening of the skin, as if much water had accumulated in it (that is, "edema").

Thyroxin deficiency may be accompanied by thyroid enlargement, or *goiter.* Here the number of thyroid cells increases and more hormone may then be secreted by the enlarged gland. This may or may not suffice to compensate for an original hormone deficiency. If it does, body functions will be normal but a *simple goiter* will be in evidence. If the deficiency is not compensated for, then cretinism in the young and myxedema in the adult may develop in spite of and in addition to the goiter. Goiter, cretinism, and myxedema may all be relieved by the administration of adequate amounts of thyroxin from an external source. As might be expected, the effects of thyroxin excess (for example, as a result of a tumor) are virtually the reverse of those of deficiency. Greatly accelerated cellular respiration liberates so much heat that the affected individual feels hot all the time. Despite voluminous consumption of food, so much is burned that body weight may decrease. Whereas the myxedemic individual is sluggish, the hyperthyroid individual is under constant nervous tension, is highly irritable by stimuli, yet is unable to perform sustained work because of lack of fuel reserves.

Apart from carrying out metabolic control functions, the thyroid hormone also regulates developmental processes, at least in amphibia. In these vertebrates the hormone is specifically required in metamorphosis. If thyroid function in an embryo or a young tadpole is in some way inhibited (for example, by excising the thyroid gland), then the animal remains a tadpole permanently. Conversely, if a young tadpole is given an excess of thyroxin, then the larva metamorphoses prematurely into a tiny froglet. This developmental role of the thyroid hormone is evidently somewhat analogous to that of the insect hormones.

PARATHYROID HORMONES

The parathyroid glands are tiny paired organs either located near but outside the thyroids (for example, rabbit) or embedded directly within the thyroids (for example, dog, man). Removal of the thyroids in dogs and rabbits therefore produces partly different results. This has been the clue which has led to the discovery of the parathyroids.

The hormone of these glands, sometimes called *parathormone,* is a protein. The basic function of parathormone is control of calcium metabolism in cells and, as a corollary, maintenance of a constant calcium level in the blood. If the hormone is in abnormally low supply, even if vitamin D is amply available, blood calcium may be deposited in abnormally large quantities in bones. Low blood calcium has another drastic effect. Lack of these ions makes muscles and nerves hyperirritable and the slightest stimulus may throw the whole body into convulsive twitching. Such attacks are completely exhausting and lead to death very quickly.

Symptoms are reversed when parathormone is present in excess. Calcium is then withdrawn from bones and the skeleton weakens. Blood calcium rises and the ions may be excreted in abnormally large quantities. Moreover, nerves and muscles become hypoirritable and an individual becomes unresponsive to stimuli.

ADRENAL HORMONES

As their name indicates, "adrenal" organs are situated near the kidneys. In man, one organ lies directly on top of each kidney. An adrenal organ consists of two structurally distinct parts, namely, an outer *cortex* and an inner *medulla*. Each part is a separate endocrine gland and produces its own distinct hormones (Fig. 22.30).

More than 100 different compounds are known to be produced by adrenal cortex. All these cortical hormones are closely related sterol compounds (see Fig. 6.15). One of the best known is *cortisone*. Secretion of cortical hormones is under the control of ACTH from the pituitary, as noted above. Insufficiency of the cortical hormones results in *Addison's disease*. Its most conspicuous symptoms include a characteristic bronzing of the skin, muscular weakness, low blood pressure, and digestive disturbances. These abnormalities have been traced to a wide range of upsets in metabolic processes within cells, involving most particularly water, inorganic ions, and carbohydrates.

Kidney cells appear to be particularly sensitive to the cortical hormones, and one of the primary actions of these compounds is control of kidney function. For example, the cortical hormones regulate the water balance of the body, a function carried out jointly with hormones from the posterior lobe of the pituitary, as noted. Cortical hormones also promote

22 · 30 Section through the adrenal gland of a mouse. Note dark cortex, inner medulla.

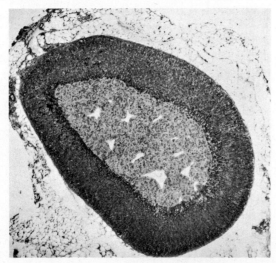

the retention of sodium and chloride ions and the excretion of potassium ions. Moreover, the cortical hormones regulate the excretion of metabolic wastes such as urea. Hormone deficiency may therefore lead to a lowering of sodium and chloride and to an accumulation of potassium and urea in the blood. In this context, recall the discussion of the evolutionary relation between excretion and endocrine-controlled salt and water balance in vertebrates (Chap. 16).

Another primary action of cortical hormones is control of carbohydrate metabolism. Like the pancreatic hormone glucagon, for example, the hormones promote the conversion of glycogen into glucose. As noted earlier, insulin directly and thyroxin indirectly have a contrary effect. Inasmuch as the pituitary controls the adrenal cortex via ACTH and the thyroid gland via TTH, the pituitary evidently plays an important role in carbohydrate metabolism. The adrenal cortex additionally influences the sex organs and is in turn influenced by them. Like the cortical hormones, the sex hormones are sterols and the chemical differences between the two groups are slight (see Fig. 6.15). As a result, abnormal hormone production in the adrenal cortex often amounts to abnormal production of sex hormones and vice versa. Even under normal conditions the adrenal cortex actually produces compounds which more or less duplicate the effects of sex hormones. Long before puberty, that is, before adult sex hormones are produced, a male is already different from a female not only in the nature of the sex organs as such but also in characteristics associated with sex generally. Such differences are produced and maintained by adrenal hormones. After puberty, sex hormones secreted by the gonads intensify the sexual differences and the production of adrenal sex hormones declines.

The cortical hormones have still other effects, for example, on membranes in joints, eyes, and skin and on other body parts. Most of these effects are consequences of cortical control over water, ion, and carbohydrate metabolism and of the influence of the adrenal cortex on other endocrine organs. By virtue of these widely divergent functions, the adrenal cortex constitutes one of the most crucial regulators in the vertebrate body.

The hormones produced by the adrenal medulla are *epinephrine* and *norepinephrine,* synthesized from the amino acid tyrosine (see Fig. 19.24). These substances are customarily referred to loosely as *adrenalin.* The adrenal medulla is largely under the control of the nervous system. Indeed, the connection between this gland and the nervous system goes even deeper, for both structures are derived from embryonic ectoderm, and certain nerves also regulate cellular functions by releasing adrenalin (see Chap. 25).

Adrenalin raises blood pressure; increases heart rate; promotes conversion of liver glycogen to blood glucose; inhibits the peristaltic movements of the gut; stimulates the tiny muscles attached to hairs and feathers, appendages which are raised as a consequence (producing "goose flesh" in man); dilates the pupils of the eye; increases muscular power and resistance to fatigue; promotes faster coagulation of blood; and generally promotes faster and sharper responses to external stimuli. Together, most or all of these effects are sometimes called the *alarm reaction*. It comes into play during danger or emergency, when an animal is under great emotional or physical stress, as, for example, in doing battle with an adversary. In such situations adrenalin is released in increased quantity from the adrenal medulla and the hormone then spurs the animal to increased effort. If the action of adrenalin is somehow inhibited, a vertebrate cannot adjust rapidly to emergencies.

SEX HORMONES

Under the stimulus of pituitary gonadotropic hormones, several male and several female steroid sex hormones are manufactured by matured testes and ovaries. We may refer to male hormones collectively as *androgens* and to female hormones as *estrogens*. The most potent androgen is *testosterone*; the most potent estrogen, *estradiol* (see Fig. 6.15). The secretion patterns and the specialized functions of sex hormones will be discussed in Chap. 28. Here we may examine the general role of these compounds.

First, the hormones maintain the *primary sex characteristics*, that is, the structural and functional integrity of the male and female reproductive systems. Second, the hormones maintain *secondary sex characteristics*, or all those features apart from the sex organs that differentiate male from female. Such secondary male-female differences include different patterns of growth and distribution of hair; voice differences; differences in physical strength, endurance, and muscular development; skeletal differences, as in the hip region; differences in the amount of fat under the skin; marked differences in the degree of mammary development; and differences in skin coloration and plumage among fish, birds, and other vertebrates (Fig. 22.31). In addition, sex hormones maintain sex urge, decisively influence mental vigor and mental development, and stimulate blood circulation. Evidently, they affect the body as a whole.

All these effects are reduced or abolished and the reproductive system atrophies if sex hormones are in deficient supply. Conversely, injection of androgens into males and of estrogens into females intensifies the sexual characteristics of the animal. However, continued injection of androgens into females and of estrogens into males tends to reverse sexual charac-

22 · 31 Secondary sex characteristics of vertebrates and their differences in males and females. The photo shows a male swordtail at top, a female at bottom. See also Fig. 8.4 for another example. All such sex differences are controlled and maintained by hormones, and they are instances of polymorphism, more specifically, of sexual dimorphism.

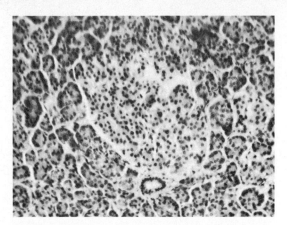

22 · 32 *Section through the pancreas. The round, lighter-colored tissue area at center is an insulin-secreting islet of Langerhans.*

teristics in the direction of the opposite sex. In a few vertebrates, a functional male can be converted in this manner into a functional female. Sperm-producing testes then become egg-producing ovaries and other parts of the reproductive system change correspondingly, and vice versa. But in most vertebrates, man included, injection of the opposite hormone merely deemphasizes the original sexual traits. For example, an estrogen-injected human male would acquire a more highly pitched voice, would accumulate increased quantities of subcutaneous fat, would develop broader hips, and would perhaps change toward other secondary sexual traits characteristic of females. Yet the sex organs would remain testes, though they would atrophy and become nonfunctional. In most respects the results here duplicate those of castration.

Both sexes normally produce *both* androgens and estrogens. The compounds are only slightly different chemically, and both are probably manufactured in testes as well as ovaries. It is the relative quantitative ratio of hormones, not their absolute amount, which is of importance. Thus, so long as a definite ratio of male and female hormones is present, regardless of which is more abundant in absolute terms, the cells of a female will respond differentially to female hormone, the cells of a male, to male hormone. When this quantitative balance is upset, cellular processes will swing more toward maleness or toward femaleness. Normal sex-hormone balances actually differ slightly for different individuals, and this probably accounts for the various degrees of masculinity and femininity widely in evidence.

OTHER HORMONES

Various other endocrine secretions have been discussed in earlier contexts. For example, the roles of the hormones *gastrin* and *secretin* have been described in the account on digestion (Chap. 17). We have also dealt with *insulin* and *glucagon*, the hormones manufactured in the pancreas in groups of endocrine cells embedded within the exocrine pancreatic tissue (Fig. 22.32). Unlike pancreatic juice, insulin and glucagon do not have access to the pancreatic duct; blood is their only exit path. The kidneys produce a hormone called *renin*, which regulates blood pressure. And in Chap. 25 we shall encounter hormones within the nervous system which participate in the transmission of nerve impulses.

Many of the hormonal substances of vertebrates are known also to occur in other groups of animals, including those without endocrine systems, and indeed in plants as well. In such organisms, however, the compounds do not *function* as specific hormones, just as auxins do not function as hormones in the many animals in which such compounds are present. Wide occurrence of certain chemicals indicates that they are fairly usual products of metabolism; and we may infer that, during the evolution of given organisms, many of the already existing chemicals happened to prove useful as control agents in newly evolved processes. In plants and most animals, chemicals which become control agents in this manner continued to be manufactured by cells performing various other functions as well. And in insects and vertebrates, manufacture came to be the specialized function of elaborate endocrine glands. It happens that, to date, only the hormone chemicals produced in plants and in endocrine glands have been studied to any extent.

As already noted, steady-state regulation in most animals is achieved not only by growth factors such as hormones and vitamins, but also by various tissue- and organ-level control systems without counterparts in plants. We shall examine these uniquely animal controls in the following chapters.

REVIEW QUESTIONS

1. Describe the chemical nature of auxins and review the experiments that have led to their discovery. What is the effect of auxins on (*a*) growth, (*b*) development? Show how these substances contribute to the control of steady-state maintenance in plants.

2. What are kinins? What are gibberellins? Discuss how gibberellins were discovered and describe their effects on plants and plant cells. What is the effect of kinins on plant cells?

3. Define the nature of different types of growth movements. Describe various tropic responses of plants and review once more the role of auxins in producing such responses. Show how differential auxin sensitivities are of importance.

4. Define the nature of different types of turgor movements. Review the mechanism of the opening and closing movements of guard cells. Describe the nature of the responses of sensitive plants to touch.

5. Review again the role of auxins in controlling developmental responses of plants. What is an abscission layer? How can fruit or leaf abscission be promoted or inhibited by artificial means? Review all nondevelopmental effects of light on plants.

6. Describe the developmental responses of plants to (a) light intensity, (b) light quality, (c) light duration. What is etiolation? What is a photoperiod? Define short-day, long-day, and indeterminate plants.

7. Describe experiments demonstrating the existence of (a) florigen, (b) vernalin. Show how the photoperiodic characteristics of given plants are reflected in the global distribution of the plants. What factors play a role in the production of a photoperiodic response and what sort of hypothesis may account for the significance of these factors?

8. Describe the nondevelopmental and the developmental effects of temperature on plants. What is vernalization and what is its practical importance? Show how vernalization requirements differ for (a) annual and perennial plants, (b) temperate-zone and tropical plants. Review the effects of other physical and also of chemical and biological stimuli on plants.

9. How do given vertebrate endocrine glands control the activity of other endocrine glands? Show how the activity of the adrenal cortex is regulated by the pituitary, and vice versa.

10. Review the general chemical nature of the principal hormones. What determines whether a medicinal hormone preparation must be injected or may be taken orally? Review the functions of arthropod hormones.

11. What are the specific hormones produced by the various endocrine glands? As far as is known, what are the primary cellular functions of each of these hormones? In each case, what are the clinical effects of (a) hormone deficiency and (b) hormone excess?

12. Inasmuch as both sexes of vertebrates produce both male and female sex hormones, how can the sexes remain distinct? What is the effect of injecting male hormone into a female, and vice versa? Distinguish between primary and secondary sex characteristics.

COLLATERAL READINGS

Braun, A. C.: Plant Cancer, *Sci. American*, June, 1952. An account of calluses and crown galls.

Constantinides, P. E., and N. Carey: The Alarm Reaction, *Sci. American*, March, 1949. Stress and the role of adrenalin are discussed.

Davidson, E. H.: Hormones and Genes, *Sci. American*, June, 1965. Preliminary evidence indicates that hormones may exert reaction control by regulating the activity of genes.

Funkenstein, D. H.: The Physiology of Fear and Anger, *Sci. American*, May, 1955. A study of the role of adrenalin in human emotion.

Gabriel, M. L., and S. Fogel: "Great Experiments in Biology," Prentice-Hall, Englewood Cliffs, N.J., 1955. This paperback includes reprints of classical original papers on both plant hormones and animal hormones. Well worth consulting.

Galston, A. W.: "The Life of the Green Plant," 2d ed., Prentice-Hall, Englewood Cliffs, N.J., 1964. Sections on plant growth and growth substances are included in this paperback.

Gorbman, A., and H. A. Bern: "Textbook of Comparative Endocrinology," Wiley, New York, 1962. An excellent source of additional data on animal hormones and the glands that produce them.

Gray, R. W.: Cortisone and ACTH, *Sci. American*, May, 1950. The role of these hormones in stress and human disease is reviewed.

Greulach, V. A.: Plant Movements, *Sci. American*, Feb., 1955. Some of the movements studied in this chapter are examined.

Jacobs, W. P.: What Makes Leaves Fall?, *Sci. American*, Nov., 1955. An account of experiments on abscission and the role of auxins in this process.

Levine, R., and M. S. Goldstein: The Action of Insulin, *Sci. American*, May, 1958. The cellular and general biological role of this hormone is discussed.

Li, C. H.: The Pituitary, *Sci. American*, Oct., 1950. A general examination of this gland and its hormones.

———: The ACTH Molecule, *Sci. American*, July, 1963. The function of this pituitary hormone is outlined in relation to its structure.

Naylor, A. W.: The Control of Flowering, *Sci. American*, May, 1952. Some of the hormonal and other controls are examined.

Rasmussen, H.: The Parathyroid Hormone, *Sci. American*, Apr., 1961. The function of this hormone in man is described.

Salisbury, F. B.: Plant Growth Substances, *Sci. American*, Apr., 1957. A review of growth factors other than auxins.

————: The Flowering Process, *Sci. American*, Apr., 1958. Experiments revealing the functioning of flowering hormones are described.

———— and R. V. Parke: "Vascular Plants: Form and Function," Wadsworth, Belmont, Calif., 1964. This paperback contains a section on photobiology, another on biological time, and a third on the flowering process, all pertinent readings in the context of this chapter.

Steward, F. C.: "Plants at Work," Addison-Wesley, Reading, Mass., 1964. A section on growth in this paperback contains accounts of tropisms, hormones, and responses of plants to various stimuli.

Sweeney, B. M.: The Measurement of Time in Plants, in "Plant Biology Today," Wadsworth, Belmont, Calif., 1963. A very interesting chapter on rhythmic behavior and biological clocks of plants.

Went, F. W.: Plant Growth and Plant Hormones, in "This Is Life," Holt, New York, 1962. An excellent review article by the discoverer of auxin. Recommended.

White, A., P. Handler, and E. L. Smith: "Principles of Biochemistry," 3d ed., McGraw-Hill, New York, 1964. A comprehensive coverage of all vertebrate endocrines and their hormones is given in this text.

CHAPTER 23 BODY FLUIDS AND CIRCULA- TION

Cells are in steady state relative to their environments. Within an animal, this environment consists of other cells and, in most instances, of body fluids, namely, *blood* and *lymph*. Lymph fills all the spaces between cells and cell layers, and, as noted in Chap. 17, this fluid originates in the blood stream in vertebrates. Blood itself comes close to most cells, for tiny blood capillaries ramify through virtually all vertebrate tissues.

The body fluids thus become not only the general transport vehicle of the body but also major controllers of steady states within and between cells; tissue cells reflect the conditions prevailing in blood and lymph, and vice versa. In their turn, the body fluids are controlled by the *circulatory system*. Unlike the transport system of plants, the circulation in animals is more than a network of channels. It also regulates the *physical* attributes of the fluids it carries, such as pressure, distribution, and rate of flow. We shall presently find that, through these activities, the circulatory system contributes materially to steady-state maintenance on all organizational levels of the animal.

BLOOD AND LYMPH

All animals characteristically possess lymph between cells and tissues. In ancestral animals lymph was probably little different from the sea water in which these animals lived; and modern animals have inherited some form of "sea water" as the universal internal medium of their bodies.

Lymph functions primarily in maintaining an adequate aqueous environment around all cells, that is, in preserving *water, salt, pH,* and *osmotic* equilibria and steady states between the interior and the exterior of cells. Secondarily lymph also provides a medium for the diffusion and transport of foodstuffs, respiratory gases, waste materials, in some cases hormones, and any other substances transiting from one body region to another. In comparatively simply constructed animals (including particularly the sponges, radiates, and acoelomates) the free spaces between cells and tissues are minimal and the quantities of body fluid are comparatively small. Also, these fluids do not circulate in any specialized manner but are merely redistributed to some extent by body movements.

All other animals possess pseudocoelomic or coelomic body cavities. Lymph here again permeates all tissues, but it also fills the body cavities and such animals therefore possess substantial accumulations of internal fluid. By its very presence in the free spaces the lymph gives the animals a measure of hydrostatic "skeletal" support, and because of its bulk its movements are readily discernible: as the animal bends and twists, lymph ebbs and flows haphazardly but nevertheless quite conspicuously. We already know that in many of these animals the body fluids are actually kept in motion on a regularized and continuous basis, by means of specialized flow channels and pumping organs, that is, circulatory systems. Any body fluid confined partly or wholly within channels may be considered to be a *blood*.

As shown in earlier chapters, the systems of blood channels in animals are either *open* or *closed* (Fig. 23.1). In the latter case the vessels form a complete, self-contained circuit, and the only access to and exit from such a system is *through* the vessel walls. By and large, the fluid portion of a blood and most materials dissolved in it pass through vessel walls quite readily, but blood proteins and blood cells largely do not. In an open system, therefore, blood and lymph are essentially indistinguishable and both body fluids contain the same components.

In a closed system, on the contrary, as in vertebrates, blood within the circulatory system differs from the general lymph outside it primarily in that the latter contains neither blood cells nor blood proteins. As pointed out in Chap. 17, vertebrates possess a system of one-way lymph channels which facilitate the return of blood-derived lymph into the blood circulation. Along the course of the larger lymph channels are *lymph nodes* (see Fig. 23.9), glandular tissues carrying out a variety of functions as we shall see.

Blood is a tissue. Approximately half the volume of vertebrate blood consists of loose blood *cells*, the other half of fluid, or blood *plasma*, in which the cells are suspended. All body tissues affect the momentary composition of blood by adding wastes and withdrawing nutrients. Several structures in particular regulate the long-term composition: the liver, the marrow of long bones, and the lymph nodes, all of which control the cellular content; and the intestine, the liver, the kidneys, and probably also the lymph nodes, all of which control the composition of plasma.

PLASMA

This fluid contains two groups of substances (Table 19). One comprises compounds that fluctuate more or less widely in concentration in accordance with the changing rates of supply and removal. In this category are a number of foods in transit, urea and other waste products in transit, hormones in transit, and many classes of materials present only occasionally. Supply of such components may take the form of absorption from the gut or release by tissue cells or manufacture and release by the liver. Removal may involve liver storage, elimination via the excretory organs, or absorption by tissue cells. The second group includes substances normally maintained at *constant* concentrations. In this category are water, most of the mineral ions, plasma proteins, and certain nutrients and waste products in transit. Quantity control here is again exercised by the alimentary and excretory organs, and in each case too high or too low a concentration of a given substance in blood is the critical stimulus for its own removal or replenishment. We already know, for example, that a moderately high blood-glucose level stimulates liver cells to lower it by storing the excess as glycogen. A still higher level stimulates storage not only in liver but also in muscle and skin, for example. And a very high concentration leads to glucose excretion from the kidneys. The differential sensitivity of these control organs to actual supply and demand of a given compound thus brings about a steady state in blood.

The main constituent of blood plasma is *water*. Its source is food and metabolic water *excreted* by cells into the body fluids. The supply of body water from these sources is carefully counterbalanced by controlled loss of water via the excretory system. Within narrow limits, therefore, the total water content of the body, hence also blood volume, remains constant. Recall here the regulating functions performed by pituitary and adrenocortical hormones.

Blood water has many functions. This store maintains an aqueous environment around all tissues and, by its very presence in a given volume within a closed channel system, blood water contributes importantly to blood pressure. After extensive blood loss through wounds, one of the foremost requirements is restoration of blood volume, that is, restoration of water. Blood water functions as the *transport vehicle* for all other plasma components, for respiratory gases, and for blood cells. Dissolved inorganic materials carried in blood water comprise the *mineral ions*. These include mainly the positively charged sodium (Na^+), potassium (K^+), calcium (Ca^{++}), and magnesium (Mg^{++}) ions and the negatively charged phosphate ($H_2PO_4^-$, $HPO_4^=$, $PO_4^\equiv$), chlorine (Cl^-), bicarbonate (HCO_3^-), and sulfate ($SO_4^=$) ions. Over half of the total mineral content of plasma (and lymph) is sodium chloride, common table salt. The

23 · 1 Open and closed circulations. *An open circulation is diagrammed at top in longitudinal and cross-sectional views and a closed circulation is diagrammed at bottom. In animals with open systems, the coelom is small, the blood sinuses are large, and access to blood vessels is provided by the open ends of such vessels. In animals with closed systems, the coelom is large, the blood spaces are confined to the blood vessels almost entirely, and access to the blood vessels is through the vessel walls only.*

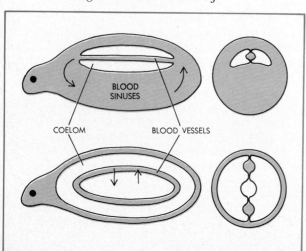

TABLE 19 THE PRINCIPAL CONSTITUENTS AND
FUNCTIONS OF BLOOD PLASMA°

COMPONENTS	FUNCTIONS
1. water	maintains blood volume and pressure; forms lymph; water supply of cells; provides vehicle for other constituents
2. mineral ions	maintain osmotic balance, pH balance; buffer capacity; varied effects on tissue cells
3. plasma proteins	all maintain osmotic and pH balance
fibrinogen	participates in blood clotting
prothrombin	participates in blood clotting
albumins, enzymes	functions obscure
globulins	basis of blood types; act as antibodies
4. glucose, other organic metabolites	in transit to and from cells
5. urea, CO_2, O_2, various foods, hormones, vitamins, and others	in transit to and from cells·

°Categories 1 to 4 are maintained at constant concentrations; materials in category 5 occur in variable concentrations.

ions are kept at constant concentrations through mineral supply in food, turnover in tissue cells, and excretion. Moreover, growth factors such as vitamin D, parathormone, and adrenocortical hormones contribute to maintenance of mineral balance (see Chap. 22).

Apart from their functions as nutrients and cellular control agents, mineral ions are essential regulators of the *osmotic pressure* of blood. This pressure is adjusted to the osmotic pressure within tissues. When either blood or the tissues acquire greater concentrations of minerals, water will move osmotically one way or the other. For example, if through intake of much salt water the mineral concentration of blood should rise, then the tissues would become dehydrated. Conversely, if through intake of too much plain water the ion concentration should fall, then the tissues would become overly hydrated. Short-term fluctuations of this sort occur frequently as a consequence of normal metabolism.

Another crucial regulating function of the plasma minerals is *pH control* and pH balance between blood and the tissues. Any small change of pH is readjusted to normal by the buffering action of the mineral ions. Ion pairs like $HPO_4^=/H_2PO_4^-$ are particularly significant as blood buffers. For example, if H^+ ions should accumulate in abnormally large quantities, then $HPO_4^=$ could combine with H^+, forming $H_2PO_4^-$. Concentrations of the former would thereby decrease, concentrations of the latter would increase, and the free H^+ ions would have been "taken out of circulation." The reverse reactions would occur if blood should tend to become too alkaline. Original ion balances may subsequently be restored by the excretory system, through removal of those ions present in relative excess.

Mineral ions exert important additional effects. For example, calcium ions regulate the sensitivity of nerves and muscles. Calcium also influences the sol-gel states within cells, and it is a component of the cementing substance between cells. Since all cells are in contact with blood or lymph, the concentration of blood calcium evidently is of enormous significance. Each of the other mineral components has its own specific biological effects.

Plasma and lymph are virtually indistinguishable with respect to their content of water, mineral ions, and most other dissolved constituents. As noted, however, plasma differs importantly from lymph in that it contains proteins.

PLASMA PROTEINS

These compounds endow blood with some of its most important regulating functions, including the function of chemical body defense. The proteins represent a permanent population of control agents maintained at constant concentrations. Some of the proteins are known to be manufactured and destroyed in the liver. Others are believed to be formed in the lymph nodes and still others possibly in the lungs. The compounds do not normally leave the circulatory vessels, as noted, and they serve a variety of nonnutritional roles.

First, inasmuch as the proteins are particles they contribute to the osmotic pressure of blood; and since most of them are ionized, they also play a role in maintaining the pH of blood, like mineral ions. Second, some of the proteins are ingredients in the clotting reaction; *fibrinogen* is one of these (see below). Third, many of the proteins are active enzymatically.

One of the catalytic agents is a clotting factor known as *prothrombin*. Others are enzymes such as are found in tissue cells generally and even in the intestine. For example, trypsin is usually present in plasma. The catalytic functions of such enzymes in plasma are still largely obscure. Similarly obscure are the specific roles of plasma proteins called *albumins*, so named because of their chemical resemblance to egg white. Fourth, proteins called *globulins* play a major role in so-called *immunological* reactions. These include reactions resulting from *blood-type* differences and reactions involving *antigens* and *antibodies*.

That bloods of different animals differ in type has been known for some time. Where type differences exist, the blood cells of one animal act as foreign bodies when introduced into another animal, and the plasma globulins of the host may cause the foreign cells to clump. Clumped blood cells clog narrow blood vessels and may cause death. Type differences in man evidently are of major clinical significance, and before a blood transfusion is made, blood compatibility must be established. Biologically, however, type differences are merely one further expression of the general phenomenon of protein specificity, that is, of protein differences among all organisms.

23 · 2 Antibodies. *A foreign protein introduced into an animal is an antigen. It elicits the formation of antibodies, which "fit" precisely the surface configuration of the antigen. These specific antibodies may then combine with the antigens, making the latter harmless.*

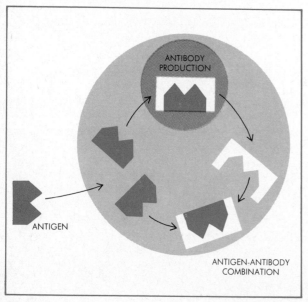

The antigen-antibody reactions referred to above likewise are an expression of protein specificity. An antigen is usually a foreign protein (in some cases it is a polysaccharide) which enters the body fluids of an animal as part of an infectious agent. For example, antigens may be introduced into an animal by viruses, bacteria, plant pollen, or any other protein-containing cell part or tissue part of a foreign organism. An antibody is a blood protein, specifically a globulin, which may make an infected animal immune to a foreign antigen. Thus, antibodies function importantly in body defense and in organismic steady-state control.

What does "making immune" mean? It means the combination of an antibody with an invading antigen. Such a union abolishes the free mobility of the antigen and thus prevents the antigen from acting in a damaging manner. The combining process is thought to be a "lock-and-key" reaction, quite like the combining of an enzyme with a reactant. The molecular configuration of the antibody protein apparently is such that it "fits" into the configuration of the foreign antigen. In other words, antigen-antibody reactions are specific, and any given antigen requires a particular kind of antibody if immunity is to be established (Fig. 23.2).

However, animals do not normally possess preexisting antibodies for all types of antigens that might possibly invade the blood. This means that an appropriate type of antibody must be manufactured after a given antigen has invaded; and the more rapidly and abundantly such antibodies are formed, the less damage the animal will sustain. Several organs are believed to produce antibodies, the liver and the lymph nodes among them. The cells of such organs probably absorb samples of invading antigens and then synthesize large quantities of appropriate globulin antibodies. Inasmuch as globulin synthesis is protein synthesis, genes should be expected to participate directly in antibody production. That this is actually the case can be demonstrated, and certain gene mutations are known to alter the antibody-response capacities of animals.

Immunization procedures in man are based on specific antibody production. In vaccination, for example, an individual is injected with nonvirulent strains of disease-producing bacteria or viruses or with killed microorganisms of virulent strains. In either case, the injection does not produce disease yet antigens of a particular type are introduced nevertheless. The body responds by manufacturing specific antibodies against these injected antigens. Virulent living strains of the microorganisms have the same antigens. Therefore, if at some later time such potentially harmful microorganisms should in-

ANTIBODY PRODUCTION

ANTIGEN

ANTIGEN-ANTIBODY COMBINATION

fect the individual, protective antibodies are already present and the disease will be expressed only in mild form or not at all. Vaccinations so establish *active immunity* for periods up to several years or often throughout life (Fig. 23.3).

In many cases active immunity arises without vaccination. Infectious agents producing disease in extremely mild and hardly noticeable form invade the body continually and induce the development of antibodies against them. Such almost harmless natural agents thus have the same effect as vaccinations and build up immunity. If later their more virulent relatives should invade the body, the protective antibodies are already deployed.

When an individual does suffer from an infectious disease, the effects of the disease can often be reduced by providing short-term *passive immunity*. Here the individual is injected with specific antibodies from an external source. Such prefabricated antibodies are obtained from rabbits, sheep, horses, guinea pigs, and other mammals. The mammal is exposed to a given infectious agent, and globulins manufactured by the mammal against the agent are withdrawn and are used to immunize man (Fig. 23.4). Diphtheria antitoxin is an example of an "immune globulin" conferring passive immunity.

An important consequence of specific antibody production is the rejection of tissues or organs transplanted into an animal from a foreign source. If a part of one animal is grafted to another, the proteins in the graft will be antigens which will induce the production of specific antibodies against them. The graft therefore will not heal in and will usually be cast off after a few days. This is true even if donor and recipient belong to the same species or indeed to the same parentage. Successful grafts can be made, however, if tissue from one animal is transplanted to another location in the same animal; the proteins of a given individual do not act as their own antigens. Analogously, grafts can be successful when a foreign tissue is transplanted to a location that does not contain blood vessels. This is the case, for example, in corneal transplants; the cornea is not vascularized. In the absence of blood, an antibody response cannot develop even though an antigen stimulus may be present.

Research in recent years has shown that the usual rejection of foreign grafts can be prevented under special circumstances. In an embryo, the antibody-forming mechanism is not fully developed as yet. Therefore, if an embryo is given tissue from a donor animal, the cells of the embryo will accept the foreign protein as if it were their own. After the embryo has become an adult, this adult may be given a graft from the original donor animal. Such

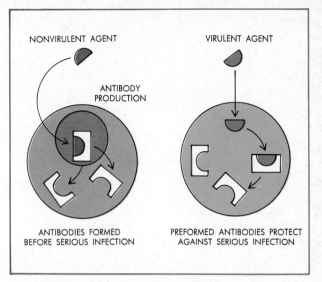

23 · 3 Active immunization. *Left, nonvirulent agents are introduced into an organism, and specific antibodies are formed. Right, if virulent forms of the foreign agents later infect the organism, specific antibodies are already present to combat the infection.*

23 · 4 Passive immunization. *Various animals may be infected and allowed to manufacture specific antibodies against the infectious agent. Blood serum of these animals, containing the antibodies, may then be used to protect man against the same infectious agent. Immunity here is not permanent, since human tissues do not produce the antibodies on their own.*

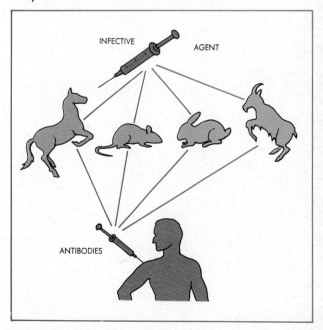

TABLE 20 THE CELLULAR CONSTITUENTS OF BLOOD AND THEIR FUNCTIONS

COMPO-NENT	ORIGIN	NUMBER PER CUBIC MILLIMETER	FUNC-TIONS
red cor-puscles	red marrow (adults) liver, spleen (embryo)	5 million	transport of O_2, CO_2
white cells		8,000	
leucocytes	red marrow		engulf bacteria, foreign bodies; aid in wound healing
lymphocytes	lymph nodes		
platelets	red marrow, lungs	250,000	release thrombokinase, aid in blood clotting

differs from lymph also in another respect, namely, the presence of blood *pigments*. Many animals possess such pigments in their blood cells, however, and inasmuch as all of them function in breathing we shall deal with them in that context in the next chapter.

Through its various constituents, blood plasma clearly plays a vital role in steady-state maintenance. Plasma constitutes a sensory and motor path interconnecting all cells of an animal. It represents a modulator contributing to the constancy of chemical and physical conditions in all tissues. And it is a receptor of infectious stimuli and a defensive effector against them. All this is in addition to the purely transportive functions of plasma, namely, delivering nutrients and collecting wastes, and in addition also to the function of plasma as lymph, through which it provides a proper operating environment for all cells.

a graft now does not induce antibody production against it, apparently because the adult cells still "remember" to accept the foreign protein as their own. Some day it may perhaps be possible to make practical use of this sort of "training" for graft acceptance.

Apart from its protein content, plasma often

BLOOD CELLS

Most bloods contain *nonpigmented* cells of various kinds, and many also contain *pigmented* cells (Table 20). Both types are usually quite specialized and normally they do not divide.

Where pigmented blood cells are present, they derive their color from hemoglobin or other oxygen-transporting compounds dissolved in their cytoplasms. Such cells usually contain nuclei, the only notable exceptions being the red cells of mammals (Color Plate XXVII, 45). These cells are manufactured in the red marrow at the ends of long bones (for example, ribs, limbs). As the red cells of mammals mature their nuclei disintegrate, and the resulting enucleated *corpuscles* then are no longer cells in the strict sense. Liver and spleen are the production

23 · 5 Control of red corpuscles. *The numbers of corpuscles produced in bone marrow and destroyed in the liver are balanced by the oxygen content of blood.*

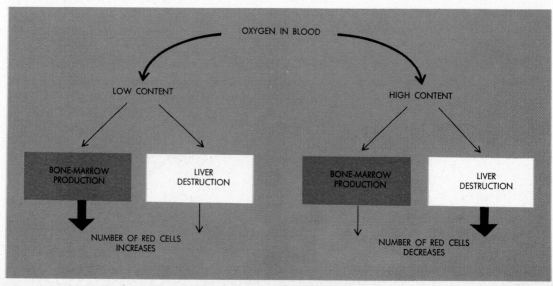

sites in the embryo, before bones mature. After the skeleton is fully formed and blood-cell production is initiated in it, the spleen becomes principally a blood-storing organ; it may contract and squeeze reserve blood into the circulation. The liver becomes the organ where red corpuscles are destroyed.

Production in bone marrow is geared to destruction in the liver. The controlling signal is the amount of oxygen carried by blood (Fig. 23.5). Low oxygen content stimulates bone marrow to produce red corpuscles at a faster rate. At the same time, the liver is inhibited from destroying corpuscles at too fast a rate. Accordingly, when inhaled air contains too little oxygen for extended periods, as at high altitudes, then more blood corpuscles are manufactured. An adequate quantity of gas thus may still be delivered to the tissues by this greater number of corpuscles. A persistently high oxygen concentration in blood has the opposite effect on liver and bone marrow. Through this mechanism, the number of red corpuscles is adjusted to oxygen requirements. Since such requirements and the composition of the atmosphere normally remain fairly constant, the number of corpuscles is correspondingly constant.

When the number of corpuscles or their hemoglobin content or both are reduced significantly, the result is *anemia*. This condition may be brought about by excessive corpuscle destruction in an abnormal liver or by extensive blood loss through wounding. In the latter case, production in bone marrow soon makes up the loss. Anemia may also arise as a result of inadequate production of corpuscles as, for example, when marrow cells are defective or when the iron content of the diet is low.

In man, each cubic millimeter of blood, roughly the volume of a pinhead, contains over 5 million red corpuscles. It has been estimated that every *second* some 10,000,000 corpuscles are manufactured and just as many are destroyed. Destruction in the liver is random and nonselective, and affects young corpuscles as well as old ones. The iron fraction of destroyed heme is salvaged and becomes available again for the synthesis of cytochrome or new hemoglobin. The tetrapyrrol part of destroyed heme becomes green *biliverdin* and red *bilirubin*, pigments excreted from the liver via bile and feces and via blood and urine; hence the characteristic colors of these elimination products. Some birds deposit the pigments in their egg shells, a disposal procedure which accounts, for example, for the blue color of robins' eggs.

To a greater or lesser extent, most of the non-pigmented cells present in blood are capable of amoeboid locomotion. Called *amoebocytes* generally and *white* cells in vertebrates, such cells may squeeze themselves between adjacent cells of a capillary vessel and may leave or reenter the circulatory system in this manner (Plate 45 and Fig. 23.6). White cells are of two main types, *leucocytes* and *lymphocytes,* each with several subvarieties. In leucocytes the amoeboid habit is developed particularly well. Once leucocytes are out in the body tissues, they may migrate toward sites of infection and engulf the bacteria causing the infection. Leucocytes are probably guided to infected regions by their sensitivity to cellular disintegration products diffusing away from such regions. An accumulation of leucoytes, bacteria, and cellular debris in wounded areas constitutes *pus*.

23 · 6 *The migration of blood cells through capillary walls.* *In each photo, a blood-filled capillary is in upper right portion. In the photo at the top, two white blood cells have just penetrated through the capillary wall into surrounding tissues. In the photo at bottom, the white cells have migrated farther into the tissue.*

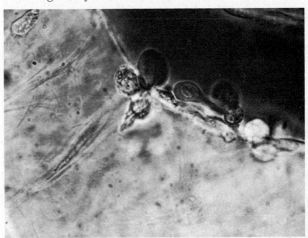

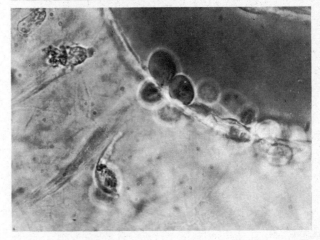

Lymphocytes too serve in body defense. These cells contribute importantly to scar-tissue formation after internal or external injury (via transformation into mesenchymal cells and fibrocytes), and in this manner they facilitate wound healing. Moreover, they aid in sealing off a surface wound against new infections. Numerous lymphocytes are normally present in the lymph nodes, where the cells act as lymph-purifying agents. For example, microscopic particles of dust, smoke, and other materials present in the atmosphere frequently get into lungs and may become embedded in lung tissue. Lymph then usually carries such particles to the lymph nodes. The lymphocytes there engulf the particles and retain them permanently.

Leucocytes are manufactured in red bone marrow, probably by the same generating tissue which gives rise to red corpuscles. Lymphocytes are formed in lymphatic tissue, principally in the lymph nodes and also in the spleen. White blood cells are much less abundant than red corpuscles; a cubic millimeter of human blood contains about 8,000 white cells. This number is fairly constant under normal conditions. It is not known where white cells are destroyed or by what mechanism the rates of production and destruction are controlled. Cancer of the bone marrow, *leukemia*, is characterized by uncontrolled, abnormally rapid formation of white cells. Other diseases similarly may raise the white-cell count excessively or may lower it to abnormal levels. The number of white cells increases temporarily during infectious diseases, as would be expected in view of the phagocytic activity of the cells.

Bone marrow and to some extent also connective tissues in the lungs are believed to be the principal generating tissues of *platelets*, a third category of cellular components in vertebrate blood. Platelets are not usually whole cells but membrane-covered cell fragments, often without nuclei (Plate 45). About 250,000 of these bodies are found in each cubic millimeter of human blood. The control system

that keeps their numbers constant is obscure. Platelets are the initiators of the *clotting reaction*. This self-sealing mechanism of the circulatory system is brought into action whenever platelets encounter obstructions and rupture. In most cases, such obstructions are the rough edges of torn blood vessels. External clotting then occurs. But air bubbles in blood (for example, when dissolved gases effervesce) or roughness of the inner surfaces of blood vessels (for example, as produced by solid deposits in hardened arteries) may suffice for the rupturing of platelets. An internal blood clot may then form.

Among the materials oozing out from ruptured platelets is an enzymatically active substance, *thrombokinase*, also called *thromboplastin* (Fig. 23.7). This substance interacts with two components of blood plasma, namely, calcium ions and the plasma protein *prothrombin*. The protein is an inactive precursor of the catalyst *thrombin*. In the presence of calcium ions and thrombokinase, prothrombin becomes converted to thrombin. Subsequently thrombin reacts with fibrinogen, another of the plasma proteins. As a result of the reaction, fibrinogen becomes fibrin, an insoluble coagulated protein. Fibrin constitutes the blood clot. It is a yellowish-white meshwork of fibers in which pigmented blood cells are trapped, hence the color of the clot. As noted in Chap. 21, vitamin K is required at some step in the clotting reaction.

Moderate heat speeds clotting time; cold slows it. Clotting can be prevented when any of the ingredients are missing or are made inoperative. For example, fibrinogen can be withdrawn fairly easily from whole blood or plasma. This procedure is often used in storing blood or plasma for transfusions. Plasma minus fibrinogen constitutes *blood serum*. Clotting can also be prevented by precipitating out the calcium of blood. Leeches, fleas, bedbugs, and other blood feeders secrete *hirudin* and mix it with ingested blood. Hirudin is a clotting inhibitor enabling leeches, for example, to store uncoagulated blood in their digestive tracts for as long as 6 months. Finally, clotting will be impossible when blood platelets are defective. In one type of (hereditary) disease, platelets are missing altogether. In another, platelets have thickened membranes which do not rupture on contact with obstuctions. In either of these *bleeder's diseases*, the slightest wound can be fatal.

We note that, through antibodies, through white cells, and through clotting, blood forms the first line of internal defense. However, this control function of blood and its other functions in transport and tissue maintenance can be exercised only if blood *circulates*. Consequently, as the activities of body tissues are dependent on blood, so the activities

23 · 7 Main reactions of the clotting process.

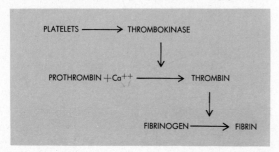

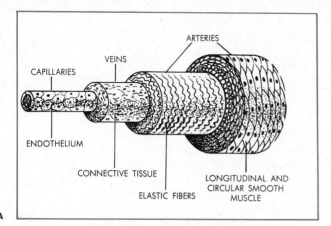

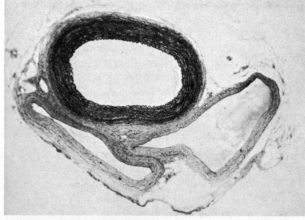

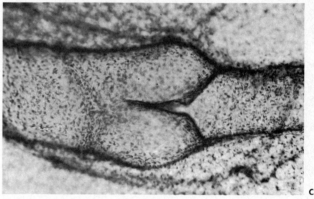

23 · 8 Circulatory vessels. *A, diagram illustrating the progressively greater thickness and tissue complexity of capillaries, veins, and arteries. The single-cell layer of squamous endothelium is continuous throughout a vessel system. Additional tissues do not necessarily occur in such neat layers as sketched here. B, photomicrographic section through an artery and two veins. Note the thicker wall of the artery and the presence of many elastic fibers (dark wavy lines) in this wall. C, longitudinal section through a lymph vessel, showing an internal valve. Such valves prevent backflow. Valves very much like this are present also in the larger veins.*

of blood in turn are dependent on the transport channels.

CIRCULATION

THE PATHWAYS: BLOOD VESSELS AND HEART BEAT

The organs of a blood-vessel system usually are *arteries, veins, hearts,* and, in most closed systems, also *capillaries* (Fig. 23.8). Arteries carry blood away from a heart, veins carry blood toward a heart. Capillaries are vessels of microscopic diameter interconnecting the narrowest arteries and veins. In closed systems the capillary beds are the most important parts of the circulation, for it is in such regions that the body tissues are serviced and exchange materials with blood, and that blood in turn obtains supplies and delivers wastes in the alimentary, breathing, and excretory systems. The only tissue component of a capillary is a one-cell thick *endothelium,* a simple squamous epithelium. This tissue is in direct contact with blood and is continuous throughout the entire circulatory system. Vessels with larger diameters possess additional tissues on the outside, principally layers of fibroelastic connective tissue and

smooth muscle. The wider a vessel, the thicker is its wall. Arteries, which carry blood under the greatest pressure, have thicker walls and more extensive layers of elastic fibers and muscles than veins. Hearts are characterized by exceptionally thick muscular walls, the muscle tissue being of the cardiac variety in vertebrates (see Chap. 7). At intervals along the larger veins are found internal *valves* which open toward the heart and so prevent backflow of blood.

The lymph vessel systems of vertebrates are composed primarily of *lymph capillaries* and *lymph veins* (Fig. 23.9). Such lymph vessels are even thinner than blood veins, and they also contain a greater number of internal valves. Along the course of the lymph vessels are present glandular *lymph nodes,* as already noted. In frogs and some other vertebrates, certain regions of given lymph vessels are enlarged into pulsating *lymph hearts.* These aid in driving lymph into the blood circulation.

The principal pumping organs are the hearts of the blood circulation, and they may be tubular as in arthropods or more compact as in most other animals. In the latter case a heart generally contains two types of chambers, namely, one or two relatively thin-walled *atria,* which receive blood, and one or

23 · 9 **The lymph system.** *Diagram: the general plan of the blood and lymph circulations. Oxygenated blood, (dark color); venous blood, (light color). Oxygenation occurs in gills or lungs. An artery carries blood away from the heart, a vein, toward the heart (regardless of the state of oxygenation of the blood carried). Fluid escaped from blood capillaries into surrounding tissues enters the lymph system through the walls of the lymph capillaries. Photo: section through a lymph node.*

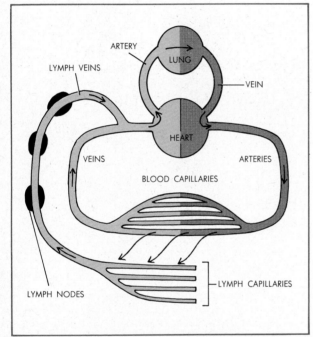

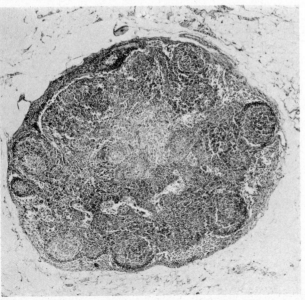

two thicker-walled *ventricles*, which pump blood out.

The mammalian heart consists of four chambers, a right and left atrium, each here called an *auricle*, and a right and left *ventricle*. Typically, one large blood vessel is connected to each (Fig. 23.10). The *aorta* leaves the left ventricle and the branches of this vessel supply all parts of the body with arterial, oxygen-rich blood. Venous, oxygen-poor blood collects from all body regions and returns through the *vena cava* into the right auricle. This chamber connects with the right ventricle through the *tricuspid valve*, an opening equipped with three flaps. The valve lets blood through from auricle to ventricle but not in the reverse direction. Venous blood collected in the right ventricle leaves this chamber via the *pulmonary artery*, a vessel leading to the lungs. Here blood is oxygenated, and arterial blood returns through the *pulmonary vein* into the left auricle.

A *bicuspid* or *mitral* valve, equipped with two flaps, separates the left auricle from the left ventricle. Like the tricuspid on the right, the mitral valve also opens into the ventricle only. The flaps of both the bicuspid and tricuspid valves are prevented from letting blood pass in the wrong direction by strands of tissue resembling parachute strings. These are attached to the free edges of the valve flaps on one end and to the ventricle walls on the other (Fig. 23.11). The bicuspid and tricuspid valves together may be referred to as the auriculoventricular valves, or *AV valves*. Smaller valves are situated where the aorta and the pulmonary artery leave the left and right ventricle, respectively. These valves open away from the heart and close toward it.

Note that the left chambers of the heart are not connected directly with the right chambers. The left carry arterial blood only; the right, venous blood only. Inasmuch as the auricles pump blood only as far as the ventricles, relatively thin muscular walls suffice. But the ventricles, the left one in particular, pump blood into the farthest parts of the body. These chambers possess proportionately thick walls.

The heart is a pressure pump. It generates pumping force on contraction, here called *systole*, and it rests during muscular relaxation, or *diastole*. A complete heart beat consisting of one systole and one diastole lasts about 0.8 sec in a normal human adult at rest. On an average, therefore, 72 beats take place per minute.

A heartbeat starts with the contraction of the auricles (Fig. 23.12). These chambers gradually distend as blood returns via vena cava and pulmonary vein. When the auricles are fully distended, their muscular walls contract. The ventricles are relaxed at that time. As the auricles contract, blood cannot

23 · 10 The heart and circulation. *Diagram: the mammalian blood circulation. Arterial blood is in the left side of the circulatory system (right side of diagram), venous blood in the right side (left side of diagram). Photo: the human heart. The large blood-vessel stump is the aorta. The auricles are partly hidden by the aorta. The size of your fist is very nearly the actual size of your heart.*

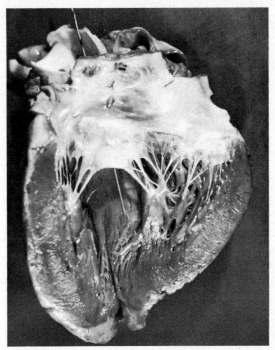

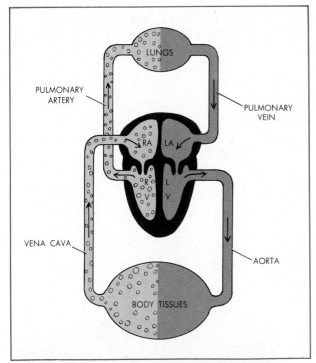

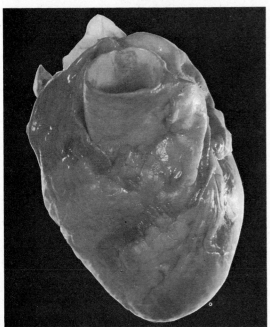

23 · 11 The human heart *cut open to show the interior of the left ventricle. Note the strands of tissue attached to the two flaps of the bicuspid valve. These strands prevent the valve from opening into the auricle (white area above the ventricle).*

23 · 12 The action of the mammalian heart. *When the atria contract (left), they force blood into the relaxed ventricles. The AV valves are open, but the pressure of blood closes all other exits. When ventricles contract (right), they force blood into the pulmonary artery and the aorta. The atria are relaxed at the same time and fill with blood in preparation for the next beat.*

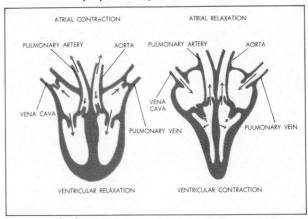

flow backward because incoming blood presses steadily *into* the auricles. Therefore, the only path open to auricular blood is through the AV valves, which lead into the ventricles. These chambers now distend as the auricles empty. The auricular phase of the heartbeat lasts about 0.1 sec. The auricles then relax for the remaining 0.7 sec of the cycle, slowly redistending during this interval in preparation for the next beat (Fig. 23.13).

When the auricles have relaxed, the ventricles are already fully distended and they then contract in their turn. Their thick walls generate much more pressure than the walls of the auricles. Also, ventricular systole lasts longer, namely, some 0.3 sec. As the contraction peak is reached, blood is forced against all ventricular openings, including the AV valves. But as blood slaps against the AV flaps, these snap shut and prevent backflow into the auricles (see Fig. 23.12). The impact of blood against the valve flaps produces a *first heart sound,* which can be felt or heard as "the" heartbeat.

The only way blood can leave the ventricles is via the aorta on the left and the pulmonary artery on the right. The exit valves into these vessels open as blood presses against them with great force. The sudden quantity of fluid now rushing out dilates portions of the exit arteries adjacent to the heart. But the arterial walls are elastic and snap back into position, thereby adding to the pressure of blood. Most of the blood is thus forced forward, where the open paths lead to the lungs and to all body tissues. But some blood tends to press back into the ventricles. This back pressure snaps the exit valves shut and blood then cannot flow in this direction. The impact of blood in closing the exit valves

23 · 13 *Time relationships between atrial and ventricular beats. The atria contract and generate pressure when the ventricles are relaxed, and vice versa. The whole heart is relaxed for half the time of a beat.*

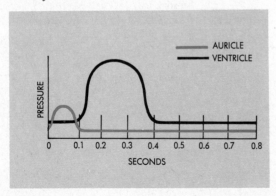

generates a *second heart sound,* fainter than the first.

Note that even the ventricles rest more than half the time. Note also that all heart chambers are always completely full with blood. The quantity of blood in different chambers does vary, however, and such blood is also under greater or lesser pressure. This differential pressure alone determines the position of the heart valves, hence the course in which blood can flow.

Arterial blood "flows" in rhythmic spurts, according to the rhythm of the heart. As each spurt of fluid impinges on the walls of arteries, it gives rise to *pulse* vibrations. With increasing distance from the heart, arterial spurts become less and less forceful. By the time blood is through capillary vessels and has reached veins, it no longer spurts but flows in a continuous, even stream. The heart here produces very little direct push. Venous blood keeps moving slowly by the push of blood from behind and by contraction of skeletal muscles which squeeze the veins. The valves in the veins impose the right direction on venous return. The pressure of lymph is even lower than that of blood. Here again, push of lymph from behind and muscular activity of the body provide the major forces which return lymph to the blood circulation.

How are heartbeat and circulation as a whole maintained?

THE CONTROL: HEART RATE AND BLOOD PRESSURE

The beat of a heart may originate *neurogenically* or *myogenically.* In a neurogenic beat, exemplified by the hearts of most arthropods, contraction is initiated by a nerve ganglion situated in or close to the heart. Such a ganglion delivers rhythmic impulses to the heart muscle. In a myogenic beat, as in the hearts of mammals (and vertebrates generally), contraction is triggered off by a special node of modified or unmodified heart muscle, a so-called *sinus node,* or *pacemaker* (Fig. 23.14). Located in the wall of the right auricle, the pacemaker produces rhythmic signals leading to contraction. Because of this built-in trigger, a myogenic heart exhibits an *intrinsic* beat; when isolated from the body and placed into an artificial nutrient medium, such a heart may for a time contract and relax in a slow rhythm. In the body, this inherent rhythm of the heart is varied and adjusted in strength and rate by control systems. Some of these operate on a nervous, some on a chemical and physical basis.

In vertebrates the main nervous regulating center of heart rate is located in the *medulla oblongata,* a region of the hindbrain near the juncture of skull and neck. Two pairs of nerves lead from a heart-rate center to the heart (see Fig. 23.14). Impulses through one pair accelerate heartbeat; impulses through the other slow it. The accelerator nerves travel through the spinal cord for some distance, emerge in the chest region, and innervate the heart. The inhibitory nerve fibers pass from the heart-rate center into the large *vagus nerves*. One vagus nerve on each side leaves the hindbrain and runs through the neck alongside the trachea. Some branches of the vagus then lead to the heart.

Both the accelerator and inhibitor nerves terminate at the pacemaker in the wall of the right auricle. When impulses through the nerves stimulate the pacemaker, a wave of contraction spreads out from it through both auricles. Auricular contraction in turn stimulates a second patch of modified muscle tissue, the *AV node*, situated in the partition which divides the left and right sides of the heart. At the AV node originates still another portion of modified heart muscle, the *bundle of His*, specialized for impulse conduction. The strands of this bundle branch out through the walls of both ventricles. Thus, auricular contraction stimulates the AV node, and impulses transmitted from there through the strands of the bundle of His initiate ventricular contraction. The time required for stimulus transmission from pacemaker to AV node ensures that the ventricles contract a fraction of a second *after* the auricles.

The frequency with which the pacemaker triggers the contraction of the heart is under the control of the heart-rate center in the brain. Like other processes, the rate of heartbeat is a restrained compromise between acceleration and deceleration. Experiments show that inhibitory signals via the vagus nerves allow a more flexible adjustment of heart rate than accelerator signals. For example, it can be demonstrated that an acceleration of the heart is brought about specifically by a *decrease* of impulse frequency through the vagus nerves; the heart beats faster primarily because of reduced braking action, not because acceleration has been stepped up. Similarly, a slowing of the heart is primarily a result of increased braking via the vagus nerves, not a result of decreased acceleration.

The heart-rate center sends out brake or accelerator signals in response to specific sensory nerve impulses that affect it. Such impulses may reach it from anywhere in the body. As is well known, heart rate can be influenced greatly by external environmental changes, via vision, hearing, and other senses. Moreover, virtually all emotions affect heart rate, and so do internal body activities. In all such cases, sensory

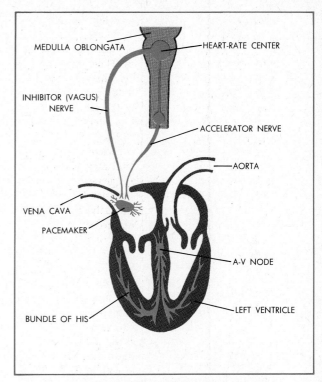

23 · 14 *The motor innervation of the mammalian heart* (color). *Impulses through both inhibitor and accelerator nerves may affect the pacemaker. Impulses from there stimulate the atria, which contract as a result, then the AV node, which in turn sends contraction signals to the ventricles through the bundle of His.*

impulses are transmitted into specific parts of the brain, and interconnected impulse pathways from there then relay signals to many other parts of the brain, the heart-rate center usually included. Depending on the kind of signal the heart-rate center receives, it accelerates or decelerates the heart.

Among the sensory messages transmitted to the heart-rate center, many originate in the circulatory system itself. For example, sensory nerves lead to the heart-rate center from the walls of the vena cava and the aorta. When these blood vessels become distended by large quantities of blood, their walls stretch and this mechanical distension stimulates the endings of the sensory nerves. If the heart-rate center receives impulses from the vena cava, the center accelerates the heart. By contrast, impulses to the center from the aorta bring about a slowing of the heart (Fig. 23.15).

Suppose that strenuous work is started. The active

body muscles now compress many veins vigorously, and much blood returns to the heart as a result. This more abundant flow distends the vena cava pronouncedly and initiates a *stretch reflex*, as described. Heart rate will increase, therefore, just when the tissues require more fuel and oxygen. Also, a heart beating more rapidly can handle the larger quantities of incoming blood by pumping them out faster. But the increased outflow dilates the walls of the aorta. Stretch reflexes now originate in this vessel and they *slow* the heart; they prevent the heart from beating *too* rapidly (Fig. 23.16).

Through these controls and the built-in feedbacks, heart rate is automatically self-adjusted to the volume of blood the heart must handle. Moreover, any excessive speedup produces signals forcing a slowdown. Similarly, if the heart should slow down, the aortic walls would be stretched less, reflex inhibition of the heart would decrease, and heart rate would increase back to normal.

In addition to nervous controls like the above,

23 · 15 *The sensory innervation of the heart. The heart-rate center receives messages through sensory nerves which originate in the vena cava and the aorta. In response to such messages, the center then may send appropriate command signals to the pacemaker, as shown in Fig. 23.14.*

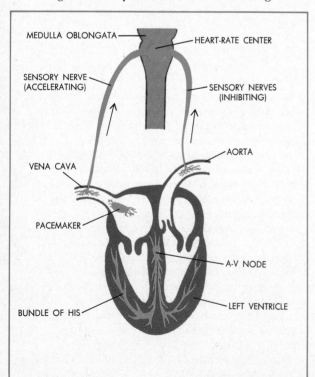

heart rate is regulated decisively by many nonnervous agencies. Most of these act directly on the heart muscle or on the pacemaker specifically. Thus, like any other metabolic process, heartbeat is affected by temperature. High temperature accelerates, low temperature decelerates. The effect of pH is equally pronounced. Relative acidity accelerates the heart, relative alkalinity decelerates it. Since carbon dioxide lowers the pH of blood, this compound increases the rate of the heart when it is present in high concentrations. This is the case during strenuous body activity, for example, when rates of respiration and CO_2 production are high. Increased CO_2 concentrations also speed up breathing, as will become apparent in the next chapter. Consequently, fast breathing and a fast heart usually go together. The mineral ions in blood and also hormones have pronounced effects on heart rate. For example, the action of adrenaline under conditions of severe stress has already been mentioned. Analogously, thyroxine, insulin, sex hormones, pituitary hormones, and others all influence heart rate directly or indirectly. At any given moment, therefore, the actual rate of the heart is a net result of many simultaneous nervous and nonnervous effects.

An appropriately controlled heart rate is one component of an adequate circulation; another is an appropriately regulated blood pressure. For if blood pressure became too high, thin blood vessels and the thin-walled auricles of the heart might burst. And if blood pressure became too low, blood would not possess sufficient momentum to circulate.

Even in the absence of a pumping mechanism, a quantity of fluid filling a confined space is under a certain pressure. The larger the volume of fluid and the smaller the available space, the greater will be the pressure. Blood pressure therefore depends on three main factors: blood *volume*, blood *vessel space*, and in addition also the *force* of the heartbeat.

Blood volume is adjusted to some extent through contractions of the spleen, which bring stored blood into circulation, and to a major extent through regulation of fluid intake into the body and fluid loss from it. Adjustments of blood pressures by such means are comparatively slow. However, virtually instant adjustments may be brought about by alterations in the force of the heartbeat and in the space within blood vessels.

The main determinant of the force of heartbeats is the *amount* of blood received and pumped out in a given span of time. This is a curious but little-understood phenomenon characteristic of all muscle. Within certain limits, the greater the work load of a muscle and the more it is thereby stretched, the stronger is its contraction. For example, when the

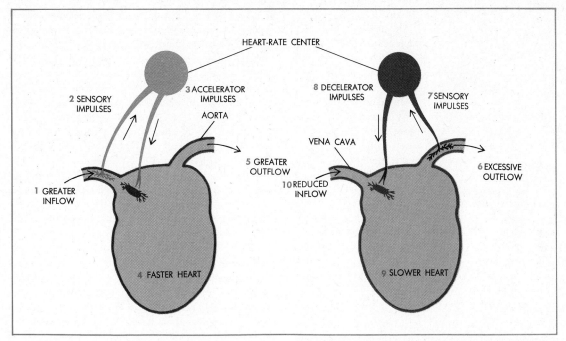

23 · 16 *Stretch-reflex control of blood flow. If the inflow of blood into the heart increases* (left), *the outflow will increase too, through reflex acceleration of the heart (1 to 5). If the outflow rate is excessive* (right), *inflow and outflow will quickly be reduced, through reflex deceleration of the heart (6 to 10).*

heart receives small quantities of blood in each beat and distends only a little, then its contraction will be weak. But when much blood distends the ventricles fully, then the pumping action will be powerful and blood pressure will increase correspondingly.

The heart distends with much blood when venous return is great. As just noted above, a stretch reflex originates under such conditions from the wall of the vena cava and heart rate is raised. Venous return evidently affects both the rate and the force of the heart, a circumstance of considerable adaptive value. During intensive activity, for example, a heart which has a fast but shallow beat could not supply the tissues with extra fuel and oxygen. However, a beat which is both fast and forceful does put the necessary drive behind blood to service the tissues adequately.

The space available within blood vessels is adjusted by contraction and relaxation of the smooth muscles in the vessel walls. *Vasoconstriction* reduces the diameter of blood vessels; *vasodilation* increases it. Vasoconstriction and vasodilation, together referred to as *vasomotion*, are controlled by a *vasomotor center* in the brain, located again in the medulla oblongata, close to the heart-rate center. Nerves lead from the vasomotor center to all blood vessels except the capillaries, which do not possess muscles. Experiments show that changes in the caliber of a blood vessel are brought about primarily by variations in the activity of constrictor muscles. Dilator muscles

play a lesser role. Consequently, a vessel ordinarily narrows as a result of more impulses from the vasomotor center to constrictor muscles. A vessel widens when fewer impulses reach these muscles (Fig. 23.17).

Vasoconstriction in all parts of the body raises overall blood pressure; vasodilation lowers it. Vasomotion may also occur in limited regions of the body, leading to localized changes in blood pressure. Actual events are controlled by the vasomotor center, which, like the heart-rate center, acts in response to nervous and chemical cues.

Nervous cues to the vasomotor center are as numerous as those affecting heart rate. Virtually any nervous signal transmitted into the brain is likely to have an effect on the vasomotor center as well. For example, pain, emotions, and stresses generally all tend to increase blood pressure, through body-wide vasoconstriction. At the same time, in specific parts of the body in which stresses are to be counteracted the local blood pressure often falls through regional vasodilation. For example, if an animal sustains a wound, overall blood pressure rises but the wounded

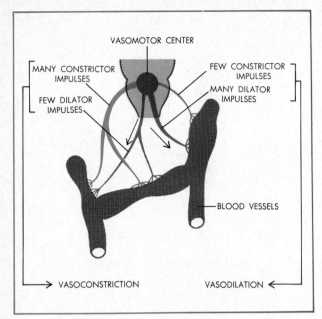

23 · 17 Vasomotion. *Vasoconstriction occurs when a blood vessel receives many constrictor impulses and few dilator impulses from the vasomotor center. Vasodilation occurs when constrictor impulses are few and dilator impulses are many.*

area swells through local vasodilation. The adaptive advantage of this response is clear. A rise of overall blood pressure produces a state of readiness enabling the animal to react to stress more effectively. And a local vasodilation in the stressed region itself permits more blood to flow into that region. More nutrients and oxygen become available there as a result (Fig. 23.18).

Like heart rate, blood pressure is normally prevented from varying excessively by stretch reflexes. Some sensory nerve fibers from the aorta lead into the vasomotor center. When the aorta is greatly distended by blood spurting out from the heart, that is, when blood pressure is high, a stretch reflex via the vasomotor center brings about body-wide vasodilation. In this manner, a high blood pressure is reduced to normal. Conversely, when the aorta distends very little or not at all, a stretch reflex leads to increased vasoconstriction and a rise of blood pressure.

The chief chemical cue to which the vasomotor center responds is carbon dioxide in the blood, as in the case of the heart-rate center. If blood reaching the vasomotor center carries a high concentration of CO_2, then the center transmits constrictor signals throughout the body and blood pressure will rise.

Conversely, low CO_2 concentrations result in a generalized fall of blood pressure. We already know that CO_2 also affects heart rate and breathing rate. Evidently, intensive CO_2 production by highly active tissues neatly stimulates the whole circulatory and breathing machinery to increased efforts, just when such efforts are actually required to sustain tissue activity.

Apart from its effects on the vasomotor center, CO_2 also has a direct, local effect on vasomotion. In tissues in which much CO_2 is produced, the gas acts directly on the blood vessels in the vicinity and dilates them. Thus, active tissues control their own increased blood supply through the local effects of the CO_2 they produce. At the same time, such tissues also promote general vasoconstriction elsewhere in the body, through the effects of their CO_2 on the vasomotor center (Fig. 23.19). Changes of this sort occur after a meal, for example, when the whole alimentary system becomes active and produces large amounts of CO_2. As a result of local vasodilation, blood may then flow freely through intestine and liver, where it is particularly needed at the time. But less blood will flow through the peripheral parts of the body, including the skeletal muscles and the head. An animal therefore tends to be sluggish after a meal and will be disinclined to undertake physical activities. Conversely, an empty digestive system facilitates blood flow through the skeletal muscles and the brain (this is why athletes do not

23 · 18 Vasomotor effects of localized stress. *Generalized vasoconstriction and localized vasodilation follow through the numbered events shown. Sensory nerves in light color, motor nerves in darker color.*

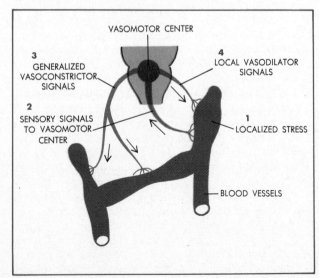

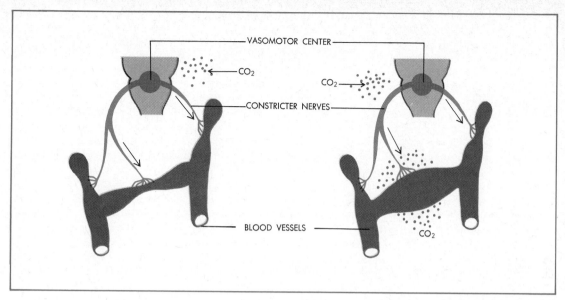

VASOMOTOR CENTER

CO_2

CO_2

CONSTRICTER NERVES

BLOOD VESSELS

CO_2

eat immediately before exerting themselves physically).

We note that vasomotor control, both nervous and chemical, regulates not only blood pressure as such but also the *distribution* of blood. The nervous and chemical effects tend to reinforce each other, and the results are adaptive, being geared to the relative activity or inactivity of body tissues. Moreover, the tissues themselves initiate the distributional changes, through automatic self-regulation via control systems with feedbacks. The controls of blood pressure and blood distribution also operate in concert with the controls of heart rate and breathing rate, and the net result is that all long-distance transport functions are carried out in interlocking and interdependent fashion. A change in heart rate may thus produce correlated changes in blood pressure, in venous return, in the force of the heart, in breathing rate, in the distribution of blood, and eventually in heart rate itself. If one condition of circulation is altered, all others are altered also. Circulatory ad-

23 · 19 Vasomotor control by carbon dioxide. Left, generalized vasoconstriction as a result of stimulation of the vasomotor center by CO_2. Right, CO_2 produced locally overrides the general vasoconstriction ordered by the vasomotor center and brings about a local vasodilation.

justments illustrate once again that control systems normally operate in such a way that they produce an appropriate, self-preserving, or "right" response to a given stimulus, and that built-in feedbacks impose restraints which prevent responses from going too far in direction, strength, and duration.

Control of the *physical* motion of blood is but one requirement if blood is to service the tissues adequately. A second requirement is control of proper *chemical* conditions in blood, despite changes produced continuously by actively metabolizing tissues. This requirement is met chiefly by the breathing and excretory systems.

REVIEW QUESTIONS

1. Define lymph and blood. What are the basic functions of lymph and blood? Distinguish between open and closed circulations. Which animal groups possess open and which closed circulations? Which are without blood circulations?

2. Review the composition of blood plasma and the functions of each group of components. How, specifically, may ions in plasma act as buffers? Give examples.

3. What are antibodies? When, where, and how are they produced? Distinguish between active and passive immunity. Why does passive immunity not give as lasting protection as active immunity?

4. What cellular components occur in blood and what are the functions of each? By what processes is the number of red corpuscles maintained relatively constant? What role do lymph nodes play in internal steady-state control? Review the reaction pattern of blood clotting.

5. What organs are the principal components of a

circulatory system? A lymph system? What is an endothelium? How do arteries differ from veins and capillaries (*a*) structurally, (*b*) functionally?

6. Name the principal parts of the mammalian heart and the principal blood vessels, and review the general course of the blood circulation. What are lymph hearts and lymph nodes and what are their functions?

7. Review the events during a complete heartbeat, with attention to durations, pressure patterns, valve positions, direction of blood flow, and heart sounds. How is blood moved through veins and lymph vessels?

8. Describe the nervous controls of the heart. How are control signals transmitted through the heart itself? Which motor signals accelerate the heart and which decelerate it? Describe stretch reflexes that (*a*) accelerate and (*b*) decelerate the heart. Through what specific processes is the heart (*a*) speeded up when physical exercise is begun and (*b*) slowed down during rest or sleep? What nonnervous agencies affect heart rate?

9. What three major factors control blood pressure and what governs each of these factors? Describe the action of the vasomotor center. What nervous and chemical agencies affect this center and how?

10. What is the interrelation between vasomotion, heart rate, and breathing rate? Suppose that physical exercise is begun; describe the specific processes leading simultaneously to (*a*) increased heart rate, (*b*) increased breathing rate, (*c*) increased blood pressure, and (*d*) redistribution of blood within the body.

COLLATERAL READINGS

Burnet, M.: How Antibodies Are Made, *Sci. American,* Nov., 1954. A hypothesis regarding this still unsolved problem is described.

————: The Mechanism of Immunity, *Sci. American,* Jan., 1961. The article examines the antibody-antigen interplay in immune reactions.

Carlson, A. J., and V. Johnson: "The Machinery of the Body," 4th ed., University of Chicago, Chicago, 1953. Detailed chapters on blood, blood flow and pressure, and the work of the mammalian heart are included in this recommended text.

Harvey, W.: On the Motion of the Heart and Blood, in "A Source Book in Animal Biology," McGraw-Hill, New York, 1951. A translation of the famous original paper by the discoverer of the closed circulation in man; published in 1616 in Latin, and one of the first works of modern science.

Kilgour, F. G.: William Harvey, *Sci. American,* June, 1952. The life and work of the discoverer of the blood circulation are described.

Mayerson, H.: The Lymphatic System, *Sci. American,* June, 1963. A good account of the biology of this system.

McKusick, V. A.: Heart Sounds, *Sci. American,* May, 1956. The production and meaning of these sounds are examined.

Ponder, E.: The Red Blood Cell, *Sci. American,* Jan., 1957. A discussion of the significance of red corpuscles in circulation and breathing.

Scholander, P. F.: The Master Switch of Life, *Sci. American,* Dec., 1963. The article describes the vasomotor mechanism of blood distribution in relation to the oxygen-carrying role of blood.

Speirs, R. S.: How Cells Attack Antigens, *Sci. American,* Feb., 1964. The role of defensive cells in protecting against foreign antigens is described.

Surgenor, D. M.: Blood, *Sci. American,* Feb., 1954. A good general discussion.

Wiener, A. S.: Parentage and Blood Groups, *Sci. American,* July, 1954. The nature of blood groups and the genetics of their inheritance are discussed.

Wiggers, C. J.: The Heart, *Sci. American,* May, 1957. The structure of the heart muscle and the quantitative work of the human heart are described.

Wood, W. B., Jr.: White Blood Cells vs. Bacteria, *Sci. American,* Feb., 1951. A good account of the phagocytic activity of white cells.

Zweifach, B. J.: The Microcirculation of the Blood, *Sci. American,* Jan., 1959. An examination of the steady-state functions of the capillary circulation.

CHAPTER 24
BREATHING
AND
EXCRETION

Both breathing and excretion control the exchange of metabolites between the interior of the animal body and the external environment, and both therefore contribute most significantly to maintenance of body-wide steady states. Breathing supplies the environmental O_2 required for respiration within cells; and the CO_2 and H_2O produced by respiration and other metabolic processes are eliminated in part by the breathing structures, in part by the excretory structures. Both types of structures eliminate other metabolic byproducts as well, but at the same time they also ensure that useful substances are not excreted. Determination of what is or is not a byproduct actually constitutes a primary function of both breathing and excretion.

All breathing and excretory structures operate by continuously screening and adjusting the chemical composition of the body fluids. In blood-possessing animals, therefore, both types of structures are associated intimately with the circulation.

BREATHING

THE BREATHING APPARATUS

The basic component of any breathing system is a *breathing surface,* a region exposed directly to the external environment where O_2 may diffuse in and CO_2 may diffuse out. In all animals, terrestrial ones included, the actual gas exchange occurs in a liquid medium; the breathing surface is exposed to water if the animal is aquatic or is kept moist by the ani-

mal if the environment is air. Gases then must dissolve in a film of liquid covering the breathing surface before they can diffuse in or out. A dry breathing surface is a dead surface.

As has become evident in the chapters of Part 4, only coelomate animals possess breathing surfaces within specialized breathing systems. In all other animals, and indeed also in some of the coelomates (for example, annelids), gas exchange essentially takes the form of *skin breathing:* O_2 and CO_2 diffuse across virtually all body surfaces exposed to the environment—the skin mainly, but also the alimentary surfaces to some extent. Internal gas distribution in such cases is accomplished adequately by direct diffusion between adjacent cells and by transport via lymph or blood. Even in animals with specialized breathing systems the skin may serve as an accessory breathing organ (for example, frogs).

Where present, specialized breathing systems may be classified into two general categories according to whether they function in an *aquatic* or an *aerial* environment (Fig. 24.1). Aquatic systems are *gills,* formed by outgrowths from the integument. Aerial systems are *lungs,* as in terrestrial vertebrates, or *tracheal tubes,* as in terrestrial arthropods. Both types are ingrowths from the integument. In both gills and lungs, the actual breathing surfaces are one-cell-thick epithelia, exposed to the environmental medium on one side and to the internal circulatory medium on the other. Where the circulatory system is open, blood usually comes into direct contact with the breathing epithelium. In closed systems, dense networks of capillaries held within thin layers of connective tissue invest the inside surfaces of the breathing epithelium. Gases here must traverse two layers of cells intervening between environment and blood.

In mammals generally and in man specifically, the air channels of the breathing apparatus are formed by several familiar organs: *nose* and *nasal passages, pharynx, larynx* (or Adam's apple), *trachea* (or windpipe), and *lungs.*

The nasal passages are narrow, winding pathways leading past intricately grooved and ridged walls (see Fig. 17.14). Along the walls are found a number of paired openings. Some of these connect with the head *sinuses,* hollow air-filled cavities within some of the skull bones. For example, one large sinus is present in each of the two frontal bones forming the forehead. Another pair of openings admits the contents of the *tear ducts* into the nasal passages. Tears are secreted continuously by glands in the outer

24 · 1 Breathing in invertebrates. *Epidermis shown as layer of cells, blood and vessels in dark color. As indicated, all such breathing organs are outfolded or infolded integumentary derivatives. External and internal gills differ in principle only in whether or not they are tucked into chambers. Tracheae occur in terrestrial arthropods, fine air tubes here reaching individual cells; muscle-enveloped sacs folded out from a main tube (as shown) often serve as air reservoirs and air pumps. Book lungs occur in most spiders, the gas-carrying medium here being blood in blood sinuses (color). Free blood rather than blood within vessels also transports gases in skin, gill, and lung systems of animals in which vessel circulations are absent. Some aquatic arthropods possess book gills, constructed like book lungs but operating in water.*

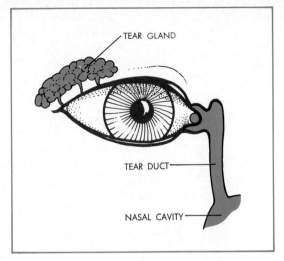

24 · 2 The tear apparatus.

corners of the eyes. The lymphlike fluid flows over and moistens the surface of the cornea, then collects in the inner corners of the eyes and runs through the tear ducts into the nose (Fig. 24.2). Near the entry of the nasal passages into the pharynx, another pair of openings leads into the *eustachian tubes* passing into the middle-ear cavities. This connection permits the equilibration of air pressure between the external atmosphere and the middle ear, a space closed off from the outside by the eardrum (see Fig. 17.14 and Chap. 25).

Nasal passages, head sinuses, tears ducts, and eustachian tubes are lined with a continuous single layer of epithelial cells. Mucus secreted by the cells moistens the exposed surfaces. The epithelial cells in the nasal passages are ciliated, and some of these cells are specialized as odor receptors. Nerves lead from them to the nearby brain, where impulses are interpreted as smell. Air passing through the narrow spaces of the nasal pathways is smelled, warmed, and moistened, and is freed of dust by the ciliated cells, which act as a filtering screen. As everyone is uncomfortably aware, inflammation of the passages as in a cold or in hay fever blocks air transmission to greater or lesser degree. The tissues swell up and obliterate the pathways. Increased secretion of mucus adds to the discomfort and smelling is impaired. Moreover, tears overflow from the eyes, since the fluid cannot easily drain off into the blocked nasal chambers. In severe cases, the inflammation may spread into the head sinuses, the middle-ear cavities, the throat, and the pathways leading from the throat to the lungs. Breathing by mouth under such conditions introduces relatively unwarmed, dust-laden, and unsmelled air.

As has been noted in Chap. 17, the air and the food channel cross in the pharynx (see Fig. 17.14).

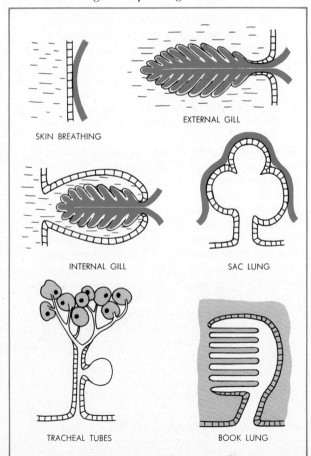

SKIN BREATHING

EXTERNAL GILL

INTERNAL GILL

SAC LUNG

TRACHEAL TUBES

BOOK LUNG

The esophagus is more or less collapsed in the absence of food, but some air may pass into it nevertheless. Most of the air enters the larynx through the *glottis*, a slit which can be closed or opened to varying degrees. The larynx consists of a number of cartilages. Held together by membranes and movable relative to one another by muscles, these cartilages enclose a hollow, cylindrical chamber. Attached to the inner surfaces of this chamber is a pair of horizontally placed fibroelastic ligaments, the *vocal cords*. These run from front to back in the laryngeal cavity, leaving an air passage in the mid-plane (Fig. 24.3).

Sound is produced when air is expelled past the vocal cords through the glottis. The shape of the glottal opening and, as in a violin string, the length and tension of the vocal cords determine tone *pitch*. The shape of the larynx may be changed at will by muscles, and such changes in turn alter the tension of the cords. Taut ligaments vibrate rapidly and produce a highly pitched sound. Also, notes are the higher the shorter and thinner the vocal cords and the narrower the glottal slit. The *volume* of the sound produced depends on the force of the air blast and on the amplitude with which the cords vibrate.

A third characteristic of voice, tone *quality*, is influenced by the size and shape of the resonating cavities: chest, pharynx, mouth, and nasal passages. That tone quality changes as the position of lips, tongue, jaws, and cheeks is changed is quite familiar. Tone quality is altered also during a cold or when the nose is pinched or when sound is produced on inhalation rather than on exhalation, as is normal. During puberty in males, the chest cavity and larynx enlarge and the vocal cords lengthen. The voice "breaks" as the individual learns to control his modified sound equipment. Deeper tones than in females are produced thereafter. The vocal cords may thicken or scar during disease or become encrusted with mucus during a cold; a rasping voice is the result.

Most mammals make sounds of some sort (the giraffe being a notable exception). In song birds, the only other vertebrate group with extensive and conspicuous voice capacity, sound is produced not in the larynx but in a *syrinx*. This cartilaginous voice box is located at the lower, not the upper, end of the windpipe (Fig. 24.4).

The larynx is continuous with the trachea. This tube is prevented from collapsing by C-shaped rings of cartilage set horizontally into its wall. As in the larynx, the inner lining of the trachea is a ciliated, mucus-secreting layer of cells. The cilia beat upward, carrying mucus, dust, and occasional bits of food which "went the wrong way" into the pharynx. Air forced out as a cough facilitates the process.

At its lower end, the trachea divides into two *bronchi*, tubes having a smaller diameter than the trachea but the same structure otherwise (see Fig. 24.4). Each bronchus subdivides after a distance into *bronchioles* and each of the latter in turn branches repeatedly. Cartilage supports are not present in these smaller ducts. Also, their walls become thinner as they branch. Only the inner ciliated lining layer and some connective tissue containing elastic fibers are carried forward into the microscopic terminations of the branch system. Each such terminus is a raspberry-shaped sac made of a single layer of thin flat cells. Such a sac is an *alveolus*, and the sum of all alveoli constitutes the lung. The alveoli are held together by connective tissue which carries nerves and a dense network of blood capillaries (see Fig. 24.4). These vessels receive oxygen-poor (venous) blood from the pulmonary artery (and the right ventricle) and they conduct oxygen-rich (arterial) blood into the pulmonary vein (and the left auricle; see Fig. 23.10). The left and right parts of the lungs are sculptured into lobes, their number corresponding to the number of main branches arising from the bronchi.

24 · 3 The vocal cords of man. The view is from above, looking into larynx and trachea. From left to right, sequence of vocal-cord positions during the transition from quiet breathing to voicing.

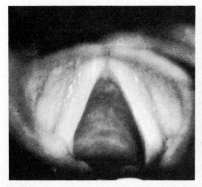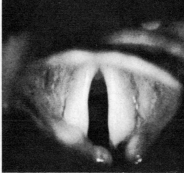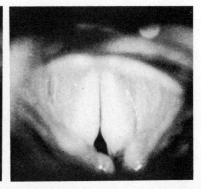

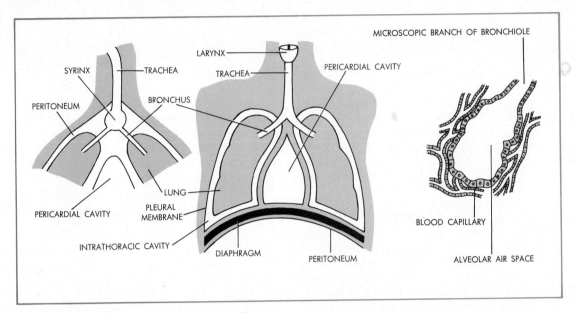

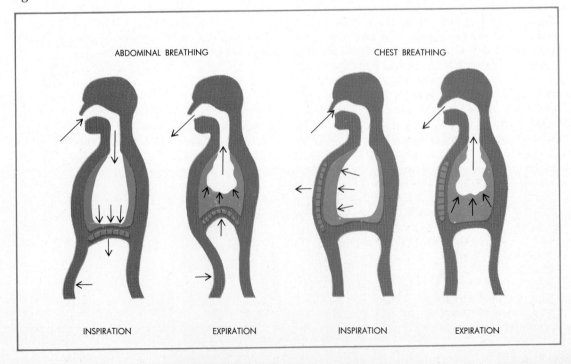

24 · 4   Lung systems. *Left and center, the anatomical relations of the lower parts of the breathing system in birds and mammals, respectively. Note the comparative position of syrinx and larynx. Note also that, in mammals, the intrathoracic cavity is sealed off. Right, an alveolus of the lung, surrounded by blood capillaries. Connective tissue* (not drawn) *envelops the entire system.*

24 · 5   Abdominal breathing and chest breathing.

The lung on each side is situated in an *intrathoracic space* which is bounded by two *pleural membranes* (see Fig. 24.4). The outer membrane lies against the diaphragm below, against the pericardial, heart-containing cavity along the mid-plane of the chest, and against the rib cage at the top and along the sides. The inner membrane covers the lung itself. Except for openings admitting the bronchi and the blood vessels to the lungs, the intrathoracic cavities are sealed off from the rest of the body. This feature is essential in breathing.

Gas Exchange

Air is moved through the breathing system by action of the *diaphragm,* the *rib muscles,* or both. The diaphragm participates in *abdominal breathing;* the rib muscles, in *chest breathing.*

The diaphragm separates the chest cavity from the abdominal cavity; stomach and liver lie directly underneath it. In relaxed condition, this thin muscular partition is dome-shaped. On contraction the upward curvature of the dome disappears and the diaphragm flattens out. A contraction pushes liver, stomach, and intestine downward and outward and so forces the abdomen out (hence the designation "abdominal breathing"). Flattening of the diaphragm also enlarges the chest cavity and this change is the effective event in *inhalation* (Fig. 24.5). As a result of the enlargement the pressure in the sealed intrathoracic space falls, and this lowered pressure now sucks the lung alveoli wide open. Air pressure within the alveoli consequently falls also, but the decrease is rebalanced instantly by air rushing in through the nose or mouth.

When the diaphragm relaxes, it resumes its original dome shape. The abdomen is pulled back, the chest cavity becomes smaller, and the intrathoracic space reattains its former volume. Pressure within the intrathoracic space is then no longer lowered, and further suction is therefore not exerted on the alveoli. As a result, the elastic fibers which cover the alveoli recoil and air is pressed out from the lungs in an *exhalation.*

Breathing movements produced by the rib cage have the same effect on the lungs. Ribs are hinged to the vertebral column along the back and to the sternum along the front. Attached between successive ribs are two layers of muscles which raise or lower the rib cage. When the chest is raised, the thoracic cavity expands and, through suction on the alveoli, inhalation occurs. A lowering of the chest results in exhalation. Chest breathing may enlarge the intrathoracic spaces much more than abdominal breathing and may therefore produce deeper breaths. In procedures of "artificial respiration," by hand or in "iron lungs," the chest is subjected to intermittent external pressure which forces air into and out of the lungs just as normal breathing does.

In view of the importance of pressure, effective breathing clearly depends on the structural wholeness of the intrathoracic space. If the chest wall is pierced by a wound, external air enters the cavity on that side and the diaphragm or the rib muscles then can no longer exert suction on the lung. The lung consequently stays collapsed. In some diseases

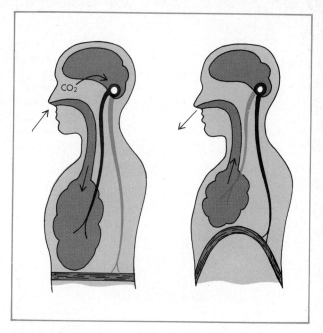

24 · 6 Control of inhalation (left) *and of exhalation* (right). *Left,* CO_2 *in blood stimulates the breathing center to send impulses via the phrenic nerves to the diaphragm, leading to inhalation. Right, impulses from the inflated lung inhibit the breathing center, leading to exhalation.*

(for example, tuberculosis), it is often desirable to rest one of the lungs. This is done by injecting air into one of the intrathoracic cavities. The lung on that side then collapses and becomes nonfunctional. The procedure may have to be repeated from time to time, for the injected air is gradually absorbed and removed by the blood circulation.

How are the bellowslike breathing movements maintained and how are they adjusted in rate and depth to changing requirements? Breathing is controlled by a *breathing center,* located in the medulla oblongata very near the centers for heart rate and vasomotion. The breathing center responds to two kinds of incoming stimuli, one nervous, the other nonnervous. The nonnervous stimulus is blood-borne CO_2, which accelerates the activity of the breathing center in proportion to its concentration. The center acts by sending nerve impulses to the breathing muscles, namely, the diaphragm or the rib muscles. Special nerves conduct such impulses; a pair of large *phrenic nerves* innervates the diaphragm, for example. When impulses from the breathing center reach the breathing muscles, these contract, the chest cavity enlarges as a result, and the lung alveoli are sucked open. Air is then inhaled (Fig. 24.6).

The very stretching of the alveoli now stimulates

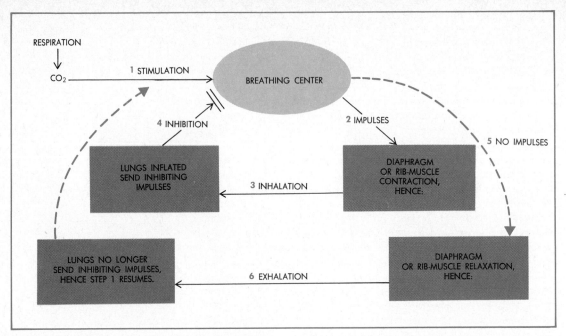

RESPIRATION

CO₂ —— 1 STIMULATION ——→ BREATHING CENTER

4 INHIBITION

2 IMPULSES

5 NO IMPULSES

LUNGS INFLATED SEND INHIBITING IMPULSES

3 INHALATION

DIAPHRAGM OR RIB-MUSCLE CONTRACTION, HENCE:

LUNGS NO LONGER SEND INHIBITING IMPULSES, HENCE STEP 1 RESUMES.

6 EXHALATION

DIAPHRAGM OR RIB-MUSCLE RELAXATION, HENCE:

24 · 7 *Breathing control is summarized in this diagram. An arrow tipped with a transverse double bar* (left center) *designates inhibition.*

special sets of nerves which originate in the alveolar walls. These nerves conduct impulses from the inflated lung to the breathing center, and when such impulses arrive there, the center is *inhibited.* That is, the impulses override and suppress the stimulating effect of blood-borne CO_2. Consequently, the center ceases to send signals to the breathing muscles. Inhalation is thus prevented from going too far, for in the absence of signals from the brain the breathing muscles relax. As they do so, the chest cavity becomes smaller, the lung alveoli recoil to their original state, and air is exhaled.

After the alveoli have recoiled, they are no longer stretched and the nerve endings in their walls therefore cease to be stimulated. Impulses then also cease to be sent to the breathing center and the center consequently will no longer be inhibited. But in the absence of inhibition, blood-borne CO_2 can again exert its effect. The breathing center can therefore resume its impulse transmission to the breathing muscles and a new inhalation so begins (Fig. 24.7). Blood-borne oxygen likewise has an effect on the breathing center, but this effect is much less powerful than that of CO_2 and it probably plays only a minor role during normal breathing. Thus, a basic breathing rhythm is maintained by an automatic control cycle, which continues to operate in self-renewing manner through carbon dioxide stimula-

tions and neural feedback inhibitions.

It should follow that, as the stimulations and inhibitions vary, so should the breathing rhythm. Indeed, both the rate and depth of breathing can be altered easily, as is well known. For example, an exercise of will or a powerful sensory emotional experience may affect breathing greatly. These are nervous influences, relayed to the breathing center over many different and often indirect nerve paths. Moreover, carbon dioxide too produces modifications of the breathing pattern. As already pointed out, breathing rate varies in direct proportion with CO_2 concentrations. High CO_2 concentrations build up whenever the rate of CO_2 production by respiration is greater than the rate of CO_2 removal via the lungs. This is the case, for example, during intensive body activity, when respiration rates are high. As CO_2 accelerates breathing under such conditions, the gas hastens its own removal through the lungs. Faster breathing at the same time increases the oxygen supply, just when the tissues require more oxygen. Recall here also that CO_2 speeds up the heart; a more rapid circulation thus aids additionally in increasing the speed of gas exchange.

The concentration of CO_2 in blood becomes extremely high when breathing is deliberately stopped altogether. But the accumulating gas then soon stimulates the breathing center so strongly that a resumption of breathing is *forced*, even against the most intense will. An animal cannot commit suicide by holding its breath.

Conversely, when the CO_2 concentration in blood is low the breathing center is stimulated rather

602

weakly and breathing slows down. This is the case during sleep or rest, when respiration and CO_2 production are minimal. The extreme here is the *hyperventilated* condition, produced, for example, when breathing is intentionally made as deep and as rapid as possible. Carbon dioxide may then be exhaled so fast that abnormally little of the gas reaches the breathing center. A similar lack of CO_2 and of oxygen may develop in the rarefied atmosphere at very high altitudes. In such situations the breathing center may temporarily cease to operate altogether and a "blackout" may ensue. Breathing will remain stopped until the CO_2 concentration has again built up to a high enough level to stimulate the center adequately.

Breathing is a means to an end. The most immediate end is the procurement of additional oxygen and the removal of excess carbon dioxide. Fresh atmospheric air as inhaled contains some 20 per cent oxygen and 0.03 per cent carbon dioxide. Exhaled air includes only 16 per cent oxygen, but some 4 per cent carbon dioxide. Evidently, a fifth of the available oxygen has been retained in the body and more than 100 times the amount of carbon dioxide has been expelled. What happens to the one and where does the other come from?

Gas Transport

The transfer of oxygen from the lung alveoli into the blood and the reverse transfer of carbon dioxide are governed primarily by diffusion. This exchange is one of the few instances when active cellular absorption and secretion do not appear to play a role. The wall of an alveolus consists of a thin, single layer of cells, and the wall of a blood capillary also consists of such a layer (see Fig. 24.4). Neither wall offers resistance to the passage of gaseous O_2 and CO_2. Gas exchange may therefore take place much more rapidly than if absorption and secretion were necessary.

The specific direction in which the gases move is determined by the prevailing pressure gradients, or *tension gradients*, between blood and lung. Specifically, atmospheric air in the lungs contains only a little CO_2, but venous blood flowing into the lungs from the body is virtually saturated with the gas. The pressure, or tension, of CO_2 in blood is therefore greater than that in the alveoli and a tension gradient points *out* of the capillaries. More CO_2 molecules consequently diffuse out of the blood than into it and blood ceases to be venous (Fig. 24.8). The pressure pattern is the reverse with respect to oxygen. Blood flowing into the lungs from the body is oxygen-poor, since the tissues have removed much of the gas. But the air in the alveoli contains a maximal

amount of O_2. Accordingly, a tension gradient points *into* the blood and more O_2 molecules diffuse into the capillaries than in the reverse direction. As a result, blood becomes arterial.

These interrelations explain why breathing is inefficient at high altitudes. In rarefied air, the atmospheric pressure of oxygen is greatly reduced and the pressure differential between lung and blood is low. Oxygen diffusion consequently does not take place so readily. We may similarly understand why the close atmosphere of an unventilated, overcrowded room makes breathing difficult. The CO_2 tension in the room is high, approaching that in blood. Hence, CO_2 cannot easily leave the blood.

Just as in the lungs, cellular gas exchange in the body tissues is governed similarly by tension gradients (see Fig. 24.8). Cells continuously use up oxygen in respiration and the tension of this gas in cells is therefore low. The tension in arterial blood is higher, however, and O_2 diffuses from blood into tissue cells. Blood consequently ceases to be arterial. At the same time, since respiratory CO_2 is produced in cells steadily, the CO_2 tension within tissue cells is high. But arterial blood has low CO_2 tensions and the gas therefore diffuses from tissue cells into blood. Blood thus becomes venous.

By what means are the respiratory gases actually carried in blood? With respect to oxygen, this gas is always dissolved in the plasma and lymph of all animals up to the limits of its physical solubility in water. In animals with blood, however, a variety of *respiratory pigments* provide an additional and far more efficient means of oxygen transport. All such

24 · 8 *Exchange of respiratory gases between the lungs and blood and between the body tissues and blood. Oxygen enters the blood in the lungs and leaves in the tissues. Carbon dioxide enters in the tissues and leaves in the lungs.*

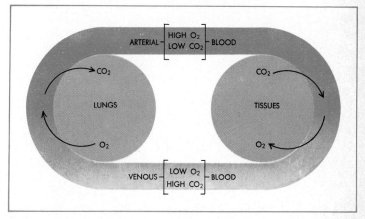

oxygen-carrying pigments are linked to protein, the latter conferring reversibility to the union with oxygen:

$$\text{protein-pigment} + O_2 \underset{\text{in body tissues}}{\overset{\substack{\text{in breathing}\\ \text{system}}}{\rightleftharpoons}} \text{protein-pigment}—O_2$$

Without the protein, the pigments combine with O_2 irreversibly. Four different types of respiratory pigments are well known: *hemoglobin, chlorocruorin, hemerythrin,* and *hemocyanin.*

Hemoglobin (Hb) is by far the most widespread; its presence has been demonstrated in all phyla except the sponges and the radiates. However, the pigment does not always occur in all groups within a phylum, and it is not always a blood constituent. For example, Hb occurs in protozoan cells, in the eggs of many animals, and within vertebrate skeletal muscle (where it is responsible for the redness of flesh and the color of "dark meat" in cooked condition). In such noncirculatory locations, Hb serves as a supplier of oxygen just as it does in blood. Blood hemoglobin occurs in the plasma of some animals, in the blood cells of others. For example, certain annelids, mollusks, and crustacea carry Hb in plasma. Other annelids, nemertine worms, sea cucumbers,

and vertebrates are among animals in which Hb is in the blood cells. A few annelids are known in which the pigment occurs both in plasma and in blood cells. Virtually the only generalization possible here is that the distribution of Hb is quite haphazard and does not appear to follow any obvious taxonomic or evolutionary pattern.

Hemoglobin is purple-red without oxygen, orange-red when combined with oxygen. It consists of the carrier protein *globin* and the pigment *heme.* The latter is a tetrapyrrol containing a single iron atom, rather similar to the cytochromes (see Fig. 6.16). Hb carries one molecule of oxygen per atom of iron. The nature of the globin fraction varies for different animal groups, and each such form of Hb endows blood with a unique oxygen-carrying capacity, as indicated in Table 21. This table shows that Hb is the most efficient of the respiratory pigments and that oxygen-carrying efficiency is correlated closely with the general level of body activity an animal can sustain. Thus, vertebrates and squids are far more active than other mollusks or worms, for example, and such differences are matched by the different oxygen-carrying capacities of their bloods. Among vertebrates, moreover, mammals are more active than reptiles, for example, and mammalian hemoglobin is actually seen to be the most efficient of all respiratory pigments.

The reaction of hemoglobin and oxygen may be symbolized as:

$$\text{Hb} + O_2 \rightleftharpoons \text{HbO}_2$$

This reaction proceeds to the right when oxygen is present in excess, as in the lungs. The product HbO_2 is *oxyhemoglobin* which, carried in blood, reaches the body tissues. These are oxygen-poor, and the reaction above therefore shifts to the left. Free Hb then reappears while the oxygen is taken up by the tissue cells (Fig. 24.9). Hemoglobin is known also to combine to some extent with CO_2 in blood, and it joins carbon monoxide (CO) in preference to O_2. Consequently, CO is an oxygen-displacing poison to hemoglobin-possessing animals.

Chlorocruorin is a green pigment with a reddish color in a concentrated state. Its composition is quite similar to that of Hb, that is, it is an iron-containing heme protein. It also functions in essentially the same way as Hb (Table 21). Chlorocruorin is found only in certain sedentary marine annelids, in which it is dissolved in the plasma. The taxonomic distribution of this pigment similarly does not follow any obvious evolutionary pattern. For example, in one particular genus of annelids, one species is known to possess Hb and red blood; a second species possesses chlorocruorin and green blood; and a third

TABLE 21 RESPIRATORY PIGMENTS AND OXYGEN-CARRYING CAPACITY OF BLOOD

PIGMENT	ANIMAL GROUP	cm³ O_2 CARRIED per 100 cm³ BLOOD	OCCURRENCE IN BLOOD
hemocyanin	*some snails*	2	*plasma*
(colorless to	*squids*	8	*plasma*
blue); Cu	*crustacea*	3	*plasma*
hemerythrin	*some annelids*	2	*cells*
(colorless to	*and*		
red); Fe	*related worms*		
chlorocruorin	*some annelids*	9	*plasma*
(green to			
reddish); Fe			
hemoglobin	*some mollusks*	2	*plasma*
(purple-red	*some annelids*	7	*plasma or cells*
to orange-			
red); Fe	*fishes*	9	*cells*
	amphibia	11	*cells*
	reptiles	10	*cells*
	birds	18	*cells*
	mammals	25	*cells*

species does not contain respiratory pigments at all and thus has colorless blood. In the annelid genus *Serpula*, moreover, both Hb and chlorocruorin are present (in plasma). This is the only clearly known instance where two different blood pigments occur together.

Hemerythrin is a colorless pigment which turns red when combined with oxygen. Its chemistry is known only poorly, but it has been shown that the pigment is an iron compound containing two atoms of iron per molecule. Thus, two Fe atoms are required for the transport of one O_2 molecule. Hemerythrin too has a highly restricted distribution, being found only in one group of annelids, in some echiuroid worms, and in one genus of brachiopods (*Lingula*). In these animals the pigment occurs exclusively in the blood cells.

Hemocyanin likewise is colorless, but it turns blue in combination with oxygen. It differs also from the pigments above in that it is a copper compound, two atoms of copper being required for the transport of one O_2 molecule. Unlike the other pigments, moreover, hemocyanin does not combine with CO. The pigment always occurs in plasma, and it is found in two phyla only, namely, in mollusks (squids, octopuses, and certain snails) and in arthropods (crustacea most particularly).

An interesting group of blood pigments with possible respiratory functions is known to occur in tunicates. The blood of these marine chordates contains high concentrations of oxides of vanadium, an element so dilute in sea water that its presence there can barely be demonstrated. The pigments are orange, green, and blue, they are linked to protein, and they occur in the blood cells. Hb is not present (and none, indeed has as yet been demonstrated in any chordates other than the vertebrates). The vanadium pigments combine readily with O_2, and they release the gas in acid media. Since tunicate blood cells actually contain free sulfuric acid (!), a respiratory role of the pigments is probable though not fully proved.

With the exception of small amounts of CO_2 carried by hemoglobin (as $HbCO_2$), transport of carbon dioxide largely does not involve the respiratory pigments. To a certain extent CO_2 is dissolved in blood water, like oxygen, and indeed blood contains dissolved aerial nitrogen as well. Thus, when the external air pressure suddenly falls, as during rapid ascents into high altitudes or up from great depths, the dissolved gases may fizz out of the blood in the form of bubbles (an effect rather like the fizzing of a bottle of soda after the cap has been removed). The bubbles block blood vessels, induce formation of internal blood clots, and produce dangerous "bends."

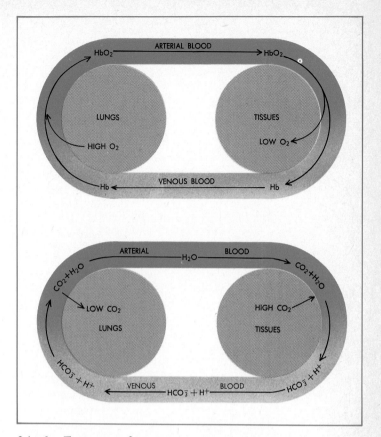

24 · 9 Transport of respiratory gases in blood. *Oxygen is carried in the form of oxyhemoglobin* (HbO_2), *carbon dioxide in the form of bicarbonate ions* (HCO_3^-).

By far the greater part of CO_2 in blood reacts chemically with the water of plasma and forms bicarbonate ions:

$$CO_2 + H_2O \underset{\substack{\textit{in breathing} \\ \textit{system}}}{\overset{\textit{in body tissues}}{\rightleftharpoons}} H^+ + HCO_3^-$$

Inasmuch as tissue cells continuously add CO_2 to blood, this reaction proceeds to the right in the tissues. Most of the CO_2 is therefore transported to the lungs in the form of HCO_3^-. In the lungs CO_2 escapes into the alveoli, the reaction above then shifts to the left, and more free CO_2 is released for exhalation (see Fig. 24.9).

We may note that *rapid* formation of HCO_3^- and H^+, as in the reaction to the right, requires the enzyme *carbonic anhydrase*. This enzyme occurs only within red blood corpuscles, and HCO_3^- is therefore formed mostly in these corpuscles. After they are formed, the bicarbonate ions largely diffuse out of the corpuscles and are carried to the lungs in the plasma. Inasmuch as bicarbonate ions are electrically negative, we might expect that as the ions leave the red corpuscles the latter would not remain electrically neutral. But it has been found that for every bicarbonate ion diffusing out from a red corpuscle, a chloride ion (Cl^-) normally present in plasma diffuses in. This exchange, called the *chloride shift*, preserves the electrical neutrality of the red corpuscles. In the lungs, these processes take place in reverse. Chloride ions move out of red corpuscles and bicarbonate ions move back in. The enzyme carbonic anhydrase then promotes the rapid re-formation of free CO_2, and this gas diffuses from the blood into the lung alveoli (Fig. 24.10).

The reaction between CO_2 and H_2O yields not only bicarbonate ions but also hydrogen ions (H^+). Blood might therefore be expected to become considerably more acid whenever it transports CO_2. The pH of blood does not change, however, for blood is strongly buffered (see Chap. 23). Among the buffering agents are various inorganic ions as well as blood proteins, including hemoglobin. These substances unite with H^+ as it is formed and the resulting combinations remain more or less nonionized. In the lungs CO_2 and H_2O are re-formed and the buffers then release the H^+ ions.

EXCRETION

Excretory systems are the ultimate controllers of chemical equilibria within the body and between the body and the environment; their primary role

24 · 10   The chloride shift. *In tissue capillaries (left), CO_2 reacts with water in the corpuscles. Bicarbonate ions appear, and as these diffuse into the plasma, chloride ions diffuse into the corpuscles. Hydrogen ions are also formed, and these are buffered (middle). In the lungs these processes occur in reverse, resulting in the liberation of gaseous CO_2 (right).*

is to maintain optimum internal balances of water volume, salt concentrations, pH, and osmotic pressure, and to eliminate metabolic wastes. The latter include principally respiratory CO_2, NH_3 or its derivatives resulting from metabolic interconversions of nitrogenous compounds, excess mineral ions from ingested food, and excess water from either ingested food or metabolic processes or osmotic intake in freshwater animals. As already noted, however, what is or is not "waste" among such substances is precisely what the excretory system must determine. To do so requires exquisite sensitivities to concentrations, for water and salts are both waste and nonwaste simultaneously, the difference being one of amount, not kind. Ammonia and derivatives such as urea or uric acid are toxic materials usually representing wastes in virtually any amounts, and CO_2 is largely waste; as a gas it is excreted primarily through the breathing surfaces, as we have seen.

As long as an animal is so constructed that all or most of its cells are exposed directly to the environment, each cell can function as its own excretory apparatus. The cell membrane is the excretory organelle, and waste substances can be eliminated into the external medium by diffusion and/or energy-requiring active transport across the cell boundary. But where all or most cells of an animal are not exposed directly to the environment, the interior cells can excrete only into lymph or blood. Specialized excretory systems must then operate in close association with the body fluids and act as screening devices, retaining valuable substances within the fluids and collecting only wastes for removal to the exterior. In all systems this excretory function appears to be performed through one or more of three basic processes: *filtration*, *reabsorption*, and *secretion* (Fig. 24.11).

Filtration takes place between the body fluids

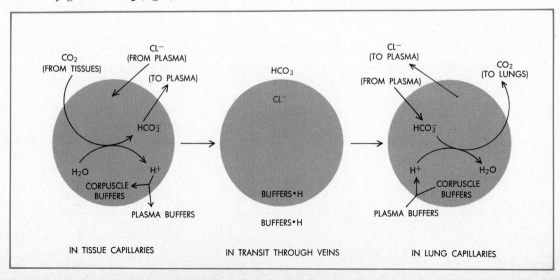

IN TISSUE CAPILLARIES   IN TRANSIT THROUGH VEINS   IN LUNG CAPILLARIES

and the interior space of an excretory system, the filter usually being a surface layer of the system in contact with the body fluids. The pressure of the body fluids (for example, blood pressure) supplies the force necessary for filtration. Cellular components and proteins in blood or lymph normally cannot pass through the filter, but most other components can; the filtration process is otherwise not too selective. Thus, the filtrate collecting within the space of the excretory structure is essentially lymph, which we may refer to here as *initial urine*. It still contains valuable substances as well as wastes. A separation of the two occurs when initial urine flows through another region of the excretory system on its way to the outside. Reabsorption then takes place; cells in contact with initial urine remove from it substances "judged" to be valuable, and they return such substances into the body fluids. We note that the reabsorbing cells represent the discriminators, and they must expend a substantial amount of energy in carrying out their functions. If salts or other dissolved materials are being reabsorbed, the remaining urine will become more dilute, that is, hypotonic to the body fluids; if water is reabsorbed, the remaining urine will become hypertonic and more concentrated than the body fluids.

The third process, secretion, may take place either in the same general region of the excretory system or in another body part altogether (for example, gills or lungs). Secretion accomplishes the removal of waste or excess materials from the body fluids into either urine or the external environment directly (see Fig. 24.11). Secretion and reabsorption therefore appear to be essentially the same process but operating in opposite directions. However, the two do not always occur simultaneously, and the substances being reabsorbed may differ greatly from those being secreted. Thus, secretion provides an additional mechanism by which the composition of the internal body fluids can be regulated. The urine ultimately present may be called *final urine*. It is discharged either continuously or, after accumulating in a *bladder*, intermittently. In many cases the excretory system opens to the outside directly; in others it empties into the hind region of the alimentary tract or into the outgoing ducts of the reproductive system.

We are already familiar with some of the types of excretory systems encountered in various animal groups (see Chaps. 14 to 16). Thus, we have referred to flame-bulb systems, in which filtration takes place through the flame cells and reabsorption and secretion through the ducts of the system. We have also spoken of metanephridia and various special excretory glands in mollusks and arthropods, in which the ducts

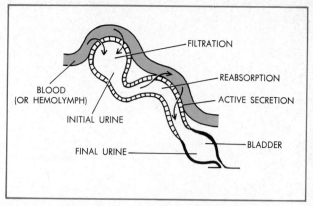

24 · 11 The actions of an excretory system. *A filtrate of blood forms initial urine, from which some materials are reabsorbed and to which other materials are secreted. These functions are performed by the cells lining the system. Final urine is the ultimate product.*

largely reabsorb and secrete, whereas filtration of coelomic fluid or blood occurs earlier through peritoneal or other membranes. And we have discussed the basic operation of the vertebrate nephron, where a capillary glomerulus first filters into a nephric capsule and where a nephric tubule from this capsule then functions in reabsorption and secretion (see Fig. 16.29). The numerous nephrons present constitute the kidney, the organ being either a pronephros, a mesonephros, or a metanephros depending on the anteroposterior body level at which the nephrons occur. A metanephros is characteristic of reptiles, birds, and mammals; and we recall that such a kidney is specialized particularly for conservation of water and elimination of salt in adaptation to the terrestrial life of these animals.

Note, however, that kidneys are not the only components of the vertebrate excretory system. In mammals, for example, the lungs contribute to the elimination of water and carbon dioxide. Sweat glands aid materially in regulating water balance and also salt balance. The large intestine makes a further contribution to mineral balance. The liver excretes many diverse materials via bile. And various excretory functions are performed also by the nasal epithelium, the tear glands, the salivary and other digestive glands—in short, by all the organs with access to the exterior of the body, either directly or via the alimentary tract (Fig. 24.12). But the kidneys exercise the major excretory control. When the kidneys are inoperative, all the above organs together are inadequate to prevent death from excretory failure. As indicated in Chap. 22, several hormones control the proper functioning of kidney cells.

In mammals specifically, each kidney consists of

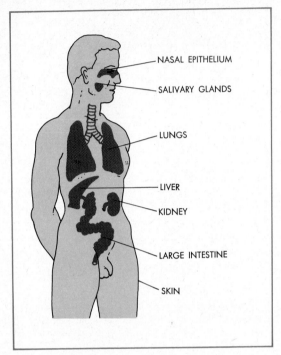

24 · 12 *The excretory system and some of its component organs.*

24 · 13 *The renal system. Left, kidneys and their ducts and the bladder (kidney on right in section). Right, a nephron unit, showing the convoluted portions of the tubule and Henle's loop. The capillary bed enveloping the coiled parts of a nephron is indicated as the shaded area.*

an outer *renal cortex* and an inner *renal medulla* (Fig. 24.13). Located partly in the cortex and partly in the medulla are the many thousands of nephrons. The nephric capsule of each continues as a highly coiled and looped nephric tubule, and note again that it is the great length of these tubules that specifically adapts the entire kidney to terrestrial operation; the whole tubule and the long *loop of Henle* particularly represent the water-reabsorbing and therefore water-conserving segments. At its far end the nephric tubule leads into a *collecting duct,* which receives the output of many neighboring nephric tubules. The numerous collecting ducts in a kidney eventually join and form a wide vessel, the *ureter.* This channel carries urine into the *urinary bladder.* A final duct, the *urethra,* connects the bladder with the outside.

A large *renal artery* enters the kidney in the region where the ureter leaves and branches out repeatedly into many smaller arteries. One of these smaller arteries leads to each nephric capsule and there forms the capillary *glomerulus.* The capillaries then rejoin into a single vessel which leaves the capsule and passes into the tubular portion of the nephron. Here the blood vessel branches out once more into a dense capillary net which envelops all parts of the nephric tubule. Near the collecting duct, the capillaries lead into a small vein and many such veins from neighboring nephrons join into larger vessels. All these eventually form a single channel, the *renal vein,* which leaves the kidney where the renal artery enters (see Fig. 24.13).

Filtration of blood through the glomeruli produces initial urine within the cavities of the nephric capsules, and after reabsorption and secretion have taken

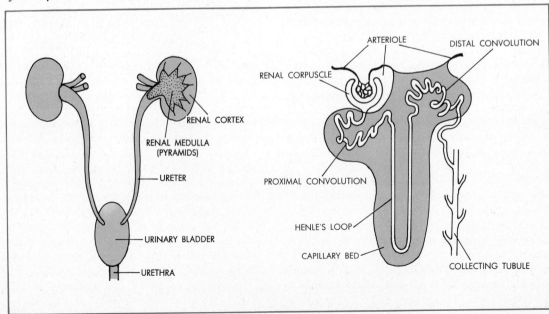

place in the nephric tubules, a final urine leaves the kidneys via the ureters and collects in the urinary bladder. The wall of the bladder stretches as urine accumulates, and at a certain stage of stretching sensory nerve endings in the wall are stimulated. A reflex initiates contraction of the muscles in the bladder wall and the organ then empties to the outside.

Of the substances filtered out from blood and subsequently returned to blood in the kidneys, the most abundant is water. In man, blood contains about 5 to 6 qt of water and this amount is filtered through the kidneys roughly once every 45 min. In a 24-hr period, therefore, the kidneys filter about 150 qt of liquid. Yet in the same period only about 1½ qt of urine, on an average, is actually excreted by the normal adult. This means that tubule cells reabsorb 99 per cent of the water in initial urine and leave only 1 per cent as final urine. As might be expected, the amount of water excreted varies with the amount of fluid intake.

Another substance always reabsorbed by the tubule cells and returned to blood is glucose. Initial urine contains glucose in the same concentration as in blood. Under normal conditions, all the glucose in initial urine is reabsorbed into the blood and none escapes into final urine. As noted in earlier contexts, however, glucose does pass into final urine when the compound is present in excessive quantities. Under such conditions, tubule cells probably cannot reabsorb this carbohydrate fast enough and some of it is then excreted. Glucose is said to be a *high-threshold substance;* a high concentration must be present in blood and initial urine before it will be excreted in final urine. Among other high-threshold materials are amino acids, fatty acids, glycerin, vitamins, hormones—in short, essential nutrients and other required metabolites in transit to tissue cells (Fig. 24.14).

On the contrary, some substances are always left in initial urine and are not reabsorbed by the tubule cells. Among such substances are urea, pigmented blood-breakdown products, and other outright wastes. Inasmuch as materials of this type are excreted even when they are present in very low concentrations, they are referred to as *low-threshold substances.* They become highly concentrated as water is withdrawn from initial urine. For example, final urine contains some 70 times more urea than an equal volume of initial urine.

Included in a third group are so-called *inter-mediate-threshold substances.* Tubule cells do or do not reabsorb a given material in this group depending on whether the material is or is not in proper balance in blood. Most mineral ions and many organic

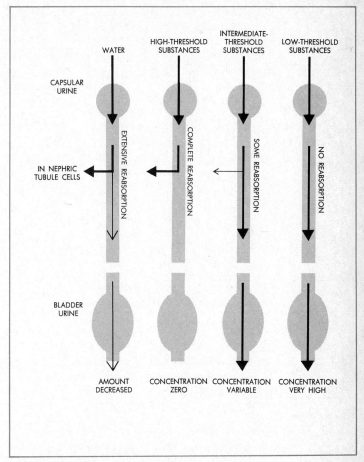

24 · 14 *Selective action of the cells of a nephric tubule. Water is reabsorbed to a very large extent; high-threshold substances like glucose are reabsorbed more or less completely; low-threshold substances like urea are not reabsorbed at all; and intermediate-threshold substances like many mineral ions are reabsorbed in part, depending on the amount already present in blood.*

substances belong to this category. For example, high salt intake will be followed by excretion of sodium and chloride ions if the supply of these ions in blood is already adequate. But if the supply is low to begin with, the tubule cells will reabsorb sodium and chloride and thus raise the salt concentration in blood. Note that water itself qualifies as an intermediate-threshold substance (see Fig. 24.14).

Note too that, as urine becomes more concentrated by withdrawal of water from initial urine back to blood, the osmotic pull of urine becomes greater. Despite this force, which tends to draw water *from* blood *into* urine, tubule cells nevertheless continue to transport more water from *urine* into *blood*. It would evidently be quite justifiable to regard kidneys, and analogously functioning organs, not merely as excretory systems but as "retention systems" as well. Moreover, it may be appreciated why examination of urine will reveal not only how well the kidneys function, but also how well chemoregulation specifically and steady state generally are maintained in the body as a whole.

REVIEW QUESTIONS

1. Distinguish between breathing and respiration. How does gas exchange occur among plants? What different types of breathing processes and systems are encountered among invertebrates? How does each of these systems operate? How is a system operating in water different from one operating in air?

2. Describe the structural organization of the breathing system in man. How is sound produced and how can sound be varied in pitch, volume, and quality? What is an alveolus and what is its relation to the lung? What chest structures surround the lungs?

3. Describe the pressure changes in the body associated with inhalation and exhalation in (*a*) abdominal breathing and (*b*) chest breathing.

4. How are inhalation-exhalation cycles controlled and maintained automatically? Review here the role of CO_2 and that of the brain. Show by what sequence of events inhalation comes to alternate with exhalation.

5. Describe the processes through which breathing rate increases when physical exercise is begun and decreases at the onset of sleep. What is overventilation and what is its effect?

6. Interpret the automatic alternation of inhalation and exhalation in terms of control activity. What parts of the breathing system serve as receptors, modulators, effectors, and transmission paths, and what are the stimulus, the feedback, and the response?

7. By what processes and specifically where does arterial blood become venous and vice versa? Show what factors govern these changes and describe the actual changes in lungs and tissues.

8. How is oxygen carried in blood in different animal groups? What reactions occur in the lungs and in the tissues with reference to oxygen transport? Why is carbon monoxide a poison?

9. How is CO_2 carried in blood? What reactions occur in the lungs and in the tissues? What is the role of red blood corpuscles in CO_2 transport? What is the chloride shift? What is the function of carbonic anhydrase and of blood buffers?

10. How are breathing and gas transport affected during ascent to high altitudes? How is nitrogen carried in blood? Why is breathing difficult in an unventilated room? What happens when a person holds his breath for a long time?

11. What is the basic structure and function of an excretory system? What does it excrete? Distinguish between excretory filtration, secretion, and reabsorption. Describe the structure and operation of flame-bulb nephridia and metanephridia.

12. Show how the pattern of water and salt excretion varies according to whether an animal lives in a marine, a freshwater, or a terrestrial environment. Describe the structure of the vertebrate pronephros, mesonephros, and metanephros. How do these differ functionally? What is a nephron and how does it operate?

13. What organs compose the mammalian excretory system and what is the specific excretory role of each? Describe the general structure of the mammalian kidney and its associated ducts and the specific structure of a nephron.

14. Review in detail the process of urine formation in man. What are the roles of filtration and reabsorption and where and how does each occur? What are high-threshold substances? Give examples.

15. Construct a table showing how final urine differs from blood and initial urine with respect to (*a*) the kinds of substances present and (*b*) the concentrations of substances present.

COLLATERAL READINGS

Baldwin, E.: "Introduction to Comparative Biochemistry," Cambridge, New York, 1949. This little booklet contains excellent discussions of gas transport in blood and excretory mechanisms (especially of nitrogen compounds) in a variety of animals. Recommended.

Carlson, A. J., and V. Johnson: "The Machinery of the Body," 4th ed., University of Chicago, Chicago,

1953. A thorough chapter on mammalian breathing and a section on excretion are included in this recommended text.

Carter, G. S.: Aquatic and Aerial Respiration in Animals, *Biol. Rev.*, vol. 6, 1931. A review paper on breathing; comparative for a variety of animals.

Clements, J. A.: Surface Tension in the Lungs, *Sci. American*, Dec., 1962. An examination of tension-lowering substances in the lungs that may aid in preventing lung collapse.

Griffin, D. R.: "Animal Structure and Function," Holt, New York, 1962. This paperback includes a very brief review of the structures of various vertebrate breathing systems.

Perutz, M. F.: The Hemoglobin Molecule, *Sci. American*, Nov., 1964. An account of the detailed configuration of the four polypeptide chains that compose hemoglobin.

Prosser, C. L., and F. A. Brown, Jr.: "Comparative Animal Physiology," 2d ed., Saunders, Philadelphia, 1961. A comprehensive coverage of breathing and excretory functions may be found in this very good text.

Smith, H.: The Kidney, *Sci. American*, Jan., 1953. A recommended article on the function of the mammalian kidney.

Williams, C.: Insect Breathing, *Sci. American*, Feb., 1953. The structure and function of the tracheal system of arthropods is discussed.

CHAPTER 25
NERVE, BRAIN, AND SENSE ORGAN

All nervous activity is based on *reflexes,* the operational units of nervous systems. A reflex is routed through a *reflex arc,* which, like any control apparatus, usually consists of five components: *receptor, sensory pathway, modulator, motor pathway,* and *effector* (see Fig. 21.6).

The neural receptors are specialized *sensory cells,* which may or may not be housed in elaborate sense organs. Receptors are sensitive to specific environmental *stimuli,* and incoming stimuli initiate *nerve impulses.* These are transmitted over *sensory nerve fibers* to the modulators, namely, specialized internal portions of a nervous system such as ganglia, spinal cords, and brains. It is the function of modulators to interpret sensory impulses and in turn to initiate appropriate, steady-state-maintaining motor impulses. The latter are sent out over *motor nerve fibers* to the effectors, namely, *muscles* and *glands.* Such effectors then act on the motor impulses they receive by carrying out explicit *responses.* These usually bear a distinct relation to the original stimuli, and they alter the internal or external activities of an animal in such a way that steady state can be preserved.

NEURAL PATHWAYS

The structural units of reflex arcs, and thus of nervous systems as a whole, are nerve cells, or *neurons.* Each typically consists of a nucleus-containing cell body, the *cyton,* and of one or more *nerve fibers,* filamentous outgrowths extending away from the cell body (Fig. 25.1). Nerve impulses normally originate at the terminal of one of the fibers, travel toward the cell body, traverse it, then lead away from the cell body through another of its fibers. Nerve fibers in which impulses travel toward the cell body are termed *dendrites;* those carrying impulses away from the cell body are called *axons.* Dendrites and axons vary greatly in length, some being quite short, others often being as much as a yard or more long. Many nerve fibers branch along their course and at their terminals. On the basis of the number and arrangement of long fibers present, neurons may be said to be *unipolar, bipolar,* or *multipolar.*

Long nerve fibers but not the cell bodies or the shorter fibers may be enveloped by one or by two sheaths. Thus, most of the long fibers of vertebrates are surrounded directly by a layer of secreted fatty material, the *myelin sheath.* This sheath in turn is enveloped by the *Schwann sheath,* composed of a single layer of thin flat cells. In other nerve fibers of vertebrates only a Schwann sheath surrounds the axon; myelin sheaths are absent in such cases. Myelin sheaths probably increase the speed of nerve-impulse transmission. It can be shown that myelinated fibers may conduct impulses at speeds of about 100 yd per sec, whereas nonmyelinated fibers conduct at about 25 yd per sec at most. The suggestion has been made that the accelerating effect of the fatty myelin layer results from an insulating action; a myelin envelope would be to a nerve fiber what a rubber envelope is to an electricity-conducting metal wire.

The Schwann sheath maintains the continued existence of the nerve fiber it envelops. It is known to supply nutritive materials to the fiber, and it also plays a critical role in fiber regeneration. If an axon is cut, for example, the disconnected part soon degenerates. But if the cut ends of the Schwann sheath are allowed to heal together, then the intact axon stump slowly grows out into the reconnected Schwann tube. A complete new axon eventually regenerates, replacing the degenerated portion (Fig. 25.2).

Adjacent neurons are never fused to one another

directly but remain structurally discrete. The fiber terminals are separated from one another by a microscopic space called a *synapse* (Fig. 25.3). Impulses are transmitted across such synapses by chemical means, from the axon terminal of one neuron to a dendrite terminal of an adjacent neuron (see below). According to their position within a reflex arc, so-called *sensory*, or *afferent*, neurons transmit impulses from sense organ to modulator; and *motor*, or *efferent*, neurons transmit from modulator to effector. Neurons within a modulator, including those which transmit impulses from incoming sensory to outgoing motor fibers, are called *interneurons*. Groups of nerve fibers frequently traverse a body region as a single collective fiber bundle. Such a bundle, usually enveloped by a sheath of connective tissue, constitutes a *nerve*. Nerves are designated as being sensory, motor, or mixed, depending on whether they contain sensory fibers, motor fibers, or both (see Fig. 25.3).

The most primitive type of neuron arrangement is a *nerve net*, characteristic particularly of the Radiata, flatworms, echinoderms, and hemichordates. In the first two of these groups such nets are the most elaborate neural structures present. But nets usually form at least part of the nervous systems of all other animals as well. For example, nets are common in the walls of the alimentary tract, as in vertebrates. In addition to nets, most animals also possess more highly specialized neural aggregations. Among these are, for example, *nerve cords* and *ganglia*. Such structures may be sensory, motor, or mixed, according to the kinds of fibers they connect with. The more complex ganglia contain meshworks of interneurons, organized into intricate internal pathways and neural circuits. Within large ganglia there are usually functional subdivisions referred to as nerve *centers*, specialized groups of interneurons regulating specific activities. Thus, some centers are specialized to interpret incoming sensory information only, others transmit motor commands only; some centers control involuntary functions only, others are concerned with voluntary activities only. Moreover, the large ganglia and groups of ganglia may also store information as memory, may acquire and store new information by learning, and may control intricate patterns of behavior. Such ganglia and ganglionic groups in effect constitute *brains*.

By far the most complex nervous systems are those of the vertebrates. The main portions arise from a hollow dorsal nerve cord, or *neural tube*, formed in the embryo as an ingrowth from the ectoderm (see Chap. 29). The anterior portion of the tube enlarges into a *brain*; the posterior portion becomes the *spinal cord*. The fluid-filled space within the tube persists

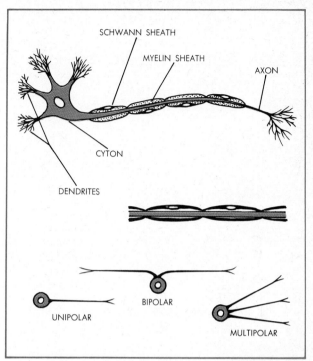

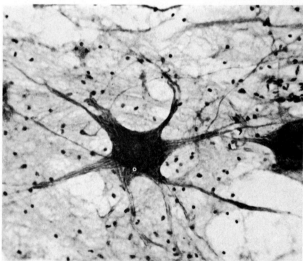

25 · 1 Neurons. *Diagrams: the labeled figure depicts the general structure of a neuron with a myelinated axon; a portion of a nonmyelinated fiber, possessing a Schwann sheath only, is sketched immediately below. At bottom are schematic drawings of different neuron types; axons only, not dendrites, are shown. The unipolar type corresponds to the labeled figure at top. Photo: micrograph of a stained (multipolar) motor neuron.*

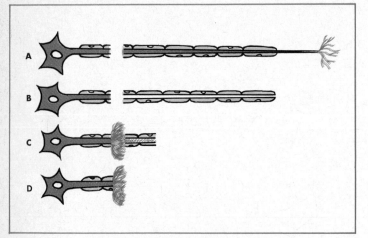

25 · 2 Neuron regeneration. *A, cut axon. B, axon on far side of cut has degenerated. C, if a Schwann sheath is present, a new axon grows into it. D, if a Schwann sheath is not present, new axon growth is random and disoriented.*

of these form the *telencephalon* anteriorly, a left and right portion containing a brain ventricle each. In all vertebrates except the birds and mammals, the telencephalon remains comparatively small, and the most conspicuous components are the *olfactory lobes* extending forward. These contain the centers for the sense of smell. In birds and mammals, the telencephalon is enlarged greatly into two *cerebral hemispheres,* which cover the rest of the brain dorsally, posteriorly, and laterally. The hemispheres contain the modulator centers for most sensory and motor activities; and they are also the seat of memory, intelligence, and all so-called "higher" mental functions. An extensive series of nerve tracts, called the *corpus callosum,* interconnects the two hemispheres.

Behind the telencephalon is the unpaired third part of the forebrain, the *diencephalon* (see Fig. 25.4). Its ventricle communicates with those anteriorly and

as the brain *ventricles* anteriorly and the *spinal canal* posteriorly (Fig. 25.4). In the mature brain, three general regions may be distinguished, namely, *forebrain, midbrain,* and *hindbrain.*

The forebrain consists of three subdivisions. Two

25 · 3 Neural pathway patterns. *Afferent fibers (color) conduct impulses from receptors to modulators, where interneurons transmit the impulses to efferent fibers. The latter send impulses to effectors. Neurons interconnect functionally across synapses. Collected bundles of neuron fibers form nerves. The photo at right depicts a cross section through such a nerve; the dark circlets are the myelin sheaths of the individual nerve fibers.*

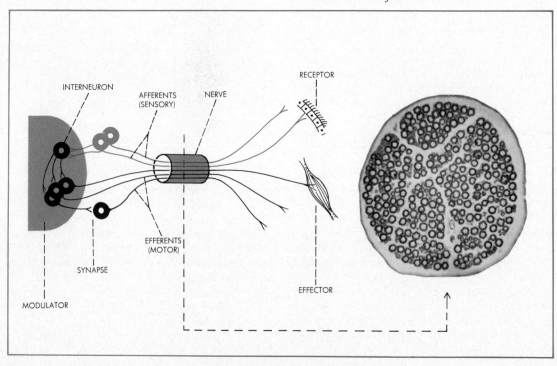

INTERNEURON

AFFERENTS (SENSORY)

NERVE

RECEPTOR

SYNAPSE

EFFERENTS (MOTOR)

MODULATOR

EFFECTOR

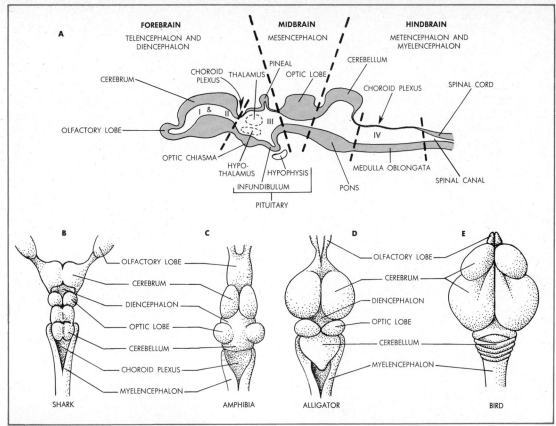

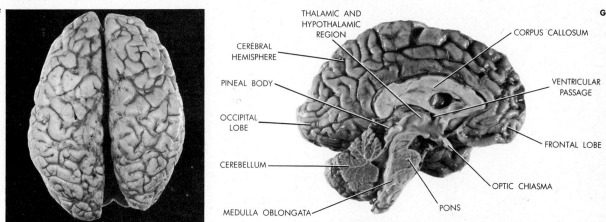

25 · 4 The vertebrate brain. *A, schematic representation of median section through primitive vertebrate brain (as in fishes), showing basic structural plan. Roman numerals refer to ventricles. Thalamus and hypothalamus regions are indicated in broken lines, since these brain parts lie on each side of the median plane (as do ventricles I and II). The hypophysis forms as an outpouching from the roof of the mouth cavity; it becomes the anterior lobe of the pituitary, the infundibulum becoming the posterior lobe. The two choroid plexi are membranous regions in which blood vessels are carried. B, C,*

D, E, dorsal views of brains of fish (shark), amphibia (frog), reptiles (alligator), and birds (goose), respectively. Note the proportionate progressive enlargement of the cerebrum in a posterior direction (and the parallel reduction of the olfactory lobes). F, photo showing dorsal view of cerebrum of human brain. Note that the left cerebral hemisphere is slightly larger than the right, a usual condition in right-handed persons. G, median section through human brain. The cerebrum here has become so large that, in dorsal view, it covers the cerebellum posteriorly.

615

those posteriorly. The principal modulator centers of the diencephalon are the *thalamus* and *hypothalamus,* lateral regions which control numerous involuntary muscular and glandular activities as well as consciousness, sleep, food intake, and the emotional state of the animal. On the ventral side of the diencephalon, the *pituitary gland* is attached to the brain. Nerves as well as blood vessels interconnect the hypothalamus and the pituitary gland, and it is through these pathways that the hypothalamus exercises major control over many glandular activities. Dorsally, the *pineal body* projects from the diencephalon. In lampreys and the reptile *Sphenodon,* this body forms a third eye on top of the head. In other vertebrates such a pineal eye is not functional, and in birds and mammals the body is covered over by the cerebral hemispheres.

The midbrain, or *mesencephalon,* contains a fourth brain ventricle and also dorsally located *optic lobes*

25 · 5 *Underside of brain and anterior part of spinal cord of man, showing the origin of the 12 pairs of cranial nerves and of a few of the spinal nerves. The names and functions of these nerves are given in the accompanying tabulation. Note that, in the spinal nerves, the dorsal roots (with ganglia) are sensory, the ventral roots, motor.*

(see Fig. 25.4). In all vertebrates except the mammals, these lobes represent the center of vision, and the nerve tracts from the eyes terminate there. In mammals, however, the optic nerve tracts are extended into newly evolved visual centers, located in the posterior regions of the cerebral hemispheres. The original optic lobes here are little more than relay stations for visual nerve impulses.

The hindbrain consists of two subdivisions, an anterior *metencephalon* and a posterior *myelencephalon,* or *medulla oblongata* (see Fig. 25.4). Dorsally, the metencephalon includes the *cerebellum,* a comparatively large lobe which coordinates all motor functions involving numerous muscles into smoothly integrated movements. For example, locomotion is regulated from this lobe. Ventrally, the metencephalon contains a conspicuous band of nerve tracts, the *pons,* in which the neural pathways between brain and spinal cord cross from the left side to the right side. Thus, the left side of the brain sends impulses to the right side of the spinal cord and thereby controls activities on the right side of the body. Analogously, the right side of the brain controls the left side of the body.

The medulla oblongata is continuous posteriorly with the spinal cord. We already know that the medulla contains the centers controlling heartbeat, breathing, and vasomotion. Twelve pairs of *cranial*

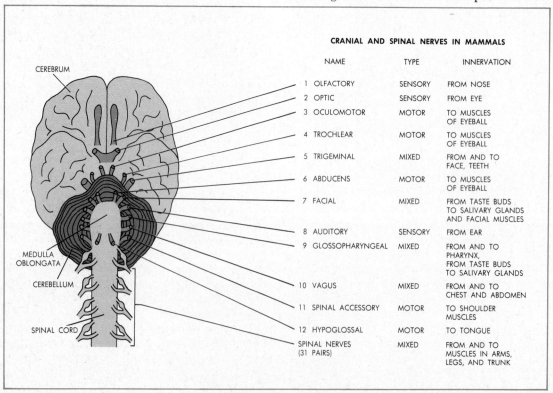

CRANIAL AND SPINAL NERVES IN MAMMALS

	NAME	TYPE	INNERVATION
1	OLFACTORY	SENSORY	FROM NOSE
2	OPTIC	SENSORY	FROM EYE
3	OCULOMOTOR	MOTOR	TO MUSCLES OF EYEBALL
4	TROCHLEAR	MOTOR	TO MUSCLES OF EYEBALL
5	TRIGEMINAL	MIXED	FROM AND TO FACE, TEETH
6	ABDUCENS	MOTOR	TO MUSCLES OF EYEBALL
7	FACIAL	MIXED	FROM TASTE BUDS TO SALIVARY GLANDS AND FACIAL MUSCLES
8	AUDITORY	SENSORY	FROM EAR
9	GLOSSOPHARYNGEAL	MIXED	FROM AND TO PHARYNX, FROM TASTE BUDS TO SALIVARY GLANDS
10	VAGUS	MIXED	FROM AND TO CHEST AND ABDOMEN
11	SPINAL ACCESSORY	MOTOR	TO SHOULDER MUSCLES
12	HYPOGLOSSAL	MOTOR	TO TONGUE
	SPINAL NERVES (31 PAIRS)	MIXED	FROM AND TO MUSCLES IN ARMS, LEGS, AND TRUNK

Labels on diagram: CEREBRUM, MEDULLA OBLONGATA, CEREBELLUM, SPINAL CORD

A

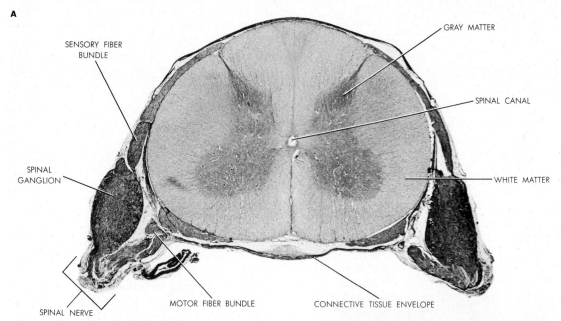

SENSORY FIBER BUNDLE

GRAY MATTER

SPINAL CANAL

SPINAL GANGLION

WHITE MATTER

SPINAL NERVE

MOTOR FIBER BUNDLE

CONNECTIVE TISSUE ENVELOPE

25·6 A, cross section through mammalian spinal cord. Note the spinal nerves, each dividing into two fiber bundles. The motor bundle connects with the cord ventrally, and the sensory bundle passes through a spinal ganglion and connects with the cord dorsally. The spinal cord itself is a dense meshwork of neurons, the cytons of which are aggregated around the center and form so-called gray matter. The axons and dendrites of these neurons are collected around the gray matter, forming white matter. The central spinal canal contains lymphlike spinal fluid. B, section through a spinal ganglion. Note the many cytons and also the nerve fibers, some seen in cross section, some in longitudinal section.

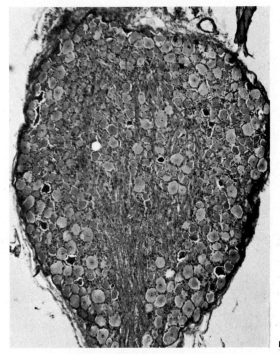

B

nerves (only ten pairs in fishes and amphibia) emerge from the entire brain, and about half of these lead away from the medulla oblongata (Fig. 25.5). The nerves are partly motor, partly sensory, partly mixed. Most fibers within these nerves control voluntary activities. The spinal cord connects with paired *spinal nerves* (31 pairs in mammals) which lead to the trunk and the appendages. Controlling voluntary activities in these body regions (for example, skeletal muscles), the nerve pairs are arranged segmentally and they are all mixed. In each such spinal nerve, sensory fibers enter the dorsal part of the spinal cord; motor fibers leave from the ventral part of the cord. The cytons of the sensory fibers lie just outside the spinal cord, in *spinal ganglia* (Fig. 25.6).

Vertebrates also possess a very well-developed *autonomic* subdivision of the nervous system, distinct from the remainder, called the *central* subdivision. Controlling the involuntary activities of smooth muscles, glands, and the heart, the autonomic system has its nerve centers located in the spinal cord and also partly in the brain, alongside the centers for voluntary functions. Leading to and from the auto-

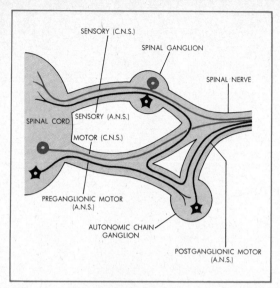

25 · 7 Interrelations of C.N.S. and A.N.S. fibers. *C.N.S. neurons are shown in color, A.N.S. neurons in black. Note that a given fiber bundle or nerve connecting with the spinal cord contains sensory fibers of both C.N.S. and A.N.S., or motor fibers of both C.N.S. and A.N.S., or both sensory and motor fibers of both C.N.S. and A.N.S. Sensory fibers of all kinds enter the spinal cord dorsally, motor fibers of all kinds leave ventrally.*

nomic centers are separate sets of sensory and motor nerve fibers. Most of these are distinguished from the fibers of the central nervous system in that they are without myelin sheaths, Schwann sheaths being their only covering.

Some of the sensory pathways of the autonomic system have already been described in earlier contexts. For example, stretch reflexes regulating heart function involve sensory neurons from the vena cava and the aorta to the heart-rate center in the medulla oblongata. Heart control is a purely autonomic, involuntary function; the heart-rate center together with the nerve fibers to and from it are part of the autonomic nervous system. Similarly, every other internal organ not controllable by force of will is innervated by sensory fibers leading to autonomic centers in brain or spinal cord. Like the sensory neurons of the central system, those of the autonomic system similarly pass through ganglia. Indeed, the cell bodies of autonomic sensory neurons lie in the same 31 pairs of spinal ganglia that also contain the cell bodies of central sensory neurons (Fig. 25.7).

With respect to the motor pathways of the autonomic system, two functionally different sets of motor fibers lead away from the autonomic centers (Fig. 25.8). Motor fibers from the brain and the most posterior part of the spinal cord constitute a so-

called *parasympathetic* outflow of the autonomic system. Such fibers pass to all involuntarily controlled organs of the body, and they either stimulate (accelerate) or inhibit (decelerate) the functioning of such organs. Some of the parasympathetic fibers travel along with the fibers of certain cranial nerves; for example, parasympathetic fibers from the medulla oblongata to the heart travel within the vagus nerve, the 10th cranial. From the middle portion of the spinal cord emanate motor fibers constituting a *sympathetic* outflow of the autonomic system. Sympathetic fibers likewise lead to all involuntarily controlled organs, and their effects are generally opposite to those of parasympathetic fibers. For example, the fibers accelerating the heart are sympathetic, those slowing the heart are parasympathetic. Analogously, vasoconstrictor fibers to blood vessels are part of the sympathetic outflow, but vasodilator fibers belong to the parasympathetic outflow. In general, if parasympathetic fibers inhibit the function-

25 · 8 The autonomic nervous system. *A, mammalian spinal cord and autonomic chains (color) on each side. B, some of the motor pathways of the autonomic nervous system. In spinal cord (center), parasympathetic centers shown in light*

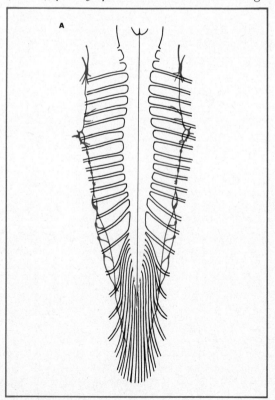

ing of a given organ, sympathetic fibers accelerate that organ; or vice versa. In effect, therefore, each organ functioning involuntarily is innervated by accelerating as well as by braking controls.

On their way to particular organs, sympathetic fibers pass through *autonomic ganglia* located just outside the spinal cord (see Fig. 25.8). These ganglia are arranged segmentally, and they are interconnected to form *autonomic ganglion chains,* one on each side of the spinal cord. The anatomical relation between a spinal ganglion and an autonomic ganglion is shown in Fig. 25.7. Note that sympathetic motor paths to given organs consist of at least two consecutive neurons. The fiber of the first neuron emanates from brain or spinal cord and either terminates in an autonomic chain ganglion or passes through to another autonomic ganglion located farther out in the body. Such fibers are referred to as being *preganglionic.* The fiber of the second neuron synapses with the axon terminal of the first and then

leads to a particular organ. Such fibers are said to be *postganglionic.* Parasympathetic motor paths do not lead through the autonomic ganglion chains, but they too consist of preganglionic and postganglionic portions, specific ganglia being located along the way to given organs.

Apart from their particular anatomies, how do nervous systems work?

NEURAL IMPULSES

The precise nature of a nerve impulse is still unknown. We may say, in general, that an impulse is a sequence of reactions propagated along a nerve fiber. After an impulse has passed, the reaction balance returns to the original state, readying the fiber for a new impulse. The processes consume oxygen and energy.

Accompanying the chemical changes are electrical phenomena. Indeed, the intriguing resemblance

color, sympathetic centers in darker color. The column left of the spinal cord represents the sympathetic chain on that side. Each neural path shown occurs pairwise, one on the left and one on the right of the body. For simplicity,

only one side is indicated in each case. Sympathetic motor paths are drawn on left, parasympathetic paths, on right. Note that each organ is innervated by both portions of the autonomic nervous system.

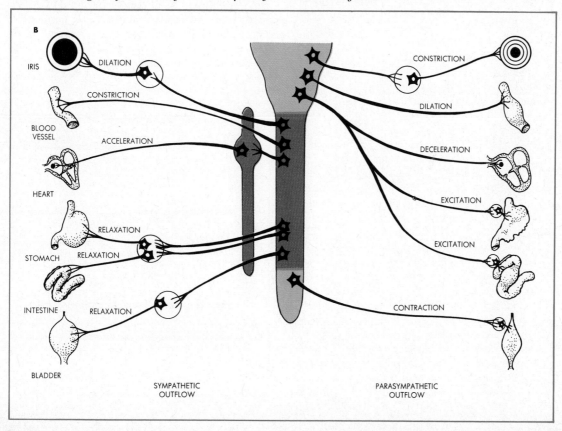

SYMPATHETIC OUTFLOW

PARASYMPATHETIC OUTFLOW

IRIS — DILATION — CONSTRICTION

CONSTRICTION — DILATION

BLOOD VESSEL — ACCELERATION — DECELERATION

HEART — EXCITATION

STOMACH — RELAXATION — RELAXATION — EXCITATION

INTESTINE — RELAXATION — CONTRACTION

BLADDER

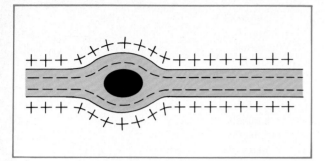

25 · 9 *Polarization of an inactive resting neuron. The positive charges on the outside and the negative charges on the inside produce an electric potential across the cell membrane.*

of the nervous system to a meshwork of electrical wires conducting electric currents has been the basis of many attempts to explain nervous activity. Moreover, just as one can measure currents in wires by galvanometers, voltmeters, ammeters, and the like, so this same electrical equipment can be used on nerves. But nerve impulses are not simply electrical impulses. The latter travel some 100,000 miles per sec in a wire, the former at most about 100 yd per sec in a nerve fiber. Nerve impulses are neither purely electrical nor purely chemical, and at present they may best be described as *electrochemical* events.

Before a nerve fiber can transmit an impulse, it must be stimulated adequately. Whereas any environmental change may represent a stimulus, not every such change represents an adequate, or effective, stimulus. To be effective, a stimulus must be at least of minimum strength, or *threshold intensity;* it must reach this threshold intensity fast enough, at an appropriately high *rate of change;* and it must last long enough and thus have appropriate *duration.* When a neuron is stimulated adequately, it will "fire," that is, transmit an impulse from the point of stimulation over its fibers. Under normal conditions within the body, stimulation occurs at a dendrite terminal and an impulse then travels through or past the cell body to an axon terminal.

Whatever else an impulse may be, it is known that it is a *wave of electrical depolarization* sweeping along a nerve fiber. It can be shown that a resting, nonstimulated neuron is electrically positive along the outer side of its surface membrane and electrically negative along the inner side (Fig. 25.9). These electric charges are carried by mineral ions attached to the two sides of the neuron membrane. The outer, positive charges are due primarily to ions such as Na^+, the inner, negative ones, to ions such as Cl^-. As a result, an *electrical potential* is maintained

across the cell membrane, and the membrane is said to be *polarized* electrically. In some ways this resembles the polarization believed to be maintained in the actomyosin units of muscles.

Polarization, as well as the integrity of a neuron membrane, appears to depend on *semipermeability.* The membrane is so constructed that it prevents the positive and negative ions from coming together. If the permeability state were altered, the membrane would depolarize; that is, the positive and negative ions would join. Conversely, if depolarization were to occur, membrane semipermeability would be abolished. When a nerve impulse sweeps along a nerve fiber, local depolarization and simultaneous changes of permeability actually do occur at successive points of the fiber membrane. As this happens at any one point, an avenue is created through which positive and negative ions of an adjacent point may meet (Fig. 25.10). In other words, the impulse itself produces the necessary conditions which allow it to advance farther. In this manner it travels wavelike along a fiber. Some short time after an impulse has passed a given point, the membrane at that point recovers; both the polarization and the original permeability state are restored.

25 · 10 *Passage of an impulse through a nerve fiber produces a local depolarization of the fiber membrane. This depolarization is propagated like a wave through successive portions of the fiber. After an impulse has passed a given region, the original polarization reappears.*

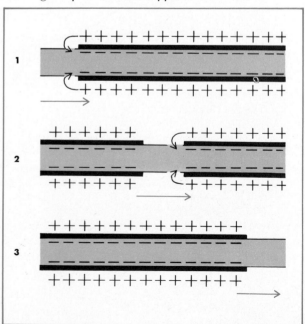

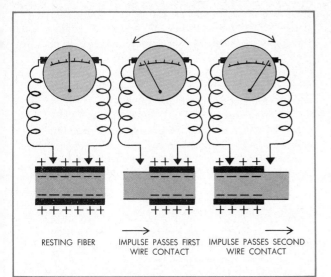

25 · 11 *The action potential of a nerve impulse. Left, resting fiber, connected to galvanometer by wire contacts. Middle, impulse passes first wire contact, which becomes electronegative relative to second contact. Hence current flows through galvanometer from right to left, as indicated by deflected galvanometer needle. Right, impulse passes second wire contact. Current now flows in opposite directions, the second contact being electronegative relative to the first. Current flow accompanying an impulse represents the action potential of that impulse.*

These electrical aspects of transmission may be demonstrated experimentally. For example, it is possible to expose a nerve of a test animal and to connect a galvanometer to this nerve with fine wires (Fig. 25.11). When the nerve is then stimulated, the needle of the galvanometer is deflected in one direction as the impulse passes the first wire contact and in the opposite direction as it passes the second. This result indicates that electrical changes occur during impulse transmission. Moreover, the test reveals that the particular portion of the fiber carrying the impulse at any given moment is electrically less positive on the surface than the remainder of the fiber. This is what should be expected if an impulse were to cause local depolarization, that is, reduction or removal of the outer positive charge. The current flow accompanying impulse transmission is called the action current, or the *action potential,* of a nerve fiber.

By measuring the action potentials of different nerves, one may determine many of the characteristics of the impulses these nerves carry, for example, speeds, frequencies, and strengths. In some nerve fibers, impulses are fired continuously and in fairly rapid succession. This is the case, for example, in the motor fibers from the heart-rate center to the heart. Adjustment of heart rate is brought about by "frequency modulation"; heart rate changes when the frequency of the impulses changes. In other cases, a fiber is normally at rest and carries impulses only when an effector response is to be brought about. In fibers to many glands, for example, impulses are sent only as long the glands are to secrete. Each type of fiber has its own characteristic pattern of impulse transmission, and it has been found also that impulse speeds tend to be directly proportional to the thickness of a nerve fiber.

How does an impulse jump across the gap of a synapse? In certain cases it can be shown that, when an impulse reaches an axon terminal, the terminal acts like a miniature endocrine gland; it secretes minute amounts of a hormone. This hormone diffuses through the synaptic gap, some of it eventually reaches dendrite terminals of adjacent neurons, and the hormone there affects a dendrite in such a way that a new impulse is initiated in it (Fig. 25.12).

Four hormonal substances functioning in this manner have been identified in vertebrates. Called *neurohumors* collectively, they are *serotonin, acetylcholine,* and the adrenalines *epinephrine* and *norepinephrine.* One or the other of the last two is secreted by the axon terminals of the sympathetic postganglionic fibers, which are therefore said to be *adrenergic.* Serotonin or acetylcholine is produced by sympathetic preganglionic fibers, all fibers of the parasympathetic system, and probably also by the

25 · 12 *Diagram of a neural synapse shows the release and local spreading of hormones* (color) *from the axon terminal of one fiber to the dendrite terminal of another. Impulses are transmitted across synapses by such chemical means.*

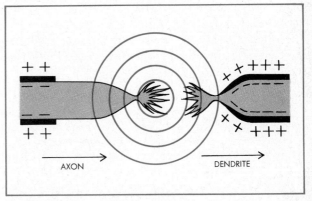

fibers of the central nervous system. Such fibers are considered to be *cholinergic*.

In synapses formed by cholinergic fibers, the enzyme *choline esterase* splits acetylcholine into separate acetyl and choline fractions and so makes the hormone ineffective. The presence of this enzyme is advantageous adaptively. If it did not exist, acetylcholine would linger in the synapse and would stimulate dendrites repeatedly. If therefore two impulses arrived in a synapse in rapid succession, acetylcholine produced by the first would still be effective when the second produced more hormone. The impulses would then merge into each other and the result would be one long drawn-out response, not two sharply distinct responses. Choline esterase prevents the merging of impulses. There is just time for acetylcholine to stimulate dendrites once or a few times and the hormone is destroyed immediately thereafter. An equivalent enzyme cannot be demonstrated in synapses formed by adrenergic fibers; the adrenalines do have a lingering effect. This circumstance contributes to the comparative slowness and sustained quality of the responses produced by the sympathetic part of the autonomic nervous system.

Synaptic impulse transmission by chemicals has important consequences. For example, diffusion takes much longer than impulse conduction within a fiber. A complete reflex, which usually passes through many synapses, consequently lasts longer than would be expected on the basis of impulse speeds within fibers alone. Moreover, nerve fibers as such rarely fatigue but synapses get "tired" fairly easily. During intensive activity, axon terminals may temporarily exhaust their hormone-secreting capacity, and synaptic transmission then slows even more or stops altogether for the time being.

Note also that the synaptic hormones impose a

one-way direction on neural pathways. A nerve fiber can be stimulated at either end or in the middle, and impulses then travel backward, forward, or in both directions. But only axon terminals are specialized to secrete hormones, and only dendrite terminals are sensitive to these hormones. As a result, impulse conduction is unidirectional.

The first nerve impulse in a reflex arc is generally produced by a receptor. Such structures start all nervous activity, and on their functioning depend all subsequent neural events. How are receptors constructed and how do they work?

NEURAL RECEPTORS

Receptor cells of two general types are known (Fig. 25.13). One type is a specialized nonnervous epithelial cell which receives stimuli at one end and is innervated by a sensory nerve fiber at the other end. The second type is a variously modified sensory neuron which carries a dendritelike stimulus-receiving nerve ending at one end and an axon at the other. Both types of receptor cells may occur in clusters and, together with accessory cells, form *sense organs*. All receptor cells of invertebrates are of the sensory-neuron type. Vertebrates possess both neural and epithelial receptors.

A light receptor is sensitive only to light and cannot be stimulated by sound waves, for example; all sensory structures are relatively *stimulus-specific*. Moreover, sensory devices as such do not give an animal any perception of sensation. Receptors merely generate nerve impulses, and it is the modulator centers which must interpret the impulses as actual perceptions. Eyes therefore do not see, and ears do not hear; eye-brain complexes are required for seeing, and ear-brain complexes for hearing. In these and other instances the perceptions become conscious, but more often they do not, even in man. Thus, when nerve impulses reach the brain from a blood vessel, for example, sensing takes place, although without conscious awareness.

Very little is known as yet about the mechanism by which specific stimuli actually produce nerve impulses in receptor cells. Environmental change as such is known to be an important factor, for when a given stimulus persists unchanged for a time, a sense dulls, or "adapts." For example, we soon become relatively insensitive to the pressure of clothes, to a persistent odor, or to a taste. Ease of adaptation varies considerably. Pain is most difficult to adapt to, but odor perception dulls very easily. We cannot judge our own body odors, for example, since we live with them constantly and adapt to them continuously.

25 · 13 *The two kinds of receptor cells.*

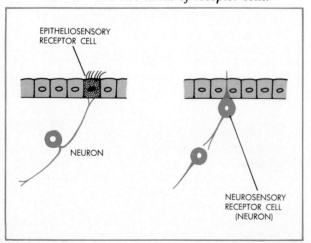

EPITHELIOSENSORY
RECEPTOR CELL

NEURON

NEUROSENSORY
RECEPTOR CELL
(NEURON)

It can be shown dramatically that different kinds of sense perceptions depend not so much on differences in the impulses produced by the receptors as on the different *central connections* of nerve fibers in the brain. For example, a fiber from a heat receptor and a fiber from a cold receptor can be cut and the cut ends can be allowed to reinnervate the sense organs in switched order. The fiber from the heat receptor would then terminate in the cold center of the brain and the fiber from the cold receptor would terminate in the heat center. Under such conditions, the animal would feel hot every time the cold receptor is stimulated and cold every time the heat receptor is stimulated. Evidently, the quality of a sensation is determined not by the receptor nor by the type of nerve impulse sent by the receptor, but by the neural centers. The sensation depends on which of various centers receives signals.

Furthermore, correct *localization* of a stimulus similarly depends on the central connections. If pain fibers from hand and foot were switched as above, then a needle prick on the foot would prompt immediate examination of the hand for blood, and vice versa. We may note that the anatomical distribution of receptors throughout the body is matched virtually point for point in the anatomical distribution of neural centers. Each receptor has its neural center, and so long as the structural relationships are preserved, impulses will be correctly interpreted as coming from particular body regions and particular receptors.

This generalization should be qualified in one respect. It is a fairly common experience that pain originating in an internal organ is often sensed as if it originated at some remote skin area or at another, distant internal region. For example, pain stimuli actually affecting the liver may be felt as pain in the shoulder region. Pain in the uterus may be erroneously thought to originate in forehead, chest, and palm of hand. Similarly, an ache in one tooth is often thought to come from the whole side of the head. In all such cases of *referred pain,* pain fibers originating in different body regions lead into the same general area in the brain. Impulses arriving through one of the fibers may stimulate a greater or lesser portion of that area, as if impulses actually arrived over more than one pain fiber. As a result, pain sensations may be diffuse and may be referred to numerous body regions.

Receptors may be classified as *exteroceptors* and *interoceptors,* that is, as structures receiving information either about the external or the internal environment of an animal. Receptors may also be classified according to the kinds of stimuli they are sensitive to, as in the following.

CHEMORECEPTORS

Some types of chemoreceptors give information about environmental *chemicals* generally; other types initiate sensations of *smell;* and still other types mediate the sense of *taste*. In most animals, the receptor structures are free sensory nerve endings which may be stimulated directly by given chemicals.

The ability to sense common environmental chemicals has particular significance for many invertebrates, aquatic ones especially. This sense permits an animal to detect the presence of irritants or poisons and the chemical exudates of enemies, prey, food, and mates. The receptors usually are distributed abundantly over all parts of the integument, as might be expected, and they are believed to be distinct from those for smell and taste.

Smell is primarily a distance sense. Aquatic animals smell traces of chemicals in solution. Thus they may smell slight differences between different kinds of waters or the presence of plants, logs, and other objects. Terrestrial animals smell vaporized chemicals, of particular importance here being traces of chemicals adhering to the ground; a worm or a four-footed mammal may receive as much information about its environment by sniffing the ground as an insect, a bird, or a man may receive by sight.

The smell receptors of vertebrates are parts of the ciliated epithelium lining the upper nasal passages (Fig. 25.14). Sensory nerve fibers from the ciliated cells lead to the olfactory lobes of the forebrain. Structural differences among the receptor cells of the nasal epithelium cannot be detected, but it is clear that the cells are functionally able to discriminate between different odor stimuli. However, it is virtually impossible to determine which receptor cells of the epithelium mediate perception of what odors. Indeed, it is difficult even to group odors into categories, and attempts to establish basic odors from which all others can be derived have met with relatively little success. A reasonably adequate scheme can be constructed on the basis of four primary odors, *rancid, vinegary, fragrant,* and *burnt,* each classified in various intensities.

The sense of taste conveys information primarily about the general chemical nature of potential food substances. In most animals the receptors are localized in and around the mouth, but animals such as flies and moths taste with their legs; the receptors are at or near the ends of the legs. The taste receptors of mammals are *taste buds,* organs in which clusters of elongated ciliated cells are embedded. Such organs occur in depressions or deep pits all over the tongue, and fiber terminals from each of the bud cells lead into the brain (see Fig. 25.14).

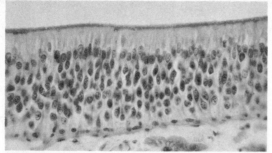

A

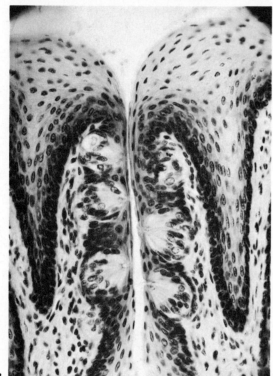

B

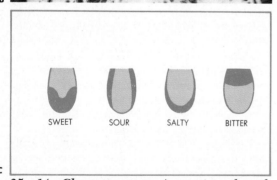

SWEET   SOUR   SALTY   BITTER

C

25 · 14 Chemoreceptors. *A, section through epitheliosensory nasal epithelium of vertebrates. B, portion of section through tongue showing taste buds; the buds are located along the deep, narrow channels leading into the tongue from the surface. C, diagrams of the tongue, showing the distribution of taste buds for the four taste sensations.*

Structural differences among buds cannot be demonstrated, but well-known functional differences exist; the four primary taste sensations, *sweet, sour, salty,* and *bitter,* arise through stimulation of buds at different regions of the tongue. Bitter substances primarily affect buds located at the back of the tongue; sweet substances, buds in the forward part of the tongue; and sour and salty materials are tasted predominantly along the tongue edges.

Numerous composite tastes are built up from different combinations and intensities of the four basic tastes, from smell, and from the other sense perceptions initiated in the mouth. For example, both a hot meal and a cold meal affect the same taste buds if the two meals are alike chemically. But the hot meal vaporizes more and therefore smells more, and it also stimulates heat receptors in the lining of the mouth and on the tongue. The hot and the cold meals consequently taste differently. Moreover, our reduced tasting ability when the nose is blocked with a cold again indicates that smell is an important component of "taste." Taste buds are highly sensitive receptors. Quinine, for example, a substance normally producing a bitter taste, can be sensed in concentrations as low as 1 part in 2 or 3 million parts of water.

We may note here that tastes, and indeed chemical perceptions of all kinds, are subjective sensations, not objective properties of given chemicals. Sugar is not intrinsically sweet, nor is quinine intrinsically bitter. Sweetness, bitterness, and all similar sensory qualities are subjective interpretations made by the brain, and the only pertinent objective properties of given chemicals are to stimulate certain taste buds. This conclusion is clearly supported by the observation that certain chemicals produce a sweet sensation when applied to the tongue tip but a bitter sensation when applied at the back of the tongue. Also, in different individuals one and the same sugar may produce qualitatively and quantitatively different sensations of sweetness. And at least one substance is known (*phenylthiocarbamide*) that one person may not taste at all, but that tastes sweet to another, bitter to a third, salty to a fourth, and sour to a fifth. Individual differences of this sort trace back to differences in heredity.

TANGORECEPTORS

These structures register stimuli of touch and of mechanical pressure generally. The receptors usually are free nerve endings, highly branched or elaborated into the meshworks in many cases. Tangoreceptors occur abundantly in most animals, both in the integument and in the body interior (for example, in muscles, tendons, and most connective tissues). The skin of vertebrates additionally contains minute touch-registering organs composed of nonnervous cells. Such organs are innervated by sensory nerve fibers (Fig. 25.15).

Tangoreceptors are stimulated by mechanical displacement or by changes in the mechanical stresses affecting surrounding parts. For example, the bending or the stretching of a part of the skin or of an internal organ is likely to result in receptor stimulation. An animal thereby receives information both about contacts with external objects and about movements of any body part. As might be expected,

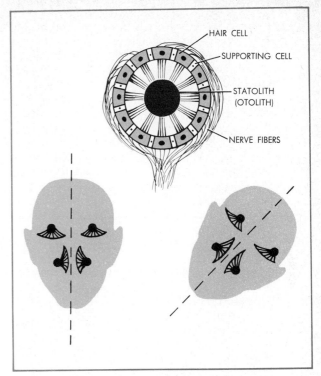

25 · 16 *Static balance. Diagram of statocyst (top) shows how hair cells support an ear stone (statolith) in the center of the cyst. (After Hyman.) Lower figures show position of the receptor organs in relation to the head, and the effect of tilting the head.*

25 · 15 *Cutaneous receptors in mammals. A, free nerve ending (pain); B, nerve net surrounding hair (touch); C, Pacinian corpuscle (pressure); D, organ of Ruffini (pressure); E, organ of Krause (cold); F, end organ of Ruffini (warmth); G, Meissner's corpuscle (touch). B, C, D, and G are tangoreceptors.*

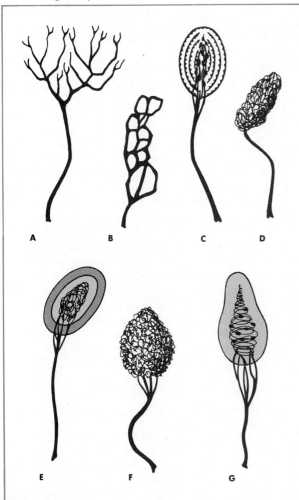

integumentary tangoreceptors are particularly abundant where contact with external objects occurs frequently—in and around the mouth, on appendages, and on the ventral body surfaces in creeping forms. In mammals, the base of each hair within the skin is surrounded by a meshlike terminal of a tangoreceptor fiber, and a nerve impulse is initiated if a hair is touched even lightly (see Fig. 25.15). Internal tangoreceptors are *stretch receptors* (also called *proprioceptors*). We have already discussed the action of some of these in the accounts on circulation and breathing. Others contribute to the control of the position and movements of body parts and thus they play an important role in maintaining posture and balance.

STATORECEPTORS

Present in many invertebrate groups and in all vertebrates, these organs are receptors for the sense of body equilibrium (Fig. 25.16). Most commonly, a statoreceptor is a small, fluid-filled sac (*statocyst*) in which is present a cluster of ciliated *hair cells*. Attached to or resting against the hairs is a *statolith*, a grain of hard, usually calcareous material (a sand grain in crayfish). When an animal moves, the statolith shifts position under the influence of gravity and it then presses against a somewhat different set of hair cells. Such a change in the pressure pattern produces a corresponding change in the pattern of nerve impulses traveling away from the sensory cells. The brain thus receives information about altered body orientations. As noted, body position is also sensed independently by information received from tangoreceptors; but the statoreceptors must function if an animal is to carry out righting activities after being turned upside down, for example, and in general if an animal is to maintain a normal orientation in relation to gravity.

In most animals, statoreceptors are located in the head or in head appendages (for example, antennae). In vertebrates they are part of the inner ear. Indeed, the vertebrate ear has evolved primarily as a statoreceptor and only secondarily as an organ of hearing. Hair cells with statoliths (here often called *ear stones*) are located at several places along the walls

25 · 17   The ear of mammals. Note ear bones in the middle-ear cavity and attachment of semicircular canals to utricle. Statoreceptors are in the utricle and the saccule.

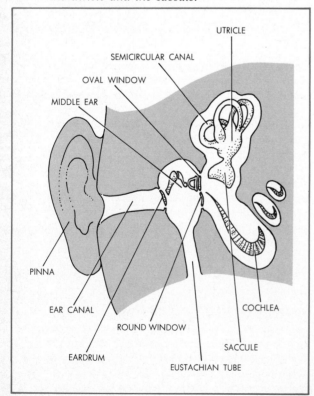

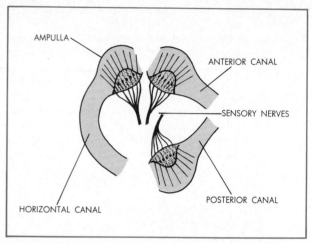

25 · 18   Semicircular canals of the left ear. *Top of diagram is anterior, right side is toward median plane of head. The three canals are set at right angles to one another, hence only the horizontal canal reveals its curvature in this view. Both ends of each canal open into the utricle. The hair cells in the ampullae function as receptors for the sense of dynamic balance. When head is moved, fluid in the canals bends the hair cells, an action which initiates sensory nerve impulses.*

of two inner-ear chambers, the *saccule* and the *utricle* (Fig. 25.17). These receptors are organs for the sense of *static body balance*. When the head is tilted or when the balance of the body as a whole changes, gravity acts on the ear stones and shifts them in a given manner. Such a change in the position of the stones produces pull on different sets of hair cells. Correspondingly, different sets of impulses to the brain then inform of the change in balance. Reflex signals from the brain to appropriate muscles subsequently ensure that equilibrium is not lost. This sense permits recognition of up, down, side, front, and back, even when visual stimuli and sensory impulses from muscles fail to provide such recognition. A blindfolded mammal with inoperative ear-stone receptors has difficulty in remaining upright. And when its position is abnormal, it does little to correct this position.

Present in addition are separate receptors, the *semicircular canals*, which inform about movement of the head and thus about *dynamic body balance*. Three semicircular canals in each ear loop from the utricle back to the utricle. The canals are placed at right angles to one another in the three planes of space (Figs. 25.17 and 25.18). At one end of each canal is an enlarged portion, the *ampulla,* in which is found a cluster of hair cells. When the head is moved, the semicircular canals move with the head. But the fluid in the canals "stays behind" temporarily as a result of its inertia and "catches up" with the head only after the head has stopped moving. This delayed fluid motion bends the hairs of the receptor cells and produces nerve impulses. Different impulse patterns are transmitted to the brain according to the direction and intensity of fluid motion in the three pairs of canals. Every straight-line motion or rotation of the head or of the body as a whole produces a distinct impulse pattern, hence a distinct sense perception.

Mammals pursue a more or less two-dimensional way of life and are relatively unaccustomed to up-and-down motion. When such motion occurs in man, it initiates reflexes via the semicircular canals leading to well-known symptoms of dizziness, nausea, and gastric upsets. Seasickness is produced in this way, as is the discomfort experienced when one rides in an elevator. The sense of dynamic balance may also be affected by rapid temperature changes in the environment; uneven cooling or warming of the fluid in the semicircular canals may produce currents which may stimulate the receptor cells. Sensations of motion or of dizziness may therefore be experienced even if the head does not move.

PHONORECEPTORS

These organs are sensitive to pressure vibrations in displaceable media, for example, water and air. Organs of hearing are particular kinds of phonoreceptors. Free nerve endings and hair cells in the integument function most commonly as the receptors for nonauditory vibrations. Many animals probably register pressure vibrations also by means of their tangoreceptors. Indeed, even where specialized phonoreceptors are absent, as in the skin of man, vibrations may still be felt. In such cases direct conduction of pressure waves through skin, muscle, and bone probably leads to stimulation of tangoreceptors in various body parts. Most aquatic vertebrates possess highly developed, specialized phonoreceptors in the integument of the head and the trunk. Present there are so-called *lateral-line systems,* essentially series of water-filled canals that communicate via pores with the external medium (Fig. 25.19). Movement of the water in the canals initiates impulses in fiber terminals of nerves traveling alongside the canals. The lateral-line system probably registers vibratory currents produced both by moving objects in the water and by the movement of the fish itself. The system thus functions like the "listening"

component of submarine sonar, and it probably serves not only to detect water turbulence as such but also to discriminate between different kinds of turbulence.

A distinct sense of hearing is restricted to some arthropods (certain crustacea, spiders, and insects) and to vertebrates; by and large, only animals that *make* sounds can also hear them. In arthropods, the

25 · 19 The lateral-line system. *A, general plan of the system in relation to body surface. B, relation of the system to the dermal scales of a bony fish; the lateral-line canal partly passes through the scales. C, schematic cross section through a lateral-line canal, showing supporting cells and sense organ, the latter with phonoreceptive hair cells embedded among supporting cells.* (After Goodrich.)

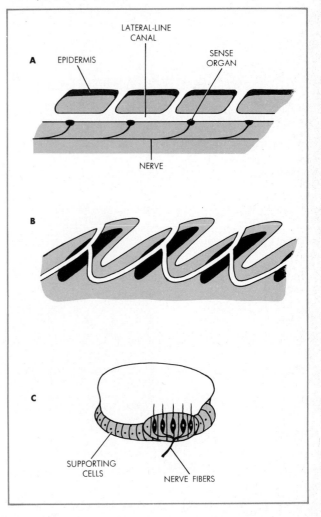

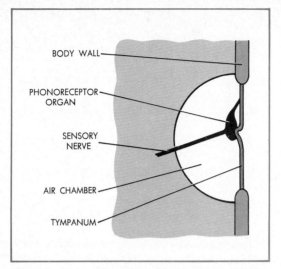

25 · 20 An arthropod ear. *An organ of this type is found, for example, on grasshopper legs. The typanum corresponds functionally to the eardrum of mammals.* (After Weever.)

25 · 21 The cochlea. *The diagram shows the coils of the cochlea and a cochlear cross section with the parts of the organ of Corti. A section through this organ is illustrated also in the photo. The tectorial and basilar members and the hair cells are clearly visible.*

receptor organs (Fig. 25.20) are located in various body regions, for example, in the antennae (mosquitos), forelegs (crickets), thorax (cicadas), or abdomen (grasshoppers). In general, the "ears" of arthropods are sensitive to rather limited sound frequencies only. For example, a male mosquito can hear only sounds having the same frequency as those produced by the wings of female mosquitos in flight.

In terrestrial vertebrates, the *outer ear* carries sound to the *eardrum,* a membrane which separates the cavity of the *middle ear* from the outside (see Fig. 25.17). The connection of this cavity with the mouth, via the eustachian tube, has already been referred to in Chap. 24. Three tiny middle-ear bones, *hammer, anvil,* and *stirrup,* moved by the smallest muscles in the body, form an adjustable bridge from the eardrum across the middle-ear cavity to the *inner ear.* The latter is closed off from the middle ear by two membranes. One stretches across a so-called *round window* and the other across an *oval window.* The stirrup bone of the middle ear is anchored to the membrane of the oval window.

The inner ear is an intricate system of interconnected canals and spaces, all surrounded by bone and filled with a lymphlike fluid. Apart from the saccule and the utricle already referred to above, the inner ear contains a *cochlea,* a coiled, very elaborate receptor organ for the sense of hearing (Fig. 25.21). The internal space of the cochlea is partitioned into canals by membranes running the

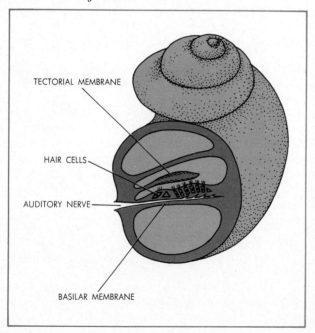

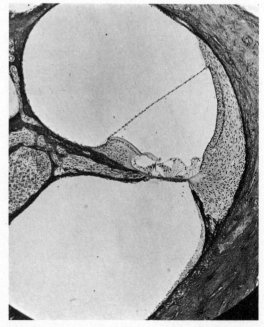

length of the cochlear coils. One of the membranes, the *basilar membrane,* supports rows of hair cells. These are the actual receptors; nerve fibers lead from them to the brain. The hairs make contact with the *tectorial membrane,* a tissue fold overhanging the receptor cells. Basilar membrane, hair cells, and tectorial membrane together constitute the *organ of Corti.*

Sound waves produce vibrations in the eardrum. This motion is communicated via the middle-ear bones to the oval window. As the membrane at this window now vibrates, it sets the fluid of the inner ear into motion. Since fluid is practically incompressible, the membrane over the round window bulges outward every time the membrane over the oval window bulges inward; and vice versa. In other words, the round window permits the fluid of the inner ear to vibrate in harmony with the oval window and thus in harmony with external sound waves (Fig. 25.22).

Fluid motion in the inner ear next affects the basilar membrane. The membrane contains strands of tough connective tissue fibers stretched transversely across the cochlear tube. These fibers are shortest at the base of the cochlear coil and longest at the tip of the coil. They may vibrate at different rates or frequencies according to their different lengths. In this respect the fibers resemble the tone strings of a piano. Thus, as the cochlear fluid vibrates at a given frequency under the impact of external sound waves, it sets into motion those basilar fibers which can vibrate at the same frequency. This is a selective *resonance* effect. In a similar way, a string of a piano may be set into resonating vibrations if a corresponding sound is produced nearby with a tuning fork, for example, or by striking an appropriate key on another piano.

As particular sets of basilar fibers now vibrate, the hair cells attached to them move up and down. And as these cells make contact with the overhanging tectorial membrane, their hairs are bent and nerve impulses are initiated. Each external sound pattern so gives rise to a particular pattern of nerve impulses, and the latter are transmitted to the hearing centers in the temporal lobes of the brain. There the incoming impulse patterns are interpreted as sounds of given pitch.

Mammals probably have the best sense of hearing. Their ears discriminate sounds of even slightly different intensity and pitch, and they are sensitive to a very wide range of sounds. For example, man may hear sounds ranging in frequency from 16 to 20,000 cycles per second. Dogs are sensitive to frequencies up to 30,000 cycles per second, and bats,

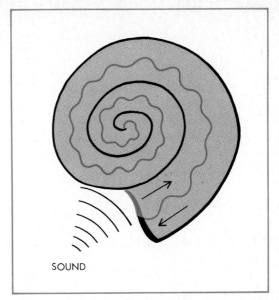

25 · 22 *Pressure of the stirrup bone* on the *oval window sets the basilar membrane into vibration* (colored serpentine line). *The round window* (heavy black line at bottom) *bulges out, compensating for the inward pressure of the oval window* (heavy colored line at bottom center).

to frequencies up to 100,000 cycles per second. The ear of man is probably unsurpassed in distinguishing tones of only slightly different pitch and tones of widely different quality. As an interpretive sense and as an important adjuster of speech, hearing has acquired a human importance second only to vision.

PHOTORECEPTORS

Notwithstanding their many differences on the organ level, all light-sensitive receptors of animals are alike on the molecular level: light-sensitive *photopigments* are present within specialized organelles of receptor cells. These pigments are unstable in light, and their breakdown in some way initiates an impulse in the sensory fiber innervating the receptor cell. Moreover, the photopigments appear to be chemically rather similar in all animals. Each consists of two joined molecular parts. One is a variant of *retinene,* an aldehyde derivative of vitamin A; the other is a variant of *opsin,* a protein to which retinene is linked. Light splits retinene away from opsin, resulting in a nerve impulse. In a subsequent series of ATP- and enzyme-requiring reactions, retinene is rejoined to opsin and the photopigment is thereby regenerated (Fig. 25.23).

Numerous invertebrate groups and all vertebrates

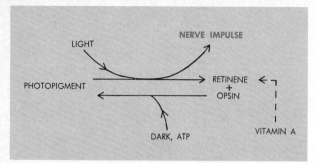

NERVE IMPULSE

LIGHT

PHOTOPIGMENT → RETINENE

\+

OPSIN

DARK, ATP

VITAMIN A

25 · 23 Photoreception. *The pattern of the chemistry of vision. The photopigment is iodopsin in the case of cone cells, rhodopsin in that of rod cells. Note that vitamin A may replenish the supply of retinene.*

possess elongated photoreceptor cells called *rods.* Their photopigment is "visual purple," or *rhodopsin.* With this pigment animals may detect different black-white intensities of light and changes in such intensities. Rods thus serve primarily as illumination- and motion-detectors. In addition to rods, a few

25 · 24 Types of eyes. *A, eye spot (as in coelenterates). B, eye cup (as in chambered nautilus). C, vesicular eye (as in snails and annelids). In all these eyes light reaches the retina directly, that is, without first passing through neuron layers.*

animal groups, notably some insects, some reptiles, most birds, and monkeys, apes, and man, possess separate color detectors. The pigment in these is some form of *iodopsin,* a combination of variants of retinene and opsin different from those in rhodopsin. Animals able to see a complete color spectrum actually appear to possess at least three different kinds of iodopsin, sensitive respectively to red, blue, and yellow wavelengths of light. From various combinations of these three primary colors all other colors can probably be derived, as in color television. In the color-detecting vertebrates, iodopsin occurs in photoreceptor cells called *cones.*

Clusters or more extensive layers of photoreceptor cells form *retinas,* the principal components of seeing organs (Fig. 25.24). Some of these organs are relatively simply constructed *eyespots,* flush with the body surface. Others are *eyecups,* and the most complex are more or less spherical *eyes.* Most types of eyes are usually equipped with accessory structures such as transparent *lenses* (see Fig. 15.33).

The vertebrate eye is made up of three coats (Fig. 25.25): an outer *sclera,* fibrous in man, cartilaginous in many other mammals; a middle *choroid,* a layer which is pigmented black and carries blood vessels to and from the eye; and an inner *retina.* In many mammals, a thin film of white-green crystalline material coats the choroid layer. This material reflects light and makes the eyes of these animals shine and glow in the dark.

In the front part of the eye the three coats are

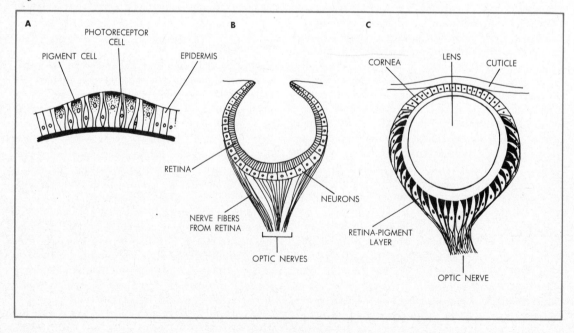

A

PIGMENT CELL

PHOTORECEPTOR CELL

EPIDERMIS

RETINA

NERVE FIBERS FROM RETINA

OPTIC NERVES

B

NEURONS

C

CORNEA

LENS

CUTICLE

RETINA-PIGMENT LAYER

OPTIC NERVE

modified structurally. The sclera merges into the transparent *cornea*. The choroid coat continues as the sometimes pigmented *iris*, which encloses the *pupil*. Just behind the iris is a ring-shaped muscle, the *ciliary body*, to which the *lens* is attached by ligaments. The spaces between lens and cornea are filled with the fluid, lymphlike *aqueous humor;* and the space between lens and retina contains a glassy, jellylike material, the *vitreous humor*.

Functionally, the eye resembles a photographic camera. But whereas a camera is focused by varying the distance between lens and film, the eye is focused by adjustment of the curvature of the lens; the distance between lens and retina remains fixed (Fig. 25.26). A beam of light passes through the cornea and through the pupil into the lens. The pupillary opening corresponds to the diaphragm of a camera; it narrows or widens and thus regulates the amount of light admitted into the eye. This control mechanism is set into operation by light itself. Intense light initiates a reflex via retina, the autonomic nervous system, and a set of circularly arranged muscles in the iris. These muscles contract and the pupil narrows. Conversely, low light intensity results in reflex signals to a set of iris muscles arranged like the spokes of a wheel. When these muscles contract, the pupil of the eye enlarges (see Fig. 25.8).

The lens focuses an object onto the retina. When

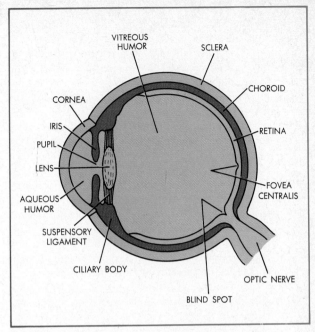

25 · 25   *The structure of the mammalian eye.*

25 · 26   *Focusing in camera and in eye. Upper figures, images fall short of photographic film and retina. Lower figures, camera is focused by changing the lens-film distance, and eye is focused by changing the curvature of the lens.*

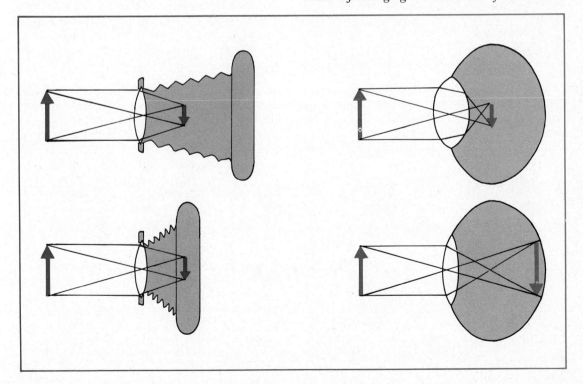

a far-off object is viewed and when the eye is at rest, the lens is fairly flat. As an object moves nearer, the lens curves out increasingly (Fig. 25.27). Lens shape is controlled by the ciliary body. When this muscular ring is relaxed, the ligaments holding the lens are taut and the lens is flat. Conversely, when the ciliary muscle contracts, the lens ligaments relax and the lens, an elastic structure, is then allowed to curve out. The ciliary muscle is under reflex control. A blurred image on the retina elicits reflex impulses to the ciliary body. These impulses produce contraction or relaxation of the ciliary body until the image is no longer blurred. The adjustment reflex then ceases and a focused image so reaches the retina. Note that the image of an object is projected on the retina in an inverted position, just as an image is inverted on the film of a camera.

The retina consists of several layers of neurons and one layer of rods and cones (Fig. 25.28). The latter is adjacent to the choroid coat, hence light must pass through the neuron layers before it reaches the rods and cones. The light-sensitive cells connect functionally with the neurons of the retina, and the neurons in turn synapse among one another in intricate ways. Nerve fibers from the whole inner surface of the retina eventually collect in one region and form the *optic nerve* to the brain. Where this nerve leaves the eye, somewhat off-center, it interrupts the continuity of the rod and cone layer and of the choroid and sclera. This area of discontinuity is the *blind spot*, so called since visual images cannot be formed in it.

The greatest concentration of cone cells is found

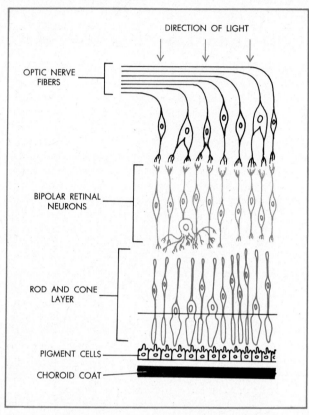

25 · 28   The mammalian retina. *Diagram: general sectional structure, greatly simplified. Note that in this type of ("inverted") retina light must pass through neuron layers before it reaches the*

in the *fovea centralis*, a tiny depression in the center of the retina. Only cones are present in this area; rods are absent. Also absent are overlying neurons, and the cones are exposed to light directly. By virtue of its dense accumulation of cones, the fovea permits the most acute vision. The concentration of cone cells decreases with increasing distance from the fovea, and at the retinal periphery cones do not occur at all. Rods, on the other hand, are particularly abundant there. These light receptors are distributed more sparsely away from the retinal periphery and are absent altogether in the fovea. Thus, reception of sharp images and of colored ones occurs most efficiently in and near the optical center of the retina, whereas movement and black-and-white vision are mediated primarily by the retinal periphery.

An external object is "pictured" on the retina as a series of points, like the points of a newspaper photograph. Each point corresponds to a rod or a cone. Impulses from these points are transmitted into the brain such that all fibers from the left sides

25 · 27   Eye adjusts focus *when object changes distance. Left, far object, flat lens. Right, near object, curved lens. Lens curves out when the muscles of the ciliary body contract.*

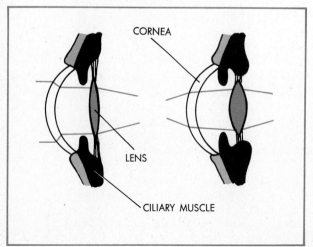

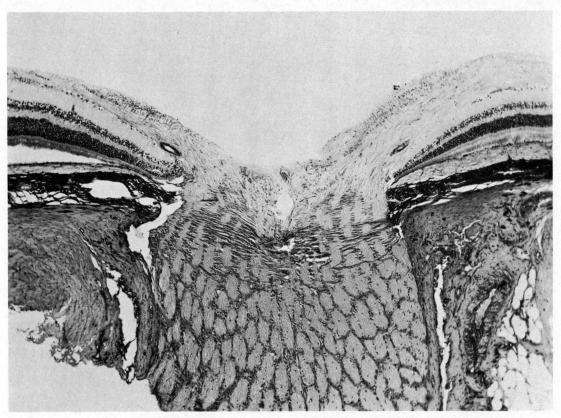

photosensitive rods and cones. Photo: section through the blind spot. The retina is toward the top of the photo. Note the neuron layers at the surface of the retina and the merging of the neu-ron fibers at the depression of the blind spot, forming the optic nerve. This thick nerve leads downward in the photo.

of *both* eyes lead into the left half of the brain, and all fibers from the right sides of both eyes lead into the right half of the brain (Fig. 25.29). In each brain hemisphere the fibers from the eyes lead to an *optic lobe* which contains the visual centers. It can be shown that for each group of rods and cones there exists a corresponding group of interpreter neurons in the visual centers. In other words, the "point picture" of an object on the retina is duplicated more or less faithfully in the optic lobes, by impulses from specific rods and cones to their correlated interpreter neurons. In these neurons the impulses register as vision.

Evidently, the left half of every external field of vision produces images in the right halves of both eyes. Similarly, the right half of what can be seen is focused onto the left halves of both retinas. There-fore, in view of the fiber patterns from the eyes to the brain, the right half of a field of vision registers in the left half of the brain and the left half of a vision field registers in the right half of the brain.

The left and right optic lobes are not directly con-tinuous. Yet interpreter activity normally is such that the "left" picture of the external world is super-imposed smoothly on the "right" picture. Moreover, both halves of the picture are sensed right side up, even though the retinas receive inverted images. Left and right pictures sometimes fail to superimpose smoothly (for example, under the influence of alcohol), in which case one "sees double."

Why is an inverted retinal image not also "seen" as an inverted picture? The answer is that the optic centers in the brain have learned to give visual ex-periences correct orientations. Recognition of up and down and of space orientation generally is based ultimately on perception of gravity via the stato-receptors. Therefore, even though retinal images might arrive in the optic lobes in an inverted posi-tion, gravity perception teaches an individual soon after birth to associate the bottom part of a picture with the idea of "up" and the upper part with the idea of "down." Without gravity (as in outer space),

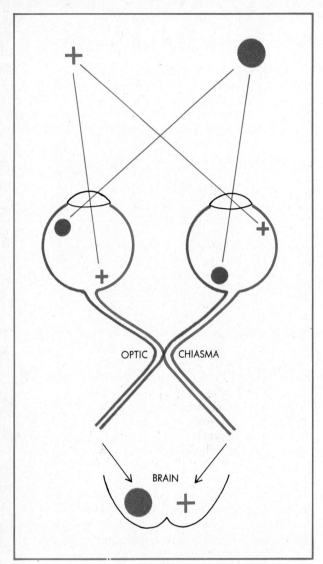

25 · 29 Nerve fiber tracts from eye to brain.
An object in the left field of vision registers on the right halves of both retinas, and impulses are transmitted into the right half of the brain.

the frame of reference for space orientation is lacking and the notion of "right-side-upness" becomes meaningless.

It is known also that the interpreter activity in the optic lobes is assisted by the neuron layers of the retina, which apparently carry out a considerable amount of "data processing" before impulses are sent to the brain. It has been found, for example, that the retinal neurons of the frog eye arrange the impulses from the photoreceptor cells into four

distinct sets of signals to the brain. One set provides the animal with a stationary black-and-white "outline drawing" of the visual field, a background picture of the world, as it were. A second set similarly provides an outline drawing, but only of illuminated objects which move across the visual field. A third set informs of objects which blot out illumination in part of the visual field and which become rapidly larger—undoubtedly indicating the approach of potentially dangerous animals. And a fourth pattern of impulses registers the presence of moving objects which blot out illumination but which remain small. This pattern probably serves as an insect-detector and thus may be of specific importance to a frog. The four sets of impulses become superimposed neatly in four adjacent neuron layers in the brain and appear to be interpreted as a single "picture." A frog evidently sees the world in its own unique and subjective manner. An analogous conclusion undoubtedly holds for light-sensitive animals of all kinds.

The human eye is among the most efficient light receptors developed during evolution. Insect eyes possibly are better adapted for the detection of motion, and many vertebrates have a larger visual field without moving their heads than man. But the human visual apparatus probably registers color more clearly than that of any other animal, and human eyes are about as light-sensitive as eyes can possibly get. Moreover, immense numbers of neural paths lead from the vision centers to almost all other centers in the brain and spinal cord. A tremendous number of reflexes can therefore be initiated through the receptor cells in the eyes, and it is this which makes the sense of vision so important.

OTHER RECEPTORS

Numerous animal groups possess *temperature receptors* in the integument, in the form of either free nerve endings or minute organs. In arthropods, for example, such receptors are found particularly in the antennae and the mouth parts. Vertebrates possess distinct heat and cold receptors in all parts of the skin, specially dense concentrations being present around the mouth and within the mouth cavity (see Fig. 25.15). Especially sensitive heat receptors occur on the tongues of snakes, reptiles which may detect the body heat of other animals from appreciable distances.

In man and in vertebrates generally, distinct sets of free nerve endings in all parts of the body serve as *pain receptors* (see Fig. 25.15). Other animals may possess such receptors as well. However, inasmuch as feelings of pain must be communicated before we can be sure of their presence, it is actually quite difficult to determine how widespread a specialized sense of pain might be. Most animals do react sharply to stimuli which, by analogy with man, could be assumed to be painful. But such actions need not necessarily indicate pain as such; they could well result from stimulation of tangoreceptors or various other types of sense organs. Collectively, the receptors for pain, pressure, touch, and temperature in the skin constitute the *cutaneous receptors*. It is estimated that the human skin contains some 4 million pain receptors, $\frac{1}{2}$ million pressure receptors, 150,000 cold receptors, and 16,000 heat receptors.

Apart from the senses here discussed, numerous others unquestionably exist. For example, man—and by inference presumably other animals as well—possesses senses of sexual excitation, hunger, thirst, and sleepiness; and man may also discriminate between sensations of burning, tickling, stinging, and limbs "falling asleep." Separate receptors need not necessarily be associated with each of these senses. It is known, for example, that some of the above sensations result when different cutaneous receptors are stimulated simultaneously and in different combinations. Thus, simultaneous impulses from heat and pain receptors may give rise to a burning sensation. In a hot shower, both hot and cold receptors may be affected and one may feel hot and cold at the same time. Ice on the skin may produce sensations of burning, through simultaneous stimulation of cold, heat, and pain points.

In some instances, however, specialized receptors for so far unidentified senses undoubtedly do exist, particularly among invertebrates. Many of these animals possess organs which clearly reveal their sensory nature by their structure, but which so far have not yet been characterized functionally as registering this or that type of stimulus. The environments of many invertebrates often produce stimuli quite different from those we would expect in a terrestrial or human environment; and it is therefore not too surprising that invertebrate senses are as yet known far less completely than those of vertebrates.

That the neural centers are as essential in sense perception as the neural receptors has become clear in this section. The neural centers are also essential in producing effector responses. How do these most crucial components of nervous systems operate?

NEURAL CENTERS

The most basic type of modulator activity is probably a *reflex relay:* an impulse arriving in a ganglion or a brain over an incoming neural path is simply relayed via one or more synapses to an outgoing path (Fig. 25.30). However, even the least complexly organized modulators are usually capable also of *reflex modification*.

One important form of modification is *suppression* or *augmentation* of a reflex. Depending in part on the characteristics of the neurons involved and in part on the nature of the incoming impulses, outgoing impulses often may not be emitted at all, or may be emitted with greater intensities or frequencies. A suppression of impulses results from *inhibition* of given modulator neurons by others. Some neurons are so organized internally that, when their dendrites are stimulated by neurohumors, the production of impulses in these neurons becomes harder rather than easier. Inhibitory processes of this sort thus provide "brakes" to impulse transmission. The opposite effect, augmentation, may result from a *summation* of impulses. In a synapse receiving many incoming impulses over numerous axon fibers, each arriving impulse may be individually too weak to produce an impulse in an outgoing fiber. However, the small quantities of neurohumors produced by the many incoming fibers may add together and may then become sufficiently powerful to initiate a strong impulse in an outgoing fiber. By virtue of its synapses, evidently, a modulator may carry out some degree of "interpretation" of the incoming signals and may exercise some measure of "decision" with regard to the outgoing signals (see Fig. 25.30).

Another, more complex form of modulator activity,

25 · 30 Modulator activities. *1, simple reflex relay; 2, suppression of impulse conduction; 3, augmentation of outgoing impulse by summation of weak incoming impulses; 4, channel selection; 5, information storage by continued impulse conduction in oscillator (cyclical) circuit.*

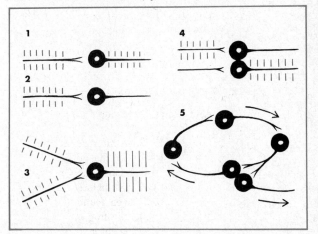

based largely on summation and inhibition, is *channel selection*. Even a simply organized neural modulator contains the terminals of a large number of incoming neurons and the starting points of a large set of outgoing neurons. If impulses arrive via the first set, outgoing signals are not usually emitted over all outgoing paths present. Instead, again depending on the nature of the neurons and on the characteristics of the incoming signals, modulator activity results in the *selection* among the hundreds or thousands of possible outgoing paths and the emission of signals only over some specifically chosen paths. The chosen paths are usually such that only *appropriate* effectors will receive motor commands. As a result, the effector response of an animal can be adaptively useful and can actually contribute to steady-state maintenance (see Fig. 25.30).

All modulator activity, no matter how complex, appears to be based ultimately on modification of impulses and on pathway selection. To be sure, little is known as yet about the internal mechanism by which some neural channels are selected in preference to others. In most cases, preferred circuits become established during the embryonic development of the nervous system. At any time thereafter, given sets of sensory impulses in a modulator result in more or less fixed, predictable sets of motor impulses to effectors. Such inherited circuit patterns govern most of the internal operations of most animals. In these operations, modulator activities are often considerably more complex than simple reflex relays. For example, sets of interneurons may be arranged as *oscillating circuits*, in which an impulse travels continuously over a circular route. Each time such an impulse passes a given synapse, a motor impulse to an effector might be initiated (see Fig. 25.30). It can be shown, for example, that the rhythmic heartbeat of certain arthropods is controlled by nine modulator neurons embedded directly in the heart muscles. The neurons form an oscillator circuit which generates periodic motor commands resulting in rhythmic contraction of the heart. Many other rhythmic, automatic activities are governed by oscillator circuits of this type.

Still more complex circuit patterns, also inherited, are represented by *stored programs*, responsible for *instinctive* overt behavior. A given external stimulus here leads to the completion of several or many simultaneous reflex responses, all occurring as a single, *integrated* pattern of activity. A good example is the startle response in man: an unexpected blow directed at the head occasions a closing of the eyes, a lowering of the head and assumption of a crouching stance, and a raising of hands to the front of the face. These several dozen separate reflexes occur simultaneously,

as a unified "program" of activity. The neural circuits are geared together and may be said to contain the program as *stored information*. In most animals, invertebrates in particular, virtually all behavior is based on inherited, instinctive, stored programs of this type. Fixed, automatic locomotor responses to particular stimuli are often referred to as animal *tropisms*.

The total number of circuit patterns a modulator may store varies with the number of interneurons available and thus with overall modulator size. In animals with small brain ganglia or brains, most available neurons are required for the establishment of inherited stored programs, and relatively few are left with which new circuit patterns could later be formed on the basis of experience. Such animals consequently are largely (though not entirely) incapable of converting experience into *learning* and *memory*. In comparatively large-brained animals, the majority of interneurons present again form inborn circuits, yet substantial numbers may remain for the later establishment of new circuits. Even so, learning and memory storage through experience are of more than incidental significance only in mammals.

It has been suggested that, where learning is possible, the establishment of new circuit patterns might occur through pathway *facilitation:* the more frequently impulses travel over a given neural circuit, the less resistance this circuit may offer to subsequent impulses. Wherever a choice of circuits exists, therefore, the often used, *facilitated* circuits may be selected in preference to the previously little used, unfacilitated ones. Conceivably, a circuit might become different in synaptic fine-structure and/or function the more often it is used. Learning might then occur by repetition and by trial and error. In a young animal, for example, few brain pathways are as yet firmly established by facilitation. Incoming impulses are transmitted more or less in all directions, and behavior is relatively uncoordinated and random. But among the random impulse paths, some will bring about advantageous effector results. The same pathway pattern may then be tried time and again and a facilitated neural route may thus be established eventually. Training, habit formation, and memory accumulation are implicit in such learning by facilitation.

Facilitation may also account for learning by association, as in *conditioned reflexes*. Here two or more stimuli are presented to an animal simultaneously and repeatedly, until the animal learns to execute the same response to either stimulus. For example, if bright light is directed into the eyes of an animal, its pupils will contract by inherited reflex action. If the light stimulus is given repeatedly and is accompanied each time with the presentation of food, then pupillary contraction can eventually be initiated by food alone, without the stimulus of bright light. Evidently, the animal learns to associate food with light, and it has come to possess not only the inherited neural circuit to the pupillary muscles, but also an additional, facilitated circuit, acquired by learning through experience. Either one alone or both together may now produce the pupillary response. Conditioning of this sort plays a considerable role in the behavioral development of any animal capable of learning, vertebrate or invertebrate.

Undoubtedly the most complex modulator activities are those which produce consciousness, emotion, intelligence, personality, and ability to think abstractly. Such modulator functions are developed to any notable degree only in the most advanced mammalian brains. Regardless of the relative complexity of given modulator functions, however, the primary role of all neural modulators is to aid in steady-state maintenance by control of *muscular movement* and of *glandular secretion*. But is it not really more than this, particularly for man? Conscious, contemplative thinking, reasoning, reading, aesthetic appreciations, higher mental functions in general—are they not more than mere reflex control of muscles and glands? Actually not. For *all* mental activity aims toward some *action*, potential or actual, present or future. On the one hand we see, hear, learn,

experience, store and correlate information—in short, we *think*. And on the other hand we speak, walk, build, vote—in short, we *do*. All this doing requires and is directly brought about by muscular and glandular activity. In the final analysis, therefore, thinking sets the stage for moving muscles, and better thinking implies more judicious and more diversified use of muscles. Because muscular control contributes powerfully to the maintenance of steady states, nervous systems have become vital components of animals.

Throughout these chapters on steady state, the central running theme has been that built-in control systems endow a living unit with a life span of maximum duration. When the controls fail for any external or internal reason, disease occurs. Intact controls may then be able to restore steady state. However, in time even the best-controlled system goes out of control. As the component parts age and wear out, functional and structural breakdowns occur so often and in so many different places at once that not enough controls remain intact to make the necessary repairs. Irreversible unsteady states and death must be the eventual outcome. But, as pointed out in Chap. 2, living systems here reveal the superiority of their organization over any nonliving system. Before final disintegration supervenes, the living controls may call into action another self-perpetuating device which circumvents even death: *reproduction.*

REVIEW QUESTIONS

1. Name the components of a reflex arc and describe the course of a reflex in a vertebrate. Review the structure of a neuron. What are nerves, nerve nets, nerve cords, and ganglia? What is the difference between a ganglion and a brain?

2. Describe the structure of the vertebrate brain. List the principal subdivisions, the principal components of each, and show how the elaboration of the subdivisions varies in different vertebrate groups. Distinguish between spinal and cranial nerves. List the mammalian cranial nerves and review the functions of each.

3. Review the structure and functioning of the autonomic nervous system. Distinguish structurally and functionally between the sympathetic and parasympathetic subdivisions of that system. What are sympathetic chain ganglia?

4. What are preganglionic and postganglionic fibers? Describe the detailed course of a reflex in (*a*) the central nervous system, (*b*) the autonomic nervous system. Review the innervation of the heart.

5. What is a nerve impulse? How is an impulse transmitted through a nerve fiber? What electrical phenomena take place during impulse transmission? What is an action potential of a nerve fiber? How is an impulse transmitted across a synapse? Distinguish between a cholinergic and an adrenergic nerve fiber. Where does each kind occur? What is choline esterase and what is its function?

6. What is the basic function of all sensory receptors? Describe the location and general structure of receptors for pain, touch, pressure, heat, and cold stimuli. How can it be proved that the kind and localization of a sensory experience depend on neural centers? Distinguish between neurosensory and epitheliosensory cells.

7. Describe the location and structure of the taste and smell receptors. What are the primary taste sensations? Are tastes and smells inherent in given substances? Discuss. What are tangoreceptors, proprioreceptors? What are their functions, and where in an animal can such receptors be found?

8. Review the structure and function of stato-receptors generally, then describe the organization of the mammalian ear and show where statoreceptors are located. Distinguish between static and dynamic body balance.

9. What is a phonoreceptor? Describe the structure and function of a lateral-line system. Which animals can hear, and by means of what kinds of receptors? Describe the structure of such receptors. What is a cochlea? Show how hearing is accomplished in man and how pitch is discriminated.

10. Review the chemistry of vision. What are rods and cones? What is a retina? Which animals have color vision? Distinguish among eyespots, eye-cups, and vesicles. Describe the structure of the mammalian eye. What components form the focusing mechanism and how is the function of focusing carried out?

11. What is the distribution pattern of rods and cones in the retina of man? What eye structures does light traverse before it reaches the rods and cones? Describe the pattern of the neural pathways between the eyes and the brain.

12. Describe simple and complex activities of neural centers. What are reflex modification, impulse summation, channel selection, oscillatory circuits, stored programs, tropisms? How are stored programs related to learning and memory? What are conditioned reflexes and what is their functional significance? What is meant by pathway facilitation?

COLLATERAL READINGS

Bekésy, G. von: The Ear, *Sci. American*, Aug., 1957. A highly recommended account.

Carlson, A. J., and V. Johnson: "The Machinery of the Body," 4th ed., University of Chicago, Chicago, 1953. Nerve and sensory physiology are well reviewed in this text.

Eccles, J.: The Synapse, *Sci. American*, Jan., 1965. An analysis of synaptic functions by electron-microscopic studies of structure.

French, J. D.: The Reticular Formation, *Sci. American*, May, 1957. A discussion of the important brain region which functions as "volume" control and governs sleep and wakeful states.

Gerard, R. W.: What Is Memory?, *Sci. American*, Sept., 1953. Experiments designed to elucidate the mechanisms of memory storage are described.

Gibson, E. J., and R. D. Walk: The "Visual Cliff," *Sci. American*, Apr., 1960. A study of depth perception in various animals.

Gray, G. W.: The Great Ravelled Knot, *Sci. American*, Oct., 1948. A review of experiments on exploring and locating various functional regions in the brain.

Haagen-Smit, A. J.: Smell and Taste, *Sci. American*, Mar., 1952. A study of the sensitivity and discriminating ability of these chemoreceptors.

Hubel, D. H.: The Visual Cortex of the Brain, *Sci. American*, Nov., 1963. Responses of individual interpreter neurons in the optic lobes of cats are examined.

Hydén, H.: Satellite Cells in the Nervous System, *Sci. American*, Dec., 1961. The probable chemical basis of memory is explored, and special attention is given to the neuroglia cells, present together with neurons.

Katz, B.: The Nerve Impulse, *Sci. American*, Nov., 1952. A recommended review on the nature of impulses.

————: How Cells Communicate, *Sci. American*, Sept., 1961. A more recent examination of the nature of nerve impulses.

Kennedy, D.: Inhibition in Visual Systems, *Sci. American*, July, 1963. The nature of neuron inhibition by other neurons is examined in relation to vision.

Keynes, R. D.: The Nerve Impulse and the Squid, *Sci. American*, Dec., 1958. The physiology of nerve impulses is studied with the aid of the giant axons of squids.

Lissman, H. W.: Electric Location by Fishes, *Sci. American*, Mar., 1963. Some fishes explore their environment by sensing changes in electric fields they have produced.

Loewenstein, W. R.: Biological Transducers, *Sci. American*, Aug., 1960. The conversion of external stimuli to nerve impulses is examined in the Pacinian corpuscle.

Melzack, R.: The Perception of Pain, *Sci. American*, Feb., 1961. Factors such as past experiences and cultural backgrounds are shown to affect the sensation of pain.

Miller, W. H., F. Ratcliff, and H. K. Hartline: How Cells Receive Stimuli, *Sci. American*, Sept., 1961. The properties of specialized sensory cells are examined, with special reference to the photoreceptors of horseshoe crabs.

Olds, J.: Pleasure Centers in the Brain, *Sci. American*, Oct., 1956. Interesting experiments on electrically self-stimulating rats have revealed the existence of distinct pleasure centers.

Pavlov, I. P.: Conditioned Reflexes, in "A Source Book in Animal Biology," McGraw-Hill, New York,

1951. A classical account by the most famous student of such reflexes.

Rushton, W. A. H.: Visual Pigments in Man, *Sci. American*, Nov., 1962. A very interesting discussion. Recommended.

Snider, R. S.: The Cerebellum, *Sci. American*, Aug., 1958. Modern experiments on the functions of this brain part are described.

Sperry, R. W.: The Growth of Nerve Circuits, *Sci. American*, Nov., 1959. An excellent account on how complex neural pathway networks may become established in the embryo.

Wald, G.: Eye and Camera, *Sci. American*, Aug., 1950. A very instructive comparison.

————: The Molecular Basis of Visual Excitation, *Am. Scientist*, vol. 42, 1954. A recommended review by one of the leading investigators in this field.

Walter, W. G.: The Electrical Activity of the Brain, *Sci. American*, June, 1954. The patterns and possible meaning of brain waves are examined.

Wooldridge, D. E.: "The Machinery of the Brain," McGraw-Hill, New York, 1963. One of the best and most stimulating recent paperbacks on brain function. Strongly recommended.

PART SEVEN
SELF-PERPETUATION: REPRODUCTION
CHAPTER 26
PATTERNS OF REPRODUCTION
CHAPTER 27
REPRODUCTION: MONERA, PROTISTA, METAPHYTA
CHAPTER 28
REPRODUCTION: METAZOA
CHAPTER 29
DEVELOPMENT

Of all living functions, reproduction happens to be among the most noticeable to the casual human observer. Metabolism occurs largely on an invisible, molecular scale. Control functions result in steady state, that is, in unchanged, even conditions. Adaptation and evolution occur on a scale so vast that man does not perceive them directly or obviously. But reproduction does take place on a directly perceivable, obvious scale. Moreover, reproductive processes are universal and very dramatic; now there is one, then there are two.

To be sure, the deep significance of reproduction lies not in its dramatic nature but in its results. We recall that we have assigned "living" properties to the first of the ancient nucleic acids largely because they possessed *reproductive* properties. These properties have been handed down in an unbroken succession from the first genes to all present genes, and they still form the basis of all reproductive events today.

Just as an organism maintains steady states from its molecules up, so it also reproduces from its molecules up; molecular reproduction is the foundation of all reproduction. In this series of chapters, therefore, we examine first the patterns of reproduction among molecules, cells, and whole organisms. We then proceed with a systematic study of specific reproductive processes encountered in all main categories of organisms, and we conclude with a discussion of processes of development, the essential events through which reproduced offspring are transformed into adult wholes.

CHAPTER 26 PATTERNS OF REPRO-DUCTION

We may define reproduction broadly as extension of living matter in space and in time. The fundamental importance of this process as a self-perpetuative device is clear, for formation of new living units makes possible replacement and addition at every level of organization. Among molecules or cells, among whole organisms or species, replacement offsets death from normal wear and tear and death from accident or disease. *Healing* and *regeneration* are two aspects of replacement. Above and beyond this purely restorative function of reproduction, addition of extra units at any level results in four-dimensional *growth,* or increase in the net amount of existing living matter.

Any new living unit resembles the old, and reproduction therefore implies reasonably exact duplication. To create new units raw materials are required. Indeed, reproduction at any level depends on ample nutrition specifically and on properly controlled metabolism generally. It is also clear that duplication of a large unit implies prior or simultaneous duplication of all constituent smaller ones. Reproduction must therefore occur on the molecular level before it can occur on the cellular level, and on the cellular level before it can occur on the level of the whole organism.

CELLULAR REPRODUCTION

The multiplication of molecules within cells may take four different forms, according to the nature of the molecule to be multiplied. We are already familiar with all four. If water or another inorganic substance is to be reproduced within a cell, additional molecules or ions of such substances must be supplied ready-made by nutrition. Thus, *accumulation* is the simplest form of molecular "reproduction."

If a carbohydrate, a lipid, an amino acid, or any of their numerous derivatives is to be duplicated, it may have to be synthesized from accumulated simpler raw materials with the aid of appropriate enzymes. So long as the enzymes of a cell remain the same, most newly synthesized organic molecules will automatically be exact duplicates of molecules synthesized earlier. The second form of molecular reproduction therefore is *enzymatic synthesis*. It includes the first form, accumulation, as a component phase.

If a protein molecule is to be duplicated, we know that enzymes are required to link amino acids together and also that DNA and RNA must provide the specific information, or template, for the joining of particular amino acids in particular sequences. The third form of molecular reproduction evidently includes the first two forms but is additionally characterized as *template-dependent synthesis*. Lastly, if genetic DNA is to be duplicated, it must serve as its own template and control its own replication. All three other forms of molecular reproduction play a part here. Phosphate must be accumulated; sugars, purines, pyrimidines must be synthesized enzymatically; and protein enzymes must be synthesized with the aid of both other enzymes and genetic templates. But in addition, duplication of DNA hinges on specific *self-duplication,* and this is the fourth form of molecular reproduction.

In viruses, where the structural organization does not exceed the level of an aggregate of molecules, molecular reproduction is equivalent to reproduction of the whole unit. In all truly living systems, accumulation, enzymatic and template-dependent synthesis, and self-duplication contribute either to normal molecular replacement within cells or to molecular additions to cells. The result is *cell growth*. The rate of these processes depends on the supply of nutrients. If the parts of the cellular framework wear down faster than they can be replaced, then a cell may actually decrease in size and undergo negative growth, or degrowth. Positive growth demands a rate of molecular reproduction exceeding the rate of molecular destruction.

Duplication of DNA in the chromosomes of a cell may actually be the stimulus which in some as yet unknown way initiates reproduction of the cell as a whole. It is known that the microscopically observable events of *cell division* are preceded by synthesis of new DNA from old, each preexisting DNA set giving rise to two identical offspring sets. This chemical reproduction follows the pattern outlined in Chap. 20 (see Fig. 20.11), and reproduction of the entire cell occurs very soon thereafter.

Few biological events are as central to life and as universally characteristic of it as cell division. It is the sole means by which unicellular organisms multiply. It creates reproductive cells and trans-

forms them into multicellular adults. It replaces dead cells in the adult and thereby offsets normal wear and tear. It heals wounds and regenerates body parts lost or destroyed. And cell division sometimes goes wild and produces tumors, cancers, and other abnormal overgrowths. Indeed, the life histories of organisms may be well described as changing dynamic equilibria between cell division and cell death.

In many cases among Protista, a mother cell may divide into *several* daughter cells simultaneously, a reproductive process known as *multiple fission*. In the vast majority of cases, however, *binary fission* or division of one cell into two is the rule. Binary fission in most organisms produces two daughter cells of roughly equal size. In some instances, as in yeasts, distinctly unequal cells may result, a form of cell division called *budding*. In all cases, daughter cells enlarge by molecular reproduction, and they may subsequently divide in their turn. The period between two succeeding cell divisions represents a cell generation (Fig. 26.1).

In Protista, Metaphyta, and Metazoa, cell division consists of at least two separate processes; cleavage of the cytoplasm into two parts, or *cytokinesis*, and reproduction of the nucleus, referred to as *karyokinesis* or *mitosis*. These two events normally take place more or less concurrently, but they may become ungeared from each other. In many cell types, for example, mitosis often occurs without cytoplasmic cleavage and a binucleate or multinucleate cell then results. The reverse is encountered as well, that is, a binucleate or multinucleate cell may cleave without nuclear duplication. Such events may also be induced by experimental means. It is unknown how, in a uninucleate cell, the normal gearing of nuclear and cytoplasmic duplications is accomplished. Since the nucleus usually begins to duplicate somewhat earlier than the cytoplasm, nuclear reproduction may possibly trigger cytoplasmic reproduction (see Fig. 26.1).

Mitosis includes a mathematically precise doubling of the chromosomes and their genes. One of the two chromosome sets so formed becomes incorporated into one of the daughter nuclei, and the second chromosome set, into the other daughter nucleus. If mitosis is accompanied by cytokinesis, as is most often the case, we may speak of both processes together as a *mitotic cell division*. Note in any event that "mitosis" is not simply another word for cell division but designates a particular kind of *nuclear* division. Monera do not possess nuclei or chromosomes like other organisms. Cell division in Monera does include gene duplication but does not include mitosis.

26 · 1 Cell division. *A, B, C, the principal forms of fission. D, in most divisions* (left), *karyokinesis and cytokinesis occur together. In some cases, however, karyokinesis alone leads to formation of binucleate or multinucleate cells* (middle), *or cytokinesis alone transforms a bi- or multinucleate cell into two or more uninucleate ones* (right).

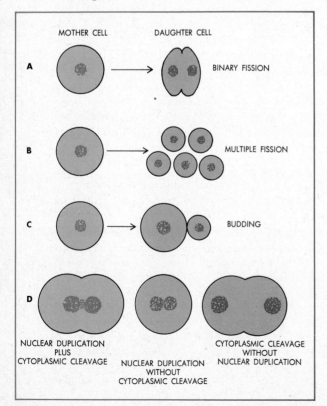

MOTHER CELL   DAUGHTER CELL

A   BINARY FISSION

B   MULTIPLE FISSION

C   BUDDING

D

NUCLEAR DUPLICATION
PLUS
CYTOPLASMIC CLEAVAGE

NUCLEAR DUPLICATION
WITHOUT
CYTOPLASMIC CLEAVAGE

CYTOPLASMIC CLEAVAGE
WITHOUT
NUCLEAR DUPLICATION

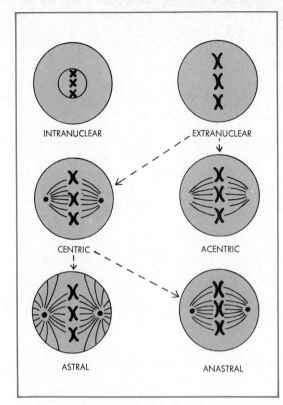

26 · 2 Patterns of mitosis. *The arrows show that, in extranuclear mitosis, for example, the pattern may be centric or acentric; and in centric mitosis, for example, the pattern may be astral or anastral. Other combinations of patterns are encountered as well.*

Among the Protista, mitotic division takes several different forms in different groups (Fig. 26.2). For example, mitosis may be *intranuclear* or *extranuclear*. In the intranuclear type, all mitotic events occur right within the nucleus, which persists with its membrane intact till near the end of fission. Then the nucleus divides along with the cytoplasm. In extranuclear mitosis, the nuclear membrane dissolves soon after mitosis starts. Subsequent events take place throughout the whole cell, which ceases to be differentiated into nucleus and cytoplasm for the time being. Two new nuclei with new membranes form at the end of mitosis, when the cell cleaves into two.

Mitosis may also be *centric* or *acentric*. In the first case a centriole is present and it participates in mitosis in a manner to be described below. In some protistan groups the centriole is situated inside the nucleus, and in such cases mitosis is centric and intranuclear. In other groups the centriole is located just outside the nucleus and mitosis here is centric

and extranuclear. Acentric mitosis occurs in species that do not possess centrioles. Division in these instances may similarly be intranuclear or extranuclear.

Protistan mitoses may be classified further into *astral* and *anastral* types. These terms refer to the presence or absence of an *aster*, a set of temporary fibrils which during mitosis radiate like a sunburst from a centriole. If centrioles are present, asters may or may not form. Thus, centric mitoses may be astral or anastral, and acentric mitoses are always anastral.

Each protistan group is characterized by its own type of mitosis, and the distribution of particular mitotic types does not appear to follow any obvious evolutionary or taxonomic pattern. Two species within a given phylum may be characterized by different mitotic types, whereas two species of different phyla may exhibit the same mitotic type. In the Metaphyta mitosis is characteristically *extranuclear, acentric,* and *anastral.* Metazoan mitoses are *extranuclear, centric,* and *astral.*

A certain amount of time elapses between DNA duplication in the cell nucleus and the visible phases of division. During this period numerous biochemical preparations are probably made throughout a cell for the actual execution of the reproductive process. The visible events consist of four successive, arbitrarily defined stages: *prophase, metaphase, anaphase,* and *telophase.* One stage merges gradually into the next and it is usually impossible to fix sharp lines of transition. Nuclear reproduction, that is, mitosis

26 · 3 Early prophase in animal mitosis. *The nuclear membrane is just dissolving and chromosomes are already visible. To either side of the nuclear region is a darkly stained centriole area. These areas develop after a single centriole has divided and the two daughter centrioles have migrated to opposite sides of the nucleus. From each centriole area fine fibrils are beginning to radiate out, that is, asters are beginning to form.*

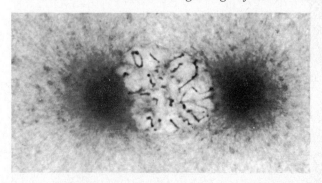

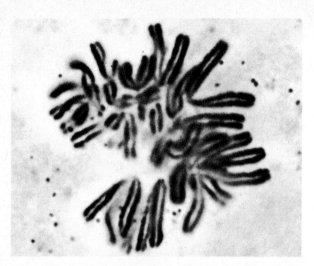

26 · 4 Later prophase in animal mitosis. *Chromosomes have already duplicated, and doubled chromosomes, each known as a chromatid, are therefore present. The members of each pair of chromatids are still held together at one point, the centromere.*

proper, encompasses all four stages; cytokinesis occurs in the last stage.

In the extranuclear, centric, astral mitosis of Metazoa, one of the first events of *prophase* is the division of the centriole (Fig. 26.3 and Color Plate XXVIII, 46). As soon as daughter centrioles have formed, the two granules behave as if they repelled each other and they migrate toward opposite sides of the cell nucleus. Concurrently, portions of the cytoplasm transform into fine gel fibrils. Some of these radiate away from each centriole like the spokes of a wheel and form *asters*. Other gel fibrils develop between the two centrioles. Looping from one centriole to the other in flat curves, these fibrils constitute a *spindle*. The centriole at each end marks a *spindle pole*. As the centrioles move farther and farther apart, the fibrils of the spindle and the asters lengthen and increase in number. Centrioles are not present and asters do not form in the acentric, anastral mitoses of Metaphyta. Spindles do develop, however.

During these stages of prophase, the nuclear membrane dissolves, the nucleoli disintegrate, and nuclear and cytoplasmic substances mix freely. Moreover, distinct chromosomes become visible. Close examination reveals that each chromosome now is a *double* filament (Fig. 26.4); each chromosome has manufactured a mathematically exact duplicate some time before prophase. Such twin chromosomes lie closely parallel and are joined to each other only at a single point, the so-called *centromere*. The location of the centromere varies for

different chromosome pairs. Two spindle fibrils become anchored to each centromere, one from each pole of the spindle. In this way, the chromosomes become linked to the spindle. At this general period, prophase comes to a close and *metaphase* begins.

Early during metaphase the chromosome pairs are still scattered randomly through the central portion of the cell, but later they begin to migrate. If we draw an imaginary line from one spindle pole to the other, we mark out a spindle axis. Chromosomes migrate into a plane set at right angles to the spindle axis, midway along it. Specifically, it is the centromere of each chromosome pair which comes to occupy a station precisely within this plane. During the migration, the chromosomes trail behind their centromeres like streamers. Lined up in one plane, the centromeres are said to form a *metaphase plate* (Fig. 26.5 and Color Plate XXVIII, 47).

The lengthwise separation of the chromosome pairs now becomes complete. Each centromere divides and entirely independent chromosomes are produced in this manner. A small gel fibril arises at once between the centromeres of formerly joined chromosomes, and such chromosomes begin to move apart. Once they are completely separated, the members of a pair of chromosomes behave as if they repelled each other. Thus, one set of chromosomes migrates away from the metaphase plate toward one spindle pole, and an identical twin set migrates in the opposite direction, toward the other spindle pole. The centromeres again lead and the arms of the chromosomes trail. Also, the gel fibrils between twin centromeres lengthen, and fibrils between the centromeres and the spindle poles shorten. This

26 · 5 Metaphase in animal mitosis. *Note asters, spindle, and the metaphase plate, halfway along and at right angles to the spindle axis. Note also the fibrils which join the chromosomes lined up in the metaphase plate with the spindle poles.*

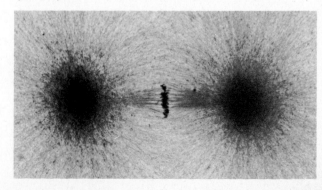

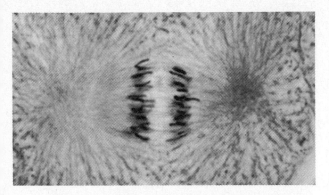

26 · 6   Anaphase in animal mitosis. *Chromosome sets are migrating toward spindle poles.*

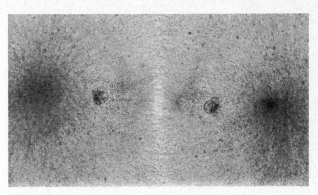

26 · 7   Telophase in animal mitosis. *Asters are subsiding, nuclei are re-forming, chromosome threads have become indistinct, and cytoplasmic cleavage is underway, in the same plane as the earlier metaphase plate.*

period of poleward migration of chromosomes represents the *anaphase* of mitotic division (Fig. 26.6 and Color Plate XXVIII, 48).

The beginning of *telophase* is marked by the appearance of a *cleavage furrow* in animal cells and a *division plate* in plant cells. Both furrow and plate form in the plane of the earlier metaphase plate. A cleavage furrow at first is a shallow groove circling the surface of a cell. This groove gradually deepens, cuts through the spindle fibrils, and eventually constricts the cell into two daughter cells. The division plate of plant cells is a partition of cellulose laid down more or less simultaneously at all points of the plane of cleavage (Fig. 26.7 and Color Plate XXVIII, 49).

While such cytokinesis is in progress, the chromo-

somes within each prospective daughter cell aggregate near the spindle pole. Spindle fibrils subside, that is, the gel composing them reverts to a sol state. A new nuclear membrane forms at each spindle pole, and this membrane surrounds the chromosomes. Concurrently, the chromosomes in each newly forming nucleus manufacture new nucleoli, in numbers characteristic of the particular cell type. These nuclear processes terminate roughly when cytoplasmic cleavage nears completion, and mitotic division then has reached its endpoint. In each of the newly formed daughter cells, the genes now resume control of *m*RNA manufacture and a new growth cycle follows (Fig. 26.8).

The mechanical forces responsible for the chromosome movements in division cannot yet be identified precisely. The behavior of the spindle fibrils is highly suggestive. Do these fibrils, like guy ropes, pull and push chromosomes first into the metaphase plate and later toward the spindle poles? This possibility has been tested in experiments (with amoebae) in which spindle fibers have been cut through with needles. Under such conditions the chromosomes

26 · 8   Summary of mitosis. *The assumption here is that cytoplasmic cleavage accompanies mitosis. Note that a "resting" cell is resting only from the standpoint of reproductive activity; in all other respects it is exceedingly active.*

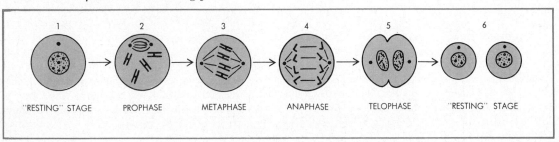

"RESTING" STAGE   PROPHASE   METAPHASE   ANAPHASE   TELOPHASE   "RESTING" STAGE

still migrate in normal fashion. In certain insects, moreover, cells have been found in which demonstrable spindle fibrils from pole to chromosome are not formed. Yet here the chromosomes migrate nevertheless. Accordingly, the gelated fibrils would not seem to be responsible for chromosome movements.

However, other lines of evidence indicate the opposite. It happens sometimes that pieces break off from chromosomes. Indeed, breaks can be induced by exposing cells to X rays or to ultrasonic vibrations. In such cases the main portion of a chromosome, which remains attached to a spindle fibril, unfailingly moves toward a pole, but detached pieces invariably stay behind and are unable to migrate. In certain animal cells, furthermore, it can be shown that aster fibrils attach to the inner surface of the cell membrane. As these fibrils shorten, the cell membrane is pulled inward and so forms the constricting groove which eventually divides the cell.

In these instances, spindle fibrils do seem to exert a positive pull. Some investigators have suggested that the fibrils contain myosin, the same protein that makes muscles contract. We note that, on the whole, existing evidence is still conflicting and for the present we must conclude that the forces responsible for mitotic movements have not yet been identified. Yet it is clear that these forces are brought into action ultimately by DNA. Moreover, they produce cells containing exactly identical gene sets incorporated in identical chromosome sets, and approximately equal quantities of all other cellular constituents. DNA is therefore the key to cellular multiplication. It controls cell growth and, through its own periodic reproduction, triggers the reproduction of the whole cell. In the process, the all-important codes of DNA are transmitted exactly from cell generation to cell generation. Such transmission in effect constitutes *cellular heredity;* to the extent that genes themselves are stable, each new cell generation inherits the same genetic codes, hence the same structural and functional characteristics, that had been present in the previous cell generation.

In unicellular organisms, cell division is equivalent to reproduction of the whole organism. Daughter cells generally separate, but in some forms they remain sticking together and form *colonies.* In multicellular organisms cell division either contributes to *cell replacement,* as in regeneration or wound healing, or adds to *cell number.* The result is the growth of tissues and organs. An organism may therefore grow either by molecular reproduction and increase in cell *size* or by cellular reproduction and increase in cell *number,* or by both. If the rate of cell division more than balances the rate of cell death, continued net growth occurs. In the opposite case degrowth will take place.

Rates of cellular reproduction actually vary greatly. One rate-limiting factor is the state of cellular nutrition, as noted, and another is the state of cellular specialization. Relatively unspecialized cells retain a fairly rapid but steadily decreasing rate of division throughout the life of an organism. By contrast, liver or muscle cells, for example, divide only rarely in the adult. And after being formed in the embryo, nerve cells do not divide at all. Nerve cells *may* grow, but only by increase in cell size. Destroyed neurons cannot be replaced. Other highly specialized cells may have lost their nuclei (for example, red corpuscles, sieve-tube cells) or their interior substance (for example, sclerenchyma), and these too do not divide. In general, the more highly specialized a cell the less frequently it divides, and vice versa (see Chap. 2).

Many cells divide when they have grown to double their original volume. However, attainment of such a volume is probably not a specific stimulus, for cells can be made to divide at any time before their volume has doubled. Moreover, they may be prevented from dividing altogether and may be allowed to grow into giant cells many times larger than twice the original. Several chemicals are known to inhibit division and several to promote it (for example, various growth hormones). Similarly, physical agents such as X rays may inhibit or promote division, depending on conditions. Experimental procedures employing such agents have gone far toward controlling cell division, but it is still not known how such control actually operates. And it is equally unknown what specific normal conditions within a cell or outside it so stimulate it that it synthesizes new DNA and then begins to divide.

Among multicellular organisms the highest rates of cell division normally occur in embryonic stages, the lowest in old age. What accounts for such a deceleration with increasing age? With few exceptions, cellular reproductive capacity in the adult remains *potentially* as great as in the embryo. This is shown, for example, by the high rates of cell division in wound healing, in regeneration, in cancers and other tumors, and in *tissue cultures.* Such cultures are prepared by separating groups of cells from an organism and growing them in artificial nutrient solutions. Under isolated conditions of this sort, cells are found to reproduce faster than if they had remained within an organism. Moreover, if newly formed cells in a tissue culture are cut away from time to time, the original bit of tissue may

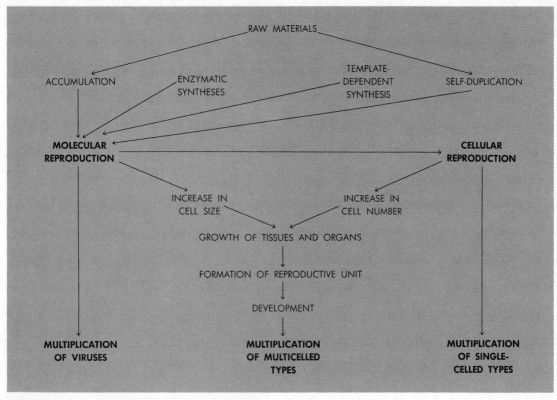

26 · 9 The overall pattern of reproduction.

live almost indefinitely long, certainly far longer than it would have lived within an organism. Through tissue culture, for example, a piece of the heart muscle of a chicken embryo has been maintained alive for over 30 years, which exceeds the life span of the whole chicken several times.

It is conceivable, therefore, that cell reproduction in intact organisms may slow down mainly because the cells are *not* isolated as in a tissue culture. Instead, cells are integrated very finely into a larger organization. Just as, in the human population, economic, social, and other checks hold the reproduction of the individual to less than maximum rates, so evidently is the rate of cell division held down by metabolic checks in the healthy cell population. Similarly, the slower expansion of an older, established society, compared with that of a new pioneer group, provides a close parallel to comparative growth rates in adult and embryo.

Although growth slows down with increasing age, it does not usually cease entirely. All plants and many animals continue to grow somewhat even in old age. The general range of body size is a genetically determined trait of the species, but within this range wide variations are possible. Trees, for example, are well known to be able to grow for hundreds of years. Some of them, particularly giant redwoods and *Eucalyptus* trees, have attained heights of about 400 ft—the largest organisms ever to exist. Here, as in whales, elephants, and other large animals, bulk arises primarily through continuing cell divisions and increase in cell number, not increase in cell size. Among animals, fish and numerous other types are known to grow throughout life. But in another series of forms, as in man, net growth stops altogether at a certain stage.

ORGANISMIC REPRODUCTION

After periods of growth by molecular and cellular reproduction, the whole organism may reproduce (Fig. 26.9). This process generally includes at least two steps. First, a *reproductive unit* separates from the parent organism. Second, a duplicate organism

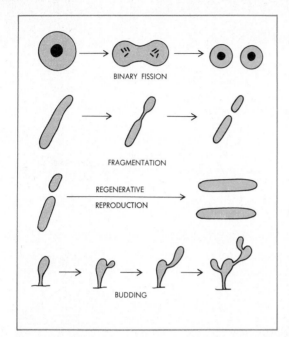

BINARY FISSION

FRAGMENTATION

REGENERATIVE
REPRODUCTION

BUDDING

26 · 10 *The basic forms of vegetative reproduction.*

forms from the reproductive unit through *development.* According to the nature and manner of formation of the reproductive unit, three basic forms of organismic propagation may be recognized, namely, *vegetative, sporulative,* and *gametic* reproduction.

In vegetative multiplication a reproductive unit may consist of any portion of the parent organism; the unit is not specialized exclusively for reproduction and may range in size from the whole parent body to a minute fragment of that body. Moreover, the unit develops into an offspring directly, in a smooth sequence of events in which successive steps are not sharply marked off from one another. The principal variants of vegetative reproduction are *fission, fragmentation, regenerative reproduction,* and *budding* (Fig. 26.10).

Fission, or cell division, is the vegetative method of reproduction in unicellular Monera and Protista, where the whole cellular body of the organism constitutes the reproductive unit. In fragmentation, a multicellular parent organism spontaneously splits up into two or more portions, each then regenerating the missing body parts. This method is quite widespread among multicellular Protista and also in Metaphyta and Metazoa. For example, in dichotomously branching algae and liverworts, two organisms may arise from one by *posterior decay;* the main por-

tion of the body dies off, leaving two branch portions as separate individuals. Among animals, analogously, certain sea anemones and flatworms occasionally fragment into two units. Other flatworms, and also certain hair worms, annelids, and echinoderms sometimes pinch off one or more smaller portions of their bodies, each such portion subsequently forming a whole new animal (Fig. 26.11).

Closely allied to fragmentation is *regenerative reproduction,* a process of multiplication in which

26 · 11 *Vegetative reproduction by fragmentation. Photo: a sea anemone is splitting lengthwise into two offspring organisms. Diagram: branching growth and posterior decay may lead to the formation of two separate individuals from one parent organism.*

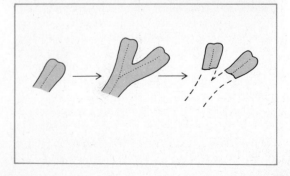

the reproductive units arise fortuitously as a result of injury to the parent by external agents. For example, many organisms may be cut into several pieces and each piece may then grow into a new, whole individual. Almost any piece of a plant, a few segments of an earthworm, an arm of a starfish, a chunk of tissue from a hydra or a sponge—each is an effective reproductive unit. The parent organisms losing such sections of their bodies usually regenerate the missing parts (Fig. 26.12). In all these cases, the size and composition of the reproductive unit obviously vary with the nature and extent of damage to the parent. It is clear, also, that regeneration may become reproduction only where the capacity of regeneration is extensive, as in the examples just cited. Regenerative capacity varies with the species, and in many organisms it is highly limited. Salamanders may regenerate a whole limb, but a limb cannot regenerate a whole salamander. In vertebrates generally, the regeneration potential is not even so great as in salamanders but, as in man, is limited to the healing of relatively small wounds.

Reproduction by budding involves the formation of reproductive units consisting initially of no more than perhaps a dozen cells each. Formed in different body regions of different organisms, a bud may retain a permanent anatomical connection with the parent, and after it has grown into an attached adult it may bud in its own turn and produce further generations of attached adults. Large colonies of joined individuals may form in this fashion. In other cases a bud at first develops in anatomical continuity with the parent, but it eventually separates and becomes

26 · 13 Reproduction by budding. *Animal budding is illustrated in Fig. 14.25. A, leaf of* Kalanchoë, *showing small, vegetatively formed plants developing along the leaf margin. B, gemmae on a thallus of the liverwort* Marchantia.

a new adult on its own (Fig. 26.13). Among plants, for example, bryophytes produce buds called *gemmae*, consisting of variously shaped groups of cells. These eventually detach from a parent plant and form separate individuals. In the angiosperm *Kalanchoë*, for example, multicellular reproductive buds may form along the margins of leaves. Animal budding is particularly widespread in sessile or sluggish types; as pointed out in the chapters of Part 4, the process occurs, for example, among sponges, coelenterates, flatworms, ectoprocts, annelids, and tunicates.

The chief adaptive advantage of all forms of vegetative reproduction is that the process can be carried out by each organism without dependence on other organisms. The only requirements are favorable environmental conditions, including ample food supplies. Thus, vegetative reproduction becomes particularly useful if the organism leads a sluggish

26 · 12 Regenerative reproduction. *An arm of a starfish regenerates all missing parts and becomes a whole animal.*

or altogether nonmotile way of life and is therefore relatively isolated from contact with other members of the species. Moreover, the method requires little tissue or cell specialization, and it also offers obvious advantages to an organism in the form of regenerative reproduction. As a result, vegetative multiplication has persisted as the only method of propagation in all unicellular forms and as a major subsidiary method in all but the most complex multicellular ones.

On theoretical grounds, a reproductive unit of a multicellular organism should not have to be so large a portion of the parent organism as it is in vegetative reproduction. The smallest unit possessing the genetic information and the operating equipment representative of an entire multicellular organism is a *single cell*. Accordingly, the minimum unit for the construction of such an organism should be one cell. This is actually the universal case. Regardless of whether or not it may also reproduce vegetatively, every multicellular organism is capable of reproducing through single *reproductive cells*. All such cells are more or less specialized for reproduction, and they are often formed in more or less specialized reproductive tissues or organs of the parent.

According to the manner of their formation and their later fate, two general classes of reproductive cells may be distinguished. One includes cells which, like vegetative reproductive units, may develop into adults *directly*. Such cells are called *spores*. The chief advantage of reproduction by sporulation is that a spore represents an excellent device for geographic dispersal. In water, a spore cell may be equipped with flagella and may swim to new territories, even far away from the parent. On land, spores may be encapsulated and protected against desiccation and may be distributed widely by wind and animals. In any environment, moreover, spores can be produced in very large numbers. As might be expected, therefore, spores or equivalent types of reproductive cells typically are formed by organisms that cannot disperse by locomotion: some Monera, most Protista, and all Metaphyta, which are uniformly sessile. Spores or sporelike cells are not produced by Metazoa; motile animals may disperse geographically at any stage of their life cycle, and sessile animals have free-swimming embryos or larvae and they may also disperse through vegetative buds.

However, both sporulation and vegetative reproduction are characterized by a major limitation which can be circumvented only by the third basic method of multiplication, gametic reproduction. This method again depends on single reproductive cells, but such cells *cannot* develop directly. Instead, they must first undergo a *sexual process*, in which two reproductive cells fuse. The cells are therefore called *sex cells*, or *gametes*. One type of gamete is often a *sperm*, the other type, an *egg*. A *mating* process makes possible the pairwise fusion of gametes. This fusion is *fertilization*, and the fusion product is a *zygote*. Development of gametes into adults cannot occur until fertilization has taken place. In other words, if sex occurs, it is interpolated between the two basic phases of the reproductive sequence, namely, between the formation of reproductive cells and the development of these cells into adults.

Note that, in a strict sense, the often-used terms "asexual reproduction" and "sexual reproduction" are essentially meaningless. In all forms of multiplication, the fundamental "reproductive" event is the formation of reproductive units. The rest is development. And it is this developmental phase which may or may not require sexual triggering. Therefore, whereas *development* may be initiated sexually or asexually, reproduction as such, or formation of reproductive units, is always "asexual."

Gametic reproduction entails a number of serious disadvantages. For example, the method depends on chance, for gametes must meet and very often they simply do not. Much of the reproductive effort of the parent organisms is then wasted. Gametic reproduction also depends on locomotion, for if gametes are to meet they either must move themselves or must be brought together by locomotion of the parents. Yet eggs in virtually all cases and parent organisms in many cases are incapable of locomotion. Above all, gametic reproduction invariably requires an aquatic medium. In air, gametes would dry out quickly unless they possessed evaporation-resistant outer shells. But if two cells were so encapsulated, they could then not fuse together. As we shall see, terrestrial organisms actually can circumvent this dilemma only by means of special adaptations.

However, all these various disadvantages are relatively minor compared to the one vital advantage offered by gametes. This advantage is sex. What is the crucial significance of this process?

SEXUALITY

THE ROLE OF SEX

Sexual processes may or may not take place in conjunction with reproductive processes. Where sex and reproduction are not associated, as in many Protista, the organisms reproduce vegetatively or by spores and sex occurs separately at some stage

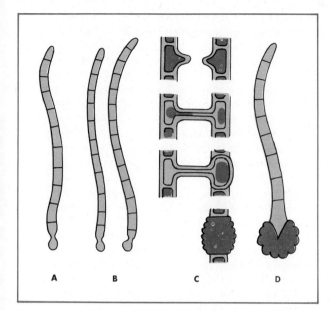

26 · 14 Sexuality in Spirogyra. A, colony of cells. B, two filaments side by side prior to conjugation. C, bridge between opposite cells (top); migration of contents of one cell into the other cell (center); formation of cyst or zygospore (bottom). D, growth of new filament from opened zygospore.

of the life cycle. Where sex and reproduction do take place together, as in most organisms, gametic reproduction is the result. Such organisms may or may not reproduce additionally by vegetative means or by spores.

The role of sex is revealed most clearly in those Protista in which sexual processes and reproduction do not occur together. A good example is *Spirogyra*, a filamentous green alga forming dense growths in freshwater ponds. Throughout spring, summer, and early fall, the cells reproduce vegetatively by mitotic division and add to the length of the filament. Pieces of the alga may break off and settle elsewhere, starting new individuals. Later in the fall, two cells from two filaments lying side by side may *conjugate;* a bridge forms which interconnects the two cells. The contents of one cell then move in amoeboid fashion through the bridge into the other cell and the two cells fuse (Fig. 26.14).

That is a sexual process. What initiates its occurrence, characteristically at that season of the year? Subsequent events provide the clue. All non-conjugated cells soon die as a result of falling autumn temperatures. But the fused double cell, or zygote,

is able to secrete a heavy wall around itself. The cyst (*zygospore*) so formed is then able to live through the winter. In the following spring, as surface ice disappears from the pond and temperatures begin to rise, the cyst wall breaks open and a new *Spirogyra* filament develops from the surviving zygote.

Analogous sexual processes occur in many other protists. Among protozoa, for example, the cells reproduce vegetatively whenever they can and sex takes place separately at some stage of the life cycle. Reproduction occurs under optimal environmental conditions, when food is plentiful, when the organisms are not too crowded together, and when the water has a proper temperature and pH. The sexual process typically manifests itself under the opposite conditions, when the environment is more or less unfavorable. For example, starvation or crowding or both usually lead to sexual response. This response takes the form of *syngamy* in some protozoa and of *conjugation* in others. In syngamy, two whole protozoa come to function as gametes and fuse into a zygote. In conjugation, two cellular individuals fuse only partially, that is, a cytoplasmic bridge forms between mating partners as in *Spirogyra*. Also, the nucleus of each conjugating protozoan gives rise to two *gamete nuclei,* and one of these migrates from each cell through the bridge into the other cell. After such a nuclear exchange, the two gamete nuclei now present in each conjugating individual fuse into a zygote nucleus and the two mating partners then separate (Fig. 26.15).

Note, first, that the sexual process is fundamentally quite distinct from reproduction. Protozoa and algae such as *Spirogyra* do not "multiply" by sex—if any-

26 · 15 Syngamy (top) *and conjugation* (bottom) *in protozoa (Paramecium, schematic).*

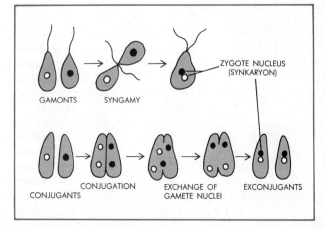

thing, quite the contrary. In *Spirogyra* and in protozoa undergoing syngamy two cells form one; and in conjugating protozoa two cells enter the process and two cells again emerge. In all other organisms sex and reproduction are equally distinct, even though in most cases the two processes do occur together.

Note further that in *Spirogyra*, protozoa, and in virtually all other organisms, man not excepted, sexual activity is particularly evident during periods of persistent environmental stress. Sexuality may be induced or intensified by unfavorable climates, by widespread food shortages, by overpopulation, or by other conditions which cannot be quickly responded to through steady-state control. Indeed, most organisms living in temperate climates manifest sexual activity typically in the fall or in the spring. In each of these two seasons, sex is a response to the stress conditions of the preceding season and anticipates the stress conditions of the following season.

Just how is sexuality effective against conditions of stress? Events in *Spirogyra* and protozoa supply the general answer: every cell resulting from the sexual process possesses the genes of both parental cells which entered the process. Stripped to its barest essentials, the sexual process may be defined as the accumulation within a single cell of genes derived from two relatively unrelated cells. One

method of achieving this is cell fusion, as in *Spirogyra*, in protozoa exhibiting syngamy, and indeed in most organisms; another method is exchange of duplicate nuclei, hence of duplicate gene sets, as in conjugating protozoa.

Sex therefore counteracts stress conditions on the principle of "two are better than one." If the self-perpetuating powers of two relatively unrelated parent organisms are joined through union of their genes, then the offspring produced later may acquire a greater survival potential than that of either parent alone. If parent *A* survives in environment *a* and parent *B* in environment *b*, then the offspring *AB* formed after sexual union may survive in environments *a* or *b* or in both (Fig. 26.16).

Moreover, a still poorly understood *rejuvenation*, on the biochemical, metabolic level, accompanies the sexual process. In certain protozoa and fungi, for example, if sex is experimentally prevented during an indefinite number of successive vegetative generations, then the vigor of the line eventually declines. The organisms ultimately die, even under optimal environmental conditions. Internal stresses apparently appear in aged generations, and only a "rejuvenation" through sex may then save the reproductive succession and prevent the line from dying out.

We may say that reproduction is a "conservative" process. Parental characteristics are passed on faithfully by reproduction from generation to generation, and so long as the external and internal environment remains favorable, succeeding generations survive as well as preceding ones. Sex, on the other hand, is a "liberalizing" process. It may offer survival under new or changed conditions. By combining the genes of two parents, sex introduces *genetic change* into the later offspring. And to the extent that such change may be advantageous for survival in new environments or under new conditions, sex has *adaptive* value. That is the key point; *sex is one of the chief processes of adaptation.* It is worth repeating that sex is *not* a process of reproduction.

Since the sexual process involves single cells, it must be carried out at a stage when an organism consists of but a single cell. Among unicellular forms, therefore, sex may occur at any stage of the life cycle regardless of when reproduction occurs, and it may be dissociated completely from reproduction. By contrast, if in the life cycle of a multicellular organism sex is to take place at all, it *must* take place at a unicellular reproductive stage. Thus, in "gametic reproduction" among multicellular types, sex occurs *after* the formation of gametes and *before* their development into multicellular adults (Fig. 26.17).

26 · 16   The role of sex in combating stress. a and b represent two different environments containing two genetically different parents; A and B symbolize their genes. Through sex, the offspring (right) acquires the genes of both parents, hence also the ability to live in either environment a or b.

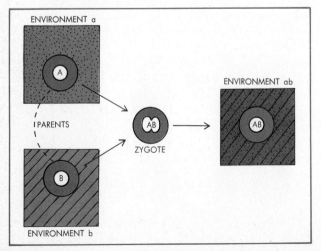

ENVIRONMENT a

A

PARENTS

B

ENVIRONMENT b

AB
ZYGOTE

ENVIRONMENT ab

AB

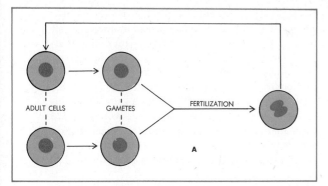

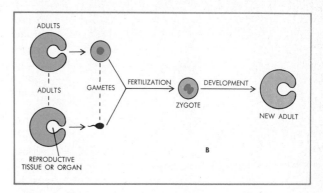

26 · 17 *Sex and life cycle. A, in unicellular organisms, there is often not much developmental difference between adult, gamete, or zygote, and sex may therefore occur at any stage of the life cycle. B, in multicellular organisms sex must occur when the organism is at a unicellular stage, for example, the gamete stage.*

FORMS OF SEXUALITY

In *Spirogyra*, the gamete cells are not visibly distinguishable as being of two different types; before an actual process of conjugation, one cannot tell which cell will move across the bridge and which will not. In protozoa, similarly, the mating partners in most cases cannot be distinguished structurally. Functional differences do exist, however, and it can be shown that mating cannot occur between just any two cells; fertilization can take place only between two cells belonging to two functionally different varieties. Such structural likeness of two gamete types is referred to as *isogamy*, a condition encountered quite frequently among Protista. In many protists, however, the two mating cells do differ visibly. In numerous cases, for example, one mating cell is distinctly smaller than the other. Such forms are said to exhibit *anisogamy;* that is, sexual processes involve gametes of unequal appearance. Still other protists, and all Metaphyta and Metazoa, exhibit a special form of anisogamy, namely, *oögamy*. Here one gamete type is always flagellate and usually small, and the other is always nonmotile or amoeboid and usually large. The small type is called a *sperm*, the large type, an *egg* (Fig. 26.18).

In many organisms, any one individual produces one gamete type only and another individual produces the other type only. The sexes then are said to be *separate*. Such a functional specialization of individuals is exhibited by most animals, numerous plants,

and many protists. The mechanisms which determine whether a given individual will belong to one sex type or the other are discussed in Chap. 30. If separately sexed organisms exhibit isogamy or anisogamy, the terms "male" and "female" are not strictly applicable. For example, there is little justification for regarding isogamous protozoa or individuals of *Spirogyra* as either males or females. Instead, the two sex types, or *mating types*, are customarily identified by distinguishing symbols such as + and − (Fig. 26.19). True male and female sexes are recognized only in cases of oögamy, that is, wherever distinct sperms and eggs are produced. In such orga-

26 · 18 *The three patterns of fertilization, distinguished on the basis of gamete types. Gametes may be of the same size and motility (isogamy), of different sizes but the same motility (anisogamy), or of different sizes and different motilities (oögamy).*

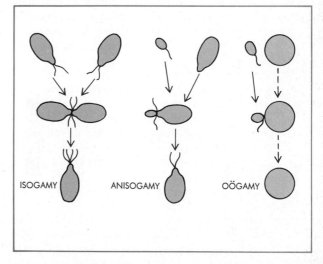

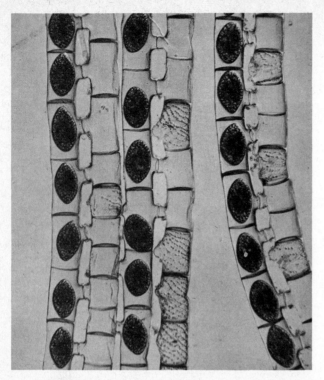

26 · 19 Zygospores of Spirogyra. *Note that all cells within a given filament have the same sexual properties: they may be either migrating sexual partners or stationary partners which receive cells from a neighboring filament. All cells of a given filament are the same* mating type, *and this accounts for their uniform sexual behavior.*

nisms males and females are often distinguished also in other ways. In Metaphyta and Metazoa, for example, sperms and eggs are produced in differently constructed sex organs. Among plants, *antheridia* form sperms, *archegonia* form eggs; among animals, *testes* form sperms, *ovaries* form eggs. Moreover, the sex organs of males and females may be components of differently constructed reproductive systems, and numerous secondary sex characteristics may provide additional distinctions. We note that where the sexes are separate, the degrees of sex distinction may vary considerably. At one extreme are the isogamous protists, where visible differences between sex types are zero. At the other extreme are the advanced Metaphyta and particularly the advanced Metazoa, in which virtually every part of the organism may exhibit characteristics of maleness or femaleness.

In numerous organisms, both gamete types are produced within the same individual. Known as *hermaphroditism*, this condition is believed to be more primitive than that of separate sexes; the latter condition may have evolved from hermaphroditism

by suppression of either the male or the female potential in different individuals. For example, all vertebrates develop in the embryo with both potentials, but only one later becomes actual in a given individual. Considerable numbers of Protista are hermaphroditic, including most conjugating protozoa, in which each individual produces a gamete nucleus of each sex type. Many, possibly most, Metaphyta are hermaphrodites, and in Metazoa hermaphroditism occurs in some groups of almost every phylum. The condition is sometimes encountered as an abnormality in vertebrates, man included.

In most cases, hermaphroditism is a direct adaptation to either a parasitic or to a sluggish or altogether nonmotile way of life. For example, since every hermaphrodite may function both as a "male" and a "female," a mating of two individuals may not even be required and *self-fertilization* may take place (Fig. 26.20). In such instances, the gametes of one sex type are genetically compatible with the gametes of the other sex type produced in the same individual. Many Protista are self-fertilizing, including most of the conjugating protozoa. In these, exchange of gamete nuclei between two individuals need not occur and the two gamete nuclei produced within one individual may fuse. Self-fertilization in such cases is called *autogamy*. Many fungi are similarly self-fertilizing, and these organisms are said to be *homothallic*. Among Metaphyta and Metazoa the phenomenon is far less common, but it does occur (for example, in parasitic forms such as tapeworms).

Other hermaphrodites must carry out *cross-fertilization;* that is, a gamete of one sex type produced by one individual must fertilize a gamete of the other sex type produced by another individual (see Fig. 26.20). Some kind of block against self-fertilization usually ensures cross-fertilization. For example, so-called "compatibility genes" are known to make self-fertilization impossible in a number of hermaphroditic Protista (fungi in particular), and these are said to be *heterothallic*. Most often, a meeting of sperms and eggs from the same individual is prevented by the anatomy of the body. Among plants such a structural block is in evidence in many flowering types, and in animals the two reproductive systems of a hermaphrodite often open to the outside in different surface regions. In several hermaphroditic animal groups, particularly among mollusks, for example, sperms and eggs are manufactured at different times during the breeding season. Some species produce ovaries first and testes next (the same sex organ often switching function and producing both eggs and sperm in succession). Other species form testes first and ovaries later.

Note that, in cross-fertilizing hermaphrodites, the

mating pattern is essentially the same as in organisms with separate sexes. Yet an adaptive advantage is apparent nevertheless; fewer reproductive cells are wasted than in species with separate sexes. Thus, if a given species is hermaphroditic and cross-fertilizing, sperms from one individual may meet eggs in *any* other individual, for every hermaphrodite does produce eggs. In species with separate sexes, by contrast, many sperms are wasted through chance misdistribution to the wrong sex. Similarly, if mutually cross-fertilizing hermaphrodites are capable of some locomotion, like earthworms, for example, then fertilization becomes possible whenever *any* two individuals meet. Since sluggish individuals are not likely to meet very frequently to begin with and

26 · 20 Separate sexes and hermaphroditism. *The symbols ♀ and ♂ in the diagram identify female and male reproductive systems, respectively. These same symbols and also ☿ outside the diagrams identify whole female, male, and hermaphroditic organisms. The pattern of self-fertilizing hermaphroditism can be envisaged readily in the lower figures.*

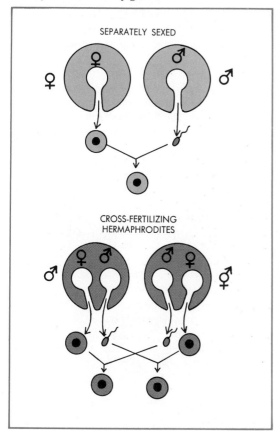

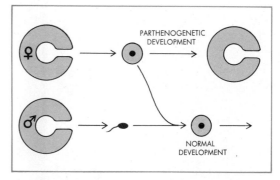

26 · 21 Parthenogenesis. *If gametes produced by adults* (left) *fuse and produce new adults via zygotes, then the pattern is regularly bisexual* (bottom). *But if a gamete develops into an adult without sexual fusion with another gamete, then the pattern is parthenogenetic* (top).

since every such meeting may result in fertilization, the adaptive value of hermaphroditism is clear (see Fig. 15.28).

In any organism, separately sexed or hermaphroditic, it happens often that given gametes fail to find compatible partners. Most of such unsuccessful gametes disintegrate very soon, but in exceptional cases this does not occur. Instead, single gametes may begin to *develop* and form normal adult organisms. This phenomenon is known as *parthenogenesis,* "virginal development" of a gamete *without* fertilization. In certain isogamous and anisogamous species, either gamete type may sometimes develop parthenogenetically. In oögamous species, only the eggs are known in some cases to develop by natural parthenogenesis without being fertilized (for example, rotifers, water fleas and other crustacea, bees and other social insects, and sporadically also birds such as turkeys and chickens). Sperms always disintegrate if they do not find an egg. In selected instances, *artificial* parthenogenesis may be induced by experimental means. For example, a frog egg can be made to develop before it has become fertilized by pricking its surface with a needle. The puncture simulates the entrance of a sperm and development then begins. But a sexual process has not taken place. By various experimental procedures, artificial parthenogenesis has also been achieved in the eggs of echinoderms, rabbits, and other animals. Note that a parthenogenetic gamete is functionally indistinguishable from a *spore;* both are single reproductive cells able to develop directly (Fig. 26.21).

One consequence of every sexual process is that

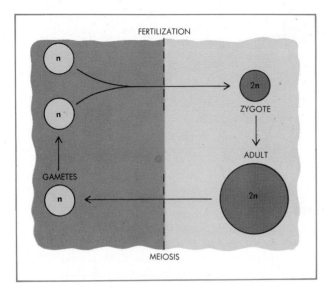

26 · 22 *Relation of meiosis and fertilization to chromosome numbers and life cycle.*

a zygote formed from two gametes possesses twice the usual number of chromosomes. Organisms counteract this increase by a series of special nuclear divisions known as *meiosis.* In many cases meiosis is accompanied by cytoplasmic divisions, and both events are then referred to collectively as meiotic cell divisions.

MEIOSIS AND LIFE CYCLE

As noted in Chap. 7, the number of chromosomes per cell is a fixed, genetically determined trait of every organism. However, whenever a sexual process takes place, the gene sets of two sex cells fuse together. In a zygote, therefore, the chromosome number is doubled. An adult organism developing from such a zygote would consist of cells having a doubled chromosome number. If the next generation is again produced sexually, the chromosome number would then quadruple, and this process of progressive doubling would continue indefinitely through successive generations.

Such events do not happen in actuality. Chromosome numbers do stay constant from one life cycle to the next, and the constancy is brought about by meiosis. *It is the function of meiosis to counteract the chromosome-doubling effect of fertilization by reducing a doubled chromosome number to half.* The doubled chromosome number, before meiosis, is called the *diploid* number, and it is symbolized as $2n$; the reduced number, after meiosis, is the *haploid* number, and it is symbolized as n (Fig. 26.22).

Meiosis occurs in every life cycle that includes a sexual process—in other words, more or less universally. Organisms differ according to when and where meiosis occurs in the life cycle. In many Protista, including the unicellular alga *Chlamydomonas,* for example, meiosis takes place in the zygote, as a first step in the further development of that zygote. Thus, fertilization produces a zygote with a diploid chromosome number and meiosis then restores the haploid condition. In such a life cycle, evidently, the only diploid stage is the zygote. The pattern is substantially different in many other Protista and in all Metaphyta and Metazoa. The essential point for the present is only that meiosis occurs at *some* stage during every life cycle which includes sex, as a counterbalance to the chromosome-doubling effect of fertilization. For purposes of illustration, we shall here continue to discuss the *Chlamydomonas* pattern specifically.

A zygote nucleus does not contain a $2n$ collection of mutually different chromosomes, but contains instead a collection of n mutually different *pairs* of chromosomes. For a zygote receives one haploid, n, set of chromosomes via the male sex cell, and a like haploid set via the female sex cell. Therefore, like shoes, the chromosomes of any diploid nucleus come in pairs. One of each pair is paternal in origin, the other maternal (Fig. 26.23). During meiosis in a diploid nucleus, chromosome reduction occurs in

26 · 23 *A diploid cell* (bottom) *contains two like sets of chromosomes representing maternal-paternal pairs. The maternal set originated in the female gamete; the paternal set, in the male gamete.*

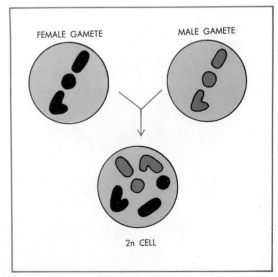

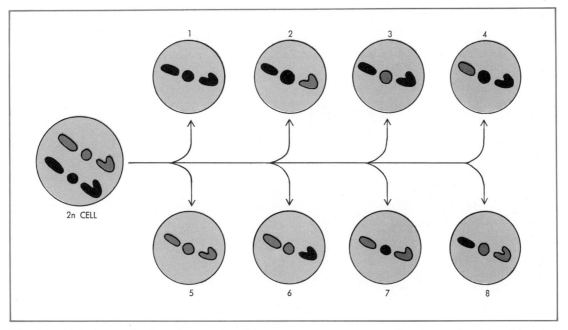

26 · 24 Meiosis and chromosome combinations. *When the chromosome number of a diploid cell is halved by meiosis, a resulting haploid cell contains a single set of chromosomes consisting of a chance-determined number of paternal and maternal chromosomes. The diagram shows the possible paternal-maternal combinations if n = 3.*

such a way that any resulting haploid nucleus contains *one of each maternal-paternal pair* of chromosomes. In this haploid nucleus, it is entirely a matter of chance which and how many chromosomes will be maternal and which and how many will be paternal. For example, after meiosis in one species of *Chlamydomonas*, eight chromosomes make up a complete haploid set. Of these eight, a chance-determined number will be paternal, the remainder maternal (Fig. 26.24).

The phrase "chromosome reduction" might imply that in a diploid cell one of each pair of chromosomes is destroyed or otherwise lost. This is not the case. Instead, the diploid chromosome number is reduced to half by two *meiotic divisions*. The general pattern of these divisions in as follows. A diploid nucleus undergoes two successive divisions, which transform the one original nucleus into four. During or before these divisions, the chromosomes of the diploid nucleus duplicate *once*. As a result, 2n becomes 4n. And of these 4n chromosomes, one n is incorporated into each of the four new nuclei formed. In sum, *one diploid* nucleus becomes *four haploid* nuclei (Fig. 26.25).

In *Chlamydomonas*, for example, a zygote nucleus contains 16 chromosomes. During meiosis the number doubles to 32 and at the same time the nucleus of the zygote divides twice in succession. Four nuclei result which share the 32 chromosomes equally.

26 · 25 The general pattern of meiosis *on the assumption that 2n = 2. During the meiotic divisions, each member of a chromosome pair is again referred to as a chromatid, as in mitosis.*

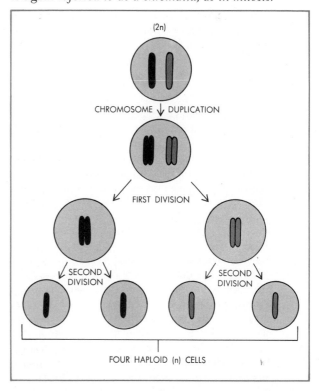

(2n)

CHROMOSOME ↓ DUPLICATION

FIRST DIVISION

SECOND DIVISION   SECOND DIVISION

FOUR HAPLOID (n) CELLS

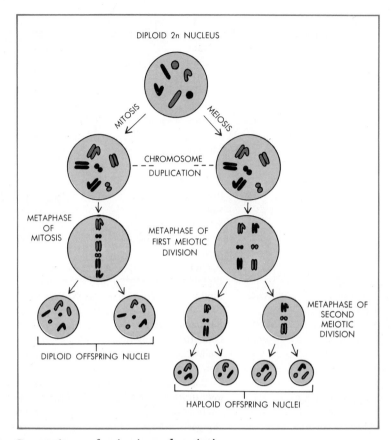

26 · 26   Comparison of mitosis and meiosis,
on the assumption that 2n = 6. The key dif-
ference between the two processes is the way the
pairs of chromatids line up in metaphase.

Hence after meiosis each nucleus of *Chlamydomonas* contains eight chromosomes, a complete haploid set.

The two meiotic divisions have many features in common with mitotic divisions. Thus, each meiotic division passes through prophase, metaphase, anaphase, and telophase, as in mitosis. Also, spindles form and other nonchromosomal events are as in mitotic divisions. In many cases, furthermore, cytokinesis accompanies meiosis and the two meiotic divisions then yield not merely four haploid nuclei but four complete haploid cells.

The critical difference between mitosis and the *first* meiotic division lies in their metaphases. In mitosis, we recall, all chromosomes, each of them already duplicated, migrate into the metaphase plate, where all the centromeres line up in the same plane. In the first meiotic division, the $2n$ chromosomes similarly duplicate during or before prophase. These $2n$ pairs, the members of each pair

again joined at the centromere, also migrate into the metaphase plate. But now only n pairs assemble in one plane. The other n pairs migrate into a plane of their own, closely parallel to the first. Moreover, every pair in one plane comes to lie next to the corresponding type of chromosome pair in the other plane. The metaphase plate is therefore made up of *paired chromosome pairs*, or *tetrads* of like chromosomes lying side by side. And there are n of these tetrads in the whole plate (Fig. 26.26).

During the ensuing anaphase, two chromosomes of each tetrad migrate to one spindle pole, two to the other. At the end of the first meiotic division, therefore, there are two cells, each with n pairs of chromosomes. In the metaphase of the subsequent second meiotic division, the n pairs of chromosomes line up in the same plane and n single chromosomes eventually migrate to each of the poles during anaphase. At the termination of meiosis as a whole, therefore, four cells are present, each with n single chromosomes, a complete haploid set.

In *Chlamydomonas*, the four haploid cells resulting from meiosis become new adult organisms. All available evidence suggests that such a meiotic pattern is primitive, inherited unchanged from the very first protists and probably even from the very first living organisms of any kind. It is reasonable to suppose that a very early ancestral cell possessed only a single complete set of genes, that is, that it was haploid, and that its life cycle consisted simply of a succession of vegetative generations, each connected to the next by cell division. In due course sporulation evolved, and any vegetative generation could then produce numerous haploid spore cells through a series of rapid cell divisions. In due course also sex evolved, and this process introduced fertilization followed by a diploid zygote stage. Meiosis in the zygote, or *zygotic meiosis*, could then have been a corollary invention. The chromosome-doubling process of fertilization may have been the stimulus to which the chromosome-reducing process of meiosis was the rapidly following response.

A life cycle characterized in this way by zygotic meiosis and haploid adults is known as a *haplontic* life cycle (Fig. 26.27). It occurs in all Monera (insofar as sex is known in this category and insofar as genetic reduction here can be called "meiosis"; see Chap. 27), in all primitive and many advanced groups among algae, in many fungi, and in sporozoan protozoa. The list suggests clearly and the next chapter will show in more specific detail that the haplontic life cycle is basic in the Monera and the Protista. Where sporulation occurs in these haplontic groups, spores are produced at some point in the life cycle between one fertilization and the next. The method of spore production is mitotic division and, like the adults which produce them, the spores are haploid. We may therefore refer to them as *haploid mitospores*.

In an organism exhibiting a haplontic life cycle, therefore, one individual may carry out any of the three basic methods of reproduction, the choice being dictated by the environment. Thus, if environmental conditions are favorable, a given individual may reproduce vegetatively or sporulatively or both. Or, if conditions are unfavorable, the same individual could produce gametes.

Haplontic patterns have probably given rise to all other types of life cycles. With regard to the timing of meiosis, we may readily guess at which points the process possibly *could* occur. Like sex, meiosis is a cellular process and it can therefore take place only at a stage when the life cycle passes through a unicellular phase. The zygote does represent such a phase even in multicellular organisms, and the haplontic life cycle is based on this. But a multicellular organism may pass through unicellular

stages on two other occasions, namely, at the stage of the *gamete* and at the stage of the *spore*. Conceivably, therefore, meiosis could occur at either of these points. As noted earlier, it is not important *when* meiosis takes place so long as it takes place at all within every sexual life cycle. In actuality, meiosis does occur at the gamete stage in many organisms and at the spore stage in many others.

In man, for example, meiosis takes place during the formation of gametes. Within the sex organs of the adult, diploid gamete-producing cells (containing 46, or 23 pairs of, chromosomes) mature into sperms and eggs. As part of this maturation, meiosis takes place in these diploid cells. Mature gametes consequently are haploid (each with 23 chromosomes). Accordingly, we may speak here of *gametogenic meiosis*. The mature haploid gametes subsequently participate in fertilization, and the zygote is then diploid. But now, as the zygote divides and develops into a mature human being, the cells *remain diploid*. The whole human adult becomes diploid in this fashion, including the sex organs it eventually forms. Gamete-producing cells consequently are diploid as well, and meiosis occurs again during their maturation.

Such a cycle, characterized by gametogenic meiosis and diploid adults, is called a *diplontic life cycle* (Fig. 26.28). The only haploid stage in it is the gamete itself, all other stages being diploid. The pattern here is evidently almost the reverse of a haplontic cycle. Diplontic cycles are very abundant. They are encountered not only in man but in all Metazoa, and among Protista such cycles occur in

26 · 27 *The haplontic life-cycle pattern.*

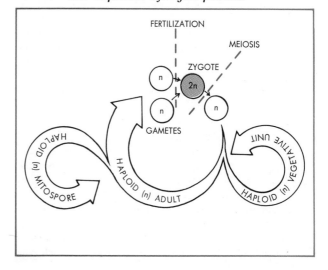

various advanced groups of algae, in some fungi, and in most protozoa. The list suggests strongly that diplontic cycles are not primitive but could have been derived from haplontic cycles.

We may readily guess how the evolutionary transition from haplontic to diplontic cycles might have been achieved. In the ancestral haplontic type, meiosis occurs in the zygote, at the very start of the life cycle. In diplontic types, meiosis is *postponed* to the time of gamete formation, the very end of the life cycle. Thus, sooner or later during the evolution of Protista, some groups probably delayed the timing of meiosis as long as it could be delayed.

There is an additional reason for regarding diplontic cycles as advanced. If we consider the time relation of fertilization and meiosis in, for example, man, the superficial impression is gained that the response *precedes* the stimulus; chromosome reduction during gamete formation here appears to be followed quickly by chromosome doubling during fertilization. However, it is quite unlikely that responses anticipate stimuli. In the same measure it is very likely that a diplontic cycle is not original but derived. Gametogenic meiosis can be reasonably interpreted only if it is assumed that it represents a much-postponed chromosome reduction. Then, properly, fertilization becomes the chromosome-doubling stimulus and gametogenic meiosis the greatly delayed response.

A postponement of meiosis is very advantageous adaptively. Inasmuch as the cells of the adult thereby become diploid, each gene (and each chromosome) in each adult cell is represented twice rather than just once. One gene of a given pair has a maternal ancestry, the other a paternal ancestry. Consequently, one advantage of paired genes (and paired chromosomes) is that they increase the genetic stability of the individual. For even if one gene of a pair changes in some way, for example, by mutation, the other gene still preserves the original genetic code. This stabilizing effect of the diploid state has evidently been of sufficient adaptive significance to make diplontic life cycles exceedingly common.

If an organism exhibiting a diplontic life cycle produces spores, such cells are manufactured by a diploid adult. The method of spore formation is again mitotic division and the spores are consequently diploid as well. We may therefore refer to them as *diploid mitospores*. They are formed by many diplontic Protista.

The third possible time of meiosis is the stage of spore production. In this case we may speak of *sporogenic meiosis*. The aquatic phycomycetous fungus *Allomyces* illustrates the pattern well. Fertilization produces a diploid zygote, and the developing adult fungus remains diploid. In due course it produces a spore-forming structure called a sporangium. In it, diploid spore-producing cells give rise to spores and meiosis occurs during this process. Mature spores are therefore haploid, and since their production includes meiosis we may refer to them as *meiospores*. A haploid meiospore subsequently germinates and develops into a new, *haploid* fungus. This adult later manufactures haploid gametes, and these subsequently participate in fertilization. A new life cycle then begins with the resulting diploid zygote.

Because meiosis here occurs during sporulation, such a life cycle is split up into two generations, each represented by a separate adult. The diploid zygote gives rise to a diploid adult; and since this adult later produces meiospores, it is called *sporophyte generation*. The haploid meiospore gives rise to a haploid adult, and since this adult later produces gametes, it is called the *gametophyte generation*. Cycles of this sort, characterized by *sporogenic meiosis* and *alternation of generations*, are known as *diplohaplontic* life cycles (Fig. 26.29). They are exceedingly widespread, occurring in numerous algae, many fungi, a few protozoa, all slime molds, and in all Metaphyta. Such cycles can again be derived from the haplontic type by a postponement of meiosis, in this case from the zygote stage to the spore-producing stage.

Diplohaplontic cycles combine the adaptive advantages of both haplontic and diplontic ones. Diploid sporophytes are genetically relatively stable and haploid gametophytes, possessing but single sets of genes, are genetically quite plastic; their characteristics can be varied fairly readily by mutation.

26 · 28   *The diplontic life-cycle pattern.*

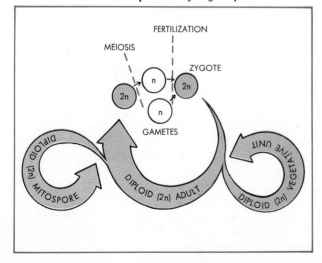

Gametophytes therefore permit comparatively rapid adaptation to changing environments, hence faster evolution. Diplohaplontic types evidently combine a measure of evolutionary conservatism with a measure of evolutionary variability.

Note that a single individual of a diplohaplontic organism is not capable of reproducing by any one of the three basic methods. For example, a sporophytic individual cannot reproduce via gametes; it must reproduce either vegetatively or sporulatively. The meiospore is its characteristic reproductive product and in most cases it is the *only* such product. However, some sporophytic adults have the additional capacity to manufacture another kind of spore. Such spores are produced by mitotic division and are therefore diploid, like the sporophytes manufacturing them. In effect, spores of this kind are diploid mitospores, like those produced by organisms with purely diplontic life cycles. When the diploid mitospores develop, they give rise to new diploid sporophytes. A whole series of successive sporophyte individuals may be produced in this manner via diploid mitospores, and the series ends only with the manufacture of haploid meiospores. This pattern is exemplified in the fungus *Allomyces*, for example (see Fig. 27.18). Diploid sporophytes here produce numerous repeat generations through diploid mitospores, and the diploid phase of the life cycle terminates only when haploid meiospores are formed. These develop into haploid gametophytes.

Analogously, among the gametophytes of various species, *most* may reproduce only vegetatively or via gametes. But in some species the gametophytes may also produce spores by mitotic divisions. Since the parent gametophytes are haploid, the spores formed are haploid mitospores like those produced by organisms with purely haplontic life cycles. For example, certain species of the brown alga *Ectocarpus* exhibit the complete diplohaplontic life cycle with all types of spores (see Fig. 27.13). Diploid sporophytes produce repeat generations through diploid mitospores. Such sporophytes then manufacture haploid meiospores which give rise to haploid gameto-

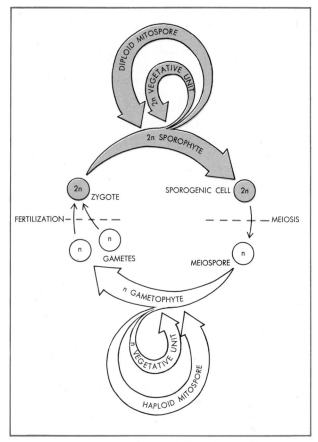

26 · 29 *The diplohaplontic life-cycle pattern. The nature of the various types of vegetative and sporulative repeating generations is indicated.*

phytes. Then these gametophytes in turn produce numerous repeat generations through haploid mitospores. The life cycle finally ends with the production of haploid gametes and subsequent fertilization (see Fig. 26.29).

The following chapters will show how these various reproductive processes and life cycles are manifested specifically in different groups of organisms.

REVIEW QUESTIONS

1. How does reproduction contribute to steady-state maintenance? To self-perpetuation in general? Review the forms of molecular reproduction and the nature of each. How does molecular reproduction contribute to organismic reproduction?

2. Define binary fission, multiple fission. What basic events occur in all forms of cell division? What is mitosis? How does cell division contribute to organismic reproduction? What different forms of mitotic division are known? Define spindle, aster, centriole, centromere. How does mitotic division differ in plant and animal cells?

3. What molecular events within cells precede the microscopically visible phases of division? De-

661

scribe the processes characteristic of prophase and metaphase. What is the metaphase plate and where is it located? What are the events of anaphase?

4. Describe the processes characteristic of telophase. Review the history of the nucleoli during mitotic division. What is the net result of mitotic division? What is known about the mechanical forces that bring about chromosome movements during mitosis?

5. What is a tissue culture? What have experiments with tissue cultures shown about rates of cell division? When and where in an organism are fission rates highest? Lowest?

6. Distinguish between reproduction and development. What is vegetative reproduction? Under what circumstances and in what forms does vegatative reproduction occur? What is sporulation? What is gametic reproduction? How is vegetative reproduction different from sporulation? How is sporulation different from gametic reproduction?

7. What are the most basic events of every sexual process? Under what conditions does sex tend to occur? In what way is sex of adaptive value? Illustrate by the example of *Spirogyra*. Define mating, fertilization, zygote, gamete, spore, isogamy, oögamy, and parthenogenesis.

8. What are the limitations of and the environmental conditions required for (*a*) gametic reproduction and (*b*) sporulation? Contrast in detail. What is hermaphroditism? What is its adaptive value? Distinguish between self-fertilization and cross-fertilization. What is autogamy?

9. What is the basic function of meiosis, and what makes such a process necessary? Where does meiosis occur? Define haploid, diploid. How many *pairs* of chromosomes are found in a diploid cell? Of these, which and how many are maternal and which and how many are paternal?

10. How many chromosome duplications and how many cell duplications occur during meiosis? In what respects are mitosis and meiosis alike? What is the essential difference between the metaphase of mitosis and the metaphase of the first meiotic division? Describe the complete sequence of events during both divisions of meiosis.

11. Describe the nature of a haplontic life cycle. Name organisms in which such a cycle occurs. Do similarly for diplontic and diplohaplontic life cycles.

12. What type of life cycle is probably primitive and how may it have given rise to the other types? Define mitospore, meiospore, gametophyte, sporophyte, alternation of generations.

COLLATERAL READINGS

Berrill, N. J.: "Sex and the Nature of Things," Dodd, Mead, New York, 1953. A beautifully and interestingly written paperback on the significance and process of sex in various organisms.

Chase, H. B.: "Sex: The Universal Fact," Dell, New York, 1965. This paperback reviews sexuality from a structural and functional viewpoint; nontechnical, with special emphasis on man.

Jensen, W. A.: "The Plant Cell," Wadsworth, Belmont, Calif., 1964. Good discussions of mitosis and meiosis in plants are included in this paperback.

Loeb, J.: On the Nature of the Process of Fertilization, in "Great Experiments in Biology," Prentice-Hall, Englewood Cliffs, N.J., 1955. The discoverer of artificial parthenogenesis describes experiments on this process in sea urchins.

Mazia, D.: Cell Division, *Sci. American,* Aug., 1953. Experiments are described in which the entire mitotic apparatus is isolated from dividing cells.

———: How Cells Divide, *Sci. American,* Sept., 1961. A review of the nature of the mitotic process.

Moscona, A. A.: How Cells Associate, *Sci. American,* Sept., 1961. A case study of tissue culture, illustrating how separated cells may reaggregate.

Raper, J. R.: Some Problems of Specificity in the Sexuality of Plants, in "Biological Specificity and Growth," Princeton, Princeton, N.J., 1955. The phenomena of separate sexuality and hermaphroditism are discussed, with special reference to fungi.

Singer, M.: The Regeneration of Body Parts, *Sci. American,* Oct., 1958. Limb regeneration in salamanders and frogs is contrasted experimentally.

Swanson, C. P.: "The Cell," Prentice-Hall, Englewood Cliffs, N.J., 1960. A general discussion of mitosis and meiosis in various organisms, plant and animal, is included in this excellent paperback.

Wenrich, D. H. (ed.): "Sex in Microorganisms," American Association for the Advancement of Science, Washington, D.C., 1954. Among the many articles in this compilation, quite a few have relevance to the topics discussed in this chapter; not introductory, but well worth consulting.

Wilson, E. B.: "The Cell in Development and Heredity," 3d ed., Macmillan, New York, 1947. A renowned large treatise in which all reproductive as well as other aspects of cellular biology are covered in great detail.

CHAPTER 27 REPRODUCTION: MONERA, PROTISTA, METAPHYTA

All three basic reproductive methods are encountered in these organisms. Very frequently, notably among Protista, a given organism is capable of reproducing by any of the three methods at different times, specific environmental conditions usually determining the particular method. In aquatic forms, spores and gametes most often are flagellate and swimming. Inasmuch as the water supply is abundant, gametic reproduction can be accomplished readily. In terrestrial forms, spores are usually encapsulated. Gametes cannot be, but despite the absence of abundant free water gametic reproduction is made possible by special evolutionary adaptations.

MONERA

Among bacteria, the main reproductive process is rapid vegetative fission. Such divisions are not mitotic and it is unknown just how gene sets of bacteria are distributed equally to daughter cells. Cells divide transversely in most bacteria but longitudinal as well as unequal binary fission is known to occur in one group, the *Hyphomicrobiales,* or budding bacteria. Many cells here may be joined end to end by filamentous secreted strands of cell-wall material.

When one cell divides longitudinally, a branch strand may be initiated. A terminal cell in such a strand may then bud and form a smaller cell by unequal division. The bud cell may subsequently grow to normal size (Fig. 27.1).

Under unfavorable conditions, many bacteria form nonreproductive *endospores,* that is, encapsulated dormant resting stages. Similarly nonreproductive despite the name are the "fruiting bodies" typically produced by the *Myxobacteriales* (see Chap. 11). The cells composing such bodies are dormant resting stages, and resemblance to the true fruiting bodies of slime molds is purely superficial.

However, the Actinomycetales do produce true reproductive spores, indeed several types of them (Fig. 27.2). In these "branching bacteria" the vegetative cells are organized into branched, multicellular, funguslike "hyphae" and "mycelia." At the ends of certain hyphae, round spore cells may be cut off either singly or in linear series. Called *conidia,* spores of this type are characteristic of the antibiotic producer *Streptomyces,* for example. In other cases, the interior substance of a hypha may break up transversely into numerous *oidiospores.* Third, some branching bacteria may develop true fruiting bodies, or sporangia, at the tips of certain hyphae. The interior substance of a sporangium may then subdivide into numerous *sporangiospores.* These are remarkable instances of parallel evolution, for all three forms of sporulation are encountered also among the fungi (see below).

Sex is now known to occur in certain bacteria as a laboratory phenomenon. Whether or not sex also takes place in nature is still undetermined. The sexual process is conjugative; cells join pairwise, exchange portions of their genetic material, and then separate. The classical experiment proving the occurrence of sex was carried out with two different strains of the eubacterium *Escherichia coli* (Fig. 27.3). One strain could respire lactose anaerobically (L+) and was also sensitive to the antibiotic streptomycin (S−). These were inherited genetic traits. The other genetically stable strain could not ferment lactose (L−), but was resistant to streptomycin (S+). When L+S− and L−S+ strains were cultured together, the vegetative offspring generations contained many

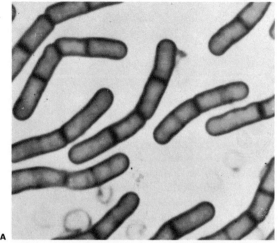

27 · 1 Bacterial reproduction. *A, fission in a species of* Bacillus. *B, budding in Hyphomicrobiales. Note the branch strand with small terminal bud cell.*

bacteria with traits exactly like the parental strains. Occasionally, however, bacteria with L+S+ traits were found; such cells could ferment lactose and at the same time were streptomycin-resistant. Other individuals were L−S−; they could not use lactose and were streptomycin-sensitive as well. Such traits are evidently mixed combinations of parental characteristics, and their occurrence indicates the occurrence of mating and of sexual exchange of genes.

Experiments of this sort have also established that vegetative bacteria are *haploid* and that some (still unknown) kind of gene-reduction process equivalent to meiosis takes place immediately after conjugation. Insofar as sex occurs in them, therefore, bacterial life cycles are haplontic.

If sex is rare, how do these organisms adapt to their changing environments? They may do so without sex by their extremely rapid vegetative multiplication. Rapid reproduction means rapid evolution, through mutations. Bacteria are haploid, which means that every mutated gene will immediately produce a change in a trait. Therefore, even if millions or billions of bacteria sucumb to one environment, a single survivor with appropriate mutations may within a few hours produce new millions or billions of readapted organisms. Bacteria evidently rely on safety through numbers and they can generally do very well without sex.

As in the bacteria, sex is now also known to occur on rare occasions in the blue-green algae. Vegetative fission takes place in all cyanophytes, and many blue-

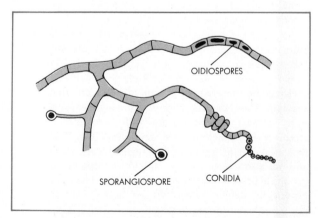

27 · 2 Three types of spores formed in Actinomycetales.

27 · 3 Gene exchange in bacteria. *L+ symbolizes lactose-utilizing capacity, and S+ symbolizes streptomycin resistance.*

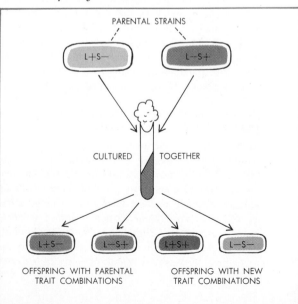

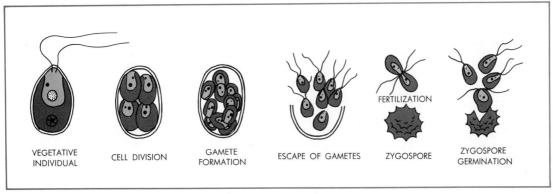

VEGETATIVE INDIVIDUAL   CELL DIVISION   GAMETE FORMATION   ESCAPE OF GAMETES   FERTILIZATION   ZYGOSPORE   ZYGOSPORE GERMINATION

27 · 4 Reproduction in **Chlamydomonas.**

green algae additionally reproduce by sporulation (for example, the Chamaeosiphonales, Fig. 11.21). In some instances the contents of a cell subdivide into numerous spore cells; in others, spores are cut off in series at one end of a cell. Spores are formed also in some of the Hormogonales, the filamentous cyanophytes. As already noted in Chap. 11, this group of blue-green algae additionally produces vegetative reproductive units called *hormogones.* Each is a multicellular section of a filament, enclosed within a common wall and located between transparent, double-walled *heterocysts.* The latter may facilitate breaks in the algal filament, and a separated hormogone may then grow into a new filament in another location (see Fig. 11.21).

PROTISTA

ALGAE

In the green algae, vegetative multiplication by binary division occurs in all except the coccine types (see Chap. 12). In unicellular forms (for example, *Chlamydomonas,* Fig. 27.4), a cell divides vegetatively within its wall and usually produces two new organisms. In multicellular types (Fig. 27.5), vegetative divisions increase the size of the organisms. Multicellular algae also reproduce vegetatively by fragmentation.

Sporulation occurs in all chlorophytes, virtually any vegetative cell usually being able to function as a *sporangium.* Sometimes the entire content of a sporangial cell may be liberated as a single spore, but more commonly a sporangial cell subdivides through successive fissions and gives rise to numerous spores, each with its own wall. Spores are released either through a pore developed in the wall of the sporangial cell or through dissolution of the entire

wall. In most species the spores are swimming *zoospores.* Some species living in damp soils produce nonmotile *aplanospores.*

All chlorophyte groups are sexual. In each of the

27 · 5 Two filaments of the green alga **Ulothrix.** *The filament on the right contains gametes within the cell walls.*

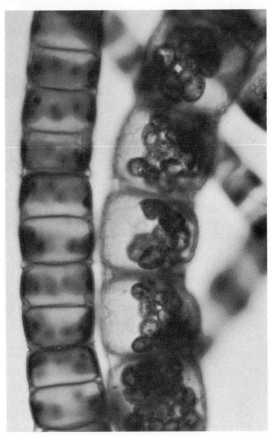

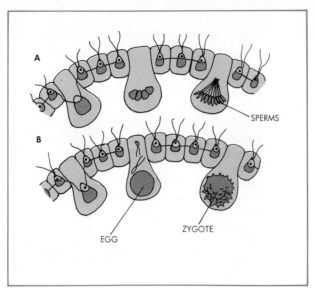

27 · 6 *Eggs and sperms in algae. A, sperm formation in* Volvox. *B, egg production and fertilization in* Volvox. *C, an egg in* Oedogonium. *Note pore in cell wall for sperm entrance.*

flagellate, sporine, and coccine lines, there has been a general progression from isogamy in primitive types to anisogamy in more advanced types to oögamy in very advanced types. In the flagellate line, for example, most species of the unicellular *Chlamydomonas* are isogamous, simple colonial forms are anisogamous, and the filamentous *Oedogonium* as well as the complexly colonial *Volvox* are oögamous (Fig. 27.6). The pattern is similar in the other lines, but it is not too rigorous. For example, *Chlamydomonas* also includes anisogamous and oögamous species despite its generally primitive character.

In most green algae, typically any vegetative cell may function as a gamete-producing *gametangium*. A cell may produce just a single gamete (for example, *Spirogyra*) or it may subdivide repeatedly and produce numerous gametes (for example, *Ulothrix*). Some chlorophytes are separately sexed (for example, *Oedogonium*), others are hermaphroditic (for example, *Ulothrix*). However, even closely related species may differ in this respect. For example, certain species of *Spirogyra* exhibit separate sexes, others, hermaphroditism.

All three types of life cycles are encountered in the green algae. The flagellate line (*Chlamydomonas, Volvox*) is typically haplontic. The sporine line is haplontic in its more primitive members (*Ulothrix, Spirogyra*) but diplohaplontic in its advanced members (*Cladophora, Ulva*). The coccine line is largely diplontic (*Acetabularia, Bryopsis*).

In the haplontic forms (Fig. 27.7), the zygotes usually encyst as in *Spirogyra* and are then known

as *zygospores*. When a zygospore germinates, the first two divisions are meiotic and result in four haploid cells. These are flagellate in most cases, and if the alga is unicellular, such cells are four whole adults (for example, *Chlamydomonas*). If the alga is multicellular, the four cells swim about for some time and then settle and grow into four new multicellular adults (for example, *Ulothrix*). In effect, the

27 · 7 *The haplontic life cycle typical of many algae.*

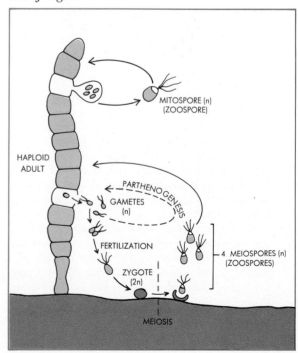

666

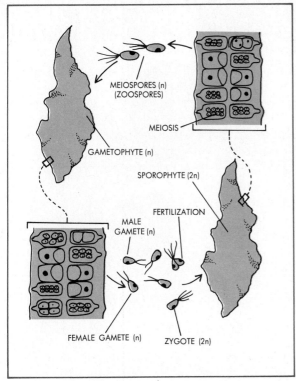

27 · 8 *The life cycle of* **Ulva,** *a typical diplohaplontic alga.*

In diplontic coccine green algae a diploid zygote is similarly motile (Fig. 27.9). After it settles, its nucleus repeatedly divides by mitosis, but the cell as a whole enlarges without division. The adult is therefore highly multinucleate and each of its nuclei is diploid. If such an adult sporulates, the spores are diploid mitospores. Gametes are usually produced in special terminal branches of an adult. The nuclei in such a branch increase in number, the divisions now being meiotic. Each resulting haploid nucleus together with some surrounding cytoplasm then becomes enveloped by a cell wall of its own and flagella develop. Mature gametes ultimately escape through a pore in the wall of the algal branch.

In the phylum Charophyta, the stoneworts may multiply vegetatively through regularly produced fragmentation bodies. The algae do not sporulate, and gametic reproduction is always oögamous. Gamete-forming structures develop on the leaflike branches, and they are true *organs*, structurally more complex than those of any other Protista. In the interior of a male sex organ, so-called *antheridial filaments* are present. The content of each cell in such a filament matures into a single sperm, which escapes through a pore in the wall of an antheridial cell. A female sex organ contains a single large egg in the interior. When the organ is mature, spirally elongated cells on the outside separate from one another at their upper ends. The organ thus opens out and a path

four cells are spores, more specifically, *meiospores* (hence the term "sporine" for protists of this type). In some cases (for example, *Spirogyra*), the four meiospores are not flagellate but nonmotile and they remain in the zygospore. Three of the four cells then usually degenerate and the fourth grows directly into a new adult. If the sexes of the algal species are separate, two of the four meiospores are of one sex type, two of the other.

In the diplohaplontic green algae (Fig. 27.8), the diploid zygote formed by fusion of biflagellate gametes is quadriflagellate, and it does not encyst but remains motile. After swimming about for some time it settles and proliferates mitotically into a diploid sporophyte adult. This organism eventually sporulates, meiosis occurring during that process. One diploid cell thereby gives rise to four haploid meiospores. Virtually any cell of the adult sporophyte may undergo meiosis and produce spores. The swimming meiospores eventually settle and grow into haploid gametophyte adults. Sporophytes and gametophytes are structurally identical in these groups. Adult gametophytes eventually form haploid gametes, any cell again being a potential gamete producer.

27 · 9 *The life cycle of* **Bryopsis,** *a typical diplontic alga. A, whole plant. B, detail of terminal branches. See also Fig. 12.8.*

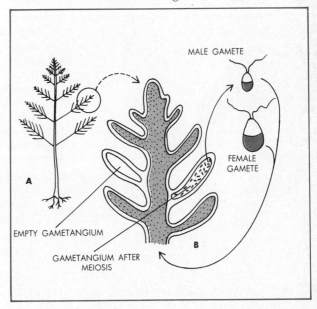

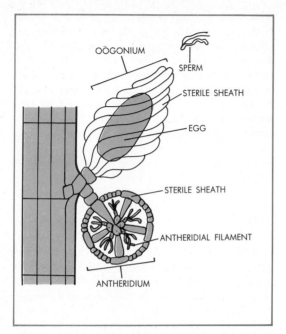

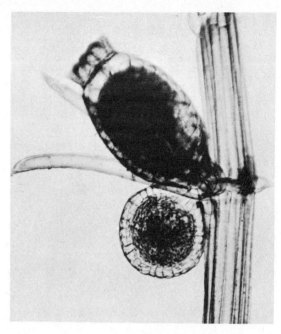

27 · 10 Sex organs of the stonewort Chara. *Diagram: the structure of an oögonium and an antheridium, located near a branch terminal of the alga. Photo: external view of an oögonium and an antheridium.*

is formed for a sperm (Fig. 27.10). As noted in Chap. 12, multicellular sex organs with sterile external tissue layers are exceptional for Protista and are encountered otherwise only in Metaphyta and Metazoa. But note that the life cycle of stoneworts is haplontic, a primitive trait not exhibited by any of the Metaphyta or Metazoa.

In euglenophytes and pyrrophytes, groups comprising mainly unicellular flagellate algae, the basic reproductive process is longitudinal vegetative cell

27 · 11 Reproduction in Vaucheria. *A, escape of zoospores. B, a filament with male and female branches. The female branch is the shorter, rounded one. C, a filament with zygospores.*

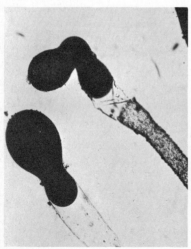

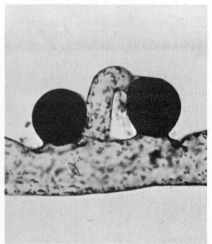

A   B   C

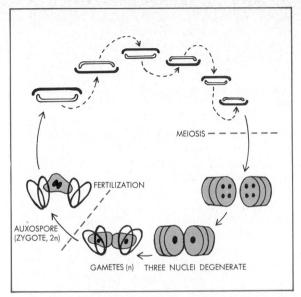

27 · 12 Reproduction in diatoms. *Top row, left to right, successive vegetative generations. Bottom row, right to left, meiosis, gametes, and fertilization.*

other and secrete a common gelatinous envelope. Each cell then undergoes meiotic nuclear division. Of the four haploid nuclei formed, three usually degenerate. The remaining uninucleate haploid cell is a gamete. It slips out of its wall and, moving in amoeboid fashion, fuses with the other similarly formed gamete within the gelatinous envelope. The resulting zygote, called an *auxospore*, photosynthesizes extensively and grows rapidly into a very large cell. Then it develops a new epitheca and hypotheca. Vegetative divisions thereafter soon restore the normal cell size characteristic of the species. Inasmuch as meiosis is gametogenic, adult diatoms are diploid and the life cycle is diplontic.

In the brown algae, phylum Phaeophyta, all

27 · 13 *Life cycles of the three classes of brown algae.*

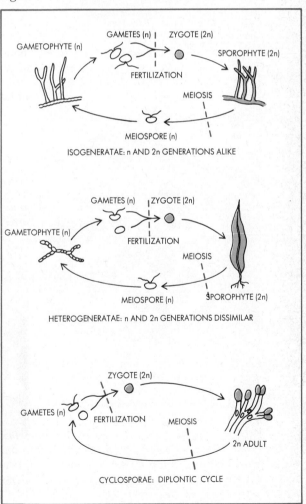

division. Sex is virtually unknown and, with the exception of multicellular sessile pyrrophytes, the organisms largely do not form spores.

The reproductive repertoire in the phylum Chrysophyta is essentially the same as in the green algae (Fig. 27.11). Reproductively the most interesting chrysophytes are the diatoms. In these predominantly unicellular organisms, successive cell divisions may give rise to progressively smaller vegetative generations (Fig. 27.12). As noted in Chap. 12, diatoms possess sculptured silica shell halves, one half fitting snugly over the other. The larger "lid" is an *epitheca*; the smaller "box," a *hypotheca*. After division, one daughter cell inherits the epitheca, the other the hypotheca. In either case, a daughter cell secretes a new wall over its exposed half and this new half-wall is always formed *within* the old half-wall. The old wall consequently is always an epitheca, regardless of what it had been originally. The new wall is always a hypotheca. Some diatoms in a population therefore may decrease in size progressively as divisions continue. However, this is not always the case in all species, for hypothecae may stretch to some extent.

Diatoms are unable to survive if they become too small. Usually well before they reach their lower size limit, they initiate sexual processes which restore them to their original size. Two small vegetative cells conjugate; they come to lie against each

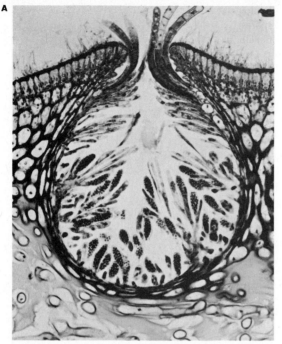

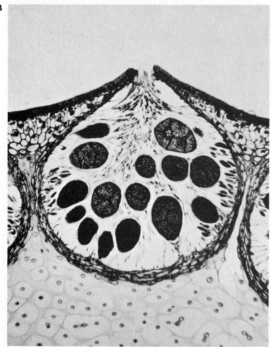

27 · 14   Conceptacles of Fucus. *A, conceptacle with a lining layer bearing antheridial branches. Note the sterile hairs (paraphyses) projecting through the opening of the conceptacle. B, conceptacle with conspicuous oögonia. Each mature oögonium contains eight eggs.*

methods of reproduction are highly developed. Vegetative divisions increase the size of a brown alga, and fragmentation increases the number of individuals. In *Sargassum*, for example, fragmentation occurs regularly by posterior decay (see Chap. 26).

The nature of the life cycle defines three classes of brown algae (Fig. 27.13). In one class, the *Isogeneratae*, the life cycle is diplohaplontic and the sporophyte and gametophyte generations are structurally alike. In the *Heterogeneratae*, the life cycle is again diplohaplontic but the two generations are structurally not alike. And in the *Cyclosporae*, the life cycle is diplontic.

To the Isogeneratae belongs *Ectocarpus*, for example, a type in which both the sporophytes and gametophytes are indistinguishably filamentous, with prostrate and erect portions. Its diplohaplontic life cycle has been outlined in Chap. 26. In the Heterogeneratae (for example, *Laminaria*), the sporophyte is always the larger and dominant generation, and the gametophyte is microscopic and structurally dissimilar. The Cyclosporae include brown algae such as *Sargassum* and *Fucus*. These diplontic types are always oögamous, separately sexed or hermaphroditic, and they do not form spores. In the rockweed *Fucus* (Fig. 27.14), tips of thallus branches accumulate gelatinous substances internally, forming swollen tips called *receptacles*. Within each, numerous cavities called *conceptacles* contain gamete-forming structures. Meiosis takes place during the maturation of sperms and eggs. In many species the receptacles shrink when an outgoing tide exposes the algae to air, and the contents of the conceptacles become loosened. The returning tide later reswells the receptacles, and the gametes in the conceptacles are thereby squeezed out into the sea. Fertilization then takes place in open water. The zygote encysts, settles on a rock, and eventually germinates into a new diploid adult.

As judged from existing Rhodophyta, reproductive evolution in the red algae appears to have started with typical haplontic life cycles, meiosis occurring in the zygote. Later evolutionary stages became characterized by progressive postponement of meiosis, leading ultimately to a life cycle consisting of *three* successive generations: a diploid *carposporophyte*, a diploid *tetrasporophyte*, and a haploid *gametophyte*. This pattern is illustrated well by the genus *Polysiphonia* (Fig. 27.15).

In a haploid gametophyte, a male sex structure is a *spermatangium*. In it, a single cell may give rise mitotically to numerous male gametes, each called a *spermatium*. A female sex structure is a unicellular *carpogonium*, one end of which is elongated into a projection called a *trichogyne*. If a spermatium is carried by sea water to a trichogyne, it may penetrate into the trichogyne. The spermatium nucleus then fuses with the nucleus of the carpogonium, and this fertilization converts the carpogonial cell into the diploid zygote.

In *Polysiphonia* the zygote gives rise to a series of compacted filaments which remain attached to the gametophyte and constitute the diploid *carposporophyte*. Some of the cells of the carposporophyte later form single diploid *carpospores* (mitospores). Each such spore eventually escapes the carposporophyte by amoeboid motion and develops into an independent, free-living *tetrasporophyte*. This adult is diploid and structurally quite similar to the gametophyte. Certain cells of the tetrasporophyte subsequently undergo meiosis, and each cell so gives rise to four

haploid amoeboid cells. These are *tetraspores* (meiospores). They ultimately complete the life cycle by developing into new independent gametophytes.

Apart from the spore types contributing to this main progression of the life cycle, additional spore types are frequently formed by one or more of the three generations. For example, gametophytes may produce haploid mitospores ("monospores") which repeat the gametophyte generation. Analogously, tetrasporophytes may produce diploid mitospores ("paraspores"), repeating the tetrasporophyte generation.

**27 · 15   *The life cycle in red algae.* A, *sexual structures. 1, whole organism; 2, male branch; 3, female branch during fertilization. B, the life cycle of* Polysiphonia. *C, 1, portion of gametophyte at time of fertilization; 2, carposporophyte borne on gametophyte; 3, tetrasporophyte.*

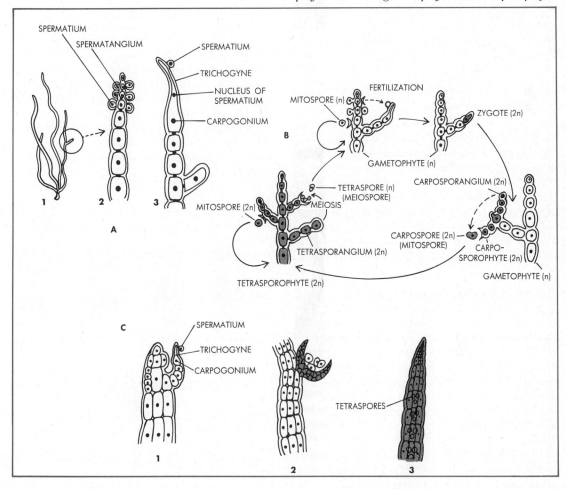

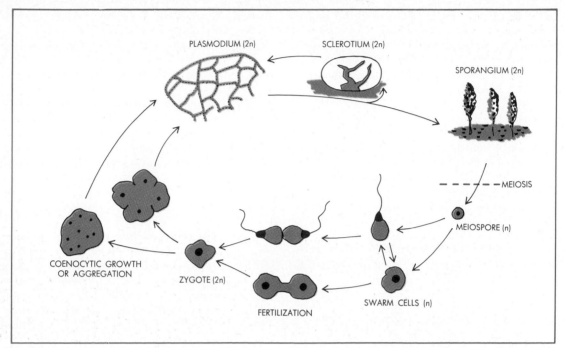

27 · 16   The life cycle of Myxomycetes.

SLIME MOLDS, PROTOZOA

The life cycle of slime molds, already outlined in
Chap. 12, is fundamentally diplohaplontic. The adult
plasmodium or pseudoplasmodium represents the
diploid sporophyte generation. It produces sporangial
fruiting bodies, and meiosis occurs during spore
formation. The unicellular swarmers resulting from
spore germination are therefore haploid. Successive
vegetative generations of such swarmers represent
the gametophyte generation, which thus consists of a
population of separate single cells, not a multicellular

*27 · 17 Protozoan reproduction and sex.
A, transverse fission in the ciliate Stentor. The
macronucleus (black) condenses into a compact
mass and then reelongates as each micronucleus
divides mitotically. Concurrently, the future
anterior offspring inherits the original set of
mouth organelles, while the future posterior one
develops a new set. After the two offspring are
constricted apart, the macronuclear portion
inherited by each renodulates. B, formation of
a ciliated bud in a suctorian. C, a mating pair
of Paramecium. Note spindles of dividing nuclei
in left individual. See Fig. 26.15 for illustration
of nuclear exchange by mating partners.*

body. Eventually such cells function as gametes and
fertilization reestablishes the diploid condition. Diploid zygotic cells subsequently grow or aggregate
into plasmodial sporophytes (Fig. 27.16).

Among protozoa (Fig. 27.17), vegetative reproduction occurs by binary fission in most cases, by multiple
fission in Sporozoa and a few other types. Binary
division is longitudinal in all zooflagellates and some
ciliates (for example, *Vorticella*), and transverse in

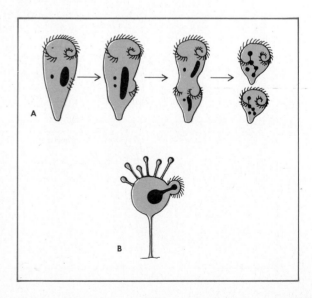

PLATE XXIX

50. Strobili of Equisetum, *on upright shoots.*

PLATE XXX

51. Section through a fern sorus,
showing arrangement of stalked
sporangia and covering indusium.

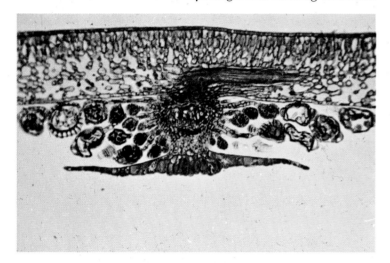

51, 52, *courtesy of Carolina Biological Supply Company*

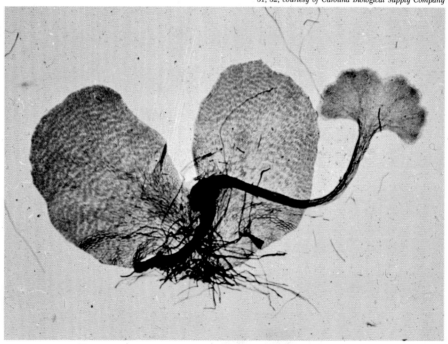

52. Fern gametophyte
with attached sporophyte,
the latter with root and
first leaf.

PLATE XXXI

53. Stages in seed germination.

PLATE XXXII

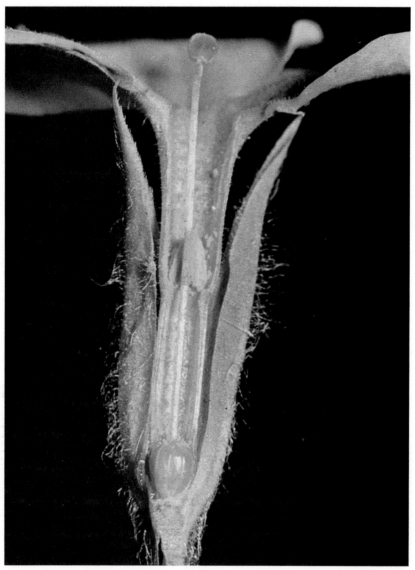

54. Anatomy of a flower.
*In this cutaway specimen, the pistil
is in the center, with stigma at top,
ovary at bottom, and the
style connecting these two parts.
Halfway along the style are the stamens,
with yellow anthers.
These various reproductive structures
are surrounded by the yellow petals, and the
latter in turn are enveloped by the green sepals.
See also Figs. 27.45 and 27.46.*

all other ciliates. Budding occurs in some protozoa (for example, Suctoria). As pointed out in Chap. 12, each ciliate protozoon possesses two kinds of nuclei. During fission, the micronuclei divide mitotically but the macronuclei, being without microscopically identifiable chromosomes, do not. Instead, a macronucleus merely constricts into two approximately equal parts.

Numerous protozoan species may encapsulate and become dormant temporarily within protective cysts. Sporulation is known to occur in Foraminifera and Sporozoa. In these organisms, a vegetative cell first becomes multinucleate and then undergoes multiple cytoplasmic fission. The cellular products, each containing one nucleus, represent spores. Foraminiferan life cycles are diplohaplontic, sporozoan life cycles, haplontic. All other protozoa are typically diplontic.

Gametic reproduction occurs universally among all protozoan groups but some individual types are without sex (for example, *Amoeba*). Fertilization is achieved either by syngamy, as in zooflagellates, or by conjugation and exchange and fusion of gamete nuclei, as in ciliates. In the latter, the macronuclei degenerate during conjugation and only the micronuclei produce gamete nuclei. After nuclear exchange and nuclear fusion, new micronuclei and macronuclei form from the zygote nuclei. Recall here that ciliates are hermaphroditic, and that the male and female gamete nuclei of a single individual may fuse in some cases (*autogamous* self-fertilization; see Chap. 26). One ciliate species, *Paramecium aurelia*, has been shown to consist of 16 distinct but structurally

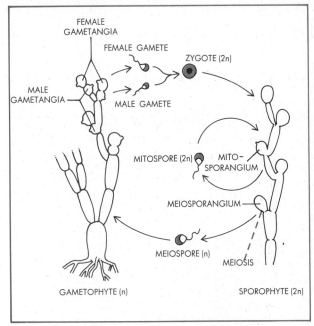

27 · 18 *Life cycle of the phycomycete fungus* **Allomyces.** *This cycle is diplohaplontic, with repeating generations in the diploid phase (via diploid mitospores).*

indistinguishable sexual varieties (syngens, see Chap. 8). Each variety in turn consists of two mating types, and cross-fertilizing conjugation requires one partner from each of these two types. Analogous sexual specializations are known to exist in other species of *Paramecium*, and indeed in several other types of ciliates.

FUNGI

In the fungal class of Phycomycetes, reproductive processes are on the whole rather like those of coccine, tubular, multinucleate algae. Vegetative nuclear divisions and cytoplasmic growth increase the extent of hyphae and mycelia. Mycelial fragmentation and dispersion may lead directly to an increase in the number of organisms. All Phycomycetes produce spores, either directly from the vegetative body or from special hyphae. Flagellate swimming spores are characteristic of aquatic types; nonmotile and encapsulated spores, of terrestrial types. All groups of the Phycomycetes are also sexual, with largely haplontic but sometimes diplohaplontic life cycles (for example, the diplohaplontic cycle of *Allomyces*, Fig. 27.18). Aquatic Phycomycetes are variously isogamous, anisogamous, and oögamous, and terrestrial types are largely isogamous with nonmotile gametes.

The reproductive repertoire of terrestrial forms

c

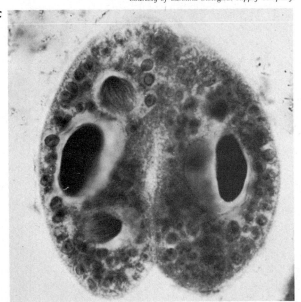

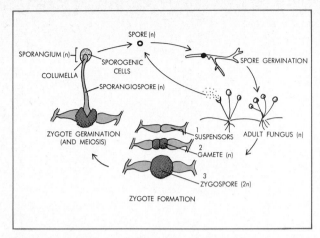

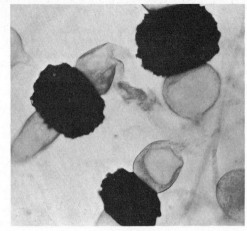

27 · 19 Rhizopus. *Diagram: the life cycle. Photo: zygospores.*

is illustrated by bread molds such as the haplontic *Rhizopus nigricans* (Fig. 27.19). The vegetative mycelium of this mold is haploid. From it in places grow upright branched hyphae with expanded tips. These tips are sporangia in which spores are produced. Such spores are formed mitotically, that is, they are haploid mitospores. Each spore is encapsulated within a wall which turns black as it matures. Dispersal and later germination of the spores repeats the haploid vegetative generation.

Rhizopus nigricans is a cross-fertilizing hermaphrodite. If two mycelia live in close proximity, each may develop a short *suspensor* hypha, one growing toward the other. The tip of each such hypha becomes walled off as a multinucleate gametelike cell. When the two gametes meet, they fuse and a cyst wall is then secreted around the fusion mass. In the

27 · 20 Ascomycete reproduction. *Photo:* Penicillium, *with conidial spores being cut off in chains from many of the hyphae. Diagram: the life cycle of diplohaplontic* (top) *and haplontic* (bottom) *yeasts.*

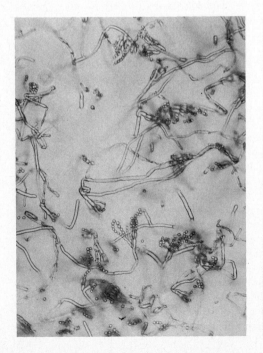

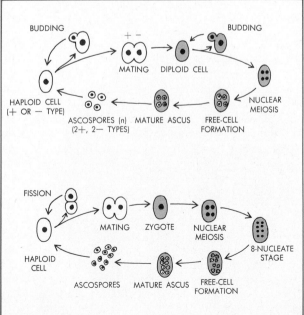

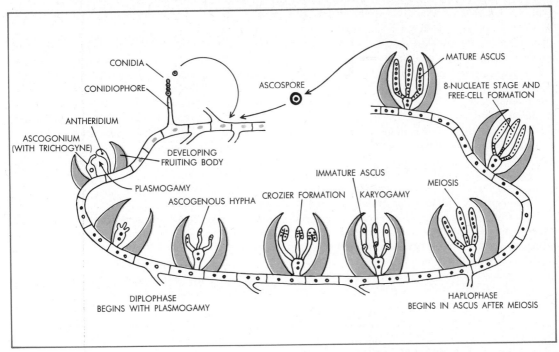

27 · 21   The life cycle of Euascomycetes. *Read counterclockwise, starting at top center. See also Fig. 12.22 and Color Plate XII, 23 for photos of asci and fruiting bodies.*

interior the nuclei pair off, one from one gamete joining one from the other. Such nuclear pairs fuse, forming diploid zygote nuclei. Unpaired nuclei degenerate. When the cyst germinates, its contents grow directly into an upright hypha with a terminal sporangium. The zygote nuclei divide in the process, and the first two divisions are meiotic. Numerous haploid nuclei are thereby formed, and these participate in spore formation in the sporangia. Mature spores grow into new vegetative mycelia as above, completing the sexual life cycle.

In the class Ascomycetes, most members produce mitospores in the form of *conidia,* that is, they are budded off in linear series from the tips of branch hyphae (Fig. 27.20). But this class of terrestrial fungi is distinguished primarily by the production of *ascospores* within *asci.* Ascospores are meiospores; meiosis occurs during their formation. Analogously, an ascus is a meiosporangium.

Yeasts exhibit ascosporulation in the simplest form (see Fig. 27.20). Brewer's yeast, *Saccharomyces cerevisiae,* exists in haploid and diploid states, and the life cycle is diplohaplontic. Both generations may reproduce vegetatively by budding. If two haploid cells of opposite sex type are brought together they fuse and form a diploid zygotic cell. Repeated fissions then produce a population of diploid sporophytic cells. Such a cell may later function as a meiosporangium, that is, as an ascus. The

diploid nucleus undergoes meiosis and the four resulting haploid nuclei are centers around which four ascospores are formed. Of these four, two are of one sex type and two are of the other. They germinate into four haploid, separately sexed yeast cells which may divide and give rise to a population of haploid gametophytic cells.

Not all yeasts are diplohaplontic and not all produce four ascospores. For example, in other genera the life cycle is haplontic and eight ascospores are formed. Here the zygote functions as an ascus immediately. Its nucleus undergoes three divisions, the first two being meiotic. Such a haplontic cycle with eight ascospores is typical for Ascomycetes generally.

In most Ascomycetes, the basic sexual process is rather different from that encountered in yeasts and in virtually all other living organisms (Fig. 27.21). A vegetative ascomycete mycelium with haploid nuclei produces special, usually multinucleate, sexual branch hyphae. "Female" ones are called *ascogonia;* "male" ones, *spermogonia.* If mating is to take place, two sexually different hyphae must be near each other and parts of their cytoplasms must become fused. The method by which fusion may be effected is shown rather clearly in some of the cup fungi. An ascogonium here develops a fingerlike outgrowth, or *trichogyne*, which curves toward and eventually fuses with the spermogonium. Nuclei from the spermogonium subsequently migrate through the trichogyne into the ascogonium. But the two types of nuclei now present do *not* fuse pairwise at this stage. They remain separate, and indeed they may increase in number by mitosis. Thus, mating, or *plasmogamy*, has occurred, but fertilization has not as yet taken place.

The mated ascogonium of cup fungi, still projecting as a branch from the vegetative mycelium, now develops a radial array of branch hyphae of its own. Each of these branches contains nuclei of the two different sex types. By a series of special processes, the tip of each branch may then become walled off as a cell with just two nuclei of opposite sex type. Such a terminal cell is a young ascus. Its two nuclei now fuse, a process representing *karyogamy* and constituting fertilization.

In most Ascomycetes, evidently, the sexual process has become separated into two subprocesses, namely, plasmogamy, or mating, and karyogamy, or nuclear fusion. In other organisms both occur more or less simultaneously, but in Ascomycetes a substantial time interval elapses between the first and the second. During this interval, the ascogonium and its branch hyphae are said to be in *diplophase*, or *dikaryophase*, that is, they contain two different sets of nuclei. By contrast, the vegetative hyphae continue to be in *haplophase*, or *monokaryophase*, with only one set of nuclei.

The zygotic fusion nucleus in the young ascus is diploid. It undergoes three divisions, the first two being meiotic. The resulting eight haploid nuclei become centers around which eight ascospores are produced. These eventually escape and germinate into new haplophasic mycelia. While ascus formation is under way after plasmogamy, vegetative hyphae may have grown up around the ascogonium and its branches, forming a fruiting body of characteristic structure (see Chap. 12).

Thus, distinct gametes are not formed in the Ascomycetes. Also, a single mating produces not just a single zygote but many. Not only may there be numerous asci, each with its own zygote nucleus, but after one ascus has performed its function, further asci may arise successively in the same location; the ascogonium and its branches contain a large store of nuclei of the two sex types. Through such continual ascus formation after a single mating, the dikaryotic state may be maintained almost indefinitely. For organisms which cannot move to find mates, this is a highly efficient adaptation to terrestrial life.

The life cycle of Ascomycetes may be considered to be essentially "haplontic," with a dominant vegetative monokaryophase and a dikaryophase restricted to special sex-associated and ascus-producing hyphae. Fungi in the class Basidiomycetes have similarly developed monokaryotic and dikaryotic states, again by a separation of plasmogamy from karyogamy. Moreover, the dikaryotic state may become much more extensive and in some cases even dominant. Consequently, the life cycles of some Basidiomycetes somewhat resemble haplontic ones, others resemble diplohaplontic ones, and still others compare with diplontic ones. In further contrast to the Ascomycetes, Basidiomycetes never develop any special sexual hyphae.

The basic basidiomycete life cycle may be considered to start with a vegetative monokaryophase (Fig. 27.22). A haploid nucleus is present in each cellular compartment of the hyphae. Mating, or plasmogamy, occurs when a hyphal cell produces a lateral outgrowth which fuses with a similar outgrowth from another cell. The fused cell now contains two nuclei, and these remain distinct. Such a cell undergoes repeated divisions and produces the dikaryophase of the life cycle. This phase may grow to become a whole mycelium itself, either still connected with the monokaryotic mycelium or separated. Later, the dikaryophase is terminated by karyogamy, meiosis, and the formation of meiospores. These processes occur in somewhat different ways in the two subclasses of Basidiomycetes, the Homobasidiomycetes and the Heterobasidiomycetes.

In the Homobasidiomycetes, terminals of hyphae each cut off a club-shaped binucleate cell, the *basidium* (see Fig. 12.24). This is a meiosporangium, equivalent to an ascus of the Ascomycetes. In a basidium, karyogamy and meiosis occur and the four resulting haploid nuclei become incorporated into four *basidiospores*. Such spores are budded off on the outside of a basidium. After being dispersed, the basidiospores germinate into new monokaryotic mycelia.

In the Heterobasidiomycetes, basidia are not formed directly from dikaryotic hyphae. Instead, hyphal cells become transformed into special thick-walled binucleate spores, named differently in different cases. Within such spores karyogamy takes place. Meiosis occurs either before or after germination, but in each case the result is a basidium. In these fungi the basidium consists of four haploid uninucleate cells joined end to end. Each cell buds off one basidiospore (see Fig. 27.22).

The dikaryophase of Homobasidiomycetes often

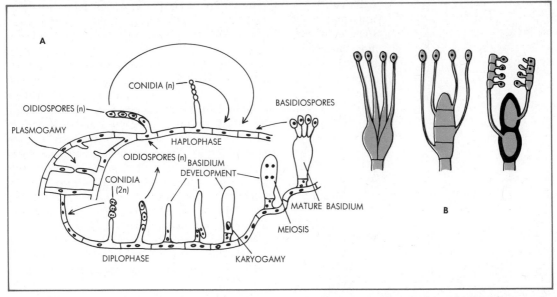

27 · 22 ***The life cycle of Basidiomycetes.***
A, read counterclockwise, starting at top center.
B, types of basidia characteristic of Heterobasid-
iomycetes. See also Figs. 12.24 and 12.26.

forms distinct fruiting bodies, for example, mushrooms, in which the basidium-forming hyphae are aggregated. The Heterobasidiomycetes, which include smuts and rusts, do not form fruiting bodies. Among these fungi are types with extreme reductions of either vegetative phase. In certain smuts, for example, the entire monokaryophase is limited to the four-celled basidia; plasmogamy occurs directly between these two pairs of cells. The whole subsequent cycle is therefore dikaryotic. In certain rusts, by contrast, the entire dikaryophase is the binucleate cell resulting from plasmogamy; the cell immediately becomes the basidium-producing spore in which karyogamy and meiosis take place. Thus, with the exception of that cell, the whole remaining cycle is monokaryotic. These instances are close approaches to purely "diplontic" and "haplontic" life cycles. Most other basidiomycete life cycles are somewhere between these extremes, that is, they are diplohaplontic, with either the monokaryophase or the dikaryophase being variously dominant.

METAPHYTA

The reproduction of all Metaphyta is characterized by diplohaplontic life cycles with *dissimilar* gametophyte and sporophyte generations; by vegetative reproduction through fragmentation and bud formation, developed to various degrees in different groups; by multicellular sex organs; by oögamy, with distinct eggs and sperms or sperm nuclei; by development of zygotes into distinct sporophytic embryos; by

multicellular sporangia with sterile external sheaths; and by production of meiospores *only*, no other types of spores being formed.

The gametophyte generation is dominant in the bryophytes, the sporophyte generation in the tracheophytes. The entire reproductive evolution of the Metaphyta has been characterized by the more or less complete development of a land-adapted life cycle out of the originally water-adapted diplohaplontic cycle probably inherited from green algal ancestors.

BRYOPHYTES

Vegetative reproduction is particularly highly developed in this phylum. Fragmentation bodies may be formed in many thallose bryophytes by posterior decay and consequent liberation of branches as separate plants. The liverwort *Marchantia* forms *gemma cups* from surface cells of the thallus (see Fig. 26.13). The floor of such a cup continuously develops vegetative buds, or *gemmae*, each an upright spindle-shaped body attached by a tiny stalk. Gemmae are readily dislodged by rain drops, and if gemmae are splashed to suitable ground they develop into new plants. Similar buds are formed by many other bryophytes.

The sex organs develop in different regions in

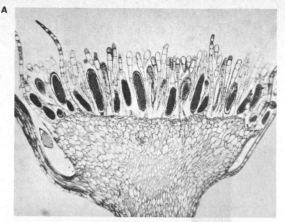

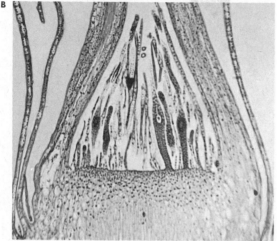

27 · 23 *Sections through the apical tips of moss shoots, showing the position of an antheridial head (A) and an archegonial head (B). Note the numerous sex organs on each head.*

27 · 24 *Sex-organ-bearing stalks in* **Marchantia.** *A, structure containing male sex organs. B, stalk bearing fingerlike processes in which female sex organs are located.*

Courtesy of Carolina Biological Supply Company.

different bryophyte groups. Mosses form such organs typically at the terminals of their upright shoots (Fig. 27.23). In many thallose liverworts, sex organs arise in the median furrow of the horizontal body of the plant, where water is likely to collect and provide a pathway from the sperms. Both types of sex organs, antheridia and archegonia, may form in separate locations of a single plant. In other thallose liverworts, groups of archegonia are located in so-called *receptacles,* which, after fertilization, grow upward on stalked extensions of the thallus. *Marchantia* is representative of a third group, in which both types of sex organs are in receptacles, both becoming raised on stalks after fertilization (Fig. 27.24). Antheridial receptacles are shaped like scalloped disks, with male sex organs set in the upper surface. An archegonial receptacle is roughly umbrella-shaped, and its rim is extended into (usually) nine fingerlike processes. The female sex organs are on the underside of the umbrella.

In all bryophytes, a sperm-producing antheridium is more or less spherical and consists of an external single-layered *jacket* and of *spermatogenous cells* in the interior. Each such interior cell matures into a biflagellate, spirally coiled sperm. An archegonium is roughly flask-shaped. The expanded portion consists of a large egg in the interior and of a single-layered *venter* on the outside. The venter continues into the narrow portion of the sex organ as the *neck,* a canal which provides a sperm path to the egg (Fig. 27.25).

Fertilization requires free water; continuous films of water must be present between nearby sex organs or fluid droplets must splash sperms to archegonia. After sperms enter an archegonium, one fertilizes

A

B

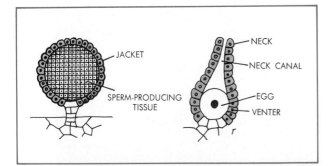

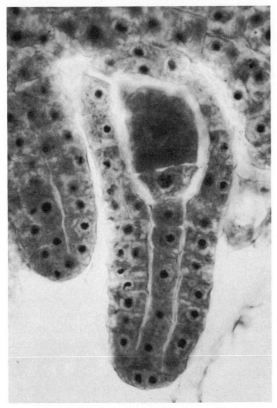

27 · 25 Bryophyte sex organs. *Diagrams: the structure of antheridia* (left) *and archegonia* (right). *Photo: section through an archegonium.*

27 · 26 The sporophyte of bryophytes. *A, moss gametophytes bearing attached sporophytes on top. B, the sporophyte of the liverwort Marchantia. C, meiosis of a spore mother cell and mature spores.* A, *courtesy of Carolina Biological Supply Company.*

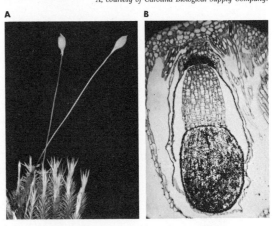

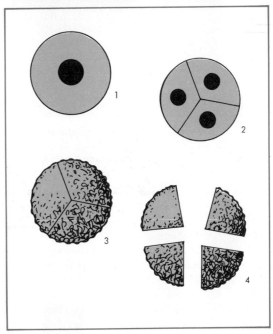

the egg. The zygote then grows into a diploid embryo, and the embryo later matures into an adult sporophyte. Such a sporophyte consists of a basal *foot*, a *stalk* of different lengths in different bryophyte groups, and a terminal sporangial *capsule* (Fig. 27.26 and see Chap. 13). Recall that the structure of the capsule differs in the three bryophyte classes, as does the nutrition of the entire sporophyte. Recall also that, as sporophyte development progresses in mosses

and liverworts, the nutritional pattern changes from autotrophism to heterotrophism.

Spore maturation in the capsule includes the process of meiosis (see Fig. 27.26). Each spore-producing cell is a *spore mother cell*. After such a cell has undergone meiosis, the four resulting haploid meiospores remain joined together temporarily as a *spore tetrad*. Each spore soon secretes a heavy wall around itself, and the tetrad thereby becomes separated into individual spores. In all bryophytes except the

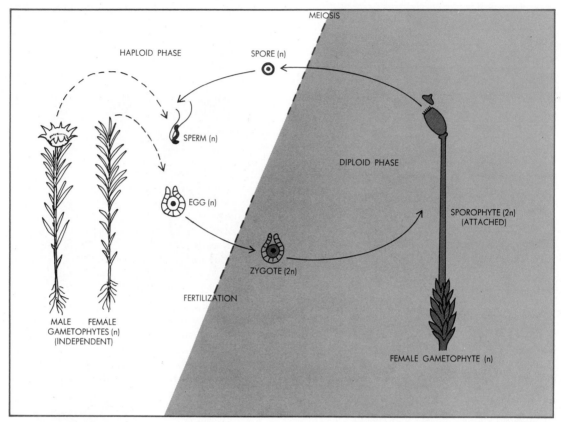

MEIOSIS

HAPLOID PHASE   SPORE (n)

SPERM (n)

DIPLOID PHASE

EGG (n)

SPOROPHYTE (2n)
(ATTACHED)

ZYGOTE (2n)

FERTILIZATION

MALE   FEMALE
GAMETOPHYTES (n)
(INDEPENDENT)

FEMALE GAMETOPHYTE (n)

27 · 27   *The life cycle of a bryophyte (moss).*

mosses, elaters develop in the spore-forming regions along with the spores (Chap. 13). After discharge from the sporangia, the spores germinate into new haploid gametophytes (Fig. 27.27).

Inasmuch as bryophytes probably descended from green algal ancestors, which possessed unicellular reproductive structures, we may ask how the multicellular sex organs and sporangia of bryophytes (and tracheophytes) might have evolved. The *potential* of forming multicellular reproductive parts undoubtedly existed in the algal ancestors. Even today, for example, practically the whole body of a chlorophyte such as *Ulva* is in effect a reproductive structure; *any* vegetative cell of a gametophyte may become gamete-producing, and *any* vegetative cell of a sporophyte may become spore-producing. If, in such an organism, reproductive capacity were to be retained only in a localized group of cells but were lost everywhere else, a multicellular reproductive *tissue* would arise. A localization of this sort may conceivably have occurred in ancestors of bryophytes (Fig. 27.28), and perhaps the evolutionary

stimulus here was the terrestrial way of life. In adapting to terrestrial conditions, the body of bryophyte ancestors became specialized internally into absorptive, conductive, and photosynthetic regions. However, effective performance of these functions may have precluded a continuing reproductive role of each cell. Moreover, once a specialized multicellular reproductive structure is in existence, the advantage of an external protective sheath is clear, especially in a terrestrial plant. We may therefore envisage that, in ancestral bryophytes, the outermost cells of a multicellular gamete- or spore-producing structure lost reproductive capacity too and came to function instead as a sterile sheath. The whole body part thus became a true organ.

We may also ask how the structural similarity of sporophyte and gametophyte in the algal ancestors would have become changed to the structural dissimilarity characteristic of bryophytes. In all probability, this bryophyte trait may likewise have evolved as an adaptation to or consequence of the terrestrial way of life (Fig. 27.29). Since the zygotes of diplohaplontic chlorophytes are typically flagellate and swimming, and since a swimming zygote would be quite inadequate on land, a first prerequisite for a diplohaplontic terrestrial plant would be oögamy; a nonmotile egg would be formed and it would be retained in the archegonium. As a result, the sporophyte developing after fertilization on the gametophyte would have to remain attached, for it could not readily swim away on land. But once a sporophyte is attached, its whole structure and metabolic nature are likely to change in correlation with its *dependent* way of life. For example, it no longer absorbs from the physical environment but from the gametophyte, and it therefore does not require rhizoids for nutrient absorption from soil. Indeed it may economize even further by becoming a heterotrophic parasite altogether, as is actually the case in most bryophytic sporophytes. It is thus conceivable that the structural and nutritional dissimilarities between gametophyte and sporophyte may be an evolutionary consequence of the attached condition of the sporophyte.

TRACHEOPHYTES

Regardless how well adapted to land the gametophyte generation of bryophytes may be in other respects, it can never be really well adapted in its reproduction; gametic reproduction requires free external

27 · 29 Evolution of the dependent sporophyte. A, *both gametophyte and sporophyte independent. B, C, oögamy and equal attached sporophyte. B, D, oögamy and reduced attached sporophyte.*

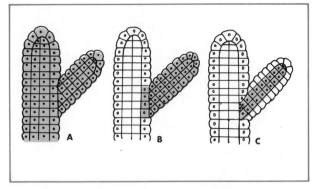

27 · 28 Probable evolution of multicellular sex organs. A, *all cells of a plant are potentially reproductive. B, reproductive potential restricted to specific groups of cells. C, reproductive cells surrounded by sterile sheath.*

water for the swimming sperms, but ample water is not always available in a terrestrial environment. As we have seen, bryophytes "make do" by gearing their sperm release to wet periods.

Primitive tracheophytes actually cannot do much better. But in their life cycles the emphasis is on the diploid sporophyte, not the gametophyte. The sporophyte produces encapsulated (meio)spores, which are excellently adapted to terrestrial conditions. And by reducing the gametophyte to microscopic dimensions and to a generally short-lived existence, they correspondingly reduce the water

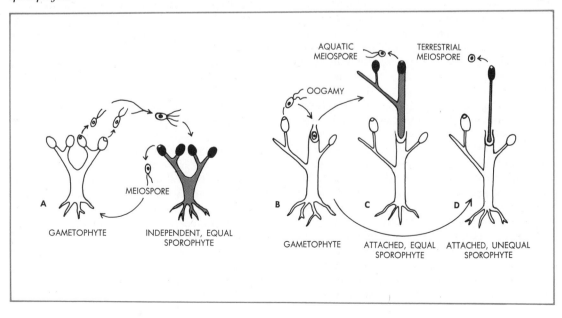

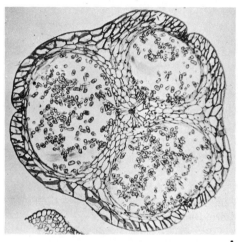
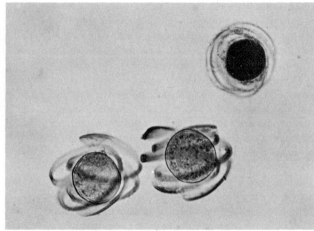

A   B

27 · 30   Sporangia. *A, cross section through a sporangium of* Psilotum. *The location of such sporangia on the plant is shown in Fig. 13.32. B, spores of* Equisetum, *with elaters aiding in dispersal.*

problem of the weak link in their life cycle. Moreover, deemphasis of the gametophyte also prepares the way for a complete circumvention of the water problem, realized in advanced tracheophytes.

Psilopsids, Lycopsids, Sphenopsids

As pointed out in Chap. 13, the sporangia of these primitive tracheophytes form either bulbous outgrowths on stems, as in psilopsids, or outgrowths on specialized cone leaves (sporophylls) as in lycopsids and sphenopsids. A sporangial sac in any of these plants consists of several layers of external protective and nutritive tissue and of an inner spore-producing tissue. The cells of the latter are spore mother cells. They undergo meiosis and form spore tetrads. Each haploid meiospore subsequently develops a thickened wall and the tetrads separate. As the spores thus mature, the sporangial sacs become dry and brittle and they open along specialized weak regions. Also, the cones of lycopsids and sphenopsids dry and open out and facilitate spore discharge in this manner (Fig. 27.30 and Color Plate XXIX, 50). Spores germinate on suitable ground and grow into tiny independent gametophytes, as described in Chap. 13. Depending on the species, gametophytes are either hermaphroditic or separately sexed.

In most species all spores are alike, and one cannot tell ahead of time whether a given spore will develop into a male or a female gametophyte. This condition of equal spores, known as *homospory*, characterizes not only most tracheophytes here under

discussion but also all bryophytes and indeed all Protista as well. However, the pattern is different in a group of lycopsids which includes *Selaginella* (Fig. 27.31). In this group the sex potential of a spore does become apparent even before a gametophyte develops. The spores come in two sizes. Smaller *microspores* always develop into *male* gametophytes, and larger *megaspores* always develop into *female* gametophytes. Microspores develop within *microsporangia*, which form on *microsporophylls;* and megaspores develop within *megasporangia*, which form on *megasporophylls*. This condition of unequal spores is called *heterospory*. Both spore types may arise within the same plant, indeed often within the same cone. Note that in a heterosporous species the gametophytes are automatically of separate sexes.

Microspores form through meiosis of *microspore mother cells*. Analogously, megaspores are the meiotic product of *megaspore mother cells*. In a megasporangium almost all potential spore-forming cells disintegrate and only one or a few actually become megaspore mother cells. These few are large, and after meiosis the resulting megaspores are correspondingly large.

When the tiny gametophytes are mature, they develop sex organs structured like those of bryophytes. Fertilization similarly takes place as in bryophytes, during wet periods. In many species of *Selaginella* fertilization occurs, as in other cases, after the gametophytes are fully developed as separate plantlets on the ground. But in certain species the gametophytes mature *precociously*, before spores are even discharged from the sporangia in the cones. It may then happen that male gametophytes, within their microspore walls, are dispersed to open megasporangia nearby, which contain mature female gametophytes within megaspore walls. Under such conditions, fertilization may occur right within the megasporangia. The resulting zygotes then remain in the body of the old sporophyte adult, and may develop there into new sporophyte embryos. The whole process is a very close—but not a complete—approach to pollination and seed formation as encountered in advanced tracheophytes (see below).

In psilopsids, lycopsids, and sphenopsids generally, a zygote within an archegonium divides and produces two cells (Fig. 27.32). One of these in many cases does not contribute to the formation of an embryo. Instead, with or without further divisions, it may function as a microscopic holdfast, or *suspensor*. This structure is equivalent to the foot of bryophyte embryos; it anchors the embryo to the archegonium and the female gametophyte. The second cell formed by the zygote does give rise to the actual embryo. Through repeated divisions it produces a cell mass which soon becomes organized into an embryonic stem and root (only a stem in psilopsids). As these early organs elongate further, they penetrate through

the tissues of the gametophyte and establish independent contact with the ground. Tiny erect branch shoots eventually break through the soil and on them then form the first microphylls. At this stage the embryo is a young adult, already far larger than the gametophyte which gave rise to it. Indeed, the gametophyte may already have degenerated completely. But note that the sporophyte is initially dependent on the gametophyte.

Ferns

In this class of the Pteropsida, sporangia develop on or within the leaves. For example, in the common stone fern *Polypodium* a single cell on the lower

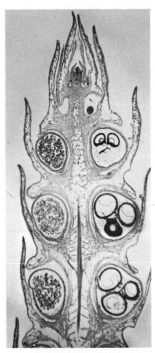

27 · 31 Reproduction in Selaginella. *Photo: longitudinal section through strobilus, showing microsporophylls with microsporangia on left and megasporophylls with megasporangia on right. Diagram: A, 1, megasporangium with megaspore mother cell and nutritive layer (tapetum) around it; 2, megaspore with wall; 3, after nuclear division and cell formation, the female gametophyte formed from the megaspore is a layer of cells on top of reserve food, all still within the megaspore wall which has broken open; an archegonium has developed as well. B, 1, microsporangium with microspores and surrounded by nutritive tapetum; 2, microspore with wall; 3, a few-celled male gametophyte develops from the microspore, and this gametophyte eventually produces sperms. These escape through a break in the microspore wall.*

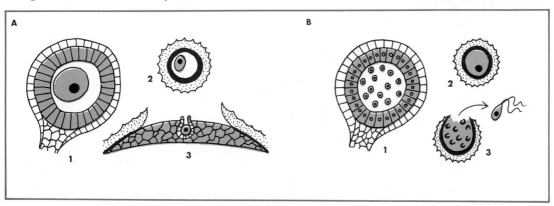

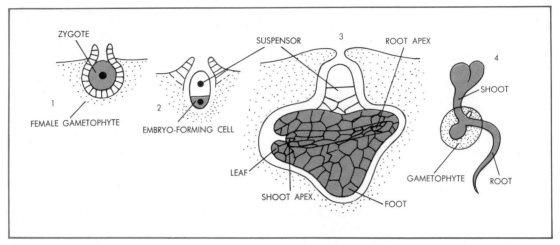

27 · 32 *Zygote development in primitive tracheophytes such as* Selaginella.

surface of a leaf divides and produces a series of cells. These become arranged into a basal stalk and a terminal lens-shaped sporangium. Numerous sporangia usually arise from the same area of the leaf, and such a sporangial group is a *sorus.* It is covered by a single-layered shield of tissue, the *indusium.* Sori appear in regular double rows, one row

27 · 33 Spores in ferns. *The mechanism of spore discharge.*

on each side of a main leaf vein (see Color Plate XXX, 51). Internally, a sporangium contains some 12 to 16 spore mother cells. These undergo meiosis and form spore tetrads, and the latter mature into 48 to 64 encapsulated meiospores.

The exterior wall of a mature sporangium is single-layered. One row of cells around the edge of the lens-shaped sporangium is specialized as an *annulus.* The cells here are boxlike, and each has a greatly thickened wall on all sides except on the outer surface. Where one end of the annulus joins the sporangial stalk, a few *lip cells* remain thin-walled on all surfaces. When the sporangium is mature, it

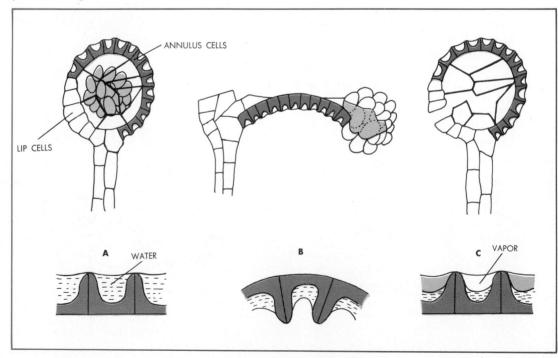

loses water by evaporation and dries. As water disappears from annulus cells they tend to shrink, but only their thin outer walls are nonrigid. Each such wall is therefore sucked inward, into the boxlike interior of the annulus cell. These suction forces are generated over the entire annulus, and they are sufficiently strong to rupture the lip cells and the side walls of the sporangium. Freed of its constraints by these ruptures, the annulus straightens out and then bends backward, acquiring an opposite curvature. Many mature spores cling to it as it curves back. But eventually the tensile strength of the water within each annulus cell is no longer sufficiently great to hold the thin outer wall in a sucked-in position. The cohesion among water molecules then ceases and liquid water is transformed into water vapor. The thin wall of an annulus cell is thereby pushed outward explosively. As this occurs simultaneously in all annulus cells, the whole annulus suddenly snaps back into its original position. In the process the spores are forcibly catapulted into the air, just as a ball is propelled by an overhand throw (Fig. 27.33).

With only a few heterosporous exceptions, ferns are homosporous. On suitable ground a spore germinates and grows into a small, heart-shaped gametophyte, rather similar in structure to a thallose bryophyte (Fig. 27.34 and Color Plate XXX, 52). Gametophytes are hermaphroditic in most cases, and the sex organs develop on the lower surfaces. After fertilization, the zygote within an archegonium undergoes repeated divisions and forms a sporophyte embryo. In it, four organ zones become recognizable: a *foot*, which anchors the whole embryo to the base of the archegonium; a *radicle*, the embryonic root; a *hypocotyl*, the embryonic stem; and a *cotyledon*, the embryonic leaf. Root and stem elongate rapidly, penetrate through the archegonial tissues, and establish the young sporophyte in soil and air, respectively. Until the leaf greens, the gametophyte nourishes the sporophyte, but thereafter the gametophyte shrivels and degenerates. The life cycle of ferns is summarized in Fig. 27.35.

SEED PLANTS

All Metaphyta considered so far exhibit essentially the same system of reproduction. Regardless of whether the sporophyte is dependent or independent, the gametophyte is independent. Moreover, the gametophyte produces sex organs of the same basic type in all groups and requires external water for fertilization. As noted, certain species of *Selaginella* suggest some of the features of the second major system of reproduction among Metaphyta, namely, the system

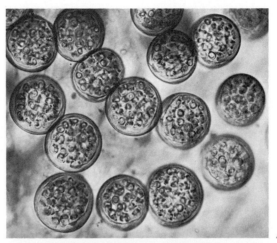

A

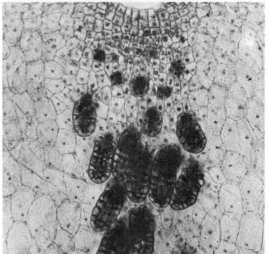

B

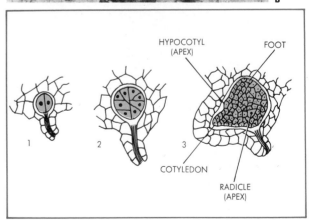

C

27 · 34   *Fern reproduction. A, some antheridia on a gametophyte. B, some archegonia on a gametophyte. See Color Plate XVII, 30 for whole view of gametophyte. C, development of a sporophyte embryo, diagrammatic.*

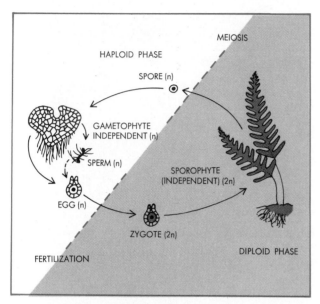

27 · 35 Fern life-cycle summary.

27 · 36 Reproduction in seed plants. A, the
basic pattern. B, the monoecious and dioecious
conditions. In a monoecious organism, a given
individual produces both micro- and megasporangia, either within the same strobilus or in
different strobili. In a dioecious organism, a
given individual produces only microsporangia
or only megasporangia.

encountered among seed plants. Here the gametophyte is always *dependent;* it is parasitic on the
sporophyte. Furthermore, external water is *not* needed
for fertilization.

The reproductive pattern of seed plants may be
characterized as follows (Fig. 27.36). First, all seed
plants are heterosporous (and thus they invariably
possess gametophytes with separate sexes). Like
Selaginella, some seed plants produce both microspores and megaspores in the same individual (*monoecious* condition). Others produce only microspores
in one individual, only megaspores in another (*dioecious* condition).

Second, a microspore gives rise to a male gametophyte consisting of a few cells only, and this whole
gametophyte is retained within the wall of the
microspore. Such a wall with gametophyte is a *pollen
grain.* Analogously, a megaspore gives rise to a few-
celled female gametophyte, retained within the wall
of the megaspore. The megaspore in turn does not
leave the megasporangium in which it is produced.
Megasporangia are often called *ovules.*

Third, pollen grains are dispersed from the microsporangia and are carried by wind or animals to the
ovules. Such dispersion, leading eventually to contact
between a pollen grain and an ovule or associated
structures, is called *pollination.*

Fourth, the male gametophyte within a pollen
grain develops a *pollen tube,* which carries sperms

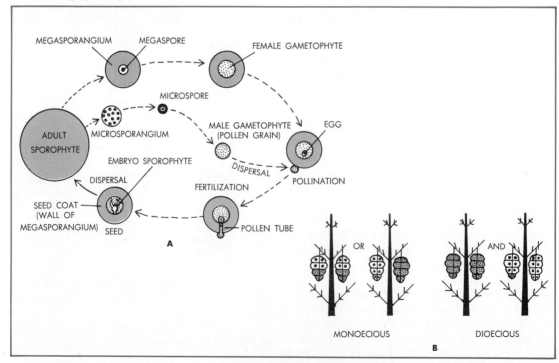

or sperm nuclei at the tip. This tube digests a path to the female gametophyte and makes contact with an egg. A sperm nucleus then enters the egg and fuses with its nucleus, a process constituting *fertilization*. Pollination and fertilization are therefore distinct and separate events; several months may in some cases intervene between them. Note that it is the pollen tube which circumvents the requirement of free water in fertilization, and that the success of seed plants rests in large measure on the evolutionary development of such tubes.

Lastly, the fertilized egg, the female gametophyte, the surrounding wall of the megaspore, and the surrounding tissues of the ovule, all together constitute a *seed*. The outer layers of the ovule usually harden into a tough *seed coat*. Within a seed, the zygote develops into a new sporophyte embryo. Through subsequent dispersion of the seed from the parent sporophyte and through seed germination, the young sporophyte becomes an independent plant. In effect, the gametophyte generation remains hidden throughout and the visible reproductive pattern of a seed plant becomes sporophyte ⟶ seed ⟶ sporophyte.

Mature seeds may usually remain *dormant*, often for very long periods (even centuries in some cases). Dormancy is adaptively advantageous, for if seed formation were followed invariably by immediate germination then the emerging seedlings would frequently find themselves in totally unsuitable environments. Actually, further development of a dormant seed appears to be triggered specifically by a favorable environment. The dormant condition is in some respects similar to the state of hibernation encountered in various mammals; the rate of respiration and of metabolism generally is exceptionally low and reserve foods are used up exceedingly slowly. The mechanisms by which such states are initiated, maintained, and terminated are as yet largely unknown.

Gymnosperms

In almost all gymnosperms the reproductive structures form in cones, or *strobili*. In a pine, for example, microstrobili develop in clusters on the ends of branches. A microstrobilus bears microsporophylls of which each develops two microsporangia on the underside (Fig. 27.37). Microspore mother cells

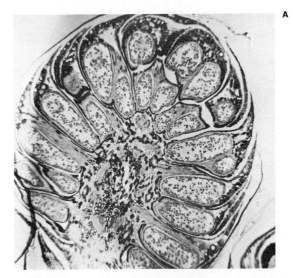

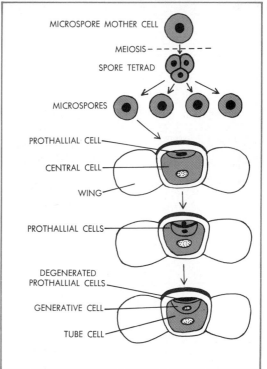

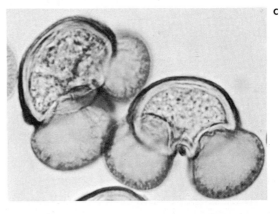

27 · 37 Pine reproduction: microspores. *A, longitudinal section through a microstrobilus. Note sporangia with microspores. B, development of a microspore into a pollen grain (bottom). C, some mature pollen grains.*

687

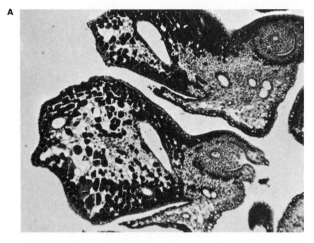

A

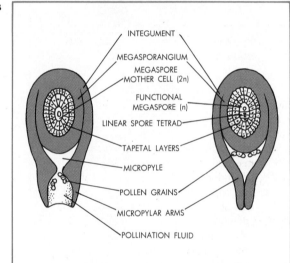

B

INTEGUMENT

MEGASPORANGIUM

MEGASPORE
MOTHER CELL (2n)

FUNCTIONAL
MEGASPORE (n)

LINEAR SPORE TETRAD

TAPETAL LAYERS

MICROPYLE

POLLEN GRAINS

MICROPYLAR ARMS

POLLINATION FLUID

27 · 38 Pine reproduction: megaspores. *A, section through ovuliferous (ovule-bearing) scale of a megastrobilus, showing megasporangia (at top right corner of each scale). In each megasporangium, note the large central megaspore mother cell, the surrounding megasporangial tissues, and the outer integument with micropylar arms (pointing to right). B, the early development of a megasporangium. Left, before meiosis; right, after meiosis.*

undergo meiosis and spore tetrads give rise to microspores. Each of the latter possesses a wall composed of two layers. The outer one subsequently separates partially and forms two conspicuous "wings." Within its wall, the microspore cell divides and forms one small and one large cell. The small cell divides once more, producing two *prothallial cells*. These represent the whole vegetative portion of the male gametophyte. They eventually disintegrate and play no further role. The larger cell also divides, forming one smaller *generative cell* and one larger *tube cell*. At such a stage of development a pollen grain is mature and is shed from the microsporangium.

Megastrobili of pines are formed on short lateral branches. Such cones are small and green at first, and they harden only after pollination and considerable growth (Fig. 27.38). The axis of a megastrobilus bears lateral scales on each of which develop two ovules. An ovule consists of an outer *integument*

27 · 39 The female gametophyte of pines. *A, cell formation in the developing female gametophyte. B, the mature female gametophyte, with eggs. C, section through the female gametophyte with egg (at bottom) and two neck cells of the archegonium (below egg, closing chamber in which gametophyte lies).*

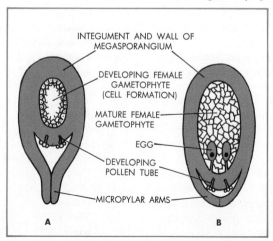

INTEGUMENT AND WALL OF
MEGASPORANGIUM

DEVELOPING FEMALE
GAMETOPHYTE
(CELL FORMATION)

MATURE FEMALE
GAMETOPHYTE

EGG

DEVELOPING
POLLEN TUBE

MICROPYLAR ARMS

A

B

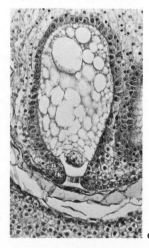

C

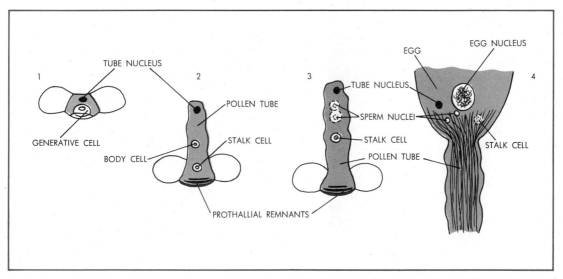

27 · 40 *Development of a pollen grain and fertilization in pines.*

and a small interior megasporangium. At the base of the ovule, that is, on the side facing the axis of the megastrobilus, the integument is extended into two flaps, the *micropylar arms*. Between the arms the integument leaves a narrow canal, the *micropyle*, leading to the megasporangium. In the latter, a single cell functions as megaspore mother cell. A *linear spore tetrad* of four haploid cells is produced by meiosis. Of these four cells, three degenerate and the remaining one is the *functional megaspore*.

When pollination occurs, the ovule is usually developed to the point where a megaspore mother cell has differentiated. Pollen grains are carried into the megastrobilus, and some fall into the space between the micropylar arms. In this region the ovule secretes a *pollination fluid*, which traps pollen grains and permits them to float into the micropyle. Pollen grains thus come to make contact with the megasporangium. After pollination the external tips of the scales of a megastrobilus grow and fuse to one another, and the whole cone thereby becomes sealed off.

Subsequent events within a pine ovule occur exceedingly slowly; about a year elapses between pollination and fertilization. During this time, the whole cone and its contents increase in size. A functional megaspore is formed, and it enlarges and elongates. The megaspore nucleus divides repeatedly, until some 2,000 haploid nuclei are present. Cell walls are then laid down between the nuclei, and in this way the megaspore is transformed into a multicellular female gametophyte. On the side of the micropyle a few highly reduced archegonia develop, each with an egg (Fig. 27.39).

In the meantime, the pollen grain resting against

the megasporangium develops also. The tube cell of each pollen grain elongates slowly, producing a pollen tube. This tube secretes enzymes which digest a path through megasporangial tissue. The generative cell of the male gametophyte divides, forming one *stalk cell* and one *body cell*. These cells migrate toward the tip of the pollen tube, where a tube-cell nucleus is already present. Later, the body-cell nucleus divides once again, forming two *sperm nuclei* within the cytoplasm of the body cell. Fertilization occurs when a pollen tube penetrates into an egg. All four nuclei at the tip of the pollen tube are usually discharged into the egg. One sperm nucleus fuses with the egg nucleus and the remaining nuclei disintegrate within the egg cytoplasm (Fig. 27.40). We may note that, in cycads and ginkgoes, division of the body cell results not in two nuclei only but in two whole sperm *cells*. These become multiflagellate and they *swim* through the pollen tube into the egg. Undoubtedly this is an evolutionary relic condition reminiscent of the swimming sperms of the pteropsid ancestors.

Several or all of the eggs present in a female gametophyte of a pine may be fertilized independently (Fig. 27.41). Such an event leads to *simple polyembryony* and is equivalent to the formation of fraternal twins in animals (that is, several embryos formed from several zygotes). In pines only one zygote usually develops much further. It soon forms 16 cells arranged as 4 groups of 4, one quartet below the other. This is the *proembryo* stage of sporophyte development. The four cells of the uppermost

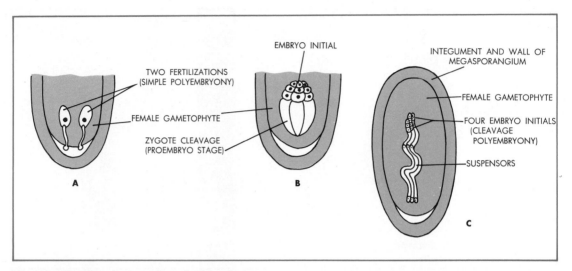

27 · 41 Fertilization and early development of the zygote in pines. A, fertilization. B, cleavage. C, formation of embryo initials. Note the two possible kinds of polyembryony.

quartet are *embryo initials;* each begins to produce an embryo. Multiple development of this sort, called *cleavage polyembryony,* is equivalent to the formation of identical twins in animals (that is, several embryos formed from a single zygote). The next lower quartet of cells elongates greatly and develops into a strand called a *suspensor* (Fig. 27.42). As it lengthens it pushes the embryo initials deep into the female gametophyte. Enzymes secreted by the embryo initials digest some of the gametophyte tissue and make room for further expansion. Of the four embryo initials, one usually develops faster than the others. Eventually only that one develops further and the other three degenerate.

Continuing divisions of this remaining embryo initial soon establish a sporophyte embryo consisting of root, stem, and two or more embryonic leaves called cotyledons. The whole embryo is embedded in the remains of the female gametophyte tissue, which in turn is surrounded by the remains of the megasporangium and the external integument. The latter has hardened by this time into a seed coat, and a flap of integument extending away from the seed coat has matured into the "wing" of the seed (Fig. 27.43 and Color Plate XXXI, 53).

Pine seeds are ripe several months after fertilization. At that time the scales of the megastrobilus spread open and the naked, exposed seeds may be dispersed. Not all conifers require two or three years for seed formation like pines, in which pollination

occurs one year and fertilization not until the next. In spruces, for example, the time interval between pollination and fertilization is only a few weeks. Many other conifers similarly complete their whole reproduction in a single season. Such time variations notwithstanding, the reproductive processes themselves are basically the same in all gymnosperms (Fig. 27.44).

Angiosperms

In this group of plants, the equivalents of gymnosperm cones are *flowers* (Color Plate XXXI, 54). Like a strobilus, a flower consists of an axis and of leaves attached to the axis. But here the internodes are

27 · 42 Two stages in the development of a pine embryo.

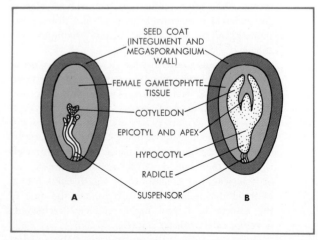

extremely shortened and the conelike arrangement becomes obscured.

A flower is formed on a *receptacle,* the terminal expanded part of a stem. From the receptacle arise a *calyx,* consisting of a whorl of *sepals;* a *corolla,* consisting of a whorl of *petals;* a circularly arranged set of *stamens,* equivalent to microsporophylls; and a central *pistil,* or *carpel,* equivalent to a megasporophyll. A stamen consists of a stalk, or *filament,* and a terminal *anther.* The latter contains the microsporangia. A pistil consists of a terminal *stigma,* a middle *style,* and an expanded basal *ovary.* Within the ovary are the ovules.

Flowers may be with or without calyx or corolla. Where these leaves are present, they may or may not be pigmented (other than green) and they may or may not produce scents. Pigments and scents are familiar adaptations attracting various pollen-dispersing animals (bees, wasps, butterflies, moths, in some cases small birds, as well as men). Plants depending on animals for pollination generally also secrete abundant nectar (sugar water) in their flowers. Many ingenious structural devices have evolved through which only particular animal types may have access to the nectar of a particular flower type. Potential "robbers" either cannot enter the flower

A   B

27 · 43 *Seeds and seed germination in pines. A, the mature winged seed at time of dispersal. B, dissected seed showing embryo and surrounding female gametophyte.*

27 · 44 *Pine life-cycle summary.*

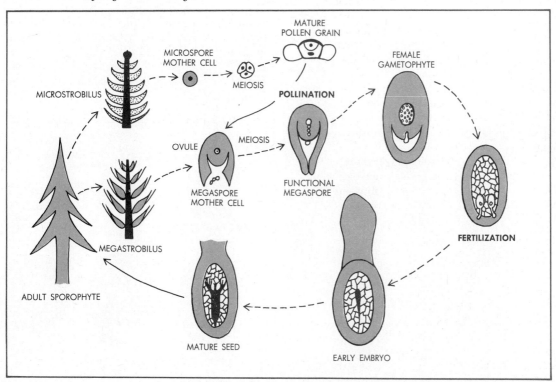

A

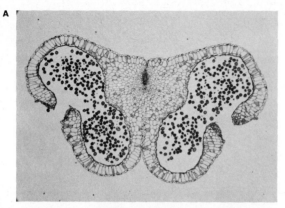

B

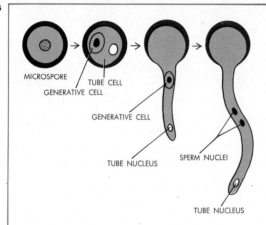

MICROSPORE

TUBE CELL

GENERATIVE CELL

GENERATIVE CELL

TUBE NUCLEUS

SPERM NUCLEI

TUBE NUCLEUS

27 · 45 Microspores. *A, cross section through the anther of a lily. Note the two spore sacs, the openings in these sacs, and the microspores (pollen grains). B, development of a microspore.*

or cannot reach the nectar stores. Qualified animals such as bees, however, may find landing platforms, colored guide marks on petals, and other conveniences. As such animals reach for nectar deep down in the flower, they brush against stamens and pistil. In the process they pick up new pollen on their body surfaces or deposit pollen from other flowers visited earlier.

Some species of angiosperms are regularly *self-pollinating;* pollen grains fall on the stigma of the same flower and develop normally thereafter. In the majority of angiosperms, however, *cross-pollination* must occur. In such cases many pollen grains undoubtedly do chance on the stigma of the same flower, but such grains may not begin to develop at all or may develop abnormally. Events proceed normally only when pollen grains from one flower are transferred to the stigma of other flowers of the same species.

In the anthers, formation of microspores occurs as in gymnosperms but the subsequent development of

27 · 46 Megagametophytes. *A, cross section through the ovary of a lily. Note the ovary wall (which will eventually give rise to the "meat" of a fruit) and the three pairs of ovules containing female gametophytes. B, the basic pattern of the development of a female gametophyte in angiosperms.*

A

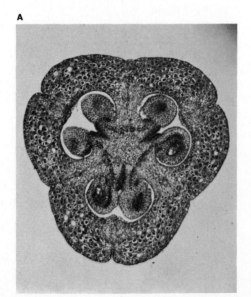

B

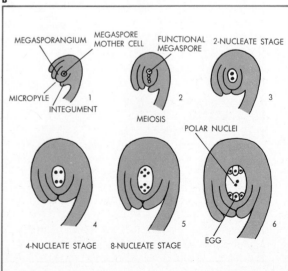

MEGASPORANGIUM MEGASPORE MOTHER CELL FUNCTIONAL MEGASPORE 2-NUCLEATE STAGE

MICROPYLE INTEGUMENT 1 2 MEIOSIS 3

POLAR NUCLEI

4 5 6

4-NUCLEATE STAGE 8-NUCLEATE STAGE EGG

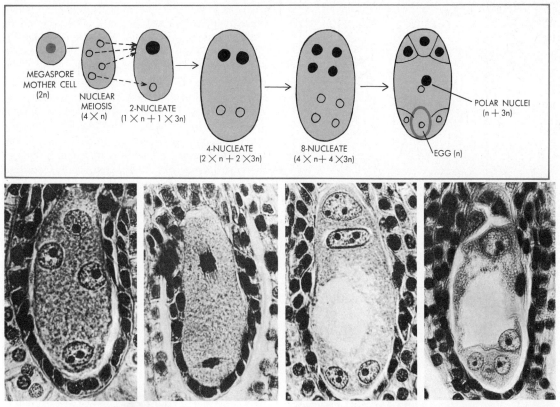

27 · 47 *The development of the female gametophyte in* Lilium. *The sequence of photos illustrates the second, third, fourth, and sixth stages sketched in the diagram.*

a male gametophyte is abbreviated still more (Fig. 27.45). The microspore nucleus divides only once, producing a *generative nucleus* and a *tube nucleus*. Prothallial cells are not formed at all. The generative nucleus subsequently divides once more, forming two *sperm nuclei*. The whole male gametophyte in a pollen grain therefore consists of one trinucleate cell.

An analogously condensed development occurs in the ovary, which may contain one or more ovules (Fig. 27.46). In each ovule, as in gymnosperms, a micropyle leads through the integument to the megasporangium. Within the latter, a single megaspore mother cell undergoes meiosis and produces a linear spore tetrad. In most cases, three of the four haploid cells degenerate (not in the lily, however; see below). In the remaining and enlarging functional megaspore, the nucleus undergoes three divisions. Four of the resulting eight haploid nuclei come to be situated at one end of the spore cell, four at the other. Three of each group of four then become partitioned off as cells and the remaining two, the so-called *polar nuclei,* migrate to the center of what is now a seventh large middle cell. These seven cells constitute the entire female gametophyte. Archegonia are not formed at all. Instead, of the three

gametophyte cells near the micropyle, one becomes an egg directly.

The lily is representative of a small group of angiosperms in which the female gametophyte develops slightly differently (Fig. 27.47). In the megaspore mother cell the meiotic divisions are *nuclear* only, and all four resulting haploid nuclei contribute to gametophyte formation. One of the four nuclei migrates to the future egg end of the spore cell. There it divides twice, forming a group of four haploid nuclei. The three remaining megaspore nuclei migrate to the other end of the spore cell and *fuse.* The result is *triploid* nucleus, containing three sets of chromosomes. Such a nucleus divides twice and produces a group of four triploid nuclei. One triploid nucleus and one nucleus from the haploid group again migrate to the center of the spore cell as polar nuclei. All remaining six nuclei become partitioned off as cells, as above. One of the haploid cells becomes the egg.

Pollen of angiosperms is dispersed partly by wind,

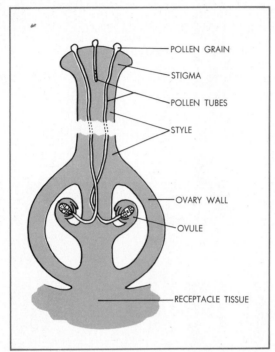

partly by insects and other animals. Numerous pollen grains may land on a stigma of a pistil. The stigma is sticky and traps the pollen grains. Each then produces (usually) one pollen tube, which grows between the cells of the style toward the ovary. Such a tube usually enters an ovule through the micropyle and then digests a path through the megasporangial tissues. The tip of the tube contains the tube nucleus and the two sperm nuclei. All three are eventually discharged into the female gametophyte (Fig. 27.48).

The next event is *double fertilization,* unique to the angiosperms (Fig. 27.49). One of the sperm nuclei enters the egg and effects fertilization. The other sperm nucleus migrates to the two polar nuclei, and all three now fuse together into a so-called *endosperm nucleus.* In most cases this nucleus is *triploid,* inasmuch as it is formed from two female and one male haploid nuclei. In the lily group of angiosperms the endosperm nucleus is *pentaploid,* being formed from one triploid and one haploid polar nucleus plus one sperm nucleus. In either case, the endosperm nucleus divides repeatedly, cell walls are then usually laid down between the nuclei, and the tissue so formed is the *endosperm.* It soon fills the space formerly occupied by the female gametophyte and the megasporangial tissues. Endosperm cells accumulate food substances from the parent sporophyte.

While the endosperm develops, the zygote divides and gives rise to a sporophyte embryo (Fig. 27.50). The latter possesses one or two cotyledons, depend-

27·48 *Growth of pollen tubes after pollination in angiosperms.*

27·49 *Fertilization and early embryos. Diagrams: 1, 2, 3, double fertilization and the early embryo in angiosperms generally. 4, 5, double fertilization in the lily. Photo: early angiosperm embryo attached by suspensor.*

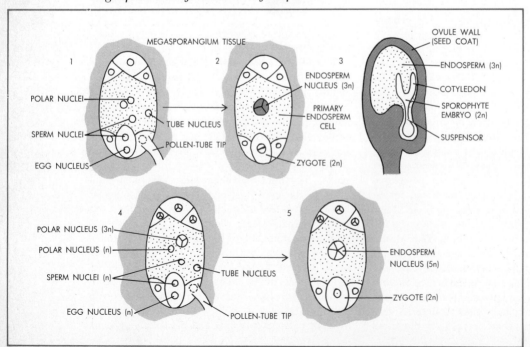

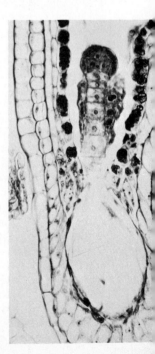

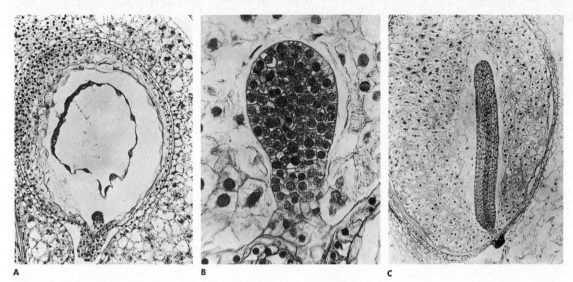

A   **B**   **C**

27 · 50 The early development of endosperm and embryo in the lily. A, the early embryo near bottom of photo and, above it, the developing tissue of the endosperm. B, later stage in embryo development. C, older embryo surrounded by endosperm. Note suspensor attaching embryo to wall of ovule.

ing on the subclass of angiosperms (see Chap. 13). The whole embryo is embedded in endosperm, and this tissue gradually contributes more or less of its food to the developing sporophyte. In a germinating seed, therefore, endosperm may or may not be present. If the endosperm is still extensive, the cotyledons are likely to be thin and leafy (for example, squash, castor beans). But if the endosperm is absent, its substance is incorporated into the cotyledons and these are likely to be massive (for example, peanuts, peas).

Soon after fertilization, the integuments around the developing embryos harden into seed coats and much of the flower withers. On the contrary, the ovary and in some cases also parts of the receptacle enlarge rapidly and mature into a *fruit*. This structure may become *dry* or *fleshy*, and it hides the seeds of angiosperms within it (Fig. 27.51).

The reproduction of angiosperms is therefore characterized by three major features not encountered in gymnosperms: the *flower* itself; double fertilization, resulting in the inclusion of *endosperm* tissue

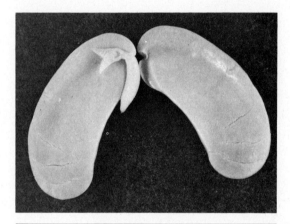

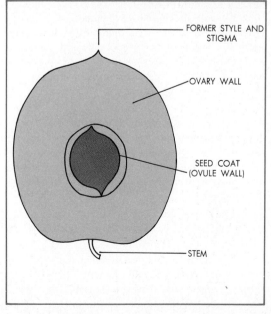

27 · 51 Seeds and fruits. Photo: dissected bean seed. Note the two large endosperm-filled cotyledons and the small embryo with rootlet and developing leaves. Diagram: the structure of a fruit.

695

within seeds; and the *fruit*, which contains a number of seeds. Each of these evolutionary innovations is of pronounced adaptive value. The flower often promotes pollination by attracting insects. The endosperm nourishes the embryo. And the fruit promotes seed dispersal and seed germination; for fleshy fruits may be eaten by animals and seeds may be spit out or may be expelled undigested with the feces, in new locations. Dry fruits like nuts may be carried about by squirrels, for example, and may be left by them in some forgotten hiding place. Fruits with burrs, hooks, or wing blades are distributed widely by animals and wind. Fruits which simply fall to the ground eventually decay, and they aid seed development by so enriching a patch of soil.

We note that the solution of the problem of terrestrial reproduction is rather similar in seed plants and terrestrial animals. As the next chapter will show, most terrestrial animals circumvent the requirement of external water by copulation and *internal* fertilization: a male animal deposits sperms directly into a female animal containing mature eggs. In seed plants the depositing is done by wind or animals, but internal fertilization in a sense takes place as well. A sporophyte produces microspores and, through them, sperms or sperm nuclei. Another sporophyte produces megaspores and, through them, eggs. The sperm nuclei then reach the eggs by means of pollen tubes, the plant equivalents of the copulating organs of animals.

REVIEW QUESTIONS

1. Review the reproductive repertoire of bacteria. What are conidia, oidiospores, sporangiospores? Which bacteria produce them? Describe experiments through which bacterial sex has been discovered. What are endospores? How do Cyanophyta reproduce? How can these organisms adapt without sexuality?

2. Describe reproductive processes among green algae. Which groups of these organisms exhibit which type of life cycle? What is a zygospore? Review the reproduction of charophytes, euglenophytes, and pyrrophytes. In what respects is charophyte reproduction atypical for Protista?

3. Describe the reproductive process of *Vaucheria*. Outline the life cycle of (*a*) diatoms, (*b*) *Ectocarpus*, (*c*) *Fucus*. What kinds of life cycles are characteristic of brown algae? Review the life-cycle pattern of red algae. Define spermatium, carpogonium, trichogyne, carpospore, tetraspore.

4. Describe the life cycle of slime molds. Review the reproductive repertoire of protozoa. What reproductive processes occur in Phycomycetes? Through what sequence of processes are ascospores produced? Describe the life cycle of (*a*) diplohaplontic yeasts, (*b*) haplontic yeasts. Define: plasmogamy, karyogamy, dikaryophase.

5. Review the life cycle of Ascomycetes and contrast it with that of Basidiomycetes. What are basidia and how are they formed?

6. List features that characterize the reproduction of Metaphyta generally. Describe the structure of the sex organs of Metaphyta. Describe the detailed life cycle of a bryophyte. In what respects is it (*a*) well, (*b*) poorly, adapted to terrestrial life?

7. Define: homospory, heterospory, microsporangium, megasporophyll, megaspore mother cell, spore tetrad. What reproductive characteristics distinguish the tracheophytes? In what ways are these characteristics adaptive? Describe the reproduction of (*a*) Psilopsida, (*b*) *Lycopodium*, (*c*) *Selaginella*, (*d*) *Equisetum*.

8. Describe the life cycle of a fern, with particular attention to the mechanism of spore discharge. Describe the structure of a fern gametophyte.

9. Review the general reproductive processes among seed plants. What are monoecious and dioecious conditions? Distinguish between pollination and fertilization. In what ways are seeds particularly advantageous for terrestrial life?

10. Describe the life cycle of a pine. Distinguish between simple and cleavage polyembryony. Review the structure and development of a sporophyte embryo of a pine. Describe the structure and adaptive significance of a flower. Distinguish between self- and cross-pollination.

11. Review the life cycle of a flowering plant. Define double fertilization, endosperm. Show how development of a female gametophyte in the lily differs from that of most other flowering plants.

12. What is a fruit and what is its adaptive significance? Review the ways in which reproductive processes of gymnosperms differ from those in angiosperms. Review the general reproductive adaptations of Metaphyta as contrasted with those of Protista.

COLLATERAL READINGS

Clevenger, S.: Flower Pigments, *Sci. American*, June, 1964. An account of the chemical structure and genetic origins of these compounds.

Delbruck, M., and M. Delbruck: Bacterial Viruses and Sex, *Sci. American*, Nov., 1948. Genetic recombination analogous to that in sexual processes may occur when different bacteriophage viruses infect a bacterial host cell.

Doyle, W. R.: "Nonvascular Plants: Form and Function," Wadsworth, Belmont, Calif., 1964. The reproduction of protistan groups and of bryophytes is among the topics of this paperback.

Galston, A. W.: "The Life of the Green Plant," 2d ed., Prentice-Hall, Englewood Cliffs, N.J., 1964. A paperback containing accounts of reproductive and developmental processes in vascular plants.

Grant, V.: The Fertilization of Flowers, *Sci. American*, June, 1961. The article discusses the adaptive features of flowers and the correlated adaptations of pollinating animals.

Haldane, J. B. S.: Some Alternatives to Sex, *New Biol.*, vol. 19, 1955. A noted biologist discusses reproductive processes not followed by sexual events.

Heslop-Harrison, J.: The Sexuality of Flowers, *New Biol.*, vol. 23, 1957. Reproductive structures and functions in flowers are described.

Koller, D.: Germination, *Sci. American*, Apr., 1959. An account of seed dormancy and escape from dormancy by chemical stimuli.

Leopold, A. C.: "Plant Growth and Development," McGraw-Hill, New York, 1964. An advanced book on the physiology of growth processes in plants, including reviews of the roles of flowering and other hormones. Extensive references to original research papers may be found at the end of each chapter.

Maheshwari, P.: "An Introduction to the Embryology of the Angiosperms," McGraw-Hill, New York, 1950. A good source book for this specific topic.

Pelczar, M. J., Jr., and R. D. Reid: "Microbiology," 2d ed., McGraw-Hill, New York, 1965. This text reviews reproductive processes not only in bacteria but also in Protista generally.

Pool, R. J.: "Flowers and Flowering Plants," 2d ed., McGraw-Hill, New York, 1941. Another good source book on angiosperm reproduction.

Salisbury, F. B., and R. V. Parke: "Vascular Plants: Form and Function," Wadsworth, Belmont, Calif., 1964. A paperback with very good coverage of reproduction in tracheophytes.

Smith, G. M.: "Cryptogamic Botany," 2d ed., vols. 1 and 2, McGraw-Hill, New York, 1955. A comprehensive series containing detailed discussions of reproductive processes in algae, fungi, slime molds, bryophytes, and ferns.

Wollman, E. L., and F. Jacob: Sexuality in Bacteria, *Sci. American*, July, 1956. The conjugative sexual process in bacteria is described and experiments referred to in this chapter are reviewed.

CHAPTER 28 REPRODUCTION: METAZOA

The principal and often the only form of multiplication in Metazoa is gametic reproduction. Gamete formation occurs in multicellular sex organs and is accompanied by meiosis. The life cycle is therefore diplontic, mature gametes representing the haploid phase. All Metazoa are oögamous, and fertilized eggs develop into distinct embryos. These may grow into adults directly or, more typically, may first become *larvae* and then adults.

Vegetative reproduction by fragmentation or budding occurs regularly in some animal groups as a normal process of propagation. Regenerative reproduction after injury is widespread, but in the majority of groups the capacity of regeneration is severely restricted. Body parts separated from the parent simply die, and in such animals the only remnant of vegetative reproduction is wound healing.

Species dispersal is achieved by locomotion of the adults or the larvae. Sporulation is therefore largely superfluous and indeed does not occur. Whatever other forms of reproduction may or may not be exhibited in given cases, gametic reproduction occurs in all cases. The sexes typically are separate, but hermaphroditism is common, particularly in sessile and sluggish animals. Virtually all hermaphroditic types are cross-fertilizing. As has become apparent in Part 4, animal reproductive systems typically consist of sex organs, testes or ovaries, or *gonads* collectively, and of ducts leading to the outside of the body.

REPRODUCTIVE PATTERNS

Gametes are formed from special groups of diploid generative cells in the gonads. Such cells become sperms or eggs by maturation processes affecting both the cell nucleus and the cytoplasm.

Nuclear maturation consists of meiosis. In a testis, a diploid generative cell undergoes both meiotic divisions in fairly rapid succession, and all four resulting haploid cells constitute functional sperms. The pattern is somewhat different in females. A generative cell in the ovary undergoes a first meiotic division and produces two cells. Of these, one is small and soon degenerates. Its remnants, now called the *first polar body*, remain attached to the other cell. This cell subsequently passes through the second meiotic division. Of the two cells produced here, one becomes the egg and the other again is small and degenerates. Its remnants form the *second polar body* which, like the first, remains attached to the egg. Each original generative cell thus gives rise to only one functional egg (Figs. 28.1 and 28.2).

In some animals, for example, coelenterates and echinoderms, egg-forming cells pass through both meiotic divisions in rapid sequence, as do the sperm-producing cells of all animals. The eggs then formed are haploid and ready to be fertilized. In most other animals, however, vertebrates included, eggs are ready for fertilization before meiosis is fully completed. Meiosis here proceeds part way, and the egg then remains in a state of meiotic arrest until fertilization occurs. At that time, the entrance of the sperm provides the stimulus for the completion of meiosis. In vertebrates, for example, egg-forming cells undergo the first meiotic division and produce the first polar body. The eggs are then fertilizable and meiosis remains incomplete until fertilization actually occurs. When a sperm enters, the second meiotic division takes place and the second polar body is formed. Thereafter, the remaining haploid nucleus of the egg fuses with the haploid nucleus of the sperm, and this event completes fertilization.

In parallel with the nuclear maturation of gametes, cytoplasmic maturation takes place. The particular form varies for different animal groups. In the maturing sperms of most animals, much of the cytoplasm degenerates altogether. The nucleus enlarges into an oval *sperm head,* and the mature sperm retains only three structures having a cytoplasmic origin: a long posterior *sperm tail,* which serves as locomotor flagellum; a *middle piece,* which contains energy-supplying mitochondria and which joins the sperm tail with the sperm head; and an *acrosome,* a derivative of Golgi bodies at the forward end of the sperm head, by means of which the sperm will make contact with an egg. As a result of losing all other cytoplasm, a mature sperm is among the smallest cells within the body (Fig. 28.3). Mature eggs, on the other hand, are among the largest cells; their cytoplasms have become specialized for the accumulation and storage of *yolk,* food reserves for the future embryos. The amount of yolk may be insignificant, as in mammals, where the embryo will be nourished by the female parent, or it may be comparatively enormous, as in birds, where yolk represents the very substance out of which an offspring will be constructed.

Regardless of whether an animal is aquatic, terrestrial, sessile, or motile, its sperms must be motile and must fuse with eggs in an aqueous environment. This requirement has led to the elaboration of two basic mating patterns among animals.

In *external fertilization,* mating partners are or come into more or less close proximity in natural bodies of water and both then simultaneously *spawn;* they release sperms and eggs directly into the water. Frequent chance collisions among the closely placed gametes then bring about many fertilizations. This

pattern is characteristic of most aquatic animals, sessile as well as motile, and also of terrestrial animals such as certain insects and amphibia, which may migrate to permanent bodies of water for reproduction.

The second pattern is *internal fertilization.* Mating partners here come into physical contact and *copulate;* by some means the male transfers sperms directly into the reproductive system of the female. Specialized copulatory organs may or may not be present in such cases. For example, birds are without copulatory organs (ostriches excepted), yet fertiliza-

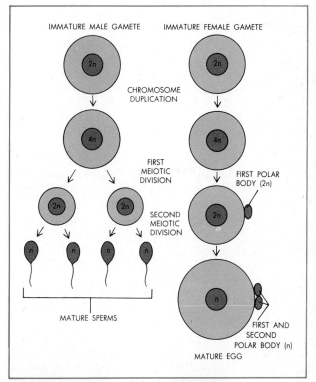

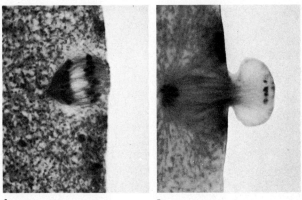

28 · 1 Meiosis. *Diagram: in males, all four haploid cells formed become functional sperms. In females, one cell formed by the first meiotic division is small and degenerates and becomes the first polar body. Similarly, one cell formed by the second meiotic division becomes the second polar body. Thus only one cell matures as a functional egg. Photos: polar-body formation. A, section through the edge of an immature whitefish egg, showing the extremely eccentric position of the spindle and the chromosomes during a meiotic division. The chromosomes are in anaphase, and cleavage, which will occur at right angles to' the spindle axis, will therefore produce an extremely large and an extremely small cell. B, cytoplasmic cleavage is under way. The small cell formed will degenerate and the remnants will persist as a polar body.*

tion is internal; mating here requires the apposition of the cloaca of the male against that of the female. In all instances of internal fertilization, the internal tissues of the female provide moisture for the sperms and the need for external water is thereby circumvented. Internal fertilization is characteristic of most terrestrial animals, but the process occurs also in numerous aquatic groups (for example, in many fishes).

Several variant forms of internal fertilization are known. For example, numerous groups of animals produce not loose sperms but compact sperm packets, or *spermatophores*. These are transferred into females in a variety of different ways. Thus, squids and octopuses use their tentacles as transferring arms. The females of certain salamanders use cloacal lips to enfold spermatophores deposited on the ground by the males. Males of certain other amphibia transfer spermatophores by mouth. In certain spiders, sperms are placed on a pedipalp and the latter is then inserted directly into the female reproductive system. Some animals transfer sperms into females by a process akin to hypodermic injection, through any part of the skin.

It should be readily apparent that, in both external and internal fertilization, mating is facilitated greatly by animal locomotion. All sessile animals are aquatic; sessile terrestrial animals could not survive because, in the absence of adult locomotion, sperms could not be brought to eggs, and sperms themselves cannot swim on land. Among the sessile aquatic animals, successful fertilization in large measure depends on the presence of reasonably dense populations of mating animals within circumscribed regions.

Where fertilization is external, development of the zygotes into new adults takes place externally as well, in natural bodies of water. In many cases where fertilization is internal, the zygotes are released from the female parent and zygote development then also occurs externally. All animals in which the eggs are shed to the outside, either in an unfertilized or a fertilized state, are said to be *oviparous*. Among vertebrates, for example, many fishes are oviparous and externally fertilizing, whereas all birds are oviparous and internally fertilizing. In all instances of oviparity, the eggs develop essentially on their own, food being supplied by yolk within each egg. Eventually the embryos *hatch* as larvae or as miniature, immature adults. Such a pattern of events is characteristic of most animals (Fig. 28.4).

If the development of oviparous animals takes place in water, the zygotes often have coats of jelly around them (for example, frog eggs) but are otherwise protected very little. Coats of this sort are

28 · 2 Meiosis in the egg maturation of the nematode Ascaris, *in which 2n = 4. A, first meiotic metaphase. Each of the two pairs of chromosomes has duplicated, and two tetrads are lined up in the metaphase plate. B, first telophase. One large and one small cell will be formed, each with four chromosomes. The small cell will degenerate and become the first polar body (see Fig. 28.1). The remaining large cell then undergoes the second meiotic division, the metaphase of which is shown in C. Of the two pairs of chromosomes here present, two (n) will go into each of the two cells yet to be formed. One of these will be the egg, the other will degenerate and become the second polar body. The first polar body may be seen as a dark spot at the top of the photo. Note also the dark central patch in A, B, and C. This is the sperm nucleus. When egg meiosis is completed, sperm and egg nuclei will fuse and fertilization will then have been accomplished.*

Courtesy of Carolina Biological Supply Company.

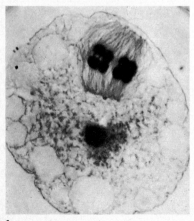

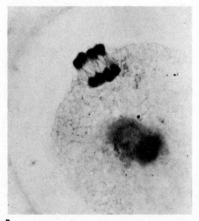

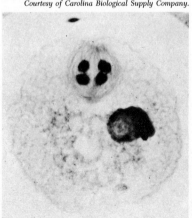

A   B   C

tribute to zygote development; as in oviparous types, food is supplied by the yolk included within each egg. Ultimately the young are *born* rather than hatched; that is, the females release fully formed animals, not eggs. Among vertebrates, some of the fishes, amphibia, and reptiles are ovoviviparous (see Fig. 28.4).

A third group of animals comprises *viviparous* types. In these, fertilization is again internal, zygotes are retained within the female, and the young are born as developed animals. However, the female body here influences the development of the young not merely by providing protection. It also supplies food and contributes to offspring metabolism generally in numerous and vital ways. The females in such cases are *pregnant*. Viviparous vertebrates include, for example, some fishes, some snakes, and the majority of the mammals (see Fig. 28.4).

28 · 4 Patterns of fertilization and offspring development in relation to the environment and the maternal body.

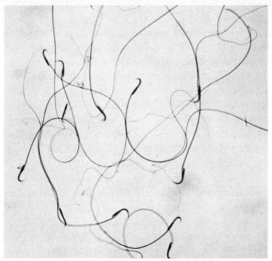

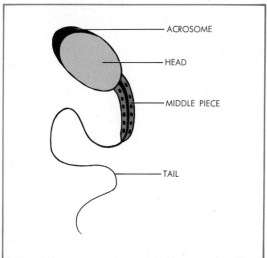

ACROSOME

HEAD

MIDDLE PIECE

TAIL

Photo, courtesy of Carolina Biological Supply Company.

28 · 3 Sperms. *Photo: rat sperms. Note sperm head (with acrosome faintly visible at forward end), sperm tail, and the middle piece (darkly stained). Diagram: sperm structure.*

secreted by the ducts of the female reproductive system before the eggs are laid. Zygotes developing on land possess more elaborate protection, particularly against evaporation. For example, earthworms, spiders, and insects such as grasshoppers and cockroaches form a cocoon or a hard casing around batches of just-laid fertilized eggs. Other insects and also reptiles and birds secrete shells around individual eggs after fertilization and before laying.

Some animals are *ovoviviparous*. Fertilization in such cases is always internal, and the zygotes are then retained within the female reproductive system. Development therefore occurs inside the female. However, beyond providing a substantial measure of protection, the female body does not otherwise con-

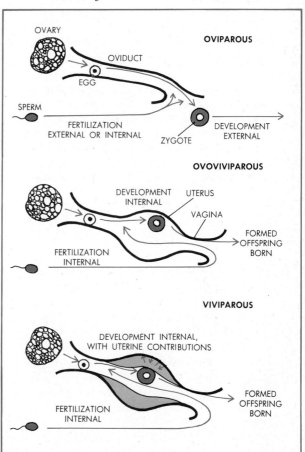

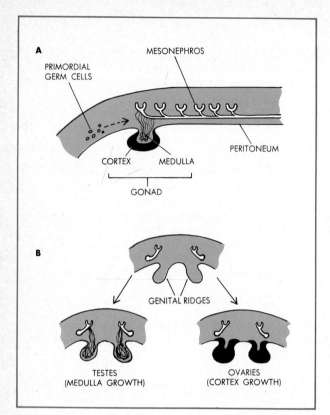

28 · 5 Development of the vertebrate gonad. *A, side view, indicating relation of the site of origin of the primordial germ cells and of gonad to mesonephros and coelom. B, cross-sectional views of the early paired genital ridges of the indifferent gonads and the differential growth of either the medullary (mesonephros-derived) tissue, resulting in testes, or the cortical (peritoneum-derived) tissue, resulting in ovaries.*

develop in either a male or a female direction. The factors determining the actual direction will be examined in Chap. 30. If the gonad becomes a testis, the cortex develops very little more but the medulla proliferates greatly and forms the bulk of the mature testis. By contrast, if the indifferent gonad transforms into an ovary, it is the medulla which undergoes little further development. The cortex on the contrary enlarges and gives rise to the bulk of the mature ovary.

In most male vertebrates, including mammals such as opossums, bats, and whales, the testes remain permanently in their original positions at mid-body. However, other male mammals are characterized by *descending* testes. In one group, which includes elephants and many rodents, for example, the testes are found within the body for most of the year. But during the breeding season, when sperms are actually produced, the testes migrate into a *scrotum,* a skin sac between the hind legs. After the breeding season the testes migrate back into the body, to their original positions. In another group, exemplified by rodents such as mice and rats, the testes pass into a scrotum when the animals reach sexual maturity, and from then on the gonads remain there permanently. And

28 · 6 Section through a mammalian testis. *Note the tubular chambers in which sperms are produced. Mature sperms accumulate in the central spaces of the tubules. The tissue between the tubules contains the interstitial endocrine cells which manufacture androgens, the male sex hormones, under the stimulus of LH from the pituitary.*

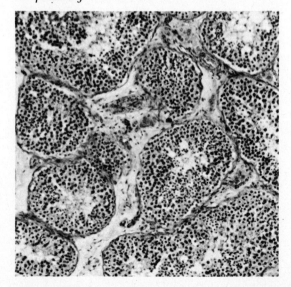

REPRODUCTIVE PROCESSES

MALE AND FEMALE SYSTEMS

In vertebrates, the gonads arise as paired pouches growing into the coelom from the dorsal coelomic lining, near mid-body (Fig. 28.5). Each such pouch proliferates and fills with tissue, the outer layers then forming the *cortex* and the interior tissue the *medulla* of the developing gonad. The gamete-producing cells, called the *primordial germ cells,* arise not in the developing gonad itself, but in the head region of the embryo. From there the cells migrate into the embryonic gonad and disperse within it. At this stage the gonad is sexually still indifferent and may

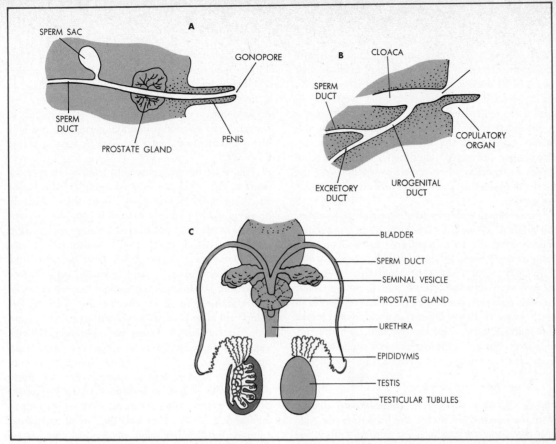

SPERM SAC

GONOPORE

SPERM DUCT

PROSTATE GLAND

PENIS

CLOACA

SPERM DUCT

COPULATORY ORGAN

EXCRETORY DUCT

UROGENITAL DUCT

BLADDER

SPERM DUCT

SEMINAL VESICLE

PROSTATE GLAND

URETHRA

EPIDIDYMIS

TESTIS

TESTICULAR TUBULES

28 · 7 Male reproductive system. *A and B, some of the common component organs and exit modifications according to whether or not a cloaca or a penis is present. See also Fig. 16.48. C, the principal features of the system in human males. The testis on left is shown in section.*

in still another group, of which man is a member, the testes are internal only during embryonic stages. The organs migrate into a scrotum before birth and then remain in this sac permanently. It is known that the temperature in a scrotum is up to 7°C lower than within the body. It is also known that lower temperatures tend to promote sperm production and that higher temperatures tend to inhibit it. Temperature, testis location, and sperm manufacture therefore are probably correlated.

The primordial germ cells, present in a testis from embryonic stages on, give rise to a gamete-forming *generative epithelium*. In man, for example, each adult testis is honeycombed extensively with *testicular tubules*, channels separated from one another by connective tissue partitions (Fig. 28.6). The lining of these tubules represents the sperm-producing epithelium. The cells of it divide mitotically at great rate, and the new cells so formed accumulate in the interior of the tubules where they mature into sperms. As noted, meiosis takes place in the process. Functional sperms may subsequently leave a testis via the *sperm duct* (Fig. 28.7).

Among accessory organs often associated with such ducts in various animals are, for example,

sperm sacs, which may store sperms before discharge. In man, sperm storage occurs primarily in the *epididymis,* a highly coiled portion of the sperm duct just outside the testis. Nerve impulses may bring about contraction of the walls in the storage regions and the collected sperms are then expelled. Also connected to sperm ducts may be *prostate glands* and *seminal vesicles,* which produce *seminal fluids.* Together with sperms such secretions make up *semen.* Sperms usually do not lash their flagella before seminal fluids mix with them, for sperm motility tends to be depressed by CO_2 accumulated in the narrow spaces of the testicular tubules. The seminal fluids may contain specific sperm-activating substances, however, and CO_2 may also become diluted sufficiently by the fluids to permit sperm movement. If an animal possesses a copulatory organ, as in many internally fertilizing types, the terminal parts of a sperm duct may or may not pass through such an organ. If it does, as in man, then the copulatory organ is called a *penis* (see Fig. 28.7). Note that in man, as in most mammals, the exit duct for sperms in the penis is the *urethra*, the channel which also carries urine from the bladder. Simultaneous discharges are prevented reflexly; the bladder-urethra juncture constricts when semen is expelled and the sperm duct–urethra juncture constricts when urine is expelled.

In the female reproductive system of vertebrates, the original primordial germ cells in an ovary analogously give rise to a generative epithelium. This tissue is represented by the outside layer of an ovary (Fig. 28.8). As in a testis the generative layer buds off new cells into the interior, but in an ovary not all such new cells become eggs. In a given batch of newly formed cells usually only one undergoes meiosis and matures into a reproductive cell, and the surrounding cells are inhibited in some unknown way from also becoming eggs. Instead, the surrounding

28 · 8 Section through a mammalian ovary. Note the two large follicles, the follicular cavities, and the large egg cell in each follicle, embedded within a mass of cells along the follicular wall. Endocrine cells secrete estrogens into the follicular cavity. When the eggs are mature they will ovulate, i.e., escape by rupture of follicle and ovary walls. Near top of photo, along the edge of the ovary, note the relatively large cells. These are immature eggs which will become mature later, within follicles yet to be formed.

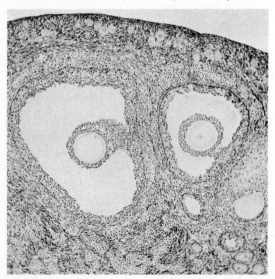

cells become arranged into a *follicle,* a ball of tissue which soon acquires an enlarging central cavity. The egg is located excentrically in such a follicle, in a thickened region of the follicular wall. An embryonic ovary of a human female is estimated to contain some 400,000 primordial germ cells; but only about 400 functional eggs are actually formed during adult life.

The reproductive channels leading away from ovaries (Fig. 28.9) are ciliated *oviducts* (also called *Fallopian tubes* in mammals). Along their course in given animals (but not in man) may be present *seminal receptacles,* pouches which store sperms after mating and before fertilization, as well as *yolk glands, shell glands,* and other glands producing nutritive or protective layers around fertilized eggs. Before its exterior termination, an oviduct may be enlarged into a *uterus,* a muscular chamber in which egg development takes place in ovoviviparous and viviparous types. If the female mates by copulation, the last section of the oviduct receiving the copulatory organ during mating is called a *vagina.* Note that, in contrast to the arrangement in human males, the reproductive tract of human females is entirely separate from the urinary tract; each exits via its own opening (see Fig. 16.48). Note also that, in all copulating animals, fertilization takes place along the course of the oviduct, after sperms have been transferred from the male into the reproductive tract of the female.

BREEDING CYCLES

Like plants, most animals produce gametes only during specific *breeding seasons.* Such seasons are largely annual, most of them occurring in spring or in fall. Among spring breeders (for example, most fishes, birds, and mammals) the offspring are usually hatched or born in the same spring or in summer, and among fall breeders (for example, deer, sheep) the offspring typically appear in the following spring. Many animals have two or more breeding seasons per year; for example, there are two in dogs. The durations of breeding seasons vary considerably, being restricted in some cases to a single day (or night, as in clamworms and many other marine invertebrates), but extending in others throughout the whole year, as in monkeys, apes, and men. Breeding seasons tend to be continuous also where environmental conditions remain uniformly favorable the year around, as in domesticated cattle, chickens, and rabbits, and in laboratory mice and rats. Even in such cases, however, fertility is usually greatest during the spring (Fig. 28.10).

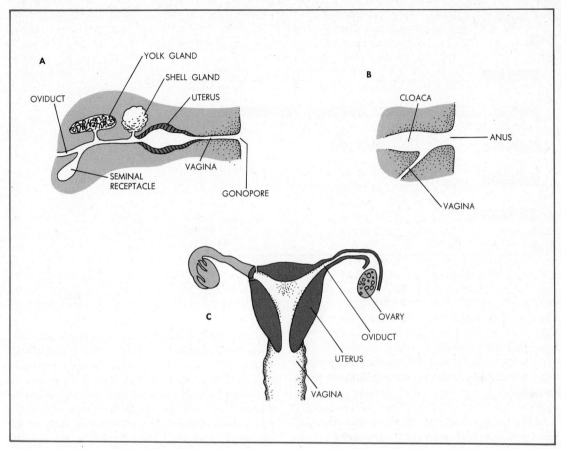

28 · 9 Female reproductive systems. *A and B, some of the common component organs and exit modifications according to whether a cloaca is or is not present. See also Fig. 16.48. C, the principal features of the system in human females.*

The external physical environment normally provides the stimulus for the onset of a breeding season. Particularly significant in this respect are light and temperature. For example, spring breeding in many, perhaps most, animals is induced by increasing temperatures and day lengths, fall breeding, by decreasing temperatures and day lengths. If habitual spring breeders or fall breeders are transported from the northern to the southern hemisphere or vice versa, their breeding time usually changes in line with the altered seasons in the new environment. In vertebrates, it can be shown that such external stimuli exert their effect via the sensory system, the brain, and the pituitary gland. Signals from the brain, including particularly blood-borne neurosecretory signals from the hypothalamus, activate the pituitary, and this gland then begins to secrete increasing amounts of gonadotropic hormones. As a result, all parts of the reproductive system increase in size considerably and become functional. Gonads may increase their weight up to 100 times. After a breeding season, the pituitary hormone output declines again, and the reproductive system becomes quiescent and reduced in size.

Initiation of a breeding season and actual mating thereafter often require biological, psychosomatic inducing stimuli. For example, female mammals such as mice can be induced to come into heat by the smell given off by the males. Many fishes and birds perform elaborate, instinctive courtship rituals, and the visual effect of one mate on the other brings about certain hormone secretions internally and thus leads to reproductive readiness. In many instances, indeed, a fixed sequence of behavioral displays by one mate initiates a corresponding sequence of necessary internal hormonal events in the other.

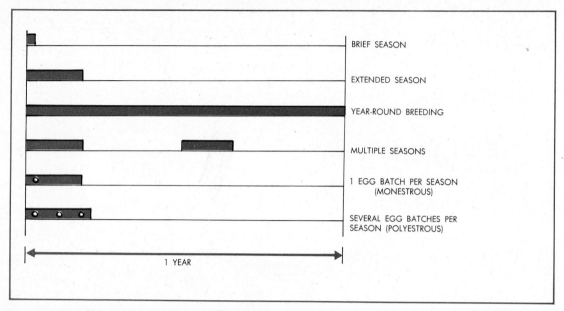

BRIEF SEASON

EXTENDED SEASON

YEAR-ROUND BREEDING

MULTIPLE SEASONS

1 EGG BATCH PER SEASON
(MONESTROUS)

SEVERAL EGG BATCHES PER
SEASON (POLYESTROUS)

1 YEAR

28 · 10   Breeding-season patterns. *The monestrous condition characterizes the majority of mammals. In polyestrous types, fertilization of any batch of eggs and the onset of pregnancy stop further egg production during that breeding season.*

Males produce sperms continuously during a breeding season and often also to a reduced extent between such seasons. In vertebrates, pituitary control is exercised mainly through *LH,* one of the three gonadotropic hormones (see Chap. 22, Table 18). Of

28 · 11   Control of androgen secretion. *LH is one of the gonadotropic hormones of the pituitary. Line tipped with transverse double bar (color) signifies inhibition.*

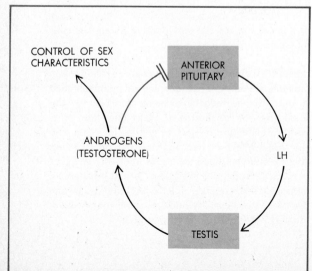

CONTROL OF SEX
CHARACTERISTICS

ANTERIOR
PITUITARY

ANDROGENS
(TESTOSTERONE)

LH

TESTIS

the other two, *FSH* and *prolactin* (or lactogenic hormone), the function of FSH in males, if any, is still obscure. Prolactin likewise may play little or no role in sperm production as such, but the hormone is known to be responsible for any paternal behavior a male vertebrate may exhibit (for example, protective attitudes toward mate and offspring, acquisition of nesting materials). Pituitary LH is the specific hormone which stimulates the testes to produce androgens, the male sex hormones. They are manufactured in cells located in the tissue partitions between the testicular tubules. The concentration of *testosterone,* the most potent of the androgens, rises sharply at the start of a breeding season under the influence of LH. The entire reproductive system then becomes operational and sperms are actively produced. Also, sex urge increases and the secondary sex characteristics become pronounced (for example, mating colors in plumage and the integument generally). If they are present in blood in excessive concentrations, androgens have an inhibitory effect on the pituitary. The latter produces less LH as a result, and androgen secretions consequently decline as well. Through such feedback control, the androgen concentration in males is maintained at a fairly steady level during the breeding season (Fig. 28.11). In man and other mammals with a year-round breeding season, sperm production begins at puberty, or sexual maturity, and may then continue for life.

Females do not produce eggs continuously during a breeding season. Rather, a given group of eggs matures together in a batch and other eggs do not

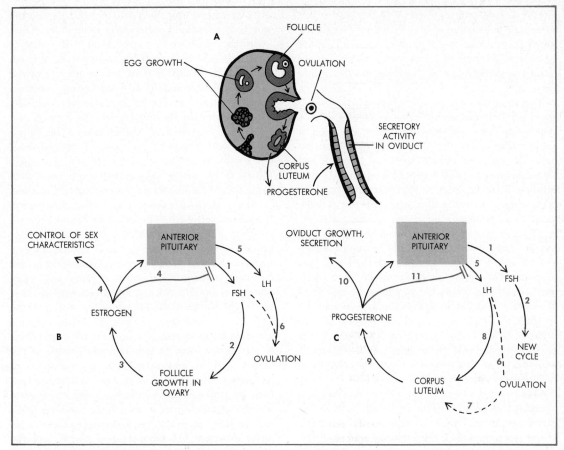

28 · 12 Egg-growth cycles. A, ovarian events from egg growth to progesterone secretion in oviparous vertebrates, and the effect of progesterone on the oviduct; the secretions of the latter may be jelly coats around eggs or shell-forming substances. B, the feedback-control pattern of hormonal changes during the follicular phase of an egg-growth cycle, leading to ovulation. Numbers indicate sequence of steps. Regular arrows denote stimulation; colored arrows indicate inhibition. Broken line indicates decreasing concentrations. C, the hormonal changes during the luteal phase of an egg-growth cycle in oviparous vertebrates. The sequence begins at step 5, equivalent to the terminal steps in diagram B, and ends at step 8. Steps 1 and 2 then repeat the first events in diagram B. Note that the feedback-control pattern is analogous to that in the follicular phase.

mature at the same time. Most animals develop only a single batch of eggs during any one breeding season. This holds also for many mammals, animals in which the periods of egg maturation are called *estrus cycles*. Female dogs, for example, come into estrus just once during a breeding season. If the eggs produced in such a cycle are not fertilized, the animals remain infertile until the next breeding season. Other mammals (for example, horses, sheep) are *polyestrous*; that is, they may produce several successive batches of eggs per breeding season if they are not fertilized. If one batch does become fertilized, however, further egg manufacture then stops for the season (see Fig. 28.10).

The cycles of egg maturation have various durations. For example, year-round breeders such as domestic chickens may lay eggs as often as once a day. Man and apes produce eggs approximately once a month. Most animals *ovulate* spontaneously; that is, the ovary releases eggs as soon as they are mature. In some animals, however, ovulation is induced only by copulation. For example, rabbits, squirrels, and cats are among animals which come into estrus and then retain the mature eggs in the ovary. Depending on whether copulation subsequently does or does not take place, the eggs either ovulate into the oviduct and become fertilized or they degenerate within the ovary.

The hormonal controls of egg production in vertebrates parallel those of sperm production (Fig. 28.12). In response to environmental stimuli at the onset of the breeding season, the pituitary secretes prolactin and FSH. Prolactin induces maternal behavior and broodiness, causing the female to contribute to nest building, to guard or sit on eggs after they are laid, or to care for the young after birth. FSH, the *follicle-stimulating hormone*, influences ovarian activity. More specifically, the follicle cells around an egg, and perhaps also the ovarian cells between follicles, are stimulated to produce *estrogens*, the female sex hormones. These correspond functionally to the male hormones; they promote the growth of the reproductive system, follicles included, the pronounced development of secondary sex characteristics, and an increase in sex urge. Developing follicles migrate within the ovary, and at maturity they are stationed just underneath the ovary surface, where they may bulge outward pronouncedly.

When estrogen concentrations in blood exceed a certain threshold level, the hormones exert an inhibitory effect on FSH production in the pituitary. At the same time also, the estrogens stimulate the pituitary to produce another gonadotropic hormone, namely, LH. As a result, LH concentrations begin to rise just when FSH concentrations begin to fall. These shifting hormone balances are the specific stimulus for ovulation; the ovary surface and the follicle wall both rupture, and the mature egg escapes into the coelom and oviduct (Figs. 28.12 and 28.13). In some animals, as noted, ovulation additionally requires nervous triggering through copulation.

An immediate consequence of ovulation is that the ruptured and eggless follicle remaining in the ovary loses its fluid and collapses. Another consequence is that, since FSH production by the pituitary has now ceased, the remnant of the follicle ceases to manufacture estrogen. Instead, under the specific influence of the LH produced in increasing quantities by the pituitary, the remnant of the follicle transforms into a yellowish body, the *corpus luteum*. The name "LH" stands for "*luteinizing hormone*." Under the continuing influence of this hormone, the corpus luteum begins to secrete a new hormone of its own, namely, *progesterone* (see Fig. 28.12).

This hormone is a steroid compound, chemically very much like the estrogens and the male hormones (see Fig. 6.15). In oviparous vertebrates, progesterone

stimulates growth of the oviducts generally and the secreting activity of these ducts specifically. Thus, under the influence of the hormone, jelly coats or shells are secreted around eggs now passing through the oviduct. Prolactin from the pituitary likewise stimulates the corpus luteum to produce progesterone. When the concentration of progesterone eventually exceeds a certain threshold level, the hormone inhibits LH production in the pituitary. The corpus luteum then ceases to manufacture progesterone, but by this time the eggs have already been shed. A new FSH-initiated egg-growth cycle may then begin if the breeding season does not come to a close.

The pattern of events is somewhat different in viviparous vertebrates, in which fertilized eggs are retained and developed in a uterus. In such cases protective layers are not secreted around an egg. Instead, the wall of the uterus thickens greatly and develops numerous glandular pockets and extra blood vessels (Fig. 28.13). Fertilized eggs become firmly embedded, or *implanted*, in this wall, and the eggs receive nourishment and oxygen from the maternal blood. In these animals, the function of progesterone is to stimulate and to maintain the growth of the uterus wall in preparation for this condition of pregnancy. However, if eggs are not fertilized on their way through the oviduct, they soon disintegrate and the uterus will have been made ready for nothing. In such an event, progesterone eventually inhibits pituitary LH production as above, and the corpus luteum then ceases to manufacture progesterone. Without the hormone, however, the ready condition of the uterus cannot be maintained, and the wall soon reverts to its normal thickness.

In Old World monkeys, apes, and men, the preparations for pregnancy in the uterus are so extensive that, if fertilization does not occur and progesterone production then ceases, the inner lining of the uterus actually disintegrates. Tissue fragments separate away, and some blood escapes from torn vessels. Over a period of a few days, all this debris is expelled through the vagina to the outside. This process is *menstruation* (see Fig. 28.13).

A *menstrual cycle* in such animals lasts about 28 days. Follicle maturation occurs during the first 10 to 14 days, under the control of FSH and estrogen. This *follicular phase* of the cycle terminates with ovulation (Fig. 28.14). During the ensuing 14 to 18 days, the uterus grows in preparation for pregnancy under the influence of LH and progesterone. If during this *luteal phase* pregnancy does not start, menstruation takes place in the course of the first few days of the next menstrual cycle. Such a new cycle begins when, in the absence of LH and progesterone, the pituitary resumes FSH production and a new follicle

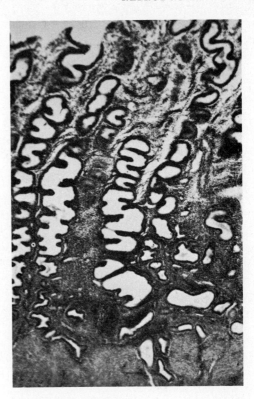

28 · 13 Egg-growth cycles in viviparous vertebrates. *Diagram: steps 1 to 8 correspond generally to events in oviparous vertebrates (see preceding figure). After progesterone production by the corpus luteum (step 9), events differ according to whether fertilization does or does not take place. If it does, pregnancy ensues (step 10); if it does not, progesterone production declines (via step 11), leading to tissue resorption in the uterus wall in most mammals and to menstruation in certain monkeys and in apes and man. The cycle then repeats (step 1). Photos: the effect of sex hormones on the structure of the uterus. The left photo shows the inner glandular tissues of a human uterus during the follicular phase of a menstrual cycle, when progesterone is absent. Note the layer of uterine muscle underneath the glandular layer (×38.5). The right photo, taken at the same magnification, shows the glandular layers during the luteal phase, when the progesterone concentration is high. Note the tremendous increase in the thickness of the glandular layer and the increased elaboration of the glandular pockets.*

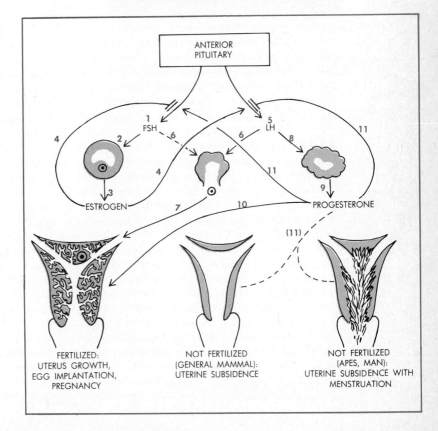

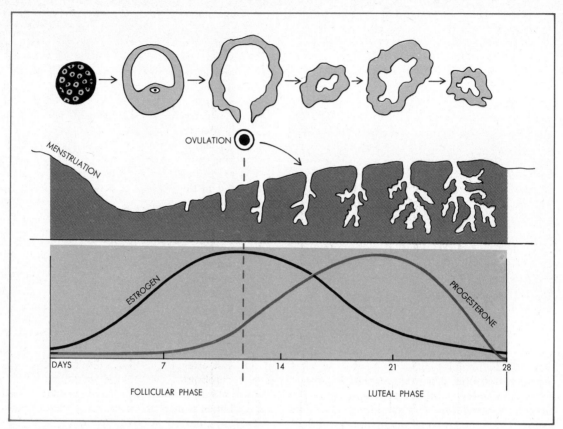

28 · 14 The menstrual cycle. *Top, events in the ovary, indicating follicle growth, ovulation, and corpus luteum formation. Middle, events in the wall of the uterus. Graph at bottom shows variations in the sex hormone concentrations.*

matures in the ovary. Evidently, a menstrual cycle (and an estrus cycle generally) is governed by two successive control cycles with built-in feedbacks. FSH and estrogen are components of one control cycle, LH and progesterone of the other; and the termination of one is the specific stimulus for the initiation of the second.

It may be noted here that estrogen is not absent altogether during a luteal phase. Some can be shown to be present in the blood even then, despite the absence of follicles at that time. Similarly, some progesterone is present during the follicular phase of a menstrual cycle (see Fig. 28.14). Exactly where these hormones come from is still undetermined. Immature follicles that will reach maturity only during future cycles might secrete some estrogen during a given luteal phase. Analogously, corpora lutea from past cycles and in process of degeneration might secrete

some progesterone during a given follicular phase. Or other ovarian tissues might secrete the hormones. Yet although both female sex hormones are present at every stage of the menstrual cycle, their quantities do fluctuate sharply. Estrogen reaches a definite peak late during the follicular phase and at the time of ovulation, whereas progesterone reaches peak concentrations during the luteal phase.

This fluctuation has far-reaching consequences. In addition to its effect on the uterus, progesterone promotes the development of the duct system in the mammary glands. A slight swelling of these glands generally occurs during the luteal phase of a menstrual cycle. Body temperature increases somewhat during the follicular phase, then falls during the luteal phase. Sex drive is likely to be more pronounced during the follicular phase, since estrogen maintains it. And inasmuch as estrogens, like androgens in males, affect mental processes, it is possible that the monthly fluctuation of these hormones contributes to the emotional fluctuations rather characteristic of females.

Estrus cycles generally and menstrual cycles specifically essentially are elaborate egg-producing mechanisms. They ensure that female gametes are formed in a controlled, rhythmically timed manner. In conjunction with sperm production, such cycles set the stage for fertilization.

FERTILIZATION

Once it is discharged from the male reproductive system, a sperm can live only a few hours. Analogously, eggs erupted from the ovary do not persist for more than a few hours. The time of greatest fertility therefore coincides roughly with the time of ovulation. Sperms deposited into the female swim from the vagina through the uterine cavity into the oviducts. Defective sperms largely succumb along the arduous path. If a ripe living egg is encountered in the upper part of the oviduct, fertilization may occur.

The fertilization of an egg generally includes two steps, namely, *plasmogamy* and *karyogamy*. Plasmogamy refers to the entrance of a sperm into an egg. If a sperm collides with an egg at an angle, it is likely to bounce off. By contrast, sperms hitting head on are likely to remain attached, for the acrosome at the sperm tip is specialized to adhere to the egg. One, and only one, sperm can normally enter any one egg. As soon as a first sperm makes contact, a *fertilization membrane* rises from the egg surface. This membrane has formed earlier, during egg maturation. On contact with a sperm, the egg rapidly secretes some water between its surface and the membrane. As a result the membrane lifts off, the sperm which has made contact is trapped inside, and any other sperms are prevented from entering (Fig. 28.15). If by chance two or more sperms do enter an egg, either all but one of the sperms disintegrate within the egg or the egg fails to develop normally and soon dies.

A successful sperm resting against the egg surface does not penetrate into the egg by boring in. Instead the egg engulfs the sperm; eggs are amoeboid at least to this extent, and in many animals they are very obviously amoeboid. During the entry of a sperm into the egg, the sperm tail drops off. At this point plasmogamy is completed, and the egg is *activated*: development of the egg has been triggered off. A mature egg is ready and able to develop, but this ability remains latent until a specific stimulus makes development start. Sperm entrance normally serves as this stimulus. Such an arrangement ensures that the sexual process occurs before development begins. As noted in Chap. 26, unfertilized eggs of many animals may become activated by natural or artificial parthenogenesis, without sperms. Such eggs remain haploid, and all the cells of the resulting embryos are correspondingly haploid.

Under normal conditions, a sperm nucleus that has activated an egg moves toward the egg nucleus, and the meeting of the two haploid nuclei then constitutes karyogamy, which completes fertilization. The membranes of the two nuclei dissolve and a mitotic spindle forms. The chromosomes, now diploid in number, line up in a metaphase plate, and the zygote undergoes its first *cleavage division*. Very shortly after fertilization, therefore, two cells are formed from the zygote. The two cells then divide again, and many successive mitotic cleavage divisions follow thereafter. The development of an animal is launched in this manner and, in viviparous forms, *pregnancy* is initiated.

PREGNANCY

Zygote development after fertilization occurs in all animals and is not unique to viviparous types. We shall defer a discussion of zygote development as such to the next chapter. Here we concentrate largely on events that *are* unique to viviparous types, namely, processes through which the body of the pregnant female contributes vitally to offspring development. The most extensive maternal contribution is made while the offspring is retained within the environment of the uterus, during the period of *gestation*. A final contribution is made when the course of pregnancy terminates, during the process of *birth*.

28 · 15   Fertilization. *A sperm enters an egg by being engulfed by the egg, through an egg cone which comes to surround the sperm (C). A fertilization membrane (colored circle) lifts off the egg surface after a sperm has made contact, preventing additional sperms from being engulfed (C,D). The sperm tail is left at the egg surface, and the sperm head (nucleus) alone migrates into the egg cytoplasm, where it fuses with the egg nucleus. An egg is fully fertilized only after sperm and egg nuclei have fused.*

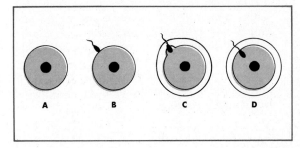

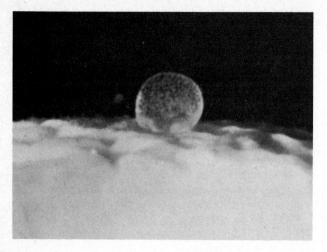

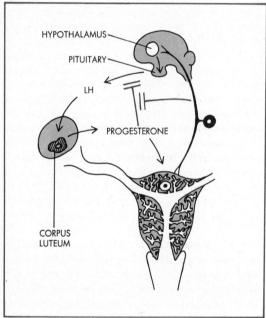

28 · 16 Implantation. *Photo: early monkey embryo just arrived in the uterus and beginning to implant. Diagram: the continuation of progesterone production during pregnancy. Nervous signals from uterus to hypothalamus and further signals from the latter to the pituitary lead to continuation of LH secretion, hence to continued progesterone manufacture and maintenance of the embryo implanted in the uterus. By this means, the usual inhibitory effect of progesterone on LH production is inhibited; that is, the inhibition is removed and LH production can actually continue.*

GESTATION

In all viviparous vertebrates, fertilization in the oviduct and egg implantation in the uterus entail a suppression of further egg production during the ensuing pregnancy. Through still poorly identified nervous pathways, the presence of an embryo in the uterus wall is signaled to the hypothalamus and from there to the pituitary. This gland then continues to produce LH and the corpus luteum continues to secrete progesterone. Consequently, the thickened wall of the uterus can be maintained intact, and the developing embryo can remain implanted in it. Menstruations are likewise suppressed during pregnancy (Fig. 28.16).

The region where an egg implants in the uterus wall becomes a *placenta*. In viviparous fishes, and indeed also in viviparous invertebrates, a fertilized egg contributes little to its own anchoring in the wall of the uterus. Such eggs receive raw materials partly from the yolk they contain, partly from maternal blood by direct diffusion and active transport in the uterus wall. Yolk also supplies many of the raw materials in the eggs of viviparous snakes, but here, and particularly also in all viviparous mammals, the developing eggs themselves contribute greatly to their firm implantation in the uterus; the eggs become anchored with the aid of so-called *extraembryonic membranes*. Evolved in ancestral reptiles, the first vertebrates to lay eggs on land, these membranes originally served as specific adaptations to egg development under terrestrial conditions. The modern reptiles and also birds and mammals have inherited the membranes, and in the oviparous members they still serve in facilitating egg development on land. But in the viviparous forms the extraembryonic membranes came to function in new ways, and one of these is aiding in egg implantation in the uterus.

Most modern reptiles, all birds, and some primitive mammals are oviparous and lay shelled eggs on land. The shells are porous enough to permit aerial gas exchange, yet not porous enough to permit leakage of water. Just inside the egg shell and enclosing all interior structures lies one of the extraembryonic membranes, the *chorion* (Fig. 28.17). It prevents undue evaporation of water through the shell. A second membrane, the *amnion*, surrounds the developing embryo everywhere except on its ventral side. This membrane holds lymphlike *amniotic fluid*, which bathes the embryo as in a "private pond." The fluid may be regarded as the equivalent of the freshwater ponds in which the aquatic ancestors of the land vertebrates developed.

Because reptiles, birds, and mammals all possess an amnion, these animals are called *amniotes* (and

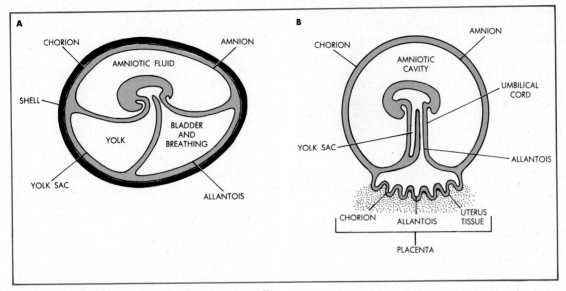

28 · 17 Extraembryonic membranes. *A, the membranes in reptile and bird eggs. Yolk sac and allantois are large and functional. B, the membranes in mammals and the placenta. The yolk sac is rudimentary and collapsed, and the allantois is no longer a bladder. However, it still functions as a breathing organ, via blood vessels it carries from placenta to embryo. In both figures, note that the amnion (and also the chorion) is ectodermal, that the yolk sac and allantois are endodermal, and that the light-colored areas correspond to mesodermal regions.*

all other vertebrates are *anamniotes*). The two remaining extraembryonic membranes pouch out from the ventral side of the embryo, more specifically, from the alimentary tract. One of these is the *allantois,* which comes to lie against the egg shell just inside the chorion. Blood vessels ramify through the allantois, and this membrane is the breathing structure of the embryo; gas exchange occurs between it and the air outside the shell. Also, the allantois serves as an embryonic urinary bladder in which metabolic wastes are stored up to the time of hatching. The second membrane on the ventral side is the *yolk sac,* which contains the ample food stores for development and which gradually gets smaller as yolk is used up during the growth of the embryo.

The viviparous land vertebrates do not produce egg shells, but the four extraembryonic membranes are still in evidence in all cases (see Fig. 28.17). In mammals, for example, the chorion again forms as an outer enclosure around the other membranes

and the embryo; it is in direct contact with the tissue of the uterus. In one region the chorion develops numerous fingerlike outgrowths which branch extensively and erode paths through the thickened uterine wall. In this manner the tissues of the chorion and the uterus become attached to each other firmly. These interfingering and interlacing tissues represent the placenta. When fully developed (in man at about the twelfth week of gestation), the placenta functions both as a mechanical and as a metabolic connection between the embryo and the maternal body.

The allantois in mammals still serves as in reptiles and birds as an embryonic breathing membrane, except that now gas exchange occurs in the placenta, between the embryonic blood vessels of the allantois and the maternal blood vessels of the uterus (Fig. 28.18). However, the allantois has entirely lost its ancestral function as urinary bladder; embryonic wastes now are carried off by the maternal blood in the placenta. The allantois in mammals is actually a collapsed, empty sac. This is true also of the yolk sac, food being supplied by maternal blood, again through the placenta. On the other hand, the fluid of the amnion still functions as in reptiles and birds as a "private pond" and shock absorber. As more and more amniotic fluid accumulates during the course of pregnancy, the amnion distends greatly and the surrounding chorion and uterus are stretched correspondingly. This enlargement, more than growth of the embryo itself, eventually leads to the characteristic bulging out of the abdomen of the pregnant female.

In the mammalian placenta, the microscopic

terminals of the chorionic outgrowths dip into pools of maternal blood which has accumulated within the placental spaces. The maternal blood circulates extensively through the maternal side of the placenta. On the embryonic side, an artery leaves the embryo proper, travels through the allantoic membrane, and capillarizes abundantly in the placenta, just underneath the chorion (see Fig. 28.18). The capillaries eventually join and form a large vein which leads back through the allantoic membrane to the embryo proper. The artery, the vein, the yolk sac, and the allantois become enveloped by connective tissue and skin, and the whole represents the *umbilical cord*. It is the lifeline between placenta and embryo, and its point of origin in the embryo leaves a permanent mark in the later offspring in the form of the navel.

Note that maternal and embryonic bloods do not mix in the placenta. The two circulations approach each other closely, but the chorion always separates them. This membrane forms a selective boundary. Nutrients of all kinds and oxygen are passed across into the embryonic circulation, and metabolic wastes are passed in the opposite direction. If a raw material is in low supply in the maternal circulation, it is usually in still lower supply in the embryonic circulation. Diffusion therefore tends to occur *into*

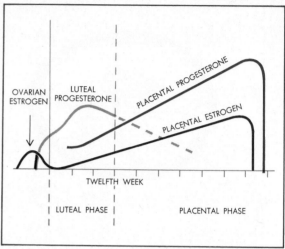

28 · 19 Hormones in pregnancy. *Curves indicate the amounts and sources of sex hormones during pregnancy in human female.*

28 · 18 The embryonic and placental blood circulations *in the mammalian placenta. Note that embryonic and maternal bloods do not mix, being separated by the chorionic and allantoic membranes.*

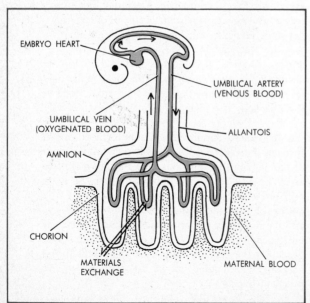

the embryo, even if this produces a pronounced deficiency in the prospective mother. In this sense, the embryo is parasitic on maternal metabolism. The placenta also ferries defensive antibodies from the maternal to the embryonic circulation. An offspring thereby acquires much of his mother's immunity for the first few months of life, usually sufficiently long to allow the young to manufacture his own antibodies in response to exposure to infectious agents.

The placenta also specializes as an endocrine organ; as it grows and develops, it manufactures slowly increasing amounts of estrogen and progesterone (Fig. 28.19). Indeed, the progesterone output eventually becomes far greater than that of the corpus luteum. The latter actually degenerates and its hormone secretion subsides at some stage during gestation (roughly the twelfth week in man). From that time on, the placenta provides the main hormonal control of pregnancy, and through its progesterone output it maintains its own existence. We may therefore say that at this stage of hormonal change a *luteal phase* of gestation changes over to a *placental phase*.

This period of phase change is rather critical in pregnancy. If the corpus luteum should degenerate a little too soon and if the placenta should reach full development a little late, then the amount of progesterone available during this gap is likely to be inadequate. In the absence of the hormone, however, placental tissues could not be maintained. Just as at the end of a menstrual cycle, the uterine lining would disintegrate and the embryo, no longer anchored securely, would be aborted. In man, miscarriages occur frequently near the end of the third month of pregnancy. Such mishaps due to hormone deficiency can be prevented by injecting some progesterone into the pregnant female.

We may note in passing that sex hormones normally produced by the placenta pass not only into the maternal but also into the embryonic circulation. As a result, the genitals and the breast region in newborn young are often precociously enlarged and swollen, superficially resembling a mature condition. After a short time, however, the sex hormones in the offspring are destroyed metabolically without being replaced till puberty, and the external effects then disappear.

At the time of hormonal phase change, it is already amply clear that the developing embryo will be a member of a particular species. For example, human traits are already well established during the

twelfth week of gestation. Basic forms and functions have become elaborated earlier, in surprisingly rapid sequence. Thus, 3 weeks after fertilization the human embryo is about the size of a coarse grain of sand, some three-quarters of it consisting of head structures. It is characteristic of the development of all animals that the head end forms earlier and faster than other regions. Four weeks after fertilization, the eyes are partly developed and the heart is already beating (Fig. 28.20). Limb buds appear in the fifth week, ears are elaborated at that time, and the embryo now responds to mechanical stimuli by muscular contractions. Human form is first vaguely recognizable 8 weeks after fertilization, when the embryo is about 1 in. long (Figs. 28.20 and 28.21). Once the species of a developing mammal can be identified, one speaks of a *fetus* rather than an embryo.

In a 12-week-old human fetus the fingers have formed, the semicircular canals in the ears are func-

28 · 20 *Four successive stages in human development,* namely, 25 days, 33 days, 6 weeks, and 8 weeks after fertilization, respectively. The series indicates that chordate features arise first (e.g., dorsal skeletal supports, gill pouches, as in A); that vertebrate features develop next (e.g., anteroposterior segments, paired limb buds, tail, as in B); that tetrapod and mammalian traits appear still later (e.g., four legs, umbilical cord, as in C); and that distinctly human traits appear last (e.g., arm-leg differences, flat face, individualized facial expression, as in D).

A   B   C   D

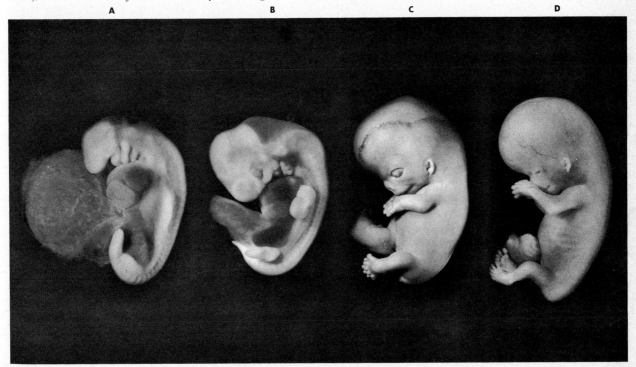

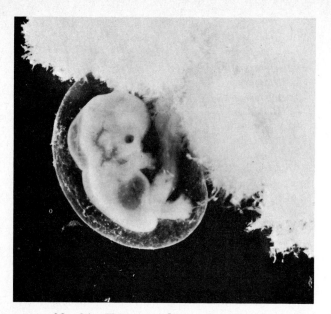

28 · 21 Human embryo, *about 8 weeks after fertilization, obtained after surgical removal of portions of the reproductive system of a female patient. The chorion is pushed to the side, revealing the amniotic sac. Note umbilical cord.*

tional, and the fetus moves of its own accord within its amniotic water pool. Eyelids are still fused, but the eyes may move underneath. Five months after fertilization, the fetus is about 8 in. long, weighs about 1 lb, and the facial features show signs of individual personality. In the ensuing weeks, the breathing machinery develops rapidly. The fetus is now in a perpetual drowsy state, neither sleeping nor waking. Overt body movement are sporadic and uneven, but important facial reflexes are being developed. For example, eyelids open and close and lips purse rhythmically, as if the fetus were learning to suck. But there is some doubt whether these prenatal movements are being "learned," in preparation for the future. In primitive vertebrates, at least, overt movement may be suppressed experimentally, yet upon hatching the animals are fully capable of performing necessary motions.

In the eighth and ninth months, periods of true wakefulness occur increasingly. Arms and legs are moved frequently and the hands open and close. Body fat is being laid down and the fetus acquires a sturdier stature generally. Growth in size has proceeded apace, and by the end of the ninth month the microscopic fertilized egg has become a whole human being.

With several exceptions, the gestation period of mammals generally is roughly proportional to adult size. For example, the period of pregnancy is 3 weeks in mice and 22 months in elephants. However, pregnancy lasts only a year, approximately, in whales.

BIRTH

In parallel with the growth and development of the fetus, the amnion gradually enlarges and the uterus stretches. Also, the mammary glands enlarge markedly during the last months of pregnancy, under the stimulus of the increasing quantities of sex hormones from the placenta. Numerous ducts form in the interior of the glands, and in later stages the milk-secreting cells mature. Flow of secretion starts soon thereafter, under the influence of lactogenic hormone (prolactin). However, the first product is not milk but *colostrum,* a watery, lymphlike fluid.

The process of birth normally begins when the chorion and the amnion rupture and when the amniotic fluid escapes to the outside. Labor contractions of the uterine muscles then occur with increasing frequency and strength, pressing against the fetus and pushing it out through the vagina. With respect to these labor contractions, recall the possible role of hormones produced in the posterior lobe of the pituitary (Chap. 22). At the time of birth, the interlocked maternal and embryonic tissues forming the placenta loosen away from the wall of the uterus. The mechanical and metabolic connection between mother and offspring is thereby severed.

An important consequence is that CO_2 produced by the offspring must accumulate in his own circulation. Within seconds or minutes, the concentration of the gas then becomes high enough to stimulate the breathing center of the newborn. In correlation with this switchover from placental breathing to lung breathing, several structural changes occur in the heart and in the large blood vessels around the heart. In the fetus before birth, the dividing wall between the right and left auricles is incomplete (Fig. 28.22). A movable flap of tissue provides an opening between these two chambers, and blood may pass freely from one chamber into the other. Once lung breathing is initiated at birth, the blood-pressure pattern within the heart changes and the tissue flap is pressed over the opening interconnecting the auricles. The flap eventually grows into place, and the left and right sides of the heart so become separated permanently.

Another structural change involves an embryonic blood vessel, the *ductus arteriosus,* which before birth conducts blood from the pulmonary artery to the aorta. The ductus arteriosus thus shunts blood around the nonfunctional lung. At birth, a specially developed muscle in the ductus arteriosus constricts, and this muscle never relaxes thereafter but degenerates into scar tissue. Blood is forced in this manner to pass through the lungs. The ductus arteriosus as a whole degenerates soon after birth.

The loosened placenta, still connected to the umbilical cord, is expelled to the outside as the *afterbirth* within an hour or so after the offspring is expelled. Mammalian mothers, modern human ones excepted, bite the umbilical cord off their young and then eat the cord and the placenta. Even herbivorous mothers do so, though they are vegetarians

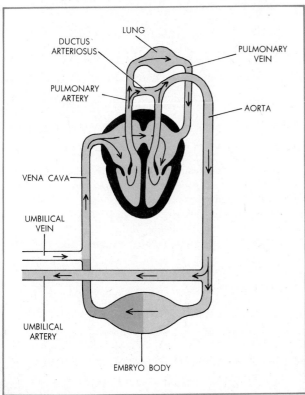

28 · 22 The embryonic circulation in mammals. *Oxygenated blood, white (only in umbilical vein, from placenta); venous blood, dark color (from embryo body to vena cava); mixed blood, light color (in vena cava, heart, lung, and aorta). The embryo lung is nonfunctional as a breathing organ, and blood may pass directly from the pulmonary artery via the ductus arteriosus to the aorta. Note also the open passage between the two atria. The ductus arteriosus is a portion of the sixth aortic arch of the vertebrate gill circulation (see Fig. 16.30). Compare the embryonic with the adult mammalian circulation (Fig. 23.10) and, in the diagram below, determine the effect on circulation if the umbilical vessels, the ductus, and the atrial passage all disappear and the lungs become functional.*

LUNG

DUCTUS ARTERIOSUS

PULMONARY VEIN

PULMONARY ARTERY

AORTA

VENA CAVA

UMBILICAL VEIN

UMBILICAL ARTERY

EMBRYO BODY

at all other times. The escaped amniotic fluid may also be lapped up. Indeed, among carnivorous mammals it is not uncommon that, in the course of drinking the fluid and eating the placenta, the just-born offspring is swallowed as well.

In the majority of mammals, litter size corresponds roughly to the number of nipples present on the mother's body. For the first few feedings mammary secretions remain lymphlike, as before birth. This fluid has some laxative action, clearing the infant's alimentary tract of debris and mucus accumulated during uterine development. Milk begins to be produced soon, however. Production continues as long as lactogenic hormones are manufactured by the pituitary and as long as milk is not allowed to accumulate in the glands. The females of certain primitive human tribes in northern Australia have been reported to produce milk for sometimes up to 6 years after a pregnancy. Cows milked after a pregnancy may "dry up" after a year or so. Incidentally, contrary to a surprisingly wide belief among urban people, cows do not give milk at just any time; they must have been pregnant first.

In man, even though the source of progesterone is removed with the expulsion of the placenta, normal menstrual cycles are generally not resumed as long as nursing continues. The manufacture of lactogenic hormones by the pituitary apparently inhibits FSH production. But once the offspring is weaned, FSH is formed again in quantity and a new ovarian follicle then begins to mature. After a few months of establishing new hormone balances, the reproductive machinery of the female reverts to rhythmic nonpregnancy operations.

The reproductive period of mammalian (and other vertebrate) females comes to a close at the time of *menopause*, reached in man during middle age. For ill-understood reasons, the sex-hormone control system ceases to operate, estrogen manufacture declines rapidly, and the reproductive system atrophies progressively during later life. Menopausal events are attended by profound readjustments of all hormone balances in the body, hence by more or less incisive changes in mental and physical functions. Menopause may occur rather abruptly. In such cases, the effects may be eased by injection of estrogen in slowly decreasing doses. In males, processes equivalent to menopause may occur in old age or may not occur at all.

Up to this point, our attention has been focused primarily on reproductive processes as such and on correlated changes taking place within the parental body of a plant or an animal. Our next concern is the fate of the reproductive unit itself, that is, the *development* of a new organism.

REVIEW QUESTIONS

1. What are the first and second polar bodies? Are they found in males as well as females? Explain. What is the general structure of a mature sperm and of a mature egg? In which animals is fertilization (*a*) external, (*b*) internal? Define oviparity, ovoviviparity, viviparity. In which vertebrates does each occur?

2. Describe the general structure of a male and a female reproductive system. How does the structure of the reproductive system generally vary for externally and internally fertilizing animals? What are primordial germ cells and where do they arise in vertebrates? Show how an indifferent vertebrate gonad develops into either a testis or an ovary.

3. Review the structure of the reproductive system of human males. Where, specifically, are sperms produced? Describe the hormonal controls of sperm production. What is semen? Describe the relation of testis location and breeding season in different mammals.

4. Review the structure of the reproductive system of human females. Specifically where, and from what tissues, are eggs produced? What is a follicle and what is its structure?

5. How do breeding seasons vary with respect to time of occurrence, durations, and numbers of egg-growth cycles? What factors initiate breeding seasons? What are monestrous and polyestrous mammals? What are the roles of prolactin in male and female vertebrates, and what are the roles of FSH and LH? Which mammalian groups exhibit menstrual cycles?

6. Describe the hormonal controls and the process of follicle growth in man up to the time of ovulation. What events take place during ovulation? After ovulation, what happens to (*a*) the egg and (*b*) the follicle?

7. Describe the hormonal controls and the events in the uterus up to the time of menstruation. What happens during menstruation? Review the entire menstrual cycle from the standpoint of (*a*) hormonal control, (*b*) events in the ovary, and (*c*) events in the uterus.

8. If fertilization occurs, what hormonal events (*a*) prevent menstruation and new menstrual cycles and (*b*) promote the further development of the uterus? Describe the hormonal controls during (*a*) the luteal phase and (*b*) the placental phase of pregnancy.

9. Distinguish between fertilization and activation of an egg. Where and when does fertilization occur? What is parthenogenesis? What happens to an egg (*a*) after fertilization and (*b*) after it arrives in the uterus?

10. Describe the location and function of the extraembryonic membranes in reptiles and birds and in mammals. In which vertebrates and how is a placenta formed? What are the functions of a placenta?

11. Review the structure of the human placenta, with attention to embryonic and maternal blood circulation through it. Describe the whole pathway of the embryonic circulation. What is a fetus?

12. What events take place in the reproductive system of a pregnant mammal during birth of offspring? What changes take place in the blood circulation of the offspring at birth? How is milk production initiated and maintained?

COLLATERAL READINGS

Berrill, N. J.: "Sex and the Nature of Things," Dodd, Mead, New York, 1953. This paperback contains interesting accounts of reproductive behavior and processes in various animals.

Bishop, D. W.: Sperm Maturescence, *Sci. Monthly,* vol. 80, 1955. A good review of the process of sperm production.

Bullough, W. S.: "Hormones and Reproduction," Methuen, London, 1952. The hormonal controls in vertebrate reproduction are discussed authoritatively.

————: "Vertebrate Reproductive Cycles," Wiley, New York, 1961. An account of breeding behavior and a more recent coverage of the subject of the preceding book.

Chase, H. B.: "Sex: The Universal Fact," Dell, New York, 1965. A paperback on animal reproduction, with special reference to man.

Corner, G. W.: "The Hormones in Human Reproduction," Princeton, Princeton, N.J., 1942.

————: "Ourselves Unborn," Yale, New Haven, Conn., 1944.

Two well-known books on reproduction and development in man.

Csapo, A.: Progesterone, *Sci. American,* Apr., 1958. A good review of the function of this hormone.

Farris, E. J.: Male Fertility, *Sci. American,* May, 1950. The fertilizing capacity of the male depends on normally structured sperms and certain proportions of them in semen.

Monroy, A.: Fertilization of the Egg, *Sci. American,* July, 1950. The fine details of the process are examined.

Nelsen, O. E.: "Comparative Embryology of the Vertebrates," McGraw-Hill, New York, 1953. Vertebrate reproductive processes are reviewed in detail in this large text.

Pincus, G.: Fertilization in Mammals, *Sci. American,* Mar., 1951. Fertilization and early development may be studied in isolated mammalian eggs.

Reynolds, S. R. M.: The Umbilical Cord, *Sci. American,* July, 1952.

———: Circulatory Adaptations at Birth, *Sci. Monthly,* vol. 77, 1953.

Two recommended articles in the context of this chapter.

Tinbergen, N.: The Courtship of Animals, *Sci. American,* Nov., 1954. A noted student of animal behavior discusses the organismic requirements for mating.

Tyler, A.: Fertilization and Antibodies, *Sci. American,* June, 1954. Experiments showing that fertilization in sea urchins is chemically analogous to an antigen-antibody reaction.

Van Beneden, E.: Researches on the Maturation of the Egg and Fertilization, in "Great Experiments in Biology," Prentice-Hall, Englewood Cliffs, N.J., 1955. A reprint of the classical paper which showed that chromosomes were reduced to the haploid number during the maturation of animal eggs and were restored to the diploid number by fertilization.

Wilson, E. G.: "The Cell in Development and Heredity," Macmillan, New York, 1953. Animal meiosis, fertilization, and early development are covered exhaustively in this renowned volume.

CHAPTER 29 DEVELOP- MENT

The scope of development is universal; any type of change, occurring on any level of living organization and at any time in living history, has developmental significance. Developmental changes can be structural or functional, quantitative or qualitative, progressive or regressive, normal or abnormal. Actually, as we shall see, development always involves all these simultaneously. But in given instances one or the other form of change may predominate or may be more readily apparent to the observer. Development is universal too with respect to the living unit in which change takes place and with respect to time. A molecule develops no less than a cell or a tissue, a whole organism no less than a whole species. And whether we measure it in microseconds as on the molecular level or in millions of years as on the species level, development occurs at every moment in living history. The developmental domain, clearly, is as extended as that of biology as a whole.

However, developmental studies traditionally have concentrated most on the particular events relating to the formation of *organisms* and of their parts. Accordingly, the account below deals first with the general *nature* of development, and then with the actual *processes* of development in specific organisms, protist, plant, and animal.

THE NATURE OF DEVELOPMENT

Inasmuch as new organisms can arise by vegetative means, from spores or sporelike cells, and from zygotes, the maximum problem of developmental studies is to explain how single cells are transformed into whole multicellular organisms. A simple answer here would be "by cell division." This answer is not in-

correct, to be sure, but it is not very informative either. The real issues are far more subtle and far more complex.

MORPHOGENESIS

If single cells are to transform into whole animals, then a first obvious developmental requirement is increase in size, or *growth*. Overall growth may occur by either or all of three types of changes. Structural parts may increase in number, they may increase in size, or the spaces between the parts may enlarge.

Singly and in combination, all these alternatives actually occur. We already know, for example, that molecules increase in number either by being accumulated ready-made from the environment or by being newly synthesized within cells; that they increase in size by combining with other molecules; and that they increase in spatial distribution by dilution with water. Together, these ways of molecular growth constitute the means by which the size of cells increases. The number of cells increases by division, and the spacing increases by the accumulation between cells of water, cementing substance, or other secreted deposits. These ways of cellular growth in turn bring about increase in the size, the number, and the spacing of tissues and organs. The net result is overall growth of the organism. Note, however, that molecular growth is the fundamental prerequisite: the living system grows from its molecules up.

Growth introduces qualitative as well as quantitative changes. For example, certain types of molecules may be synthesized or accumulated at a greater rate or in greater amount than others. Indeed, some molecular types may disappear altogether, whereas others, not previously present, may appear for the first time. Similarly, the growth of cells, of tissues, or of organs may take place disproportionately in different parts of the developing organism. As a result of such *differential growth*, the structure and composition of the organism may be altered not only quantitatively but also qualitatively (Fig. 29.1).

Moreover, growth does not proceed randomly in all directions. How does it happen, for example, that developmental growth stops just when the nose, the brain, the rootlet, the leaflet, and all other body parts are of the "right" proportional size and the "right" proportional shape? How does it happen that the different parts of the fully grown adult *retain* correct proportions and shapes? And how does it happen that, when the limb of a salamander is cut off, regenerative growth stops just when the newly developing limb has the size and the shape of the original one? In short, what determines the *form* of an organism, with respect to both size of parts and geometrical configuration of parts? Evidently, development of form, in addition to growth as such, is a second requirement if a reproductive unit is to be converted into a whole organism.

At any level of living organization, the basic aspects of form are *polarity* and *symmetry*. If *they* are given, a great deal about the general appearance of an object is already specified. The polarity of a structure indicates its orientation with reference to the three axes of space. A structure is polarized if one axis is in some way dominant. For example, the head-tail axis in most animals is longer than the other two. This axis is the principal guide line around which the whole animal is organized, and such organisms are said to be polarized longitudinally. Symmetry indicates the degree of mirror-image regularity. A structure may be symmetrical in three, two, one, or in no dimensions; that is, it may be *spherical, radial, bilateral,* or *asymmetrical.*

Each organism exhibits a certain polarity and a certain symmetry. These features are the first and most permanent expressions of living form. Invariably, the earliest definitive traits to appear during the development of any plant or animal are its polarity and its symmetry. Many traits of an organism can be changed by experimental means, but its original polarity and symmetry can hardly ever be changed. Millions of years later, long after the organism has become a fossil, polarity and symmetry may still be recognizable even if all other signs of form have disappeared. It is a fairly general principle of development that the earlier a particular feature appears, the later it disappears.

Form is first blocked out in the rough, through establishment of polarity and symmetry, and then it becomes progressively more refined in regional detail. Whereas an organism grows from the molecule up, it forms from gross shape down. For example, the organ system is delineated ahead of its component organs. The tissue acquires definitive shape in advance of its component cells. And the molecules of the organism are last to assume final form. Evidently, form develops as in a sculpture, from the coarse to the fine, from the general to the specific. In both instances, this may be the only feasible way to ensure that the small remains appropriately subordinated to the large, structurally as well as functionally.

Specifically, establishment of form requires that cellular aggregates be molded into various configurations. Cells must become arranged and rearranged to produce regional enlargements and diminutions, to transform compact masses into sheets and vice versa, to produce channels, openings, cavities, and the like. Two general types of processes bring about such changes: *directed differential growth* and *form-regulating movements.*

For example, if differential growth proceeds differently in different parts of a developing system, so that the amount and rate of growth vary for different directions of space, then regional enlargements and diminutions will be produced. Local elongations, thickenings, overgrowths, altered contours, layers, and other new shapes can arise in this manner. Also, a solid mass can become hollow if the outer layers of the mass grow faster than the core. And a hollow structure can become solid if the inner layers of the rind grow faster than the outside.

Form-regulating movements involve shifts and migrations of growing parts relative to one another. Directed migrations of parts can result in the piling up of material in one region and in attenuation in others. Sheets or compact masses can slide over one another, can fuse together, or can separate. Compact masses can spread out and become sheets or loose aggregations, or aggregations can condense and form

29 · 1 Differential growth. *The right claw of this crab has been lost and is regenerating. The new claw grows differentially at a far faster rate than the rest of the animal, for in the time the regenerate takes to reach the size of the left claw the rest of the body does not increase in size appreciably.* Courtesy of Carolina Biological Supply Company.

larger masses. In short, if we add directed movements to directed growth, a sufficient machinery is available to translate the form of the reproductive unit into the specific form of the adult.

Growth, form, and all their qualitative and quantitative expressions together determine the architecture of the living unit. This architectural aspect of development is called *morphogenesis*. It is the first major component of the developmental process.

DIFFERENTIATION

An organism develops not only architecturally but also operationally. Thus, growth of a zygote produces not simply an aggregate of many identical cells, but an aggregate of mutually different cells; for example, some become nerve cells, some liver cells, some skin cells, etc. How does a reproductive unit give rise to a multitude of differently specialized cells? Cell division as such certainly does not alter the characteristics of a cell. As already noted, daughter cells inherit the same set of genes and the same kinds of cellular components generally as are present in a mother cell. Cell division does copy faithfully and a dividing reproductive cell therefore *should* give rise to many identical cells. Yet it does not; cell characteristics do change radically during development (Fig. 29.2).

Such inconstancy holds for every other organizational level as well. Molecules, tissues, organs, whole

organisms, all change their operational characteristics in the course of time. The changes are often in the direction of progressively greater operational novelty, but they may also be in the direction of regressively less operational novelty. As a result, every living unit possesses structures and carries out functions which are not yet in existence at earlier developmental stages and which may no longer be in existence at later stages. For example, an apical meristem cell today may be a photosynthetic cortex cell tomorrow; a cortex cell today may be a suberized cork cell tomorrow. A mature organism reproduces, but the senile organism no longer can.

Such dramatic changes of operational potential are brought about by the second and perhaps the most important major component of the developmental process, namely, by *differentiation*. A developing system need not necessarily grow and it need not necessarily change form, but by the very meaning of development, it must differentiate. Through differentiation, structural units become functionally *specialized* in various ways. It is sometimes useful to distinguish between "chemodifferentiation," "cytodifferentiation," "histodifferentiation," "organ differentiation," and so forth, according to the level of organization at which operational change takes place.

The basis of differentiation, as of any living process, is *interaction*. In most interactions of living parts with one another or with their physical environment, the operational potentialities of the system are not altered lastingly. But in some cases they are, and then the result is differentiation. For example, if some of the many interactions among molecules lead to the continuing production of novel categories of molecules, then these interactions contribute to chemodifferentiation. Or if a cell produces a hormone which,

29 · 2 Differentiation. *In the cross section through an onion root on the left, the tissues are not yet differentiated. In the section on the right, taken farther back from the root apex, tissue differentiation has already occurred.*

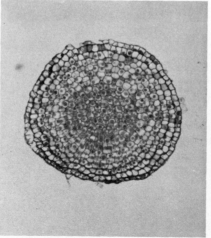
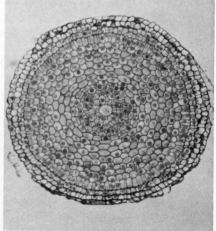

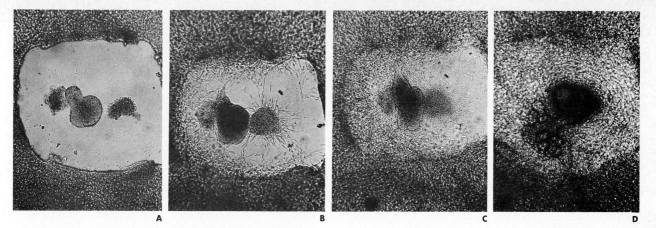

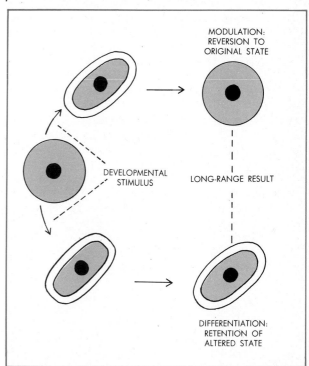

29 · 3 Salivary gland development in tissue culture, *an example of differentiation by interaction. A piece of undifferentiated salivary ectoderm and two pieces of undifferentiated salivary medoderm from a mouse embryo were put together into a culture (A). These pieces grew and interacted (B, C) and eventually differentiated into secretion pockets and ducts characteristic of normal salivary glands (D).*

on reaching a second cell, causes that second cell to mature, to become abnormal, or to change operationally in some other lasting way, then this is an instance of cytodifferentiation. Or again, if in response to a persisting climatic change, organisms transform into new types able to withstand the altered conditions, then this is a case of organismic differentiation, otherwise known as evolution (Fig. 29.3).

In short, to be differentiation, operational changes must have a certain degree of permanence. We may make an animal vitamin-deficient, for example, and many of its cells will then behave differently. But if we now add the missing vitamin to the diet, normal cellular operations will probably be resumed very promptly. Here cellular capacities have not been changed in any fundamental way. Only their expression has changed temporarily, in response to particular conditions. Such easily alterable, transient, reversible changes are spoken of as *modulations*. The concept of differentiation, on the contrary, implies a more or less fundamental, relatively lasting alteration of operational potentials. A vitamin-deficient cell which, after addition of the missing vitamin, *maintained* its altered characteristics would have differentiated (Fig. 29.4).

How does differentiation come about? On the organismic level, the process is understood comparatively well, and we shall discuss it in detail in the chapters on evolution. However, differentiation on the molecular and cellular levels is not fully understood as yet. Three general possibilities exist.

First, cell differentiation might be a result of progressive changes in gene action. Genes them-

selves probably do not change during development, for, as already noted, their stability is an essential requirement for the preservation of species characteristics. But the activity of different genes could vary with time. For example, in a given cell some genes might become active at certain developmental stages, whereas others might become inactive. The operon hypothesis (Chap. 21) now gives us some indication of how gene activity may become switched, and how thereby one particular set of reaction pathways would be followed out of many potentially pos-

29 · 4 Differentiation versus modulation. *In differentiation, the developmental change is permanent; in modulation, it is not.*

MODULATION: REVERSION TO ORIGINAL STATE

DEVELOPMENTAL STIMULUS

LONG-RANGE RESULT

DIFFERENTIATION: RETENTION OF ALTERED STATE

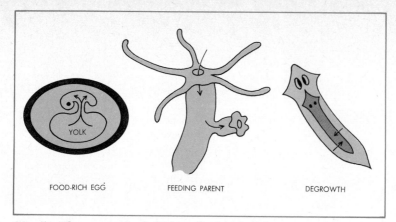

29 · 5 *Three principal forms of nutrition in developing systems: inclusion of food in the embryo, as in yolky egg or starchy corn kernel (photo); attachment of embryo to parent and embryo nourishment by parent, as in hydra buds; degrowth, that is, food obtained by partial breakdown of body and reorganization on smaller scale, as in planarians.*

sible pathways. Such differential activity patterns might occur differently in different cells, and this might contribute to differentiation.

Or, second, gene actions might remain the same, but the operations of the cytoplasm could become altered progressively. For example, one round of cytoplasmic reactions might use up a certain set of starting materials; and in the subsequent absence of these, similar reactions could then no longer take place. A next round of reactions would proceed with different starting materials and would therefore produce different endproducts. The new result could be progressive differentiation.

Or, third, nuclear and cytoplasmic changes might both occur, in reciprocal fashion. This is the likeliest possibility.

Like growth, differentiation occurs from the molecule up. Just as a house cannot be any more serviceable than its component rooms will permit, so also the operational capacities of any living level are based on the capacities of subordinated levels. Chemodifferentiation therefore is the key to all differentiation. It is this which makes the problem of understanding so enormous. For if the process of differentiation is as complex as the totality of molecular interactions in cells, then it cannot be any less complex than the very process of life itself.

METABOLISM

Morphogenesis and differentiation are two of the forces which drive development processes. A third is metabolism. To be sure, metabolism is not a uniquely developmental requirement, but there could be no

growth, no establishment of form, no differentiation, if energy were not available and if molecular syntheses did not occur. On the other hand, there could be no metabolism if morphogenesis and differentiation did not develop it.

Rates of metabolism are correlated with rates of development. At no point in the life cycle of any organism is metabolism more intensive and development more rapid than during the earliest stages. Both then decline in rate, until the zero point is reached at death; the metabolic clock is wound only once, at the beginning.

This circumstance introduces a number of major problems. Early in development, just when metabolic fires burn most fiercely, well-developed means of nutrition are not yet in existence. Neither the zygote nor the spore nor in many cases the regenerating fragment possesses a functioning food-procuring machinery. Three general solutions of this dilemma are possible; all three occur. First, enough food may be packed into the reproductive unit to last till it differentiates a functioning nutritional apparatus of its own. The endosperm-filled seed of plants and the yolk-filled egg of animals are the best examples. Or, second, the developing unit may be fed more or less continuously by the parent, via a persisting functional connection between the two. This is well illustrated by the parasitic sporophytes of bryophytes, the parasitic gametophytes of seed plants, and the placental mechanism of most mammals.

A third solution is frequently necessary in vegetative regeneration, when injury has put the nutritional apparatus out of commission and reserve food sources are not available. Under such conditions, the regenerating unit may be able to draw foods from its own structural framework. One result of such partial self-destruction is decrease in size, or *degrowth*. Another is the mobilization of enough raw materials for effective redevelopment on a smaller scale. Mouthless fragments of many animals may degrow and regenerate with the foods so obtained (Fig. 29.5).

724

With fuel supplies assured, respiration and synthesis become possible. But initial dilemmas must be resolved here as well. Intensive respiration requires oxygen and reproductive cells must exchange gases through their cell surfaces. But this requirement limits the size of a reproductive cell, for diffusion alone could not be effective in too large a cellular mass. The requirement of smallness, however, limits the amount of food that can be stored in the reproductive cell, and this in turn places a time limit on the amount of development possible. Clearly, the developmental consequences of so "simple" a requirement as oxygen supply are quite-far-reaching.

Once gas-supply problems are solved, respiration may proceed. The molecular equipment for energy production is inherited complete by all reproductive units and is more or less fully functional from the start. This is an absolute necessity for survival. But such is not the case for cellular syntheses; only relatively few kinds of synthetic reactions are possible initially. Most of the molecular equipment required for intricate development syntheses must itself first develop. Endproducts of a first round of synthesis must become the starting materials for a second, more complex round. In this manner, synthetic capacities must be increased and broadened progressively. Evidently, synthesis metabolism is as much a result of development as it is a prerequisite; it is one aspect of chemodifferentiation.

Morphogenesis, differentiation, and metabolism are three of the universal components of every developmental process. A fourth is perhaps the most essential.

CONTROL

How does a reproductive unit happen to give rise to just the right kinds and right numbers of parts? For example, how does the zygote of a seed plant produce just one stem apex and one root apex, not two stem apices at opposite ends or, alternatively, two root apices at opposite ends? Later, in the mature plant, if the stem apex is cut off, a node lower down develops a new apex: not a root-forming apex but a stem-forming one. Yet if that same node together with the stem system above it is cut off and put into soil, the node now will form a new root apex, not a stem apex. In another example, if the head of an earthworm is cut off, the worm develops a new head: not two or three heads or half a head, but one and only one; and not another tail, but another head. Even more strikingly, a single animal zygote does not yet possess any of the features of the adult. How then does it happen to produce just one head and one tail, not two or more of each, but in a man, for example, two arms and two legs, not one of each? And why arms and legs at all—why not wings or fins?

Considerations such as these bring us to the most puzzling of all aspects of development. What integrates development? How do morphogenesis, differentiation, and metabolism mesh together to produce an elegant, sensibly functioning whole? By any standard, this smooth, seemingly unerring advance toward wholeness is probably the most remarkable property of development. The headless earthworm, for example, never ceases its quiet internal revolution till it

29 · 6 Regeneration. *Both arms of this salamander larva were amputated, one above and the other below the elbow. The sequence of four photos shows the degree of regeneration attained after 1, 14, 22, and 31 days, respectively. Note that, although a salamander can regenerate its limbs, an isolated limb cannot regenerate the missing salamander.*

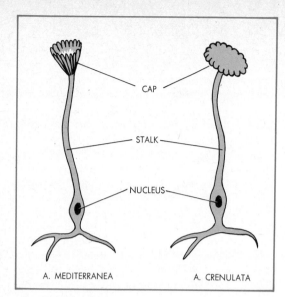

29 · 7 Acetabularia, *gross structure of two species. See also Fig. 12.8.*

has a new head. The transfigurations of the egg do not stop before the adult whole has come into being. Evidently, the healthy developing system behaves as if it "knew" its objectives precisely, and it proceeds without apparent trial and error. For normally there is no underdevelopment, no overdevelopment, and there are no probing excursions along the way. Development is directed straight toward wholeness (Fig. 29.6).

Only one conclusion can be drawn: the course of development must somehow be rigorously controlled. However, recognition of the occurrence of control does not of itself provide an explanation of it. We know in general terms that the control systems must reside within a developing unit itself and that, like any other living process, development must be self-controlling. But the nature and operations of these built-in control systems have in most cases not yet been identified. Today it is fashionable to say that genes control development, as they control every other living process. This is unquestionably correct. But such an answer is not very informative and is actually little more than a restatement of the problem. *How* do genes control development? More specifically, how does a particular gene, through control over a particular enzyme or other protein, regulate a particular developmental occurrence? Answers to such small problems are just beginning to be obtained. The collective larger issue, that is, the controlled, directed emergence of wholeness in an entire organism, remains a matter of future research. But even though we cannot now describe how the controls operate, we can nevertheless describe the results of such operations.

CELLULAR DEVELOPMENT

The general developmental question to be answered is roughly the same for each level of the living organization: how do the internal structural and functional components interact with one another and with the external environment, and how do such interactions produce given developmental changes? On the cellular level, for example, what are the relative contributions of the nucleus and the cytoplasm to the morphogenesis and differentiation of a whole cell? And if several whole cells develop together, how if at all do the cells interact and how does such interaction affect the developmental result?

NUCLEUS AND CYTOPLASM

Acetabularia

One of the most elegant studies of the roles of the nucleus and the cytoplasm in cellular development has been carried out on the coccine green alga *Acetabularia*. This unicellular marine protist is large (1 to 3 in. in height) and consists of a rhizoidal base, a stalk with a single basal nucleus, and a terminal cap (see Chap. 12). In one species, *A. mediterranea* (*med*), the cap is umbrellalike; it is composed of closely joined fingerlike outgrowths radiating away from the tip of the stalk. In another species, *A. crenulata*

29 · 8 Grafting experiments *with two species of* Acetabularia *to show nuclear control of cytoplasmic development. A and B illustrate reciprocal graft series.*

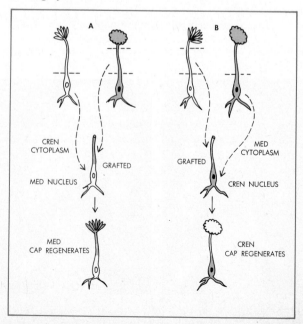

726

(*cren*), the cap contains fewer fingerlike outgrowths and these project outward freely (Fig. 29.7).

In either species, a new stalk and cap may regenerate if the original upper parts of the cell are cut away. Suppose that a nucleated *med* base is prepared and onto it is grafted a piece of *cren* stalk without nucleus. Will the regenerating cap be of a *med* or a *cren* type? The experimental answer is clear: the newly developing cap is of the *med* type. An analogous result is obtained in the reverse experiment: if to a nucleated *cren* base is grafted an enucleated piece of *med* stalk, then the new cap formed will be of the *cren* type. In other words, morphogenesis of the cap is always in line with the nature of the nucleus, regardless of the nature of the cytoplasm (Fig. 29.8).

Other kinds of experiments reinforce this conclusion. For example, if a nucleated *med* base is grafted to a nucleated *cren* base, then a single stalk grows out near the graft area of this binucleate combination. The stalk eventually regenerates a new cap and the characteristics of the cap are intermediate between a purely *med* and a purely *cren* type of cap. Evidently, both nuclei control cap development here and the cap exhibits mixed features as a result. If three nucleated bases are grafted together, then the single new cap formed again follows the predominant nuclear type. For example, if two nuclei are *cren* and one is *med*, then the cap will be of the *cren* type. But if one nucleus is *cren* and the other two are *med*, then the cap will be of the *med* type. It is quite clear, therefore, that cap development is under nuclear—hence presumably genic—control. Moreover, a given nucleus directs the cytoplasm not simply to develop a cap; it directs development of a cap of a particular structural type. Nuclear control is clearly species-specific (Fig. 29.9).

However, it can be shown that the nuclear effect on cytoplasmic development is not direct. If an enucleated piece of stalk is isolated and maintained independently, then a new cap may still regenerate on this piece even though a nucleus is now not present. This result indicates that, in an intact alga, the nucleus secretes certain "morphogenetic substances" into the cytoplasm and that these substances accumulate and then control cap development. Even if the nucleus is removed, therefore, cap formation may still occur so long as the morphogenetic substances persist in the cytoplasm. Evidently, nuclear control is indirect and long-range. The nature of the postulated morphogenetic substances has not been fully determined as yet; they may be associated with or derived from messenger RNA (Fig. 29.10).

It can also be shown that just as the nucleus controls cap development, so the cap controls nuclear

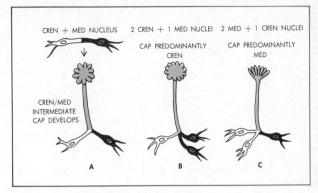

29 · 9 Double and triple grafts with two species of Acetabularia.

development. In a mature intact alga, the nucleus sooner or later divides repeatedly and the resulting nuclei are then carred by cytoplasmic streaming into the cap. Gametes are subsequently formed in the cap. It can be demonstrated readily that if the cap of a mature plant is cut off, nuclear division is suppressed. Division will remain suppressed until a new cap has developed. Moreover, one may prepare a capless nucleated base of a young immature alga and one may graft to it an enucleated stalk and cap of an old mature alga. In the original young alga, nuclear division would normally not have occurred for two months or more. But with the mature cap now grafted on, nuclear division occurs within two weeks. It is clear that the mature cap induces premature nuclear division and that the cap therefore controls nuclear division. Thus, the cytoplasm governs the development of the nucleus (see Fig. 29.10).

The results obtained from experiments on *Acetabularia* have provided a model applicable to developmental processes in cells generally. Numerous investigations on cells from a large variety of organisms, protist, plant, and animal, have shown fairly conclusively (1) that cellular morphogenesis and differentiation are under basic nuclear control, (2) that the nucleus acts via products released into the cytoplasm, and (3) that developmental processes in the cytoplasm act back on the nucleus and control its development in turn. Does nuclear control mean gene control? Probably yes, as the following experiments suggest.

Paramecium

If paramecia are injected into the bloodstream of a rabbit, the surface proteins of the paramecia, particularly the proteins of the cilia, will act as antigens;

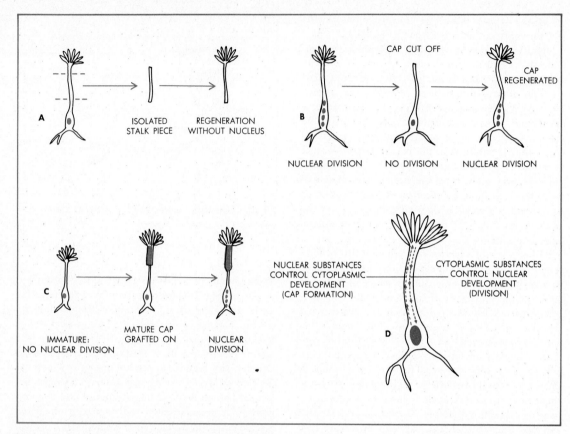

29 · 10 Interaction of cytoplasm and nucleus in morphogenesis. *A, experiment suggesting the release of morphogenetic substances from the nucleus in the control of cytoplasmic development. B, C, D, experiments illustrating the role of the cytoplasm in controlling nuclear events.*

the rabbit will manufacture specific antibodies against the ciliary proteins. If then rabbit blood serum containing such antibodies is placed into a dish in which the same kinds of paramecia are growing, the specific antibodies will become attached to the cilia of the paramecia. As a result, the cilia will stick to one another and the paramecia will become immobilized (Fig. 29.11).

By such means, it has been shown that protozoa of the species *Paramecium aurelia* may manufacture different ciliary proteins at different times. If we symbolize a series of ciliary proteins as *a*, *b*, *c*, etc., then a given paramecium and its immediate descendants may produce protein *a*, for example. But later descendants may manufacture protein *b*, still later ones may form protein *c*, and so on. Thus, although the cilia are visibly and functionally the same at all

times, their proteins are of a particular *antigenic type* at any given time and this antigenic type may change at some later time. Such changes represent processes of molecular development, or chemodifferentiation. What controls the development of a given antigenic type and what controls the change from one type to another?

A first set of experiments has shown that antigenic types are controlled by both the nucleus and the cytoplasm of paramecium. A paramecium known to be able to manufacture only protein *a*, for example, may be mated to another paramecium known to be able to produce only protein *b*. As shown in Chap. 26, mating in these organisms involves nuclear exchange such that after a mating both partners possess genetically identical nuclei. Accordingly, when antigenic type *a* mates with antigenic type *b*, the mating will yield two paramecia with identical nuclei. It is then found that, despite such genetic identity, the paramecium of type *a* and its descendants *remain* of type *a*. Similarly, the paramecium of type *b* and its descendants remain of type *b*. This result indicates that, inasmuch as the nuclei are alike in both cases, the antigenic types must be controlled by the cytoplasm (Fig. 29.12).

However, it can also be shown that later descendants of the *a* parent may on occasion change to the *b* type. Analogously, descendants of the *b* parent may occasionally change to the *a* type. Evidently, the original mating has endowed *both* mating partners and their respective descendants with the capacity to produce *both* antigenic types. This capacity does not become apparent immediately, yet it exists nevertheless and is a result of mating. And since mating means nuclear exchange, nuclear control of antigenic type may be inferred. It may be concluded, therefore, that both the nucleus and the cytoplasm contribute to type control (see Fig. 29.12).

A second set of experiments has shown that changes of antigenic type can be induced at will by alterations of the temperature at which paramecia are grown. For example, organisms raised at 18°C may exhibit type *a*, but if the organisms subsequently are raised at 25°C, their descendants will soon exhibit type *b*. Numerous mating tests carried out be-

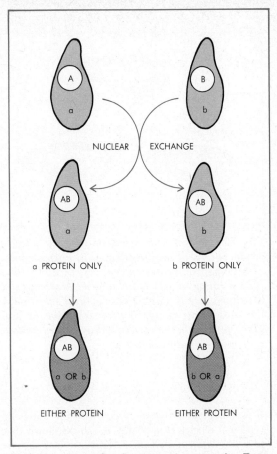

29 · 12 Control of antigenic type in Paramecium. *One organism containing A genes and a ciliary proteins is mated to another organism containing B genes and b ciliary proteins. After nuclear exchange, both organisms contain identical genes (A, B), yet the ciliary proteins are manufactured as before. This indicates cytoplasmic control of antigenic type. In later generations, however, the offspring of both original mating partners may manufacture either a or b proteins, indicating ultimate nuclear, genetic control of antigenic type.*

29 · 11 Antigen-antibody reactions *with* Paramecium. *If paramecia (dark color) are injected into a rabbit, the protozoa will act as antigens and the rabbit will produce specific antibodies against them. If rabbit blood serum containing the antibodies is then placed into the original* Paramecium *population, the cilia of the protozoa will be immobilized by the antibodies and the organisms will be unable to move.*

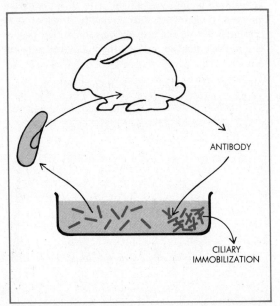

tween different strains of paramecia raised at various temperatures have yielded the following significant conclusions. First, each antigenic type is under the ultimate control of a specific gene. Any given paramecium possesses an experimentally identifiable series of such genes. Thus if an organism contains the genes *A*, *B*, *C*, and *D*, it will have the capacity to manufacture antigenic types *a*, *b*, *c*, and *d*. Second, at any given time only one gene is active and only one antigenic type may actually be exhibited. If gene *A* is active, antigenic type *a* will be manufactured. Later gene *A* may become inactive and gene

729

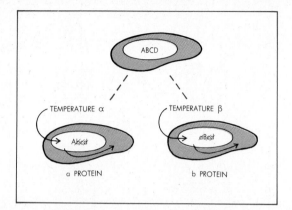

29 · 13 Temperature selection *of gene activity in the control of antigenic types in* Paramecium. *If an organism possesses genes A, B, C, D, then a temperature* α *will activate gene A selectively, a temperature* β *will activate gene B selectively, etc. According to which gene is active at any given time, only the corresponding ciliary protein will then be manufactured.*

B may become active, in which case the antigenic type will change to *b*. Third, it can be shown that it is the cytoplasm which determines what specific gene type will be active at any given time. Thus if a paramecium is raised at a given temperature, this environmental condition will affect a (so far unidentified) cytoplasmic control system. The system in turn will then affect the genes in such a way that a particular gene will become activated and all others in the series will become inactivated. A particular antigenic type will then be the result (Fig. 29.13).

The *Paramecium* data thus show again that cellular development—in this case development of a structural protein—is controlled by both nucleus and cytoplasm. Nuclear control is also clearly suggested to mean direct gene control. Moreover, cells appear to be capable of developing several *alternative* states of differentiation, but, only one of the possible states is actually exhibited. Such differential activation of one of several alternative gene-controlled pathways may be explained quite readily on the basis of an operon-governed switch-on, switch-off mechanism (see Fig. 21.12); and the *Paramecium* data show in addition that cytoplasm can itself be the selector of a particular pathway. The nucleo-cytoplasmic interaction is therefore cyclical: nuclear genes provide the control apparatus for the development of cytoplasmic traits such as ciliary proteins, but the cytoplasm provides the control apparatus for the effective activation of one of the genes. The experiments also show that environmental factors can have a decisive influence on the particular course of development a cell will follow.

Entirely analogous conclusions have been obtained from many other kinds of studies on many other kinds of organisms. Like *Acetabularia*, therefore, *Paramecium* provides a broadly applicable model of developmental processes in cells generally.

CELL-CELL INTERACTIONS

Slime Molds

The effect of one cell on the development of another is illustrated most strikingly in the life cycle of the Acrasieae, the cellular slime molds. Much of the pertinent experimental work has been done on the species *Dictyostelium discoideum*. In this slime mold, spores germinate and form vegetative amoebae. These increase in size by feeding on bacteria and increase in number by cell divisions. When food becomes unavailable, the amoebae cease their independent existence and aggregate into a pseudoplasmodium, a united multicellular mass (see Color Plate XIV, 25).

What directs these cells to stream and stick together and to behave subsequently as a cooperative unit? Experiments show that certain of the amoebae secrete a diffusible substance, *acrasin*, which has a powerful orienting and attracting effect: other amoebae are stimulated to migrate into regions of increasing acrasin concentrations. Since the highest concentrations are in the immediate vicinity of an acrasin-producing cell, all the cells in a population eventually aggregate into a clump around the secreting cells. Acrasin also changes the surface properties of the amoebae, making them adhere to one an-

29 · 14 Formation of a fruiting body *in the slime mold* Dictyostelium.

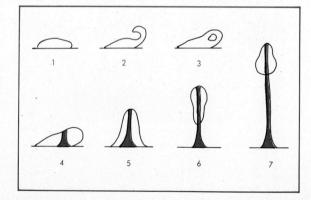

other quite readily. Accordingly, cells which collide during their migration to a common center tend to remain sticking together. A pseudoplasmodium is formed in this manner. It is still not fully known what factors determine which cell in an amoebal population will become acrasin-producing. However, it is quite clear that such a cell influences the subsequent activity and development of all others.

Once a pseudoplasmodium, or "slug," has formed, it secretes a thin slime sheath over the surface on which it glides. The slug is therefore never in direct contact with the surface itself and the moving organism may somehow gain traction on its own slime track. After a period of moving and feeding, the slug comes to rest and develops into a fruiting body (Fig. 29.14). In this morphogenetic process, the forward tip of the slug turns upward and curves back, into the main mass of its body. The cells of the tip then secrete a cellulose envelope around themselves and become arranged as the base of a hollow stalk. Other amoebae migrate upward on the outside of this stalk and add to its height. The last group of cells flowing up the stalk forms the terminal sporangium.

It can be shown that the developmental fates of different amoebae are determined long before construction of a fruiting body actually begins. If, in preliminary experiment, independent vegetative amoebae are fed on red-colored bacteria, a correspondingly red-colored pseudoplasmodium may be obtained. Similarly, by supplying colorless bacteria to another group of amoebae, the slug they form will be unpigmented. Pieces of two such slugs may now be grafted together. It is found that, in graft combinations of this sort, red-colored cells tend to remain together in one portion of the moving slug and unpigmented cells tend to remain together similarly. The amoebae in a normal pseudoplasmodium therefore appear to intermix relatively little; each largely maintains the same position relative to the other cells in the united population.

The position of a given cell in a slug then apparently determines the role of this cell in the development of the fruiting body. If the forward portion of a slug is red-colored, the stalk will be formed by red cells and the terminal sporangium by unpigmented cells. Conversely, if the leading part of a slug is unpigmented, that part will form stalk and the red trailing part will form sporangium (Fig. 29.15). Such results suggest that, when amoebae aggregate into a pseudoplasmodium, the cells soon differentiate either into stalk-forming or into spore-forming types, depending on their position within the cellular mass. Indeed, several chemical differences between these two cell groups have been discovered. Slime molds therefore demonstrate that cells originally equal in

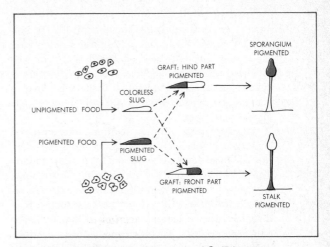

29 · 15 *Grafting experiments with* **Dictyostelium.** *Vegetative amoebae (as at left) are fed either unpigmented or pigmented bacteria, and reciprocal graft combinations are then made between the resulting slugs. The fruiting bodies formed subsequently will have different pigmented and unpigmented parts.*

developmental potential may differentiate unequally, as a result of their mutual interaction and their fate-directing effect on one another. These data again form a model for a generally applicable principle of cellular development.

Isolation Cultures

In such cultures, parts of an organism—populations of loose cells, compact tissues, or whole organs—are isolated and grown aseptically in various artificial media to which nutrients and growth factors have been added. One may then observe the developmental behavior of the isolated cells or cell groups, investigate their changing chemical characteristics, and determine how their development is affected by changes in the composition of the medium. The technique has been applied successfully to both plant and animal material.

Tissue culture studies have shown that undeveloped embryonic cells differentiate chemically well before their microscopically visible structure becomes differentiated. For example, at a time when the future heart region of a chicken embryo is still unrecognizable on the basis of cell structure, that is, when distinct cardiac muscle is not yet present, the region already contains a unique kind of myosin, a muscle protein characteristic of the heart. Analogous findings have been obtained in experiments on plants.

For example, well before embryonic root tissues of onions are distinguishable microscopically as epidermis, cortex, xylem, and phloem, the later fates of these undeveloped tissues are already foreshadowed by characteristic chemodifferentiations. The general conclusion appears warranted that cells develop first on the molecular level and only later on the microscopic level.

Moreover, tissue culture work has demonstrated convincingly that soon after cells have developed on the chemical level they behave as if they already "knew" what tissues they are to form. For example, undeveloped tissue taken from a future cartilage region of an embryo may be treated in such a way that the tissue becomes disaggregated into a population of loose cells. These cells may then be grown in isolation culture. Before long, the cells are found to migrate toward one another and to form a compact tissue again. This tissue soon differentiates as cartilage. Analogously, one may treat undeveloped tissue from a future kidney region so that the cells no longer adhere to one another. Placed into culture, the loose cells of such a population similarly migrate into a compact mass and the latter eventually differentiates as kidney tissue.

Populations of both types of loose cells may now be mixed and may be grown together in the same culture dish. If this is done, it is found that the mixed cells appear to become "unscrambled" and that they migrate to form *two* compact masses. One of these later differentiates as cartilage, the other as kidney tissue. It may be concluded that cells in which chemodifferentiation is already under way are able to "recognize" if other cells are of like or of unlike type. Perhaps the molecular properties of the cell surfaces are already developed sufficiently to permit only cells of like type to adhere to one another (Fig. 29.16).

Indeed, it can be shown that cellular properties predetermine not only the differentiation but also the morphogenesis of tissues. For example, cells from the future lung region of a mouse embryo will, when grown in tissue culture, form into a portion of lung exhibiting a perfectly normal architecture; lung alveoli and air ducts become well developed and are clearly recognizable as such. By similar experiments, isolated portions of normally formed kidneys, salivary glands, and other organs may be produced in culture. Experiments of this sort indicate generally that embryonic cells already launched on a particular path of development continue to develop in culture more or less as they would in an intact organism (Fig. 29.17).

A different result is obtained when a culture consists of cells that have not yet started to develop in given directions and thus are still more or less completely undeveloped. For example, if single cells from very early embryos of certain animals (for example, sea urchins, frogs) are isolated, each such cell may develop into a *whole* animal. Analogously, isolated embryonic cells of plants (obtainable even from adult plants, for example, various meristem cells) may develop into whole new plants under appropriate culture conditions. Evidently, undifferentiated cells exhibit a far greater developmental potential in isolation than in the intact organism; the capacity of forming entire plants or animals actually resembles the similar capacity of vegetative reproductive units. Later, after such cells have begun to differentiate and have become specialized to a certain extent, their developmental potential becomes restricted progressively. They then form only parts of an organism under isolated conditions—the same parts they would have formed had they not been isolated.

This restriction of developmental potentials be-

29 · 16 Reaggregation. *If a compact tissue such as embryonic cartilage is disaggregated and the loose cells are grown in a culture medium, then the cells tend to migrate together and reaggregate into compact cartilage tissue (A). If two tissues such as embryonic cartilage and kidney are disaggregated and the loose cells are mixed and grown in the same culture medium, then the cells will correspondingly tend to reaggregate into two separate tissue masses (B).*

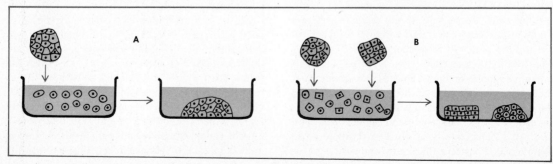

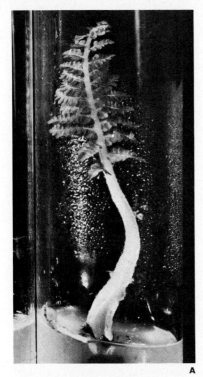

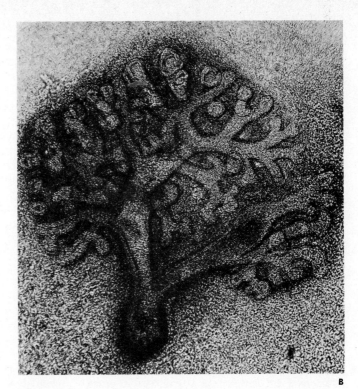

29 · 17 Tissue cultures. A, a fern leaf grown in culture from a leaf bud. B, future lung tissue of an 11-day-old mouse embryo was placed into tissue culture. After 6 days of growth in the culture, the well-formed lung shown in this photo had developed. Note ducts, branches, and alveoli.

comes greatest when cells reach the fully differentiated adult state. Such cells at best may be able to produce more of themselves if they are capable of division, but they may no longer form any other kind of cell type. Tissue culture data at first glance seem to suggest a different answer. For when a single adult tissue is grown in culture, the cells usually do not remain differentiated but appear to *dedifferentiate;* they lose their adult specializations and come to exhibit a less developed, more or less embryonic state. It can be shown, however, that such dedifferentiation does not change the fundamental characteristics of the cells. For if a dedifferentiated tissue from a culture is grafted back into an intact organism, the tissue soon redifferentiates and then exhibits the same adult properties it did originally; it cannot redifferentiate into another kind of tissue. Clearly, the developed characteristics of a greatly specialized adult tissue appear to be fixed and irreversible, even though these characteristics may become obscured temporarily when the tissue exists in isolation (Fig. 29.18).

The result suggests that dedifferentiation in culture might occur because an isolated tissue may be unable to interact with other tissues, as it would normally do in an intact organism. Returning a cultured tissue to an intact organism would again make tissue-tissue interaction possible, and the observed redifferentiation could be a consequence. Such an interpretation is supported by experiments with *organ cultures,* in which whole isolated organs are grown in artificial media. The several closely associated tissues of the organ then do not dedifferentiate but tend to retain their adult characteristics; presumably, normal tissue-tissue interaction may still occur. It appears, therefore, that the cells and tissues of multicellular organisms are interdependent developmentally; in isolation they do not develop in quite the same manner as in integrated groups. This finding again underscores a conclusion already reached in various earlier contexts, namely, group integration is a necessary condition for the formation and maintenance of a properly organized living whole.

For often poorly understood reasons, group integration sometimes breaks down in intact organisms. Various developmental abnormalities then result, tumors and cancers among them. Investigation of such abnormal expressions of development is likewise aided greatly by the technique of isolation culture. For example, tumor tissues may be grown in culture and their chemical characteristics may be compared with those of normal tissues. Drugs and other agents

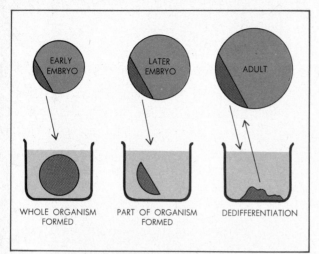

EARLY EMBRYO

LATER EMBRYO

ADULT

WHOLE ORGANISM FORMED

PART OF ORGANISM FORMED

DEDIFFERENTIATION

29 · 18 Dedifferentiation. *If isolated cells from a very early embryo are cultured, the cells may form a whole organism* (left). *Cells from a later embryo tend to form only that part of the organism they would have formed if they had been left intact in the embryo* (middle). *Cells from an adult tend to dedifferentiate* (right), *but if replanted into the adult donor, they will redifferentiate the structural and functional characteristics they had before they were isolated.*

may be introduced into the culture medium and their effects may be observed. Moreover, by growing normal tissues in culture and by changing the environmental conditions in various ways, one may discover some of the factors that produce abnormal development.

To be sure, cells, tissues, or organs largely do not develop in man-made cultures but in naturally forming organisms. Ultimately, therefore, every developmental problem refers back to and is suggested by events in whole organisms.

ORGANISMIC DEVELOPMENT

THE PATTERN

The course of development varies considerably according to whether the starting unit is a zygote produced by a sexual process or an asexually developing spore or vegetative body.

Zygotic development starts with *fertilization* and continues with the formation of an *embryo*. During the embryonic period, all basic structures and functions of the future adult body are elaborated in at least rough detail. In plants, the embryonic phase merges imperceptibly into the young adult phase, the general time of transition being the establishment of a self-supporting sporophyte in soil and air. In oviparous animals, the embryonic phase typically terminates with a process of *hatching*, in which the embryo emerges from its original egg envelopes and becomes a free-living *larva*. A larval phase is characteristic of animals in virtually all phyla, but it is often absent in some of the more advanced subgroups within a phylum or subphylum (for example, reptiles, birds, and mammals among vertebrates). Animals without larvae are usually (but not necessarily) ovoviviparous or viviparous.

Larvae largely play one or both of two functional roles. In many animals, sessile ones in particular, the larvae are the chief agents for geographic distribution of the species. In some cases, indeed, a mouth may not be functional as yet and larvae then serve exclusively as nonfeeding dispersal devices (for example, tunicate tadpoles). As might be expected, locomotor structures are well developed in such species-distributing larvae. For example, we already know that chordate tadpoles possess strongly muscled tails, and that the swimming larvae of many invertebrates have greatly enlarged, variously folded and ciliated epidermal surfaces, with bands and tufts of extra long cilia in given regions. In many other animals, larvae can disperse geographically far less well than the adults (for example, insect caterpillars), and the primary function of larvae then appears to be nutritional. Embryonic development alone evidently provides only enough building materials for the construction of a transitional feeding apparatus in the form of a larva. The latter must subsequently accumulate the necessary food reserves for the ultimate formation of a more complex adult body. Larvae of this type have particularly well developed alimentary systems. Note that the larvae of numerous animals function both as dispersal and as feeding machines. And note also that, in many cases, feeding larvae have nutritional requirements differing from those of the adults. The existence of two distinct stages may therefore permit more complete utilization of foods available in the environment and may reduce competition for food within a population.

In due course, larvae undergo *metamorphosis*, a more or less gradual but in many cases quite sudden transformation into the *adult* condition. In animals without larvae, the embryo becomes a young adult directly (the stage of transition being marked by birth in ovoviviparous and viviparous forms). Note that this last phase in the developmental history of an individual is not any more static than preceding phases. On the contrary, as shown in the chapters on metabolism, the components of the adult are steadily being demolished and redesigned or replaced. In this continuing turnover, internal as well as external features become altered. Youth and adolescence so pass into maturity, marked by the onset of reproductive capacity. Maturity then gives way to senescence, and only death brings development to a halt.

Thus, the typical developmental pattern following gametic reproduction is either fertilization ⟶ embryo ⟶ adult, as in plants and some animals, or fertilization ⟶ embryo ⟶ larva ⟶ adult, as in most animals. In sharp contrast to this lengthy multistage course of sexual development, all forms of asexual development are exceedingly direct. In the development of spores or vegetative units of any type, there is no sex, hence no fertilization; there is no larva, hence also no metamorphosis. Instead, the reproductive unit becomes an adult in a smoothly continuous, single developmental step (Fig. 29.19).

Without doubt, this marked difference between sexual and asexual patterns of development must be due to the presence or absence of the sexual process itself. Unlike a spore or a vegetative body, an egg is *more* than simply a reproductive unit. As we have seen, it is also the agent for sex and therefore an *adaptive* device. Through fertilization the egg acquires new genes, which may endow the future offspring with new, better-adapted traits. However, before any new traits can actually be displayed, they must be *developed* during the transition from egg to adult. Embryonic and larval periods appear to be the result. These phases may be considered to provide the means and the necessary time for translating the genetic instruction acquired sexually by the zygote into the adaptively improved structures and functions of the adult. Vegetative units do not acquire new genetic instructions through sex, and equivalent developmental processes for executing such instructions would then not be needed. Correspondingly, embryos and larvae are absent here.

We note that, in addition to their developmental and functional roles as just outlined above, embryos and larvae also play a major genetic role. Moreover, to the extent that the genetic instructions received by an egg may be different from those received by earlier generations of eggs, embryos and larvae permit the introduction of *evolutionary* changes into developmental histories. We shall find, indeed, that evolutionary change is achieved not by alteration of adults but primarily by modifications of eggs, embryos, and larvae, that is, incompletely developed stages still plastic enough to be capable of executing changed genetic instructions.

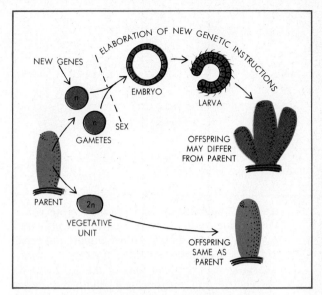

29 · 19 Sexual versus asexual development. *In sexual development* (top), *new genetic instructions are introduced into the zygote via the gametes, and during subsequent embryonic and larval stages these instructions are elaborated explicitly. Hence the mature offspring may differ to greater or lesser extent from the parent. In asexual development* (bottom), *new genetic instructions are not introduced, and the offspring therefore resembles the parent fully.*

Of all forms and phases of development in various plants and animals, the embryonic phase of animals has been studied most. Particular attention has been given to externally fertilizing types such as frogs and sea urchins. The sperms and eggs of animals of this kind may be put into a dish of water, where fertilization and development may be observed under the microscope and where experiments may be performed readily. Much has also been learned by cutting windows into developing chicken eggs and by observing and experimenting on the exposed embryos. Comparative studies have shown that, although the details often vary considerably, certain basic processes are common in the development of all animal embryos.

THE EMBRYO

The first clearly visible event after fertilization is *cleavage*, the subdivision of an egg into progressively smaller cells called *blastomeres*. Eggs are generally larger than the average adult cell size characteristic of the species. During cleavage, divisions occur so

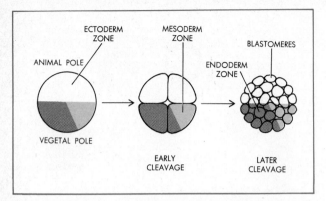

29 · 20 Germ-layer- and organ-forming zones in egg and early cleavage stages. *The principal egg axis is marked by so-called animal and vegetal poles at opposite points of the egg. As cleavage progresses, a given zone of the egg becomes segregated into progressively small but larger numbers of blastomeres.*

rapidly that the blastomeres have little opportunity to grow, hence the egg subdivides without enlarging as a whole. Cleavage divisions typically continue until adult cell sizes are attained. The early cleavages are unusual also in that they occur synchronously; all blastomeres present cleave simultaneously. However, such synchrony generally disappears after a few dozen blastomeres have formed.

The function of cleavage actually is not merely to subdivide an egg into a random set of appropriately small cells. Sooner or later, different regions of an egg develop into qualitatively different *organ-forming zones,* areas which will later give rise to the various body parts of the adult. Cleavage *segregates* these zones into different cells and cell groups (Fig. 29.20). On the basis of how soon the zones become established, and thus how soon the later fate of the various egg parts becomes fixed, two categories of eggs may be distinguished; *mosaic* or *determined* eggs and *regulative* or *undetermined* eggs.

The first type is encountered generally among most protostomial animals. In these, the future developmental fate of every portion of the egg becomes fixed unalterably before or at the time of fertilization. The zygote therefore is already fully polarized and the head-tail, dorsal-ventral, and left-right axes are firmly established. Moreover, experiments show that each portion of the egg behaves as if it already "knew" what it is going to develop into. For example, after cleavage in such an egg has produced two or more cells, it is possible to separate these cells from one another. Each isolated blastomere then continues to develop and forms a *partial* embryo. More specif-

ically, it produces the same portion of the embryo it would have produced if the cleaving egg had been left intact. In other words, the determined egg is like a quiltwork, a mosaic, in which each portion of the cytoplasm develops into a fixed, unalterable part of the whole embryo; and the nature of the mosaic is established before or, at the latest, during the time of fertilization (Fig. 29.21).

By contrast, the eggs of most deuterostomial animals, vertebrates included, are of the regulative variety. In these, the future fate of various egg portions similarly becomes unalterably fixed, but such fixing occurs comparatively much later, during the

29 · 21 Mosaic vs. regulative development. *If the cells of early cleavage stages of mosaic eggs are isolated experimentally (left), then each cell develops as it would have in any case. The inference is that the fates of cytoplasmic regions in such eggs (the dark colored central parts) are determined very early. But if the cells of early cleaving regulative eggs are isolated experimentally (right), then each cell develops into a smaller whole animal. The inference here is that the fate of the cytoplasm is still undetermined. Thus the dark colored central cytoplasm, which normally would form central body parts, actually forms left structures in one case, right structures in the other, if the two-cell-stage blastomeres are separated.*

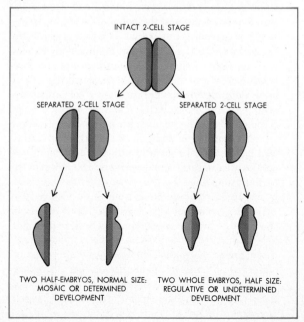

embryonic phase. Moreover, different features become determined at different times. For example, at fertilization only the main egg axis is determined. That is, the direction of "top" and "bottom" is already given, but other aspects of polarity and symmetry or of any other feature are not as yet fixed.

That this is so can be demonstrated very strikingly by experiment. If the two blastomeres formed by the first cleavage division are left as they are, then they will eventually form the left and right halves of the future animal. Further, cytoplasm in the center of the egg will develop into central internal structures of the adult. But if the two blastomeres are separated from one another, then they do *not* develop into two half animals as would be the case in a mosaic egg. Instead, the two blastomeres develop into two whole animals. Moreover, the central cytoplasm of the original egg now gives rise to the right side of one whole animal and to the left side of another. Evidently, central material at the two-cell stage does not yet "know" whether to form left, right, or internal mid-body structures. In short, it is not yet determined (see Fig. 29.21).

Analogously, if the cells of later cleavage stages are isolated and grown separately, then each may again give rise to a whole instead of a partial animal. But a limit is reached fairly soon. After the first three cleavages, for example, eight blastomeres are present. If these are separated from one another, eight whole animals cannot be obtained. Instead, each blastomere forms only one-eighth of an embryo, as it would have done if the eight-cell stage had been left intact. In other words, the developmental fate of the cells has become determined by now, and the embryo henceforth is like a mosaic.

We may conclude that mosaic and regulative eggs differ mainly in the timing of developmental determination. The early timing in mosaic eggs contrasts with the comparatively late timing in regulative eggs. During the undetermined phase in regulative eggs, any cell may substitute for any other cell and may develop into any structure, including a whole animal. Note here that developmental determination is a form of differentiation, particularly chemodifferentiation, and that the underlying mechanism is still completely unknown.

Note also that the formation of two or more whole animals from separated blastomeres is equivalent to the production of identical twins, triplets, quadruplets, and so on. Natural *twinning* undoubtedly occurs through similar separations. However, the forces or accidents which actually isolate such blastomeres in nature are not understood. If the blastomeres are separated incompletely, Siamese twins result. This too can be demonstrated by laboratory experi-

29 · 22   X-ray photo of Siamese twinning in fish. *Abnormalities like these result from incomplete divisions of cells during early cleavage.*

ments (Fig. 29.22). Twins are *identical* when they develop from a single fertilized egg, as above. They are *fraternal* when two or more whole eggs are fertilized separately at the same time. The offspring here may be of different sexes, and they need not resemble one another. By contrast, identical twins are of the same sex and they do resemble one another. Indeed, they tend to be structural mirror images.

The ultimate result of normal cleavage is a ball of a few hundred cells, called a *blastula*. This ball may be hollow or solid, and it represents a developmental stage characteristic of virtually all Metazoa (Fig. 29.23). Cell divisions continue in a blastula, but growth now occurs as well and successive cell generations thus no longer become smaller. The next major developmental event is the establishment of the three primary germ layers of the embryo—*ectoderm* exteriorly, *endoderm* interiorly, and *mesoderm* between. The processes which transform a blastula into such a developmental stage are collectively called *gastrulation*, and the resulting embryo itself is a *gastrula*.

There are almost as many different specific methods of gastrulation as there are animal types. In the majority of animals, the regions which will give rise to the three germ layers are already determined on the surface of the blastula and indeed even on the egg surface, as revealed by studies of organ-forming zones (see Fig. 29.20). Therefore, gastrulation here must involve an *interiorization* of the endoderm- and mesoderm-forming regions. Interiorization of the endoderm-forming regions usually takes place first, either by overgrowth of the ectoderm-forming regions around the endoderm-forming regions, or by ingrowth of the endoderm-forming regions under the ectoderm-forming regions (see Fig. 29.23). The latter process occurs, for example, in echinoderm embryos. When such embryos gastrulate, one side of the hollow spherical blastula *invaginates*, or becomes indented. A two-layered cup-shaped structure results, the outer layer now being the ectoderm, the inner layer the endoderm. An essentially analogous end result is obtained where gastrulation takes place by overgrowth of ectoderm-forming regions around endoderm-forming ones.

Regardless of how the first two germ layers become established, the gastrula at this stage is a two-layered ball with an opening in one region (Fig. 29.24).

29 · 23 Gastrulation. Diagrams: future and actual endoderm shaded. A, gastrulation by ectodermal overgrowth (epiboly). B, gastrulation by endodermal ingrowth (emboly, or invagination). Photos: early development and invaginative gastrulation in starfish. 1, egg; 2, two-cell stage; 3, late cleavage; 4, blastula; 5, embolic invagination, early gastrula; 6, late gastrula, beginning of mesoderm formation; 7, mesoderm formation under way.

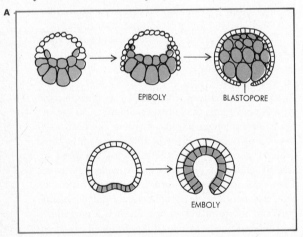

This opening is a *blastopore*. It subsequently develops into the single alimentary opening of adult radiate animals and flatworms, into the adult mouth of *Protostomia*, and into the adult anus of *Deuterostomia*. In later stages a second perforation breaks through at the opposite side of the embryo, and this opening becomes the anus in the Protostomia and the mouth in Deuterostomia. The two-layered gastrula also contains an interior cavity, which communicates with the outside through the blastopore. This space is a *gastrocoel* or *archenteron*, the future alimentary cavity. The endoderm layer enclosing it will later develop into the alimentary system, in vertebrates also the breathing system, and into all glands and ducts associated with these: liver, pancreas, salivary glands, trachea, and so forth. The ectoderm will give rise to the whole nervous system and to the skin, including hair, nails, and skin glands.

Development of the third germ layer, the mesoderm, usually begins as soon as endoderm has become interiorized. We already know from Chap. 14 that mesoderm arises in different ways in different animal groups and that the specific way categorizes the animal as an acoelomate, a pseudocoelomate, a schizocoelomate, or an enterocoelomate (see Fig. 14.10). The mesoderm will later form the remaining body parts, including (in vertebrates) bones, muscles, and the circulatory, excretory, and reproductive systems. The endocrine system arises partly from ectoderm, partly from mesoderm, and partly from endoderm.

The late gastrula evidently represents a key stage in embryonic development. At this stage the germ layers are established in proper positions, the prospective head and hind ends of the developing animal are marked, and in many cases the top-bottom and left-right axes are determined as well. Moreover, the extent and position of the pseudocoelomic or coelomic body cavities or both are already foreshadowed. In effect, the fundamental architecture of the future animal has become elaborated in rough

1   2   3   4   5   6   7

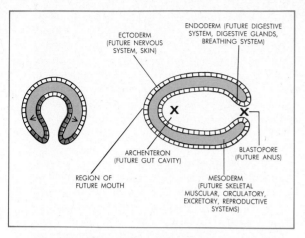

29 · 24 The vertebrate gastrula. *Left, most of the mesoderm-forming zone (color) becomes interiorized by gastrulation, hence the adult vertebrate mesoderm is largely endoderm-derived endomesoderm. Right, the general structure of a vertebrate gastrula and the adult organ systems formed by each of the primary germ layers.*

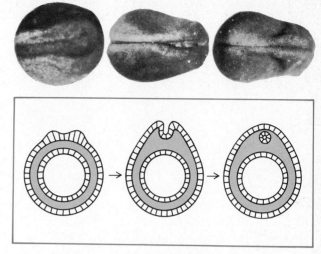

outline. All later development consists essentially of a sculpturing of detail—formation of organ systems, then of organs within each system, then of tissues within organs, and so on.

How do organ systems actually arise in later embryos?

LATER DEVELOPMENT

The detailed patterns by which the germ layers are transformed into well-defined body parts differ vastly in different animals. Nevertheless, certain basic processes appear to be common to all such patterns. We may illustrate these by considering the development of the vertebrate nervous system (Fig. 29.25).

On the upper surface of the gastrula develop two ectodermal ridges, one along each side of the midline. These ridges grow upward and toward each other and soon meet along the mid-line. As their edges fuse, they form a tube of ectoderm which runs from front to back and is covered over by an outer ectoderm layer. This tube is the basis of the nervous system; it develops into brain in the front part of the embryo and into spinal cord in the hind part.

The essential event here is the outfolding of a tissue layer, followed by fusion of the fold edges. Almost all other formative processes of later em-

29 · 25 The initial development of the vertebrate nervous system. *Top, left to right, dorsal views of progressive stages in neural tube formation in frogs. The anterior ends of the embryos are toward the right. Middle, diagrammatic cross sections corresponding to the stages shown above. Bottom, left and right, cross sections corresponding to the first and last stages illustrated in top series. Note the large amounts of yolk. Middle, chicken embryo cross section corresponding to middle stage shown above. Note the mesoderm cells to either side of the developing neural tube and the notochord just below the tube.*

bryonic development similarly consist of outfolding or infolding, outpouching or inpouching, of portions of the three germ layers of the gastrula. For example, limb buds arise by combined outpouchings from ectoderm and mesoderm. Lungs and digestive glands develop in part as outpouchings from various levels of the endoderm. The eye develops in part as an outpouching from the brain. All other body parts develop analogously. The ultimate result of these processes of morphogenesis and differentiation is a fully formed embryo, clearly recognizable as a young stage of a particular species.

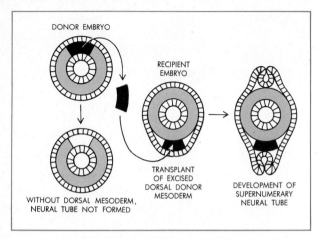

DONOR EMBRYO

RECIPIENT EMBRYO

TRANSPLANT OF EXCISED DORSAL DONOR MESODERM

DEVELOPMENT OF SUPERNUMERARY NEURAL TUBE

WITHOUT DORSAL MESODERM, NEURAL TUBE NOT FORMED

29 · 26 Neural induction. *If the dorsal meso-derm of a donor embryo* (black wedge) *is trans-planted under the belly ectoderm of a host embryo, then the transplant will induce the for-mation of an abnormally located neural tube in the host (and the host's own neural tube will develop as well).*

Experiments have shown how these orderly se-quences of development may come about (Fig. 29.26). In amphibian embryos it is possible to cut out the dorsal ectoderm which, under normal circumstances, would fold up and form a neural tube. If this excised tissue is then transplanted to another region of the embryo, it will not form a neural tube and its cells will not differentiate into neurons. This result suggests that the dorsal mesoderm, which in an intact embryo

lies just under the dorsal ectoderm, normally affects this ectoderm in such a way that it will fold out and differentiate into neural tissue. That this is actually so can be shown by another experiment. The dorsal mesoderm can be cut out and can be transplanted, for example, into the belly region of an embryo just under the belly ectoderm. Normally, belly ectoderm forms only skin. But if dorsal mesoderm lies under it, it will form a neural tube and its cells will differentiate into neural tissue.

The implications are clear. Somehow, the dorsal mesoderm of a normal embryo *induces* the outfolding of the overlying ectoderm, the formation of ridges, and the later differentiation of neural tissue. Such induction can actually be shown to occur whenever outfoldings or infoldings and outgrowths or ingrowths develop in the embryo. The formation of the verte-brate eye provides a particularly striking example.

Eye development (Fig. 29.27) begins with the evagination of a pocket from the side of the future brain. This pocket is narrow at the base and bulbous at the tip. Soon the bulbous portion invaginates from the forward end and a double-layered cup is formed. The cup represents the future eyeball. As it grows outward from the brain, its rim comes into contact with the outer ectoderm layer which overlies the whole nervous system and which represents the future skin. Just where the eyecup rests against it, the ectoderm layer now begins to thicken. This thick-ening eventually grows into a ball of cells, which is nipped off toward the inside. It fits neatly into the mouth of the eyecup and represents the future lens. The cells of this ball and the ectoderm overlying them later become transparent. The basic structure of the eye is then established.

29 · 27 Development of the vertebrate (am-phibian) eye. *This series of diagrams shows the successive outgrowth of a pocket from the brain, contact of this pocket with the outer body ecto-* *derm, formation of an eyecup, gradual formation of a lens from the outer ectoderm, and develop-ment of the pigmented and other tissue layers of the eyeball.*

Courtesy of Dr. Dietrich Bodenstein, from figs. 2 and 3, J. Exp. Zool., vol. 108, pp. 96, 97.

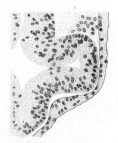
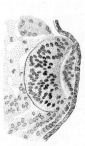
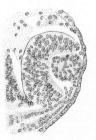
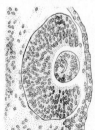

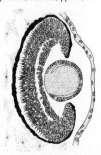

The following type of experiment has shown dramatically how these developmental processes are controlled. It is possible to cut off the eyecup and its stalk before they have grown very far. Eyecup and stalk may then be transplanted. For example, they may be inserted into a region just under the belly ectoderm of an embryo. Under such conditions, the patch of belly ectoderm overlying the eyecup soon thickens, a ball of cells is nipped off toward the inside, and a lens differentiates. Moreover, lens and overlying skin become transparent. In effect, the transplanted structures have caused the formation of a structurally normal eye in a highly abnormal location (Fig. 29.28).

A common conclusion emerges from this and many similar types of experiments. One embryonic tissue layer interacts with an adjacent one, and the latter is thereby induced to differentiate, to grow, to develop in a particular way. This developed tissue then interacts with another one in turn and induces it to develop. In short, sequential induction must occur if progressive development is to take place. As in the induction sequence: dorsal mesoderm ⟶ neural tube ⟶ eyecup ⟶ lens, so also generally; one tissue provides the stimulus for the development of the next. The phenomenon of *embryonic induction* consequently may account well for the orderly, properly timed, and properly spaced elaboration of body parts.

Although inductive processes among embryonic tissues may be identified and described, the nature of such interactions in terms of reactions within and among cells is still obscure in many respects. Even so, the ultimate result of these various occurrences is a fully formed embryo, which may later hatch and become a larva or may develop into an adult directly. A new individual emerges in either event, and when this individual becomes mature the entire cycle of reproduction and development will be repeated.

Courtesy of Drs. S. R. Detwiler and R. H. Van Dyke, from fig. 16, J. Exp. Zool., vol. 69, p. 157.

29 · 28 Experiments in eye transplantation. *If an embryonic eyecup is excised from a donor embryo and is transplanted into an abnormal location in a host embryo, then a structurally perfect eye may develop at that abnormal location. The photo shows a larva of a salamander* (Amblystoma) *with two supernumerary eyes grafted into abnormal locations. The photo was taken 43 days after the transplant operation.*

This concludes the series of chapters on reproduction. Throughout the discussion we have found that the ultimate controlling role of genes either has been demonstrated already or is strongly suspected. In this regard, reproductive processes do not differ from those of steady-state control. This consideration brings us directly to the last ingredient of self-perpetuation, namely, adaptation. In adaptation even more obviously than in reproduction or steady-state control, genes are again at the root of all happenings. As genes reproduce, these time capsules of living tradition become the basis of heredity, and out of heredity is woven the fabric of evolution.

REVIEW QUESTIONS

1. Define morphogenesis, differential growth, form-regulating movements, polarity. Through what types of growth processes does an organism enlarge in size? Explain the meaning of the phrase "Organisms grow from their molecules up."

2. What different types of symmetries are exhibited by living units? In what ways do polarity and symmetry circumscribe the form of an organism? Specify the polarity and symmetry of (*a*) man and (*b*) a tree. What is the role of differential growth in the development of form?

3. Define and distinguish between differentiation and modulation. What is the relation between differentiation and specialization? Cite examples of differentiative changes on the level of (*a*) molecules, (*b*) cells, (*c*) organisms, and (*d*) societies. What kinds of changes within cells might bring about cytodifferentiation?

4. What role does metabolism play in development? How does metabolic rate vary during the developmental history of an organism? In what different ways may an incompletely developed reproductive unit acquire (*a*) nutrients and (*b*) respiratory gases? What cellular metabolic capacities (*a*) are and (*b*) are not in existence in a zygote?

5. Describe experiments performed on the development of *Acetabularia* and indicate what general principles of cellular development these experiments illustrate. Similarly review experiments on (*a*) control of antigenic type in *Paramecium*, and (*b*) cellular aggregation in *Dictyostelium*. What is the general significance of the results obtained?

6. What is a tissue culture? What kinds of developmental studies can be undertaken with the aid of tissue cultures? What has been learned about the developmental behavior of cells, tissues, and organs grown in tissue culture?

7. Describe and define the principal developmental phases in the life history of an animal if this history (*a*) includes and (*b*) does not include a sexual process. What is the significance of the greater number of phases under condition *a*? What events usually terminate (*a*) the embryonic period and (*b*) the larval period?

8. What events occur during the cleavage of an egg? What is meant by developmental determination? Distinguish between mosaic and regulative eggs. How can it be established by experiment whether a given egg is mosaic or regulative? In which animals do each of these egg types occur? How are twins formed? Distinguish between identical and fraternal twinning. Can identical twinning take place in mosaic eggs?

9. Describe the processes leading to the formation of (*a*) a blastula and (*b*) a gastrula. Define ectoderm, endoderm, mesoderm, blastopore, archenteron. How does mesoderm form in vertebrates? Which structural components of an adult vertebrate develop from each of the primary germ layers?

10. By what general processes of morphogenesis do the primary germ layers develop into adult structures? Illustrate this in the development of the nervous system and the eye. What differentiative role does induction play in such transformations? Again illustrate in the development of the nervous system and the eye and describe supporting experiments.

COLLATERAL READINGS

Balinsky, B. I.: "An Introduction to Embryology," Saunders, Philadelphia, 1960. A standard basic text on animal development.

Barth, L. J.: "Development," Addison-Wesley, Reading, Mass., 1964. This paperback deals with selected developmental topics; special emphasis is on cellular and early embryonic development.

Berrill, N. J.: "Growth, Development, and Patterns," Freeman, San Francisco, 1961. Numerous special aspects of embryonic and later development in both plants and animals are discussed in this highly recommended book.

Dahlberg, G.: An Explanation of Twins, *Sci. American*, Jan., 1951. Obviously pertinent in the context of this chapter.

Ebert, J. D.: "Interacting Systems in Development," Holt, New York, 1965. A strongly recommended analytical paperback on some of the mechanisms at work in developing units.

Fischberg, M., and A. W. Blackler: How Cells Specialize, *Sci. American*, Sept., 1961. Progressive differentiation from the egg stage onward is discussed.

Gray, G. W.: The Organizer, *Sci. American*, Nov., 1957. An examination of egg differentiation in plants and animals.

Jensen, W. A.: The Problem of Cell Development in Plants, in "Plant Biology Today," Wadsworth, Belmont, Calif., 1963. Patterns of plant development are studied in relation to the characteristics of individual cells.

Konigsberg, I. R.: The Embryological Origin of Muscle, *Sci. American*, Aug., 1964. The differentiation of muscle is described.

McElroy, W. D., and B. Glass: "The Chemical Basis of Development," Johns Hopkins, Baltimore, 1958. A collection of advanced technical papers, but very useful for background on specific points.

Moscona, A. A.: How Cells Associate, *Sci. American*, Sept., 1961. Reaggregation of isolated cells in tissue culture is examined.

Nelsen, O. E.: "Comparative Embryology of the Vertebrates," McGraw-Hill, New York, 1953. A comprehensive volume of the details of vertebrate development.

Puck, T. T.: Single Human Cells in Vitro, *Sci. American*, Aug., 1957. The article shows how from single starting cells human cells can be cultured like bacteria in artificial media.

Sussex, I. M.: Plant Morphogenesis, in "This Is Life," Holt, New York, 1962. A brief review of experiments on developmental processes involving the apical tip of vascular plants.

Sussman, M.: "Animal Growth and Development," Prentice-Hall, Englewood Cliffs, N.J., 1960. A partly comparative and partly analytical discussion of developmental processes; recommended.

Waddington, C. H.: How Do Cells Differentiate? *Sci. American*, Sept., 1953. 'A review of the embryonic and genetic aspects of differentiation during egg development.

————: "Principles of Embryology," G. Allen, London, 1956. A standard basic text on animal development.

Wardlaw, C. W.: "Morphogenesis in Plants," Methuen, London, 1952. A noted student of plant development discusses the experimental work done, much of it by the author himself.

White, P. R.: Plant Tissue Cultures, *Sci. American*, Mar., 1950. An interesting discussion of the technique and its potential.

Wigglesworth, V. B.: Metamorphosis and Differentiation, *Sci. American*, Feb., 1959. The developmental processes and control mechanisms of insect metamorphosis are examined.

PART EIGHT
SELF-PERPETUATION: ADAPTATION
CHAPTER 30
GENETIC SYSTEMS: HEREDITY
CHAPTER 31
EVOLUTION: MECHANISMS
CHAPTER 32
DESCENT: PALEONTOLOGY

On the molecular as on the organismic level, in structure as in function, every organism is *adapted* to its environment. For example, among thousands of different shapes that a fish *might* possess, its actual shape is well suited for rapid locomotion in water. A bird is cast in a form eminently suited for aerial life, yet its ancestry traces to fish. Over long periods of time, clearly, organisms may change their particular adaptations in response to new environments.

Being adapted is a universal attribute of all organisms, and adaptation is the long-range process of development which creates and maintains this attribute. Through adaptation organisms change *with* their environments, and this property makes them potentially immortal as a group.

We already know that, based on steady-state control and reproduction, adaptation consists of three components: *sex*, *heredity*, and *evolution*. Of these, the adaptive role of sex has already been discussed. In this last series of chapters, therefore, we begin with an analysis of the adaptive roles of *heredity* and continue with a similar analysis of *evolution*.

CHAPTER 30 GENETIC SYSTEMS: HEREDITY

Life began after the first nucleic acids had originated. Creation of original life took billions of years, for it had to occur by physical and chemical chance; there was no blueprint to follow. But after nucleic acids were in existence, creation of new life could become a very rapid process. Today it takes only 20 minutes to create a new bacterium, only 22 months to create a new elephant. This great acceleration is made possible by genes, the modern descendants of the first nucleic acids. Genes do provide a blueprint, a recipe, for the creation of new generations; through gene inheritance, construction of new life ceases to be a matter of chance and becomes a matter of controlled planning. Heredity therefore has adaptive significance, like sex, for what an organism inherits will determine its survival potential in large measure.

It should be clear that organisms do *not* inherit strong muscles, green leaves, sensitive hearing, red blood, beautiful flowers, or any other trait. Organisms inherit genes, not traits. Moreover, they do not inherit genes only, but all the contents of reproductive units, that is, *whole cells*. Visible traits then *develop* in an offspring, under the control of inherited genes and within the limitations imposed by given intracellular and extracellular environments.

The key problem in studies of heredity is to explain the inheritance of *likeness* and of *variation:* how an offspring usually comes to resemble its parents in certain major respects but differs from the parents in many minor respects. Are such hereditary patterns in any way regular and predictable, and if

so, what are the underlying principles? Answers can be found by examining the traits of successive generations of organisms and inferring from the visible likenesses and variations what the inheritance of the genes has been. The first important studies of this sort were made in the last half of the nineteenth century by the Austrian monk Gregor Mendel. He discovered two basic rules of inheritance which laid the foundation for all later advances in understanding of processes of heredity.

Accordingly, this discussion of heredity will include an examination of the general relationship between *genes* and *traits,* an account of the rules of *Mendelian inheritance,* and a survey of the main aspects of *non-Mendelian inheritance* brought to light since the time of Mendel.

GENES AND TRAITS

The pattern of inheritance varies according to whether reproduction is uniparental or biparental. If an organism is produced by a single parent, as in vegetative reproduction or sporulation, the genes of the parent are passed on unchanged to the offspring. In uniparental reproduction, therefore, offspring and parent are genetically identical and usually display the same visible traits. The only source of genetic variation in such cases is *mutation.* Thus, if some gene in a cell forming a bud or a spore undergoes a mutational change, then, and only then, may the offspring become genetically different from the parent. Trait variations may then also be displayed.

By contrast, two sources of genetic variation exist in cases of biparental, gametic reproduction. One is again mutation, in this instance mutation in one or both gametes. The other is a direct result of sex; *two* sets of genes are pooled in the zygote. The genetic endowment of the offspring consequently may differ from that of either parent, and through such *sexual recombination* of genes the offspring may become unlike the parents. We conclude, for both uniparental and biparental reproduction, that likeness to parents will be inherited to the extent that the genes of the offspring are the same as those of the parents, and that variation will be inherited to the extent that mutation, recombination, or both have changed the genes of the offspring (Fig. 30.1).

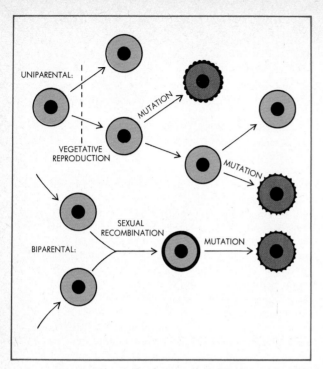

30 · 1 Sources of genetic variations. *In uni-parental inheritance the only source is mutation. In biparental inheritance genetic variations may arise both by mutation and by sexual recombination of genes.*

But inheriting a certain gene is not automatically equivalent to developing a certain trait, for the development of traits is affected by the environment. Genes supply a reasonable promise, as it were, and the total environment of the genes subsequently permits or does not permit the translation of promise into reality. The environment of genes includes, first of all, other genes. Indeed, gene interactions are exceedingly common (see below). The functional integration of genes in a cell is actually so intimate and so complex that it becomes relatively meaningless to speak of "a" gene, as if it were an independently acting particle. Only the interacting totality of genes in a cell, called the *genome*, has functional reality.

The environment of genes also includes the cell cytoplasm, and it too influences the development of traits in major ways. We know that, in the cytoplasm, genes indirectly exercise their basic function; that is, they control protein synthesis. We may regard proteins as the *primary* traits of a cell, and indeed we may formulate an acceptable definition of "gene" on this basis: a gene is that minimum section of a chromosome which controls the synthesis of a single type of protein molecule. Genes may therefore be regarded as *units of biochemical action*. In the form of enzymes or structural components, the proteins manufactured under gene control then bring about

the development of various *secondary,* often visible traits. But such traits usually differ in different cell types and in the same cell type at different times, even though the genes are the same in all. Thus, all cells of a flowering plant possess flower-color genes but only cells in the petals express that color. All cells of man possess eye-color genes, for example, but only iris cells actually develop the color. Evidently, the cytoplasms of different cells may react differently to the genes they contain, and trait expression will then differ correspondingly. The various developmental differentiations and specializations of cells and larger body parts are the result.

We may therefore distinguish between *inherited* traits, controlled by genes, and noninherited *acquired* traits, superimposed on the inherited ones and produced by nongenetic environmental and developmental effects. And we are led to the fundamental conclusion that visible traits are always a product of inherited genes and of the nongenetic environment. To the extent that variations of traits may be advantageous to an organism in its way of life, heredity then has adaptive value.

Note here that, unless we refer to a particular cellular protein synthesized under gene control, we must exercise caution in designating a given characteristic of an organism as "a" trait. For example, the hereditary characteristic of disease resistance is not really "a" trait. Inasmuch as it is a functional property of a whole organism, it is a composite property of millions of cooperating cells. Each of these contributes some particular function to the total trait, and specific genes in each of these cells control each of these functions. Therefore, disease resistance must be a combination of perhaps millions of different cellular activities controlled by a large, equally unknown number of genes.

In very many instances, what is normally regarded

30 · 2 Traits and genes. *One trait (for example, D) is often controlled by many genes, and one gene (for example, B) often controls many traits.*

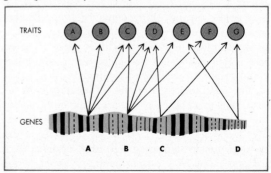

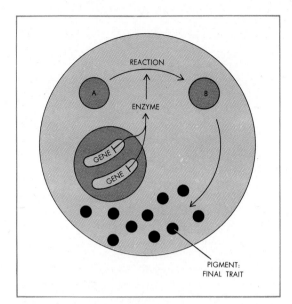

30 · 3 *One gene is known to control just one trait in certain special cases. Here a cytoplasmic pigment is the final trait. A single gene governs the manufacture of the enzyme necessary to produce the pigment.*

as one trait is of such composite nature. Body size, the fine structure and the functional capacities of organs, general vigor, intelligence, fertility, and many others—all are interaction products of several dozens or hundreds or thousands of different genes. Indeed, there is reason to believe that most of such highly composite traits are controlled by the collective action of possibly all genes of an organism, each contributing a tiny effect to the total trait. Such traits may then be expressed in a correspondingly great variety of ways. As is well known, for example, the expression of traits like body size or intelligence in different individuals may range from one extreme to another, through enormously varied series of intergradations.

But if all genes contribute to the control of a trait like body size, for example, and if all genes also control disease resistance and other highly composite traits, then any one gene clearly must contribute to the control of more than one trait. We are led to the generalization that *one composite trait may be controlled by many genes, and one gene may contribute to the control of many composite traits* (Fig. 30.2).

In some instances, the functional relation between genes and traits is comparatively less complex. We know from Chap. 21 that the general pattern of gene action within a cell may be symbolized by the sequence: gene $\longrightarrow$ $\longrightarrow$ enzyme $\longrightarrow$ reaction

$\longrightarrow$ reaction product. Sometimes such a reaction product does not participate in the elaboration of a more complex trait but constitutes a final trait itself. For example, a pigment produced within a cell is a gene-controlled reaction product, and it is often a visible endproduct, a final trait. In cases of this sort, a readily specifiable unit trait is correlated directly with one particular gene (Fig. 30.3). From the pattern in which such a trait is expressed visibly in successive generations, one may readily infer the pattern of gene inheritance. It was from studies of just such color traits in plants that Mendel deduced his two rules of heredity. If he had happened to investigate, instead, any of the numerous composite traits of organisms, then regularities in hereditary patterns would not have been clearly apparent and his name might not be immortal today.

MENDELIAN INHERITANCE

THE CHROMOSOME THEORY

If two red-flowered snapdragon plants are mated, all offspring produced are exclusively red-flowered. Moreover, all later generations also develop only red flowers. Similarly, a mating of two white-flowered snapdragons yields exclusively white-flowered progeny in all subsequent generations. Red and white flower colors in this case are said to be *true-breeding* traits (Fig. 30.4).

When a red-flowered snapdragon is mated with a white-flowered plant, all offsping develop *pink* flowers. In Mendel's time, it was generally supposed that

30 · 4 *True-breeding in snapdragons. If two red-flowered plants (P) are mated, all offspring (F₁, first filial generation) will be red-flowered (left); and if two white-flowered plants are mated, all offspring will be white-flowered (right).*

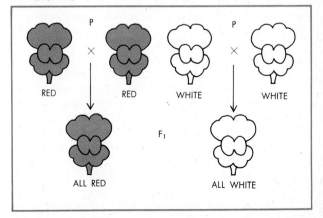

results of this kind were due to a *blending* of traits. Thus if red and white plant pigments were mixed together, like paints, a pink color would be produced. Moreover, if blending really occurred, pinkness should be equally true-breeding; for mixed traits, like mixed paints, should be incapable of "unblending." In reality, however, the results of cross-breeding are strikingly different: two pink-flowered snapdragons consistently produce pink *and* red *and* white offspring. Numerically, an average of 50 per cent of the offspring are pink, roughly 25 per cent are red, and the remainder are white (Fig. 30.5). Evidently, pinkness does *not* breed true, for from pink can be re-created pure red and white as well as pink. Hence pink color cannot be a permanent blend of red and white.

Large numbers of tests of this kind have clearly established that, quite generally for any trait, blending inheritance does not occur and that traits remain distinct and intact. They may become joined together in one generation, but they may then again become separated, or *segregated*, from one another in a following generation. Mendel was the first to reach such a conclusion from his studies on plants, and this denial of blending was his most significant contribution. It ultimately reoriented the thinking about heredity completely and paved the way for all modern insights. Mendel himself supplied the first of such in-

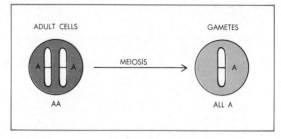

30 · 6

sights, for he not only negated the old interpretation but also postulated a new one.

He realized that traits trace back to the sperm and the egg which produce an organism, and he suspected that some specific components within the gametes controlled the later development of traits. Mendel called these hypothetical components "factors." For any given trait, he argued, an organism must inherit at least one factor from the sperm and one from the egg. Therefore, the offspring must possess at least two factors for each trait. When that offspring then becomes an adult and produces gametes in its own turn, each gamete must similarly contribute *one* factor to the next generation. Hence, at some point before gamete production, two factors must be reduced to one. Mendel consequently postulated the existence of a factor-reducing process.

With this he in effect predicted the occurrence of meiosis. When near the end of the nineteenth century meiosis was actually discovered, it was recognized that the reduction of chromosomes at some point before fertilization matched precisely the postulated reduction of Mendel's factors. Chromosomes then came to be regarded as the carriers of the factors, and so the *chromosome theory of heredity* emerged. This theory has since received complete confirmation, and Mendel's factors became the genes of today.

30 · 5 All offspring are pink if a red-flowered snapdragon is mated with a white-flowered one (P). And if two of these pink-flowered F₁ plants are then mated in turn, their offspring (F₂) will be red, pink, and white in the ratios shown.

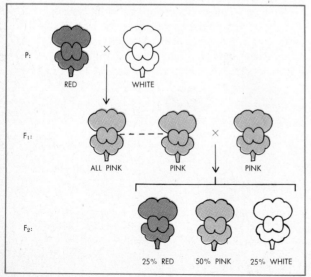

THE LAW OF SEGREGATION

On the basis of the chromosome theory, we may interpret the snapdragon data above as follows. A true-breeding red-flowered plant (parental generation, *P*) possesses a pair of red-pigment-producing genes in each cell. These genes, which may be symbolized by the letters *AA*, are located on a given pair of chromosomes, one of which is maternal and one paternal in origin. We say that the *genotype*, or gene content, of the plant is *AA* and that the *phenotype*, or visible appearance, is red. Before such a plant produces gametes, meiosis occurs. Mature gametes therefore contain only one of the two chromosomes, hence only one of the two genes (Fig. 30.6).

Note that it is entirely a matter of chance which of the two adult chromosomes will become incorporated into a given gamete. Since both adult chromosomes here carry the same color gene, all gametes will be genetically alike in this respect. We may understand now why AA plants are true-breeding, that is, why a mating of $AA \times AA$ will produce only red-flowered, AA offspring (F_1, first filial generation; Fig. 30.7).

In precisely analogous manner, we may symbolize the genotype of a true-breeding white-flowered snapdragon as aa. The letters here represent genes which do not produce any pigment at all, and the white color of such flowers is a result of this lack of pigment. A mating of two such plants (P) will yield only white-flowered (F_1) offspring (Fig. 30.8).

If we now mate a red-flowered and a white-flowered plant, *all* F_1 offspring will be *pink* (Fig. 30.9). An Aa offspring plant of this type possesses only *one* pigment-producing gene per cell, namely, A. Such a cell consequently develops only *half* as much pigment as an AA cell, which possesses two pigment-producing genes. This lesser amount of pigment in the Aa offspring appears as a dilute red, that is, pink.

If now two pink-flowered F_1 plants are mated, after meiosis each plant will give rise to two types of gametes. Given the genes Aa, either the A gene or the a gene could become incorporated into any given gamete. What actually happens in each specific case is determined by chance. Hence if, as is usually the case in plants, large numbers of gametes are produced, each possibility will be realized with roughly

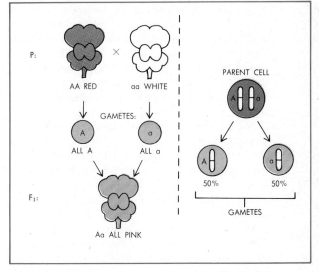

30 · 9

30 · 10

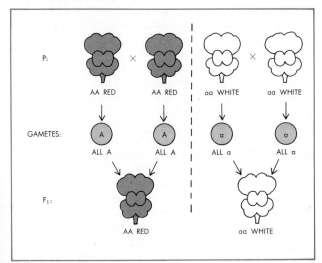

30 · 7

30 · 8

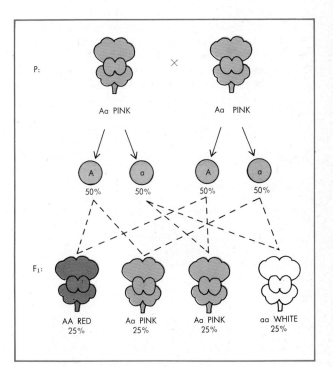

30 · 11

equal frequency. Consequently, approximately 50 per cent of the gametes will carry the A gene, the other 50 per cent, the a gene. We may write: Aa parent $\longrightarrow$ 50 per cent A gametes, 50 per cent a gametes (Fig. 30.10).

Now fertilization occurs. There are two genetically different sperm types and two genetically different egg types, and it is wholly a matter of chance which of the two sperm types fertilizes which of the two egg types. If many fertilizations occur simultaneously, as is usually the case, then all possibilities will be realized with appropriate frequency (Fig. 30.11).

We note that half the offspring (F_2, second filial generation) are pink-flowered and resemble their parents (F_1) in this respect. One-quarter are red-flowered, one-quarter white-flowered, and these offspring resemble their grandparents (P). We may conclude that the visible results can be explained adequately on the basis of nonblending, freely segregating genes and the operations of chance. Genes like A and a, which control the same trait but produce different expressions of that trait, are called allelic genes, or *alleles*. In the snapdragon example above, trait expression evidently depends on the number of A alleles. Presence of A in a single dose, as in Aa plants, gives only half as much pigment as presence of A in a double dose, as in AA plants. Most traits are affected in this way by gene dosage.

In some cases, however, a maximum trait may be produced even if an allele is present only in single dose. In garden peas, for example, as in snapdragons, true-breeding red-flowered plants may be symbolized as AA, true-breeding white-flowered plants as aa. But when two such plants are mated, *all F_1 offspring are red*, not pink (Fig. 30.12).

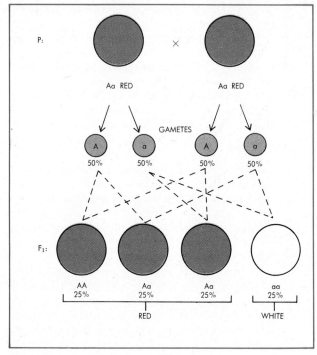

30 · 13

Evidently, the single A gene in Aa garden pea plants suffices to bring out the full red color. Two A genes, as in AA, do not produce substantially more redness. Therefore, if two red-flowered Aa (F_1) plants are mated, three out of every four F_2 offspring will be red-flowered (Fig. 30.13).

Genes producing a maximum trait even when present only in single dose, like the A's of garden peas, are called *dominant* genes. They mask more or less completely the effect of other alleles, like the a's of garden peas. The latter are *recessive* alleles. Offspring in ratios of $3/4 : 1/4$ are characteristic for matings involving dominant and recessive alleles, as above.

But complete dominance of this sort is far rarer than the allelic relationship illustrated earlier for snapdragons. There the A gene is said to be *incompletely* dominant, the a gene, *incompletely* recessive. Offspring ratios of $1/4 : 1/2 : 1/4$ are then characteristic. We may note in this connection that allelic pairs like AA or aa, in which both genes are the same, are called *homozygous* combinations. By contrast, Aa pairs are *heterozygous* combinations. Thus an AA genotype in garden peas is said to be "homozygous dominant," an aa genotype, "homozygous recessive."

In modern terminology, Mendel's first law, the *law of segregation*, may now be stated as follows: *Genes do not blend, but behave as independent units. They pass intact from one generation to the next, where*

30 · 12

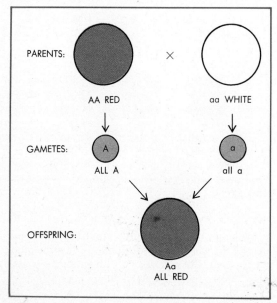

they may or may not produce visible traits depending on their dominance characteristics. And genes segregate at random, thereby producing predictable ratios of traits in the offspring. Implied in this law are chromosome reduction by meiosis and the operation of chance in the transmission of genes.

THE LAW OF INDEPENDENT ASSORTMENT

Organisms do not express traits one at a time but exhibit all their traits simultaneously. Analogously, genes are not inherited one at a time, but are all inherited together. Therefore, given certain parents, what will the offspring be like with respect to two or more simultaneous traits?

Mendel discovered a fundamental rule here. Phrased in modern terms, this *law of independent assortment states: The inheritance of a gene pair located on a given chromosome pair is unaffected by the simultaneous inheritance of other gene pairs located on other chromosome pairs.* In other words, two or more traits produced by genes located on two or more chromosome pairs "assort independently"; each trait will be expressed independently, as if no other traits were present.

The meaning of the law may be demonstrated readily if we analyze, as Mendel did, the simultaneous inheritance of two traits of garden peas, *seed shape* and *seed color*. Seed shape can be either *round* or *wrinkled*. Round can be shown to be dominant over wrinkled, and the possible alleles can be sym-

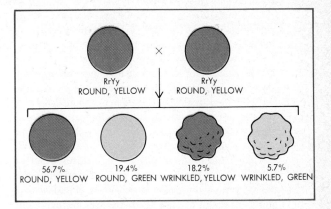

30 · 15   Parental pea plants *matured from seeds* (top) *produce offspring seeds of types and numbers shown below.*

bolized as *R* for round and *r* for wrinkled. Therefore, on a given chromosome pair of peas is located either an *RR*, an *rr*, or an *Rr* pair of alleles. Similarly *yellow* seed color (*Y*) is dominant over *green* seed color (*y*). Hence on another chromosome pair is located a *YY* or a *yy* or a *Yy* pair of alleles (Fig. 30.14).

Mendel mated two *RrYy* plants, that is, individuals developed from round, yellow seeds but heterozygous for both traits. He obtained four categories of offspring, in the proportions given in Fig. 30.15. Mendel here noted that a total of 76.1 (56.7 plus 19.4) per cent of the offspring were round-seeded, and that a total of 74.9 (56.7 plus 18.2) per cent were yellow-seeded. In other words, each of the two dominant traits, considered *separately*, amounted to very nearly 75 per cent, or three-fourths, of the total. The two recessive traits, considered separately, each amounted to about 25 per cent, or one-fourth, of the total. Evidently, as expected on the basis of the law of segregation, each dominant and its correlated recessive appeared in a ratio of $3/4 : 1/4$; dominants were three times as abundant as recessives.

Moreover, the two dominants were also three times as abundant *even if they were considered together.* Thus among the 76.1 per cent total of round-seeded offspring, 56.7 per cent, or very nearly three-fourths, were at the same time also yellow-seeded. And among the 74.9 per cent total of yellow-seeded offspring, 56,7 per cent, or again nearly three-fourths, were at the same time also round-seeded. In other words, the 56.7 per cent round- *and* yellow-seeded offspring amounted to *three-fourths of three-fourths,* or *nine-sixteenths,* of the total. The overall ratio was therefore very nearly $9/16 : 3/16 : 3/16 : 1/16$. Mendel con-

30 · 14   Color and shape of seeds *in garden peas. Four seed types may occur: round-yellow, round-green, wrinkled-green, and wrinkled-yellow. Some of the possible gene combinations which could produce these types are shown in the diagram.*

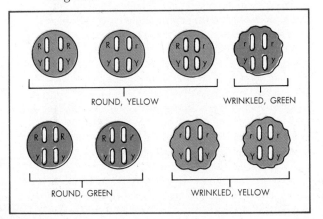

cluded that such a ratio could be obtained only if *each* trait obeyed the law of segregation, and if it were also expressed independently of other traits; hence his law of independent assortment.

The validity of this second law may be appreciated readily if we consider chromosomes, meiosis, and gametes. In the mating above, the cells of the parents are as shown in Fig. 30.16. After meiosis, each gamete will contain only *one* seed-shape gene and only *one* color gene. But which of each pair? The dominant or the recessive gene? This is a matter of chance and there are four possibilities: a gamete might contain the genes *R* and *Y*, or *R* and *y*, or *r* and *Y*, or *r* and *y*. Many gametes are produced and all four combinations will therefore occur with roughly equal frequency (see Fig. 30.16).

Fertilization is similarly governed by chance. Consequently, *any* one of the four sperm types might fertilize *any* one of the four egg types. Hence there are 16 different ways in which fertilization can occur. If large numbers of fertilization take place simultaneously, all 16 ways will be realized with roughly equal frequency. We may determine these 16 ways by using a grid where the gametes of one parent are put along a horizontal edge and the gametes of the other parent along a vertical edge (Fig. 30.17). Among the 16 offspring types now formed, we find some individuals that contain *both* dominant genes at least once, some that contain one *or* the other of the dominant genes at least once, and some that contain none of the dominant genes. A count reveals round-yellow, round-green, wrinkled-yellow, and wrinkled-green to be present in a ratio of 9:3:3:1. This is the ratio Mendel actually obtained.

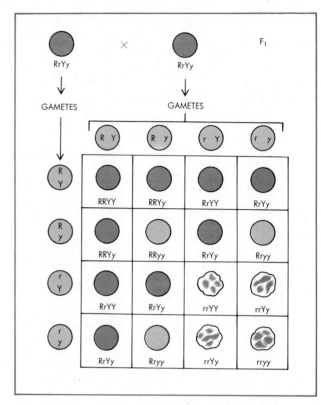

30 · 17

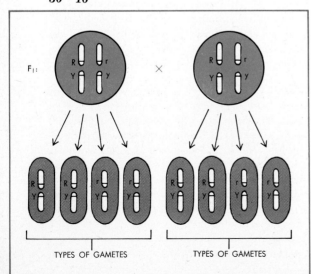

30 · 16

Mendel's second law applies specifically to gene pairs located on *different* chromosome pairs. The law will therefore hold for as many different gene pairs as there are chromosome pairs in each cell of a given organism. Suppose we considered the inheritance of *three* different gene pairs, each located on a different chromosome pair. For example, what would be the offspring of a mating of two triple heterozygotes, such as *AaBbCc* × *AaBbCc?*

We have found above that a double heterozygote *AaBb* produces *four* different gamete types. It should not be too difficult to verify that a triple heterozygote produces *eight* different gamete types, namely *ABC*, *ABc*, *AbC*, *Abc*, *aBC*, *aBc*, *abC*, and *abc*. To determine all possible genotypes of the offspring, we may make a grid 8 squares by 8 squares and place the 8 gamete types of each parent along the sides of the grid, as above; and 64 offspring types will then result. Of these, 27 will express all three traits in dominant form. The complete phenotype ratio may easily be verified as 27:9:9:9:3:3:3:1.

Two quadruple heterozygotes, *AaBbCcDd*, would manufacture 16 gamete types each, and we would need a grid 16 by 16 to represent the 256 different genotype combinations. Evidently, the possibilities rapidly become astronomical once we consider more than a few traits simultaneously.

Organisms heterozygous for a large number of traits are known as *hybrids. Aa* types are sometimes referred to as *monohybrids, AaBb* types as *dihybrids, AaBbCc* types as *trihybrids.* In man there are 23 pairs of chromosomes per cell. Consequently, Mendel's second law will apply to any 23 different traits controlled by genes located on different chromosome pairs. We might then study a mating of, for example, two 23-fold hybrids: *AaBb . . . Ww* × *AaBb . . . Ww.* How many gamete types would each such hybrid produce? We know that:

a monohybrid yields $2^1 = 2$ gamete types
a dihybrid yields $2^2 = 4$ gamete types
a trihybrid yields $2^3 = 8$ gamete types
a quadruple hybrid yields $2^4 = 16$ gamete types

Carrying this progression further, we find that a 23-fold hybrid will produce 2^{23} or over 8 million genetically different gamete types. Therefore, in considering just 23 traits, we would require a grid 8 million by 8 million to represent the over 64 trillion possible genotypes.

A particular individual then inherits just one of these genotypes. Of all the possible genotypes, a few millions or billions will produce resemblance to parents and another few millions or billions to grandparents or earlier ancestors. But there are bound to be a good many million or billion genotypes which have never yet become expressed during the entire history of man. Accordingly, there is a very excellent chance that every newly born human being differs from every other one, past or present, in at least some genes controlling just 23 traits. And the genetic differences for *all* traits must be enormous indeed. Here is one major reason for individual variations and a genetic basis for the universal generalization that no two organisms are precisely identical.

Any given chromosome contains not just one gene but anywhere from a few hundred to a few thousand genes. What is the inheritance pattern of two or more gene pairs located on the *same* chromosome pair? This question leads us beyond Mendel's two laws.

THE LAW OF LINEAR ORDER

Genes located within the same chromosome are said to be *linked:* as the chromosome is inherited, so are all its genes inherited. Such genes clearly do *not* assort independently but are transmitted together in a block. The traits controlled by linked genes are similarly expressed in a block. For example, assume

that in the heterozygote *AaBb* the two gene pairs are linked. When such a dihybrid produces gametes, only *two* different gamete types are expected, 50 per cent of each (Fig. 30.18). We recall that if the gene pairs *Aa* and *Bb* were not linked, we should expect *four* gamete types through independent assortment, namely, *AB, ab, Ab,* and *aB,* 25 per cent of each.

Linkage studies were first undertaken by T. H. Morgan, a renowned American biologist of the early twentieth century. Experimenting with fruit flies, *Drosophila,* Morgan discovered a curious phenomenon. When genes were linked, the expected result of two gamete types in a 50:50 ratio was obtained relatively rarely. Instead, there were usually somewhat fewer than 50 per cent of each gamete type, and there were correspondingly small percentages of two additional, completely unexpected gamete types.

For example, fruit flies possess a gene for *gray* body color (*B*), dominant over a gene for *black* body color (*b*). These alleles are located on the same chromosomes which also carry genes controlling wing shape: all allele for *normal* wings (*V*), dominant over an allele for highly reduced, *vestigial* wings (*v*). If now a gray-bodied, normal-winged heterozygous female fly, *BbVv,* produces gametes, only two types should be expected, namely, *BV* and *bv* (Fig. 30.19). However, Morgan consistently obtained *four* gamete types, in the proportions given in Fig. 30.20.

If these four types had formed to an extent of about 25 per cent each, the experiment could have

30 · 18

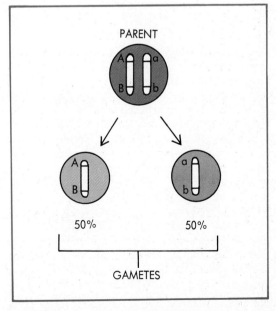

PARENT

50% 50%

GAMETES

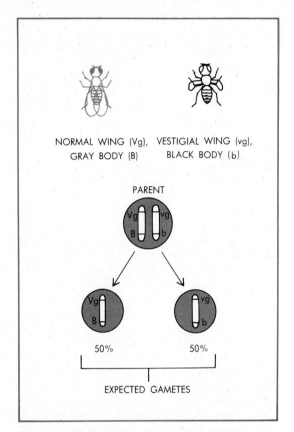

30 · 19 **Phenotypes of two traits** (*wing shape and body color*) *of* Drosophila (*top*) *controlled by linked genes.* (*See also Fig. 30.23.*) *Bottom, the expected gametes of a heterozygous fly,* VgvgBb.

deed, and the phenomenon of *crossing over* was so proved.

The implications of this discovery were far-reaching. It was reasoned that the frequency of crossovers should be an index of the *distance* between two genes. If two genes on a chromosome are located near each other, the chances should be relatively small that a break and fusion will occur between these close points. But if two genes are relatively far apart, then breaks between these points should be rather frequent. In general, the frequency of crossovers should be proportional to the distance between two genes on a chromosome (Fig. 30.22).

Inasmuch as the crossover percentage of two genes could be determined by breeding experiments, it became possible to construct *gene maps* showing the actual location of given genes on a chromosome. Since Morgan's time, the exact position of few hundred genes has been mapped in the fruit fly. Smaller numbers of genes have similarly been located in corn plants, in mice, and in various other organisms. Many of these determinations have been corroborated by X-ray work. When irradiated, a chromosome may break into pieces and a small piece of this sort may be lost from a gamete. Offspring resulting from such deficient gametes will be abnormal in certain traits. In many cases, microscopic examination can show where a chromosome piece is missing and a trait thus can be correlated with a particular spot on a chromosome.

A second implication of crossing over is that genes on a chromosome must be lined up single-file. Only if this is the case can linkage and crossing over occur as it actually does occur. This generalization has become known as the *law of the linear order of genes.* It constitutes the third major rule governing Mendelian inheritance.

Third, crossing over has provided a functional

been regarded simply as a case without linkage, governed by Mendel's second law. But the actual results included significantly *more* than 25 per cent each of the expected gamete types and significantly *fewer* than 25 per cent each of the unexpected types. To explain these odd results, Morgan proposed a new hypothesis. He postulated that, during meiosis, paired chromosomes in some cases might *twist around each other* and might break where they are twisted. The broken pieces might then fuse again in the "wrong" order (Fig. 30.21).

Such a process would account for the large percentage of expected and the small percentage of unexpected gamete types. To test the validity of this hypothesis, cells undergoing meiosis were examined carefully under the microscope: could chromosome twists and breaks actually be seen? They could in-

30 · 20

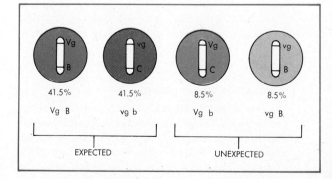

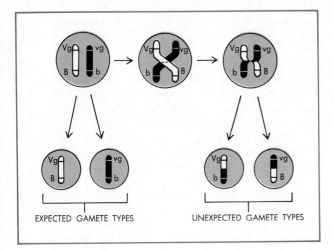

EXPECTED GAMETE TYPES   UNEXPECTED GAMETE TYPES

30 · 21

definition of "gene": *A gene is the smallest section of a chromosome within which crossovers do not take place.* The assumption here is that the minimum chromosome unit able to cross over is one *whole* gene, not a fractional part of one gene. Evidently, genes may be regarded either as units of biochemical action or as *crossover units.* A third possible definition will emerge below. It follows that a gene is not a singularly definable object; what we mean by "a gene" depends entirely on the techniques we use to study it. Put another way, genes are *operational concepts.*

A final implication of crossing over during meiosis is that meiosis is a source of genetic variations. For example, when a diploid cell in a testis undergoes meiosis and produces four haploid sperms, these four do not contain merely the same whole chromosomes as the original cell, even though redistributed. For if the original diploid cell possesses a chromosome pair M' and M'', then a given sperm will not simply receive either the M' or the M'' chromosome. Instead, as a result of crossing over, it will receive a quiltwork chromosome composed of various joined pieces of *both* M' and M''. In each set of four sperms, actually, two will contain like chromosomes composed of one set of M' and M'' pieces, and two will contain like chromosomes composed of the remaining, complementary M' and M'' pieces. Moreover, the original diploid cell possesses not just a single chromosome pair but several, and each such pair is likely to be subject to crossing over in an unpredictable fashion. Chances are therefore excellent that the four sperms will be genetically different from one another as well as from the original diploid cell. Further, even two

genetically identical diploid cells are not likely to give rise to genetically identical sets of sperms. In general, the gene-shuffling effect of crossing over is in evidence wherever or whenever meiosis occurs. Genetic variations consequently are produced by both phases of sex, that is, by chromosome doubling through fertilization as well as by chromosome reduction through meiosis.

The three rules of heredity here outlined describe and predict the consequences of sexual recombination, that is, the various results that can be obtained when different sets of genes become joined through fertilization and are pooled in the zygote. In other words, sexual recombination of genes leads to Mendelian inheritance. However, a great many hereditary events have been found that do not obey the three basic rules. Some of these non-Mendelian processes will be the subject of the following section.

NON-MENDELIAN INHERITANCE

MUTATION

Two instances of non-Mendelian heredity are bacterial *transformation* and *transduction,* already discussed in Chap. 20. In these cases, the gene content of bacteria is altered by the introduction of additional genetic material through the agency of either human experimenters or viruses (see Figs. 20.1 and 20.2). However, transformation and transduction have strictly limited significance. A far more important type of non-Mendelian variation, of universal significance, is *mutation.*

Any stable, inheritable change in the genetic ma-

30 · 22 Crossover frequency in relation to gene distances. If two genes are far apart, crossing over between them is likely to occur rather frequently (top). But if genes are close together, crossing over between them is less likely. In general, the farther apart given genes are on a chromosome, the more frequent crossing over will be.

GENES FAR APART   CROSSOVER FREQUENCY HIGH

GENES CLOSE TOGETHER   CROSSOVER FREQUENCY LOW

terial present in a cell constitutes a mutation. For example, the accidental doubling, tripling, and so on, of the normal chromosome number represents a stable, transmissible *chromosome mutation*. Accidental loss or addition of a whole chromosome, loss of a chromosome piece, fusion of such a piece with another chromosome or fusion with the original chromosome in inverted position—these also are chromosome mutations. But by far the most common type of mutation is a *point mutation*, a stable change of one gene. A third definition of "gene" is that it is a *unit of mutation*, that is, that minimum part of a chromosome which, after becoming altered in a stable manner, changes just one trait of a cell (Fig. 30.23).

It has been known for many years that mutational changes can be induced by high-energy radiation such as X rays. The frequency of mutation has been found to be directly proportional to the amount of radiation a cell receives. Are naturally occurring mutations similarly produced by radiation, that is, by cosmic rays and other space radiation or by radioactive elements in the earth? Probably not entirely; it can be shown that unavoidable natural radiation affecting all living organisms is not sufficiently intense to account for the mutation frequency characteristic of genes generally. This frequency has been estimated as about one mutation per million cells, on the average. However, natural "background" radiation does produce some mutations. Most others probably represent errors in gene reproduction (see Fig. 20.13). And still others are undoubtedly caused by

man-made radiation, which adds to and so increases the natural background radiation. Mutations can also be produced experimentally by physical agents other than radiations and by various chemical agents.

Apart from limitations as to numbers, types, and range of possible effects, mutations occur entirely at random. Any gene may mutate at any time, in unpredictable ways. A given gene may mutate several times in rapid succession, then not at all for considerable periods. It may mutate in one direction, then mutate back to its original state or in new directions. There is little question that *every* gene existing today is a *mutant* which has undergone many mutations during its past history.

The effect of a mutation on a trait is equally unpredictable. Some are "large" mutations, that is, they affect a major trait in a radical, drastic manner. Others are "small," with but little effect on a trait. Some mutations are dominant, producing immediate positive alterations of traits. Other mutations are recessive, and in diploid cells they remain masked by normal dominant alleles.

Most mutations are disadvantageous. Indeed, inasmuch as a living cell is an exceedingly complex, very finely adjusted whole, it is to be expected that *any* permanent change in cellular properties would be more or less disruptive and harmful. In many cases, therefore, dominant mutations tend to be eliminated as soon as they arise, through death of the affected cell. In other cases, the effect of a dominant mutation, particularly a "small" dominant mutation, may become integrated successfully into cellular functions. Such a cell may then survive even though it exhibits an altered trait. By and large, however, recessive mutations are likely to persist more readily in diploid cells, since their effects may be masked by normal dominant alleles. Accumulated

30 · 23 *Mutant types resulting from point mutations. The photos give the actual appearance of wild type* (left) *and vestigial-winged* (right) *fruit flies* (Drosophila melanogaster).

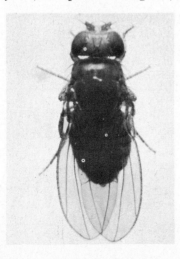

evidence actually shows that surviving mutations are very largely recessive ones.

A small percentage of mutants produces advantageous traits and new traits that are neither advantageous nor disadvantageous. Consider mutations in man for example. Many trillions of cells compose the human body and mutations occur at an average rate of one in every million cells. Therefore, several million mutations are likely to occur in each individual. Many of these may be lethal to the cells in which they occur and many others will remain masked by normal dominants. But some mutations may produce nonlethal traits. Such new traits arising in individual cells are then transmitted to all cells formed from the original ones by division. For example, "beauty spots" probably develop in this manner.

Gene changes of this type, occurring in body cells generally, are known as *somatic mutations.* They affect the heredity of the cell progeny, that is, a patch of tissue at most. But in multicellular organisms such mutations have little direct bearing on the heredity of the individual. Entire multicellular offspring are affected only by so-called *germ mutations,* stable genetic changes in immature and mature reproductive cells. Such mutations will be transmitted to all cells that ultimately compose the offspring (Fig. 30.24). To the extent that germ mutations may be recessive and masked by normal dominants, the traits of the offspring will not be altered. But if the offspring is haploid, or is diploid but homozygous recessive for a mutation, or if a mutation is dominant, then a particular trait may be expressed in altered form. Provided such a new trait is not lethal, it will persist as an individual (and non-Mendelian) variation. Mutations may therefore affect the adaptation of an individual as much as sexual recombination of genes.

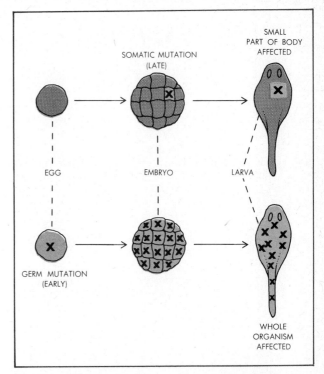

30 · 24 Germ mutations and somatic mutations. *If a mutation occurs late during development, in a somatic cell, then only the progeny of that cell will inherit the mutation and the total effect on the adult animal will be small. But if a mutation occurs early during development, for example, in a reproductive cell, then all cells of the resulting adult will inherit such a germ mutuation and may be altered.*

MUTONS, RECONS, CISTRONS

We already know from Chap. 20 that a mutation need not change the structure of an entire gene; an alteration of a single nitrogen base in a code triplet of DNA probably suffices to produce an effective mutational change. If so, should a whole gene be regarded as the "minimum" unit of heredity? If a gene represents a series of joined nucleotides in a DNA chain, could not the internal parts of such a section of DNA represent functional *subunits* of a gene?

That a gene actually might contain functional subunits can be inferred from the phenomenon of *multiple alleles.* Many genes are known to occur in not just two but in several dozens of alternative allelic forms, each allele having a specifically different

effect on the expression of the same trait. Thus, all allelic forms of a gene might affect eye color, but the actual color produced by one of the alleles might differ slightly from that produced by any of the other alleles. Inasmuch as allelic forms do affect the same trait, it is quite unlikely that their DNA's are totally different. It is far more likely that all alleles of a gene have essentially the same basic sequence of joined nucleotides, and that the functional differences between alleles are due to relatively slight chemical differences. For example, one or perhaps a few of the nucleotides present at a given point along the DNA chain of one allele might differ from the nucleotides present at the corresponding point of another allele. In terms of molecular structure, therefore, any given allelic state of a gene might differ from any other by not more than one or at most a few nucleotides along otherwise identical DNA chains.

New allelic states are produced by gene mutation. Thus, a detectable new allele could be produced if a mutation affected only a small segment within a gene. The creation of new allelic genes in this fashion has actually been demonstrated, and the term *muton* has been proposed to designate the smallest segment within a gene which by mutation can produce an altered trait. A muton has been estimated to consist of perhaps just one and probably no more than three joined nucleotides, and a whole gene may be envisaged to consist of a linear array of very many mutons.

If consecutive segments within a single gene may mutate independently, a gene should include a linear series of functionally different regions. That this is actually the case has been shown in recent studies on gene-controlled enzyme synthesis (principally in bacteria). These studies indicate that small, functionally distinguishable segments of genes can become transferred to other chromosomes. Such transfers are not crossovers. As outlined earlier, crossing over takes place between whole genes, and we recall that a possible definition of a whole gene is that it is the smallest chromosome unit capable of crossing over. Crossing over is also a reciprocal process. For example, suppose that genes A and B are linked on one chromosome and that the corresponding alleles a and b are linked on the other chromosome of a pair. If crossing over occurs between A and B, the result will be the combination Ab as well as the reciprocal combination aB.

By contrast, transfers of small segments within a gene are occasionally nonreciprocal. Suppose that a gene R contains the subunits R_1 and R_2 and that an allele r on the other chromosome of a pair contains the corresponding subunits r_1 and r_2:

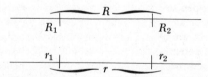

When the genes R and r reproduce and form duplicates, it happens in some cases that one of the genes appears to make a reproduction error. For example, R_1R_2 may form a normal duplicate but r_1r_2 may not. The r_1 region may be duplicated correctly, but instead of also forming a copy of the r_2 region, the gene copies the R_2 region of the nearby allele on the other chromosome. The result is a new gene containing the subunits r_1R_2:

The combination r_1R_2 is clearly nonreciprocal, for R_1r_2 is not formed.

Evidently, the r_2 region behaves as if it could make a *copy choice* during reproduction; it may produce either another r_2 or an R_2 region. Recombinations of subunits within genes generally appear to result from "wrong" copy choices. The smallest segment within a gene capable of forming new recombinations as just described has been called a *recon*. Such a unit may consist of perhaps not more than a single nucleotide. It is therefore conceivable that, in some cases at least, a recon may be identical with a muton.

Can a genetic function continue to be performed if the mutons and recons of a gene are not united together on the same chromosome? For example, suppose that a given gene A controls the synthesis of a particular enzyme protein and that this gene consists of a series of consecutive mutons. Suppose also that the mutons form two adjacent groups A_1 and A_2, and that an allelic recessive gene a contains the corresponding muton groups a_1 and a_2:

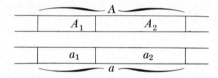

So arranged on the same chromosome, the muton groups A_1 and A_2 are said to be in a *cis* position. Under such conditions the whole gene A will function normally and will control the synthesis of the enzyme, as assumed.

What is the effect on genetic function if the muton groups A_1 and A_2 are not within the same chromosome? For example, A_1 and A_2 may come to be located on different chromosomes and may be arranged in a *trans* position:

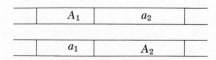

In such a *trans* arrangement, control of enzyme synthesis may or may not continue normally, depending on the specific nature of the gene and its muton groups A_1 and A_2. If the genetic function of A does continue normally, the muton groups A_1 and A_2 are said to *complement* each other. In this case, evidently, the functional effectiveness of the gene is not interfered with even though the gene is subdivided structurally and each muton group is located on a different chromosome. In other cases, however, a *trans* arrangement of muton groups does lead to cessation of enzyme synthesis; complementation does not occur and genetic function then stops.

Such results can be explained if it is assumed that given numbers of consecutive mutons (or recons) within a gene form larger functional sets. For example, if a gene consisted of 50 mutons, 30 of these might form an integrated block which might have to stay intact structurally if function is to be maintained. Thus, if this block of 30 were on one chromosome and the remaining 20 were in *trans* position on another chromosome, then complementation could occur and genetic function could continue. But if only 29 mutons were on one chromosome and the remaining 21 were on the other, then complementation could not occur since an intact block of 30 mutons would no longer be present. The actual existence of such integrated blocks of mutons within genes has been verified. The term *cistron* has been coined for the smallest set of mutons or recons of a gene which must remain together on one chromosome if genetic activity is to be preserved. The mutons within a cistron undoubtedly interact with one another in some intimate way, and if the interaction is prevented by a subdivision of the cistron, then the whole cistron will become nonfunctional. Tests show that a single gene consists of relatively few cistrons, one adjacent to the next and each composed of specific numbers of mutons (or recons).

We may conclude, therefore, that for each operational definition of a whole gene we now also have a corresponding operational definition of a genic subunit. A whole gene is a unit of mutation, or a unit of recombination by crossing over, or a unit of biochemical action. Within a gene, analogously, the mutational unit is the muton, the recombinational unit is the recon, and the functional unit is the cistron. Both sets of definitions are operational ones reflecting the nature and refinement of the experimental methods we use. If we regard a whole protein molecule as the smallest genetically controlled trait, then our experimental methods will lead us correspondingly to a smallest unit of heredity; we have called such a unit a gene. Until recently, the best conclusion actually permitted by available methods was that a whole gene controlled the synthesis of a whole protein molecule. However, we know that a protein molecule has subtraits, namely, amino acids

and polypeptide chains. And it is now possible to study the inheritance of such subtraits by means of refined experimental methods. The results have shown that a whole Mendelian gene is a relatively crude hereditary unit within which finer subunits may be identified—mutons, recons, and cistrons. Conceivably, mutons and recons may control the synthesis of individual amino acids, and cistrons may control the synthesis of polypeptide chains. In any event, a gene must be regarded as a complex chromosome region composed of many interacting functional parts. The latter appear to have a definite though not yet fully specified relation to the structural units of the DNA chain.

Interaction is known to occur not only among the parts within a gene but also among whole genes. As pointed out earlier, the activity of a gene is influenced by its environment and this environment includes other genes. Like the interactions within genes, those among genes again tend to produce non-Mendelian results, that is, results that cannot be predicted by the three rules of Mendelian inheritance.

GENE-GENE INTERACTIONS

Groups of genes within a cell often cooperate in controlling a highly composite trait. One of the best illustrations is the trait of sexuality, which in numerous organisms is controlled not by individual genes acting separately but by whole chromosomes acting as functionally integrated units.

Sex Determination

Each organism is believed to possess genes promoting the development of male traits as well as genes promoting the development of female traits. Such genes are not usually specialized "sex genes," but they tend to be of a type which, among other effects, also happen to influence the sexual development of a plant or an animal. Fundamentally, therefore, all organisms are potentially *bisexual;* each possesses a genetic potential for both maleness and femaleness. Organisms may be classified into two categories according to how this genetic potential is translated into actual sexual traits.

In one category, comprising probably the majority of all types of organisms, the masculinizing genes are equal in effect to the feminizing genes. The two genetic influences are matched exactly in "strength," and in the absence of other influences an organism will then develop as a hermaphrodite. In many cases, however, other sex-determining factors do exert an effect. Such factors are nongenetic and environ-

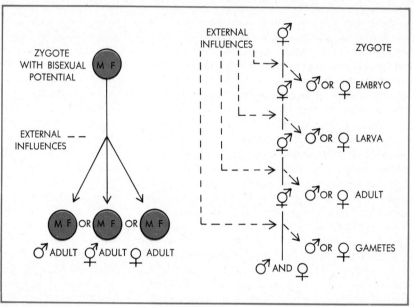

30 · 25 Nongenetic sex determination. *Left, M and F in zygote and adults indicate that male- and female-determining genetic factors are equally balanced. The actual maleness, femaleness, or hermaphroditic condition of the adult will depend on external nongenetic influences acting at some point during development. Right, such influences act at different developmental stages in different types of organisms. Thus, separate sexuality may already become manifest in the embryo or, by contrast, not until the adult produces gametes. Up to such an externally influenced determination stage, the organism retains a bisexual (hermaphroditic) potential.*

mental; different conditions in the external or internal environment affect an organism in such a way that it develops either as a male or as a female. The genetic characteristics of the species determine whether nongenetic influences will or will not play a role and thus whether the species will be separately sexed or hermaphroditic (Fig. 30.25).

Also the genetic nature of the species determines *when* during the life cycle the sex of an organism may become fixed by nongenetic means. For example in hydras and other animal groups, sex determination does not occur until the animals are fully adult and ready to produce gametes. Up to that time, an individual is sexually indifferent, and all cells retain a bisexual potential. Later, certain environmental influences affect the gamete-producing cells in such a way that they mature either as sperms or as eggs. The precise nature of these influences has in most cases not yet been identified. In hermaphroditic species, the gamete-producing cells remain unaffected and both sperms and eggs are formed.

In other instances, nongenetic sex determination

takes place earlier in the life cycle, for example, during the larval phase. After metamorphosis, therefore, such animals are no longer bisexual but are already determined as males, females, or hermaphrodites. In at least one case, namely, the echiuroid worm *Bonellia* (see Chap. 15), the sex-determining factor is known to be environmental CO_2. The relatively low concentrations of CO_2 in sea water cause free-swimming larvae of this worm to develop as females. But if a sexually still indifferent larva happens to come into contact with an adult female or with a larva already determined as a female, then the added respiratory CO_2 produced by the latter causes the indifferent larva to be determined as a male; it becomes a small, sperm-producing, and structurally quite distinct parasitic animal, permanently attached within the body of the female (see Fig. 15.30). In still other animal groups, nongenetic sex determination occurs even earlier during the life cycle, for example, after cleavage or within the fertilized egg itself. The sexually indifferent period then is reduced correspondingly.

An altogether different pattern of sex determination characterizes a second category of organisms, again represented by various protists, plants, and animals. In these, the masculinizing genes are not equal in effect to the feminizing genes, and the primary determination of sex has a purely genetic basis. Any individual becomes either a male or a female; hermaphroditism does not occur except as an abnormality. Also, the determination of sex always takes place at the time of fertilization, and every cell of the embryo, the larva, and the adult is therefore genetically male or female (Fig. 30.26).

Organisms in this category possess a pair of special *sex chromosomes*, different in size and shape from all other chromosomes. The latter are referred to as *autosomes*. The sex chromosomes are structurally of two types and are referred to as X and Y chromo-

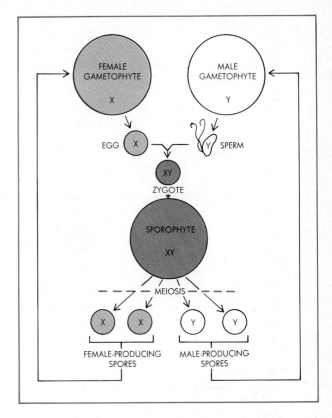

30 · 26 Genetic sex determination. 1. In the zygote, either the male-determining genes outweigh the effect of the female-determining genes (M over f), or vice versa (F over m); all subsequent stages are then separately sexed, and hermaphroditic or bisexual conditions do not (normally) occur. 2. If X chromosomes determine femaleness and autosomes (A) maleness, then the cells of the two sexes will have the chromosome balances shown (many pairs of A are assumed to be present here). This pattern occurs, for example, in insects such as fruit flies and in mammals; actual chromosome balances for man are indicated in 3. The reverse of 2 is shown in 4, X here determining maleness, A, femaleness. This pattern is encountered, for example, in butterflies, fishes, and birds. The Y chromosomes in 2, 3, and 4 are genetically inert.

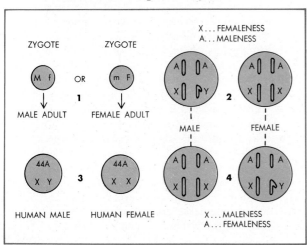

30 · 27 Sex determination in the bryophyte Sphaerocarpos. *The sex chromosomes are named X and Y, the former determining femaleness, the latter maleness. Note that gametophytes are haploid and thus carry only a single sex chromosome per cell; sporophytes are diploid and carry two, namely X and Y. This endows sporophytes with potential genetic bisexuality, even though structurally the plants represent the asexual generation.*

somes. In the liverwort *Sphaerocarpos*, for example, the gametophytes are separately sexed. Examination reveals that each cell of a female gametophyte contains one X chromosome. Analogously, each cell of a male gametophyte contains one Y chromosome (Fig. 30.27). Eggs and sperms are then similarly X and Y, respectively. Fertilization therefore produces a diploid zygote which is XY in constitution. Each cell of the sporophyte subsequently inherits the XY chromosomes. Where a spore-producing cell of the sporophyte later undergoes meiosis, the two sex chromosomes become segregated into different spore cells. The final result is that, of the four mature spores formed, two contain an X chromosome each and two a Y chromosome each. Thus, even though all spores look alike, they are genetically of two different sex types. Spores with X chromosomes subsequently mature into female gametophytes and spores with Y chromosomes mature into male gametophytes. Evidently, the whole X chromosome appears to determine femaleness, the whole Y chromosome, maleness. We may conclude that, probably in addition to serving in other trait-controlling roles, each gene of a sex chromosome also contributes toward the control of the sexual characteristics of the plant.

An entirely similar sex-determining mechanism exists in a number of other bryophytes and also in several protists. The pattern of sex inheritance is somewhat different in other organisms in which genetic sex determination is known to occur, for example, in tracheophytes such as *Elodea* and strawberry plants and in animals such as insects and vertebrates. In each diploid cell of such organisms a pair

30 · 28 Chromosomes of the fruit fly Drosophila (top). *In each cell, $2n = 8$. Note the differences in the sex chromosomes of males and females. Bottom, sex and chromosome balances in the fruit fly. The sexual character of an individual is determined by the specific balances of autosomes and X chromosomes.*

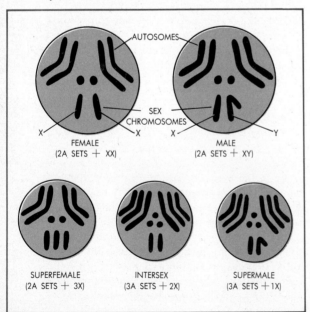

X — — X   X — — Y
FEMALE
(2A SETS + XX)   **MALE**
(2A SETS + XY)

AUTOSOMES

SEX CHROMOSOMES

SUPERFEMALE
(2A SETS + 3X)   **INTERSEX**
(3A SETS + 2X)   **SUPERMALE**
(3A SETS + 1X)

of sex chromosomes is present, and these may consist either of one X and one Y chromosome or of two X chromosomes. For example, in holly, *Elodea*, mammals, and flies, all cells of adult *males* contain an XY pair, all cells of *females*, an XX pair. By contrast, in strawberries, butterflies, most moths, some fishes, and in birds, the cells of females contain an XY pair and the cells of males, an XX pair (see Fig. 30.26). In either case, the Y chromosomes are in most instances inert from the standpoint of sex determination; they may be lost from cells without appreciable effects. But the X chromosomes and the autosomes do determine sexual traits. Where the males are of the XY type, the X chromosomes promote the development of femaleness and the autosomes promote the development of maleness. Conversely, where the males are of the XX type, the X chromosomes promote male traits, the autosomes, female traits.

In man, for example, each adult cell contains 22 pairs of autosomes plus either an XY or an XX pair. The chromosome complement of male cells may be symbolized as $44A + XY$, that of female cells, as $44A + XX$ (see Fig. 30.26). In view of the inertness of the Y chromosome, the cells of human females thus possess 46 functional chromosomes but male cells possess only 45. This difference of one whole X chromosome, with it hundreds of genes, lies at the root of the sexual differences between males and females. More specifically, in a $44A + XX$ cell, the total feminizing influence of the two X chromosomes outweighs the total masculinizing effect of the 44 autosomes, and such cells are therefore female. But in a $44A + XY$ cell, the total masculinizing effect of the 44 autosomes outweighs the feminizing influence of the single X chromosome and such cells are male.

That the sexual nature of an individual does indeed depend on a particular balance of X chromosomes and autosomes has been proved by experiments in fruit flies. In these animals, it is possible by certain laboratory procedures to vary the numbers of X chromosomes and autosomes normally present in the sperms and eggs. One may then obtain offspring characterized by normal paired sets of autosomes, but by three X chromosomes instead of two. Such individuals grow into so-called *superfemales;* all sexual traits are generally accentuated in the direction of femaleness. *Supermales* and *intersexes* may be produced analogously. In intersexes, sexual traits are intermediate between those of males and females. The chromosome balances are shown in Fig. 30.28. Paradoxically, supersexes and also intersexes are generally sterile; as a result of the abnormal chromosome numbers, meiosis occurs abnormally and the sperms and eggs then produced are defective.

In the light of such balances, we may appreciate readily how the sex of an offspring is normally determined at the time of fertilization. For example, human females, 44A + XX, produce eggs of which each contains 22A + X after meiosis. Males, 44A + XY, produce two kinds of sperms, namely, 22A + X and 22A + Y, in roughly equal numbers. Fertilization now occurs at random, that is, a sperm of either type may unite with an egg. Therefore, in about 50 per cent of the cases the result will be (22A + X) + (22A + X), or 44A + XX, or zygotes developing into females. In the remaining 50 per cent of the cases, the zygotes will be (22A + X) + (22A + Y), or 44A + XY, or prospectively male (Fig. 30.29).

Note that it is the paternal gamete that, at the moment of fertilization, determines the sex of the offspring. When only a single offspring is produced, there exists a 50:50 chance of its being a son or a daughter. When many offspring are produced, the number of males will generally equal the number of females. Note also that the absence of a functional mate to the X chromosome in males has other genetic consequences. In females, the effect of a recessive gene located on one X chromosome may be masked by the effect of a dominant located on the other X chromosome. But in males recessive genes on the X chromosome may exert their effect, since another X chromosome with masking dominants is never present. Genes located on X chromosomes are called *sex-linked* genes.

Because males possess only a single X chromosome, such genes are inherited according to a characteristic pattern. For example, red-green color blindness in man is traceable to a sex-linked recessive gene c. Suppose that a color-blind male, $X_c Y$, marries a normal female, XX. In this symbolization, an X chromosome without the subscript c is tacitly assumed to contain the dominant gene C, which prevents the expression of color blindness. The offspring of such a mating, shown in Fig. 30.30, include sons and daughters in equal numbers. The daughters carry recessive gene c, but *all* offspring have normal vision.

Suppose now that one of these daughters marries a normal male, as shown in Fig. 30.31. All daughters resulting from such a mating are normal, but half the sons are color-blind. Thus the trait has been transmitted from color-blind grandfather via normal mother to color-blind son. Such a zigzag pattern of inheritance is characteristic of all recessive sex-linked traits. Males typically exhibit the trait, females merely transmit it. The second X chromosome in females prevents expression of recessive sex-linked traits.

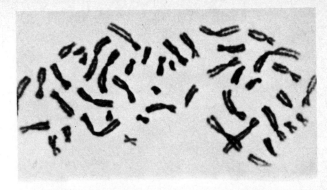

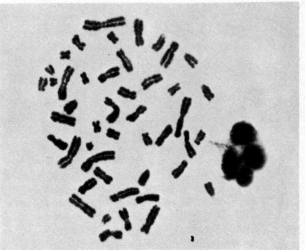

Courtesy of Carolina Biological Supply Company.

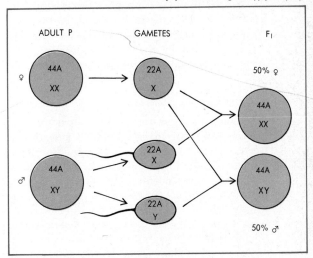

30 · 29 Sex determination in man. Photos: *isolated chromosomes from cells of a human male and a human female respectively. In each case the photo shows 46 chromosomes (or 23 pairs), each already duplicated as a preliminary to cell division. Diagram: males produce two genetically different types of sperms, roughly 50 per cent of each. Offspring will then be male and female in a 1:1 ratio.*

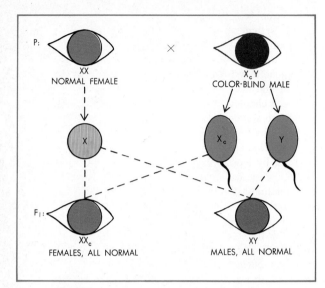

30 · 30

to a cell; only their position relative to one another is rearranged. Under such conditions the cell may nevertheless develop altered traits, a clear indication that genes normally interact with their neighbors.

The phenomenon of dominance provides another good illustration of the interdependence of genes. A dominant gene acts as it does not only because of its inherent characteristics, but also because other genes permit it to act in dominant fashion. If the functional characteristics of the recessive allele of a given dominant were to change, then the status of dominance of that gene would change correspondingly. And if the functional characteristics of any other genes in the cell were to change, then the status of dominance of that gene would again change. It is now well established that given genes boost, suppress, partially inhibit, or otherwise change the effects of other genes. For example, *modifier* genes are known which intensify or minimize the traits produced by other genes. Analogously, *suppressor* genes completely prevent traits produced by other genes from becoming expressed explicitly. Some genes affect not the traits produced by other genes but the other genes themselves. Among them are the *operator* and *regulator* genes we have discussed in Chap. 21, in the context of the operon hypothesis. As in that earlier instance we may now therefore conclude again that genes are of two general types, namely, "structural" genes, effective in producing cellular traits, and "coordinating" genes of various kinds, effective in influencing the activity of the structural genes and their products. Indeed it is quite possible that every

Color blindness is only one of several characteristically male, sex-linked abnormalities. Another is *hemophilia,* for example, a bleeder's disease resulting from absence of blood platelets.

The discussion above applies specifically to organisms in which the males are of the XY type. Where the females are of the XY type, all generlizations apply equally if every reference to "male" above is changed to "female" and vice versa.

Genetic Systems

The examples of genetic sex determination just described show clearly that genes of one or more chromosomes may act in concert and control one highly composite trait. The implication is that genes are not merely independent "beads on a string," lined up haphazardly on given numbers of chromosomes. On the contrary, the genes in every chromosome appear to interact in very specific ways, and the expression of traits is influenced by such interactions.

Many other illustrations of this principle are known. For example, if genes were simply independently functioning units, then it should not matter if the position of genes relative to one another were rearranged. But experiment shows that such rearrangement actually does matter. It is possible to change the position of given sections of a chromosome. A piece lost by one chromosome may become attached to another, or it may become reattached to the same chromosome but in inverted position or at the other end. Genes here are neither removed from nor added

30 · 31

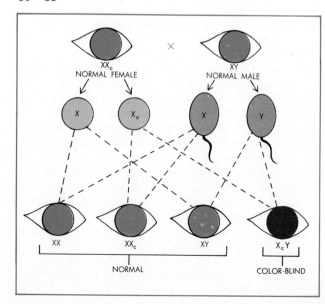

gene in a cell might have a trait-producing role in some hereditary functions and a coordinating role in others.

Thus, whereas the pre-Mendelians thought that traits were inherited, and whereas the Mendelian era advanced to the concept that individual factors, or genes, were inherited, the modern post-Mendelian era recognizes that actually neither traits nor genes nor even subunits of genes are inherited. Instead, what are inherited are whole chromosome sets, co-ordinated complexes of genes, subtly integrated and interacting *genetic systems*. Moreover, even genetic systems are not inherited by themselves but are transmitted within *whole* cells. The functional integration between genetic system and cell system is never lost, and it is biologically almost meaningless to consider one without the other. Actually, the cell cytoplasm is a carrier of heredity too. For example, cell membranes, mitochondria, kinetosomes, nuclear membranes, and many other intracellular organelles are inherited not through genes but through "self-

duplication" of preexisting parental structures. The genetic system of a cell undoubtedly controls such cytoplasmic self-duplication, but the cytoplasmic system certainly also controls the self-duplication of the genetic system. Ultimately, therefore, the smallest real unit of inheritance is one whole cell.

In this chapter we have found that the inheritance of genetic systems and of the traits they control is governed by the biological nature of sex, by various probabilistic Mendelian rules, by random mutational changes, by interactions within genes and between genes, and by the effects of the environment on gene-trait relationships. To the extent that this interplay between sex, heredity, and environment remains the same in the course of successive generations, it maintains the traits of organisms and given degrees of individual adaptation. And to the extent that the interplay changes as the reproductive succession continues, it produces *evolution* and altered adaptations.

REVIEW QUESTIONS

1. What are the sources of genetic variations in (*a*) uniparental, (*b*) biparental inheritance? Distinguish between inherited and acquired variations. What contributions are made to the expression of traits by (*a*) genes, (*b*) the environment? What is an "inherited disease"?

2. What was meant by "blending inheritance"? Describe breeding experiments showing that blending does not occur. What hypothesis did Mendel substitute for the blending concept? State the chromosome theory of heredity. What is the evidence that genes are actually contained within chromosomes?

3. Define: genome, true-breeding, phenotype, genotype, allele, dominant gene, recessive gene, homozygous, heterozygous, hybrid.

4. Review the experiments on inheritance of flower color in snapdragons in terms of genes and chromosomes. What are the quantitative results of the mating $Aa \times Aa$ if (*a*) A is dominant over a, (*b*) neither gene is dominant over the other?

5. In your own words, state the law of segregation. If A is dominant over a, what phenotype ratios of offspring are obtained from the following matings: (*a*) $Aa \times aa$, (*b*) $AA \times aa$, (*c*) $Aa \times Aa$, (*d*) $Aa \times AA$?

6. In your own words, state the law of independent assortment. What kinds of breeding experiments and what reasoning substantiate this law? Interpret

the law in terms of genes, meiosis, and gametes. How many genetically different gamete types will be produced by an organism heterozygous in 10 gene pairs? If two such organisms were mated, how many genetically different offspring types could result?

7. Define linkage. Why does inheritance of linked genes not obey Mendel's second law? What are the quantitative and qualitative differences here? What were Morgan's observations which led him to the hypothesis of crossing over? Describe this hypothesis. How do crossover data permit the construction of gene maps? State the law of the linear order of genes. What definition of gene is based on the phenomenon of crossing over? Review other definitions.

8. Distinguish between chromosome mutations and point mutations and between somatic mutations and germ mutations. What is the relation between mutation frequency and radiation intensity? What are the characteristics of mutations from the standpoint of (*a*) predictability, (*b*) functional relation to normal alleles, (*c*) effects on traits, and (*d*) relative advantage to the organism?

9. What are mutons, recons, and cistrons? Review the patterns of sex determination based on (*a*) non-genetic, (*b*) genetic mechanisms. How is sex determined in (*a*) *Sphaerocarpos*, (*b*) man? What is the significance of a given numerical balance between autosomes and sex chromosomes? What are super-sexes and intersexes?

10. What are sex-linked genes? Describe the inheritance pattern of the sex-linked recessive hemo-philia gene *h*, assuming that a hemophilic male mates with a normal female. What are modifier genes? Describe specific instances of gene-gene interactions.

COLLATERAL READINGS

Beadle, G. W.: The Genes of Men and Molds, *Sci. American*, Sept., 1948. A noted geneticist discusses the inheritance mechanism in the fungus *Neurospora* and the basis of the "one gene, one enzyme" hypothesis.

Bearn, A. G., and J. L. German: Chromosomes and Disease, *Sci. American*, Nov., 1961. Visually demonstrable abnormalities in human chromosomes are correlated with genetic diseases.

Benzer, S.: The Fine Structure of the Gene, *Sci. American*, Jan., 1962. A review of experiments that have led to the concept of mutons, cistrons, and recons.

Bonner, D. M.: "Heredity," Prentice-Hall, Englewood Cliffs, N.J., 1961. A paperback covering general aspects of both Mendelian and non-Mendelian genetics.

Cook, S. A.: "Reproduction, Heredity, and Sexuality," Wadsworth, Belmont, Calif., 1964. This paperback represents an introduction to general genetic principles and deals particularly with inheritance in protists and plants.

Deering, R. A.: Ultraviolet Radiation and Nucleic Acid, *Sci. American*, Dec., 1962. A discussion of mutations induced by this form of energy.

Goldschmidt, R. B.: "Understanding Heredity," Wiley, New York, 1952. A nontechnical book reviewing general principles.

Hollaender, A., and G. E. Stapleton: Ionizing Radiation and the Cell, *Sci. American*, Sept., 1959. The primary and secondary genetic effects of radiation are discussed.

Knight, C. A., and D. Fraser: The Mutation of Viruses, *Sci. American*, July, 1955. An examination of genetic change and the possibility of inducing such change predictably by chemical means.

Kormondy, E. J.: "Introduction to Genetics," McGraw-Hill, New York, 1964. A programmed paperback designed for self-instruction in general genetic principles; recommended as a study aid.

Mendel, G.: "Experiments in Plant Hybridization," Harvard, Cambridge, Mass., 1941. A translation of the 1865 original on which modern genetics is based.

Mittwoch, U.: Sex Differences in Cells, *Sci. American*, July, 1963. Differences in sex chromosomes and in other cellular traits of males and females are examined.

Moore, J. A.: "Heredity and Development," Oxford, Fair Lawn, N.J., 1963. A paperback containing a good historical review of the growth of genetic concepts.

Muller, H.: Radiation and Human Mutation, *Sci. American*, Nov., 1955. The discoverer of the genetic effects of radiation discusses the influence of mutations of human evolution.

Sinnott, E. W., L. C. Dunn, and T. Dobzhansky: "Principles of Genetics," 5th ed., McGraw-Hill, New York, 1958. A standard basic text.

Sonneborn, T. M.: Partner of the Genes, *Sci. American*, Nov., 1950. A recommended article, showing that genetic control is exercised not only by genes but also by cytoplasmic factors.

Srb, A., and R. D. Owen: "General Genetics," 2d ed. Freeman, San Francisco, 1965. A standard basic text.

Stahl, F. W.: "The Mechanics of Inheritance," Prentice-Hall, Englewood Cliffs, N.J., 1964. An excellent nonintroductory paperback on "molecular" genetics; virus and bacterial research is reviewed in detail, and references to original papers are given.

CHAPTER 31 EVOLUTION: MECHANISMS

No biologist today seriously questions the principle that species arise from preexisting species. Evolution on a small scale can actually be brought about in the laboratory, and the forces which drive and guide evolutionary processes are understood quite thoroughly.

That evolution really occurs did not become definitely established till the nineteenth century. For long ages man was unaware of the process, but he did wonder about the origin of his kind and of other living creatures. Indeed, he developed a succession of simple and rather crude theories about evolution. Unsupported by real evidence, these were ultimately proved untenable one by one. Yet the early ideas occasionally still color the views of those who are unacquainted with the modern knowledge.

It is advisable, therefore, that we begin this chapter with a brief survey of the historical *background* of evolutionary thought. Based on such a perspective, we may then discuss the *forces of evolution,* as these are understood today, and follow with an analysis of the *nature of evolution,* as determined by the underlying forces.

BACKGROUND

EARLY NOTIONS

The earliest written discussion of organic creation is contained in the Old Testament: God made the world and its living inhabitants in six days, man coming last. Later ideas included those of *spontaneous generation* and of *immutability of species,* which largely held sway until the eighteenth and nineteenth centuries. Each species was considered to have been created spontaneously, completely developed, from dust, dirt, and other nonliving sources. And once created, a species was held to be fixed and immutable, unable to change its characteristics.

In the sixth to fourth centuries B.C., Anaximander, Empedocles, and Aristotle independently considered the possibility that living forms might represent a *succession* rather than unrelated, randomly created types. However, the succession was thought of in an essentially philosophical way, as a progression from "less nearly perfect" to "more nearly perfect" forms. The historical nature of succession and the continuity of life were not yet recognized. Nor was the notion of continuous succession exploited further in later centuries, for clerical dogma by and large discouraged thinking along such lines.

Francesco Redi, an Italian physician of the seventeenth century, was the first to obtain evidence against the idea of spontaneous generation, by showing experimentally that organisms could not arise from nonliving sources. Contrary to notions held at the time and earlier, Redi demonstrated that maggots would never form spontaneously in meat if flies were prevented from laying their eggs on the meat. But old beliefs die slowly, and it was not until the nineteenth century, chiefly through the work of Louis Pasteur on bacteria, that the notion of spontaneous generation finally ceased to be influential.

By this time, the alternative to spontaneous generation, namely, the idea of continuity and historical succession, or *evolution,* had occurred to a number of thinkers. Some of them recognized that any concept of evolution demanded an earth of sufficiently great age, and they set out to estimate that age. Newton's law of gravitation provided the tool with which to calculate the weight of the earth. One could then bring a small weighed ball of earth to white heat and measure its rate of cooling. From such measurements, one could calculate how long it must have taken the whole earth to cool to its present state. Determinations of this sort provided the many millions of years required to fit evolution into, and this time span gradually lengthened as techniques of clocking improved. As a result of these efforts, the notion of evolution was clearly in the air when the nineteenth century began. In 1809, the first major theory of evolution was actually published. This was the theory of the French naturalist Lamarck.

LAMARCK

Lamarck considered the reality of evolution as established. He believed, correctly, that to explain how evolution occurred was equivalent to explaining adaptation—how individual variations arise among organisms and how such variations lead to the emergence of different species suited to different environments and ways of life. To account for such evolution, Lamarck proposed the two ideas of *use and disuse of parts* and of *inheritance of acquired characteristics*. He had observed that if a body part of an organism was used extensively, such a part would enlarge and become more efficient, and that if a structure was not fully employed, it would degenerate and atrophy. Therefore, by differential use and disuse of various parts during its lifetime, an organism would change to some extent and would acquire individual variations. Lamarck then thought that such acquired variations were inheritable and could be transmitted to offspring.

According to the Lamarckian scheme, evolution would come about somewhat as follows. Suppose a given short-necked ancestral animal feeds on tree leaves. As it clears off the lower levels of a tree, it stretches its neck to reach farther up. During a lifetime of stretching, the neck becomes a little longer, and a slightly longer neck is then inherited by the offspring. These in turn feed on tree leaves and keep on stretching their necks; and so on, for many generations. Each generation acquires the gains of previous generations and itself adds a little to neck length. In time, a very long-necked animal is formed, something like a modern giraffe.

This theory was exceedingly successful and did much to spread the idea of evolution. But Lamarck's views ultimately proved to be untenable. That use and disuse do lead to acquired variations is quite correct. For example, it is common knowledge that much exercise builds powerful muscles. However, Lamarck was mistaken in assuming that such (nongenetic) acquired variations were inheritable. We may say categorically that *acquired characteristics are not inheritable*. They are effects produced by environment and development, not by genes. Only *genetic* characteristics are inheritable, and then only if such characteristics are controlled by the genes of the reproductive cells. What happens to cells other than reproductive cells through use and disuse, or in any other way for that matter, does not affect the genes of the gametes. Accordingly, although Lamarck ob-

served some of the effects of use and disuse correctly in some cases, such effects cannot play a role in evolution.

One famous attempt at experimental refutation of Lamarckism was carried out by Weismann, an eminent biologist of the nineteenth century. The tails of mice were cut off for very many successive generations. According to Lamarck, such enforced disuse of tails should eventually have led to tailless mice. Yet mice in the last generation of the experiment still grew tails as long as their ancestors.

DARWIN AND WALLACE

The year in which Lamarck published his theory was also the year in which Charles Darwin was born. During his early life, Darwin undertook a 5-year-long circumglobal voyage as the biologist on the naval expeditionary ship *H.M.S. Beagle*. He made innumerable observations and collected a large number of different plants and animals in many parts of the world. Returning home, he spent nearly 20 years sifting and studying the collected data. In the course of this work, he found evidence for certain generalizations. Another biologist, Alfred R. Wallace, had been led independently to substantially the same generalizations, which he communicated to Darwin. Darwin and Wallace together then announced a new theory on the mechanism of evolution, which was to supplant that of Lamarck. Darwin subsequently elaborated the new theory into book form. This famous work, entitled "On the Origin of Species by Means of Natural Selection, or the Preservation of Favored Races in the Struggle for Life," was published in 1859.

In essence, the Darwin-Wallace *theory of natural selection* is based on three observations and on two conclusions drawn from these observations.

Observation. Without environmental pressures, every species tends to multiply in geometric progression.

In other words, a population doubling its number in a first year possesses a sufficient reproductive potential to quadruple its number in a second year, to increase eightfold in a third year, etc.

Observation. But under field conditions, although fluctuations occur frequently, the size of a population remains remarkably constant over long periods of time.

We have already referred to this point in the discussion of food pyramids (Chap. 9).

Conclusion. Evidently, not all eggs and sperms will become zygotes; not all zygotes will become adults; and not all adults will survive and reproduce.

Consequently, there must be a "struggle for existence."

Observation. Not all members of a species are alike; considerable individual variation is in evidence.

Conclusion. In the struggle for existence, therefore, individuals exhibiting favorable variations will enjoy a competitive advantage over others. They will survive in proportionately greater numbers and will produce offspring in proportionately greater numbers.

Darwin and Wallace thus identified the environment as the principal cause of natural selection. Through the processes above, the environment would gradually weed out organisms with unfavorable variations but preserve those with favorable variations. Over a long succession of generations and under the continued selective influence of the environment, a group of organisms would eventually have accumulated so many new, favorable variations that a new species would in effect have arisen from the ancestral stock.

Laymen today often are under the impression that Darwin and Wallace's theory is *the* modern theory of evolution. This is not the case. Indeed, Darwinism was challenged even during Darwin's lifetime. What, it was asked, is the source of the all-important individual variations? How do individual variations arise? Here Darwin actually could do no better than fall back on the Lamarckian idea of inheritance of acquired characteristics. Ironically, the correct answer regarding variations began to be formulated just 6 years after Darwin published his theory, when a monk named Mendel announced certain rules of inheritance. But Mendel's work remained unappreciated for more than 30 years and progress in understanding evolutionary mechanisms was retarded correspondingly.

Another objection to Darwinism concerned natural selection itself. If this process simply preserves or weeds out what already exists, it was asked, how can it ever create anything new? As we shall see, natural selection actually does create novelty. The earlier criticism arose in part because the meaning of Darwin's theory was—and still is—widely misinterpreted. Social philosophers of the time and other "press agents" and disseminators of "news," not biologists, thought that the essence of natural selection was described by the phrase "struggle for existence." They then coined alternative slogans like "survival of the fittest" and "elimination of the unfit." Natural selection so came to be conceived almost exclusively as a negative, destructive force. This had two unfortunate results. First, a major implication of Darwin's theory, namely, the creative role of natural selection, was missed, and, second, the wrong emphasis was often accepted in popular thinking as the last and final word concerning evolution.

Such thinking proceeded in high gear even in Darwin's day. Many still did not accept the reality of evolution and were prompted variously to debate, to scorn, and to ridicule the merits of the evidence. It was felt also that evolution implied "man descended from the apes," and man's sense of superiority was duly outraged. Moreover, because evolutionary views denied the special creation of man, they were widely held to be antireligious. In actuality, the idea of evolution is not any more or less antireligious than the idea of spontaneous generation. Neither really strengthens, weakens, or otherwise affects belief in God. To the religious person, only the way God operates, not God as such, is in question.

But many were properly convinced by the evidence for evolution. However, under the banner of phrases like "survival of the fittest," evolution was interpreted to prove an essential cruelty of nature; and human behavior, personal and national, often came to be guided by the ethic of "jungle law," "might is right," "every man for himself." Only in that way, it was thought, could the "fittest" prevail. Even today, unfortunately, the mechanism of evolution is still commonly—and erroneously—thought to be a matter of "survival of the fittest."

By now, a full century after Darwin and Wallace, the emotion-charged atmosphere has cleared and the impact of their theory may be assessed calmly. That Darwin made the greater contribution cannot be questioned. In voluminous writings, he, far more than Wallace, marshaled the evidence for the occurrence of evolution so extensively, and so well, that the reality of the process has never been in doubt since. Moreover, the theory of natural selection was the most convincing explanation of the evolutionary mechanism offered up to that time. Indeed, carrying new meaning today, it still forms an essential part of the modern theory of evolution. As now understood, however, natural selection has very little to do with "struggle," "weeding out," or "the fittest." Also, we know that Darwin and Wallace, like Lamarck, were unsuccessful in identifying the actual sources of individual variations. In short, the explanation supplied by Darwin and Wallace was incomplete, but as far as it went, theirs was the first to point in the right direction.

The modern theory of evolution is not the work of any one man and it did not arise by "spontaneous generation," fully developed. Rather, it evolved slowly during the first half of the current century, many biologists of various specializations contributing to it. The theory is the spiritual offspring of Mendel and of Darwin, but the family resemblance, though present, may not be immediately evident. We shall be concerned with this modern theory in what follows.

THE FORCES OF EVOLUTION

THE EVOLUTIONARY PROCESS

The medium of evolution is the *population*, a geographically localized aggregation of members of a given species. The raw materials of the evolutionary process are the *inheritable variations* which appear among the individuals of such a population. And the mechanism of evolution may be described as *natural selection acting on the inheritable variations of a population.*

In a population, the members interbreed preferentially with one another and they also interbreed occasionally with members of neighboring sister populations (see Chap. 8). The result of the close sexual communication within a population is a *free flow of genes.* Hereditary material present in a part of a population may in time spread to the whole population, through the gene-pooling and gene-combining effect of sex. Therefore, in the course of successive sexual generations, the total genetic content of a population may become shuffled and reshuffled thoroughly. We may say that a population possesses a given *gene pool* and that the interbreeding members of the population have free access to all components of that pool. Moreover, inasmuch as sister populations are in occasional reproductive contact, the gene pool of one population is connected also to the gene pools of sister populations. In this way, the total genetic content of an entire species continues to be

31 · 1   Concept of a gene pool. *In a species, genes flow within and between populations. The total gene content of the species thus represents a gene pool to which all members of the species have access. Genes normally cannot flow between the gene pools of two different species.*

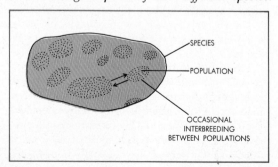

SPECIES

POPULATION

OCCASIONAL
INTERBREEDING
BETWEEN POPULATIONS

shuffled about among the member organisms (Fig. 31.1).

Evolution operates via the gene pools of populations. We already know from Chap. 30 how changes in genetic systems, hence inheritable variations, may arise: by sexual recombination and by mutation. In each generation, some individuals may appear exhibiting new trait variations, as a result of either recombinational or mutational processes (see, for example, Fig. 8.1). If these variant organisms survive and have offspring of their own, then their particular (mutational) genetic innovations will persist in the gene pool of the population. In the course of successive generations, the genetic novelty may spread to many or all members of the population.

Whether or not such spreading actually takes place depends on natural selection. This term is synonymous with *differential reproduction.* Either "natural selection" or "differential reproduction" means simply that some individuals of a population have more offspring than others. Clearly, those leaving more offspring will contribute a proportionately greater percentage of genes to the gene pool of the next generation than those leaving fewer offspring. If, therefore, differential reproduction continues in the same manner over many generations, the abundant reproducers will contribute a progressively larger number of individuals to the whole population. As a result, *their* genes will become preponderant in the gene pool of the population (Fig. 31.2).

Which individuals leave more offspring than others? Usually, but by no means necessarily, those that are best adapted to the environment. Being well adapted, such individuals on the whole are healthier and better fed, may find mates more readily, and may care for their offspring appropriately. However, circumstances may on occasion be such that comparatively poorly adapted individuals have the most offspring. Instances of this are sometimes encountered in human populations, for example. In any event, what counts most in evolution is not how well or how poorly an organism copes with its environment, but how many offspring it manages to leave. The more there are, the greater a role will the parental genes play in the total genetic content of the population. By and large, the well-adapted organism contributes most to the gene pool.

Therefore, if an inheritable variation appears in an organism and if, through differential reproduction in successive generations, the progeny of that organism becomes numerically more and more abundant, then a given genetic novelty will spread rapidly throughout the population. As a result, a trait variation originating in one organism will have become a standard feature of the population as a whole.

This is the unit of evolutionary change. Many such unit changes must accumulate in a population before the organisms are sufficiently altered in structure or function to be established as a new species. All evolution operates through the basic process just described. In brief, it consists of:

1. appearance of inheritable variations by sexual recombination and mutation

2. spreading of these variations through a population by differential reproduction in successive generations

Inasmuch as inheritable variations originate at random, evolutionary innovations similarly appear at random. But inasmuch as the best reproducers are generally the best adapted, evolution as a whole is directed by adaptation and is oriented toward continued or improved adaptation. It is therefore not a random process.

Note that, in this modern view of evolution, natural selection is fundamentally a creative force; for its important effect is to spread genetic novelty, hence new traits, through a population. It is also a peaceful force, involving reproduction, not "struggle for existence" or "survival of the fittest." Organisms actually struggle rather rarely. Indeed, animals try to avoid struggle and attempt to pursue life as inconspicuously as possible, eating when they can, reproducing when they can. And plants have never been seen to engage in struggles at all. Moreover, natural selection does not "eliminate the unfit." The "fit" may be the mightiest and grandest organism in the population, but it might happen to be sterile. And the "unfit" could be a sickly weakling, yet have numerous offspring. The point is that neither "survival" nor "elimination" is actually at issue. The only issue of consequence here is comparative reproductive success. Indirectly, to be sure, health, fitness, and even actual physical struggles may affect the reproductive success of organisms. To that extent such factors can have evolutionary consequences. But what in Darwin's day was regarded as the whole of natural selection is now clearly recognized to have only a limited, indirect effect on evolution. The whole of natural selection, directly and indirectly, undoubtedly is differential reproduction.

THE GENETIC BASIS

The Hardy-Weinberg Law

From the preceding, we may conclude that evolution is characterized by *a progressive change of gene frequencies*. Thus, in the course of successive generations, the proportion of some genes in the population

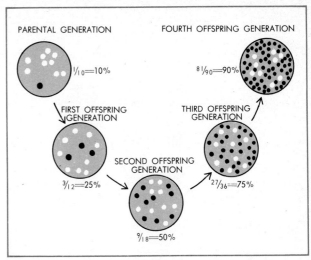

31 · 2 The effect of differential reproduction, or natural selection. Assume that a variation arises in one individual of a parental generation (dark dot) *and that the variant organism is able to leave three offspring. Each nonvariant organism* (white dots) *on the other hand only manages to leave one offspring. The complexion of the population will then change as shown during subsequent generations; that is, the variant type will represent a progressively larger fraction of the numerical total. Such spreading of variations, brought about by differential reproduction, constitutes natural selection.*

increases and the proportion of others decreases. For example, a mutation may at first be represented by a single gene, but if by natural selection this mutation spreads to more and more individuals, then its frequency increases whereas the frequency of the original unmutated gene decreases. Clearly, the rates with which gene frequencies change will be a measure of the speed of evolution. What determines such rates?

Suppose we consider a large population in which two alleles, A and a, occur in certain frequencies. In such a population, three kinds of individuals will be found, namely, AA, Aa, and aa. Let us assume that the numerical proportions happen to be

AA	Aa	aa
36%	48%	16%

Assuming further that the choice of sexual mates is entirely random, that all individuals produce roughly equal numbers of gametes, and that the genes A and a do not mutate, we may then ask how the frequency of the genes A and a will change from one generation to the next.

Since AA individuals make up 36 per cent of the

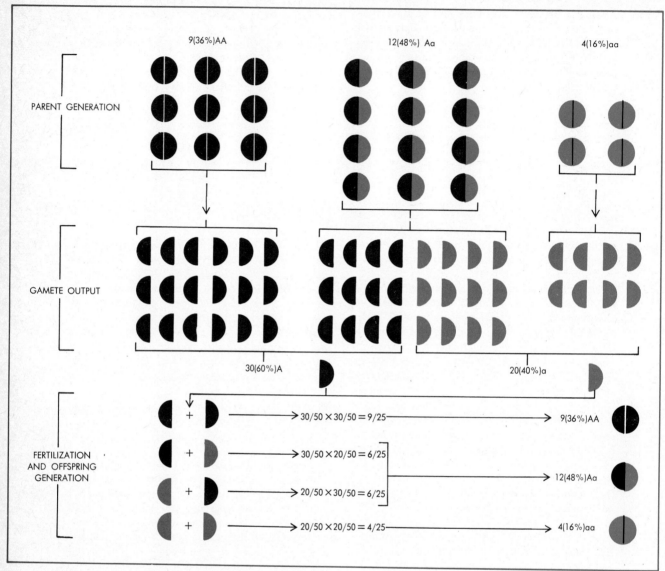

31 · 3. The Hardy-Weinberg law. *If mating is random, if mutations do not occur, and if the population is large, then gene frequencies do not change from one generation to the next.*

parents	gametes	parents	gametes
36% AA	$\longrightarrow$ 36% A	16% aa	$\longrightarrow$ 16% a
48% Aa	$\longrightarrow$ 24% A	48% Aa	$\longrightarrow$ 24% a
	60% A		40% a

total population, they will contribute approximately 36 per cent of all the gametes formed in the population. These gametes will all contain one A gene. Similarly, *aa* individuals will produce 16 per cent of all gametes in the population, and each will contain one *a* gene. The gametes of *Aa* individuals will be of two types, A and *a*, in equal numbers. Since their total amounts to 48 per cent, 24 per cent will be A and 24 per cent will be *a*. The overall gamete output of the population will therefore be

Fertilization now occurs in four possible ways: two A gametes join; two *a* gametes join; an A sperm joins an *a* egg; and an *a* sperm joins an A egg. Each of these possibilities will occur with a frequency dictated by the relative abundance of the A and *a* gametes. There are 60 per cent A gametes. Accordingly, A will join A in 60 per cent of 60 per cent of the cases, that is, 60×60, or 36 per cent of the time. Similarly, A sperms will join *a* eggs in 60×40, or 24 per cent of the cases. The total result:

sperms	eggs		offspring
A	$+$ A	$\longrightarrow$ 60×60 $\longrightarrow$	36% AA
A	$+$ a	$\longrightarrow$ 60×40 $\longrightarrow$	24% Aa
a	$+$ A	$\longrightarrow$ 40×60 $\longrightarrow$	24% Aa
a	$+$ a	$\longrightarrow$ 40×40 $\longrightarrow$	16% aa

We note that the new generation in our example population will consist of 36 per cent AA, 48 per cent Aa, and 16 per cent aa individuals. These are precisely the same proportions we started with originally. Evidently, gene frequencies have not changed.

It can be shown that such a result is obtained regardless of the numbers and the types of gene pairs considered simultaneously. The important conclusion is that, *if mating is random, if mutations do not occur, and if the population is large, then gene frequencies in a population remain constant from generation to generation.* This generalization is known as the *Hardy-Weinberg law.* It has somewhat the same central significance to the theory of evolution as Mendel's laws have to the theory of heredity (Fig. 31.3).

The Hardy-Weinberg law indicates that, when a population is in genetic equilibrium, that is, when gene frequencies do not change, the rate of evolution is zero. Genes then continue to be reshuffled by sexual recombination and, as a result, individual variations continue to originate from this source. But the overall gene frequencies do not change. Of themselves, therefore, the variations are *not* being propagated differentially. Evolution consequently does not occur.

What does make evolution occur are deviations from the "ifs" specified in the Hardy-Weinberg law. Thus, mating is decidedly not random whenever natural selection takes place; genes actually do mutate; and populations are not always large. Singly and in combination, these three factors may disturb the genetic equilibrium of a population and may produce evolutionary change.

The Effect of Nonrandom Mating

This effect may be appreciated readily if we assume that, in our example above, AA, Aa, and aa individuals are not adapted equally well. Suppose that the A gene in double dose, as in the AA combination, has a particular metabolic effect, such that death in embryonic stages will occur in one-third of the individuals possessing these genes. Under these conditions, 36 per cent AA individuals will be produced as zygotes, but only two-thirds of their number will reach reproductive age. Consequently, the Aa and aa individuals will constitute a proportionately larger fraction of the reproducing population and will contribute proportionately more to the total gamete output. The ultimate result over successive genera-

tions will be a progressive decrease in the frequency of the A gene and a progressive increase of the a gene. A certain intensity of natural selection, or *selection pressure,* here operates against the A gene and for the a gene (Fig. 31.4). Whenever such selection pressures exert an effect, Hardy-Weinberg equilibria are not maintained. Instead, as gene frequencies become altered more or less rapidly, given traits spread or disappear, and such a flux represents evolutionary change. In nature, most traits are steadily being selected for or selected against. In the course of many generations, even a very slight selection pressure affects the genetic makeup of a population substantially.

The Effect of Mutations

Inasmuch as mutations do occur in populations, Hardy-Weinberg equilibria change for this reason also. Depending on whether a mutation has a beneficial or harmful effect on a trait, selection will take place either for or against the mutated gene. In either case gene frequencies will change, for the mutated gene will either increase or decrease in abundance.

Mutations in haploid organisms affect traits immediately. But the evolutionary effect of mutations in diploid organisms varies according to whether the gene changes are dominant or recessive. A newly originated mutation with dominant effect will influence traits immediately, and selection for or against the mutation will take place at once. But if a mutation has a recessive effect, it does not influence traits immediately. Natural selection therefore does not influence the mutation immediately either. This is the case with most mutations, since, as noted in Chap. 30, most actual mutations produce recessive effects.

Nevertheless, such mutations may spread through a population. For example, an organism may carry mutant gene a' having a recessive effect, and it may also carry a linked gene B producing an adaptively very desirable dominant trait. Natural selection could then operate for the gene B; the organism possessing B might reproduce abundantly, and its genes would spread through the population. As a result, the linked mutant gene a' would be spread at the same time. Many mutations with recessive effects actually do propagate in this way, by being inherited along with other, adaptively useful genes having dominant effects. Note, moreover, that many genes have only incompletely recessive effects and will therefore be subject to natural selection even more directly.

Completely recessive mutants simply accumulate in the gene pool without visible expression. However, if two individuals carrying the same mutation happen to mate, then one-fourth of their offspring will be

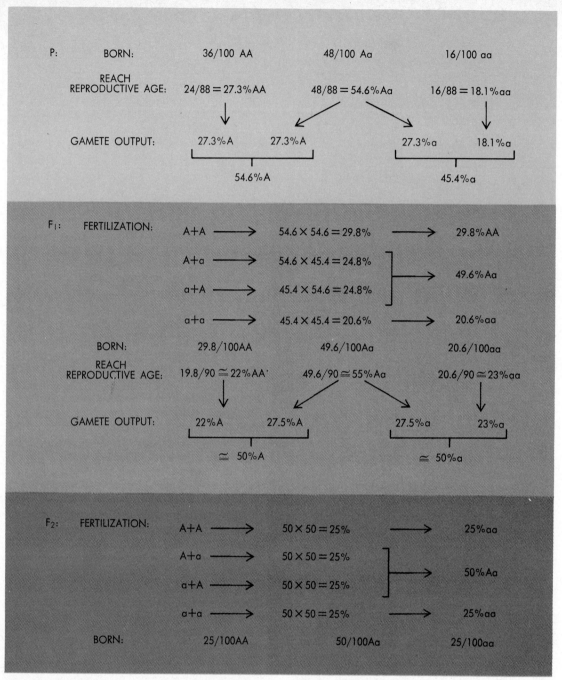

31 · 4 The effect of nonrandom mating. *If only two-thirds of all AA individuals reach reproductive age, then in the course of two generations the frequency of the A gene will decrease and the frequency of the a gene will increase, as shown in the calculation.*

homozygous recessive: $Aa' \times Aa' \longrightarrow 25$ per cent $a'a'$. These offspring will exhibit altered visible traits, and natural selection will then affect the mutation directly (Fig. 31.5).

Mutational effects in evolution also vary according to how greatly a given mutation influences a given trait. A "large" mutation affecting a vital trait in major ways is likely to be exceedingly harmful and will usually be lethal. For example, *any* change in the principal structure and function of the heart of an animal is likely to cause immediate death. Indeed, large variations are usually eliminated as soon as they arise. By contrast, an organism may survive far more readily if a mutation is "small." Evolutionary alterations of organisms actually occur almost exclusively through the accumulation of many small changes in traits, not through single large changes.

The Effect of Population Size

The third condition affecting Hardy-Weinberg equilibria is population size. If a population is large, any regional imbalances of gene frequencies arising by chance are quickly smoothed out by the many random matings among the many individuals. The underlying principle here holds in statistical systems generally. In a coin-flipping experiment, for example, heads and tails will each come up 50 per cent of the time, but only if the number of throws is large. If only three or four throws are made, it is quite likely that all will come up heads, by chance alone. Analogously, gene combinations attain Hardy-Weinberg equilibria only if a population is large. In small groups, chance alone may produce major deviations.

Assume, for example, that *AA*, *Aa*, and *aa* individuals are expected in a certain ratio, in accordance with existing gene frequencies. If the population contains many hundreds of individuals, this ratio will actually materialize. But if the population consists of a few individuals only, all these might by chance turn out to be of the same genotype, rather than of the three expected genotypes. We say that, in small populations, chance leads to *genetic drift*, the random establishment of genetic types numerically not in accord with Hardy-Weinberg equilibria (Fig. 31.6).

This effect resembles that of natural selection; if several genotypes are possible, a particular one would likewise come to predominate if there were a selection pressure for it. But whereas natural selection normally propagates the adaptive trait, genetic drift is governed primarily by chance and is initially not oriented by adaptation. The result is that, in small populations, nonadaptive and often bizarre traits may become established. These may actually be harmful to the population and may promote its getting even smaller. On the other hand, genetic drift may happen to adapt a given small population rather well to a given environment, and such a population might subsequently evolve selectively and eventually give rise to a new species. Genetic drift is often observed among plants and animals on islands and in other small, reproductively isolated groups of organisms.

By way of summary, the forces of evolution may now be described as follows. First, recombinational or mutational genetic novelty originates at random among certain individuals of a population. If this novelty happens to be adaptively advantageous in a given environment and if the population is large, then greater or lesser selection pressure for the novelty will disturb the equilibria of existing gene frequencies. Consequently, this pressure of natural selection, operating through differential reproduction, will bring about a correspondingly rapid or slow propagation of the genetic innovation throughout the population. The final result will be the establishment of new adaptive traits.

Evolution as it actually occurs must be interpreted in terms of this mechanism. That it in fact can be interpreted on this basis will become clear in the following section.

31 · 5 Gene spreading. *If a recessive mutation a' appears in an organism and if that organism also carries a gene B which is strongly selected for, then both B and a' may spread through a population. The appearance of mutant phenotypes a'a' then becomes rather likely.*

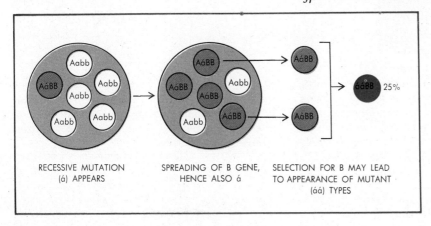

RECESSIVE MUTATION (á) APPEARS

SPREADING OF B GENE, HENCE ALSO á

SELECTION FOR B MAY LEAD TO APPEARANCE OF MUTANT (áá) TYPES

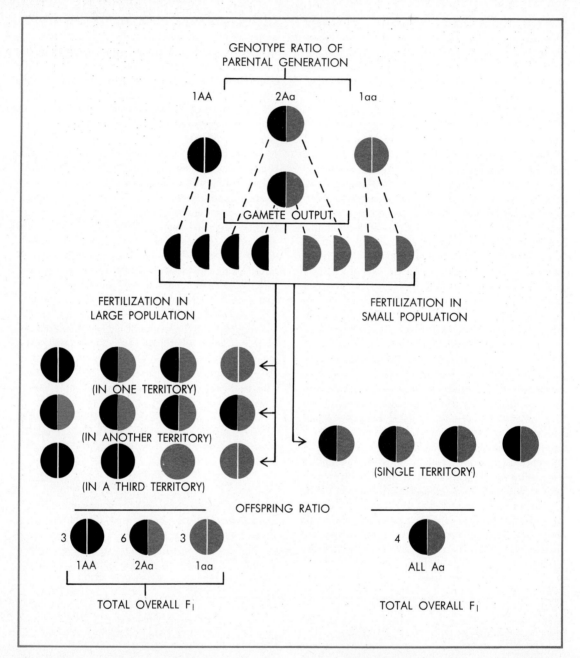

31 · 6   Genetic drift. *In a population like the one at top, the genetic constitution of offspring populations is influenced by population size. In large populations (left), gene combinations produced in different territories will average out to form a total offspring population in which gene frequencies are as in the parent generation. But in small populations (right), chance alone may produce significant deviations from Hardy-Weinberg expectations.*

THE NATURE OF EVOLUTION

SPECIATION

The key process to be explained is how unit evolutionary changes in a population eventually culminate in the establishment of new species and higher taxonomic categories. As already shown in Chap. 8, a species may be defined as a collection of populations within which reproductive communication is maintained by interbreeding. We may now define a species alternatively as a group of populations sharing the same gene pool (see Fig. 31.1). Within the pool a free flow of genes is maintained, but genetic flow between two such pools does not occur; a reproductive barrier isolates one species from another. The problem of speciation, therefore, is to show how reproductive barriers arise.

Geographic barriers between sister populations usually develop before biological reproductive barriers come into existence. Among geographic barriers, distance is probably the most effective. Suppose that, in the course of many generations, the populations of a given species grow in size and number and that, as a result of the increasing population pressure, the organisms radiate into a progressively larger territory. In time, two populations A and Z at opposite ends of the territory may be too far apart to permit direct interbreeding of their members. Although gene flow still takes place via the interconnecting populations between A and Z, individuals of A and Z no longer come into reproductive contact directly (Fig. 31.7).

It is then almost certain that, by chance, different genetic innovations arise in A and Z and that different ones will be propagated within A and Z by natural selection. Such an effect will be particularly pronounced if the environments of A and Z are or become more or less different. If now the evolutionary changes within A and within Z occur faster than the speed of genetic flow between A and Z, then A and Z will actually become progressively different in structure or function. These two populations thus may come to represent two distinct *subspecies* (Fig. 31.8).

Geographic isolation here has set the stage for the development of initial differences between members of A and Z. If the differences accumulate, they may eventually become so great that gene flow between A and Z will stop altogether. For example, population A (or Z) may undergo a change in the reproductive organs such that mating with neighboring populations becomes mechanically impossible. Or the protein specificities of A may so change that the gametes become incompatible with those of neighboring populations. Or the time of the annual breeding season in A may become advanced or delayed relative to that of neighboring populations. Or the individuals of A may become changed psychologically, so that they no longer accept mates from neighboring populations. Biological barriers of this sort will interrupt all gene flow between A and Z. These subspecies, isolated reproductively, then in effect will have become two different *species* (Fig. 31.9).

Although an initial isolation due to distance is probably the most common kind, other forms of geographic isolation are encountered as well. The development of terrestrial islands surrounded by water or of aquatic islands surrounded by land, the interposition of a forest belt across a prairie or of a prairie belt across a forest, the appearance of mountain barriers, river barriers, temperature barriers, or of many another physical barrier, each may result in

31 · 7 *Species populations may in time become separated by distance, resulting in comparative reproductive isolation and a reduction of gene flow.*

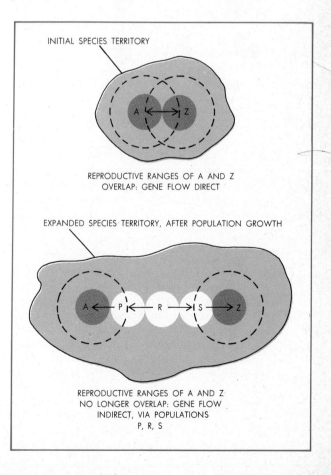

INITIAL SPECIES TERRITORY

REPRODUCTIVE RANGES OF A AND Z
OVERLAP: GENE FLOW DIRECT

EXPANDED SPECIES TERRITORY, AFTER POPULATION GROWTH

REPRODUCTIVE RANGES OF A AND Z
NO LONGER OVERLAP: GENE FLOW
INDIRECT, VIA POPULATIONS
P, R, S

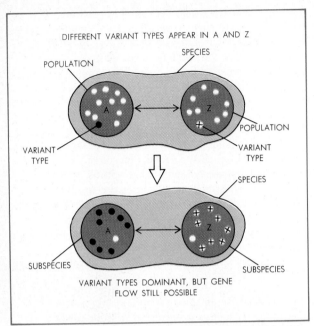

31 · 8 *Different subspecies may develop from different populations of a species by selective spreading of variant types. See also Fig. 8.1.*

geographic isolation. With reproductive contact then lost between two populations, evolution in each may henceforth follow entirely different courses. In effect, the parental species will become split into two new ones. At first, the descendant species will still be rather similar structurally and functionally. In time, however, evolutionary changes are likely to introduce progressively pronounced differences, including biological barriers to interbreeding. These add to and reinforce the environmental ones already in existence.

In two just-formed sister species, interbreeding often may still take place if the isolating condition is removed, but in nature such removals do not normally occur. Therefore, when two different species do not interbreed in nature, this does not always mean that they cannot interbreed. In many cases, members of different species may be brought together in the laboratory and there they interbreed perfectly well. For example, swordtails and platys, two species of tropical fish (Fig. 31.10), may under certain conditions have offspring in the laboratory. But in nature they almost never do because they are isolated reproductively; although they live together in the same rivers, biological barriers discourage crossbreeding. And after two sister species have been separated for long periods, interbreeding will no longer be possible even

if members of the two are brought together artificially. Biological differences sooner or later become sufficiently pronounced to preclude interbreeding.

Speciation by this means is the principal way in which new species evolve. Such a process takes, on an average, about 1 million years. Consciously or unconsciously making use of this principle of reproductive isolation, man has been and is now contributing to the evolution of many other organisms. Here may be found direct proof that evolution actually occurs and, indeed, that it operates according to the mechanism described above.

The most ancient evolution-directing effort of man is his successful *domestication* of various plants and animals. Darwin was the first to recognize the theoretical significance of domestication, and it was this, actually, which led him to his concept of natural selection. He reasoned that if man, by *artificial selection* and isolation, can transform wild varieties of given plants and animals into domesticated varieties, then perhaps natural selection and isolation, acting for far longer periods, can bring about even greater evolutionary transformations in nature. We know now that the domesticating process in fact does involve all the elements of natural evolution: first, deliberate physical, hence reproductive and genetic,

31 · 9 *The origin of two new species from two subspecies of a single ancestral species.*

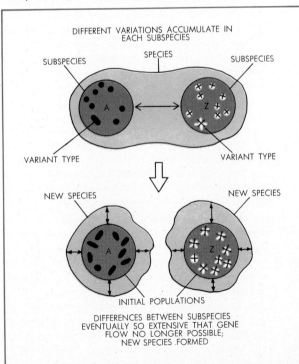

31 · 10 Platyfish female at top, swordtail male at bottom. These animals belong to different species, and in nature they do not interbreed. But they can and do interbreed in the laboratory.

isolation of a wild population by man; and second, long-continued, carefully controlled, differential reproduction of individuals "adapted" to human desires, that is, of individuals exhibiting traits considered desirable by man. The result is the creation of new strains, races, subspecies, and even species (Fig. 31.11).

Furthermore, during the last few decades, rather rapid, man-directed evolution has taken place among certain viruses, bacteria, insects, various parasites, and other pest organisms. These live now in an environment in which antibiotics and numerous pest-killing drugs have become distinct hazards. And the organisms have evolved and are still evolving increasing resistance to such drugs. Indeed, the very rapid evolution of viruses and bacteria becomes a problem in research; laboratory populations of microorganisms may evolve resistance to a drug even while the drug is being tested. Because microorganisms have exceedingly short generation times, because their populations are physically small, compact, and easily reared, and because high mutation rates may be induced readily by X rays, they have become favorite test objects in evolution experiments.

Clearly, then, small-scale evolution unquestionably occurs and is observable directly. Moreover, it may be made to occur under conditions based on the postulated modern mechanism of evolution. That this mechanism actually operates as implied by theory is therefore no longer in doubt.

Does the same mechanism operate in large-scale evolution, that is, in the formation of higher taxo-

nomic categories? In the recent past, a few biologists have expressed the belief that small-scale and large-scale evolution are not governed by the same forces. Differences between orders, classes, and phyla are far too great, it has been argued, to be accounted for by a gradual accumulation of many small, minor variations among organisms. Whereas the origin of species and even of genera can be explained on this basis, it has been held that for higher taxonomic categories a different machinery may be required.

31 · 11 A, wild boar; ancestral forms of animals such as this have also given rise to domesticated pigs, as a result of man-directed artificial selection. B, red jungle fowl, another example of a wild animal from which man has bred domesticated varieties.

A

B

A mechanism involving "large" mutations has therefore been postulated. According to this hypothesis, a major mutation affecting many vital traits simultaneously transforms an organism suddenly, in one jump, into a completely new type representing a new, high-ranking taxonomic category. In most cases such an organism could not survive, for it would undoubtedly be entirely unsuited to the local environment. But it is assumed that, in extremely rare cases, such "hopeful monsters" might have arisen by freak chance in environments in which they could survive. Only a few successes of this sort would be needed to account for the existing major taxonomic variants among organisms. Evolution by jumps would also explain why transitional fossil forms between various phyla are rare, whereas transitional fossils between different species and different genera, created by gradual evolution, are extremely common.

Few biologists today accept the hypothesis of jump evolution. In studies of natural and experimental mutations over many years, it has always been found that sudden genetic changes with major effects are immediately lethal. This is the case not only because the external environment is unsuitable, but also, and perhaps mainly, because the internal metabolic upheaval caused by a major mutation is far too drastic to permit continued survival. Indeed, large mutations lead to death well before hatching or birth. But even supposing that a hopeful monster could develop beyond birth, it would by definition be so different from the other individuals of the population that it certainly could not find a mate. Also, although transitional fossils between major taxonomic categories are rare, they are by no means nonexistent. On the whole, therefore, it is far more consistent with available evidence to explain the evolution of high taxonomic categories on a basis other than that of fortuitous hopeful monsters.

The almost universally accepted view is that large-scale evolution is governed by the very same mechanism as small-scale evolution. Thus, the origin of high-ranking taxonomic categories is again envisaged to involve isolation and accumulation of small trait variations, only more of them than in the case of a species and accumulating for a longer period of time. Although the differences between phyla and other major categories are great, they are not so great that one such category could not have evolved gradually from another category. Indeed, the evidence from fossils and embryos shows reasonably well how such derivations might have been achieved (see Fig. 14.15). Moreover, as the next section will show, important aspects of the evolutionary process cannot be explained in terms of jump evolution but can be explained rather well in terms of gradual evolution.

CHARACTERISTICS OF EVOLUTION

Rates of Change

Even on the species level, evolution is an exceedingly slow process. As noted, a very large number of very small variations of traits must accumulate, bit by bit over many generations, before a significant structural or functional alteration of organisms is in evidence. Moreover, genetic innovations occur at random, whereas natural selection is directed by adaptation. Therefore, if a substantial environmental change necessitates a correspondingly substantial adaptive change in a group of organisms, then the organisms must *await* the random appearance of appropriate genetic innovations. If useful innovations do not happen to arise by chance, then the organisms will not be able to readapt and will die out. Yet even if useful genetic novelty does arise in a given generation, there is no guarantee that more novelty of similar usefulness will originate in the next generation. In short, even though evolution may occur, it could occur too slowly to permit successful adaptation to changed environments.

The actual speeds of past evolution, though slow in all instances, have varied considerably for different types of organisms, differently at different times. As a rule, the more stable a given environment has been, the slower has been the evolution of the organisms living in it. Thus, terrestrial types by and large have evolved faster than marine types. Also, during periods of major geologic upheavals, for example, in times of glaciation or of mountain building (see Chap. 32), evolution has been fairly rapid generally. On the contrary, in a few existing types of organisms the rate of evolution has been practically zero for hundreds of millions of years. Horseshoe crabs, certain brachiopod lamp shells, and some of the radiolarian protozoa are among the oldest of such "living fossils" (see Chap. 15). In these and similar cases, the specific environment of the organisms has been stable enough to make the ancient way of life still possible. Given the general evolutionary mechanism of small random variations acted on by adaptively oriented natural selection, it is not at all surprising that speeds of evolution should have varied in step with environmental changes.

Adaptive Radiation

A general feature of evolution is the phenomenon of *adaptive radiation*. We have seen how, in speciation, one original parent species gives rise simultaneously to two or more descendant species. A similar pattern of *branching* descent characterizes evolution on all levels. A new type evolves and it then becomes a potential ancestor for many different, simultaneous descendant lines. For example, the ancestral mammalian type has given rise simultaneously to several lines of grazing plains animals (for example, horses, cattle, goats), to burrowing animals (for example, moles), to flying animals (for example, bats), to several lines of aquatic animals (for example, whales, seals, sea cows), to animals living in trees (for example, monkeys), to carnivorous predators (for example, dogs, cats), and to many others. Evidently, the original mammalian type branched out and exploited many different available environments and ways of life. Each descendant line thereby became adaptively specialized in a particular way. The sum of the various lines, all leading away from the common ancestral type, formed an "adaptive radiation."

Within each such line, furthermore, adaptive radiations of smaller scope can take place. For example, the line of tree-living mammals in time evolved several simultaneous sublines, and each of these in turn gave rise to subsublines, etc. The specific results today are animals as varied as monkeys, lemurs, tarsiers, apes, and men. Evidently, man did not descend from the apes, if by "apes" we mean modern ones such as gorillas or gibbons. Rather, living apes and man have had a common ancestor, and they are contemporary members of the same adaptive radiation.

The important implication here is that evolution is not a "ladder" or a "scale." As also pointed out in Chap. 2, the pattern is more nearly that of a greatly branching bush, where the tips of all uppermost branches represent currently living species (see Fig. 2.16). Of these, none is "higher" or "lower" than any other. Instead, they are simply contemporary groups of different structure, function, and history. Thus, the all-too-frequent picture of evolution as a "progression from amoeba to man" is and always has been utterly without foundation. Leading down from the branch tips to progressively thicker branches, the evolutionary bush goes backward in time. Junctions of branches represent common ancestors, and these are the higher in taxonomic rank the more closely the main stem is approached.

Extinction

Not all the branches on a bush ramify right to the top, but some terminate abruptly at various intermediate points. In evolution, similarly, *extinction* has been a general feature. In many actual cases of extinction, the specific causes may never be known.

But the general cause of all extinctions emerges from the nature of the evolutionary mechanism. That cause is change in environment without rapid enough readaptation of organisms to the change. Evidently, unlike death, which is inherent in the life history of every individual, extinction is not a foregone conclusion inherent in the evolutionary history of every group. Rather, extinction occurs only if and when the group cannot make adaptive adjustments to environmental change (Fig. 31.12).

Such change need not necessarily be physical. For example, biological competition between two different types occupying the same territory often has led to the extinction of one. However, note that competition most often does not involve direct combat or "struggle." Characteristically, the competition is usually quite indirect, as when two different types of herbivores draw on the same limited supply of grass (see Chap. 8). The more narrowly specialized type here usually prevails over the more generalized type. For example, a herbivore like a rabbit is specialized to feed on vegetables. It is therefore likely to have the competitive advantage over an omnivore like a man or a bear if that omnivore happens by circumstance to be forced to eat only vegetables. The rabbit will be able to find vegetables more easily and to make more efficient use of them. On the other hand, if vegetables should disappear locally, the specialized herbivore would quickly become extinct whereas the generalized omnivore might find other food and survive. Clearly, specialization and adaptive flexibility each has certain evolutionary advantages and certain disadvantages. The issue of survival or extinction depends on a fine balance between the two.

This circumstance probably accounts for the observation that extinction is the more common the lower the taxonomic category. Extinction of species and even of genera has been a nearly universal occurrence, but relatively few orders and still fewer classes have become extinct. And virtually all phyla that ever originated continue to be in existence today. The phylum evidently includes so broad and so far-flung an assemblage of different adaptive types that at least some of them have always persisted, regardless of how environments have changed. Species, on the other hand, are usually adapted rather narrowly to limited, circumscribed environments. Given these rigid conditions, the chances for extinction are therefore greater.

Replacement

In conjunction with extinction, *replacement* has been another common occurrence in evolution. As noted,

31 · 12   Restorations of animals which have become extinct relatively recently. A, dodo. B, Irish elk. C, sabertooth cat. D, woolly mammoths. Of these, the dodo survived the longest (till just a few hundred years ago), Mammoths and sabertooths became extinct some 20,000 years ago, and Irish elks, some thousands of years before that.

competition may be a direct cause for the replacement of one group in a given environment by another. For example, pouched marsupial mammals were very abundant in the Americas a few million years ago, but with the exception of forms like the opossum, they were replaced in the Western Hemisphere by the competing placental mammals. Competition is not a necessary prerequisite for replacement, however. A group may become extinct for some other reason and another group may then evolve into the vacated environment and way of life. A good example is provided by the *ammonites,* fossil mollusks related to the living chambered nautilus (see Chap. 32). Some 200 million years ago, am-

monites were represented by about a dozen families. All but one of these later became extinct, and the surviving group rapidly evolved into some two dozen new families of ammonites. The latter then exploited the adaptive niche vacated by the earlier ammonites.

Replacement in this case was more or less immediate. On occasion, however, many millions of years may elapse before a new group evolves into a previously occupied environmental niche. *Delayed replacement* of this sort took place, for example, in the case of the ichthyosaurs. These large, marine, fishlike reptiles became extinct some 100 million years ago, and their particular niche subsequently remained unoccupied for about 40 million years.

Dolphins and porpoises evolved then, and these mammals replaced the ichthyosaurs. Similarly delayed replacement occurred between the flying reptilian pterosaurs and the later mammalian bats (Fig. 31.13).

Convergence and Divergence

The phenomenon of replacement is often accompanied by that of convergence, a frequent feature in evolution generally. We have seen how, in an adaptive radiation, a common ancestral type gives rise to two or more descendant lines, all adapted in different ways to different environments. Such development of dissimilar characteristics in closely related groups is often called evolutionary *divergence*. By contrast, when two or more unrelated groups adapt to the same type of environment, then their evolution is oriented in the same direction. Such organisms may come to resemble one another in one or more ways. Evolution of a common set of characteristics in groups of different ancestry is called *convergence* (Fig. 31.14).

For example, the development of wings in both pterosaurs and bats or of finlike appendages in both ichthyosaurs and dolphins illustrates evolutionary convergence in replacing forms. Inasmuch as the replacing type occupies a similar adaptive niche as the type being replaced, the appearance of convergent features is not surprising. But convergence is also encountered in nonreplacing forms. For example, the eyes of squids and of fish are remarkably alike. Squids and fish are not related directly and neither replaces the other. However, both groups comprise large, fast swimmers, and good eyes of a particular construction are a distinct advantage in the ways of life of both. Selection actually has promoted variations which have led to eyes of similar structure, and the observed convergence is the result.

Opportunism

Although the eyes of squids and fish are strikingly alike, they are by no means identical. Similarly, although the wings of pterosaurs and bats or of insects and birds are convergent, in the sense that all carry out the same functions of flying, the various wing types are quite different structurally and operate in different ways. Convergence leads to *similarity*, never to identity. Moreover, neither squids nor fish possess a theoretically "best" eye structure for fast swimmers, and none of the flying groups possesses a theoretically "best" wing design. Actually, the structure of an organ or of a whole organism need not be theoretically "best" or "most efficient." The construction only needs to be practically workable and just ef-

ficient enough for a necessary function. In a way of life based on flying, wings of some sort are clearly essential. But virtually all requirements for living can have *multiple* solutions, and so long as a given solution works at all it does not matter how the solution is arrived at. The various animal wings do represent multiple solutions of the same problem, each evolved from a different starting point and each functioning in a different way. All other instances of evolutionary convergence are similar in these respects.

We are led to one of the most important and most universal characteristics of evolution, that of *random opportunism*. Evolution has produced not what is theoretically desirable or best, but what is practically possible. There has been no predetermined plan, no striving for set "goals," but only the exploitation of actually available opportunities offered by selection among random hereditary changes. For example, it might have been adaptively exceedingly useful for terrestrial plants to grow legs or for terrestrial animals to grow wheels. But neither occurred because it could not occur; the ancestors simply did

31 · 13 Evolutionary replacement.

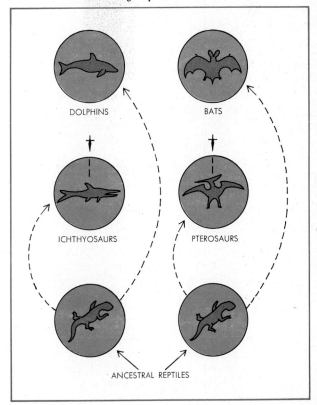

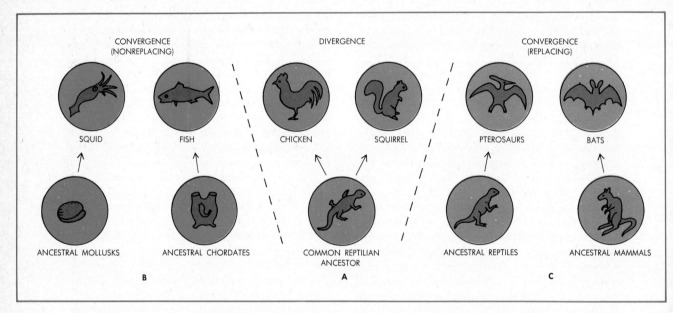

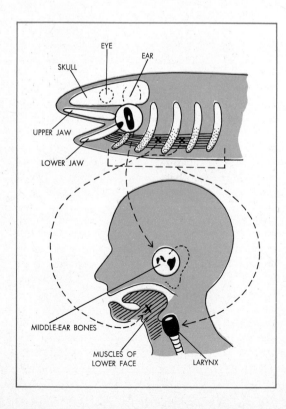

31 · 14 Divergence and convergence. *In evolutionary divergence (A), a common ancestor gives rise to different descendant lines. In evolutionary convergence (B, C), relatively unrelated ancestors give rise to rather similar lines.*

not possess the necessary structural and functional potential. However, they did possess the potential to evolve adequate, workable, alternative solutions. In the case of plants, already existing spores could be encapsulated and distributed by wind, and in the case of vertebrates, already existing fins could be reshaped into walking legs.

Clearly, evolution can only remodel and build on what already exists, in small, successive steps. Since, given a long enough time span, *every* feature of every organism undergoes random variations in many different directions, opportunities for diverse evolutionary changes have been and still are very numerous. Some of these opportunities have been and are actually exploited.

Therefore, every organism, man not excepted, is a patchwork of good opportunities seized by selection at the right time. In man, for example, the bones of the middle ear have arisen opportunistically from pieces of earlier vertebrate jaw bones. The musculature of the lower face has evolved from the gill muscles of ancestral fish. The larynx has developed from the skeletal gill supports of ancient fish (Fig.

31 · 15 Evolutionary opportunism. *Parts of the lower jaw and the upper bone of the next bony gill arch of ancestral fishes have been the evolutionary sources of the middle-ear bones of man. Analogously, parts of the other gill supports of fishes have evolved into the cartilages of the mammalian larynx, and the gill musculature of fishes has contributed the muscles of the lower face of mammals.*

31.15). Such instances of evolutionary opportunism are legion. We consequently conclude that specific organisms are not the result of any planned, goal-directed, or predetermined course of creation. Instead, they are the result of a cumulative, opportunistic process of piece-by-piece building, based on preexisting organisms and governed entirely by natural selection acting on random variations.

The above outlines the general characteristics of the evolutionary process. We have found that, in the past, evolution has proceeded at various rates through successive adaptive radiations, has led to extinction here and to replacement there, to further divergence in some instances, to convergence in others, and to opportunistic exploitation of possibilities in all. As an overall result, the living mass on earth has been increasing fairly steadily in individual numbers and types and has seeped into practically all possible environments. Indeed, it has created new environments in the process. For example, the evolution of trees has created new possibilities of life in the treetops, exploited later by very many new animals, including our own ancestors. The evolution of warm-blooded birds and mammals has created a new environment in the blood of these animals, exploited later by many new parasites. The evolution of man has created numerous new environments in human installations, and these have been exploited by a large variety of new plants and animals.

We recognize here yet another general characteristic of evolution: a progressive, creative *expansiveness,* as regards both living mass and ways of life. The expansion is still under way, faster in some cases than in others, and the end cannot be predicted as yet.

REVIEW QUESTIONS

1. Describe the essential points of the evolutionary theories of (*a*) Lamarck, (*b*) Darwin and Wallace. How could the evolution of giraffes from short-necked ancestors be explained in terms of each of these two theories? What were the weaknesses of each theory?

2. What different kinds of inheritable variations may arise in organisms? Do such variations appear randomly or are they oriented toward usefulness? How do noninheritable variations arise and what role do they play in evolution?

3. Define the modern meaning of natural selection. Show how natural selection has little to do with "survival of the fittest" or "struggle" or "weeding out" and how it is both a peaceful and a creative force. How does it happen that natural selection is oriented toward improved adaptation?

4. State the Hardy-Weinberg law. If a population consists of 49 per cent *AA*, 42 per cent *Aa*, and 9 per cent *aa* individuals, show by calculation how the law applies. If a Hardy-Weinberg equilibrium exists in a population, what are the rate and amount of evolution?

5. What three conditions disturb Hardy-Weinberg equilibria? For each condition, show in what way such equilibria are disturbed and how evolution is therefore affected. How do recessive genes spread through a population? What is genetic drift and where is it encountered?

6. Define "species" in genetic terms. Describe the process of speciation. What are some common geographic isolating conditions and what is their effect on gene pools? What is a subspecies? How do reproductive barriers arise between populations?

7. Review some actual evidence for past and present evolution. Describe the hypothesis of jump evolution. What are its weaknesses and what is the commonly accepted alternative hypothesis?

8. How have rates of evolution varied in the past? What is an adaptive radiation? Illustrate in the case of mammals. What are the general causes of extinction? What has been the pattern of extinction on different taxonomic levels?

9. How do narrow specialization and broad adaptability contribute to either extinction or survival? What is evolutionary replacement? Distinguish between immediate and delayed replacement and give examples. Distinguish between evolutionary divergence and convergence and give examples.

10. In what important way is evolution randomly opportunistic? List 10 structural and functional features of man and show for each (*a*) how it has evolved opportunistically, and (*b*) that it cannot be labeled as being "theoretically best." What has been the general evolutionary trend regarding the total quantity of life on earth? Show how evolution has created new environments, hence new opportunities for evolution.

COLLATERAL READINGS

Crow, J. F.: Ionizing Radiation and Evolution, *Sci. American,* Sept., 1959. A discussion of the effects of radiation-induced mutations on evolution.

Darwin, C.: "The Origin of Species and The Descent of Man," Modern Library, New York, 1948. A reprint of two of Darwin's classic books.

———— and A. R. Wallace: On the Tendency of Species to form Varieties; and of the Perpetuation of Varieties and Species by Natural Means of Selection, in "Great Experiments in Biology," Prentice-Hall, Englewood Cliffs, N.J., 1955. A reprint of the original 1858 statement of the theory of natural selection.

Dobzhansky, T.: The Genetic Basis of Evolution, *Sci. American,* Jan., 1950. Genetic experiments on evolution are described, including the production of bacterial strains resistant to bacteriocides.

————: "Genetics and the Origin of Species," 3d ed., Columbia, New York, 1951. A well-known and recommended analysis of evolutionary theory.

Dodson, E. O.: "Evolution: Process and Product," Reinhold, New York, 1960. A very good text on general principles and specific evolutionary processes and phenomena.

Ehrlich, P. R., and R. W. Holm: "Process of Evolution," McGraw-Hill, New York, 1963. A nonintroductory, recommended book on genetics, populations, and evolutionary principles.

Eiseley, L. C.: Charles Darwin, *Sci. American,* Feb., 1956. A biographical article.

Hardin, G.: "Population, Evolution, Birth Control," Freeman, San Francisco, 1964. A compilation of controversial readings on the social and religious aspects of evolutionary thought. Very worthwhile.

Huxley, J. S.: "Evolution: the Modern Synthesis," Harper & Row, New York, 1943. A nontechnical book on modern evolutionary theory by a well-known biologist.

Kettlewell, H. B. D.: Darwin's Missing Evidence, *Sci. American,* Mar., 1959. A study of evolution in progress; the case of body colors of certain species of moths is analyzed.

Lack, D.: Darwin's Finches, *Sci. American,* Apr., 1953. An examination of the famous Galapagos birds on which Darwin based much of his theory.

Lamarck, J. B. P. A. de: Evolution through Environmentally Produced Modifications, in "A Source Book in Animal Biology," McGraw-Hill, New York, 1951. A translation of the original 1809 statement of Lamarck's theory.

Mayr, E.: "Animal Species and Evolution," Harvard, Cambridge, Mass., 1963. An important (nonintroductory) recent book on speciation and evolutionary theory.

Pasteur, L.: Examination of the Doctrine of Spontaneous Generation, in "Great Experiments in Biology," Prentice-Hall, Englewood Cliffs, N.J., 1955. A translation of the famous 1862 original.

Redi, F.: Experiments on the Generation of Insects, in "Great Experiments in Biology," Prentice-Hall, Englewood Cliffs, N.J., 1955. A translation of the 1688 refutation of the doctrine of spontaneous generation.

Ross, H. H.: "A Synthesis of Evolutionary Theory," Prentice-Hall, Englewood Cliffs, N.J., 1962. A very stimulating book on all kinds of evolving systems, from galaxies and stars to living populations on earth.

Savage, J. M.: "Evolution," Holt, New York, 1963. A recommended paperback reviewing general evolutionary theory and principles.

Simpson, G. G.: "The Meaning of Evolution," Yale, New Haven, Conn., 1949, or Mentor Books, M66, New York, 1951. A most highly recommended analysis of modern evolutionary theory by one of the principal students of the subject; hard cover or paperback.

CHAPTER 32 DESCENT: PALEON- TOLOGY

One of the main lines of investigation revealing the time course of past evolution is *paleontology*, the study of fossils. Representing the remains of formerly living individuals, fossils provide the most direct evidence of the kinds of organisms in existence at various earlier times.

Unfortunately, a reasonably extensive fossil record does not go back more than 500 million years, a span of time representing only the last quarter or so of living history. Events during the crucial first three-quarters must therefore be inferred indirectly through *comparative morphology*, the study of the structure of presently living organisms. Being the products of past organisms, modern ones reflect in their architecture the evolutionary history of their antecedents; from molecules to organ systems, all body parts of organisms existing today embody the record of past evolution. Molecular and cellular evolution consequently can be inferred from studies in *comparative biochemistry* and *comparative cytology*, and tissue and organ evolution, from studies in *comparative embryology* and *comparative anatomy*.

In this chapter, we begin with a survey of the geologic record as a whole and continue with a more detailed survey of the past evolution of plants and animals.

THE GEOLOGIC RECORD

FOSSILS

Any long-preserved remains of organisms are fossils. They may be skeletons or shells, perhaps recrystal- lized under heat and pressure and infiltrated with mineral deposits from surrounding rock. They may be footprints later petrified or the remnants of organisms trapped in arctic ice, amber, quicksand, gravel pits, tar pits, and swamps. Or they may be imprints of carbon black on rock, left when the soft parts of plants or animals vaporized under heat and pressure. Whenever a buried organism or any part of it be- comes preserved in some way before it decays, it will be a fossil.

Fossils formed in the past are embedded in earth layers of different ages. In a geologically undisturbed section of the earth's crust, the deeper layers are the older layers. Material eroded from high-lying land gradually piles up on low land and on the sea bottom. A deep layer today therefore was on the surface in past ages and the earth's surface today will be a deep layer in the future. Fossils embedded in successive layers so provide a time picture of evolu- tion. To be sure, deep-lying fossils are normally not accessible. But on occasion a canyon-cutting river, an earthquake fracture, or an upbuckling and con- sequent breaking of the earth's crust may expose a cross section through the rock strata. Moreover, erosion gradually wears away top layers, exposing deeper rock. Geologic changes of this sort have been sufficiently abundant to expose layers of all different ages in various parts of the world (Fig. 32.1).

How is the actual age of a rock layer determined? Very excellent clocks are built right into the earth's crust: radioactive substances. The disintegration rate of these substances is known accurately, as are the endproducts of disintegration. For example, a given quantity of radium is known to "decay" into lead in a certain span of time. When radium and lead are found together in one mass within a rock, the whole mass presumably had been radium originally, when the rock was formed. From the relative quantities of radium and lead present today, one can then cal- culate the time required for that much lead to form. This dates the rock, with an error of about 10 per cent of its total age.

An analogous principle underlies age determina- tions by potassium-argon dating and by radiocarbon dating. In the potassium-argon process, one measures how much of the unstable isotope potassium 40 has decayed into the isotope argon 40. Radiocarbon dating

32 · 1 Rock layers of different ages are often exposed to view. Generally speaking, the deeper a layer in the earth's crust, the older it is.

involves measurements of carbon 14, an isotope of "natural" carbon 12. Whereas the potassium-argon method can be used for dating fossils many millions of years old, the carbon 14 method is accurate only for fossils formed within the last 50,000 years. Fossils themselves often help in fixing the age of a rock layer. If such a layer contains a fossil which on the basis of other evidence is known to be of a definite age (*index fossil*) then the whole layer, including all other fossils in it, is likely to be of the same general age.

Based on data obtained from radioactive and fossil clocks, geologists have constructed a *geologic time table* which indicates the age of successive earth layers and so provides a calendar of the earth's past history. This calendar consists of five successive main divisions, or *eras*. The last three of these are subdivided in turn into a number of successive *periods*. The names of the eras and periods and their approximate durations are indicated in Table 22.

The beginning and terminal dates of the eras and periods have not been chosen arbitrarily but have been made to coincide with major geologic events known to have occurred at those times. The transitions between eras in particular were times of great upheaval, characterized by mountain building and by severely fluctuating climates. For example, the transition from the Paleozoic to the Mesozoic dates the *Appalachian revolution,* during which the mountain range of that name was built up. By now, these mountains are already greatly reduced by erosion. Similarly, the transition between the Mesozoic and the Cenozoic was marked by the *Laramide revolution,* which produced the high mountain ranges of today: the Himalayas, the Rockies, the Andes, and the Alps. As we shall see, these major geologic events led to major biological ones, marked by evolutionary crises and large-scale replacement of types.

THE PRECAMBRIAN ERA

The first geologic era, the immensely long Azoic, spans the period from the origin of the earth to the origin of life. Living history begins with the next era, the Precambrian.

Fossils are not lacking altogether from these distant Precambrian ages. But the record is exceedingly fragmentary and it shows mainly that life, simple cellular life at least, already existed about 2 billion years ago. This must mean that the actual origin of life must have occurred earlier; we place it at about 3 billion years ago, at the start of the Precambrian. We also know how far evolution must have proceeded by the end of the Precambrian, for from that time on we have a continuous and abundant fossil record.

It is a very curious circumstance that rocks older than about 500 million years are so barren of fossils whereas rocks younger than that are comparatively rich in them. Many hypotheses have been proposed to account for this, but to date a satisfactory explanation has not been found. Did the Precambrian environment somehow preclude the formation of fossils? Were fossils destroyed in some way before the Paleozoic? Or is the Precambrian fossil record so scanty because the organisms then were still too insubstantial to leave fossilizable remains? We simply cannot be sure.

But we are reasonably sure that Precambrian evolution must have brought about not only the origin of life and the origin of cells but also the origin of three of the four present main groups of organisms, namely, the Monera, the Protista, and the Metazoa. Moreover, virtually all phyla within these three groups were in existence by the end of the Precambrian. To be sure, the organisms then representing these phyla were not the same kinds as those living today; extinction and replacement by new types was still to occur many times. But the ancient types nevertheless did belong to the same phyla we recognize now.

In what sequence these various ancient organisms evolved from the first cells must, in the absence of fossils, be inferred from the nature of presently living forms. In different contexts, we actually have already made such inferences in various earlier chapters. Thus, primitive ancestral cell types are believed to have given rise to two major descendant lines, the Monera and the Protista. Ancestral forms of these in turn each evolved several subgroups; and among the early Protista so appeared the algal types, the fungal types, and the protozoan types. Each of these subsequently produced adaptive radiations of their own, leading to the various protistan phyla we know today. Out of one or more of these adaptive radiations also came a new group, the Metazoa. These ancestral animals sooner or later gave rise to the Radiata, the Acoelomata, the Pseudocoelomata, and the Coelomata. Primitive representatives of them eventually produced ancient organisms which typified the various animal phyla of today and which we now find as fossils dating back some 500 million years.

Inasmuch as this presumed sequence of Precambrian events is based on an analysis of actual structures and functions among current organisms, it probably incorporates a measure of validity as well as a measure of error. The degree of validity is certain to be improved and to be made more detailed through research; but a given degree of error may never be resolved, for direct evidence is simply unobtainable. Note that the sequence has the form of a bush and consists of a succession of adaptive radiations. This is as it should be on the basis of known evolutionary mechanisms.

Evidently, the long Precambrian spanned not only three-quarters of evolutionary time but also three-quarters of evolutionary substance. Nearly all the organisms in existence at the end of the Precambrian were aquatic. With the probable exception of some of the bacteria and some of the Protista, the land apparently had not been invaded as yet. The ensuing last quarter of evolution brought about principally a rich and extensive further diversification within the existing phyla. This process resulted in a replacement of ancient forms by new ones, including in each of the three main groups the evolution of types that could live on land. And among the land-adapted descendants of the Protista, more specifically the green algae, there were organisms which established a new main group, namely, the Metaphyta. These appear to have been the last to evolve among the four main categories now living.

Starting with the Cambrian period of the Paleozoic era, the course of evolution is documented fairly amply by fossils. These show that, on the phylum level, every group in existence in the Cambrian has persisted to the present. But on the species level, no group has persisted.

PLANT EVOLUTION

The Cambrian and Ordovician periods lasted for almost half of the entire 300-million-year-long Paleozoic era. During this time, the land surface remained free of living organisms (some microscopic forms probably excepted, as noted). But the seas and later also the fresh waters abounded with many diverse moneran, protistan, and metazoan types. The first Metaphyta appear in the fossil record of

the Silurian. Terrestrial Metazoa had not yet evolved at this time.

It is interesting to note that these earliest land plants were tracheophytes, specifically, psilopsids and lycopsids. Bryophytes seem to have evolved much later; their first fossils do not appear till the Carboniferous.

THE PALEOZOIC

In 1903, the French botanist Lignier proposed the hypothesis that the ancestors of the terrestrial tracheophytes were green algae with a dichotomously branching, rather *Fucus*-like structure. Such an ancestral stock was postulated to have become terrestrial by development of an epidermis with cuticles and stomata; by gradual straightening of some of the dichotomous branches, leading to the formation of a main stem with lateral branches; by growth of some of the lowest branches into the ground as roots; by development of vascular tissue in the interior of stem and root; and by restriction of reproductive capacity to the terminals of stems. Lignier considered that the evolution of alga into tracheophyte might have occurred along sea or freshwater shores, where intermittent terrestrial conditions would have promoted the development of adaptations to land life (Fig. 32.2).

Later evidence has amply supported this hypothesis, and it is now accepted quite widely. Numer-

TABLE 22 THE GEOLOGIC TIME TABLE°

ERA	PERIOD	DURATION		BEGINNING DATE
Cenozoic ("new life")	Quaternary	75	1	1
	Tertiary		74	75
Mesozoic ("middle life")	Cretaceous	130	60	135
	Jurassic		30	165
	Triassic		40	205
Paleozoic ("ancient life")	Permian	300	25	230
	Carboniferous		50	280
	Devonian		45	325
	Silurian		35	360
	Ordovician		65	425
	Cambrian		80	505
Precambrian		1,500		3,000
Azoic ("without life")		3,000		5,000

° *All numbers refer to millions of years; older ages are toward bottom of table, younger ages toward top.*

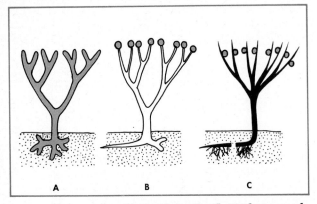

32 · 2   The Lignier hypothesis. Dichotomously branching algae as in A may have evolved via stages as in B into primitive, rhizome-possessing tracheophytes as in C.

ous psilopsid fossils have been discovered in the Rhynie deposits of Scotland, regions which probably were swamps during the Paleozoic. Ancient psilopsids living there must have become flooded and their bodies impregnated with silica. As a result, the plants are very well preserved today and even the internal organization of cells is still recognizable in amazing detail. These earliest land plants were structured more or less exactly as postulated by the Lignier hypothesis.

32 · 3   Fossil psilopsids. A, Rhynia. B, Horneophyton (after Kidston and Lang). C, Psilophyton (after Dawson). D, Pseudosporochnus (after Krausel and Wayland). E, Asteroxylon. Note rhizomes, dichotomous branching, terminal sporangia, and microphylls in C and D and absence of leaves in A, B, and E.

Silurian and Devonian

One of the Silurian fossil psilopsids is *Rhynia*, named after the Rhynie region. This plant (Fig. 32.3) possessed a rhizome with rhizoids, dichotomous upright branches about 1 ft in height, and terminal sporangia. Leaves were absent. Quite similar to this plant were two others, *Horneophyton* and *Psilophyton*. The latter carried short spines which were probably microphyllous leaves. Only the sporophytes of these fossil psilopsids have been found. Various other extinct psilopsids show clearly that these early vascular plants could indeed have been ancestral to all other evolutionary lines of tracheophytes. For example, the psilopsid *Asteroxylon* exhibited rootlike branches, numerous microphylls, and other characteristics indicating a trend of evolution in a lycopsid direction. The sphenopsid direction is suggested by fossil plants such as *Hyenia*, which possessed microphylls arranged in nodal whorls and is believed to have been closely related to the psilopsids. Several fossil psilopsids, among them *Pseudosporochnus*, point to the pteropsid direction of evolution. In these 9-ft-high treelike plants the leaves were terminal and flattened, with a webbing which may have foreshadowed the macrophyllous condition characteristic of ferns.

The fossil record of the Silurian and early Devonian thus appears to warrant the same conclusion suggested independently by a study of vascular plants now living: psilopsids are the most primitive tracheophytes and they must have been ancestral to all other lines of tracheophyte evolution. By middle and late Devonian times, the lycopsid, sphenopsid, and pteropsid lines were already in existence and flourishing (Fig. 32.4).

The Devonian lycopsids were represented by *lepidodendrids*, the giant club mosses (Fig. 32.5). All were huge trees up to 120 ft in height, with active secondary growth, leaves some 20 in. long and cones

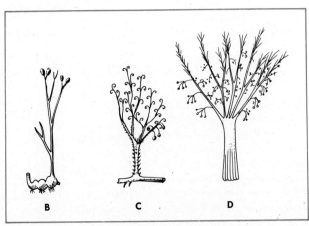

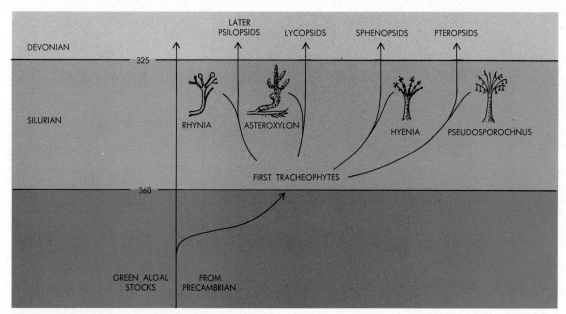

32 · 4 *Early Paleozoic fossil history of plants. Numbers at left indicate past time in millions of years.*

up to 1 ft long. The "scale tree" *Lepidodendron* became particularly abundant, as did *Sigillaria*, the "seal tree." The 60-ft-high stem of this tree bore leaves in a terminal tuft which gave the plant the general appearance of a giant paint brush. The lepidodendrids were largely heterosporous. In some of them the female gametophytes developed precociously in the megasporangia (as in *Selaginella* today). Other lepidodendrids came exceedingly close to forming true seeds.

The sphenopsids of the Devonian are represented by fossils such as *Calamophyton, Sphenophyllum,* and *Calamites* (Fig. 32.6). The first-named possessed a jointed stem, with narrow leaves arranged in nodal whorls. Secondary growth occurred in *Sphenophyllum,* characterized by whorls of triangular leaves, and in *Calamites,* the giants of the Devonian sphenopsids, which formed trees up to 100 ft high. Both homospory and heterospory were common in all the ancient sphenopsids.

In comparison with the large lycopsids and sphenopsids, the pteropsids of the Devonian were still relatively small and had not yet attained the stature they were to achieve later. All known fossil ferns, the Coenopteridales, were homosporous (Fig. 32.7). This stock must have produced an adaptive radiation which included a line leading to the seed plants; fossil seed plants appear for the first time in late Devonian rocks. These plants were gymnosperms

belonging to two groups, the *seed ferns* and the *fossil conifers.* The former (which were not really "ferns" despite their name) probably arose first and in turn gave rise to the latter. But neither achieved prominence until the next period of the Paleozoic (Fig. 32.8).

32 · 5 *Fossil lycopsids.* A, *reconstruction of* Lepidodendron. B, *reconstruction of* Sigillaria.

A   B

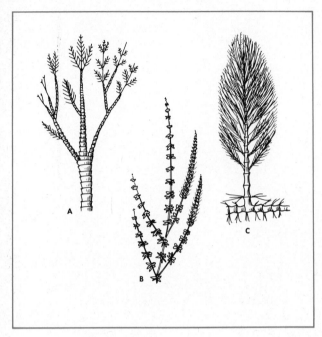

32 · 6 Fossil sphenopsids. A, Calamophyton. B, Sphenophyllum. C, Calamites. (*After Krausel and Wayland, Zeiller, and Hirmer.*)

Carboniferous and Permian

During the Carboniferous most of the tracheophytes which had evolved during the Devonian reached their peak abundance. Lycopsids and sphenopsids produced huge forests, and ferns too attained the stature of trees. Bryophytes appear for the first time in the fossil record of this period. It is possible that their evolution was promoted by the generally wet, tropical and subtropical conditions then prevailing over much of the earth. In addition, gymnosperms came to be important members of the world's flora. The two already existing groups, seed ferns and fossil conifers, became dominant during the Carboniferous. A third gymnospermous group, the *fossil cycads*, evolved in this period from the seed ferns but did not achieve prominence until much later.

The Carboniferous is sometimes called the "age of seed ferns." These plants, the *Cycadofilicales*, were at first thought to be ferns, which they resembled greatly; and after their seeds were discovered the misleading name persisted nevertheless (Fig. 32.9). The seed ferns gave rise to an extensive and important adaptive radiation. It probably included lines that sooner or later may have led to all other gymnosperms, extinct as well as living; and it is possible that one of the seed fern stocks later also

evolved into the flowering plants. Among the derived gymnospermous groups were the fossil conifers. They had been in existence since the Devonian, as noted, but attained their peak during the Carboniferous. A giant representative was *Cordaites*, a tree up to 100 ft high with parallel-veined leaves that sometimes reached lengths of 3 ft.

During the later part of the Carboniferous many regions became so wet that they were transformed into vast tracts of swamps and marshes. In these, much of the woody flora of the time died. Later geological changes converted the bodies of the plants into coal. Hence the name of the whole period, "coal-bearing." The rich coal beds of Pennsylvania and West Virginia came into being at that time, and the coal itself represents the remains of forests of lepidodendrid lycopsids, calamite sphenopsids, tree ferns, seed ferns, and fossil conifers.

However, many of these plants survived and persisted into the Permian. They were joined then by the newly evolved ginkgoes. Yet for many of the ancient forms the time of dominance was about over. The long Paleozoic terminated with the geological upheavals of the Applachian revolution, which in turn precipitated a so-called *Permo-Triassic crisis* among living organisms. This unstable time of transition was marked by widespread extinction of archaic forms and later replacement with rapidly evolving

32 · 7 A fossil fern. (*After Hirmer.*)

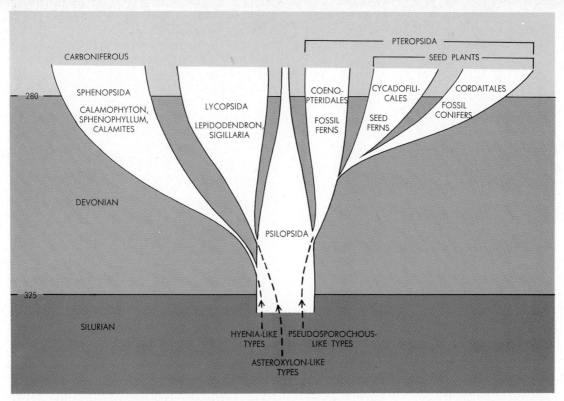

CARBONIFEROUS

PTEROPSIDA

SEED PLANTS

280

SPHENOPSIDA

CALAMOPHYTON,
SPHENOPHYLLUM,
CALAMITES

LYCOPSIDA

LEPIDODENDRON,
SIGILLARIA

COENO-
PTERIDALES

CYCADOFILI-
CALES

CORDAITALES

FOSSIL
CONIFERS

FOSSIL
FERNS

SEED
FERNS

DEVONIAN

PSILOPSIDA

325

SILURIAN

HYENIA-LIKE
TYPES

PSEUDOSPOROCHOUS-
LIKE TYPES

ASTEROXYLON-LIKE
TYPES

32 · 8 *Devonian fossil history of plants. Numbers at left indicate past time in millions of years.*

32 · 9 *Fossil gymnosperms. Diagrams (after Oliver): 1, seed fern; 2, external view of megasporangium of seed fern; 3, section through seed fern megasporangium. Photo: reconstruction of Cordaites.*

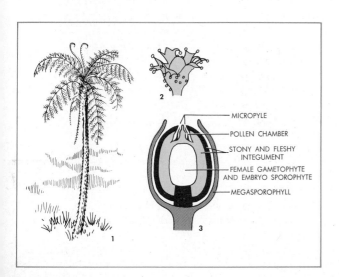

MICROPYLE

POLLEN CHAMBER

STONY AND FLESHY
INTEGUMENT

FEMALE GAMETOPHYTE
AND EMBRYO SPOROPHYTE

MEGASPOROPHYLL

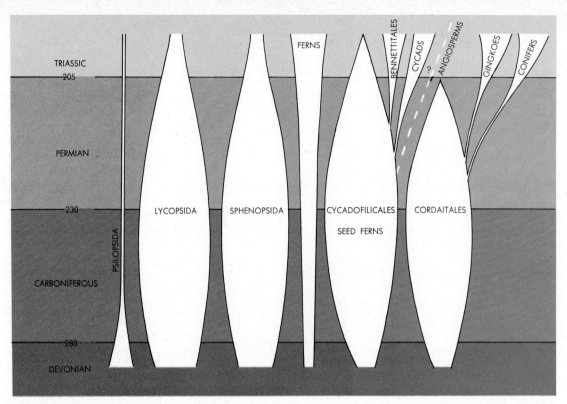

PSILOPSIDA · LYCOPSIDA · SPHENOPSIDA · FERNS · CYCADOFILICALES SEED FERNS · CORDAITALES · BENNETTITALES · CYCADS · ? · ANGIOSPERMS · GINGKOES · CONIFERS

TRIASSIC 205 · PERMIAN · 230 · CARBONIFEROUS · 280 · DEVONIAN

32 · 10 Late Paleozoic and early Mesozoic fossil history of plants. Numbers at left indicate past time in millions of years.

new types. Also, the total amount of life decreased temporarily. Evolutionary turnover in the sea was extensive, particularly among animals (see below). On land, many plant groups became extinct: virtually all of the psilopsids, lepidodendrids, and early sphenopsids, as well as many of the ancient ferns, gymnospermous seed ferns, and fossil conifers. Some of the archaic lycopsids and sphenopsids lingered on into the Triassic, but eventually they died out altogether. Other remnant groups of psilopsids, lycopsids, and sphenopsids managed to survive, and from these later arose the relic genera living today. After the Permo-Triassic crisis, however, none of the psilopsids, lycopsids, and sphenopsids achieved major stature again (Fig. 32.10).

On the contrary, the surviving groups of ferns and gymnosperms began to flourish anew, and they became the ancestors of the expanding flora of the new Mesozoic era.

THE MESOZOIC

The Mesozoic as a whole is often called the "age of gymnosperms" in plant evolution. Within the era,

the Triassic and Jurassic periods qualify as the "age of cycads," and the Cretaceous as the "age of conifers."

As noted, fossil cycads had evolved from the seed ferns and had already been in existence since the Carboniferous. This group reached its peak during the Jurassic, when it formed extensive forests. The representative type *Bennettites* (Fig. 32.11) was a tree some 10 ft high, with terminal leaves almost as long as the tree trunk. The reproductive structures were arranged in a somewhat flowerlike manner. This circumstance has on occasion given rise to the suggestion that fossil cycads may have been the ancestors of the flowering plants. It is now clear, however, that the resemblance is superficial and that it probably represents little more than an instance of convergent evolution. The fossil cycads died out during the Cretaceous (and their ample remains may still be found, for example, in the Fossil Cycad National Monument in the Black Hills of South Dakota). The group was replaced on a reduced scale by the true cycads, probably evolved independently from seed ferns. Descendants of these plants are still living in various warm-climate areas today.

During the early part of the Mesozoic the ginkgoes steadily increased in abundance, and they reached their peak during the Jurassic and early Cretaceous. Concurrently, new groups of coniferous gymno-

794

sperms, related to the earlier Cordaites, came into ascendancy. These groups dominated the whole later part of the Mesozoic and included many of the present living conifers, for example, cypresses, yews, redwoods, and pines.

The forests formed by these large trees did not dominate the late Mesozoic landscape alone. They had to share space with the *angiosperms,* which produced a first extensive radiation at that time. Fragmentary fossils of angiosperms date back to the Jurassic, but the first ample finds occur in Cretaceous layers. The origin of angiosperms is quite obscure; the best guess at present is that they evolved from some seed fern stock that had survived into the Mesozoic. As will become apparent below, the late Mesozoic expansion of angiosperms coincided with a similarly extensive radiation of insects. Most of the Mesozoic angiosperms were woody. They included many of the tree-forming types still living today, for example, elms, oaks, maples, magnolias, and palms. Forests of these were already flourishing, and in the closing phases of the Mesozoic they began to rival those of the conifers (Fig. 32.12).

THE CENOZOIC

If the Mesozoic was the age of gymnosperms, the Cenozoic was unquestionably the "age of angiosperms" in plant evolution. The increasing dominance of the angiosperms and the corresponding decline of the

gymnosperms was in large measure a consequence of the Laramide revolution which terminated the Mesozoic.

This revolution brought on a crisis similar to the one at the end of the Paleozoic. As noted earlier, the main effect of the Laramide revolution was the formation of the high mountain ranges of today. Their emergence substantially changed the pre-Cenozoic patterns of air circulation between ocean and land, and the new patterns led to new climatic conditions. For example, the east-west barrier of the Himalayas in Asia and of the Alps in Europe prevented warm south winds from reaching the northern portions of Eurasia. These regions became colder as a result. Such cooling in turn undoubtedly facilitated the development of ice ages during the last million years.

Ice ages had occurred before during the earth's history, and during the last million years there were four. In each, ice sheets spread from the North Pole southward, covered much of the land of the Northern Hemisphere, then receded. Warm interglacial periods intervened between successive glaciations. The last recession began some 20,000 years ago, the beginning of the recent epoch, and it is still in progress; polar regions are still covered with ice (see Chap. 10).

The Laramide revolution had immediate effects on animals, as we shall see, but the effect on plants was more gradual. High, even temperatures had predominated during previous ages, when much of the earth was tropical and subtropical and when the poles were ice-free. This was an advantageous climate which offered a continuous, uninterrupted growing season. The early gymnosperms and angiosperms of the time were well adapted to such conditions; they evolved secondary growth and the woody perennial

32 · 11 **Bennettites.** *Photo: model of the "flower" of* Bennettites. *Diagram (after Wieland): section through the "flower."*

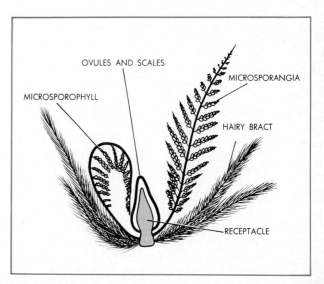

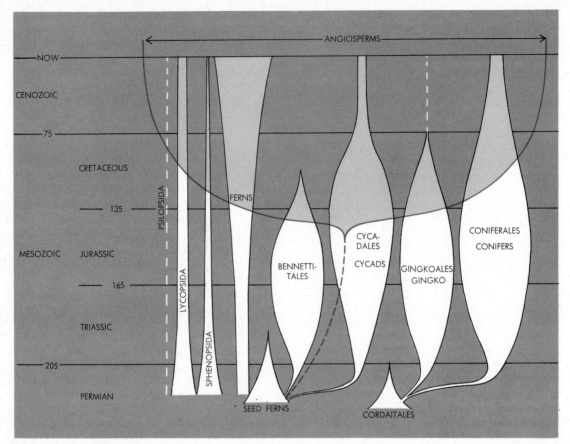

32 · 12 *Mesozoic and Cenozoic fossil history of plants. Numbers at left indicate past time in millions of years.*

habit, adding more and more wood with each passing year. Indeed, fossil trees from the Mesozoic and early Cenozoic are without annual rings, indicating the existence of even, warm conditions. The trees were typically warm-climate forms; for example, angiosperms included types such as figs, laurels, sycamores, eucalyptus, and palms.

But as climates became cooler during the later Cenozoic, distinct tropical, temperate, and cold polar zones became established on earth. As a result, seed plants already living in the tropics could remain tropical, but species in other regions could not. Three choices were open to them. They could migrate to the tropics, or they could die and become extinct, or they could readapt right where they lived to the succession of winter and summer. All three possibilities were actually realized in different groups. Of the groups that did not migrate, many became extinct. The decline of gymnosperms traces to this time. To-day only some 700 species are left, and these survive

because they now manage to protect themselves against the cold through processes of winter-harden-ing. Many woody angiosperms similarly survive to-day in temperate and northern regions, but they have adapted to winter conditions by becoming deciduous, that is, by shedding their leaves. Even so, the luxuri-ant forests of gymnosperms and angiosperms once characteristic of northern regions thinned out and became less extensive. Fossil trees from the later Cenozoic do show annual rings like trees today, in-dicating clearly that uninterrupted year-round growth was no longer possible.

Furthermore, in response to late Cenozoic climates the surviving angiosperms of temperate and northern regions produced a whole new adaptive radiation. The plants of this radiation coped with the cool seasons in new ways: they either reduced their cam-bial activity or lost cambia altogether, which left them as nonwoody herbaceous biennials and annuals. Winter then could not harm them, for during the winter they simply died and became nonexistent as mature plants. For the rest of the year their primary growth gave them only a minimum body, just barely large enough to permit them to reproduce. Thus the small herbaceous angiosperms now do not waste energy and materials in accumulating wood, which soon becomes nonfunctional in any case; yet they are winter-protected nevertheless. In effect, therefore, the long-range consequences of the Laramide revolution were the reduction of the woody seed plants in all regions except the tropics, and the gradual emergence of the modern small-bodied flowering herbs. These became dominant in the northern and arctic zones. Such areas today are inhabited by about 80 per cent of all the herbaceous angiosperms, whereas the tropics are inhabited by a similar percentage of all the woody angiosperms. As will become apparent below, the reduction of forests during the middle and late Cenozoic was to prove highly significant also for animal evolution. For example, arboreal temperate-zone mammals were forced out of the tree tops, which no longer provided continuous overhead canopies. Some of these mammals then evolved walking feet on the ground, and during the last million years they transformed into men.

ANIMAL EVOLUTION

Since most metazoan phyla recognized today appear to have been already established 500 million years ago, the various basic animal types must have evolved during the Precambrian. This early evolution consequently cannot be documented by fossils but must be inferred from the nature of the animal groups now in existence.

EARLY HISTORY

One of the notable attempts at inferring the course of animal evolution from existing forms was made by E. Haeckel, a German biologist of the late nineteenth century. Most of his views are now largely discredited, but they were once so influential that many of them still persist today under various guises. For this reason, even though the issues are quite dated, it may nevertheless be of some value to review them briefly.

Haeckel recognized, as did others before him, that the early embryonic development of all Eumetazoa passed through certain common stages. Thus, development starts with the unicellular zygote, proceeds by cleavage to a blastula stage, then to a gastrula stage, and continues later with mesoderm formation. Haeckel then thought that each such stage corresponded to an adult form of an ancestral type.

Accordingly, the succession of embryonic stages would mirror a succession of past evolutionary stages

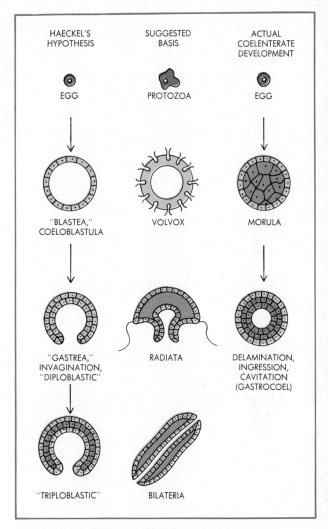

32 · 13 *Haeckel's "gastrea" hypothesis. It exemplifies the recapitulatory view that successive developmental stages of animals repeat the successive evolutionary stages of their ancestors. Based primarily on coelenterate development, the hypothesis is at variance with the actual developmental patterns typical of most coelenterates (right column). Thus, most coelenterates do not gastrulate by invagination, and mesoderm usually arises by delaminative and ingressional methods, a gastrocoel forming by central cavitation. Contrary to Haeckel's hypothesis, the presence of mesoderm actually makes not only the Bilateria but also the Radiata (hence all Eumetazoa) "triploblastic," or formed from three primary germ layers.*

(Fig. 32.13). The zygote would represent the unicellular protistan stage of evolution. The blastula would correspond to an evolutionary stage when animals were, according to Haeckel, hollow one-layered spheres. Haeckel coined the term *blastea* for such hypothetical adult animals, and he thought that his ancestral blasteas may have been quite similar to currently living green algae such as *Volvox*. Analogously, the gastrula stage in animal development would correspond to a hypothetical ancestral adult type which he called a *gastrea*. He believed that gastreas were still represented today by the living coelenterates, which in some respects do resemble early gastrulae; for example, the body consists chiefly of an ectodermal and an endodermal layer, and the single alimentary opening is reminiscent of the blastopore of a gastrula.

On such grounds, Haeckel considered the gastrea to have been the common ancestor of all Eumetazoa.

32 · 14 Developmental divergence. Top, the pattern of evolution according to Haeckel by addition of extra stages to a preexisting ancestral path of development. Bottom, the actual pattern of evolution, by divergence of new developmental paths (2, 3, 4, 5) from various points of a preexisting ancestral path (1). Thus, if divergence occurs comparatively late, as in adult 2, its embryonic and most of its larval development may be very similar to that of adult 1. But if divergence takes place early, as in adult 5, then almost the whole developmental pattern may be quite dissimilar from that of adult 1. Adults 1 and 5 then might represent different phyla, whereas adults 1 and 2 might belong to the same class or order.

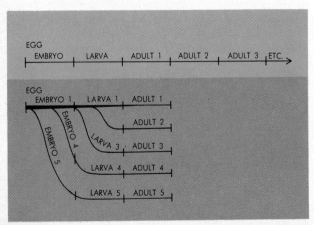

Moreover, he assumed the two-layered gastrealike condition to represent a *diploblastic* stage in animal evolution, attained by the coelenterates and the ctenophores. Further evolution then added mesoderm to the gastrealike radiates and so produced a three-layered *triploblastic* condition, as in flatworms and all other Bilateria. Thus, he considered coelenterates to represent a stage in flatworm evolution. By extension, this Haeckelian hypothesis also came to imply, for example, that a caterpillar larva represented an annelid stage in insect evolution, that a frog tadpole represented a fish stage in frog evolution, and that a human embryo, which exhibits rudimentary gill structures at certain periods, represented a fish stage in man's evolution.

Haeckel condensed his views into a *law of recapitulation*, the essence of which is described by two phrases, namely, "ontogeny recapitulates phylogeny" and "phylogeny causes ontogeny." The first statement means that the embryonic development of an egg (ontogeny) repeats the evolutionary development of the phyla (phylogeny); and the second, that "because" animals have evolved one phylum after another, their embryos still pass through this same succession of evolutionary stages.

Therefore, if one wishes to determine the course of animal evolution, he need only study the course of embryonic development. For, according to the law, evolution occurs by the addition of extra embryonic stages to the end of a given sequence of development. If to a protozoon is added cleavage, the protozoon becomes a zygote and the new adult is a blastea. If to a blastea is added the process of gastrulation, then the blastea becomes a blastula and the new adult is a gastrea. Similarly, if to a fish are added lungs and four legs, then the fish represents a tadpole and the new adult is a frog. And if to such an amphibian are added a four-chambered heart, a diaphragm, a larger brain, an upright posture, and a few other features, then the frog is a human embryo and the new adult is a man.

We can attribute to the lingering influence of Haeckel, not to Darwin, this erroneous idea of an evolutionary "ladder" or "scale," proceeding from "simple amoeba" to "complex man," with more and more rungs being added on top of the ladder as time proceeds. All such notions are invalid because Haeckel's basic thesis is invalid. Indeed, Haeckel's arguments were shown to be unsound even in his own day, but his generalizations were so neat and they seemed to explain so much so simply that the fundamental difficulties were ignored by many.

For example, it was already well known in Haeckel's time that, apart from exceptional forms, the radiate animals do not really have two-layered bodies

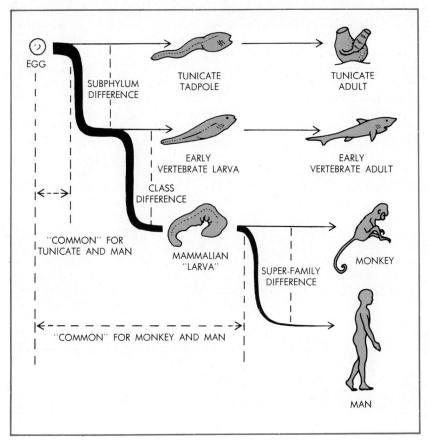

EGG

SUBPHYLUM
DIFFERENCE

TUNICATE
TADPOLE

TUNICATE
ADULT

EARLY
VERTEBRATE LARVA

EARLY
VERTEBRATE ADULT

CLASS
DIFFERENCE

"COMMON" FOR
TUNICATE AND MAN

MAMMALIAN
"LARVA"

MONKEY

SUPER-FAMILY
DIFFERENCE

"COMMON" FOR MONKEY AND MAN

MAN

32 · 15 Evolution by developmental divergence. Tailed, tadpolelike early stages are characteristic of all chordates, and the earlier the developmental paths diverge from the ancestral one, the more different the adult and taxonomic results. Keep in mind, however, that chordate eggs, for example, are not all the "same"; they are merely similar. Analogously, "common" developmental stages of two animals are merely similar.

but distinctly three-layered ones, even though the middle mesoderm remains poorly developed. Thus, two-layered animals virtually do not exist and a distinction between diploblastic and triploblastic types cannot actually be made. The central conceptual foundation on which the recapitulatory law was based was therefore never valid.

We know also that the evolution of new types generally does not occur through addition of extra stages to ancestral adults. Instead, new evolution occurs for the most part by *developmental divergence:* a new path of embryonic or larval development branches away from some point along a preexisting developmental path (Fig. 32.14). The best example is evolution by larval *neoteny,* a mechanism which probably has been responsible for a great deal of animal evolution. In such cases, a new group arises from the larva of an old group. The existing larva does not metamorphose into the customary adult, but instead develops sex organs precociously and becomes established in this larval form as a new type of adult animal. The evolution of tunicates into vertebrates provides a good illustration (Fig. 32.15). Tunicates develop via tadpole larvae into sessile

adults; and it is now considered to be most probable that vertebrates represent neotenous tunicate tadpoles. The tadpoles of certain tunicate ancestors appear to have retained their tails, with notochord and dorsal hollow nerve cord intact, and to have become reproductively mature in such a larval condition. These permanent larvae then came to represent a new chordate subphylum, namely, the vertebrates (see also Chap. 16).

Numerous other instances of evolution by neoteny are known. In all of them, the new developmental path branches away sooner or later along the course of the old path. And it should be clear that the sooner

32 · 16 Seascapes of the early Paleozoic, restorations. *A, Cambrian seas. Various algae, trilobites (in center foreground), eurypterids (in center background), sponges, jellyfishes, brachiopods, and different types of worms are the most prominent organisms shown. B, Ordovician seas. The large animal in foreground is a straight-shelled nautiloid.*

two such paths do diverge, the more dissimilar will be the two types of resulting adults. For example, the embryos of man and of apes resemble each other till relatively late in development, and the developmental paths diverge only then. The embryos of man and of tunicates are similar for considerably shorter periods; their developmental paths correspondingly diverge much sooner (see Fig. 32.15).

Such developmental correlations were clearly recognized before Haeckel and even before Darwin. We know today that they have evolutionary meaning, but not in the Haeckelian sense. It is quite natural that related animals descended from a common ancestor should resemble one another in some of their adult as well as some of their embryonic features. Such resemblances may or may not be pronounced, depending entirely on how widely the evo-

lutionary paths have diverged. Accordingly, human embryos resemble those of fish and frogs in certain respects not because an egg of man becomes a fish embryo first, changes to a frog embryo next, and transforms into a human embryo last. The similarities arise, rather, from the common ancestry of all these three animal types, including their common developmental histories up to certain stages. Beyond such stages, each type has modified its developmental processes in its own specific way.

The mechanism of developmental divergence is consistent also with our present understanding of evolutionary patterns: evolution must have occurred in bushlike fashion. A branching pattern of developmental divergence is fully in line with this knowledge, but ladderlike end addition is not. It is quite obvious also that mammalian development, for example, does not really represent a successive transformation of an actual protozoon into an actual coelenterate, flatworm, tunicate, fish, etc. Indeed it is hardly conceivable that the billion or more years of animal evolution could be crowded into the few weeks or months of animal development. The common stages in animal development may give evidence of general similarities, not of specific identities.

For these various reasons, the conclusion is certainly warranted that recapitulation in the Haeckelian sense simply does not occur; the embryonic stages of given animals do not repeat the adult stages of other animals. Moreover, phylum evolution also cannot be the "cause" of the progressive stages in animal development. If anything, just the reverse probably holds; as pointed out above, developmental stages provide the sources from which new groups may evolve.

We are thus left with the recognition that similarities among paths of development do exist, and that, inasmuch as they are consequences of common ancestries, they may indicate degrees of evolutionary interrelations among animals. This hypothesis predates Haeckel, but he then converted or subverted it into the recapitulation law. In the latter sense the hypothesis is no longer acceptable today, but in the former sense it is still valid: the development of two individuals or groups on the whole does tend to be similar if the animals are related, and the similarity lasts the longer the closer the relationship. Indeed, as has become apparent in Chap. 14, developmental resemblances are important aids both in classifying animals taxonomically and in determining how, Haeckel notwithstanding, animals may actually have evolved before they left fossils. Figure 14.15 may be considered to represent a summary of these currently held views.

THE PALEOZOIC

Every animal phylum in existence in the Cambrian has persisted to the present, but not a single species has persisted. So far as is known, only a single genus has survived from the Ordovician, the period after the Cambrian. This genus is *Lingula*, of the phylum Brachiopoda (see Chap. 15). Apart from this 400-million-year-old relic, all ancient genera have become extinct as well. Indeed, the dominant theme of the animal fossil record as a whole has been very extensive and repeated replacement within major groups and relatively few additions of new major groups.

Cambrian and Ordovician

During these first two periods of the Paleozoic, the land remained free of animals but life in the sea was already abundant (Fig. 32.16). Sponge fossils are known from earliest Cambrian times onward, and the fossil history of coelenterates begins with Cambrian jellyfishes and Ordovician corals and sea anemones. A variety of tube-forming worms is known from these and even earlier periods, and stalked brachiopods already existed in the Cambrian. The Ordovician marks the beginning of a rich record of endoprocts and ectoprocts (*bryozoa*), whose exoskeletons form extensive crusts on rocks and algae even today.

Echinoderms were amply represented by several archaic groups. Most of these have since become extinct, but the stalked sessile *crinoids* and the ancient *asteroids* and *echinoids* gave rise to the present-day echinoderms (see Fig. 32.17). Mollusks too were

32 · 17 Fossils. *A, fossils of trilobites. B, fossil of eurypterid. C, fossil of crinoid sea lily.*

A   B   C

A

B

C

32 · 18 Fossils. *A and B, restorations of two ostracoderms, ancient jawless fishes. C, restoration model of an ammonite, an ancient cephalopod mollusk; compare with modern nautilus, Fig. 15.19.*

prominent. Archaic clams and snails were exceedingly abundant, as were the *nautiloids,* a group related closely to modern squids and octopuses and still represented today by the chambered nautilus. The early nautiloids included types with coiled and uncoiled shells, and the uncoiled forms may have been the largest animals of the time; some of their shells reached lengths of 5 to 6 yd.

Of several groups of ancient arthropods, one was that of the *trilobites,* believed to have been the most primitive of all arthropod types (Fig. 32.17). Their body was marked into three lobes by two longitudinal furrows, hence the name of the group. The animals resembled crustacea and they may have been their ancestors. Trilobites were already exceedingly abundant when the Cambrian began, and they are among the most plentiful of all fossil forms. Another group of arthropods comprised the *eurypterids,* large animals which resembled the scorpions of today. Eurypterids may well have been ancestral to the whole present assemblage of chelicerate arthropods, that is, horseshoe crabs and arachnids such as scorpions and spiders. We may note that *Limulus,* a surviving genus of horseshoe crabs, has existed unchanged for the last 200 million years.

Vertebrate history begins in the late Ordovician. The marine tunicate ancestors probably were already present at or near the start of the Paleozoic, and the vertebrates evolved from them as freshwater

forms. The first fossil vertebrates are named the *ostracoderms* because they were "shell-skinned," that is, covered with bony armor plates (Fig. 32.18). These animals were members of the class Agnatha, the *jawless fishes.* From their ancestral freshwater home some of them invaded the ocean, and the whole group flourished until the end of the Devonian. Most of them became extinct then, and their only surviving descendants today are the lampreys and the hagfishes. In these modern Agnatha, the cartilage skeleton formed in the embryo remains cartilaginous and all traces of external bone have been lost. A summary of the Cambrian-Ordovician record is included in Fig. 32.19.

Silurian and Devonian

The Silurian was the period during which the first Metaphyta evolved. Providing a food source for animals, these land plants were soon followed by land animals; late Silurian land scorpions, probably evolved from earlier sea scorpions, are the earliest known terrestrial animals. Additional groups of arthropods invaded the land during the latter part of the Silurian and the beginning of the Devonian. The first mites and centipedes and the first insects appeared during these times. Also, the first spiders evolved, probably from marine eurypterid stocks. In the sea, the nautiloids gave rise to a new molluscan group, the shelled *ammonites,* which were to flourish for long ages (see Fig. 32.18). Echinoderms underwent major evolutionary changes and the ancient asteroids branched into two descendant groups, the brittle stars and the starfishes. Moreover, the vertebrates produced a major adaptive radiation during the Silurian and Devonian (Fig. 32.20).

The Devonian as a whole is often called the "age of fishes." During the early Silurian, some of the jawless ostracoderms had given rise to a new line, the *placoderms*, or *jawed fishes*. The name of this separate class of vertebrates again refers to the bony armor plates with which the skins of these fishes were equipped (see Fig. 2.5). Probably evolved in fresh water, the placoderms became abundant when the Devonian began and some stocks then spread into the ocean. Thus the placoderms replaced their own ancestors, the ostracoderms, more or less completely in all aquatic environments. Some of the placoderms were small, but others reached lengths of 12 yd or more. Most exploited the possession of jaws by adopting a fiercely carnivorous way of life.

The placoderms remained dominant for some 70 million years. During the later Silurian, ancestral placoderms gave rise to two new lines of fishes

32 · 19 *The fossil record of various animal groups. The varying widths of each vertical graph indicate roughly the time changes in the abundance of a given animal group, as judged by the numbers of fossil species found. Such widths are directly comparable only for different times within a group, not between groups. For example, the absolute Cenozoic abundance of insects would equal or exceed that of all other groups combined. The graphs clearly show the major decline which took place at the end of each era, particularly so during the Permo-Triassic transition, less so during the Mesozoic-Cenozoic transition.* (Adapted from Dunbar, Romer, and other sources.)

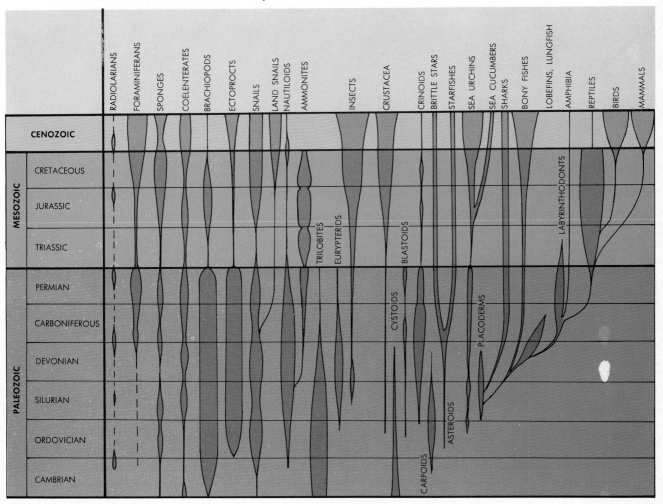

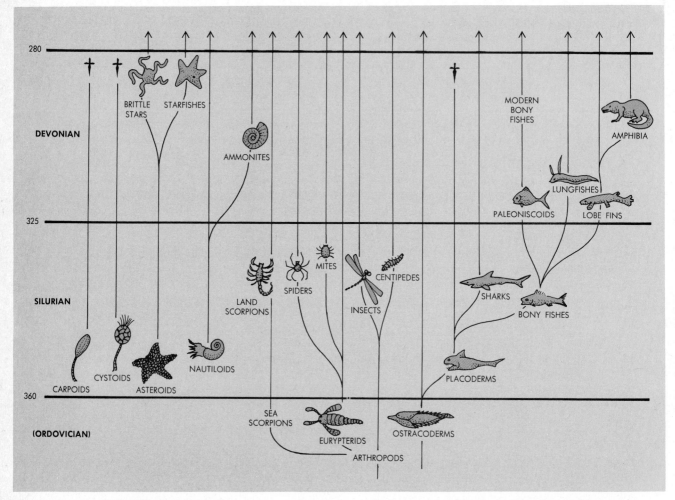

32 · 20 Silurian-Devonian events among animals. *The chart shows only newly evolved groups and those which became extinct during the periods; groups established during earlier periods are not otherwise indicated. The level at which a given group is placed corresponds roughly to the time of its first appearance in the fossil record. Daggers indicate when a group became extinct. Numbers at left indicate past time in millions of years.*

which slowly came to replace the later placoderms. By the end of the Devonian placoderms had become reduced greatly in numbers, and by the end of the Paleozoic they had disappeared completely. They represent the only vertebrate class and one of the few classes of animals generally that has become extinct.

The two new types of fishes evolved from placoderms during the late Silurian were the *cartilage fishes* and the *bony fishes,* each representing a separate class. Both groups arose in fresh water, but the cartilage fishes rapidly adopted a marine habit and their present membership of sharks, skates, and rays is almost exclusively marine. The bony

fishes at first remained in fresh water, where they soon radiated into three main subgroups: the so-called *paleoniscoid fishes,* the *lungfishes,* and the *lobe-finned fishes.* The paleoniscoids later spread into the ocean and became the ancestors of virtually all bony fishes in existence today, both freshwater and marine. The lungfishes were common in Devonian and later Paleozoic times, but thereafter they declined and today they are represented by only three surviving genera. The lobe-fins similarly are almost extinct today (Fig. 32.21).

But the Devonian representatives of the lobe-fins included the ancestors of the first land vertebrates, the *amphibia.* The lobe-fins probably lived in fresh waters which dried out periodically, and their lungs and fins may have enabled them to crawl overland to other bodies of water or to embed themselves in mud and to breathe air through the mouth. It appears, therefore, that terrestrial vertebrates arose not because certain fish preferred the land, but because they had to become terrestrial if they were to survive as fish.

Thus, when the Devonian came to a close, sharks dominated in the ocean and bony fishes in fresh waters. On land, terrestrial arthropods had become abundant and the first amphibia had made their appearance. Many of the land animals could shelter in the stands of lycopsid and sphenopsid trees already established at that time. Figure 32.19 includes a summary of Silurian-Devonian events.

Carboniferous and Permian

During these later Paleozoic times, the character of aquatic animal life did not change in major ways. The ancient coelenterates experienced a decline, and the first advanced crustacea appeared in the form of crablike and crayfishlike animals. On land the changes were more pronounced. Additional terrestrial groups evolved from aquatic ancestors, and some other groups, already terrestrial, began to diversify. More specifically, land snails appeared for the first time during the early Carboniferous, and spiders and scorpions became more abundant. Above all, insects

produced extensive adaptive radiations during the later Carboniferous and the Permian. Some of these ancient insect types reached sizes well above the modern maximum. A Permian dragonfly, for example, is known to have had a wingspread of close to a yard.

Among vertebrates, the early amphibia gave rise to a large variety of more or less clumsy, often bizarre forms, the *labyrinthodonts* (Fig. 32.22). These became the ancestors of two groups, namely, types which later evolved into the modern amphibia and types which formed a new vertebrate class, the *reptiles*. The latter were represented at first by one main group, the stem reptiles, or *cotylosaurs* (see Fig. 32.23). They were the first amniotes and the first completely terrestrial vertebrates. The animals produced a major reptilian radiation during the Permian, which brought about the decline of the labyrinthodonts and also set the stage for a subsequent "age of reptiles" during the Mesozoic era.

As noted earlier, the Paleozoic era terminated with a major *Permo-Triassic crisis* precipitated by the Appalachian revolution. This crisis was characterized as among plants by widespread extinction of archaic animal forms, by replacement and rapid evolution of new groups, and by a general, temporary decrease in the total amount of animal life. Brachiopods and ectoprocts, abundant in the sea since Cambrian times, became almost extinct. All mollusks passed through a major decline, nautiloids becoming virtually extinct and ammonites being reduced to a small group. Trilobites and eurypterids disappeared altogether, and crinoids were left with only a few surviving types. Similarly, only a single echinoid type survived into the Triassic. Placoderms died out, and extensive intragroup replacement occurred among the cartilage and bony fishes. Land animals were less affected on the whole, though their numbers did decline temporarily. Labyrinthodonts lingered

32 · 21 Fossil fishes. *A, restoration of fossil lobe-finned fishes. B, a modern lungfish* (Protopterus) *from West Africa.*

A

B

32 · 22 Fossil amphibians. A, reconstruction of Diplovertebron, *a Permian labyrinthodont amphibian.* B, reconstruction of Seymouria, *a transitional amphibian type probably related to the stock from which reptiles appear to have evolved.*

on into the Triassic, but soon they too became extinct.

The reptiles on the contrary survived the crisis well and when the new Mesozoic era opened they were already dominant.

THE MESOZOIC

The era as a whole was characterized by a re-expansion of virtually all groups that survived the Permo-Triassic crisis and by extensive intragroup replacements. Thus, sponges and coelenterates underwent major adaptive radiations during the Jurassic, with the result that these animals exist today in greater numbers than ever before. Ectoprocts and brachiopods similarly expanded; but whereas the former still appear to be gaining today, the latter became virtually extinct again at the end of the Mesozoic.

Among mollusks, clams and snails diversified greatly, and land snails in particular became abundant. The nautiloids did not regain their Paleozoic importance, however, and the chambered nautilus is their sole present survivor. The ammonites re-expanded during the late Mesozoic, yet at the end of the era all became extinct. In the echinoderm group, the crinoids managed to linger on as relics, and the more abundant brittle stars and starfishes held their own. But the single echinoid group which

survived from the Paleozoic underwent an explosive expansion during the late Mesozoic. In the course of it the modern sea urchins and sea cucumbers evolved. The crustacea gained slowly and steadily in numbers and types. Insects reradiated enormously, and their present importance traces to this Mesozoic expansion. As noted earlier, this rise of insects paralleled the evolution of flowering plants.

An extensive radiation also occurred among the bony fishes. During the Cretaceous, the paleoniscoid fishes gave rise to a multitude of new freshwater and marine types, the modern bony fishes. These became the dominant animals of the aquatic environment, a status they still retain today. The most spectacular Mesozoic event was the expansion of the reptiles. These animals not only evolved many different terrestrial ways of life but also invaded the water and the air. As a group they reigned supreme on earth for 130 million years, longer than any other animals to date. When their dominance was eventually broken, they were replaced by two new groups they themselves had given rise to, the birds and the mammals.

At the beginning of the Mesozoic five major reptilian stocks were in existence, all evolved during the Permian from the cotylosaurian stem reptiles (Fig. 32.23). One group, the so-called *thecodonts*, reradiated extensively during Triassic and in turn gave rise to the following types: the ancestral *birds;* the ancestors of the modern *crocodiles*, *lizards*, and *snakes;* the flying *pterosaurs;* and two other groups, referred to collectively as *dinosaurs.* A second reptilian stock was ancestral to the modern *turtles*. A third and fourth produced two kinds of marine reptiles, the porpoiselike *ichthyosaurs* and the unique, long-necked *plesiosaurs*. The fifth stock comprised the so-called *therapsids*, reptiles which included the ancestors of the mammals (Fig. 32.24).

These various reptilian types did not all flourish at the same time. The Triassic was dominated largely by the ancestral thecodonts and the therapsids. The former were rather birdlike in appearance. They possessed large hind limbs for walking, an enormous supporting tail, and diminutive forelimbs, often not even long enough to shovel food into the mouth.

Therapsids were four-footed walkers. Mammals evolved from some of them during the late Triassic or early Jurassic, but these new fur-bearing vertebrates still were greatly overshadowed by the reptiles. Mammals actually remained small and inconspicuous during the whole remainder of the Mesozoic, that is, for a period of about 80 or 90 million years.

During the Jurassic, ichthyosaurs became abundant in the ocean and one of the thecodont groups evolved into birds. This transition is documented beautifully by a famous fossil called *Archeopteryx* (Fig. 32.25). The animal possessed teeth and a lizard-like tail, two distinctly reptilian features. But it also possessed feathers and wings, and presumably it flew like a bird. Like the previously evolved mammals, birds remained inconspicuous during the whole remaining Mesozoic. They were overshadowed particularly by their thecodont kin, the pterosaurs. These flying reptiles had their heyday during the

32 · 23   The great reptilian radiation of the Mesozoic. *Placement of groups corresponds roughly with the time of their greatest abundance. Numbers at left indicate past time in millions of years.*

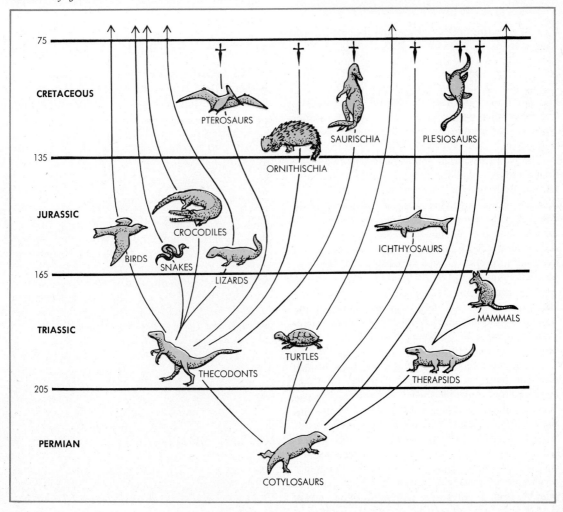

32 · 24 A *therapsid*, a mammallike reptile of the Triassic.

environments, as their modern descendants still are. However, climates appear to have become cooler toward the close of the Cretaceous, as a result of the Laramide revolution. Much tropical and subtropical vegetation may then have died out, which must have meant that herbivorous reptiles lost their food supplies. And as the herbivorous stocks so declined, the carnivorous reptiles would have had to die out as well. Whatever the precise causes, the extinction of the Mesozoic reptiles cleared the way for a great expansion of mammals and birds.

THE CENOZOIC

Just as each geologic era may be subdivided into periods, so each period may be subdivided into *epochs*. The periods and epochs of the Cenozoic era are shown in Table 23 (page 810). As noted earlier, the era as a whole began with the great upheavals of the Laramide revolution, which produced the present high mountain ranges and led to pro-

Cretaceous, the period when reptiles as a whole attained their greatest abundance and variety. Plesiosaurs then were common in the ocean, and the dinosaurs came into undisputed dominance on land (Fig. 32.26).

The two dinosaurian groups belong to two taxonomic orders called the *Ornithischia* and the *Saurischia*. Both evolved from the thecodonts. Not all dinosaurs were large, but some of the group were enormous. The saurischian *Brontosaurus* was the largest land animal of all time, exceeded in size only by the modern blue whale. This dinosaur was herbivorous and it probably lived in swamps or lagoons, where it could support its 20- to 30-ton bulk in water. Another saurischian, the giant *Tyrannosaurus*, probably was the fiercest land carnivore of all time. Among its victims undoubtedly were animals like *Ankylosaurus* and *Triceratops*, herbivorous and heavily armored ornithischian giants (Fig. 32.27).

As the Cretaceous came to a close, most of the reptilian multitude became extinct. Today the class is represented only by turtles, crocodiles, lizards, snakes, and the tuatara (see Chap. 16). The specific reasons for this large-scale dying out have been sought for a long time, but fully satisfactory explanations have not yet been found. Climatic changes at the end of the Mesozoic, coincident with the Laramide revolution, are believed to have played a decisive role. Mesozoic reptiles were adapted to rather warm

32 · 25 *Plaster cast of Archeopteryx. Note feathered tail, wings. The head is bent back, and the tooth-bearing mouth is not easily visible here.*

32 · 26 *Reconstruction of plesiosaurs* (left) *and ichthyosaurs* (right).

gressively cooler climates during the Tertiary period. These climatic changes culminated in the four ice ages spread throughout most of the last million years, the Pleistocene epoch. The biological importance of Cenozoic climates in general and of Pleistocene ice in particular is great, for these environmental conditions materially influenced the evolution of all organisms, plant or animal, man not excepted. Man in a sense is one of the products of the ice ages.

The radiation of mammals and birds came to be the main feature of animal evolution during the Cenozoic era. Terrestrial mammals replaced the dinosaurs; aquatic mammals eventually took the place of the former ichthyosaurs and plesiosaurs;

and bats, but more especially birds, gained the air left free by the pterosaurs. The Cenozoic is often designated as the "age of mammals"; it might equally well be called the "age of birds."

When the Cenozoic began, the great mammalian radiation was just getting under way. A total of some two dozen independent lines came into existence, each ranked as an order and belonging to one of three larger taxonomic units, namely, egg-laying, marsupial, or placental mammals (see Chap. 16).

The fossil record of this mammalian radiation is fairly extensive for most types and extremely good for a few, such as horses and elephants (Fig. 32.28). As outlined in Chap. 16, each mammalian line descended from the common ancestral stock exploited a particular way of life available at the time. The animals came to occupy either a new environmental niche or one left free after the extinction of the Mesozoic reptiles. One mammalian line is of particular interest, for it eventually led to man. This line exploited a relatively new environmental possibility; that is, its members took to the trees and adapted to an *arboreal* life.

32 · 27 *Restoration of extinct saurians. Left,* Triceratops, *a Cretaceous horned herbivore; right,* Tyrannosaurus, *a giant Cretaceous carnivore.*

TABLE 23 THE EPOCHS AND PERIODS OF THE CENOZOIC ERA°

PERIOD	EPOCH	DURATION	BEGINNING DATE
Quaternary	*Recent*	*20,000 years*	*20,000* B.C.
	Pleistocene	*1*	*1*
	Pliocene	*11*	*12*
	Miocene	*16*	*28*
Tertiary	*Oligocene*	*11*	*39*
	Eocene	*19*	*58*
	Paleocene	*17*	*75*

° *Unless otherwise stated, all figures refer to millions of years.*

Soon after such a stock of arboreal mammals had evolved during the early Paleocene, it must have re-radiated and produced two major sublines, the order *Insectivora* and the order *Primates* (Fig. 32.29). Most modern insect-eating mammals, particularly the moles and the hedgehogs, are clearly distinct from modern primates, of which man is a late member. But some of the shrews now living are exceedingly like insectivores on the one hand and like primitive living primates on the other. Indeed, one group of shrews is actually classified with the Insectivora and another with the Primates. Fossil data similarly support the view that insectivorous mammals and primates are very closely related, through a common, shrewlike, arboreal, insect-eating ancestor (Fig. 32.30).

The first distinct primates evolved from this insect-eating ancestor during the Paleocene may be referred to as the *early prosimians*. They were still small, shrewlike in appearance, with a fairly long snout and a long bushy tail. They probably had poor sight and good smelling ability, like the primitive first mammals; and although they lived in trees their close evolutionary connection with ancestral ground animals is still apparent from their fossils. Of the many sublines evolved from the early prosimians during the Paleocene, five major ones survive today; the *lemuroids*, the *tarsoids*, the *ceboids*, the *cercopithecoids*, and the *hominoids* (Fig. 32.31). Each of these has adapted to an arboreal existence and, roughly in the order listed, the extent of this adaptation has become progressively greater.

The lemuroids include the *lemurs* and *aye-ayes*, found today largely on the island of Madagascar (Fig. 32.32). These animals are a little larger than the ancestral primates, and they still possess long snouts and tails. However, instead of claws and paws they possess strong flat nails, a general characteristic of all modern primates. Long nails are probably more useful than claws in anchoring the body on a tree branch. In a tree, moreover, smelling is less important than seeing, and lemuroids have made a beginning toward improved vision. For example, each of their eyes can be directed forward independently, permitting better perception of branch configurations than if the eyes were fixed on the side of the head.

The tarsoids, represented today by the *tarsiers* of southern Asia and Indonesia, have evolved several additional improvements. In these animals the ancestral "smell brain" has become a "sight brain"; the olfactory lobes have become small but the optic lobes have increased in size. In parallel with this reduction of the olfactory lobes, the snout has receded and a fairly well-defined face has appeared (see Fig.

32 · 28 *Reconstruction of evolution of the horse during the Cenozoic. The evolutionary sequence begins at left, with the fossil horse* Eohippus, *and proceeds via* Mesohippus, Hypohippus, *and* Neohipparion *to* Equus, *the modern horse at right. The drawings are to scale and show how the average sizes and shapes of horses have changed. Progressive reduction in the number of toes took place, as well as changes in dentition. Note, however, that the animals shown represent a highly selected series, and it should not be inferred that horse evolution followed a straight-line pattern. Here, as elsewhere, a bush pattern is actually in evidence.*

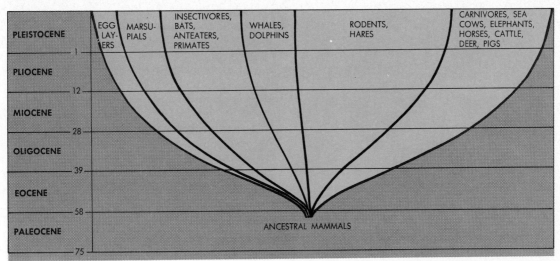

| | EGG LAY-ERS | MARSU-PIALS | INSECTIVORES, BATS, ANTEATERS, PRIMATES | WHALES, DOLPHINS | RODENTS, HARES | CARNIVORES, SEA COWS, ELEPHANTS, HORSES, CATTLE, DEER, PIGS |

PLEISTOCENE
 — 1
PLIOCENE
 — 12
MIOCENE
 — 28
OLIGOCENE
 — 39
EOCENE
 — 58
PALEOCENE
 — 75

ANCESTRAL MAMMALS

32 · 29 *The mammalian radiation during the Cenozoic. The animal types are grouped according to their evolutionary affinities (see Chap. 16). Extinct groups are not shown. The groups now living have not undergone so steady and progressive a quantitative increase as this simplified diagram might tend to suggest. It is true, however, that the rodent-hare group today is the most abundant in terms of species number. Numbers at left indicate past time in millions of years.*

32.32). The eyes have actually moved into the face and, though they are still movable independently, both eyes can be focused on the same point. As a result, tarsiers are endowed with stereoscopic vision and efficient depth perception, traits that all other primates also share. Such traits evidently are of considerable adaptive value if balance is to be maintained in a tree. Tarsiers also possess independently movable fingers and toes, with a branch-gripping pad at the end of each. Moreover, the several offspring typical in a litter of most mammals are reduced in tarsiers to a single offspring, clearly a safer reproductive pattern among the branches of a tree.

The ceboids comprise the *New World monkeys*, confined today to South and Central America. These animals are characterized by long strong tails used as fifth limbs. The cercopithecoids are the *Old World monkeys*, found in Africa and Asia. They are identified by tails not used as limbs. Both groups of

monkeys attained their present diversity during the Oligocene and Miocene, and note that monkey status evolved twice independently; the two groups represent separate, though remarkably similar, evolutionary developments. In both groups, adaptations to arboreal life have evolved a good deal farther than in the primates above.

If tarsoids possess a "sight brain," monkeys may be said to possess a "space brain." The two eyes are synchronized and can be focused in different directions without movement of the head as a whole. Each eye also possesses a fovea centralis, a retinal area of most acute vision (see Chap. 25). Above all, monkeys are endowed with cone cells and color vision, the only mammals other than the hominoids so characterized. And colors are actually there to be seen: flowers, foliage, sky, and sun provide an arboreal environment of light and space, far different from the dark forest floor which forced early mammals literally to keep the nose to the ground. The smelling capacity of monkeys has actually become as poor as their sight has become excellent. Correspondingly, the cerebrum has enlarged greatly and its posterior regions contain not only extensive

32 · 30   An arboreal squirrel shrew, order In-sectivora.

vision-control centers but also vision-memory areas; monkeys store visual memories of shape and color as we do, for reference in future activities.

The evolution of an enlarged brain has been cor-related additionally with the adoption of a pre-dominantly sitting way of life. Sitting on branches and in branch forks was probably not only safer than lying, but this posture also relieved the fore-limbs of locomotor functions and resulted in a new freedom to use hands for touch exploration. The consequences were many, and monkeys today still exhibit them. The ability to feel out the environ-ment and one's own body led to a new self-aware-ness and to curiosity. The ability to touch offspring and fellow inhabitants of the tree led to new pat-terns of communication and social life, reinforced greatly by good vision, by voice, and by varied facial expressions. Touch-control areas of the brain increased apace, centers controlling hand movements became extensive, and the brain as a whole thus en-larged in parallel with the new patterns of living. The mind quickened as a result, and the level of intelligence increased well above the earlier primate average. Thus, whereas a ground mammal such as a dog sniffs its environment, the later arboreal pri-mates began to explore it by sight and by touch. And we may note that evolution of intelligence has been correlated particularly with the improvement of coordination between eye and hand. Fundamen-tally, therefore, primate intelligence too is an adapta-tion to the arboreal way of life.

Tree life also became a basically secure way of life. Actually only two types of situations constituted significant dangers, namely, the hazard of falling off

32 · 31   The main lines of the primate radia-tion. Numbers at left indicate past time in mil-lions of years.

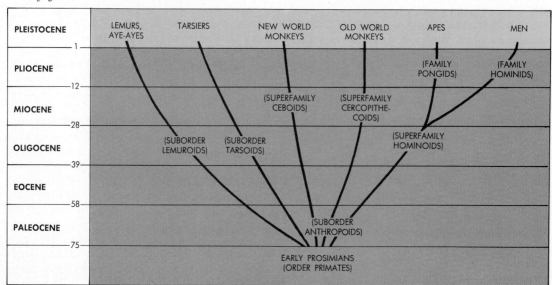

32 · 32 *A, a modern lemur from Madagascar. B, a modern tarsier from Indonesia.*

a tree and the hazard of encountering snakes. The first was minimized by the evolution of opposable thumbs and of precocious gripping ability in general (as displayed also in newborn human babies). The second was countered by the strength of the body, which increased as the evolution of larger bodies continued. As a result of this increase in body size, and perhaps aided also by the emancipation from perpetual fear, the inherent life span lengthened considerably. Monkeys may become up to four decades old compared with a life expectancy of a single year in shrews. Moreover, absence of danger and continuously warm climates led to a breeding season spanning the whole year (and in Old World monkeys the year-round breeding potential came to be accompanied by menstrual cycles).

Trends of the same kind, but developed very much farther than in monkeys, are apparent also in the hominoids. During the early Miocene, some 30 million years ago, the hominoid line branched into two main sublines. One of these led to the *pongids,* or apes, the other to the *hominids,* the family of man. Before this branching took place, the whole hominoid stock evolved important skeletal modifications over and above those attained by the monkeys. Early hominoids developed a fully upright posture, and by hand-over-hand locomotion between two levels of branches they became tree walkers more than tree sitters. Also, limbs lengthened generally, and universal limb sockets evolved as well. As a result, only an ape or a man can rotate the

arm completely within its socket, and even a monkey can match neither the acrobatics of an ape in a tree nor that of a man on a trapeze. Moreover, only apes and men are capable of swiveling their hips, and only they have broad chests with lengthened and strengthened collar bones. Tree walking was also facilitated by a reduction of the tail and its interiorization between the hind limbs. In this position the tail helped to counteract the internal sag produced by gravity acting on an upright body.

After the hominoid stock split into a pongid and a hominid line, each of these gave rise to an adaptive radiation of its own. Apes today are represented by four genera, namely, gibbons, orangutans, chimpanzees, and gorillas. Gibbons are survivors of an early branch of ape evolution, characterized by comparatively light bodies and retention of a fully arboreal way of life. Indeed, the gibbon is undoubtedly the most perfectly adapted arboreal primate. But the other three types of apes, representing later and heavier pongid lines, have abandoned life in the trees to a greater or lesser extent. Orangutans and especially chimpanzees can be quite at home out of trees, and gorillas are ground animals as fully as we are. It appears that these later apes ceased to be completely arboreal when their bodies had become so large and heavy that trees could no longer support them aloft. The feet of the apes give ample evidence of the weight they have to support; foot bones are highly foreshortened and stubby, as if crushed by heavy loads. Correspondingly, the agile grace of the arboreal gibbon is not preserved in the ground ape. Large apes cannot and do not walk, but they scamper along in a crouching shuffle-gait.

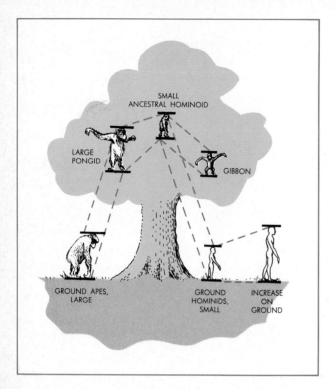

SMALL
ANCESTRAL HOMINOID

LARGE
PONGID

GIBBON

GROUND APES,
LARGE

GROUND
HOMINIDS,
SMALL

INCREASE
ON
GROUND

32 · 33 *One group of apes probably developed to a large size in the trees, and their modern descendants such as the gorilla therefore were already heavy when they adopted life on the ground. Another group, exemplified by the gibbon, remained light and arboreal. Early hominids likewise probably remained light and small. They presumably left the trees as small types and their evolutionary size increase then occurred on the ground.*

MAN

So far as is known, the hominid line left the trees completely and almost as soon as it split away from the common hominoid stock, that is, just when the adaptations to tree life had finally become perfected. Was this descent prompted by great body weight, too, as in the case of the large apes? Probably not, or else the hominid foot would resemble that of a ground ape, and man would scamper rather than walk. In actuality the hominid foot is very much like that of a gibbon, and as a gibbon swings in a tree so a man literally swings on the ground; the human bipedal gait is unique among ground forms. It is likely, therefore, that the hominid line left the trees when its evolution has progressed to a level comparable to that of the early gibbonlike

apes, that is, when the body was still comparatively small and light. On the ground the foot could then remain efficient and not overloaded unduly, and the grace won in the trees could persist. The early hominids may therefore have been small creatures originally and, in contrast to the later apes, their size may have increased only after they had come out of the trees (Fig. 32.33).

But if not body weight, what other conditions could have forced hominids to the ground? The chief cause appears to have been a change in climate. As pointed out earlier, the progressively cooler climates during the Tertiary led to a thinning out of forests, and continuous overhead canopies of branches and foliage therefore disappeared in many regions. Our prehuman ancestors then would have had to travel on the ground if they wished to move from one stand of trees to another. Such forced excursions may well have been fraught with considerable danger, however, for saber-toothed carnivores and other large mammals dominated the ground at those times. Consequently, ability to dash quickly across open spaces may have had great selective value, and strong muscles would be required to move the hind limbs in new ways. Indeed, a unique trait of the hominid line is the possession of such muscles in the form of curving calves, thighs, and buttocks. In this respect, man is also different from apes.

These and other features which now distinguish men and apes came to be superimposed on the characteristics of pre-Miocene arboreal primates. The modern human type evidently could not have evolved if the ancestral type had not first been specialized for life in trees.

THE HOMINID RADIATION

After the hominid stock had originated in the Miocene, each of its evolving main lines must have produced various sublines and subsublines in turn. The detailed pattern of this hominid radiation is unknown, but that it occurred can be inferred from available fossil evidence. To be sure, this evidence is tantalizingly scanty; we can trace the recent evolution of almost any mammal far better than our own. Nevertheless, such fossils of hominid types as have been found show clearly that a substantial number of separate lines of descent must have arisen. The exact path of descent of our own species remains undiscovered as yet and other known hominids are related to us somewhat as uncles or cousins (Fig. 32.34).

With the exception of the line leading to ourselves, all other lines of the hominid radiation have

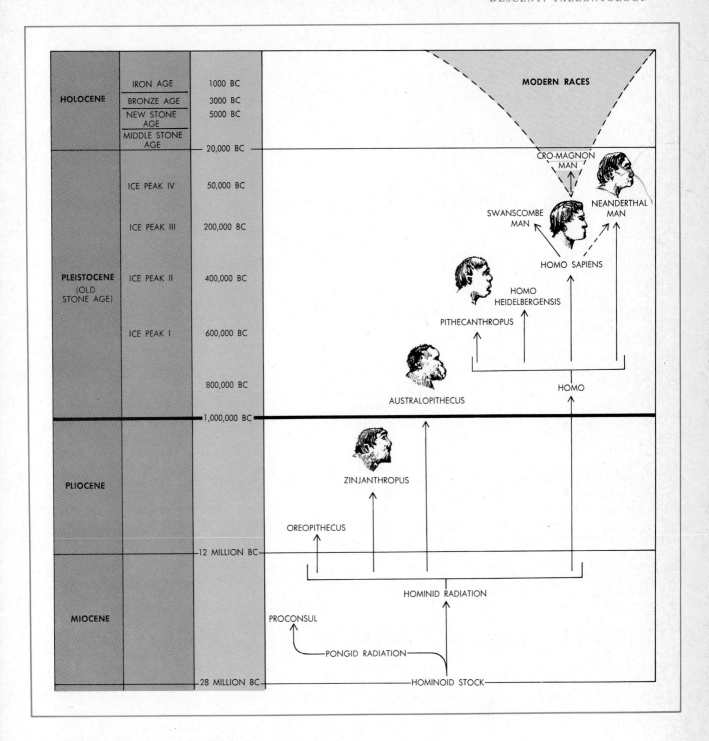

32 · 34 The hominid radiation and some of its principal members. Each hominid type is shown roughly at a time level at which it is known to have existed. Detailed interrelations of the various hominid lines are unknown.

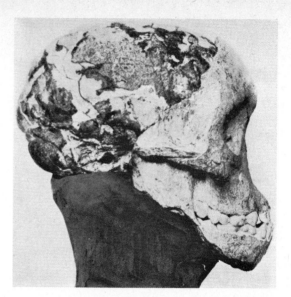

Adapted from painting by Peter Bianchi, National Geographic Society, 1961.

32 · 35 Zinjanthropus, the East Africa man (*drawing*). *Note the exceptionally low forehead and small brain case. Photo: skull of* Australopithecus.

become extinct at various periods during the last 30 million years. It is not necessary to find whole fossilized skeletons to reconstruct the probable appearance of their once-living owners. The proportions of body parts to one another may be deduced with reasonable accuracy from living man, from apes, and from such whole skeletons of hominid types as have been found. For example, a tooth, a jaw bone, a skullcap, or a leg bone may not only be identified from its shape as belonging to a particular hominid, but may also give important clues about the missing remainder. By and large, the skull gives the greatest amount of information. Thick or thin bones, prominent or reduced eyebrow ridges, receding or vertical forehead, small or large brain cases, poorly or well-defined chin, all indicate fairly well whether or not a given fossil is a primitive or an advanced hominid.

Much may also be learned from various signs of cultural activity often associated with a fossil find. For example, the type of tool, the type of camp site, the type of weapons found with a fossil, each may reveal a great deal about the evolutionary status of the hominid in question. Indeed, apart from their biological distinctions, hominids are regarded as being prehuman or truly human on the basis of cultural achievements. Any hominid which *made* tools in addition to using them can be called a "man." If a hominid only used stones or sticks found ready-made in his environment, he is considered prehuman; if he deliberately fashioned natural objects into patterned tools, no matter how crude, he is considered

human. By this criterion, quite a few hominid types were men.

The early parts of hominid history are almost completely unknown. Some clues about the common ancestor from which both the pongids and the hominids have arisen are provided by 25-million-year-old fossil apes of the genus *Proconsul*, found in East Africa. *Proconsul* clearly belongs to the pongid radiation, but certain features of the skull, particularly the teeth, suggest that the base of the hominid radiation could well have been represented by an animal similar to this ape.

Also more nearly allied to the pongid rather than the hominid radiation is *Oreopithecus*, the "mountain ape," whose remains were found in northern Italy. This primate dates back some 10 million years, to the early Pliocene. The teeth and the organization of the jaw of *Oreopithecus* were rather hominid, but in other respects the animal was apelike.

The hominid record of the Tertiary notably includes *Zinjanthropus*, the "East Africa man," discovered in Tanganyika in 1959 (Fig. 32.35). Potassium-argon dating has shown that *Zinjanthropus* lived $1\frac{3}{4}$ million years ago, in the late Pliocene. This hominid made tools and thus was a true man. The tools included wooden clubs and stone hammers with which *Zinjanthropus* killed small animals and broke open their bones. The diet was mainly coarse vegetation, however, as the large molars clearly indicate. Bone structure in the skull reveals that the head was held very erect and that jaw muscles were attached as in modern man, suggesting that *Zinjanthropus* probably knew speech. On the other hand, a forehead was almost absent; the volume of the brain could not have been larger than 600 cm³, comparable to the brain volume of a modern gorilla. Also, a low bony ridge was present on top of the skull, another apelike characteristic. *Zinjanthropus* is not the most ancient man known, for the location where he was found gives evidence of another, even more ancient tool-making hominid called *Homo habilis*. As the genus name indicates, this man appears to have been fairly close to our own line of descent.

All other known hominid fossils are of Pleistocene origin, not older than 1 million years. The oldest of these form a group of several genera of which *Australopithecus*, the "southern ape," is representative (see Fig. 32.35). The remains of this australopithecine group have been discovered in South Africa and have been shown to date back roughly 1 million years or somewhat less. Although the australopithecines thus lived much later than *Zinjanthropus*, they probably were not so far advanced. For example, they apparently did not make tools. Their brain volume averaged 600 cm³, and they probably walked erect or almost erect. Skulls and skeletons reveal a mixture of apelike and manlike traits, but the latter predominate and it is clear that the australopithecines are within the hominid family. Indeed, some investigators regard these near men to be fairly closely related to the line which gave rise to modern man.

A more recent and comparatively much better known hominid is *Pithecanthropus erectus*, also called *Homo erectus*, a true man who made tools of stone and bone and used fire for cooking (Fig. 32.36). Remains of several species of *Pithecanthropus* were found in Java and China and were shown to be about 500,000 years old. The brain volume of this "erect apeman" averaged 900 to 1,000 cm³. The skull had a flat, sloping forehead and thick eyebrow ridges, and the massive protruding jaw was virtually chinless. Like several other hominids, *Pithecanthropus* probably practiced cannibalism. His fossil remains include separate skullcaps detached cleanly from the rest of the skeleton; sheer accident does not appear to have caused such neat separations.

Homo heidelbergensis, the Heidelberg man, appears like *Pithecanthropus* to have lived about 500,000 years ago. Unfortunately, Heidelberg man is known only from one fossil jaw, and his status therefore cannot be fully assessed. Far more complete information is available about another representative of the genus *Homo*, namely, *Homo sapiens neanderthalis*, a subspecies of our own species and the best known of all prehistoric men (Figs. 32.36 and 32.37). Neanderthal man probably arose some 150,000 years ago, flourished during the period of the last ice age, and became extinct only about 25,000 years ago, when the ice sheets began to retreat. The brain of the Neanderthalers had a volume of 1,450 cm³, which compares with a volume of only 1,350 cm³ for modern man. The Neanderthal brain was also proportioned differently; the skull jutted out in back, where we are relatively rounded, and the forehead was low and receding. Heavy brow ridges were still present, and the jaw was massive and again almost without chin.

Culturally, the Neanderthalers were Stone Age cavemen. All Pleistocene hominids are generally regarded as belonging to the *Old Stone Age*. But whereas earlier hominids made only crude stone implements, Neanderthal man fashioned a variety of weapons, tools, hunting axes and clubs, and household equipment. Yet he was still a nomad living from hand to mouth and he had neither agriculture nor domesticated animals. He did not make pottery and did not leave any art. His territory covered most of Europe, with fringe populations along the African and Asian coasts of the Mediterranean. He was a contemporary of modern man, and it appears that the Neanderthal type may have become integrated genetically with modern man.

32 · 36 *Reconstruction of* **Pithecanthropus.**

HOMO SAPIENS SAPIENS

The time of origin of our own subspecies, *H. sapiens sapiens,* cannot be pinpointed very precisely. The oldest representative appears to be *Swanscombe man,* known only through a few skull bones. These are from 500,000 to 250,000 years old. Early groups of modern man thus may have been contemporaries of *Pithecanthropus.*

Later groups include *Cro-Magnon man* (see Fig. 32.36), who lived from about 50,000 to 20,000 years ago and who may have caused the extinction of Neanderthal man in Europe. Cro-Magnon was 6 ft tall on the average, with a brain volume of about 1,700 cm³. His culture still belongs to the Old Stone Age. In addition to stone implements, Cro-Magnon used bone needles with which he may have sewn animal skins into crude garments. The dog became his companion, but he still did not domesticate food animals and he did not practice agriculture; Cro-Magnon was a cave-dwelling hunter. He developed a remarkable art, however, as his murals on cave walls indicate.

Cro-Magnon man was a contemporary of other groups of men living in different parts of the world. The racial division of modern man into *caucasoids,* *negroids,* and *mongoloids* may have taken place then. However, any original racial traits became diluted or obliterated fairly rapidly, through interbreeding among the extensively migrating human populations. None of the present types of man (or any other animal for that matter) represents a "pure" race.

By the time the Pleistocene came to a close, some 20,000 or 25,000 years ago, all human species and subspecies other than our own had become extinct. The ice started to retreat, milder climates gradually supervened, and eventually man no longer needed to shelter in caves. For the next 15,000 years he produced what is known as the *Middle Stone Age* culture. It was characterized chiefly by great improvements in stone tools. Man was still a nomadic hunter.

The *New Stone Age* began about 5000 B.C., about the time Abraham settled in Canaan (see Fig. 32.34). A great cultural revolution took place then. Man learned to fashion pottery; he developed agriculture; and he was able to domesticate animals. From that period on, modern civilization moved on with rapid strides. By 3000 B.C. man had entered the *Bronze Age.* Some 2,000 years later the *Iron Age* began. And not very long afterward man discovered steam, electricity, and now the atom and outer space. Measured by geologic standards, the hairy beast which lumbered down from the trees 30 million years ago turned into a college professor in a flash.

That modern man has evolved through the operation of the same forces which produced all other creatures is clear. And it should also be clear that this creature is by far the most remarkable product of evolution. Man is sometimes described rather offhandedly as being "just" another animal. Often, on the contrary, he is considered to be so radically distinct that the appellation "animal" assumes the character of an insult. Neither view is justified.

Man certainly *is* an animal, but an animal with unique attributes. Structurally, man is fully erect and possesses a double-curved spine, a prominent

32 · 37 *Reconstruction of Neanderthal man.*

chin, and walking feet with arches. He is a fairly generalized type in most respects, being not particularly specialized for either speed, strength, agility, or rigidly fixed environments.

At some stage during this evolution, his rate of embryonic development slowed down and his whole life cycle became stretched out in duration. Thus man became perhaps the longest-lived of all animals. This stretching of the life cycle also lengthened substantially the period of postnatal growth and adolescence. In this manner, another uniquely human characteristic emerged, namely, a proportionately very long *youth*. A chimpanzee, mature at the age of 5 or 6, is senile at the age of 30, when man is just attaining adulthood. Man therefore has *time* to learn and to gather experiences, and in his learning capacity man is also unique. To be sure, other animals may also learn, but the quantitative difference is so great that it is in effect a qualitative difference.

Learning presupposes a powerful brain, and in this department man clearly has no equal. Note here again that the human nervous system develops as it does because it has *time* to do so, because the embryonic period is greatly stretched out. Man has acquired his brain by an exceedingly rapid, explosive process of evolution. Judging from Miocene fossils and living apes, the hominoids 30 million years ago may have had a brain volume of about 300 to 400 cm³, comparable to that of a newborn human baby today. From then to the beginning of the Pleistocene, brain volume increased to an average of 600 cm³, as in *Zinjanthropus* and the australopithecines. Thus, in a span of about 29 million years, brain size almost doubled. But during the first half of the Pleistocene, in only ½ million years, brain size more than doubled again, from 600 cm³ to the 1,400 to 1,700 cm³ range in modern man (Fig. 32.38).

Evidently, the human brain has become considerably larger than might be expected on the basis of general increase in body size alone. Moreover, the increase is not due simply to a proportional enlargement of all brain parts; certain parts have grown far more than others. The greatest growth has occurred in the temporal lobes, which participate in the control of speech, and especially in the frontal lobes, which control abstract thought. As a result, a basic qualitative difference between man and an ape or any other primate is that man has the capacity to think in a new time dimension, namely, the future. An ape or any other mammal has a mind which may grapple well with problems of the present and to a certain extent also with those of the past. But such an animal at best has only a rudimentary conception of future time. It does not possess elaborate control centers for this dimension of existence, namely,

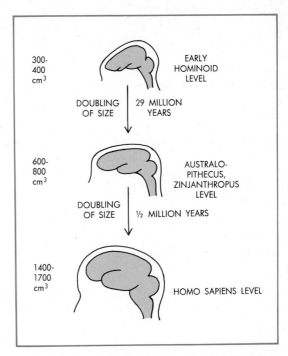

32 · 38 *The hominid brain* has not only doubled in overall size twice in succession, but it has also changed in the relative proportion of parts during the last 29 million years. The frontal and temporal lobes increased more than proportionately, which is indicated also by the changes in the contours of the skull.

frontal lobes. Man does, and he alone therefore, far more so than even a genius chimpanzee, is able to plan, to reason out the consequences of future actions not yet performed, to choose by deliberation, and to have aims and purposes. Also, only man is able to any appreciable extent to think in symbolic terms, to generalize, and to envision beauty and to weep and to laugh. Directly or indirectly, all such unique attributes of human mentality are based on ability to deal with the nonconcrete, the nonspecific, and on abstract forward projections of consequences. Such attributes in effect are fundamentally future-directed. Man has rightly been called a "time-binder," and he may be regarded also as the only philosophical animal.

As a result, also, only man has *traditions* and only he *accumulates* knowledge over successive generations. This transmission of knowledge occurs by nonbiological means, and we actually deal here with a new kind of evolution. The old is biological evolution, and its vehicle is the gene. The new is social evolution, and its vehicle is spoken and written *speech*.

Man is unique in having evolved and in continuing to evolve through inherited traditions passed on not only by genes, but also by words.

Conceivably, this change-over from the merely biological to the human may have as much future significance as the earlier change-over, 3 billion years ago, from the inorganic to the biological. The first transition gave rise to totally new opportunities through which matter became organized into a wealth of previously nonexistent arrangements. The recent transition may create new possibilities of like scope. But the realization of this potential is now in the hands of man, for with the coming of man, the chance operations of nature have begun to be modified and manipulated by human purpose. The activities of man block chance increasingly and man's fate will therefore be decided by man's purpose.

REVIEW QUESTIONS

1. What is a fossil? How can the age of a fossil be determined? Review the names and dates of the geologic eras and periods. What were the Appalachian and Laramide revolutions? List the major groups of plants not yet in existence 500 million years ago.

2. Describe the key events of plant evolution during the Cambrian and Ordovician periods. Review Lignier's hypothesis regarding the origin of tracheophytes.

3. Describe the characteristics of various fossil psilopsids. Cite fossil evidence in support of the view that psilopsids were ancestral to all other vascular plants.

4. Describe the key events of plant evolution during the Silurian and the Devonian periods. What were the characteristics of lepidodendrids? Name and describe fossil sphenopsids. Which pteropsid groups were in existence by the end of the Devonian?

5. Describe the key events of plant evolution during the Carboniferous and the Permian periods. What were the seed ferns? Which other plant groups are they believed to have given rise to?

6. Describe the causes and events of the Permo-Triassic crisis. At what date did it take place? Review the key events of plant evolution during (a) the Mesozoic era, and (b) the Cenozoic era. Name the time and the events of the Laramide revolution. What were the consequences of the Laramide revolution on plants? Review the evolutionary events of the whole Cenozoic era. When did the last ice ages occur?

7. Review the recapitulatory hypotheses of Haeckel and show why they are not tenable. Does comparative animal embryology give any clues about the probable course of early animal evolution? Discuss.

8. Describe the key events of animal evolution during the (a) Cambrian-Ordovician, (b) Silurian-Devonian, (c) Carboniferous-Permian. Review the course of vertebrate evolution during the entire Paleozoic.

9. Review the evolutionary happenings during the Mesozoic among groups other than reptiles. Make an analogous review for reptile evolution. Which reptilian groups exist today and what ancient groups did they derive from? What group was ancestral to mammals?

10. Describe the principal features of the Cenozoic mammalian radiation, with special attention to the origin of primates. Describe the major features and the time pattern of the primate radiation and name living animals representing each of the main lines. When and from where did the line leading to man branch off?

11. Describe the various adaptations of each of the primate stocks to arboreal life. Which structural, functional, and behavioristic features of man trace back specifically to the arboreal way of life of his ancestors? How does the hominoid line differ from other descendants of early prosimians? How does the hominid line differ from the pongid line?

12. Describe the known members of the hominid radiation. When was each of them probably in existence? What culture was associated with each? Roughly when did Homo sapiens arise? Review the biological characteristics which Homo sapiens shares with (a) all other hominids, (b) all other hominoids, (c) all other primates, (d) all other mammals.

COLLATERAL READINGS

Abelson, P. H.: Paleobiochemistry, *Sci. American*, July, 1956. A study of amino acids in 300-year-old fossils.

Andrews, H. N.: "Ancient Plants and the World They Lived In," Comstock, Ithaca, N.Y., 1947. A book on plant fossils and evolution.

Arnold, C. A.: "An Introduction to Paleobotany," McGraw-Hill, New York, 1947. Another good source on plant fossils and evolution.

Berrill, N. J.: "Man's Emerging Mind," Dodd, Mead, New York, 1955, or Premier Books, Fawcett World Library Pocketbooks, New York, 1957. An extremely fascinating and stimulating account of human evolution. Highly recommended.

————: "The Origin of Vertebrates," Oxford, Fair Lawn, N.J., 1955. A documentation of the probable evolution of ancestral vertebrates from ascidian stocks.

Broom, R.: The Ape-men, *Sci. American,* Nov., 1949. The article gives an account of the australopithecines; written by the discoverer of their fossils.

Clark, J. D.: Early Man in Africa, *Sci. American,* July, 1958. Another personal account of searches for human fossils.

Colbert, E. H.: The Ancestors of Mammals, *Sci. American,* Mar., 1949. Therapsids and other Triassic reptiles are examined.

————: "Evolution of the Vertebrates," Wiley, New York, 1955. A good text on fossil vertebrates.

Coon, C. S.: "The Origin of Races," Knopf, New York, 1962. Recommended for background on this aspect of human evolution.

Deevey, E. S.: Radiocarbon Dating, *Sci. American,* Feb., 1952. This technique of age determination in fossils is described.

Dobzhansky, T.: The Present Evolution of Man, *Sci. American,* Sept., 1960. A discussion of how human evolution is influenced by man's control over his environment.

Ericson, D. B., and G. Wollin: Micropaleontology, *Sci. American,* July, 1962. The new field of fossil study by microscope is described.

Glaessner, M. F.: Precambrian Animals, *Sci. American,* Mar., 1961. Recent fossil finds predating the 500-million-year mark are discussed.

Hockett, C. F.: The Origin of Speech, *Sci. American,* Sept., 1960. The article traces the development of human speech from more primitive systems of animal communication.

Leakey, L. S. B.: Finding the World's Earliest Man, *Nat. Geographic,* Sept., 1960.

————: Exploring 1,750,000 Years into Man's Past, *Nat. Geographic,* Sept., 1961.

Two articles by the discoverer of *Zinjanthropus* and other early human types.

Millot, J.: The Coelacanth, *Sci. American,* Dec., 1955. An account of a recently discovered living lobe-finned fish, formerly believed to have been extinct for 300 million years.

Moore, R. C., C. G. Lalicker, and A. G. Fisher: "Invertebrate Fossils," McGraw-Hill, New York, 1952. A good source book for further information on extinct invertebrates.

Napier, J.: The Evolution of the Hand, *Sci. American,* Dec., 1962. The ancestry of the human hand may trace back more than 1 million years, as shown by fossil finds described in this article.

Newell, N. D.: Crises in the History of Life, *Sci. American,* Feb., 1963. An examination of the several geologic periods during which organisms died out on a large scale.

Romer, A. S.: "Vertebrate Paleontology," University of Chicago, Chicago, 1945. A very good reference book on vertebrate fossils; well illustrated.

Sahlins, M. D.: The Origin of Society, *Sci. American,* Sept., 1960. A subordination of sexual drives appears to have been basic in the development of human society; see also Berrill's first-listed reference on this point.

Simpson, G. G.: "Life of the Past," Yale, New Haven, Conn., 1953. A very good review of paleontological events; see also the reference by the same author at the end of Chap. 31.

Stebbins, G. L.: "Variation and Evolution in Plants," Columbia, New York, 1950. For further background on this subject.

Washburn, S. L.: Tools and Human Evolution, *Sci. American,* Sept., 1960. The article shows how inferences about human evolution may be made from fossil tools.

Weckler, J. E.: Neanderthal Man, *Sci. American,* Dec., 1957. A hypothesis about the relation of modern man and Neanderthalers is discussed in this article.

GLOSSARY

SECTION A

COMMON PREFIXES, SUFFIXES, AND
ANATOMICAL TERMS IN BIOLOGICAL USAGE*

NOTE: The meaning of many terms not specifically listed in section B, can be ascertained from section A. For example, certain fishes are known as the *Actinopterygii*. The parts of this term are the prefix *actino-* and the suffix *-pterygii;* the list below indicates the meanings of these word parts as "ray" and "fin," respectively. Hence the whole term denotes "ray-finned." In general, a very large number of technical designations may be translated into English equivalents by separating the words into parts and consulting this first section of the glossary.

a- [Gr. not]: negates succeeding part of word: for example, *acoel,* without coelom; *Acrania,* without head.

ab- [L. away, off]: opposite of *ad,* for example, *aboral,* away from mouth; *abductor,* muscle which draws away from given position.

acro- (ăk′rô) [Gr. *akros,* outermost]: for example, *acromegaly, acrosome.*

actino- (ăk′tĭ·nô) [Gr. *aktis,* ray]: for example, *actinopodial,* ray-footed; *actinotroch,* ray-wheel.

ad- [L. toward, to]: opposite of *ab-;* for example, *adrenal,* at (near) the kidney; *adductor,* muscle which draws toward given position.

afferent (ăf′ĕr·ĕnt) [L. *ad* + *ferre,* to carry]: to lead or carry toward given position, opposite of efferent; for example, afferent nerve, afferent blood vessel.

amphi- (ăm′fĭ) [Gr. on both sides]: for example, *amphioxus,* pointed at both ends; *amphipod,* possessing both thoracic and abdominal types of legs.

an- [Gr. not]: like *a-,* used before vowel or "h"; for example *anamniote, anhydride.*

ana- [Gr. up, throughout, again, back]: for example, *analogy,* likeness, resemblance; *analysis,* thorough separation; *anatomy,* cutting up.

andro- (ăn′drô) [Gr. *aner,* man, male]: for example, *androgen,* male-producing hormone.

anterior, antero- (ăn·tēr′ĭ·ēr, ăn′tĕr·ô) [L. *ante,* before, in front of]: at, near, or toward front end.

antho- (ăn′thô) [Gr. *anthos,* flower]: for example, *Anthozoa,* flowerlike coelenterate animals; *anther,* part of flower.

anthropo- (ăn′thrô·pô) [Gr. *anthrōpos,* man, human]: for example, *anthropoid,* manlike ape.

apical (ăp′ĭ·kăl) [L. *apex,* tip]: belonging to an apex, being at or near the tip; as in apical meristem, the embryonic plant tissue at the tip of root or stem.

apo- (ăp′ô) [Gr. away, off, from]: comp. to L. *ab-;* for example, *apothecium,* case with far-lying spore sacs (in fungi).

arch-, archeo- (ärch, är′kê·ô) [Gr. *archos,* chief]: first, main, earliest; for example, *archenteron,* first embryonic gut; *archeocyte,* chief cell; *archiannelid,* primitive annelid.

arthro- (är′thrô) [Gr. *arthron,* joint]: for example, *arthropod,* jointed-legged; *arthritis,* joint inflammation.

asc-, asco- (ăs′kô) [Gr. *askos,* sac]: for example, *aschelminth,* sac worm; *ascogonium,* sac-forming structure.

aster-, -aster (ăs′tēr) [Gr. star]: for example, *asteroid,* star-shaped.

auto- (ô′tô) [Gr. same, self]: for example, *autogamy,* self-fertilization; *autotroph,* self-feeding organism.

axo- (ăk′sô) [fr. Gr. *axine,* axis]: pertaining to an axis; for example, *axoneme,* axial filament.

bi- (bī) [L. *bis,* twice, double, two]: for example, *bilateral; bicuspid,* having two points.

bio- (bī′ô) [Gr. *bios,* life]: pertaining to life; for example, *biology; amphibia,* living both in water and on land.

-blast, blast-, blasto- (blăst, blăst′ô) [Gr. *blastos,* embryo]: pertaining to embryo; for example, *blastocoel,* embryonic cavity; *mesoblast,* mid-layer of embryo.

* The system of indicating pronunciation is used by permission of the publishers of Webster's New Collegiate Dictionary. Copyright 1949, 1951, 1953, 1956, 1958 by G. C. Merriam Co.

brachio- (brā′kĭ·ō) [L. *brachium*, arm]: for example, *brachiopod*, arm-footed animal; *brachiolaria*, arm-possessing larva.

-branch, branchio- (brăng′kĭ·ō) [Gr. *branchia*, gills]: for example, *branchiopod*, animal with gills on feet; *branchial* sac, breathing sac.

cardio- (kär′dĭ·ō) [Gr. *kardia*, heart]: for example, *pericardial*, around the heart.

caudal (kô′dăl) [L. *caudo*, tail]: at, near, or toward the tail.

cephalo- (sĕf′ă·lō) [Gr. *kephalē*, head]: for example, *cephalothorax; cephalopod*, head-footed animal.

cerci, cercal, cerco- (sûr′sĭ, sûr′kăl, sûr·kō) [Gr. *kērkos*, tail]: pertaining to tail: for example, *cercaria*, tailed fluke larva; *cercopithecoid*, tailed monkey; *anal cerci*.

cervical (sûr′vĭ·kăl) [L. *cervix*, neck]: at, near, or toward the neck region.

chaeto- (kē′tō) [Gr. *chaitē*, bristle, hair]: for example, *chaetognath*, bristle-jawed animal.

chloro- (klō′rō) [Gr. *chloros*, green]: for example, *chlorophyte*, green alga; *chlorocruorin*, green blood pigment.

choano- (kō′ă·nō) [Gr. *choanē*, funnel]: for example, *choanocyte*, funnel-bearing cell.

chondro- (kŏn′drō) [Gr. *chondros*, cartilage]: for example, *chondrocranium*, cartilage skull; *Chondrostei*, cartilage-possessing fish group.

-chord, chorda- (kôrd, kôr′dă) [L. *chorda*, cord, string]: for example, *notochord*, cord along back; *chordate*, notochord-possessing animal.

-chrome, chromo-, chroma- (krōm, krō′mō) [Gr. *chroma*, color]: for example, *cytochrome*, cell pigment; *chromatophore*, pigment-carrier cell.

-clad, clado- (klăd, klā′dō) [Gr. *klādos*, branch, sprout]: for example, *triclad*, three-branched.

cocco-, cocci- (kŏkō, kŏk′sĭ) [Gr. *kokkos*, grain]: for example, *coccine*, grainlike; *coccus*, grainlike (spherical) bacterium.

-coel, coela-, coelo- (sēl) [Gr. *koilos*, hollow, cavity]: for example, *pseudocoel*, false coelomic cavity; *coelenterate*, possessing "gut cavity."

coeno- (sē′nō) [Gr. *koinos*, common]: refers particularly to aggregated or colonial groupings; for example, *coenocyte*, multinuclear cell.

cranio- (krā′nĭ·ō) [Gr. *krānion*, skull]: for example, *craniate*, skull-possessing.

crypto- (krĭp′tō) [Gr. *kryptōs*, hidden]: for example, *cryptobranch*, hidden-gilled.

cten-, cteno- (tĕn) [Gr. *kteis*, comb]: for example, *ctenoid*, comblike scale or gill structure; *Ctenophora*, comb-bearing animals.

cyano- (sī·ă′nō) [Gr. *kyanos*, dark-blue]: for example, *cyanophyte*, blue-green alga; *cyanotic*, blue (bloodless) facial color.

-cyst (sĭst) [Gr. *kystis*, bladder, pouch, sac]: for example, *sporocyst*, spore-containing cyst.

-cyte, cyto- (sīt) [Gr. *kytos*, vessel, container]: pertaining to cell; for example, *cytoplasm*, cell substance; *fibrocyte*, fiber-forming cell.

-dactyl, dactylo- (dăk′tĭl) [Gr. *daktylos*, finger, toe]: for example, *pterodactyl*, wing-fingered; *dactylozooid*, fingerlike individual.

de- (dē) [L. away, from, off]: like Gr. *apo-*; for example, *dehydration*, removal of water.

-dent, denti- (dĕnt) [L. *dens*, tooth]: like Gr. *-dont;* for example, *denticle*, little tooth.

dermis, -derm (dûr′mĭs) [Gr. *derma*, skin]: for example, *ectoderm*, outer skin tissue; *epidermis*, overskin (that is, exterior layer).

di- (dī) [Gr. twice, double, two]: like L. *bi-*, for example, *disect*, to cut in two (distinct from *dis-;* see below).

dia- (dī′ă) [Gr. through, across, thorough]: for example, *diaphragm*, across the midriff; *dialysis*, separation (dissolution) through a membrane.

dino- (dī′nō) [Gr. *dinos*, whirling]: for example, *dinoflagellate; dinosaur*, "whirling lizard."

diplo- (dĭ′plō) [Gr. *diploos*, twofold]: for example, *diploid*, with two chromosome sets; *diplontic*, having two life-cycle phases.

dis- [L. apart, away]: for example, *dissect*, cut apart (distinct from *di-*, see above).

distal (dĭs′tăl): situated away from or far from point of reference (usually the main part of body); opposite to *proximal*.

-dont (dŏnt) [Gr. *odontos*, tooth]: for example, *thecodont*, having encased (socketed) teeth.

dorsal (dôr′săl) [L. *dorsum*, back]: at, near, or toward the back; opposite to *ventral*.

dys- (dĭs) [Gr. hard, bad]: for example, *dysfunction*, malfunction; *dysentery* "bad intestine."

echino- (ē·kĭ′nō) [Gr. *echinos*, spiny, bristly]: for example, *echinoderm*, spiny-skinned; *echiuroid*, having spines at hind end.

eco- (ēkō) [Gr. *oikos*, house, home]: for example, *ecology*, study of organism-habitat (home territory) relationships.

ecto- (ĕk′tō) [Gr. *ektos*, outside]: for example, *ectoproct*, outside-anus (that is, exterior to tentacle ring).

-ectomy (ĕk′tō·mĭ) [Gr. *ek*, out of, + *tomein*, to cut]: excision; for example, *thyroidectomy*, partial or complete excision of the thyroid gland.

efferent (ĕf′ēr·ĕnt) [L. *ex*, out, away + *ferre*, to carry]: that is, to lead or carry away from given position; opposite of *afferent*, for example, efferent nerve, efferent blood vessel.

endo- (ĕn′dō) [Gr. *endon*, within]: for example,

endoderm, inner skin (tissue) layer; *endothermic,* requiring heat (that is, within reacting system).

entero-, -enteron (ĕn′tē·rô) [Gr. *enteron,* intestine]: for example, *enterocoel,* coelom formed from intestine; *archenteron,* first intestine.

ento- (ĕn′tô) [Gr. var. of *endo-,* within]: for example, *entoproct,* inside-anus (that is, within tentacle ring); *entoderm,* endoderm.

entomo- (ĕn′tô·mô) [fr. Gr. *entomon,* insect]: for example, *entomology,* study of insects.

epi- (ĕp′ĭ) [Gr. to, on, over, against]: for example, *epitheca,* outer capsule.

erythro- (ê·rĭth′rô) [Gr. *erythros,* red]: for example, *erythrocyte,* red (blood) cell.

eu- (ū) [Gr. good, well, proper]: for example, *Eumetazoa,* metazoa proper; *eustele,* stele proper.

ex-, exo-, extero- (ĕks, ĕk′sō, ĕks′tēr·ô) [L. out, from, exterior]: for example, *exopterygote,* exterior-winged; *exothermic,* releasing heat (that is, out of reacting system).

-fer, -fera (fēr, fê′rȧ) [L. *ferre,* to carry]: like Gr. *-phore;* for example, *foraminifer,* hole-carrier; *rotifer,* wheel-carrier; *Porifera,* pore-carrying animals (sponges).

flori- (flō′rĭ) [L. *flos,* flower]: pertaining to flowers; for example, *florigen,* flower-producing (hormone).

-form, -formes (fôrm, fôr′mēz) [L. *-formis,* having the form of]: for example, *perciform,* perchlike; *Galliformes,* order of chickenlike birds.

frontal [L. *front, frons,* forehead]: in a horizontal plane separating dorsal half from ventral half.

fusiform (fū′zĭ·fôrm) [L. *fusus,* spindle]: spindle-shaped, tapered at the ends.

gamo-, -gamy (gă′mô) [Gr. *gamein,* to marry]: pertaining to gametes or fertilization; for example, *gamocyst,* capsule around zygote; *autogamy,* self-fertilization.

gastro- (găs′trô) [Gr. *gaster,* stomach]: for example, *gastrozooid,* feeding individual; *gastrocoel,* stomach cavity.

-gen, -genic, geno- [Gr. *genēs,* born, created]: for example, *hydrogen,* water-producing; *myogenic,* produced by muscles; *genotypic,* according to genetic constitution (gene content).

geo- (jê·ŏ) [Gr. *gē,* earth]: for example, *geotropic,* growing toward the center of the earth.

-gest, gest- (jĕst) [L. *gestare,* to carry]: for example, *ingest,* to carry in (food); *gestation,* period of fetus-carrying within pregnant female.

glosso-, -glossus (glŏs′ô) [Gr. *glossa,* tongue]: for example, *glossopharyngeal,* pertaining to tongue and pharynx.

gluco-, glyco- (gloō′kô, glī′kô) [Gr. *gleukos,* sweet]: pertaining to sugars; for example, *glucogenic,* sugar-producing; *glycolysis,* breakdown of sugar.

gnatho-, -gnath (nā′thô) [Gr. *gnathos,* jaw]: for example, *gnathobase,* jawlike base; *chaetognath,* bristle-jawed; *agnath,* jawless.

gon-, gono-, -gonium (gŏn′ô) [Gr. *gonos,* seed, generation]: pertaining to reproduction; for example, *gonozooid,* reproductive individual; *gonopore,* reproductive opening: *oögonium,* egg-forming structure.

gymno- (jĭm′nô) [Gr. *gymnos,* naked]: for example, *gymnosperm,* naked-seed former.

gyn-, -gyne, gyno- (jĭn′nô) [Gr. *gynē,* woman, female]: opposite of *andro-;* for example, *gynogenic,* female-producing, *trichogyne,* female receptor hair.

haem- : see *hem-*

haplo- (hăp′lô) [Gr. *haploos,* single]: for example, *haploid,* with one chromosome set; *haplontic,* having single life-cycle phase.

-helminth (hĕl′mĭnth) [Gr. *helminthos,* worm]: for example, *platyhelminth,* flatworm; *aschelminth,* sac worm.

hem-, hemo-, hemato- (hēm, hē′mô, hĕm′ȧ·tô) [Gr. *haima,* blood]: var. of *haem-;* for example, *hemoglobin,* red blood pigment.

hemi- (hĕm′ĭ) [Gr. half]: like *semi-;* for example, *hemichordate,* similar to chordate.

hetero- (hĕt′ēr·ô) [Gr. *heteros,* other, different]: opposite to *homo-;* for example, *heterotrophic,* feeding on other living things.

hex-, hexa- (hĕks, hĕk′sȧ) [Gr. six]: for example, *hexapod,* six-legged; *hexose,* six-carbon sugar.

holo- (hŏl′ô) [Gr. *holos,* whole, entire]: for example, *holotrophic,* feeding on whole animals; *holoblastic,* cleavage into whole blastomeres in embryo.

homo-, homeo-, homoio- (hō′mô, hō′mē·ô, hō·moi′ô) [Gr. similar]: for example, *homeostatic,* remaining similar in state; *homoiothermic,* possessing constant temperature.

hydro- (hī′drô) [Gr. *hydōr,* water]: for example, *hydrolysis,* dissolution by water.

hyper- (hī′pēr) [Gr. above, over]: opposite of *hypo-;* for example, *hypertrophy,* overgrowth.

hypo- (hī′pō) [Gr. under, less]: opposite of *hyper-;* for example, *hypodermis,* "underskin."

ichthyo- (ĭk′thĭ·ô) [Gr. *ichthyos,* fish]: for example, *Osteichthyes,* bony fishes; *ichthyosaur,* fishlike reptile.

inter- (ĭn′tēr) [L. between, among]: for example, *intercellular,* between cells.

intra- (ĭn′trȧ) [L. within]: for example, *intracellular,* within cells.

iso- (ī′sô) [Gr. *isos,* equal]: like *homo-;* for example, *isolecithal,* having evenly distributed yolk.

-lecithal (lĕs′ĭ·thăl) [Gr. *lekithos,* egg yolk]: for example, *lecithin,* any of several complex nitrogenous substances found especially in the brain and nerve tissue and in egg yolk.

leuco- (lū′kô) [Gr. *leukos*, white]: for example, *leucocyte*, white (blood) cell.

lip-, lipo- (lĭp, lĭ′pô) [Gr. *lipos*, fat]: pertaining to fats and fatty substances; for example, *lipase*, fat-digesting enzyme.

-logy (lŏ′jĭ) [Gr. *logos*, discourse, study]: for example, *biology*, study of living things.

lumbar (lŭm′ bēr) [L. *lumbus*, loin]: at, near, or toward loin region.

-lysis, -lytic, -lyte [Gr. *lysis*, a loosening]: pertaining to dissolving; for example, *electrolytic*, dissolution by electricity; *autolysis*, self-dissolution.

macro- (mă′krô) [Gr. *makros*, long]: opposite of *micro-*; for example, *macromere*, large embryo cell.

mastigo- (măs′tĭ·gô) [Gr. *mastix*, whip]: for example, *Mastigophora*, flagellum-bearing (protozoa); *mastigoneme*, whip hair.

mega- (mĕg′ ȧ) [Gr. *megas*, large]: opposite of *micro-*; for example, *megaspore*, large spore; used like *macro-*.

meri-, mero-, -mere, -mer (mĕr′ĭ, mḛ′rô, mḛr, mĕr) [Gr. *meros*, part]: for example, *blastomere*, embryo part (cell); *polymer*, chemical of many (similar) parts; *meroblastic*, cleavage into partial blastomeres in embryo; *meristem*, dividing region.

meso- (mĕs′ô) [Gr. *mesos*, middle]: for example, *mesoderm*, middle "skin"; *mesophyll*, middle of leaf.

meta- (mĕt′ȧ) [Gr. after, behind]: for example, *metacoel*, hind cavity; *Metazoa*, later (advanced) animals.

micro- (mĭ′krô) [Gr. *mikros*, small]: for example, *micromere*, small embryo cell.

mono- (mŏn′ô) [Gr. *monos*, single]: for example, *monosaccharide*, single sugar (unit).

-morph, morpho- (mŏrf, mŏr′fô) [Gr. *morphē*, form]: for example, *morphology*, study of form (structure); *metamorphosis*, process of acquiring later (that is, adult) structure.

myc-, myco- (mīk, mī′kô) [Gr. *mykēs*, mushroom]: pertaining to fungi; for example, *mycelium*, fungus filaments; *Mycophyta*, the phylum of fungi.

myo- (mī′ô) [Gr. *mys*, muscle]: for example, *myocyte*, muscle cell; *myoneme*, muscle (-like) hair; *myocoel*, muscle-associated coelom.

myx-, myxo- (mīks, mīk·sô) [Gr. *myxa*, slime]: for example, *myxomycete*, slime mold.

-neme, nemato- (nē′mĕ, nĕm′ä tô) [Gr. *nema*, thread]: for example, *nematocyst*, thread-containing capsule; *nematode*, threadlike worm; *protonema*, first thread (filament in moss).

nephro- (nĕf′rô) [Gr. *nephros*, kidney]: for example, *nephric tubule*, excretory tubule.

neuro- (nū′rô) [Gr. *neuron*, nerve]: for example, *neuropore*, opening from nervous system.

noto- (nō′tô) [Gr. *nōton*, the back]: for example, *notopodium*, foot along back; *notochord*, cord along back.

octo- [Gr. *okto*, eight]: for example, *octopus*, eight-"legged" animal.

-oid, -oida, -oidea (oid, oid′ȧ, oi′dē·ȧ) [Gr. *eidos*, form]: having the form of; like L. *-form;* for example, *echinoid*, like *Echinus*.

oligo- (ŏl′ĭ·gô) [Gr. *oligos*, few, small]: for example, *oligochaete*, having few bristles.

omni- (ŏm′nĭ) [L. *omnis*, all]: for example, *omnivore*, animal eating all kinds of foods.

onto- (ŏn′tô) [Gr. *on*, being]: for example, *ontogeny*, production of being (=development).

oö- (ō′ô) [Gr. *ōion*, egg]: for example, *oöcyte*, egg cell; *oögonium*, egg-forming structure.

oral (ō′rȧl) [L. *or-, os*, mouth]: at, near, or toward the mouth.

osteo- (ŏs′tê·ô) [Gr. *osteon*, bone]: for example, *osteoblast*, bone-forming cell; *osteology*, study of bones; *periosteum*, tissue layer covering a bone.

ostraco- (ŏs′trȧ·kô) [Gr. *ostrakon*, shell]: pertaining to a skeletal (calcareous) cover or shield; for example, *ostracoderm*, armor-skinned.

oto-, otic (ō′tô, ō′tĭk) [Gr. *ous*, ear]: for example, *otic* vesicle; *otolith*, ear stone.

ovi- ovo- (ō′vĭ, ō′vô) [L. *ovum*, egg]: for example, *oviduct; ovary*, egg-producing organ.

paleo- (pā′lê·ô) [Gr. *palaios*, old]: for example, *paleontology*, study of ancient (fossil) life.

para- (păr′ȧ) [Gr. beside]: for example, *parapodium*, side foot; *Parazoa*, animals on side branch of evolution (sponges).

pectin- (pĕk′tĭn) [L. *pecten*, comb]: for example, *pectinibranch*, having comblike gills; *pectine*, comb-like organ.

pectoral (pĕk′tô·rȧl) [L. *pectorale*, breastplate]: at, near, or toward chest or shoulder region.

-ped, -pedia, pedi- (pĕd, pĕd′ĭ·ȧ, pĕd′ĭ) [L. *pes*, foot]: like Gr. *-pod;* for example, *bipedal*, two-footed; *pedipalp*, leglike appendage.

pelvic (pĕl′vĭk) [L. *pelvis*, basin]: at, near, or toward the hip region.

pent-, penta- (pĕnt, pĕn′tȧ) [Gr. *pente*, five]: for example, *pentose*, five-carbon sugar; *pentaradial*.

peri- (pĕr′ĭ) [Gr. around]: for example, *peristomial*, around the mouth; *perianth*, around the flower; *peristalsis*, wavelike compression around tubular organ, for example, gut.

phago-, -phage (făg′ô, fāj) [Gr. eating]: for example, *phagocyte*, cell eater; *bacteriophage*, bacterium eater (virus).

phello- (fĕl′ô) [Gr. *phellos*, cork]: pertaining to cork region of bark; for example, *phellogen*, cork-producing tissue (cambium).

phono-, -phone (fōn′ō, fōn) [Gr. *phonē*, sound]: for example, *phonoreceptor*, sound-sensitive sense organ.

phoro-, -phore (fŏr′ō, fōr) [Gr. *phoros*, bearing, carrying]: like L. *-fer;* for example, *trochophore*, "wheel"-bearing (larva).

photo-, photic (fō′tō, fō′tĭk) [Gr. *photos*, light]: for example, *photophore*, light-possessing part or organ; *photosynthesis*, synthesis with aid of light.

-phragm (frăm) [Gr. barrier]: for example, *diaphragm; endophragm*, internal skeletal plates.

phyco- (fī′kō) [Gr. *phykos*, seaweed]: refers to aquatic protists; for example, *phycomycete*, primitive (often aquatic) fungus; *phycobilin*, pigment of marine algae.

phyllo-, -phyll (fĭl′ō, fĭl) [Gr. *phyllon*, leaf]: for example, *phyllopodium*, leaf-shaped foot; *chlorophyll*, green pigment in leaf.

phyto-, -phyte (fī′tō, fīt) [Gr. *phyton*, plant]: for example, *phytoplankton*, plankton consisting of plant life; *Metaphyta*, later (advanced) plants.

-pithecus (-pĭ·thē′cŭs) [Gr. *pithēkos*, ape]: for example, *Australopithecus*, southern ape; *Pithecanthropus*, manlike ape.

placo- (plă′kō) [Gr. *plax*, tablet, plate]: for example, *placoderm*, plate-skinned; *placoid*, platelike.

-plasm, plasmo-, -plast (plăz′m, plăz′mō, plăst) [Gr. *plasma*, form, mold]: for example, *protoplasm*, first-molded (living matter); *plasmotomy*, cutting (division) of protoplasm; *chloroplast*, green-formed (body).

-pleur, pleuro- (ploōr, ploōr′ō) [Gr. *pleuron*, side, rib]: for example, *pleuron*, lateral exoskeletal plate; *pleura*, membrane lining rib cage.

-ploid [Gr. *-ploos*, -fold]: number of chromosome sets per cell; for example, *haploid, diploid, polyploid.*

poly- (pŏl′ĭ) [Gr. *polys*, many]: for example, *polymorphic*, many-shaped; *polychaete*, many-bristled animal.

post-, postero-, posterior (pōst, pŏs′tĕr·ō) [L. behind, after]: opposite of *pre-, antero-;* at, near, or toward hind end or part.

pre- (prē) [L. before, in front of]: opposite of *post-;* for example, *preoral*, in front of mouth.

pro- (prō) [Gr. before, in front of]: like L. *pre-;* for example, *prostomial*, in front of mouth; *procambium*, cambium precursor tissue.

-proct, procto- (prŏkt, prŏk′tō) [Gr. *proctos*, anus]: for example, *ectoproct*, having anus outside of ring of tentacles; *proctodeal*, anal.

proto- (prō′tō) [Gr. *prōtos*, first]: for example, *Protozoa*, first animals; *protostome*, first mouth; *protocoel*, first coelom.

proximal (prŏk′sĭ·măl) [L. *proximus*, near]: situated near to point of reference (usually the main part of body); opposite of distal.

pseudo- (sū′dō) [Gr. *pseudēs*, false]: for example, *pseudocoel*, false coelom; *pseudopodium*, false foot.

ptero-, -ptera, -ptery (tĕr′ō, tĕr′a, tĕr′ī) [Gr. *pteron*, wing, fin]: for example, *Aptera*, wingless animals (insects); *pterodactyl*, wing-fingered; *exopterygote*, exterior-winged.

-pyge, pyg- (pī′jē, pīj) [Gr. *pygē*, rump]: for example, *cytopyge*, cellular elimination pore in protozoa; *pygidium*, posterior abdominal region (in arthropods); *uropygial gland*, oil-secreting gland near tail base in birds.

rami-, -ramous (răm′ī, rā′mŭs) [L. *ramus*, branch]: for example, *biramous*, two-branched; *ramified*, branched.

renal (rē′năl) [L. *renes*, kidneys]: pertaining to the kidney.

rhabdo- (răb′dō) [Gr. *rhabdos*, rod]: for example, *rhabdite*, rod-shaped organelle; *rhabdocoel*, flatworm possessing straight (rodlike) intestine.

rhizo- (rī′zō) [Gr. *rhiza*, root]: for example, *rhizopod*, having rootlike feet; *rhizoplast*, rootlike organelle; *rhizoid*, rootlike hair.

-rhynch, rhyncho- (rĭngk, rĭng′kō) [Gr. *rhynchos*, snout]: for example, *kinorhynch*, having movable snout; *rhynchocoel*, snout (proboscis) cavity.

sagittal (săj′ĭ·tăl) [L. *sagitta*, arrow]: at, near, or toward plane bisecting left and right halves; in median plane.

sarco-, -sarc (sär′kō, särk) [Gr. *sarx*, flesh]: for example, *coenosarc*, common flesh (living portions).

saur-, -saur (sôr) [Gr. *sauros*, lizard]: for example, *saurian*, pertaining to lizards (and reptiles generally, including extinct); *pterosaur*, flying reptile.

schizo- (skĭz′ō) [Gr. *schizein*, to split, part]: for example, *schizocoel*, coelom formed by splitting of tissue layer; *schizophyte*, fission "plant" (bacterium).

sclero- (sklēr′ō) [Gr. *sklēros*, hard]: for example, *scleroprotein*, hard (horny) protein; *sclereid*, hard-walled cell.

scypho- (sī′fō) [Gr. *skyphos*, cup]: for example, *Scyphozoa*, cupshaped animals (jellyfish); *scyphistoma*, cupped-mouth-possessing larva.

semi- (sĕ′mĭ) [L. half]: for example, *semiherbaceous*, intermediate between herbaceous and woody.

seti-, seta (sēt′ī, sēt′a) [L. *seta*, bristle]: like Gr. *chaeto-; setiferous*, bristle-bearing.

sipho-, siphono- (sī′fō) [Gr. *siphōn*, a pipe]: for example, *siphonaceous*, tubular.

-soma, -some, somato- (sō′ma, sōm, sō′ma·tō) [Gr. *sōma*, body]: for example, *chromosome*, pigmented body; *somatocoel*, body coelom; *somatic mesoderm*, outer mesoderm.

-sperm, spermo-, sperma-, spermato- (spûrm, spûr′mō, spûr′mȧ, spûr′mȧ·tō) [Gr. *sperma*, seed]: for example, *spermatophore*, sperm (-bearing) capsule; *endosperm*, interior (region of) seed.

splanchno- (splăngk′nō) [Gr. *splanchnon*, entrails]: for example, *splanchnic mesoderm*, inner mesoderm.

spora-, sporo- (spō′rȧ, spō′rō) [Gr. *sporā*, seed]: for example, *Sporozoa*, spore-forming (protozoa); *sporogenous*, spore-producing.

stato- (stăt′ō) [Gr. *statos*, standing stationary, positioned]: for example, *statolith*, position (-indicating) stone; *statoblast*, stationary embryo.

stereo- (stĕr′ê·ō) [Gr. *stereos*, solid]: for example, *stereoblastula*, solid blastula.

-stome, -stoma, -stomato- (stōm, stōm′ȧ, stōm′ȧ·tō) [Gr. *stoma*, mouth]: *peristomial*, around the mouth; *stomatogenesis*, mouth formation.

sub-, sus- (sŭb, sŭs) [L. under, below]: for example, *subepidermal*, underneath the epidermis; *suspensor*, suspending structure.

sym-, syn-, (sĭm, sĭn) [Gr. *syn*, together, with]: like L. *con-*; for example, *syngamy*, coming together of gametes; *synapse*, looping together (of neurons); *synthesis*, construction, putting together; *symbiosis*, living together.

tango- (tăng′gō) [L. *tangere*, to touch]: for example, *tangoreceptor*, touch-receptive sense organ.

taxo-, taxi-, -taxis (tăk′sō, tăk′sī, tăk′sīs) [Gr. *taxis*, arrangement]: for example, *taxonomy*, "arrangement" laws; *taxidermy*, skin arrangement; *chemotaxis*, arrangement (movement) produced by chemicals.

tel-, tele-, teleo- (tĕl, tĕl′ê, tĕl′ê·ō) [Gr. *telos*, end]: for example, *telophase*, end phase; *teleost*, (fish with) bony end (adult) state; *teleology*, knowledge of end conditions.

tetra- (tĕt′rȧ) [Gr. four]: for example, *tetrabranch*, four-gilled; *tetrapod*, four-footed.

thallo- (thăl′ō) [Gr. *thallos*, young shoot]: for example, *prothallium*, precursor of definitive plant (fern gametophyte); *thallophyte*, old term for plantlike protists, that is, those without leaf, stem, or root.

theco-, -theca (thē′kō, thē′kȧ) [Gr. *thēkē*, case, capsule]: for example, *thecodont*, having socketed teeth; *spermatheca*, sperm receptacle.

thigmo- (thĭg′mō) [Gr. *thigma*, touch]: like L. *tango-*; for example, *thigmotropy*, movement due to touch.

thoracic (thô·răs′ĭk) [L. *thorax*, chest]: at, near, or toward chest region, or region between head and abdomen.

-tome, -tomy (tōm, tō′mĭ) [Gr. *tomē*, section, a cutting apart]: for example, *autotomy*, self-dismemberment (of appendage); *myotome*, muscle-producing part.

trans- [L. across]: for example, *transpiration*, water evaporation from exposed plant parts.

transverse (trăns′vûrs) [L. *transversare*, to cross]: at, near, or toward plane separating anterior and posterior; cross-sectional.

tri- (trī) [L. *tria*, three]: for example, *triclad*, three-branched (digestive tract).

-trich, tricho- (trĭk, trĭk′ō) [Gr. *trichos*, hair]: for example, *heterotrich* (ciliate), possessing different types of hairs (cilia); *trichocyst*, hair-containing sac.

-troch, trocho- (trŏk, trŏk′ō) [Gr. *trochos*, wheel]: for example, *trochophore* (larva), bearing wheel (of cilia).

-troph, tropho- (trŏf, trō′fō) [Gr. *trophos*, feeder]: for example, *autotrophic*, self-nourishing.

uro-, -ura (ū′rō, ū′rȧ) [Gr. *oura*, tail]: for example, *uropod*, tail foot; *urochordate*, tailed *chordate; Anura*, tailless animals (amphibia).

ventral (vĕn′trăl) [L. *venter*, belly]: opposite to *dorsal;* at, near, or toward the belly or underside.

xantho- (zăn′thô) [Gr. *xanthos*, yellow]: for example, *xanthophyll*, yellow pigment (of leaf).

xero- (zē′rô) [Gr. *xēros*, dry]: for example, *xerophyte*, dry-climate plant.

zoo-, -zoa, -zoon (zō′ô, zōȧ, zō′ŏn) [Gr. *zōion*, animal]: for example, *zooplankton*, animal life of the plankton; *protozoon; zooid*, individual animal (usually in a colony).

zygo- (zī′gō) [Gr. *zygon*, yoke, pair]: for example, *zygote*, fertilized egg.

SECTION B

GENERAL LISTING OF TECHNICAL TERMS

NOTE: In most cases in this section where derivations of particular word parts are not given, such parts and their derivations may be found in section A, above.

abdomen (ab′dŏ·měn) [L.]: region of animal body posterior to thorax.

abscission (ăb·sĭzh′ŭn) [L. *abscindere*, to cut off]: separation of a body part from a plant, particularly after a special layer of cells weakens and dies.

Acanthocephala (ȧ·kăn′thô·sĕf′ȧ·lȧ) [Gr. *akantho*, thorn]: spiny-headed worms, a phylum of pseudocoelomate parasites.

acentric (â·sĕn′trĭk): without center; applied specifically to type of mitosis in which a centriole is absent.

acicula (ȧ·sĭk′û·lȧ) [L. dim. of *acus*, needle]: needle-like bristle embedded within polychaete parapodium.

acid (ăs′ĭd) [L. *acidus*, sour]: a substance which releases hydrogen ions in water; having a pH of less than 7.

acoel, acoelomate (â·sēl'): (1) without coelom; also a group of free-living flatworms without digestive cavity; (2) an animal without coelom; flatworms, nemertine worms.

Acrania (â·krā'nǐ·a) [Gr. *kranion*, skull]: headless chordates, including urochordates and cephalochordates.

acromegaly (ăk'rô·měg'a·lǐ): a condition in man characterized by skeletal overgrowths, particularly in the extremities, produced by excessive growth-hormone secretion from the pituitary.

acrosome (ăk'rô·sōm): structure at the tip of the head (nucleus) of animal sperm which makes contact with the egg during fertilization.

actinostele (ăk·tǐn'ô·stēl) [Gr. *stēlē*, upright post]: a type of protostele in which the cross-sectional arrangement of vascular tissues has the form of a star with various numbers of points.

adenine (ăd'ê·nēn): a purine component of nucleotides and nucleic acids.

adenosine (di-, tri-) phosphate (*ADP, ATP*) (a·děn'-ô·sēn): adenine-ribose-phosphates functioning in energy transfers within cells.

adenylic acid: equivalent to adenosine monophosphate, or AMP.

adipose (ăd'ǐ·pōs) [L. *adipis*, fat]: fat, fatty; fat-storing tissue.

ADP: abbreviation of adenosine diphosphate.

adrenal, adrenaline (ăd·rē'năl, ăd·rěn'ăl·ǐn) [L. *renalis*, kidney]: (1) endocrine gland; (2) the hormone produced by the adrenal medulla.

adrenergic (ăd'rěn·ûr'jǐk): applied to nerve fibers which release an adrenalinelike substance from their axon terminals when impulses are transmitted across synapses.

adventitious (ăd'věn·tǐsh'ǔs): appearing not in usual place; as in adventitious root, which may sprout from anywhere on a stem.

aerobe, aerobic (ā'ēr·ōb, -ō'bǐk) [Gr. *aeros*, air]: (1) oxygen-requiring organism; (2) pertaining to oxygen-dependent form of respiration.

Agnatha (ăg'na·tha): jawless fishes, a class of vertebrates including lampreys and hagfishes.

aldaric acid (ăl·dă'rǐk): a sugar derivative in which both the first and last carbon positions carry carboxyl groups.

aldehyde (ăl'dê·hīd) [L. abbr. for *alcohol dehydrogenatum*, dehydrogenated alcohol]: organic compound possessing a —CHO grouping.

aldonic acid (ăl·dō'nǐk): a sugar derivative in which the first carbon position carries a carboxyl group.

aldose (ăl'dōs): one of a series of sugars possessing a terminal aldehyde grouping.

alga (ăl'ga), pl. **algae** (-jē): any member of a largely photosynthetic superphylum of protists.

aliphatic (ă·lǐ·fā'tǐk): refers to chainlike organic compounds; contrasts with aromatic (ringlike) types.

alkaline (ăl'ka·lǐn): pertaining to substances which release hydroxyl ions in water; having a pH greater than 7.

allantois (ă·lăn'tô·ǐs) [Gr. *allantoeides*, sausage-shaped]: one of the extraembryonic membranes in reptiles, birds, and mammals; functions as embryonic urinary bladder or as carrier of blood vessels to and from placenta.

allele (ă·lēl') [Gr. *allēlōn*, of one another]: one of a group of alternative genes which may occupy a given locus on a chromosome; a dominant and its correlated recessive are allelic genes.

alula (ăl' û·la) [L. dim. of *ala*, wing]: the first digit (thumb) of a bird wing; reduced in comparative size.

alveolus (ăl·vē'ôl·ǔs), pl. **alveoli** (-lī) [L. dim. of *alveus*, a hollow]: a small cavity or pit, for example, a microscopic air sac of lungs.

ambulacrum, ambulacral (ăm'bû·lā'krǔm, -ăl) [L. walk, avenue]: (1) tube-feet-lined ciliated groove leading over arm to mouth in certain echinoderms; conducts food to mouth; (2) adjective.

amino, amino acid, amination (ă·mē'nô, ă·mǐnā'-shǔn): (1) —NH₂ group; (2) acid containing amino group, constituent of protein; (3) addition of amino group to other compound.

ammocoete (ăm'ô·sēt) [Gr. *ammos*, sand]: lamprey larva.

amnion, amniote, amniotic (ăm'nǐ·ǒn) [Gr. dim. of *amnos*, lamb]: (1) one of the extraembryonic membranes in reptiles, birds, and mammals, forming a sac around the embryo; (2) any reptile, bird, or mammal, that is, any animal possessing an amnion during the embryonic state; (3) pertaining to the amnion, as in *amniotic fluid*.

amphiblastula (ăm'fǐ·blăst'û·la): larval stage in certain sponges.

amphineura (ăm'fǐ·nū'ra): a class of mollusks, including the chitons.

ampholyte (ăm'fô·līt): a compound (for example, amino acid or protein) carrying both positive and negative electric charges.

ampulla (ăm·pŭl'a) [L. vessel]: enlarged saclike portion of a duct, as in ampullae of semicircular canals in mammalian ear, or in ampullae of echinoderm tube feet.

amylase (ăm'ǐ·lās) [L. *amylum*, starch]: an enzyme promoting the decomposition of polysaccharides into smaller carbohydrate units.

amyloplast (ăm'ǐ·lô·plăst'): a starch-storing, nonpigmented plastid; a type of leucoplast.

amylose (ăm′ĭ·lōs): a polysaccharide composed of glucose units, a usual component of starch.

anaerobe, anaerobic (ăn·ā·ĕr·ōb, -ō′bĭk): (1) an oxygen-independent organism; (2) pertaining to an oxygen-independent form of respiration.

anamniote (ăn·ăm′nĭ·ōt): any vertebrate other than a reptile, bird, or mammal, that is, one in which an amnion does not form during the embryonic phase.

anaphase (ăn′a·fāz): a stage in mitotic division, characterized by the migration of chromosome sets toward the spindle poles.

anastral (ăn·ăs′trăl): without stars; applied specifically to type of mitosis in which asters around the centrioles are absent.

anatomy (a·năt′ō·mĭ): the gross structure of an organism, or the science which deals with gross structure; a branch of the science of morphology.

androgen (ăn′drô·jĕn): one of a group of male sex hormones.

angiosperm (ăn′jĭ·ô·spûrm′) [Gr. *angeion*, a vessel]: a member of a class of tracheophytic plants, characterized by the possession of flowers and fruits; a flowering plant.

anion (ăn′ī′ŏn): a negatively charged ion, that is, one that migrates toward the positive electrode (anode) in an electric field.

anisogamy (ăn·ī′sŏg′ăm·ĭ): sexual fusion in which the gametes of opposite sex types are unequal in size.

Annelida (ăn′ĕ·lĭd·a) [L. *anellus*, a ring]: the phylum of segmented worms.

annual (ăn′ū·ăl): yearly; as in annual plant, which lives for one year and forms seeds before dying.

annulus (ăn′ū·lŭs) [L. *ring*]: a ringlike structure.

anomer (ă′nô·mēr): one of two structural variants of an aldose sugar, defined according to how the groups on carbon 1 are aligned when the molecule is considered as a ring structure.

anther (ăn′thēr): the microsporangia in a stamen of flowering plants.

antheridium (ăn′thēr·ĭd′ĭ·ŭm) [Gr. *antheros*, flowery]: the sperm-producing organ of plants.

anthocyanin (ăn′thô·sī′a·nĭn): a water-soluble pigment in plants, producing red, purple, and blue colors.

antibody (ăn′tĭ·bŏd′ĭ): a substance produced within an organism which opposes the action of another substance; in specific usage, an antibody is a globulin type of protein which combines and renders harmless an antigen, that is, a foreign protein introduced into an animal by infectious processes.

antigen (ăn′tĭ·jĕn): a foreign substance, usually protein in nature, which elicits the formation of specific antibodies within an animal.

Anura (ă·nŭ′ra): order of tailless amphibia, including frogs and toads.

aplanospore (â·plăn′ô·spōr) [Gr. *planos*, roaming]: a nonmotile spore.

apodeme (ăp′ô·dēm) [Gr. *demos*, district]: breakage plane in crustacean appendage where autotomy may occur readily.

apothecium (ăp′ô·thē′shĭ·ŭm) [Gr. *apothēkē*, storehouse]: disk- or cup-shaped fruiting body in ascomycetous fungi.

Arachnida (a·răk′nĭd·a) [Gr. *arachnē*, spider]: class of chelicerate arthropods including spiders, scorpions, mites, ticks, and other orders.

archegonium (är′kê·gō′nĭ·ŭm) [Gr. *archegonos*, first of a race]: the egg-producing organ of plants.

archenteron (är·kĕn′tēr·ŏn): the central cavity of a gastrula, lined by endoderm, representing the future digestive cavity of the adult.

aromatic: refers to ringlike organic compounds; contrasts with aliphatic (chainlike) types.

Arthropoda (är·thrô′pŏd·a): the phylum of jointed-legged invertebrates.

Aschelminthes (ăs·kĕl·mĭn′thēs): bladderlike or bladder-forming worms; a pseudocoelomate phylum including rotifers, roundworms, and other groups.

ascogonium (ăs′kô·gō′nĭ·ŭm): a female sexual hypha of Ascomycetes which receives antheridial nuclei and produces asci or ascus-forming hyphae.

asconoid (ă′skŏn·oid): saclike; refers specifically to a type of sponge architecture.

ascus (ăs′kŭs): the tubular spore sac of a class of fungi; eight spores typically form within an ascus.

astral (ăs′trăl): applied specifically to type of mitosis in which asters around centrioles are present.

atactostele (ă·tăkt′ô·stēl) [Gr. *tassein*, to arrange]: type of stele in which vascular bundles are scattered throughout stem, as in monocots.

atom (ăt′ŭm) [Gr. *atomos*, indivisible]: the smallest whole unit of a chemical element; composed of given numbers of protons, neutrons, and other particles which form an atomic nucleus, and of given numbers of electrons which orbit around the nucleus.

ATP: abbreviation of adenosine triphosphate.

atrium, atrial (ā′trĭ·ŭm, -ăl) [L. yard, court, hall]: entrance or exit cavity, for example, entrance chamber to heart, exit chamber from chordate gill region.

auricle (ô′rĭ·k′l) [L. dim. of *auris*, ear]: ear-shaped structure or lobelike appendage; for example,

atrium in mammalian heart, lateral flap in vertebrate hindbrain, lateral flap near eyes in planarian worms.

auricularia (ô·rĭk′ū·lā′rĭ·à) [L. *lar*, larva]: larva of holothuroid echinoderms, with earlobelike ciliated bands.

autolysis (ô·tŏl′ĭ·sĭs): enzymatic self-digestion or dissolution of tissue or other part of an organism.

autosome (ô′tô·sōm): a chromosome which is not a sex chromosome.

autotroph, autotrophism (ô′tô·trŏf′, -ĭz′m): (1) an organism which manufactures organic nutrients from inorganic raw materials; (2) a form of nutrition in which only inorganic substances are required as raw materials.

auxin (ôk′sĭn) [Gr. *auxein*, to increase]: a plant hormone promoting cell elongation, hence growth.

auxospore (ôk′sô·spōr): a zygote of diatoms.

avicularium (à·vĭk′ū·lā′rĭ·ŭm) [L. dim. of *avis*, bird]: a specially differentiated polymorphic individual in a colony of ectoprocts, shaped like a bird's head, serving a protective function.

axenic (ā·zĕn′ĭk) [Gr. *xenos*, foreigner]: pertaining to a culture medium in which the available food sources are completely and specifically identified.

axil, axillary (ăk′sĭl) [L. *axilla*, armpit]: (1) the angle between a branch or leaf and the stem from which it arises; (2) adjective.

axon (ăk′sŏn): an outgrowth of a nerve cell, conducting impulses away from the cell body; a type of nerve fiber.

bacillus (bà·sĭl′ŭs) [L. dim. of *baculum*, rod]: any rod-shaped bacterium.

bacteriophage (băk·tēr′ĭ·ô·fāj) [*bacterium* + Gr. *phagein*, to eat]: one of a group of viruses which infect, parasitize, and eventually kill bacteria.

bacterium (băk·tēr′ĭ·ŭm) [Gr. dim. of *baktron*, a staff]: a small, typically unicellular organism characterized by the absence of a formed nucleus; genetic material is dispersed in clumps through the cytoplasm.

basidium (bà·sĭd′ĭ·ŭm) [Gr. dim. of *basis*, base]: a spore-bearing structure of a class of fungi; typically, four spores are formed on each basidium.

benthos, benthonic (bĕn′thŏs) [Gr. depth of the sea]: (1) collective term for organisms living along the bottoms of oceans and lakes; (2) adjective.

beriberi (bĕr′ĭ·bĕr′ĭ) [Singhalese *beri*, weakness]: disease produced by deficiency of vitamin B$_1$ (thiamine).

bicuspid (bī·kŭs′pĭd) [L. *cuspis*, point]: ending in two points, as in bicuspid heart valve, two flaps of tissue guarding opening between left auricle and left ventricle; see *mitral*.

biennial (bī·ĕn′ĭ·ăl) [L. *annus*, year]: occurring once in two years; as in biennial plant, which flowers and forms seeds the second year.

bioluminescence (bī′ô·lū′mĭ·nĕs′ĕns) [L. *lumen*, light]: emission of light by living organisms.

biome (bī′ōm): habitat zone, for example, desert, grassland, tundra.

biota, biotic (bī·ō′tä, -ŏt′ĭk): (1) the community of organisms of a given region; (2) adjective.

bipinnaria (bī′pĭn·ăr′ĭ·à) [L. *pinna*, feather, fin]: larva of asteroid echinoderms, with ciliated bands suggesting two wings.

blastopore (blăs′tô·pōr): opening connecting archenteron of gastrula with outside; represents future mouth in some animals, future anus in others.

blastula (blăs′tū·là): stage in early animal development, when embryo is a hollow or solid sphere of cells.

blepharoplast (blĕf′à·rô·plăst′) [Gr. *blepharon*, eyelid]: the basal granule of a flagellum or cilium; equivalent to *kinetosome*.

brachiopod, Brachiopoda (brā′kĭ·ô·pŏd, brā·kĭ·ŏp′-ô·dà): (1) a sessile, enterocoelomate, marine animal possessing a pair of shells (valves) and a lophophore; (2) phylum name.

bronchus, bronchiole (brŏng′kŭs, brŏng′kĭ·ōl) [Gr. *bronchos*, windpipe]: (1) a main branch of the trachea in air-breathing vertebrates; (2) a smaller branch of a bronchus.

bryophyte, Bryophyta (brī′ô·fīt) [Gr. *bryon*, moss]: (1) a moss, liverwort, or hornwort, that is, any metaphyte that is not tracheophytic; (2) phylum name.

buffer (bŭf′ēr): a substance that prevents appreciable changes of pH in solutions to which small amounts of acids or bases are added.

bulb (bŭlb): an underground stem with thickened leaves adapted for food storage.

bursa (bûr′sà) [L. sac, bag]: saclike cavity.

byssus (bĭs′ŭs) [Gr. *byssos*, flax, linen]: silky threads secreted by mussels for attachment to rocks.

caecum (sē′kŭm) [L. *caecus*, blind]: cavity open at one end, for example, the blind pouch at the beginning of the large intestine, connecting at one side with the small intestine.

callus (kăl′ŭs) [L., hardened skin]: a tissue consisting of parenchymalike cells, formed as a tumorous overgrowth, or over a wound, or in tissue culture.

calorie (kăl′ô·rĭ) [L. *calor*, heat]: unit of heat, defined as that amount of heat required to raise the temperature of 1 g of water by 1°C; a *large*, or *dietary*, *calorie* is a thousand of the units above, which are often designated as "small" calories.

calyx (kā′lĭks) [Gr. *kalyx*]: the outermost whorl of leaves (sepals) in a flower.

cambium (kăm′bĭ·ŭm) [L. exchange]: embryonic tissue in roots and stems of tracheophytes, giving rise to secondary xylem and phloem.

captaculum (kap·ta′kŭ·lŭm) [L. *captare*, to capture]: tentaclelike outgrowth from head of tooth-shell mollusks, serving in food capture.

carapace (kăr′a·pās) [Sp. *carapacho*]: a hard case or shield covering the back of certain animals, for example, many crustacea.

carbohydrate, carbohydrase (kär′bô·hī′drāt): (1) an organic compound consisting of a chain of carbon atoms to which hydrogen and oxygen, present in a 2:1 ratio, are attached; (2) an enzyme promoting the synthesis or decomposition of a carbohydrate.

carnivore, Carnivora (kär·nĭv′ô·rȧ) [L. *carnivorus*, flesh-eating]: (1) any holotrophic animal subsisting on other animals or parts of animals; (2) an order of mammals; includes cats, dogs, seals, walruses.

carotene, carotenoids (kăr′ô·tēn, kȧ·rŏt′ê·noid) [L. *carota*, carrot]: (1) a pigment producing cream-yellow to carrot-orange colors; precursor of vitamin A; (2) a class of pigments of which carotene is one.

carpogonium (kär′pô·gōn′ĭ·ŭm) [Gr. *karpos*, fruit]: the female sex cell in red algae.

catalysis, catalyst, catalytic (kȧ·tăl′ĭ·sĭs) [Gr. *katalysis*, dissolution]: (1) acceleration of a chemical reaction by a substance that does not become part of the endproduct; (2) a substance which accelerates a reaction as above; (3) adjective.

cation (kăt′ī′ŏn): a positively charged ion, that is, one that migrates toward the negative electrode (cathode) in an electric field.

ceboid (sē′boid): a New World monkey; uses its tail as a fifth limb.

Cenozoic (sē′nô·zō′ĭk) [Gr. *kainos*, recent]: geological era after the Mesozoic, dating approximately from 75 million years ago to present.

centric (sĕn′trĭk): adjective applied specifically to type of mitosis in which centrioles are present.

centriole (sĕn′trĭ·ōl): cytoplasmic organelle forming spindle pole during mitosis and meiosis.

centrolecithal (sĕn′trô·lĕs′ĭ·thȧl): pertaining to eggs with yolk accumulated in center of cell, for example, in arthropods.

centromere (sĕn′trô·mēr): region on chromosome at which spindle fibril is attached during mitosis and meiosis.

Cephalochordata, Cephalopoda, cephalothorax (sĕf′-ȧ·lô-): (1) a subphylum of chordates; the lancelets or amphioxus; (2) a class of mollusks; squids, octopuses, nautiluses; (3) the fused head and thorax in certain arthropods, for example, crustacea.

cercaria (sûr·kā′rĭ·ȧ): a larval stage in the life cycle of flukes; produced by a redia and infects fish, where it encysts.

cercopithecoid (sûr′kô·pĭ·thē′koĭd): an Old World monkey; possesses tail, which is not used as limb.

cerebellum (sĕr′ê·bĕl′ŭm) [L. dim. of *cerebrum*]: a part of the vertebrate brain, controlling muscular coordination.

cerebrum (sĕr′ê·brŭm) [L. brain]: a part of the vertebrate brain, especially large in mammals; controls many voluntary functions and is seat of higher mental capacities.

chaetognath, Chaetognatha (kē′tŏg·năth, -ä): (1) small marine wormlike enterocoelomate, with curved bristles on each side of mouth; (2) phylum name.

charophyte, Charophyta (kā′rô·fīt, kä·rŏf′ĭ·tä): (1) a stonewort; (2) phylum name.

chelate (kē′lāt) [Gr. *chēlē*, claw]: claw-possessing, esp. a limb or appendage.

chelicera (kê·lĭ′sĕr·ȧ): a pincerlike appendage in a subphylum of arthropods (chelicerates).

chemolithotroph (kĕm′ô·lĭth′ô·trŏf) [Gr. *lithos*, stone]: an organism which manufactures food with the aid of energy obtained from chemicals and with inorganic raw materials.

chemoorganotroph (kĕm′ô·ôr·găn′ô·trŏf): an organism which manufactures food with the aid of energy obtained from chemicals and with organic raw materials.

chemosynthesis (kĕm′ô·sĭn′thê·sĭs): a form of autotrophic nutrition in certain bacteria, in which energy for the manufacture of carbohydrates is obtained from inorganic raw materials.

chemotropism (kĕ·mŏt′rô·pĭz′m): the growth or movement response of organisms to chemical stimuli.

chitin (kī′tĭn): a horny organic substance forming the exoskeleton of arthropods, the epidermal cuticle or other surface structures of many other invertebrates, and the cell walls of Protista such as certain fungi.

chloragogue (klô′rȧ·gŏg) [Gr. *agōgos*, leader]: excretory cell in annelids and some other invertebrates, leading wastes from body fluids to epidermis.

chlorocruorin (klô′rô·krōō′ôr·ĭn) [L. *cruor*, blood, gore]: green blood pigment in the plasma of certain annelids.

chloroplast, chlorophyll, chlorophyte (klō′rô-): (1) chlorophyll-containing plastid; (2) green light-trapping pigment essential as electron donor in photosynthesis; (3) a green alga, member of the phylum Chlorophyta.

cholinergic (kō′lĭn·ûrjik): refers to a type of nerve fiber which releases acetycholine from the axon terminal when impulses are transmitted across synapses.

Chondrichthyes (kŏn·drĭk'thĭ·ēz): fishes with cartilage skeleton, a class of vertebrates comprising sharks, skates, rays, and related types.

Chordata (kôr·dā'tȧ): animal phylum in which all members possess notochord, dorsal nerve cord, and pharyngeal gill slits at least at some stage of life cycle; three subphyla, the Urochordata, Cephalochordata, and Vertebrata.

chorion (kō'rĭ·ŏn) [Gr.]: one of the extraembryonic membranes in reptiles, birds, and mammals; forms outer cover around embryo and all other membranes and in mammals contributes to structure of placenta.

choroid (kō'roid): mid-layer in wall of vertebrate eyeball, between retina and sclera; carries blood supply to eye and contains light-absorbing black pigment; also blood–vessel—carrying membranes in vertebrate brain.

chromatophore (krō'mȧ·tô·fōr'): pigment-containing body; specifically applied to chlorophyll-bearing granules in bacteria and to pigment cells in animals.

chromoplast (krō'mô·plăst): a pigmented plastid which does not contain chlorophyll; carotenoids are among pigments usually present.

chromosome (krō'mô·sōm): gene-containing filamentous body in cell nucleus, becoming conspicuous during mitosis and meiosis; the number of chromosomes per cell nucleus is constant for each species.

chrysophyte, Chrysophyta (krĭs'ô·fĭt) [Gr. *chrysos,* gold]: (1) a golden-brown alga, for example, a diatom; (2) phylum name.

Ciliophora (sĭl'ĭ·ôf'ô·rȧ) [L. *cilium,* eyelid]: a protozoan subphylum, in which member organisms possess cilia on body surface; includes ciliates, for example, *Paramecium.*

cilium (sĭl'ĭ·ŭm): microscopic bristlelike variant of a flagellum, present on surfaces of many cell types and capable of vibratory motion; functions in cellular locomotion and in creation of currents in water.

circinate (sûr'sĭ·nāt) [Gr. *kirkinos,* circle]: rolled up along an axis, with the apex as center, as in young fern leaves.

circumnutation (sûr'kŭm·nû·tā'shŭn): curve or ellipse described by growing portion of a plant; akin to twining.

cirrus (sĭr'ŭs) [L. tuft, fringe]: a movable tuft or fingerlike projection from a cell or a body surface.

cleistothecium (klĭs'tô·thē'shĭ·ŭm) [Gr. *kleistos,* closed]: fruiting body without opening in ascomycetous fungi.

cloaca (klô·ā'kȧ) [L. sewer]: exit chamber from alimentary system; also serves as exit for excretory and/or reproductive system.

Cnidaria (nĪ·dā'rĭ·ȧ) [Gr. *knidē,* nettle]: coelenterates; the phylum of cnidoblast-possessing animals.

cnidoblast (nĪ'dô·blăst): stinging cell characteristic of coelenterates; contains nematocyst.

cnidocil (nĪ'dô·sĭl): spike or hair trigger on cnidoblast serving in nematocyst discharge.

coccine (kŏk'sēn) [Gr. *kokkos,* grain]: pertaining to sessile protistan state of existence in which reproduction does not take place during vegetative condition.

coccus (kŏk'ŭs), pl. **cocci** (kŏk'sī): a spherical bacterium.

cochlea (kŏk'lê·ȧ) [Gr. *kochlias,* snail]: part of the inner ear of mammals, coiled like a snail shell; houses the organ of Corti.

coelenterate (sê·lĕn'tēr·ât): an invertebrate animal possessing a single alimentary opening and tentacles with sting cells, for example, jellyfish, corals, sea anemones, hydroids.

coelom (sē'lŏm): body cavity lined entirely by mesoderm, especially by peritoneum.

coenobium (sê·nō'bĭ·ŭm): colonial aggregate of independent protistan cells held together by a common sheath, with cells arranged in an orderly pattern.

coenocyte (sē'nô·sĪt): a multinucleate cell found particularly among Protista.

coenosarc (sē'nô·särk): the living parts of a coelenterate hydroid colony, as distinguished from external secreted perisarc.

coenzyme (kō·ĕn'zĪm): a cofactor, usually organic, required if a given enzyme is to be active.

cofactor (kō·făk'tēr): a required participant in many reactions; usually a mineral ion or a coenzyme.

coleoptile (kō'lê·ŏp'tĭl) [Gr. *koleos,* sheath]: the tissue mantle surrounding a shoot of plants such as oats.

collenchyma (kŏ·lĕng'kĭ·mȧ) [Gr. *kolla,* glue]: a slightly specialized type of plant cell, elongated, with walls somewhat thickened, especially at the angles; frequently present as support in maturing plant tissues.

colloblast (kŏl'ô·blăst): adhesive cell type in tentacles of ctenophores.

colloid (kŏl'oid): a substance divided into fine particles, where each particle is larger than one of a true solution but smaller than one in a coarse suspension; a colloidal system contains particles of appropriate size and a medium in which the particles are dispersed.

colon (kō'lŏn): the large intestine of mammals; portion of alimentary tract between caecum and rectum.

colostrum (kô·lŏs′trŭm): the first, lymphlike secretion of the mammary glands of pregnant mammals.

columella (kŏl′ū·mĕl′a) [L. little column]: an axial shaft within a sporangium or a capsule.

commensal, commensalism (kŏ·mĕn′săl, -ĭz′m) [L. *cum,* with, + *mensa,* table]: (1) an organism living symbiotically with a host, where the host neither benefits nor suffers from the association; (2) noun.

compound (kŏm′pound) [L. *componere,* to put together]: a combination of atoms or ions in definite ratios, held together by chemical bonds.

conceptacle (kŏn·sĕp′ta·k′l) [L. *conceptaculum,* container]: a cavity containing gametangia, as in *Fucus.*

conidium, conidiophore (kô·nĭd′ĭ·ŭm, -ô·fōr′) [Gr. *konis,* dust]: (1) one of a linear series of spores formed on a conidiophore; (2) a spore-producing branch hypha in fungi.

conjugation (kŏn·joo·gă′shŭn) [L. *conjugare,* to unite]: a mating process characterized by the temporary fusion of the mating partners; occurs in various Protista; (2) alternation of double and single bonds in a chemical compound.

convergence (kŏn·vûr′jĕns) [L. *convergere,* to turn together]: the evolution of similar characteristics in organisms of widely different ancestry.

Copepoda (kō′pê·pŏd·a) [Gr. *kope,* oar]: a subclass of crustaceans.

corm (kôrm) [Gr. *kormos,* tree trunk]: an axially shortened and enlarged underground stem.

corolla (kô·rōl′a) [L. little crown]: the whorl of petals in a flower.

corona (kô·rō′na) [L. garland, crown]: any wreath or circlet of cilia, tentacles, or cells.

corpus allatum (kôr′pŭs a·lā′tŭm) pl. **corpora allata** [L. added body]: endocrine gland in insect head, behind brain, secreting hormone inducing larval molt.

corpus callosum (kôr′pŭs ka·lō′sŭm) pl. **corpora callosa** [L. hard body]: broad tract of transverse nerve fibers uniting cerebral hemispheres in mammals.

corpuscle (kôr′pŭs′l) [L. dim. of *corpus,* body]: a small, rounded structure, cell, or body; for example, blood corpuscle, renal corpuscle.

corpus luteum (kôr′pŭs lū′tê·ŭm) pl. **corpora lutea** [L. yellow body]: progesterone-secreting bodies in vertebrate ovaries, formed from remnants of follicles after ovulation.

cortex (kôr′tĕks) pl. **cortices** [L. bark]: the outer layers of an organ or body part, for example, adrenal cortex, cerebral cortex, stem cortex.

costa (kŏs′ta) [L. rib, side]: a rib or riblike supporting structure.

cotyledon (kŏt′ĭ·lē′dŭn) [Gr. *kotylēdōn,* a cup shape]: the first leaf of a seed plant, developed by the embryo within the seed.

cotylosaur (kŏt′ĭ·lô sôr′) [Gr. *kotylē,* something hollow]: a member of a group of Permian fossil reptiles, evolved from labyrinthodont amphibian stock and ancestral to all other reptiles.

coxopodite, coxal (kŏks·ô′pô·dĭt, kŏk′săl) [L. *coxa,* hip]: (1) the first, most basal joint of a segmental appendage of arthropods; (2) adjective.

Craniata (krā′nĭ·ā′ta) [Gr. *kranion,* skull]: head-possessing chordates, that is, vertebrates.

cretinism (krē′tĭn·ĭz′m) [fr. L. *christianus,* a Christian]: an abnormal condition resulting from under-activity of the thyroid in the young mammal, specifically man.

crinoid (krī′noid) [Gr. *krinoeides,* lilylike]: a member of a class of echinoderms; a sea lily or feather star; also used as adjective.

Crustacea (krŭs·tā′shē·a) [L. *crusta,* shell, rind]: a class of mandibulate arthropods; crustaceans.

Cryptophyceae (krĭp′tô·fī′sê·ē) [Gr. *kryptos,* hidden]: a class of algae, vaguely related to dinoflagellates.

crystalloid (krĭs′tăl·oid) [Gr. *krystallos,* ice]: a system of particles within a medium, able to form crystals under appropriate conditions; a true solution.

Ctenophora (tê·nŏf′ô·rä): a phylum of radiate animals characterized by comb plates; the comb jellies.

CTP: abbreviation of cytidine triphosphate.

cutaneous (kû·tā′nê·ŭs) [L. *cutis,* skin]: pertaining to the skin; for example, cutaneous sense organ.

Cyanophyta (sī′·ă·nŏf′·ĭta): the moneran phylum of blue-green algae.

cyclosis (sī·klō′sĭs) [Gr. *kyklos,* circle]: circular streaming and eddying of cytoplasm.

cyphonautes (sī′fŏ·nôt′ēs) [Gr. *kyphos,* crooked, + *nautēs,* sailor]: a larva of ectoprocts.

cytidine (di-, tri-) phosphates (sī′tĭ·dēn): cytosine-ribose-phosphates (CDP, CTP) functioning in some energy transfers in cells.

cytidylic acid: equivalent to cytosine monophosphate, or CMP.

cytochrome (sī′tô·krōm): one of a group of iron-containing hydrogen carriers in aerobic respiration.

cytolysis (sī·tŏl′ĭ·sĭs): dissolution or disintegration of a cell.

cyton (sī′tŏn): the nucleus-containing main portion (cell body) of a neuron.

cytoplasm (sī′tô·plăz′m): the living matter of a cell between cell membrane and nucleus.

cytosine (sī′tô·sēn): a nitrogen base present in nucleotides and nucleic acids.

deamination (dē·ămĭ·nā′shŭn): removal of an amino group, especially from an amino acid.

decapod (dĕk′ä·pŏd) [Gr. *deka*, ten]: 10-footed animal, specifically decapod (malacostracan) crustacean (for example, lobster), decapod (cephalopod) mollusk (for example, squid); order Decapoda; also used as adjective.

decarboxylation (dē·kär·bŏk′sĭ·lā′shŭn): removal of a carboxyl group (—COOH).

deciduous (dē·sĭd′ū̱·ŭs) [L. *decidere*, to fall off]: to fall off at maturity, as in trees which shed foliage during the autumn.

dedifferentiation (dē′dĭf·ēr·ĕn′shĭ·ā′shŭn): a regressive change toward a more primitive, embryonic, or earlier state; for example, a process changing a highly specialized cell to a less specialized cell.

degrowth (dē′grōth): negative growth; becoming smaller.

dehydrogenase (dē·hī′drŏ·jĕn·ās): an enzyme promoting dehydrogenation.

denaturation (dē·nā′tûr·ā′shŭn): disruption of the tertiary or secondary structure of a protein molecule.

dendrite (dĕn′drīt) [Gr. *dendron*, tree]: filamentous outgrowth of a nerve cell, conducting nerve impulses from its free end toward the cell body.

denitrify, denitrification (dē·nī′trĭ·fī): (1) to convert nitrates to ammonia and molecular nitrogen, as by denitrifying bacteria; (2) noun.

denticle (dĕn′tĭ·k′l) [L. *denticulus*, small tooth]: small toothlike scale on shark skin.

deoxyribose (dē·ŏk′sĭ·rī′bōs): a 5-carbon sugar having one oxygen atom less than parent-sugar ribose; component of deoxyribose nucleic acid (DNA).

Deuterostomia (dū′tēr·ô·stō′mē·à) [Gr. *deuteros*, second]: animals in which blastopore becomes anus and mouth forms as second embryonic opening opposite blastopore.

diabetes (dī′à·bē′tēz) [Gr. *diabainein*, to pass through]: abnormal condition marked by insufficiency of insulin, sugar excretion in urine, high blood-glucose levels.

diastole (dī·ăs′tô·lē) [Gr. *diastolē*, moved apart]: phase of relaxation of atria or ventricles, during which they fill with blood; preceded and succeeded by systole, that is, contraction.

diastrophism (dī·ăs′trô·fiz′m) [Gr. *diastrophē*, distortion]: geologic deformation of the earth's crust, leading to rise of land masses.

dichotomy (dī·kŏt′ô·mĭ) [Gr. *dicha*, in two + *temnein*, to cut]: a repeatedly bifurcating pattern of branching.

dicotyledon (dī·kŏt′ĭ·lē′dŭn) [Gr. *kotylēdōn*, a cup shape]: a plant having two seed leaves or cotyledons; often abbreviated as dicot.

dictyostele (dĭk′tĭ·ô·stē′lē): a type of stele in which the vascular tissue is arranged in cylindrically placed bundles.

diencephalon (dī′ĕn·sĕf′a·lŏn) [Gr. *enkephalos*, brain]: hind portion of the vertebrate forebrain.

differentiation (dĭf′ēr·ĕn′shĭ·ā′shŭn): a progressive change toward a permanently more mature or advanced state; for example, a process changing a relatively unspecialized cell to a more specialized cell.

diffusion (dĭ·fū′zhŭn) [L. *diffundere*, to pour out]: migration of particles from a more concentrated to a less concentrated region; the process tends to equalize concentrations throughout a system.

dimorphism (dī·môr′fĭz′m): difference of form between two members of a species, for example, as between males and females; a special instance of polymorphism.

Dinophyceae (dī′nô·fī′sê·ē): a class of Pyrrophyta.

dioecious (dī·ē′shŭs) [Gr. *oikos*, house]: with megaspores and microspores produced in different individuals among heterosporous plants.

dipleurula (dī·ploor′ŭ·là): hypothetical ancestral form of most deuterostomial animals, resembling developmental stage of hemichordates and echinoderms.

diplococcus (dĭp′lô·kŏk′ŭs): member of a bacterial colony composed of two joined cocci.

diplohaplontic (dĭp′lô·hăp·lŏn′tĭk): designating a life cycle with sporogenic meiosis, that is, with alternation of diploid and haploid generations.

diploid (dĭp′loid): a chromosome number twice that characteristic of a gamete of a given species.

diplontic (dĭp·lŏn′tĭk): designating a life cycle with gametogenic meiosis, that is, with diploid adults.

diplophase (dĭp′lô·fāz): a phase in the life cycle of ascomycetous and basidiomycetous fungi characterized by binucleate conditions, the nuclei of a pair being of opposite sex type; the phase between plasmogamy and karyogamy; also called *dikaryophase*.

disaccharide (dī·săk′à·rīd) [Gr. *sakcharon*, sugar]: a sugar composed of two monosaccharides; usually refers to 12-carbon sugars.

dissociation (dĭ·sô′sĭ·ā′shŭn) [L. *dissociare*, to dissociate]: the breakup of a covalent compound in water, resulting in the formation of free ions.

diurnal (dī·ûr′năl) [L. *diurnalis*, daily]: for example, as in daily up and down migration of plankton in response to absence or presence of sunlight.

divergence (dī·vûr′jĕns) [L. *divergere*, to incline apart]: evolutionary development of dissimilar characteristics in two or more lines descended from the same ancestral stock.

diverticulum (dī′vēr·tĭk′ŭ lŭm) [L. byway]: branch or

sac off a canal or tube; for example, digestive diverticulum.

DNA: abbreviation of deoxyribose nucleic acid.

doliolaria (dŏ·lǐ·ô·lā'rǐ·à) [L. *dolium,* small cask]: yolky barrel-shaped larva of crinoid echinoderms and transient larval stage in holothuroid development.

dominance: a functional attribute of genes; a dominant gene exerts its full effect regardless of the effect of its allelic partner.

DPN: abbreviation of diphosphopyridine nucleotide, a hydrogen carrier in respiration; now called NAD, (see below).

ductus arteriosus (dŭk'tŭs är·tē'rǐ·ô'sŭs): an artery present in the embryo and fetus of mammals which conducts blood from the pulmonary artery to the aorta; shrivels at birth, when the lungs become functional.

duodenum (dū'ô·dē'nŭm) [L. *duodeni,* twelve each]: most anterior portion of the small intestine of vertebrates; continuation of the stomach, bile duct and pancreatic duct open into it.

Echinodermata (ê·kī'nô·dûr'mà·tà): the phylum of spiny-skinned animals; includes starfishes, sea urchins.

Echiuroida (ê·kī'ûr·oi'dà): a phylum of wormlike, schizocoelomate animals, characterized by spines at hind end.

ectoderm (ĕk'tô-): outer tissue layer of an animal embryo.

Ectoprocta (ĕk'tô·prŏk·tà): a phylum of sessile coelomate animals, in which the intestine is U-shaped, the mouth is surrounded by a lophophore with ciliated tentacles, and the anus opens outside this lophophore.

egestion (ê·jĕs'chŭn) [L. *egerere,* to discharge]: the elimination from the alimentary system of unusable and undigested material.

elasmobranch (ê·lăs'mô·brăngk) [Gr. *elasmos,* plate]: a member of a subclass of cartilage fishes (sharks and rays); also used as adjective.

elater (ĕl'à·tẽr) [Gr. *elatēr,* driver]: a hygroscopic filament in the capsule of spore-bearing plants; functioning in spore dispersal.

electrolyte (ê·lĕk'trô·līt) [Gr. *ēlektron,* amber]: a substance which dissociates into ions in aqueous solution and so makes possible the conduction of electric current through the solution.

electron (ê·lĕk'trŏn): a subatomic, or elementary, particle, representing a unit of negative electric charge; orbits around atomic nucleus.

electrophoresis (ê·lĕk'trô·fô·rē'sĭs): the migration of ampholytes such as proteins in an electric field, until the isoelectric point is attained.

element (ĕl'ê·mĕnt): one of about 100 distinct natural or man-made types of matter, which, singly or in combination, compose all materials of the universe; an atom is the smallest representative unit of an element.

elytron (ĕl'ĭ·trŏn) pl. **elytra** [Gr. cover, sheath]: for example, the hardened forewings of beetles.

embolus (ĕm'bô·lŭs) [Gr. *embolos,* peg, stopper]: blood clot formed within a blood vessel.

emboly (ĕm'bô·lĭ): invaginative gastrulation.

embryo (ĕm'brĭ·ō) [Gr. *en* in, + *bryein,* to swell]: an early developmental stage of an organism, produced from a fertilized egg.

emulsion (ê·mŭl'shŭn) [L. *emulgere,* to milk out]: a colloidal system in which both the dispersed and the continuous phase are liquid.

enantiomer (ĕn·ăn'tĭ·ô·mēr): equivalent to optical isomer, that is, one of a group of compounds identical in chemical structure but differing in optical activity.

endemic (ĕn·dĕm'ĭk) [Gr. belonging to a district]: pertaining to a limited locality; ecologically, occurring in a particular region only; opposite of cosmopolitan.

endergonic (ĕn'dēr·gŏ·nĭk): energy-requiring, as in a chemical reaction.

endocrine (ĕn'·dô·krīn) [Gr. *krinein,* to separate]: applied to type of gland which releases secretion not through a duct but directly into blood or lymph; functionally equivalent to hormone-producing.

endoderm, endodermis (ĕn'dô·dûrm): (1) inner tissue layer of an embryo; (2) single layer of tissue in a root or stem which separates the cortex from the stele; the layer is waterproofed with suberin, but contains nonwaterproofed passage cells.

endoplasm, endoplasmic (ĕn'dô·plăz'm): (1) the inner portion of the cytoplasm of a cell, that is, the portion immediately surrounding the nucleus; contrasts with ectoplasm or cortex, that is, the portion of cytoplasm immediately under the cell surface; (2) adjective.

endosperm (ĕn'dô·spûrm): triploid, often nutritive tissue within seed, formed by union of one sperm nucleus with two nuclei of female gametophyte.

endospore (ĕn'dô·spōr): a resting cell commonly formed in Monera by the walling off of a central portion of a vegetative cell.

energy (ĕn'ēr·jĭ) [Gr. *energos,* active]: capacity to do work; the time rate of doing work is called power.

enterocoel, enterocoelomate (ĕn'tēr·ô·sēl'): (1) a coelom formed by the outpouching of a mesodermal sac from the endoderm; (2) an animal possessing an enterocoel, for example, echinoderms, vertebrates.

enterokinase (ĕn'tēr·ô·kī'nās) [Gr. *kinētos,* moving]:

an enzyme present in intestinal juice of vertebrates; it converts trypsinogen into trypsin.

enteropneust (ĕn′tēr·ôp·nūst) [Gr. *pnein,* to breathe]: a member of a class of hemichordates; an acorn worm.

enthalpy (ĕn′thăl·pĭ) [Gr. *enthalpein,* to warm in]: a measure of the amount of energy in a reacting system.

Entoprocta (ĕn′tô·prŏk′ta): a phylum of sessile, pseudocoelomate animals, possessing a U-shaped alimentary tract, a mouth surrounded by a ring of ciliated tentacles, and an anus opening within this ring.

entropy (ĕn′trô·pĭ) [Gr. *entropia,* transformation]: a measure of the distribution of energy in a reacting system.

enzyme (ĕn′zīm) [Gr. *en,* in + *zymē,* leaven]: a protein produced within an organism, capable of accelerating a particular chemical reaction; a type of catalyst.

ephyra (ĕf′ĭ·ra) [L. a nymph]: free-swimming larval stage in scyphozoan coelenterates; larval jellyfish.

epiboly (ê·pĭb′ô·lĭ) [Gr. *epibolē,* throwing over]: gastrulation by overgrowth of animal region over vegetal region of embryo.

epidermis (ĕp′ĭ·dûr′mĭs): the outermost surface tissue of an organism.

epididymis (ĕp′ĭ·dĭd′ĭ·mĭs) [Gr. *didymos,* testicle]: the greatly coiled portion of the sperm duct adjacent to the mammalian testis.

epiglottis (ĕp′ĭ·glŏt′ĭs) [Gr. *glōssa,* tongue]: a flap of tissue above the mammalian glottis; contains elastic cartilage, and in swallowing folds back over the glottis, so closing the air passage of the lungs.

epinasty (ĕp′ĭ·năs′tĭ) [Gr. *nastos,* pressed together]: faster growth on the upper or inner surface of a leaf or other flattened plant part, leading to outfolding.

epiphyte (ê′pĭ·fīt): a plant living commensalistically on another plant.

epitheca (ĕp′ĭ·thē′ka): the larger half or valve of the shell of a diatom.

epithelium (ĕp′ĭ·thē′lĭ·ŭm) [Gr. *thēlē,* nipple]: animal tissue type in which the cells are packed tightly together, leaving little intercellular space.

esophagus (ê·sŏf′a·gŭs) [Gr. *oisō,* I shall carry]: part of alimentary tract connecting pharynx and stomach.

estrogen (ĕs′trô·jĕn) [Gr. *oistros,* frenzy]: one of a group of female sex hormones of vertebrates.

estrus (ĕs′trŭs) [L. *oestrus,* gadfly]: egg production and fertilizability in mammals; for example, estrus cycle, monestrous, polyestrous.

etiolation (ē′tĭ·ô·lā′shŭn) [F. *étioler,* to blanch]: pathological condition in plants produced by pro-

longed absence of light; characterized by whitened leaves, excessively long, weak stems.

eurypterid (ū·rĭp′tēr·ĭd) [Gr. *eurys,* wide]: extinct Paleozoic chelicerate arthropod.

Eustachian (û·stā′kĭ·an): applied to canal connecting middle-ear cavity with the nasopharynx of mammals.

eustele (ū′stēl): a type of dictyostele derived from a siphonostele; in a vascular bundle, phloem is on the outside, xylem on the inside.

exergonic (ĕk′sēr·gŏ·nĭk): energy-yielding, as in a chemical reaction.

exocrine (ĕk′sô·krīn): applied to type of gland which releases secretion through a duct.

exteroceptor (ĕk′stēr·ô·sĕp′tēr): a sense organ receptive to stimuli from external environment.

FAD: abbreviation of flavin adenine dinucleotide.

feces (fē′sēz) [L. *faeces,* dregs]: waste matter discharged from the alimentary system.

femur, femoral (fē′mēr, fĕm′ô·răl) [L. *thigh*]: (1) thighbone of vertebrates, between pelvis and knee: (2) adjective.

fermentation (fûr′mĕn·tā′shŭn): synonym for anaerobic respiration, that is, fuel combustion in the absence of oxygen.

fetus (fē′tŭs) [L. offspring]: prenatal stage of development in man and other mammals, following the embryonic stage; in man, roughly from third month of pregnancy to birth.

fiber (fī′bēr) [L. *fibra,* thread]: a strand or filament produced by cells but located outside cells; a type of sclerenchyma cell.

fibril (fī′brĭl) [L. dim. of *fibra*]: a strand or filament produced by cells and located within cells.

fibrin, fibrinogen (fī′brĭn, fī·brĭn′ô·jĕn): (1) coagulated blood protein forming the bulk of a blood clot in vertebrates; (2) a protein present in blood which upon coagulation forms a clot.

fibula (fĭb′û·lă) [L. buckle]: the usually thinner of the two bones between knee and ankle in the vertebrate hind limb.

filopodium (fī·lô·pō′dĭ·ŭm) [L. *filum,* thread]: a filamentous type of pseudopodium in sarcodine protozoa.

flagellate, flagellum (flăj′e·lāt, -ŭm) [L. whip]: (1) equipped with one or more flagella; an organism possessing flagella; (2) a microscopic, whiplike filament serving as locomotor structure in flagellate cells.

flavin: multiple-ring compound present as component in riboflavin and hydrogen carriers such as FAD and FMN.

floridean (flô·rĭd′ê·ăn): pertaining to Florideae, or red algae generally.

florigen (flô′rĭ·jĕn): flowering hormone, believed to be produced as a result of appropriate photoperiodic treatment of plants.

fluorescence (floo͞'ô·rĕs'ĕns) [L. *fluere*, to flow]: emission of radiation (light) by a substance that has absorbed radiation from another source.

FMN: abbreviation of flavin mononucleotide.

follicle (fŏl'ĭ·k'l) [L. *folliculus*, small ball]: ball of cells; as in egg-containing balls within ovaries of many animals, or cellular balls at base of hair or feather.

Foraminiferida, foraminifera (fŏ·rămĭ·nĭ'fĕr'ĭ·dȧ, -nĭf'ĕr·ȧ) [L. *foramen*, hole]: an order of sarcodine protozoa, characterized by delicate calcareous shells with holes through which pseudopods are extruded.

fovea centralis (fō'vē·ȧ sĕn·trā'lĭs) [L. central pit]: small area in optic center of mammalian retina; only cone cells are present here and stimulation leads to most acute vision.

fucoxanthin (fū'kô·zăn'thĭn): a brownish pigment found in diatoms, brown algae, and dinoflagellates.

funiculus (fū·nĭk'ū·lŭs) [L. dim. of *funis*, rope]: tissue strand, as in attachment of stomach to body wall of ectoprocts.

gamete (găm'ēt): reproductive cell which must fuse with another before it can develop; sex cell.

gametophyte (găm·ē'tô·fīt): a gamete-producing plant; phase of life cycle in diplohaplontic organisms which alternates with a sporophyte phase.

ganglion (găng'glĭ·ŭn) [Gr. a swelling]: an aggregated collection of cell bodies of neurons typically less complex than a brain.

ganoid (găn'oid) [Gr. *ganos*, brightness]: pertaining to shiny, enamel-covered type of fish scale.

gastrin (găs'trĭn): a hormone produced by the stomach wall of mammals when food makes contact with the wall; stimulates other parts of the wall to secrete gastric juice.

Gastropoda (găs·trŏp'ô·dȧ): a class of mollusks; comprises snails and slugs.

Gastrotricha (găs'trŏt'rĭ·kȧ): class of minute, aquatic, pseudocoelomate animals, possessing cilialike bristles on the ventral side and often elsewhere; members of the phylum Aschelminthes.

gastrula, gastrulation (găs'troo·lȧ, -lā'shŭn): (1) a two-layered and later three-layered stage in the embryonic development of animals; (2) the process of gastrula formation.

gel (jĕl) [L. *gelare*, to freeze]: quasi-solid state of a colloidal system, where the solid particles form the continuous phase and the liquid forms the discontinuous phase.

gemma (jĕm'ȧ) [L. a bud]: cup-shaped vegetative bud in bryophytes, capable of developing into whole plant.

gemmule (jĕm'ūl): vegetative, multicellular bud of (largely freshwater) sponges.

gene (jēn): a segment of a chromosome, definable in operational terms: repository of a unit of genetic information.

genome (jēn'ōm): the totality of genes in a haploid set of chromosomes, hence the sum of all different genes in a cell.

genotype (jĕn'ô·tīp): the particular set of genes present in an organism and its cells; the genetic constitution.

genus (jē'nŭs) [L. race]: a rank category in taxonomic classification between species and family; a group of very closely related species.

geotropism (jē·ŏt'rô·pĭz'm) [Gr. *tropē*, a turning]: behavior governed and oriented by gravity, for example, growth of roots toward center of earth.

gestation (jĕs·tā'shŭn): process or period of carrying young in uterus.

globulin (glŏb'ū·lĭn): one of a class of proteins present in blood plasma of vertebrates; may function as antibody.

glochidia (glô·kĭd'ĭȧ) [Gr. *glochis*, arrow point]: pincer-equipped bivalve larvae of freshwater clams, parasitic on fish.

glomerulus (glô·mĕr'ū·lŭs) [L. dim. of *glomus*, ball]: small meshwork of blood capillaries or channels; for example, in the nephron of vertebrates, the renal organ of hemichordates.

glottis (glŏt'ĭs) [Gr. *glōssa*, tongue]: slitlike opening in the mammalian larynx, formed by the vocal cords.

glucogenic (gloo͞'kô·jĕn'ĭk): glucose-producing, especially amino acids which, after deamination, metabolize like carbohydrates.

glucose (gloo͞'kōs): a 6-carbon sugar; principal form in which carbohydrates are transported from cell to cell.

glycerin (glĭs'ĕr·ĭn): an organic compound possessing a 3-carbon skeleton; may unite with fatty acids and form a fat.

glycogen (glī'kô·jĕn): a polysaccharide consisting of joined glucose units; a principal storage form of carbohydrates.

glycolysis (glī·kŏl'ĭ·sĭs): respiratory breakdown of glucose (or starch or glycogen) to pyruvic acid; anaerobic respiration of carbohydrates.

glycoside (glī'kô·sīd): a molecule consisting of two or more monosaccharides.

goiter (goi'tĕr) [L. *guttur*, throat]: an enlargement of the thyroid gland; may be an overgrowth resulting in excessive secretion of thyroid hormone or may be a compensatory overgrowth occasioned by undersecretion of thyroid hormone.

Golgi body (gôl'jē): a cytoplasmic organelle playing

a role in the manufacture of certain cell secretions.

gonad (gōn′ăd) [Gr. *gonē*, generator]: animal reproductive organ; collective term for testes and ovaries.

gradation (grâ·dā′shŭn) [L. *gradus*, step]: leveling of land by the geological effects of erosion.

granum (grăn′ŭm) [L. grain]: a functional unit of a chloroplast; smallest particle capable of carrying out photosynthesis.

guanine (gŭ′â·nēn): a purine component of nucleotides and nucleic acids.

guanosine (di-, tri-) phosphates (gū·â′nô·sēn): guanine-ribose-phosphates (GDP, GTP) functioning in some energy transfers in cells.

guanylic acid: equivalent to guanosine monophosphate, or GMP.

guttation (gŭ·tā′shŭn) [L. *gutta*, drop]: extrusion of water droplets from leaf pores by root pressure.

gymnosperm (jĭm′nô·spûrm): a plant belonging to a class of seed plants in which the seeds are not enclosed in an ovary; includes the conifers.

haem-: see *hem-*.

haploid (hăp′loid): a chromosome number characteristic of a mature gamete of a given species.

haplontic (hăp·lŏn′tĭk): designating a life cycle with zygotic meiosis and haploid adults.

haplophase (hăp′lô·fāz): a uninucleate phase in the life cycle of ascomycetous and basidiomycetous fungi; the phase between the meiospore and the succeeding plasmogamy; also called *monokaryophase*.

haplostele (hăp′lô·stēl): the simplest type of protostele, with central xylem and surrounding phloem.

hectocotylus (hĕk′tô kŏt′ĭ·lŭs) [Gr. *hekto-*, hundred, + *kōtylē*, cup]: modified arm of male cephalopod mollusks serving in sperm transfer to female.

helix (hē′liks) [L. a spiral]: spiral shape; for example, polypeptide chain, snail shell.

heme (hēm): an iron-containing, red, cyclic pyrrol pigment.

Hemichordata (hĕm′ĭ·kŏr dā′tà): a phylum of deuterostomial, enterocoelomate animals.

hemoglobin (hē′mô·glō′bĭn) [L. *globus*, globe]: oxygen-carrying constituent of blood; consists of red pigment heme and protein globin.

hemophilia (hē′mô fĭl′ĭà) [Gr. *philos*, loving]: a hereditary disease in man characterized by excessive bleeding from even minor wounds; clotting mechanism is impaired by failure of blood platelets to rupture after contact with torn edges of blood vessels.

hepatic (hê·păt′ĭk) [Gr. *hēpar*, liver]: pertaining to the liver; as in hepatic vein, hepatic portal vein.

herbivore (hûr′bĭ·vôr) [L. *herba*, herb + *vorare*, to devour]: a plant-eating animal.

hermaphrodite (hûr·măf′rô·dīt) [fr. Gr. *Hermes* + *Aphrodite*]: an organism possessing both male and female reproductive structures.

heterocyst (hĕt′ēr·ô·sĭst′) colorless cell in filamentous blue-green algae, permitting easy fragmentation of a filament.

heterosporous (hĕt′ēr·ôs′pô·rŭs): producing two different types of spores, namely, microspores and megaspores; microspores give rise to male gametophytes, megaspores to female gametophytes.

heterothallic (hĕt′ēr·ô·thăl′ĭk): hermaphroditic and cross-fertilizing; applied primarily to fungi.

heterotroph, heterotrophism (hĕt′ēr·ô·trŏf): (1) an organism which must obtain both inorganic and organic raw materials from the environment; (2) form of nutrition characteristic of heterotrophs.

heterozygote, heterozygous (hĕt′ēr·ô·zī′gōt): (1) an organism in which a pair of alleles for a given trait consists of different (for example, dominant and recessive) kinds of genes; (2) adjective.

holothuroid (hŏl·ô·thū′·roid) [L. *holothuria*, water polyp]: a member of a class of echinoderms; a sea cucumber; also used as adjective.

holotroph, holotrophism (hō′lô·trŏf): (1) a bulk-feeding organism in which nutrition includes the process of alimentation; an animal; (2) form of nutrition characteristic of animals.

hominid (hŏm′ĭ·nĭd) [L. *homo*, man]: a living or extinct man or manlike type; the family of man or pertaining to this family.

hominoid (hŏm′ĭ·noid): a superfamily including hominids, the family of man, and pongids, the family of apes, living or extinct.

homology (hô·mŏl′ô·jĭ) [Gr. *homologia*, agreement]: similarity in embryonic development and adult structure, indicative of common evolutionary ancestry.

homosporous (hô·mŏs′pô·rŭs): producing spores of the same size or form; each gives rise either to a male or to a female gametophyte.

homothallic (hō′mô·thăl′ĭk): hermaphroditic and self-fertilizing; applied primarily to fungi.

homozygote, homozygous (hō′mô·zī′gōt): (1) an organism in which a pair of alleles for a given trait consists of the same (for example, either dominant or recessive, but not both) kinds of genes; (2) adjective.

hormogone (hôr′mô·gōn): a section of a filament of blue-green algae, located between two consecutive heterocysts.

hormone (hôr′mōn) [Gr. *hormaein*, to excite]: a secretion produced within an organism and affecting another part of that organism.

humerus (hū′mēr·ŭs) [L. shoulder]: the bone of the vertebrate upper forelimb, between shoulder and elbow.

humoral (hū′mĕr·ăl) [L. *humor*, moisture, liquid]: pertaining to body fluids, esp. biologically active chemical agents carried in body fluids; for example, hormones or similar substances.

humus (hū′mŭs) [L. soil]: the organic portion of soil.

hybrid (hī′brĭd) [L. *hibrida*, offspring of tame sow and wild boar]: an organism heterozygous for one or more (usually many) gene pairs; in chemical usage, a combination of two or more orbitals, or the descriptive formulas of a resonating compound.

hydathode (hī′dȧ·thōd) [Gr. *hydatis*, water vesicle]: channel or gland in leaf for water excretion.

hydranth (hī′drănth): flowerlike terminal part of hydroid polyp, containing mouth and tentacles; a feeding polyp.

hydrolysis (hī·drŏl′ĭ·sĭs): dissolution through the agency of water; especially decomposition of a chemical by the addition of water.

hydrophyte (hī′drô·fīt): a water plant, or one living in water-rich areas.

hydroponics (hī′drô·pŏn′ĭks) [Gr. *ponos*, labor]: growing plants without soil by immersing the roots in a nutrient-rich water medium.

hyperparasitism (hī′pĕr-): infection of a parasite by one or more other parasites.

hypertonic, hypertonicity (hī′pĕr·tŏn′ĭk): (1) exerting greater osmotic pull than the medium on the other side of a semipermeable membrane, hence possessing a greater concentration of particles and acquiring water during osmosis; (2) noun.

hypha (hī′fȧ) [Gr. *hyphē*, a web]: a filamentous structural unit of a fungus; a meshwork of hyphae forms a mycelium.

hyponasty (hī′pô·năs′tĭ) [Gr. *nastos*, pressed together]: faster growth on the lower or outer surface of a leaf or other flattened plant part, leading to infolding.

hypothalamus: a region of the forebrain, containing various centers of the autonomic nervous system.

hypotheca (hī′pô·thē′kȧ): the smaller half or valve of the shell of a diatom.

hypothesis (hī·pŏth′ê·sĭs) [Gr. *tithenai*, to put]: a guessed solution of a scientific problem; must be tested by experimentation and, if not validated, must then be discarded.

hypotonic, hypotonicity (hī′pô·tŏn′ĭk): (1) exerting lesser osmotic pull than the medium on the other side of a semipermeable membrane; hence possessing a lesser concentration of particles and losing water during osmosis; (2) noun.

ichthyosaur (ĭk′thĭ·ô·sôr): extinct marine Mesozoic reptile, with fish-shaped body and porpoiselike snout.

imago, imaginal (ĭ·mā′gō, ĭ·măj′ĭ·nȧl) [L. image]: (1) an adult insect; (2) adjective.

induction, inductor (ĭn·dŭk′shŭn) [L. *inducere*, to induce]: (1) process in animal embryo in which one tissue or body part causes the differentiation of another tissue or body part; (2) an embryonic tissue which causes the differentiation of another.

indusium (ĭn·dū′zĭ·ŭm) [L. undergarment]: tissue covering sori in ferns.

ingestion (ĭn·jĕs′chŭn) [L. *ingerere*, to put in]: intake of food from the environment into the alimentary system.

inosine (ĭn′ô·sēn): a purine, occurs in cells as inosine-ribose-phosphates (IDP, ITP) which participate in some energy-transfer reactions.

instar (ĭn′stär) [L. likeness, form]: period between consecutive molts in insect development.

insulin (ĭn′sû·lĭn) [L. *insula*, island]: a hormone produced by the islets of Langerhans in the pancreas; promotes the conversion of blood glucose into tissue glycogen.

integument (ĭn·tĕg′û·mĕnt) [L. *integere*, to cover]: covering; external coat; skin.

intermedin (ĭn·tĕr·mē′dĭn): hormone produced by the mid-portion of the pituitary gland; adjusts degree of extension of pigment cells in skin of certain vertebrates, for example, frogs.

internode (ĭn′tĕr·nōd′): section of a plant stem located between two successive nodes.

interoceptor (ĭn′tĕr·ô·sĕp′tĕr): a sense organ receptive to stimuli generated in the interior of an organism.

invagination (ĭn·vaj′ĭ·nā′shŭn) [L. *in*, in + *vagina*, sheath]: local infolding of a layer of tissue, leading to the formation of a pouch or sac; as in invagination during a type of embolic gastrulation.

invertase (ĭn·vûr′tās) [L. *invertere*, to invert]: enzyme promoting the splitting of sucrose into glucose and fructose.

ion, ionization (ī′ŏn, -ī·zā′shŭn) [Gr. *ienai*, to go]: (1) an electrically charged atom or group of atoms; (2) addition or removal of electrons from atoms.

isoelectric point: the pH at which ampholytes such as amino acids and proteins no longer migrate in an electric field.

isogamy (ī·sŏg′ȧ·mĭ): sexual fusion in which the gametes of opposite sex types are structurally alike.

isolecithal (ī′sô·lĕs′ĭ·thăl): pertaining to animal eggs with yolk evenly distributed throughout egg cytoplasm.

isomer (ī′sô·mĕr): one of a group of compounds identical in atomic composition but differing in structural arrangement (structural isomer) or optical activity (optical isomer).

isotonic (ī′sô·tŏn′ĭk): exerting same osmotic pull as medium or other side of a semipermeable membrane, hence possessing the same concentration of particles; net gain or loss of water during osmosis is zero.

isotope (ĭ′sô·tōp) [Gr. *topos,* place]: one of several possible forms of a chemical element, differing from other forms in atomic weight but not in chemical properties.

karyogamy (kăr·ĭ·ôg′·a·mĭ) [Gr. *karyon,* nut]: fusion of nuclei in process of fertilization.

keratin (kĕr′a·tĭn) [Gr. *keratos,* horn]: a protein formed by certain epidermal tissues, for example, those of vertebrate skin.

ketogenic, ketone, ketose (kē′tô·jĕn′ĭk, -tōn, -tōs): (1) keto acid–producing, especially amino acids which after deamination metabolize like fatty acids; (2) organic compound possessing a —CO— grouping; (3) one of a series of sugars characterized by a (nonterminal) ketone group.

kinetosome (kĭ·nĕt′ô·sōm) [Gr. *kinētos,* moving]: granule at base of flagellum, presumably motion-controlling.

Kinorhyncha (kĭn′ô·rĭng′ka): a class of pseudocoelomate animals; members of the phylum Aschelminthes.

labium, labial (lā′bĭ·um, -ăl) [L. lip]: (1) any liplike structure; especially underlip, posterior to mouth, in insect head; (2) adjective.

labrum (lā′brum) [L. lip]: a liplike structure; especially upper lip, anterior to mouth, in arthropod head.

labyrinthodont (lăb′ĭ rĭn′thô·dŏnt) [Gr. *labyrinthos,* labyrinth]: extinct, late-Paleozoic fossil amphibian.

lacteal (lăk′tē·al) [L. *lactis,* milk]: lymph vessel in a villus of intestinal wall of mammals.

lactogenic (lăk′tô jĕn′ĭk): milk-producing; as in lactogenic hormone, secreted by vertebrate pituitary.

lamella (la·mĕl′a) [L. small plate]: pectin-containing layer cementing adjacent plant cells in a tissue; usually called middle lamella.

lamina (lăm′ĭ·na) [L. thin plate]: the blade of a leaf.

larva (lär′vä) pl. *larvae* (-vē) [L. mask]: period in developmental history of animals between embryo and adult; the larval period begins at hatching and terminates at metamorphosis.

larynx (lăr′ĭngks) [Gr.]: voice box; sound-producing organ in mammals.

lemniscus (lĕm·nĭs′·kus) [L. a ribbon hanging down]: an elongated, paired, interior extension of the body wall in the anterior region of acanthocephalan worms.

lenticel (lĕn′tĭ·sĕl) [F. *lenticelle,* little lentil]: porous region in periderm of woody stem, aiding gas exchange.

leucocyte (lū′kô·sīt): a type of white blood cell

in vertebrates characterized by a beaded, elongated nucleus.

leucoplast (lū′kô·plăst): an unpigmented plastid; see also *amyloplast.*

leukemia (lū·kē′mĭ·a): a cancerous condition of blood, characterized by overproduction of leucocytes.

lichen (lī′kĕn) [Gr. *leichēn*]: a symbiotic, mutualistic association of an algal type and a fungal type.

lignin (lĭg′nĭn) [L. *lignum,* wood]: a complex substance present in substantial quantities in wood.

lipase (lī′pās): an enzyme promoting the conversion of fat into fatty acids and glycerin, or the reverse.

lipid, lipoid (lĭp′ĭd): (1) fat, fatty, pertaining to fat; (2) fatlike.

lithosphere (lĭth′ô·sfēr) [Gr. *lithos,* stone]: collective term for the solid, rocky component of the earth's surface layers.

littoral (lĭt′ô·răl) [L. *litus,* seashore]: the sea floor from the shore to the edge of the continental shelf.

lophophore (lō′fô·fōr) [Gr. *lophos,* crest]: tentacle-bearing arm in anterior region of certain coelomates (lophophorate animals): serves in food trapping.

luciferase, luciferin (lū·sĭf′ĕr·ās, -ĭn) [L. *lux,* light]: (1) enzyme contributing to the production of light in organisms; (2) a group of various substances essential in the production of bioluminescence.

lutein (lū′tē·ĭn) [L. *luteus,* yellow]: a yellow xanthophyll pigment.

lycopsid (lī·kŏp′sĭd) [Gr. *lykos,* wolf]: a member of a subphylum of tracheophytes; the club mosses.

lymph (lĭmf) [L. *lympha,* goddess of moisture]: the body fluid outside the blood circulation.

lymphocyte (lĭm′fô·sīt): a type of white blood cell of vertebrates characterized by a rounded or kidney-shaped nucleus.

macromolecule (măk′rô-): a molecule of very high molecular weight; refers specifically to proteins, nucleic acids, polysaccharides, and complexes of these.

macronucleus (măk′rô·nū′klē·us): a large type of nucleus found in ciliate protozoa; controls all but reproductive functions in these organisms.

madreporite (măd′rē·pô·rīt) [It. *madre,* mother, + *poro,* passage]: a sievelike opening on the surface of echinoderms, connecting the water-vascular system with the outside.

Malacostraca (măl′a·kŏs′tra·ka) [Gr. *malakostraka,* soft-shelled]: a subclass of crustaceans.

maltose (môl′tōs): a 12-carbon sugar formed by the union of two glucose units.

mandible (măn′dĭ·b'l) [L. *mandibula,* jaw]: in arthropods, one of a pair of mouth appendages, basically biting jaws; in vertebrates, the principal bone or cartilage of the lower jaw.

marsupial (mär·sū'pĭ·ăl) [Gr. *marsypion*, little bag]: a pouched mammal, member of the mammalian subclass Metatheria.

mastax (măs'tăks) [L. *masticare*, to chew]: horny, toothed chewing apparatus in pharynx of rotifers.

Mastigophora (măs'tĭ gŏf'ō·rȧ): a subphylum of primarily unicellular flagellate protozoa; zooflagellates.

maxilla (măk·sĭl'ȧ) [L.]: in arthropods, one of the head appendages; in vertebrates, one of the upper jawbones.

maxilliped (măk·sĭl'ĭ·pĕd): one of three pairs of segmental appendages in decapod crustacea, located posterior to the maxillae.

medulla (mê·dŭl'ȧ) [L.]: the inner layers of an organ or body part, for example, adrenal medulla; the medulla oblongata is a region of the vertebrate hindbrain which connects with the spinal cord.

medusa (mê·dū'sȧ): the free-swimming stage in the life cycle of coelenterates; a jellyfish.

megagametophyte (mĕg'ȧ·gȧ·mē'tô·fīt): in heterosporous plants, the gametophyte produced by a megaspore; the female gametophyte.

megaphyll (mĕg'ȧ·fĭl): a leaf with numerous vascular bundles in a vein; it leaves a leaf gap in the stele of the stem.

megasporangium (mĕg'ȧ·spô·răn'jĭ·ŭm): a sporangium which produces megaspores.

megaspore (mĕg'ȧ·spōr'): a meiospore formed in a megasporangium and developing into an megagametophyte.

megasporophyll (mĕg'ȧ·spō'rô·fĭl): a leaf or modified leaf on which a megasporangium is formed.

megastrobilus (mĕg'ȧ·strŏ'bĭ·lŭs) [Gr. *strobilos*, a pine cone]: a cone formed by a series of megasporophylls.

meiosis (mī·ō'sĭs) [Gr. *meioun*, to make smaller]: process occurring at different points in the life cycles of different organisms in which the chromosome number is reduced by half; compensates for the chromosome-doubling effect of fertilization.

meiospore (mī'ô·spōr): a spore produced by meiosis within a sporangium; it is always haploid.

melanin (mĕl'ȧ·nĭn) [Gr. *melas*, black]: black pigment of organisms; occurs in animals in cytoplasmic granules of chromatophore cells known as melanocytes.

menopause (mĕn'ô·pôz) [Gr. *menos*, month + *pauein*, to cause to cease]: the time at the end of the reproductive period of (human) females when menstrual cycles cease to occur.

menstruation (mĕn'stroo·ȧ'shŭn) [L. *mensis*, month]: the discharge of uterine tissue and blood from the vagina in man and apes at the end of a menstrual cycle in which fertilization has not occurred.

meristem (mĕr'ĭ·stĕm): embryonic tissue in plants, capable of giving rise to additional tissues.

mesencephalon (mĕs'ĕn·sĕf'ȧ·lŏn) [Gr. *enkephalos*, brain]: the vertebrate midbrain.

mesenchyme (mĕs'ĕng·kĭm) [Gr. *enchyma*, infusion]: nonepithelial mesoderm, especially abundant in embryos and in primitive adult animals; often jelly-secreting.

mesogloea (mĕs'ō·glē'ȧ) [Gr. *gloios*, glutinous substance]: the often jelly-containing layer between the ectoderm and endoderm of coelenterates and comb jellies.

mesophyll (mĕs'ō·fĭl): tissue in the interior of leaves, composed of chlorophyll-containing cells arranged either into compact layers (palisade mesophyll) or into loose aggregations (spongy mesophyll).

mesophyte (mĕs'ō·fīt): a plant adapted to live in regions with intermediate amounts of water supply.

metabolism (mē·tăb'ô·lĭz'm) [Gr. *metabolē*, change]: a group of life-sustaining processes including principally nutrition, production of energy in usable form (respiration), and synthesis of more living substance.

metabolite (mē·tăb'ô·līt): any chemical participating in metabolism; a nutrient.

metachronous (mĕt'ȧ·crō'nŭs) [Gr. *chronos*, time]: pertaining to successive beating of adjacent cilia in a row, resulting in wavelike progression of beat.

metamorphosis (mĕt'ȧ·môr'fô·sĭs) [Gr. *metamorphoun*, to transform]: transformation of a larva into an adult.

metaphase (mĕt'ȧ·fāz): a stage during mitotic division in which the chromosomes line up in a plane at right angles to the spindle axis.

Metaphyta (mē·tăf'ĭ·tȧ): a major category of living organisms, consisting of the phyla Bryophyta and Tracheophyta; the category is distinguished in part by possession of reproductive structures which are organs and by the presence of embryo stages during sporophyte development.

Metazoa (mĕt'ȧ·zō'ȧ): a major category of living organisms, consisting of all multicellular animals.

metencephalon (mĕt'ĕn·sĕf'ȧ·lŏn) [Gr. *enkephalos*, brain]: anterior portion of vertebrate hindbrain.

micrococcus (mī'krô·kŏk'ŭs): member of a type of colony of spherical bacteria in which the cells are arranged as irregular plates or clumps.

microgametophyte (mī'krô-): in heterosporous plants, the gametophyte produced by a microspore; the male gametophyte.

micron (mī'krŏn) pl. **microns, micra**: one-thousandth part of a millimeter, a unit of microscopic length.

micronucleus (mī'krô·nū'klê·ŭs): a small type of

nucleus found in ciliate protozoa; controls principally the reproductive functions of these organisms.

microphyll (mī′krô·fĭl): a leaf with a vein consisting of a single vascular bundle; it does not leave a leaf gap in the stele of the stem.

micropyle (mī′krô·pīl) [Gr. *pilē*, gate]: an opening in the integument of an ovule, permitting entry of a pollen grain or pollen tube.

microsporangium (mī′krô·spô·răn′jĭ·ŭm): a sporangium which produces microspores.

microspore (mī′krô·spōr): a meiospore formed in a microsporangium and developing into a microgametophyte; in seed plants, equivalent to pollen grain.

microsporophyll (mī′krô·spō′rô·fĭl): a leaf or modified leaf on which a microsporangium is formed.

microstrobilus: a cone formed by a series of microsporophylls.

mictic (mĭk′tĭk) [Gr. *mixis*, act of mixing]: pertaining to fall and winter eggs of rotifers, which if fertilized produce males and if not fertilized produce females.

mimicry (mĭm′ĭk·rĭ) [Gr. *mimos*, mime]: the superficial resemblance of certain animals, particularly insects, to other more powerful or more protected ones, or to leaves and other plant parts, resulting in a measure of protection for the mimics.

mineral (mĭn′ēr·ăl) [L. *minera*, ore]: a compound or substance of the inorganic world; an inorganic material.

miracidium (mī′ră·sĭd′ĭ·ŭm): a larval stage in the life cycle of flukes; develops from an egg and gives rise in turn to a sporocyst larva.

mitochondrion (mī′tô·kŏn′drĭ·ŏn) [Gr. *mitos*, thread, + *chondros*, grain]: a cytoplasmic organelle serving as site of respiration.

mitosis (mī·tō′sĭs): a form of nuclear division characterized by complex chromosome movements and exact chromosome duplication.

mitospore (mī′tô·spōr): a spore produced by mitosis within a sporangium; may be haploid or diploid, depending on the ploidy of the parent organism.

mitral (mī′trăl) [fr. *miter*]: applied to valve between left auricle and ventricle of heart; syn. *bicuspid*.

molecule (mŏl′ê·kūl) [L. *moles*, mass]: a compound in which the atoms are held together by covalent bonds.

Mollusca, mollusk (mô·lŭs′kȧ, mŏl′ŭsk) [L. molluscus, soft]: (1) a phylum of nonsegmented schizocoelomate animals; (2) a member of the phylum Mollusca.

Monera (mŏn·ē′rȧ) [Gr. *monos*, alone]: a major category of living organisms comprising the bacteria and the blue-green algae; characterized in part by absence of nuclear membranes.

monestrous (mŏn·ĕs′trŭs) [Gr. *oistros*, frenzy]: having a single estrus (egg-producing) cycle during a given breeding season.

monocotyledon (mŏn′ô·kŏt′ĭ·lē′dŭn): a plant having a single seed leaf or cotyledon; often abbreviated as monocot.

monoecious (mô·nē′shŭs) [Gr. *oikos*, house]: in heterosporous plants, a given individual producing both megaspores and microspores.

monophyletic (mŏn′ô·fī·lĕt′ĭk) [Gr. *phylon*, tribe]: developed from a single ancestral type; contrasts with polyphyletic.

monopodial (mŏn′ô·pō′dĭ·ăl): a growth pattern in which a main axis continues to elongate in one direction but produces lateral branch axes at intervals.

monosaccharide (mŏn′ô·săk′ȧ·rīd) [Gr. *sakcharon*, sugar]: a simple sugar such as 5- and 6-carbon sugars.

morphogenesis (môr′fô·jĕn′ê·sĭs): development of size, form, and other architectural features of organisms.

morphology (môr·fŏl′ô·jĭ): the study or science of structure, at any level of organization, for example, cytology, study of cell structure; histology, study of tissue structure; anatomy, study of gross structure of organisms.

morula (mŏr′û·là) [L. little mulberry]: solid ball of cells resulting from cleavage of egg; a solid blastula.

mucosa (mū·kō′sà) [L. *mucosus*, mucus]: a mucus-secreting membrane, for example, the inner lining of the intestine.

mutation (mū·tā′shŭn) [L. *mutare*, to change]: a stable change of a gene, such that the changed condition is inherited by offspring cells.

mycelium (mī·sē′lĭ·ŭm): the vegetative portion of a fungus, consisting of a meshwork of hyphae.

Mycophyta (mī′kô·fī′tà): the phylum comprising the fungi.

myelencephalon (mī′ĕ·lĕn·sĕf′ȧ·lŏn) [Gr. *myelos*, marrow]: the most posterior part of the vertebrate hindbrain, confluent with the spinal cord; the medulla oblongata.

myelin (mī′ĕ·lĭn): a fatty material surrounding the axons of nerve cells in the central nervous system of vertebrates.

myofibril (mīô·fī′brĭl): a contractile filament within a cell, especially in a muscle cell or muscle fiber.

myosin (mī′ô·sĭn): a protein which can be isolated from muscle; forms an integral component of the contraction machinery of muscle.

myxedema (mĭk′sê·dē′mà) [Gr. *oidēma*, a swelling]:

a disease resulting from thyroid deficiency in the adult characterized by local swellings in and under the skin.

myxomycete (mĭk'sô·mī·sēt'): a slime mold, member of one of the classes of the Myxophyta.

Myxophyta (mīks·ŏf'ĭ·tá): the protistan phylum of slime molds.

nacre, nacreous (nā'kēr, -krê·ŭs) [Pers. *nakdra*, pearl oyster]: (1) mother-of-pearl; (2) adjective.

NAD: abbreviation of nicotinamide-adenine-dinucleotide, previously called DPN.

NADP: abbreviation of nicotinamide-adenine-dinucleotide-phosphate; previously called TPN.

nastic (năs'tĭk): pertaining to a change in position, as in nastic growth movement; see *epinasty, hyponasty.*

nauplius (nô'plĭ·ŭs) [L. shellfish]: first in a series of larval phases in crustacea.

nekton (něk'tŏn) [Gr. *nēktos,* swimming]: collective term for the actively swimming animals in the ocean.

Nematoda (něm'ä tō'dá): the class of roundworms, of the pseudocoelomate phylum Aschelminthes.

Nematomorpha (něm'ä·tô·môr'fä): the class of hairworms, of the pseudocoelomate phylum Aschelminthes.

Nemertina (něm·êr tīn'ä): ribbon or proboscis worms, an acoelomate phylum (also called Rhynchocoela).

neoteny (nê·ŏt'ê·nĭ) [Gr. *neo,* new + *teinein,* extend]: a permanent, sexually mature, larval state.

nephric, nephron (něf'rĭk, -rŏn): (1) pertaining to a nephron or excretory system generally; (2) a functional unit of the vertebrate kidney.

neritic (nê·rĭt'ĭk) [fr. Gr. *Nereus,* a sea god]: oceanic habitat zone, subdivision of the pelagic zone, comprising the open water above the continental shelf, that is, above the littoral.

neuron (nū'rŏn) [Gr. nerve]: nerve cell, including cyton, dendrites, and axons.

neutron (nū'trŏn): a subatomic, or elementary, particle, representing a unit of mass; it is uncharged and present in an atomic nucleus.

nicotinamide: a derivative of nicotinic acid (niacin, one of the B vitamins), a component of hydrogen carriers such as NAD and NADP.

nictitating (nĭk'tĭ·tāt'ĭng) [L. *nictare,* wink]: pertaining to thin transparent eyelidlike membrane in many vertebrates, which opens and closes laterally across cornea.

nidamental (nĭd'á·měnt·ăl) [L. *nidus,* nest]: pertaining to gland in female cephalopod mollusks which secretes protective capsule around eggs.

nitrify, nitrification (nī'trĭ·fī, -fĭ·kā'shŭn): (1) to convert ammonia and nitrites to nitrates, as by nitrifying bacteria; (2) noun.

node (nōd) [L. *nodus,* knot]: in plants, a joint of a stem; place where branches and leaves are joined to stem.

notochord (nō'tô·kôrd): longitudinal elastic rod of cells serving as internal skeleton in the embryos of all chordates and in the adults of some; in most adult chordates the notochord is replaced by a vertebral column.

nucleic acid (nū·klē'ĭk): one of a class of molecules composed of joined nucleotide complexes; the principal types are deoxyribose nucleic acid (DNA) and ribose nucleic acid (RNA).

nucleolus (nū·klē'ô·lŭs): an RNA-containing body within the nucleus of a cell; a derivative of chromosomes.

nucleoprotein (nū'klê·ô-): a molecular complex composed of nucleic acid and protein.

nucleotide (nū'klê·ô·tīd): a molecule consisting of joined phosphate, 5-carbon sugar (either ribose or deoxyribose), and a purine or a pyrimidine (adenine, guanine, uracil, thymine, or cytosine).

nucleus (nū'klê·ŭs) [L. a kernel]: a body present in all cell types except those of the Monera, and consisting of external nuclear membrane, interior nuclear sap, and chromosomes and nucleoli suspended in the sap; also the central body of an atom.

nutation (nū·tā'shŭn) [L. *nutare,* to nod]: a slow, nodding growth movement in plants, more or less rhythmical, produced by autonomic stimuli.

nutrient (nū'trĭ·ĕnt) [L. *nutrire,* to nourish]: a substance usable in metabolism; a metabolite; includes inorganic materials and organic materials (foods).

ocellus (ô·sĕl'ŭs) [L. dim. of *oculus,* eye]: eye or eyespot, of various degrees of structural and functional complexity; in arthropods, a simple eye, as distinct from a compound eye.

oidiospore (ô·ĭd'ĭ·ô·spōr) [Gr. *eidos,* form]: a spore formed by partitioning of a hyphal filament.

olfaction, olfactory (ŏl·fǎk'shǔn, -tô·rĭ) [L. *olfacere,* to smell]: (1) the process of smelling; (2) pertaining to smell.

ommatidium (ŏm'á tĭd'ĭ·ŭm) [Gr. *omma,* eye]: single visual unit in compound eye of arthropods.

omnivore (ŏm'nĭ·vŏr) [L. *omnis,* all]: an animal which may subsist on plant foods, animal foods, or both.

Oncopoda (ŏn·kŏ'pô·dá) [Gr. *onkos,* bulk]: tentative phylum comprising three small groups related to arthropods, namely, Onychophora, Tardigrada, Pentastomida.

Onychophora (ŏnĭ·kŏ'fŏr·á) [Gr. *onych,* claw]: a subphylum of Oncopoda, comprising *Peripatus* and related types.

oögamy (ô·ŏg'á·mĭ): sexual fusion in which the gametes of opposite sex type are unequal, the female gamete being an egg, that is, nonmotile, the male gamete being a sperm, that is, motile.

oögonium (ō′·ŏ·gō′nĭ·ŭm): the female gametangium of oögamous fungi and other Protista; contains one or more eggs.

operculum (ō·pûr′kŭ·lŭm) [L. a lid]: a lidlike structure.

ophiuroid (ŏf′ĭ·ŭ·roid) [Gr. *ophis*, snake]: a member of a class of echinoderms; a brittle star; also used as adjective.

orbital (ôr′bĭt·ăl): the space within which an orbiting electron may move in an atom.

organ (ôr′găn) [Gr. *organon*, tool, instrument]: a group of different tissues joined structurally and cooperating functionally to perform a composite task.

organelle (ôr·găn·el′): a formed body in the cytoplasm of a cell; a cytoplasmic structure.

organic (ôr·găn′ĭk): pertaining to organisms or living things generally; chemically, compounds of carbon of nonmineral origin.

organism (ôr′găn·ĭz′m): an individual living creature, either unicellular or multicellular.

ornithine (ôr′nĭ·thēn) [Gr. *ornithos*, bird]: an amino acid which, in the liver of vertebrates, contributes to the conversion of ammonia and carbon dioxide into urea.

osmosis (ŏs·mō′sĭs) [Gr. *ōsmos*, impulse]: the process in which water migrates through a semipermeable membrane, from a side containing a lesser concentration of particles to the side containing a greater concentration; migration continues until particles concentrations are equal on both sides.

ossicle (ŏs′ĭ·k′l) [L. dim. of *ossis*, bone]: a small bone or hard bonelike supporting structure.

Osteichthyes (ŏs·tê·ĭk′thĭ·ēz): a class of vertebrates, comprising the bony fishes.

ostium (ŏs′tĭ·ŭm) [L. door]: orifice or small opening; for example, one of several pairs of lateral pores in arthropod heart, pore for entry of water in certain sponges.

ovary (ō′vȧ·rĭ): the egg-producing organ of animals; the ovule- (megasporangium-) containing organ of flowering plants.

oviparity, oviparous (ō′vĭ·păr′ĭ·tĭ, ō·vĭp′ȧrŭs) [L. *parere*, to bring forth]: (1) animal reproductive pattern in which eggs are released by the female and offspring development occurs outside the maternal body; (2) adjective.

oviparity, oviparous (ō′vĭ·păr′ĭ·tĭ, ō·vĭp′ȧ·rŭs) [L. vō·vī vĭp′ȧ·rŭs): (1) animal reproductive pattern in which eggs develop within the maternal body, but without nutritive or other metabolic aid by the female parent; offspring are born as miniature adults; (2) adjective.

ovulation (ō′vŭ·lā′shŭn): expulsion of an animal egg from the ovary and deposition of egg into the oviduct.

ovule (ō′vūl): the integument-covered megasporangium of a seed plant.

oxidation (ŏk′sĭ·dā′shŭn): one half of an oxidation-reduction (redox) process at the end of which the free energy change is negative, that is, the process is exergonic and the endproducts are more stable than the starting materials; often takes the form of removal of hydrogen or electrons from a compound, as in respiration.

paleoniscoid (pā′lê·ŏ·nĭs′koid): extinct Devonian bony fish, ancestral to modern bony fishes, lungfishes, and lobe-fin fishes.

paleontology (pā′lê·ŏn·tŏl′ō·jĭ): study of past geologic times, principally by means of fossils.

Paleozoic (pā′lê·ô·zō′ĭk) geologic era between the Precambrian and the Mesozoic, dating approximately from 500 to 200 million years ago.

palmelloid (păl·mĕl′oid): a transient or permanent state in algal life histories, characterized by nonmotility and the secretion of jellylike envelopes around cells.

palp (pălp) [L. *palpus*, feeler]: a feelerlike appendage; for example, labial palp in clams, pedipalp in chelicerate arthropods.

Pantopoda (păn·tŏp′ô·dȧ) [Gr. *pantos*, all]: a subphylum of Oncopoda, comprising Linguatula and related types.

papilla (pȧ·pĭl′ȧ) [L. nipple]: any small nipplelike projection.

paramylum (pȧ·răm′ĭ·lŭm) [L. *par*, equal, + Gr. *amylon*, fine meal]: characteristic carbohydrate food-storage compound in Euglenophyta; starchlike.

paraphysis (pȧ·răf′ĭ·sĭs) [Gr. *physis*, nature]: one of the sterile filaments in the reproductive organs of many organisms (for example, *Fucus*).

parapodia (păr′ȧ·pō′dĭ·ȧ): fleshy segmental appendages in polychaete worms; serve in breathing, locomotion, and creation of water currents.

parasite (păr′ȧ·sīt) [Gr. *sitos*, food]: an organism living symbiotically on or within a host organism, more or less detrimental to the host.

parasympathetic (păr′ä·sĭm′pȧ·thĕt′ĭk): applied to a subdivision of the autonomic nervous system of vertebrates; centers are located in brain and most anterior part of spinal cord.

parathyroid (păr′ȧ·thī′roid): an endocrine gland of vertebrates, usually paired, located near or within the thyroid; secretes parathormone, which controls calcium metabolism.

parenchyma (pä·rĕng′kĭ·mȧ) [Gr. *para* + *en*, in + *chein*, to pour]: name applied to (1) mesenchymal

846

tissues of acoelomate animals; (2) a type of adult cell in plants, relatively little specialized, thin-walled, often 14-sided, and containing chlorophyll; may function in food storage and is a component of many tissue types.

parthenogenesis (pär'thê·nô·jĕn'ê·sĭs) [Gr. *parthenos,* virgin]: development of an egg without fertilization; occurs naturally in some animals (for example, rotifers) and may be induced artificially in others (for example, frogs).

pathogenic (păth'ô jĕn'ĭk) [Gr. *pathos,* suffering]: disease-producing.

pectin (pĕk'tĭn) [Gr. *pektos,* curdled]: one of a group of compounds frequently present in cell walls of plants.

pedicellaria (pĕd'ĭ·sĕl·ā'rĭ·ȧ) [L. *pedicellus,* little stalk]: a pincerlike structure on the surface of echinoderms; protects skin gills.

pedipalp (pĕd'ĭ·pălp): one of a pair of head appendages in chelicerate arthropods.

peduncle (pê·dŭng'k'l) [L. *pedunculus,* little foot]: a stalk or stemlike part.

pelagic (pê·lăj'ĭk) [Gr. *pelagos,* ocean]: oceanic habitat zone, comprising the open water of an ocean basin; subdivided into the neritic zone and the oceanic zone.

Pelecypoda (pĕ'lê·sĭp'ô·dȧ): a class of the phylum Mollusca, comprising clams, mussels, oysters.

pellicle (pĕl'ĭ·k'l) [L. dim. of *pellis,* skin]: a thin, membranous surface "skin," as on the exterior of many protozoa.

pepsin (pĕp'sĭn) [Gr. *peptein,* to digest]: a protein-digesting enzyme present in gastric juice of vertebrates.

peptidase (pĕp'tĭ·dās): an enzyme promoting the liberation of individual amino acids from a peptide, that is, an amino acid complex smaller than a whole protein.

peptide (pĕp'tīd): the type of bond formed when two amino acid units are joined end to end; the resulting double unit is a dipeptide, and a joining of many amino acid units into a chain results in a *polypeptide,* the basic structural component of a protein molecule.

perennial (pĕr·ĕn'ĭ·ȧl) [L. *perennis,* throughout a year]: a plant which lives continuously throughout the year and persists in whole or in part from year to year.

perianth (pĕr'ĭ·ănth): collective term for calyx and corolla, that is, all sepals and petals.

pericycle (pĕr'ĭ·sī'k'l) [Gr. *perikyklos,* spherical]: a tissue layer composed of parenchymatous or sclerenchymatous cells surrounding the vascular tissues of the stele; may be reduced or absent in stems.

periderm (per'ĭ·dûrm): collective term for cork cambium and its products, namely, cork and phelloderm.

peristalsis (pĕr'ĭ·stăl'sĭs) [Gr. *peristaltikos,* compressing]: successive contraction and relaxation of tubular organs such as the alimentary tract, resulting in a wavelike propagation of a transverse construction.

perithecium (pĕr'ĭ·thē'shĭ·ŭm) [Gr. *thēkē,* capsule]: spherical or flask-shaped fruiting body in ascomycetous fungi, usually opening by a terminal pore.

peritoneum (pê·rĭ'tô·nē'ŭm) [Gr. *peritonos,* stretched over]: a mesodermal epithelial membrane lining the coelomic body cavity in coelomate animals.

permeability (pûr'mê·ȧ·bĭl'ĭ·tĭ) [L. *permeare,* to pass through]: penetrability, as in membranes which let given substances pass through.

petal (pĕt''l) [Gr. *petalos,* outspread]: one of the leaves of a corolla in a flower.

petiole (pĕt'ĭ·ōl) [L. *petiolus,* little foot]: leafstalk; the slender stem by which a leaf blade is attached to a branch or a stem.

pH: a symbol denoting the relative concentration of hydrogen ions in a solution; pH values normally run from 0 to 14, and the lower the value, the more acid a solution, that is, the more hydrogen ions it contains.

Phaeophyta (fē'ô·fīt'ȧ): the phylum of brown algae.

pharynx (făr'ĭngks) [Gr.]: the part of the alimentary tract between mouth cavity and esophagus; in mammals it is also part of the air channel from nose to larynx.

phellem (fĕl'ĕm) [Gr. *phellos,* cork]: cork, the exterior product of the cork cambium.

phelloderm (fĕl'ô·dûrm): the parenchymatous tissue formed by the cork cambium toward the inside; becomes part of cortex.

phellogen (fĕl'ô·jĕn): cork cambium.

phenotype (fē'nô·tīp) [Gr. *phainein,* to show]: the physical appearance of an organism resulting from its genetic constitution (genotype).

phloem (flō'ĕm) [Gr. *phloos,* bark]: one of the vascular tissues in tracheophytic plants; consists of sieve tubes and companion cells and transports organic nutrients both up and down.

Phoronida (fô·rŏn'ĭ·dȧ): a phylum of wormlike, marine, tube-dwelling, coelomate animals, characterized by a lophophore.

phosphagen (fŏs'fȧ·jĕn): collective term for compounds such as creatine-phosphate and arginine-phosphate, which store and may be sources of high-energy phosphates.

phosphorylation (fŏs'fô·rĭ·lā'shŭn): the addition of a phosphate group (for example, $-H_2PO_3$) to a compound.

photolithotroph (fō'tō·lĭth'ō·trōf) [Gr. *lithos*, stone]: an organism which manufactures food with the aid of light energy and with inorganic raw materials.

photolysis (fō·tŏl'ĭ·sĭs): a component process of photosynthesis in which water is dissociated and the hydrogen is joined to NADP under the indirect influence of solar energy.

photoorganotroph (fō'tō·ôr·găn'ō·trōf): an organism which manufactures food with the aid of light energy and with organic raw materials.

photoperiod, photoperiodism (fō'tō·pēr'ĭ·ŭd, -ĭz'm): (1) day length; (2) the responses of plants to different day lengths.

photosynthesis (fō'tō·sĭn'thē·sĭs) [Gr. *tithenai*, to place]: process in which energy of light and chlorophyll are used to manufacture carbohydrates out of carbon dioxide and water.

phototropism (fō·tŏt'rō·pĭz'm) [Gr. *tropē*, a turning]: behavior oriented by light, for example, growth of plant stems toward light source.

phrenic (frĕn'ĭk) [Gr. *phrenos*, diaphragm]: pertaining to the diaphragm, for example, phrenic nerve, innervating the diaphragm.

phycobilin (fī'kō·bĭ'lĭn) [L. *bilis*, bile]: straight-chain tetrapyrrol compounds, some being pigments in blue-green and red algae.

phycocyanin, phycoerythrin (fī'kō·sī'ă·nĭn, fī'kō·ê·rĭth'rĭn): blue and red phycobilin pigments found in blue-green and red algae; those of blue-green algae differ from those of red algae, and they are distinguished accordingly by the prefixes "c-" for cyanophytes and "r-" for rhodophytes.

Phycomycetes (fī'kō·mī·sē'tēz): the class of nonseptate fungi.

phyllotaxy (fĭl'ō·tăk'sĭ): the arrangement of leaves on a stem.

phylogeny (fī·lŏj'ê·nĭ) [Gr. *phylon*, race, tribe]: the study of evolutionary descent and interrelations of groups of organisms.

phylum (fī'lŭm), pl. **phyla**: a category of taxonomic classification, ranked above class.

physiology (fĭz'ĭ·ŏl'ō·jĭ) [Gr. *physis*, nature]: study of living processes, activities, and functions generally; contrasts with morphology, the study of structure.

phytoplankton (fī'tō·plăngk'tŏn) [Gr. *planktos*, wandering]: collective term for the plants and plantlike organisms present in plankton; contrasts with zooplankton.

pilidium (pī·lĭd'ĭ·ŭm) [L. *pilus*, hair]: a larval type characteristic of many nemertine worms.

pinacocyte (pĭn'ă·kō·sīt') [Gr. *pinax*, tablet]: an epithelial cell type on the body surface of sponges.

pineal (pĭn'ē·ăl) [L. *pinea*, pine cone]: a structure in the brain of vertebrates; functions as a median dorsal eye in a few (for example, lampreys), but does not have a demonstrable function in most.

pinna, pinnule (pĭn'ă, pĭn'ūl) [L. feather, fin]: a featherlike structure (for example, the pinnules on the arms of crinoids).

pinocytosis (pĭ'nō·sī·tō'sĭs) [Gr. *pinein*, to drink]: cell "drinking"; the intake of fluid droplets into a cell.

pistil (pĭs'til) [L. *pistulus*, a pestle]: the megaspore-producing organ of a flower; consists of stigma, style, and ovary.

pituitary (pĭ·tū'ĭ·tĕrĭ) [L. *pituita*, phlegm]: a composite endocrine gland in vertebrates, attached ventrally to the brain; composed of anterior, intermediate, and posterior lobes, each representing a functionally separate gland.

placenta (plà·sĕn'tà) [L. cake]: a tissue complex formed in part from the inner lining of the uterus and in part from the chorion of the embryo; develops in most mammals and serves as mechanical, metabolic, and endocrine connection between the adult female and the embryo during pregnancy.

placoderm (plăk'ō·dûrm) [Gr. *plakos*, flat plate]: a member of a class of Devonian vertebrates (fishes), all now extinct; ancestral to cartilage and bony fishes.

planarian (plà·nâr'ĭ·ăn) [L. *planarius*, level]: any member of the class of free-living flatworms.

plankton (plăngk'tŏn) [Gr. *planktos*, wandering]: collective term for the passively floating or drifting flora and fauna of a body of water; consists largely of microscopic organisms.

planula (plăn'ü·là) [L. dim. of *planus*, flat]: basic larval form characteristic of coelenterates.

plasmodesma (plăz'mô·dĕz'mà), pl. **plasmodesmata** [Gr. *desmos*, chain]: fine cytoplasmic strand interconnecting adjacent cells in many plant tissues.

plasmodium (plăz·mō'dĭ·ŭm): multinucleate coenocytic amoeboid mass, representing aggregated diploid phase in slime molds of the class Myxomycetes.

plasmogamy (plăz·mō'gă·mĭ): mating union of cytoplasms, a component of fertilization; plasmogamy is followed by karyogamy (see above), the time interval being appreciable in many Basidiomycetes.

plastid (plăs'tĭd): a cytoplasmic, often pigmented body in cells; three types are leucoplasts, chromoplasts, and chloroplasts.

plastron (plăs'trŏn) [It. *piastrone*, breastplate]: the ventral shell part, as in turtles.

Platyhelminthes (plăt'ĭ·hĕl·mĭn'thēz) [Gr. *platys*, flat]: flatworms, a phylum of acoelomate animals; comprises planarians, flukes, and tapeworms.

plectostele (plĕk'tō·stēl) [Gr. *plektos*, twisted]: a

type of protostele in which the vascular tissues have a cross-sectional arrangement of parallel bars or bands.

plesiosaur (plē′sĭ·ô·sôr) [Gr. *plesios*, near]: a long-necked, marine, extinct Mesozoic reptile.

plexus (plĕk′sŭs) [L. braid]: a network, especially of nerves or of blood vessels.

pluteus (ploot′ê·ŭs) [Gr. *plein*, to sail, float, flow]: the larva of echinoids and ophiuroids; also called echinopluteus and ophiopluteus, respectively.

Pogonophora (pō·gŏ′nô·fôr′à) [Gr. *pōgōn*, beard]: beard worms, a phylum of deuterostomial deep-sea animals.

poikilothermic (poi′kĭ·lô·thûr′mĭk) [Gr. *poikilos*, multicolored]: pertaining to animals without internal temperature controls; "cold-blooded."

pollen (pŏl′ĕn) [L. fine dust]: microspore of seed plants.

pollination (pŏl′ĭ·nā′shŭn): transfer of pollen to the micropyle or to a receptive surface associated with an ovule (for example, a stigma).

polyclad (pŏl′ĭ·klăd): a member of an order of free-living flatworms, characterized by a digestive cavity with many branch pouches.

polymer, polymerization (pŏl′ĭ·mēr, -ĭ·zā′shŭn): (1) a large molecule composed of many like molecular subunits; (2) process of polymer formation.

polymorphism (pŏl′ĭ·môr′fĭz′m): differences of form among the members of a species; individual variations affecting form and structure.

polyp (pŏl′ĭp) [L. *polypus*, many-footed]: the sessile stage in the life cycle of coelenterates.

polyphyletic (pŏl′ĭ·fi·lĕt′ĭk) [Gr. *phylon*, tribe]: derived from more than one ancestral type; contrasts with monophyletic.

polyploid (pŏl′ĭ·ploid): possessing many complete chromosome sets per cell.

polysaccharide (pŏl′ĭ·săk′a·rīd): a carbohydrate composed of many joined monosaccharide units, for example, glycogen, starch, cellulose, all formed out of glucose units.

Porifera (pô·rĭf′ĕr·à): the phylum of sponges.

Priapulida (prī′ă·pū′lĭ·dà): a small class of pseudo-coelomate animals in the phylum Aschelminthes.

primordium (prī·môr′dĭ·ŭm) [L. beginning]: the earliest developmental stage in the formation of an organ or body part.

proboscis (prô·bŏs′ĭs) [L.]: any tubular process or prolongation of the head or snout.

procambium (prô·kăm′bĭ·ŭm) [L. *cambium*, exchange]: one of the three primary meristems; gives rise to vascular tissues and pericycle.

proembryo (prô·ĕm′brĭ·ō) [Gr. *bryein*, to swell]: a few-celled stage in the development of seed plants.

progesterone (prô·jĕs′tĕr·ōn): hormone secreted by the vertebrate corpus luteum and the mammalian placenta; functions as "pregnancy hormone" in mammals.

proglottid (prô·glŏt′ĭd): a segment of a tapeworm.

prophase (prō′fāz′): a stage during mitotic division in which the chromosomes become distinct and a spindle forms.

proprioceptor (prô·′prī·ô·sĕp′·tēr) [L. *proprius*, one's own]: sensory receptor of stimuli originating in internal organs; for example, as for muscle sense.

prosimian (prô·sĭm′ĭ·ăn) [L. *simia*, ape]: an ancestral primate.

protein (prō′tê·ĭn) [Gr. *prōteios*, primary]: one of a class of organic compounds composed of many joined amino acids.

proteinase (prō′tê·ĭn·ās): an enzyme promoting the conversion of a protein into smaller units, for example, amino acids, or the reverse; also called protease.

prothallium (prô·thăl′ĭ·ŭm): the gametophyte of a fern.

prothrombin (prô·thrŏm′bĭn) [Gr. *thrombos*, clot]: a constituent of vertebrate blood plasma; converted to thrombin by thrombokinase in the presence of calcium ions, and so contributes to blood clotting.

Protista (prô·tĭs′tà) [Gr. *prōtistos*, first]: a major category of living organisms, including all groups of algae, slime molds, protozoa, and fungi; characterized by usually unicellular reproductive structures, true nuclei, and chromosomes.

protoderm (prō′tô·dŭrm): one of the three primary meristems; gives rise to epidermis.

proton (prō′tŏn): a subatomic, or elementary, particle, representing a unit of positive electric charge with a mass of 1, a component of an atomic nucleus.

protonema (prō′tô·nē′mà): the prostrate first-formed portion of a moss gametophyte, filamentous or thallose.

protoplasm (prō′tô·plăz′m): synonym for living matter, living material, or living substance.

protostele (prō′tô·stēl′) [Gr. *stēlē*, upright post]: a general type of stele in which the vascular tissues form a solid central aggregation within the stem or root, phloem being outside the xylem; the principal protostelic variants are haplosteles, actinosteles, and plectosteles.

protozoon (prō′tô·zō′ŏn): a member of either of four subphyla (Mastigophora, Sarcodina, Ciliophora, Sporozoa) of a protistan phylum.

pseudocoel, pseudocoelomate (sū′dô·sēl, -ô·māt): (1) an internal body cavity lined not by mesoderm but by ectoderm and endoderm; (2) an animal possessing a pseudocoel, for example, rotifers, roundworms.

pseudoplasmodium (sū·dô·plăz·mō′dĭ·ŭm): multicellular amoeboid mass, representing aggregate diploid phase in slime molds of the class Acrasieae.

pseudopodium (sū·dô·pō′dĭ·ŭm): a cytoplasmic protrusion from an amoeboid cell; functions in locomotion and feeding.

Psilopsida (sī·lŏp′sĭ·dȧ) [Gr. *psilos*, bare]: a subphylum of tracheophytes; includes the earliest representatives of the vascular plants; evolved probably from green algae and in turn ancestral to all living tracheophytes.

Pteropsida (tê·rŏp′sĭ·dȧ) [Gr. *pteridos*, fern]: a subphylum of tracheophytes; includes ferns and all seed plants, that is, large-leafed vascular plants; probably evolved from psilopsids.

pterosaur (tĕr′ô·sôr): a flying, extinct Mesozoic reptile.

pulmonary (pŭl′mô·nĕr′ĭ) [L. *pulmonis*, lung]: pertaining to the lungs, for example, pulmonary artery, vein.

pulvinus (pŭl·vī′nŭs) [L., cushion, elevation]: an enlargement of a petiole at its base; in the sensitive plant *Mimosa* it is the effector of the response to touch.

pupa (pū′pȧ) [L. doll]: a developmental stage, usually encapsulated or in cocoon, between the larva and the adult in holometabolous insects.

purine (pū′rēn): a nitrogen base such as adenine or guanine; together with sugar and phosphate is a component of nucleotides and nucleic acids.

pylorus (pī·lō′rŭs) [Gr. *pylōros*, gatekeeper]: the opening from stomach to intestine.

pyranose (pī′rȧ·nōs): a sugar molecule considered as a ring structure.

pyrenoid (pī·rē′noid) [Gr. *pyrēn*, fruit stone]: starch-containing granular bodies on or near a chloroplast in many Protista.

pyrimidine (pĭ·rĭ′mĭ·dēn): a nitrogen base such as cytosine, thymine, or uracil; together with sugar and phosphate is a component of nucleotides and nucleic acids.

pyrophosphate (pī′rô-): a molecule composed of two joined organic phosphate groups (PP_i).

Pyrrophyta (pĭ·rŏf′ĭ·tȧ) [Gr. *pyrros*, fiery]: a phylum of algae; includes dinoflagellates and possibly also Cryptophyceae.

Radiata (rā·dĭ·ā′tȧ) [L. *radius*, ray]: a taxonomic grade within the Eumetazoa, comprising animals with primary and secondary radial symmetry; namely, coelenterates and ctenophores.

Radiolarida, radiolaria (rā′dĭ·ô·lär′ĭ·dä, -ȧ): an order of sarcodine protozoa, characterized by silicon-containing shells.

radula (răd′ū·lȧ) [L. *radere*, to scrape]: the horny rasping organ in the alimentary tract of chitons, snails, squids, and other mollusks.

receptacle (rê·sĕp′tȧ·k'l) [L. *receptaculum*, receiver]: (1) conceptacle-containing thallus tip in *Fucus;* (2) modified branch of thallus bearing sex organs in *Marchantia;* (3) expanded terminal of stalk bearing the components of a flower.

recessive (rê·sĕs′ĭv) [L. *recedere*, to recede]: a functional attribute of genes; the effect of a recessive gene is masked if the allelic gene is dominant.

rectum (rĕk′tŭm) [L. *rectus*, straight]: a terminal nonabsorptive portion of the alimentary tract in many animals; opens via the anus.

redia (rē′dĭ·ȧ): a larval stage in the life cycle of flukes; produced by a sporocyst larva and in turn gives rise to many cercariae.

reduction (rê·dŭk′shŭn) [L. *reducere*, to lead back]: one half of an oxidation-reduction (redox) process; the phase of such a process which yields the net energy gain; often takes the form of addition of hydrogen or electrons to a compound, as in respiration.

reflex (rē′flĕks) [L. *reflectere*, to bend back]: the unit action of the nervous system; consists of stimulation of a sense receptor, interpretation and emission of nerve impulses by a neural center, and execution of a response by an effector organ.

renal (rē′nȧl) [L. *renes*, kidneys]: pertaining to the kidney.

rennin (rĕn′ĭn) [Middle Engl. *rennen*, to run]: an enzyme present in mammalian gastric juice; promotes the coagulation of milk.

resonance: in chemical usage, a property of any compound that cannot be described completely by a single structural formula.

respiration (rĕs′pĭ·rā′shŭn) [L. *respirare*, to breathe]: the liberation of metabolically useful energy from fuel molecules within cells; may occur anaerobically or aerobically.

reticulum, reticulate (rê·tĭk′ū·lŭm, -lȧt) [L. *reticulum*, little net]: (1) a network or mesh of fibrils, fibers, or filaments, as in *endoplasmic reticulum* within cytoplasm; (2) netlike.

retina (rĕt′ĭ·nȧ) [L. *rete*, a net]: the innermost tissue layer of the eyeball; contains the receptor cells sensitive to light.

rhabdocoel (răb′dô·sēl) [Gr. *rhabdos*, rod]: member of a group of free-living flatworms having a straight, unbranched digestive cavity.

rhizoid (rī′zoid) [Gr. *rhiza*, root]: rootlike absorptive filament.

rhizome (rī′zōm) [Gr. *rhizōma*, mass of roots]: underground stem.

Rhodophyta (rô′dŏf′ĭ·tȧ) [Gr. *rhodon*, red]: the phylum of red algae.

ribosome (rī′bô·sōm): a cytoplasmic organelle which contains RNA and is site of protein synthesis.

ribotide (rī′bô·tīd): a nucleotide in which the sugar component is ribose.

rickettsia (rĭk·ĕt′sĭ·à) [after H. T. Ricketts, American pathologist]: a type of microorganism intermediate in nature between a virus and a bacterium, parasitic within cells of insects and ticks.

RNA: abbreviation of ribonucleic acid.

Rotifera (rō·tĭf′ĕr·à) [L. *rota*, wheel]: a class of microscopic pseudocoelomate animals within the phylum Aschelminthes.

rudimentary (roo′dĭ·mĕn′tà·rĭ) [L. *rudis*, unformed]: pertaining to an incompletely developed body part.

saccule (săk′ūl) [L. *sacculus*, little sac]: portion of the inner ear of vertebrates containing the receptors for the sense of static balance.

saprotroph (săp′rô·trōf) [Gr. *sapros*, rotten]: an organism subsisting on dead or decaying matter.

sarcina (sär′sĭ·nà) [L. *sarcina*, bundle]: a type of colony of spherical bacteria in which the cells divide in three planes of space, resulting in cuboidal arrangements.

Sarcodina (sär′kô·dī′nà): a subphylum of protozoa; amoeboid protozoa.

Scaphopoda (skà·fŏp′ô·dà) [Gr. *skaphē*, boat]: tooth shells, a class of the phylum Mollusca.

schizocoel, schizocoelomate (skĭz′ô·sēl): (1) a coelom formed by a splitting of embryonic mesoderm; (2) an animal possessing a schizocoel, for example, mollusks, annelids, arthropods.

Schizophyta (skĭ·zŏf′ĭ·tà): the phylum of bacteria.

sclera (sklē′rà): the outermost coat of the eyeball, continuous with the cornea.

sclereid (sklĕr′ê·ĭd): a type of sclerenchyma cell, characterized by irregular and different shapes in different cases.

sclerenchyma (sklê·rĕng′kĭ·mà) [Gr. *en*, in, + *chein*, to pour]: plant cells with greatly thickened and lignified walls and without living substance when mature; two variants of sclerenchyma are fibers and sclereids.

scolex (skō′lĕks) [L. worm, grub]: the head of a tapeworm.

scrotum (skrō′tŭm) [L]: external skin pouch containing the testes in most mammals.

sebaceous (sê·bā′shŭs) [L. *sebum*, tallow, grease]: pertaining to sebum, an oil secreted from skin glands near the hair bases of mammals.

seminal (sĕm′ĭ·nàl) [L. *semen*, seed]: pertaining to semen, or sperm-carrying fluid.

septum, septate (sĕp′tŭm, -tāt) [L. enclosure]: (1) a complete or incomplete partition; (2) adjective.

sere (sēr) [fr. L. *series*, series]: a stage in an ecological succession of communities, from the virginal condition to a stable climax community.

serum (sē′rŭm) [L.]: the fluid remaining after removal of fibrinogen from vertebrate blood plasma.

simian (sĭm′ĭ·ăn) [L. *simia*, an ape]: pertaining to monkeys; also used as noun.

sinus (sī′nŭs) [L. a curve]: a cavity, recess, space or depression; for example, blood sinus, bone sinus.

siphon (sī′fŏn): tubular structure for drawing in or ejecting fluids, as in mollusks, tunicates.

siphonaceous (sī′fŏn·ā′shŭs): tubular; applied specifically to coccine, elongate Protista.

siphonoglyph (sī·fŏn′ô·glĭf) [Gr. *glyphein*, to carve]: flagellated groove in pharynx of sea anemones; creates water current into gastrovascular cavity.

siphonostele (sī′fô·nô·stēl): a general type of stele in which the vascular tissues are arranged around a central pith or a central hollow cavity.

siphuncle (sī′fŭngk′l): gas-filled canal passing through coiled shell of chambered nautilus.

Sipunculida (sī′pŭng·kū′lĭ·dà): a phylum of wormlike schizocoelomate animals.

sol (sŏl): quasi-liquid state of a colloidal system, where water forms the continuous phase and solid particles the dispersed phase.

somatic (sô·măt′ĭk): pertaining to the body; for example, somatic mutation, stable gene change occurring in a cell of the body generally, rather than in a reproductive, or germ, cell.

somite (sō′mīt): one of the longitudinal series of segments in segmented animals; especially an incompletely developed embryonic segment or a part thereof.

sorus (sō′rŭs) [Gr. *soros*, heap]: a cluster of sporangia on a fern leaf.

species (spē′shĭz), pl. **species** (spē′shēz) [L. kind, sort]: a category of taxonomic classification, below genus rank, defined by breeding potential or gene flow; interbreeding and gene flow occur among the members of a species but not between members of different species.

specificity (spĕs′ĭ·fĭs′ĭ·tĭ): uniqueness, especially of proteins in a given organism and of enzymes in given reactions.

spectrum (spĕk′trŭm) [L. image]: a series of radiations arranged in the order of wavelengths, for example, solar spectrum, visible spectrum.

spermatangium (spûr′mà·tăn′jĭ·ŭm): sperm-producing structure; male gametangium.

spermatium (spēr·mā′shĭ·ŭm): name for the male gamete in red algae and some fungi.

spermatogenous (spûr′mà·tŏj′ê·nŭs): sperm-producing.

Sphenopsida (sfê·nŏp′sĭ·dà) [Gr. *sphēn*, a wedge]: a subphylum of tracheophytes; includes the horsetails.

sphincter (sfĭngk'tẽr) [Gr. *sphingein*, to bind tight]: a ring-shaped muscle capable of closing a tubular opening by constriction, for example, pyloric sphincter, which closes the opening between stomach and intestine.

spicule (spĭk'ūl) [L. *spiculum*, little dart]: a slender, pointed, often needle-shaped secretion of sponge cells; serves as skeletal support.

spiracle (spī'rȧ·k'l) [L. *spirare*, to breathe]: reduced evolutionary remnant of first gill slit in fishes; surface openings of breathing systems in terrestrial arthropods.

spirillum (spī·rĭl'ŭm) [L. *spirilla*, little coil]: any bacterium possessing a wavy, coiled, or spiral body.

sporangiospore (spô·răn'jĭ·ô·spōr') : a spore produced in a sporangium (as distinct from conidia and oidiospore).

sporangium (spô·răn'jĭ·ŭm) : a spore-producing structure, unicellular or multicellular.

spore (spōr) : a reproductive cell capable of developing into an adult directly.

sporine (spō'rên) : pertaining to a sessile state of protistan existence in which cell division may take place during the vegetative condition.

sporocyst (spō'rô·sĭst) : a larval stage in the life cycle of flukes; produced by a miracidium larva and in turn gives rise to many rediae.

sporogenous (spô·rŏj'ê·nŭs) : spore-producing.

sporophyll (spō'rô·fĭl) : a sporangium-bearing leaf.

sporophyte (spōr'ô·fīt) : a spore-producing organism; phase of diplohaplontic life cycle which alternates with a gametophyte phase.

Sporozoa (spō'rô·zō'ȧ) : a subphylum of parasitic protozoa; most familiar member is the organism which produces malaria.

stamen (stā'mĕn) [L. a thread]: the microspore-producing organ of a flower; consists of stalk and anther.

stele (stēl) [Gr. *stēlē*, upright post]: collective term for those portions of stem and root which contain vascular tissues and, where present, pericycle and pith.

stereomer (stĕ'rĕ·ô·mẽr) : equivalent to structural isomer, one of a group of compounds identical in atomic composition but differing in atomic arrangements.

sternum (stûr'nŭm) [Gr. *sternon*, chest]: in arthropods, ventral exoskeletal plate of a body segment; in vertebrates, breastbone, articulating with ventral ends of ribs on each side.

sterol, steroid (stĕr'ōl, stĕr'oid) : one of a class of organic compounds containing a molecular skeleton of four fused carbon rings; includes cholesterol, sex hormones, adrenocortical hormones, and vitamin D.

stigma (stĭg'mȧ) [Gr. the mark of a pointed instrument]: the uppermost part of a pistil, serving as receptive surface for pollen grains.

stimulus (stĭm'ū·lŭs) [L. goad, incentive]: any internal or external environmental change which activates a receptor structure.

stipule (stĭp'ūl) [L. *stipula*, stalk]: one of a pair of appendages at the base of the petiole in many plants.

stolon (stō'lŏn) [L. *stolo*, shoot, branch]: in colonial animals, a (usually) horizontal branch or runner from which upright individuals may bud.

stoma (stō'mȧ) pl. **stomata** [Gr. a mouth]: a microscopic opening in the epidermis of a leaf, formed by a pair of guard cells; interconnects the interior air spaces of a leaf with the external atmosphere.

streptococcus (strĕp'tô·kŏk'ŭs) [Gr. *streptos*, curved]: member of a type of colony of bacterial cocci in which the cells divide in one plane only, forming chains.

strobilation (strō·bī·lā'shŭn) [Gr. *strobilos*, pine cone]: process of segmentlike budding in sessile scyphistoma larvae of scyphozoan coelenterates, resulting in cutting off of successive free-swimming ephyra larvae.

strobilus (strŏb'ĭ·lŭs) : a cone or conelike aggregation of sporophylls.

stroma (strō'mȧ) [Gr. couch, bed]: the connective tissue network supporting the epithelial portions of an organ.

style, stylet (stīl, stī'lĕt) [Gr. *stylos*, pillar]: (1) a stalklike or elongated body part, often pointed at one end; (2) stalklike part of a pistil, connecting the stigma with the ovary.

suberin (sū'bẽr·ĭn) [L. *suber*, cork tree]: a waterproofing material secreted by cork and endodermis cells.

substrate (sŭb'strāt) [L. *substratus*, strewn under]: a substance which is acted upon by an enzyme.

suspensor (sŭs·pĕn'sẽr) [L. *suspensus*, suspended]: an elongated strand connecting a plant embryo to the surrounding tissue layers.

symbiont, symbiosis (sĭm'bī·ŏnt, sĭm'bī·ō'sĭs) : (1) an organism living in symbiotic association with another; (2) the intimate living together of two organisms of different species, for mutual or one-sided benefit; the principal variants are mutualism, commensalism, and parasitism.

sympathetic (sĭm'pȧ·thĕt'ĭk) : applied to a subdivision of the autonomic nervous system; centers are located in the mid-portion of the spinal cord.

synapse (sĭ·năps') : the microscopic space between the axon terminal of one neuron and the dendrite terminal of another, adjacent neuron.

syncytium (sĭn·sĭ'shĭ·ŭm) : a multinucleate animal tissue without internal cell boundaries.

synergistic (sĭn′ĕr·jĭs′tĭk) [Gr. *ergon*, work]: cooperative in action, for example, hormones or other growth factors which reinforce each other's activities.

syngen (sĭn′jĕn): a mating group (or variety) within a protozoan species; mating may occur within a syngen but not usually between syngens; a functional (as distinct from taxonomic) "species."

synthesis (sĭn′thē·sĭs) [Gr. *tithenai*, to place]: the joining of two or more molecules resulting in a single larger molecule.

syrinx (sĭr′ĭngks) [Gr. a pipe]: the vocal organ of birds, located where the trachea branches into the bronchi.

systole (sĭs′tō·lē) [Gr. *stellein*, to place]: the contraction of atria or ventricles of a heart.

taiga (tī′gȧ) [Russ.]: terrestrial habitat zone characterized by large tracts of coniferous forests, long, cold winters, and short summers; bounded in the north by tundra; found particularly in Canada, northern Europe, and Siberia.

tardigrade (tär′dĭ·grād) [L. *tardigradus*, a slow stepper]: a member of a subphylum of Oncopoda; water bears.

tarsus (tär′sŭs) [Gr. *tarsos*, sole]: in insects, the terminal parts of a leg; in vertebrates, the ankle.

taxon (tăks′ŏn) pl. **taxa**: the specific organisms in a taxonomic rank.

taxonomy (tăks·ŏn′ō·mĭ) [Gr. *nomos*, law]: classification of organisms, based as far as possible on natural relationships.

tectorial membrane (tĕk·tō′rĭ·ȧl) [L. cover, covering]: component of the organ of Corti in cochlea of ear.

telencephalon (tĕl′ĕn·sĕf′ȧ·lŏn) [Gr. *enkephalos*, brain]: the vertebrate forebrain.

telolecithal (tĕl′ō·lĕs′ĭ·thăl): pertaining to eggs with large amounts of yolk accumulated in the vegetal half of the cell; for example, as in frog eggs.

telophase (tĕl′ō·fāz): a stage in mitotic division during which two nuclei form; usually accompanied by partitioning of cytoplasm.

telson (tĕl′sŭn) [Gr. boundary, limit]: terminal segmentlike body part of an arthropod (not generally counted as a segment).

template (tĕm′plĭt): a pattern or mold guiding the formation of a duplicate; term applied especially to gene duplication, which is explained in terms of a template hypothesis.

temporal lobe (tĕm′pô rȧl) [L. *tempora*, the temples]: a part of the vertebrate cerebrum; contains neural centers for speech and hearing.

tergum (tûr′gŭm) [L. the back]: the dorsal exoskeletal plate of a body segment in arthropods.

testis, pl. **testes** (tĕs′tĭs, -tēz) [L.]: sperm-producing organ in animals.

tetracoccus (tĕt′rȧ·kŏk′ŭs): member of a type of colony of bacterial cocci in which the cells divide into two planes, forming quartets.

tetrad (tĕt′răd): a pair of chromosome pairs present during the first metaphase of meiosis.

Tetrapoda (tĕ·trăp′ô·dȧ): four-legged vertebrates; a superclass including amphibia, reptiles, birds, and mammals.

tetrapyrrol (tĕt′rȧ·pī′rŏl): a molecule consisting of four united pyrrol units, each of the latter being a five-membered ring of carbon and nitrogen; the four pyrrols may be joined linearly or as a larger ring; tetrapyrrols include pigments such as heme and chlorophyll.

thalamus (thăl′ȧ·mŭs) [Gr. *thalamos*, chamber]: a lateral region of the diencephalic portion of the vertebrate forebrain.

thallus, thallose (thăl′ŭs, -ōs): (1) a body without differentiation into root, stem, and leaf, usually flat and prostrate, sometimes filamentous; name applied mainly to some fungi, algae, and bryophytes; (2) adjective.

theory (thē′ô rĭ) [Gr. *theōrein*, to look at]: a scientific statement based on experiments which verify a hypothesis; it is the last step of the scientific method.

therapsid (thē·răp′sĭd) [Gr. *thērion*, beast]: extinct Mesozoic mammallike reptile; true mammals evolved from same group.

thigmotropism (thĭg·mŏt′rô·pĭz′m) [Gr. *thigma*, touch]: growth of organisms toward or away from contact stimuli.

thorax (thō′răks) [L.]: part of animal body between neck or head and abdomen.

thrombin (thrŏm′bĭn) [Gr. *thrombos*, clot]: a substance participating in vertebrate blood clotting; formed from prothrombin and in turn converts fibrinogen into fibrin.

thrombokinase (thrŏm′bô·kĭn′ās): enzyme released from vertebrate blood platelets during clotting; transforms prothrombin into thrombin in presence of calcium ions; also called thromboplastin.

thrombus (thrŏm′bŭs): a blood clot within the circulatory system.

thymidine (di-, tri-) phosphates (thī′mĭ·dēn): thymine-deoxyribose-phosphate (TDP, TTP).

thymidylic acid (thī·mĭ·dī′lĭk): equivalent to thymine monophosphate (TMP).

thymine (thī′mēn): a pyrimidine component of nucleotides and nucleic acids.

thymus (thī′mŭs) [Gr.]: a lymphoid gland in most young and many adult vertebrates; disappears in man at puberty; located in lower throat and upper part of thorax.

thyroxine (thī·rŏk′sēn): the hormone secreted by the thyroid gland.

tibia (tĭb′ĭ·a̤) [L.]: in vertebrates, usually the larger shin bone of the hind limb between knee and ankle; in insects, the leg portion between femur and tarsus.

tissue (tĭsh′ū) [L. *texere*, to weave]: an aggregate of cells of similar structure performing similar functions.

tornaria (tôr·nā′rĭ·a̤) [L. *tornus*, lathe, chisel]: the larva of certain enteropneust hemichordates.

TPN: abbreviation of triphosphopyridine nucleotide; now called NADP (see above).

trachea, tracheal (trā′kê·a̤) [Gr. *trachys*, rough]: (1) air-conducting tube, as in windpipe of mammals and breathing system of insects; (2) adjective.

tracheid (trā′kê·ĭd): plant cell type formed from procambium and maturing into a conducting component of xylem.

tracheophyte, Tracheophyta (trā′kê·ô·fĭt): (1) a vascular plant, that is, one possessing xylem and phloem; (2) phylum name.

transduction (trăns·dŭk′shŭn): transfer of genetic material from one bacterium to another through the agency of a virus.

translocation (trăns·lô·kā′shŭn): transport of organic substances in phloem.

transpiration (trăn′spĭ·rā′shŭn) [L. *spirare*, to breathe]: evaporation of water from leaves or other exposed surfaces.

trichogyne (trĭk′ô·jĭn): in red algae and some fungi, an elongated projection from the female gamete receptive to the male gamete or gamete nucleus.

triclad (trī′klăd): a member of a group of free-living flatworms, characterized by a digestive cavity with three branch pouches; a planarian.

tricuspid valve (trī·kŭs′pĭd) [L. *cuspis*, a point]: valve consisting of three flaps, guarding opening between right auricle and right ventricle of mammalian heart.

trilobite (trī′lô·bīt): an extinct, marine, Paleozoic arthropod, marked by two dorsal longitudinal furrows into three parts or lobes.

triploid (trĭp′loid) [Gr. *triploos*, triple]: possessing three complete chromosome sets per cell.

trochanter (trô·kăn′tēr) [Gr. *trechein*, to run]: in insects, the part of a leg adjoining the coxa, equivalent to the basipodite of arthropods.

trochophore (trŏk′ô·fōr): a free-swimming ciliated marine larva, characteristic of schizocoelomate animals.

tropic, tropism (trŏp′ĭk) [Gr. *tropē*, a turning]: (1)

pertaining to behavior or action brought about by specific stimuli, for example, phototropic (light-oriented) motion, gonadotropic (stimulating the gonads); (2) noun.

trypsin (trĭp′sĭn) [Gr. *tryein*, to wear down]: vertebrate enzyme promoting protein digestion; acts in small intestine, produced in pancreas as inactive trypsinogen.

tuber (tū′bēr) [L. knob]: a short, fleshy, underground stem with axillary buds, for example, potato.

tundra (tōōn′dra̤) [Russ.]: terrestrial habitat zone, between taiga in south and polar region in north, characterized by absence of trees, short growing season, and frozen ground during much of the year.

Turbellaria (tûr′bĕ·lär′ĭ·a̤) [L. *turba*, disturbance]: the class of free-living flatworms; planarians.

turgor (tûr′gŏr) [L. *turgere*, to swell]: the distention of a cell by its fluid content.

typhlosole (tĭf′lô·sōl) [Gr. *typhlos*, blind]: dorsal fold of intestinal wall projecting into the gut cavity in oligochaete annelids such as earthworms.

umbilicus (ŭm·bĭl′ĭ·kŭs) [L.]: the navel in mammals; during pregnancy, an umbilical cord connects the placenta with the offspring, and the point of connection with the offspring later becomes the navel.

umbo (ŭm′bō) [L. boss of shield]: rounded prominence near hinge of clam valve; oldest part of shell.

ungulate (ŭng′gū·lât) [L. *ungula*, hoof]: hoofed, as in certain orders of mammals.

uracil (ū′ra̤·sĭl): a pyrimidine component of nucleotides and nucleic acids.

urea (û·rē′a̤) [Gr. *ouron*, urine]: an organic compound formed in the vertebrate liver out of ammonia and carbon dioxide and excreted by the kidneys; represents principal means of ammonia disposal in mammals and some other animal groups.

ureter (û·rē′tēr) [Gr.]: duct carrying urine from a metanephric kidney to the urinary bladder.

urethra (û·rē′thra̤) [Gr.]: duct carrying urine from the urinary bladder to the outside of the amniote body; in the males of most mammals, the urethra also leads sperms to the outside during copulation.

uridine (di-, tri-) phosphates (ū′rĭ·dēn-): uracil-ribose-phosphates (UDP, UTP).

uridylic acid (ū·rĭ·dĭ′lĭk): equivalent to uridine monophosphate (UMP).

Urochordata (ū′rô·kôr·dā′ta̤): a subphylum of chordates; comprises the tunicates.

Urodela (û′·rŏ·dĕ′la̤) [Gr. *dēlos*, visible]: a subclass of tailed amphibia, comprising newts and salamanders.

uronic acid (û·rŏ′nĭk): a sugar derivative in which the groups on the last carbon are replaced by a carboxyl group.

uropod (ū'rô·pŏd): an abdominal appendage in lobsters and other crustaceans; contributes to the formation of a "tail."

uterus (ū'tĕr·ŭs) [L. womb]: enlarged region of a female reproductive duct in which animal embryo undergoes all or part of its development.

utricle (ū'trĭ·k'l) [L. *utriculus*, little bag]: portion of the vertebrate inner ear containing the receptors for dynamic body balance; the semicircular canals lead from and to the utricle.

vacuole (văk'û ōl) [L. *vacuus*, empty]: a small, usually spherical space within a cell, bounded by a membrane and containing fluid, solid, solid matter or both.

vagina (và·jī'nà) [L. sheath]: the terminal, penis-receiving portion of a female reproductive system in animals in which fertilization is internal.

vagus (vā'gŭs) [L. wandering]: the tenth cranial nerve in vertebrates; it is a mixed nerve, innervating many organs in the chest and the abdomen.

valence (vā'lĕns) [L. *valere*, to have power]: a measure of the bonding capacity of an atom; an atom may be monovalent, divalent, trivalent, etc., indicating the number of other atoms it may bond with; bonds may be electrovalent, formed through electron transfer, or covalent, formed through electron sharing.

vasomotion (văs'ô·mō'shŭn) [L. *vasum*, vessel]: collective term for the constriction (vasoconstriction) and dilation (vasodilation) of blood vessels.

veliger (vēl'ĭ·jĕr) [L. *velum*, veil]: posttrochophoral larval stage in many mollusks.

velum (vē'lŭm): a membranous curtainlike band of tissue, for example, on underside of many hydroid medusae.

venous (vē'nŭs) [L. *vena*, vein]: pertaining to veins; also applied to oxygen-poor, carbon dioxide–rich blood.

ventricle (vĕn'trĭ·k'l) [L. *ventriculus,* the stomach]: a chamber of a heart which receives blood from an atrium and pumps out blood from the heart.

vernalization (vûr'năl·ĭ·zā'shŭn) [L. *vernalis*, spring]: induction of flowering by cold (or heat) treatment of seeds or later developmental stages.

vernation (vŭr·nā'shŭn) [L. *vernare*, to be verdant]: the arrangement of leaves within a bud, for example, circinate vernation, a rolled-up arrangement of a young leaf, as in ferns.

vestigial (vĕs·tĭj'ĭ·ăl) [L. *vestigium*, footprint]: degenerate or incompletely developed, but more fully developed at an earlier stage or during the evolutionary past.

villus (vĭl'ŭs) pl. villi [L. a tuft of hair]: a tiny finger-like process projecting from the intestinal lining into the cavity of the mammalian gut; contains blood and lymph capillaries and is bounded by the intestinal mucosa.

virus (vī'rŭs) [L. slimy liquid, poison]: a submicroscopic noncellular particle, composed of a nucleic acid core and a protein shell; parasitic, and within a host cell it may reproduce and mutate.

viscera (vĭs'ĕr·à), sing. viscus [L.]: collective term for the internal organs of an animal.

vitamin (vī tà·mĭn) [L. *vita*, life]: one of a class of organic growth factors contributing to the formation of coenzymes and therefore to the action of cellular enzymes.

vitreous (vĭt'rê·ŭs) [L. *vitrum*, glass]: glassy; as in vitreous humor, the clear transparent jelly which fills the posterior part of the vertebrate eyeball.

viviparity, viviparous (vĭv'ĭ·păr'ĭ·tĭ, vī·vĭp'à·rŭs) [L. *vivus*, living + *parere*, to bring forth]: (1) animal reproductive pattern in which eggs develop within female body with nutritional and other metabolic aid of maternal parent; offspring are born as miniature adults; (2) adjective.

volvant (vŏl'vănt) [L. *volvere*, to roll, twist]: closed-ended adhesive thread in a type of nematocyst of coelenterates.

xanthophyll (zăn'thô·fĭl): one of a group of yellow pigments, members of the carotenoid group.

xerophyte (zē'rô·fĭt): a plant adapted to live under dry or desert conditions.

Xiphosura (zĭf'ô·sū'rà) [Gr. *xiphos*, sword]: a class of chelicerate arthropods; the horseshoe crabs (*Limulus*).

xylem (zī'lĕm) [Gr. *xylon*, wood]: tissue which conducts water from roots upward; consists of tracheids, vessels, and other cell types; in bulk represents wood.

zoaea (zō·ē'ä) pl. zoaeae: a larval form of crustaceans.

zooid (zō'oid): an individual animal in a colonial aggregation; often physically joined with fellow zooids and may be a polymorphic variant.

zooplankton (zō'ô·plăngk'tŏn): collective term for the nonphotosynthetic organisms present in plankton; contrasts with phytoplankton.

zoospore (zō'ô·spōr): a motile, flagellate spore.

zwitter ion (tsvī'tĕr) [Germ., *hybrid*]: an ampholyte, or compound carrying both positive and negative electric charges.

zygospore (zī'gô·spōr): an encysted zygote, as in *Spirogyra*.

zygote (zī' gōt) [Gr. *zygōtos*, paired together]: the cell resulting from the sexual fusion of two gametes; a fertilized egg.

INDEX

Note: if an entry on a given page is referred to only in an illustration or a table, the page number is marked with an asterisk